technical mathematics with calculus

technical mathematics with calculus

third edition

Harold S. Rice

Professor Emeritus of Mathematics,
Wentworth Institute

Raymond M. Knight

Professor Emeritus of Mathematics,
Hudson Valley Community College

McGraw-Hill Book Company

New York *St. Louis* *San Francisco* *Düsseldorf* *Johannesburg* *Kuala Lumpur* *London* *Mexico* *Montreal* *New Delhi* *Panama* *Paris* *São Paulo* *Singapore* *Sydney* *Tokyo* *Toronto*

Library of Congress Cataloging in Publication Data

Rice, Harold S.
Technical mathematics with calculus.

1. Mathematics—1961- I. Knight, Raymond M., joint author. II. Title.
QA37.2.R49 1974 510 74-3264
ISBN 0-07-052205-7

Technical Mathematics with Calculus

2 3 4 5 6 7 8 9 0 KPKP 7 9 8 7 6 5

The editors for this book were Gerald O. Stoner and Susan L. Schwartz, the designer was Marsha Cohen, and its production was supervised by Laurence Charnow. It was set in Medallion by York Graphic Services, Inc.
It was printed and bound by Kingsport Press.

contents

preface

Every textbook should have a definable purpose and point of view. As in the previous editions, the authors intend to help students of the engineering technologies learn how to use the techniques of mathematics not only in the study of the engineering sciences and technical specialities but also on the job in their careers as engineering technicians. The authors are well aware that there are other values of mathematics. Those, however important and worthwhile they are, are definitely subordinate to the central theme of this text.

The authors are also well aware that there are many functions and many techniques that are not even hinted at in this volume. They have been omitted intentionally because experience has shown that these functions and techniques are not ordinarily encountered by the beginning engineer and engineering technician. The authors feel very strongly that the classroom time and the textbook space can much more profitably be devoted to building skills in the use of the more elementary aspects of mathematics. Therefore such topics as infinite series, differential equations, Laplace transforms and the like have been omitted with the suggestion that they be reserved for a somewhat more advanced course.

This text is the outgrowth of years of classwork with students at Wentworth Institute and Hudson Valley Community College, who are high school graduates who have had at least a year or two of algebra and have shown a considerable aptitude for mathematics. Although they expect to enter industry and work closely with craftsmen, they must also be at ease in the more precise atmosphere of engineering. With today's and tomorrow's needs in mind, the general approach of this edition has been modernized. The emphasis is still on problem solving, and the problems, which include space-technology topics, have been revised with great care and new ones have been added. The trend toward greater use of the metric system has been recognized in the statement of some problems in metric units and the inclusion of Appendix E (Weights and Measures). Simple numbers have been intentionally used in the illustrative examples. This allows the student to concentrate on the explanation of the principle rather than getting bogged down in the arithmetic.

The text has been divided into twenty-one chapters and six appendixes. Chapters 1 through 13 are devoted to a review of the elementary algebra, geometry and trigonometry normally encountered by a student in high school mathematics courses. However, in this text in particular, there is strong emphasis on applications in technology. The slide rule (Chapter 1) and logarithms (Chapter 8) are used extensively in the solution of these problems. Determinants are also discussed in considerable detail in Chapter 7. There is increased emphasis on the Compound Interest Law in the treatment of common logarithms (Chapter 8). Chapters 15 through 18 are intended especially, but by no means exclusively, for electricity students. The treatment of curve sketching in Chapter 11, together with the extensive discussion of slopes in Chapter 6 and of graphical methods of calculus in Chapter 19 provide a particularly strong preparation for the study of the elementary calculus in Chapters 20 and 21. The topics and their sequence in these last two chapters constitute a fairly traditional course in elementary calculus. The intention of the authors here is to introduce those techniques of calculus which will be useful to engineering students in the pursuit of their major subjects. It is written for student engineers and student engineering technicians. It is definitely not written for physics majors.

Throughout the text important equations are numbered at the right side of the page to facilitate reference to them. Those equations that are especially vital for students' comprehension are numbered in boldface type.

Several changes in the order of the topics have been made to improve the teachability of the text. Exponents and radicals are presented as part of the review of algebra in Chapter 2. The chapter on ratio, variation, and proportion is presented earlier to follow directly after linear equations in one variable. Geometry now appears as Chapter 5. In this order use can be made of basic algebra, linear equations, and ratio, variation and proportion. There is a wide range in the difficulty of the geometry problems. The demarcation between the basic and the more stimulating nonroutine problems has been clearly indicated. Some "word problems" in linear equations are now to be solved using two variables instead of one.

The authors, in their courses, devote about a year and a half to the material in this book; but in courses that give a greater proportion of time to shopwork, the material may occupy two full years.

Thanks are due to the authors' colleagues for their continued interest and constructive criticisms. The authors are also grateful to the users of the first and second editions who have taken the trouble to make suggestions for an improved third edition.

In particular, the authors wish to express their appreciation to Barclay V. Huiell of Voorhees Technical Institute for his valuable suggestions about problem material and to Mr. John W. Cell, author of *Engineering Problems Illustrating Mathematics,* for permission to adapt problem material from his book.

Harold S. Rice

Raymond M. Knight

technical mathematics with calculus

1 slide rule and numerical tables

From time to time we shall review some of the methods whereby much of the drudgery of computation may be eliminated and the effectiveness of work increased. These methods include the use of the slide rule, tables, approximations, and graph paper, to name a few. In this chapter we shall obtain practice in the use of the slide rule and tables.

In this chapter and in Chap. 5 any commonly used handbook of tables may be referred to. For example, see the later editions of Burington's "Handbook of Mathematical Tables and Formulas," McGraw-Hill Book Company; Hudson's "Engineer's Manual," John Wiley & Sons, Inc.; "Standard Mathematical Tables," Chemical Rubber Publishing Co.

1.1 Scope of the Slide Rule

It is essential to have a clear idea of what can and what cannot be done on a slide rule. The slide rule is an instrument used for processes of multiplication, division, proportion, and calculation of simple powers and roots. Further discussion of the slide rule will be found in Secs. 8.31, 8.32, 14.6 and 14.14; this chapter will deal only with the processes named above. Addition and subtraction cannot be performed on the slide rule. One of the most frequently asked questions is, "Is slide-rule computation good

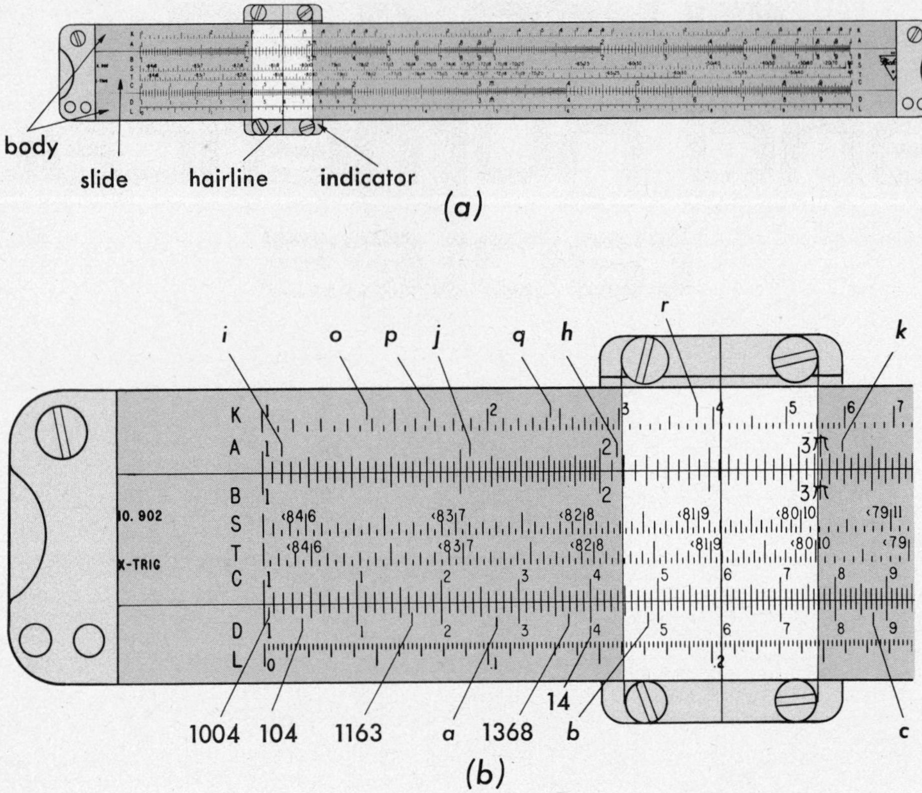

FIGURE 1.1

enough?" The answer depends upon the nature of the problem. Many experimental data are accurate to no more than three significant figures. In such cases slide-rule computation is sufficiently accurate. Even in problems requiring more precise methods, the slide rule is accurate enough to detect gross errors and to estimate the order of magnitude of the answer.

The slide rule will not think for you. Like an automobile, it will take you to your destination if you provide the proper direction.

There are many types of slide rules, but our discussion will be limited to the general technique of operation common to most basic 10-in rules. (More versatile slide rules feature inverted and folded scales as well as log-log scales. Instruction in their use is given in the manual provided with the rule. Almost as many operations can be performed on the basic rule as on the rule having additional scales. The chief advantage of the latter lies in its greater ease of operation.) Additional practice in using the slide rule may be gained by solving many of the problems in Chap. 5.

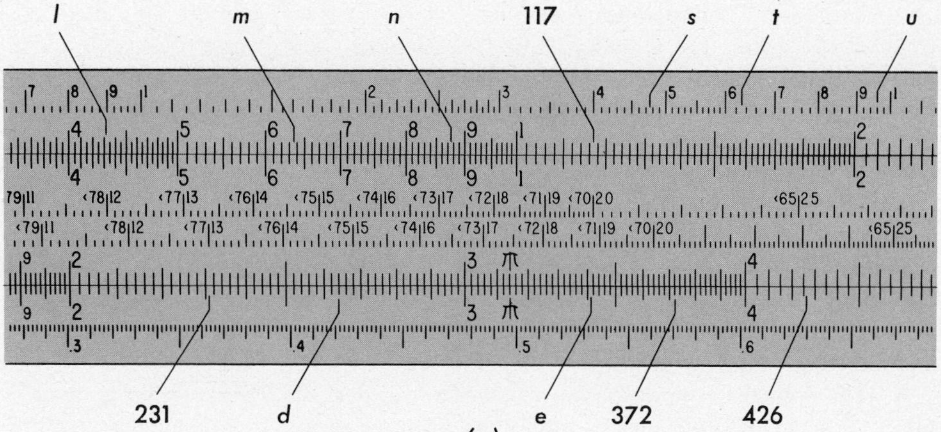

(c)

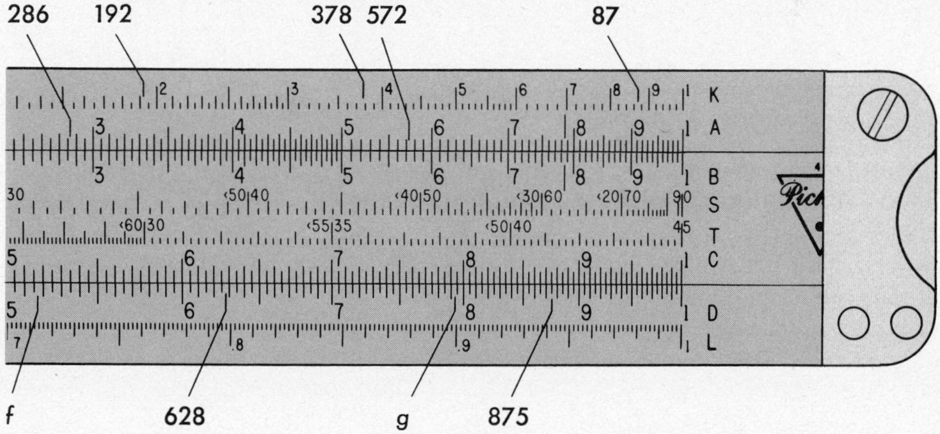

(d)

1.2 Description of the Slide Rule

The slide rule consists of three parts (Fig. 1.1): the *slide*, or central sliding part; the *body*, or the upper and lower bars between which the slide operates; and the *indicator*, which is the movable glass plate marked with a hairline.

The mark associated with the numeral 1 at an end of a scale is called the *index* of the scale. Two positions on two different scales are said to be *opposite* if the hairline can be made to cover both simultaneously.

To perform the operations mentioned in Sec. 1.1, we need use only the C, D, A, B, and K scales. The C and D scales are identical. The A and B scales are also identical, and the distance between two successive integers is one-half the distance between the same two integers on the C and D scales. The K scale is compressed even further, so that the distance between any two integers is one-third the distance between the same two integers on scales C and D.

The C and D scales are divided into nine principal divisions by *primary marks* bearing the large numbers 1, 2, 3, . . . , 8, 9, 1. The space between any two primary marks is divided into ten parts by *secondary marks*. These are not numbered, except between the primary marks 1 and 2, where they bear the small numerals 1 to 9. The space between two successive secondary marks is divided into two, five, or ten spaces by unnumbered *tertiary marks*.

The A and B scales each have two identical portions. Each portion is divided into nine principal divisions by numbered primary marks. Unnumbered secondary marks further divide each principal division, and still finer division is supplied by tertiary marks between the primary marks numbered 1 and 5.

The K scale is divided into three identical portions. They are divided much as the A and B scales are, but more coarsely.

1.3 Location of Numbers on the Scales; Accuracy of the Slide Rule

It must be remembered that the decimal point plays no part in locating a number on the C and D scales. The first significant digit is located by reference to the primary marks, the second by reference to the secondary marks, and the third by reference to the tertiary marks or to some point between tertiary marks, according to the portion of the scale being used. By estimating fractions of a graduation, a fourth digit may be located for numbers occurring between primary marks 1 and 2 on the C and D scales. This means that the maximum accuracy ordinarily available with a 10-in slide rule is 1 part in 1,000. Location of actual numbers will be best illustrated by referring to the examples in Fig. 1.1*b* to *d*.

EXERCISE 1

Read as closely as possible the points indicated in Fig. 1.1*b* to *d*.

D scale: *a b c d e f g*
A scale: *h i j k l m n*
K scale: *o p q r s t u*

1.4 Multiplication

Either the C and D scales or the A and B scales may be used. Ordinarily the C and D scales are preferable, since their larger-scale divisions make for greater accuracy. Their use is illustrated in Fig. 1.2 and in the following example.

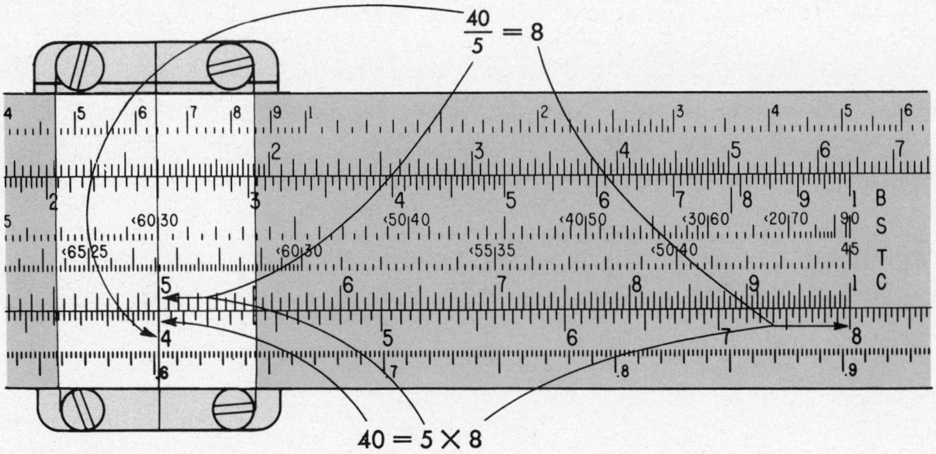

FIGURE 1.2

Example 1. Multiply 8 by 5.

Set the right index of C opposite 8 on the D scale. Move the indicator so the hairline covers 5 on the C scale. Directly below this 5 will be found the "slide-rule product" 4 on the D scale. The student must locate the decimal point himself, and common sense indicates that the answer is 40, not 4.

We can see that the same setting would be used for multiplying 80 by 50; 8,000 by 0.5; 0.08 by 500; etc.

If we were to try to use the above setting of the right index to multiply 8 by 12, a reading would be impossible, because the 12 on the C scale is located beyond the end of the D scale. In this case we would set the *left* index of the C scale over 8 on the D scale and locate on the D scale our answer 96, immediately under 12 on the C scale. It will be useful to remember that when the product of the first significant figures in multiplicand and multiplier is less than 10, the student should use the left index; when it is greater than 10, he should use the right index.

When you multiply more than two numbers, use the hairline to mark the position of the product of the first two. Without reading this product, use it as the multiplicand for the next multiplication.

If the magnitude of the product is not immediately obvious, a rough mental check will suffice.

Example 2. The slide-rule product of 1,440 × 37.5 × 0.08125 is 439. It is evident that our product is approximately 1,500 × 40 × 0.08, or 4,800. Hence the answer must be 4,390.

To multiply two numbers:

1. *Set the proper index of C opposite either factor on the D scale.*
2. *Place the hairline over the other factor on the C scale, and read the significant digits of the product under the hairline on the D scale.*
3. *Determine the position of the decimal point by a rough mental estimate.*
4. *In the above steps, C and D may be replaced by B and A, respectively.*

EXERCISE 2

Perform the following multiplications, retaining in the product as many significant figures as you think are justified:

1. 4.00×17.00
2. 7.50×1.20
3. 3.30×9.0
4. 64.0×0.375
5. 288×382
6. $321 \times 1{,}069$
7. $728 \times 1{,}218$
8. $617 \times 1{,}645$
9. $1{,}006 \times 902$
10. $1{,}258 \times 1{,}562$
11. 862×482
12. 66.2×10.3
13. $1.475 \times 1{,}520$
14. 0.981×0.693
15. 329×0.00352
16. 0.342×1.306
17. 8.14×0.0309
18. $2.46 \times 330{,}000 \times 3.14$
19. $3.1 \times 920 \times 0.486 \times 1{,}520$
20. $0.1038 \times 0.0063 \times 28 \times 9.82$
21. $512 \times 62.5 \times 0.0027 \times 87$
22. $0.1047 \times 0.00774 \times 0.349 \times 0.0562$

1.5 Division

Since division is the inverse of multiplication, Fig. 1.2 may be used to illustrate division as well as multiplication. In this example we have the setting for $40 \div 5 = 8$.

To divide one number by another:

1. *Bring the divisor on the C scale opposite the dividend on the D scale by means of the hairline.*
2. *Opposite the index of the C scale, read the significant figures of the quotient on the D scale. If desired, the indicator may be used to aid in this reading.*
3. *Determine the position of the decimal point by a rough mental estimate.*
4. *C and D may be replaced by B and A, respectively, as in multiplication.*

EXERCISE 3

Perform the following divisions, retaining in the quotient as many significant figures as you think are justified:

1. 18.00 ÷ 50.0	2. 25.0 ÷ 3.00	3. 750 ÷ 5.50
4. 12.8 ÷ 72	5. 69.8 ÷ 4.78	6. 197.2 ÷ 858
7. 0.924 ÷ 21.0	8. 17.5 ÷ 1,646	9. 1 ÷ 37.5
10. 0.0752 ÷ 0.000718	11. 0.1804 ÷ 363	12. 1 ÷ 2.73
13. 0.1875 ÷ 0.078125	14. 0.005632 ÷ 18.432	

1.6 Location of Decimal Point in Scientific Notation

Use of scientific notation makes work with very large or very small numbers easier and reduces the likelihood of error. (See Appendix A.)

Example 3. Multiply 538,000 by 0.00377.

In scientific notation, we have, roughly, $(5 \times 10^5) \times (4 \times 10^{-3})$. This product may be written $5 \times 4 \times 10^2 = 2 \times 10^3$. Since the product of 5.38 and 3.77 on the slide rule is 203 (before locating the decimal point), our answer must be 2.03×10^3, or 2,030.

Example 4. Divide 538,000 by 0.00377.

In scientific notation, we have, roughly, $(5 \times 10^5)/(4 \times 10^{-3}) = 1.2 \times 10^8$. Since the slide-rule reading is 1,427, our answer must be 1.427×10^8, or 142,700,000.

1.7 Combined Multiplication and Division

The easiest method of computing the quotient of two products is to alternate between division and multiplication. If we do all the multiplying first, and then all the dividing, more moves are required, and the chance of error is greater.

Example 5. Evaluate

$$\frac{825 \times 184}{227 \times 316}$$

Divide 825 by 227 in the usual way. The quotient will be found on the D scale under the C index. However, we do not read the value, since it serves merely as the multiplicand for 184. Without moving the slide, we move the indicator so that the hairline covers 184 on the C scale. The product will be found on the D scale under the hairline. Since this product is to be divided by 316, we do not read the value, nor do we move the hairline, but we move the slide so that 316 is under the hairline. Directly beneath the C index read approximately 2115. The answer is 2.115, with the last figure in doubt.

Sometimes the slide must be moved so that one C index is moved to the spot formerly occupied by the other C index (as marked with the hairline). This situation might have been avoided, with some sacrifice of accuracy, by using the A and B scales.

EXERCISE 4

Perform the following computations, expressing the answer in scientific notation. Retain in the answer as many significant figures as conditions justify.

1. $2.4 \times 6.5 \times 10.37$
2. $1{,}476 \times 37.8 \times 54.0$
3. $0.00842 \times 0.295 \times 6.1875$
4. $67.1 \times 0.000418 \times 3.0$
5. $32.00 \times 5.000 \times 1.900 \times 0.4000$
6. $\dfrac{1}{0.00532 \times 0.0612}$
7. $\dfrac{1.28 \times 3.56}{74.4}$
8. $\dfrac{15.8 \times 1.35}{0.031}$
9. $\dfrac{21.3 \times 0.054}{97.4 \times 3.80}$
10. $\dfrac{1{,}927}{412 \times 0.00592 \times 483}$
11. $\dfrac{24.6 \times 0.359}{296 \times 4.61 \times 98.7}$
12. $\dfrac{560{,}000 \times 0.0045 \times 12{,}500}{1{,}050{,}000 \times 0.072}$

1.8 Proportion

Proportions may usually be solved with only one setting of the slide. Observe in Fig. 1.3 that when 8 on the C scale is opposite 64 on the D scale, we find 5 opposite 4. This setting could therefore illustrate the solution of the proportion $5/x = 8/6.4$, in which we set 8 opposite 64 and, opposite 5 we read $x = 4$. Note that all other pairs of numbers opposite each other have the same ratio (for example, $^{60}/_{48}$, $^{70}/_{56}$, $^{75}/_{60}$, $^{90}/_{72}$).

To solve a proportion, locate the numbers on the C and D scales in the same

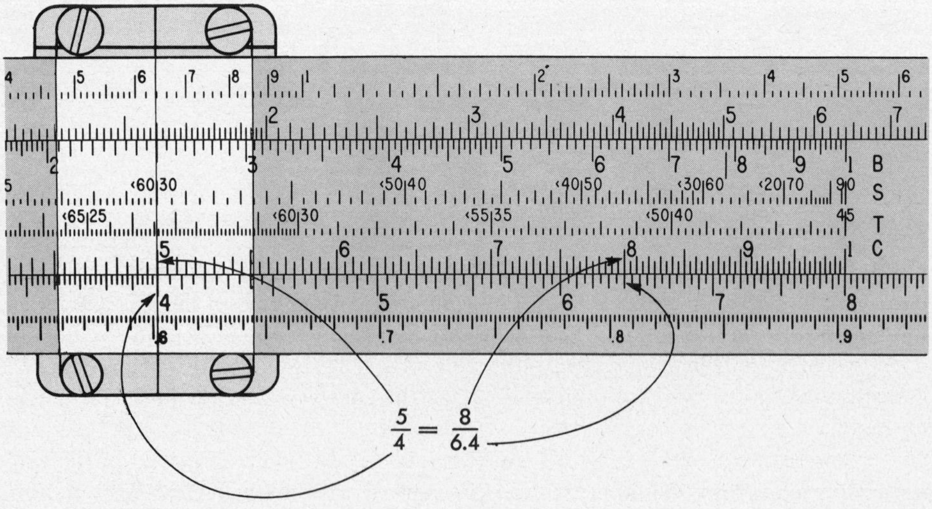

FIGURE 1.3

relative position as in the proportion $a/b = c/d$ (or $c/d = a/b$ if the setting for a falls to the right of the setting for c). When the C and D scales cannot accommodate the simultaneous settings of a over b and c over d, the A and B scales may be used.

Of course we can solve for x, obtaining $x = (5)(6.4)/8$ and, using the principle of Sec. 1.7, again obtain $x = 4$.

EXERCISE 5

In the following proportions, calculate x to three significant figures:

1. $\dfrac{x}{8.5} = \dfrac{32}{28.9}$
2. $\dfrac{x}{21.5} = \dfrac{89}{79}$
3. $\dfrac{372}{x} = \dfrac{637}{9.31}$
4. $\dfrac{8.2}{377} = \dfrac{0.323}{x}$
5. $\dfrac{18.3}{63.6} = \dfrac{x}{29}$
6. $\dfrac{267}{8.75} = \dfrac{x}{192}$
7. $\dfrac{0.716}{x} = \dfrac{10.1}{168}$
8. $\dfrac{795}{0.109} = \dfrac{42.3}{x}$

Note that in Prob. 5, for example, we may estimate the value of x by comparing either vertically or horizontally. Since 18.3 is about (0.3)(63.6), x must be about (0.3)(29), or 9. Again, since 29 is about ($\frac{1}{2}$)(63.6), x must be about ($\frac{1}{2}$)(18.3), or 9.

1.9 Squares and Square Roots

To find the square of a number, set the hairline of the indicator over that number on the D scale, and under the hairline read the square of that number on the A scale. We can also read from the C to the B scale in the same way. Figure 1.4 shows that $4^2 = 16$ (D to A scale), that $5^2 = 25$ (C to B scale), and that $8^2 = 64$ (right C index reading to right B index setting).

Figure 1.5 illustrates that $(1.428)^2 = 2.04$ and that $(2.53)^2 = 6.4$.

Example 6. Find 6^2.

Set the hairline over 6 on the D scale. Read 36 under the hairline on the A scale.

Example 7. Find $(8.62)^2$.

Set the hairline over 8.62 on the D scale. Read 74.3 under the hairline on the A scale.

Example 8. Find $(71{,}700)^2$.

On the A scale read 514 directly above the 717 on the D scale. Since $(71{,}700)^2 = (7.17 \times 10^4)^2$, the answer must be $51.4 \times 10^{4\times2} = 51.4 \times 10^8 = 5{,}140{,}000{,}000$.

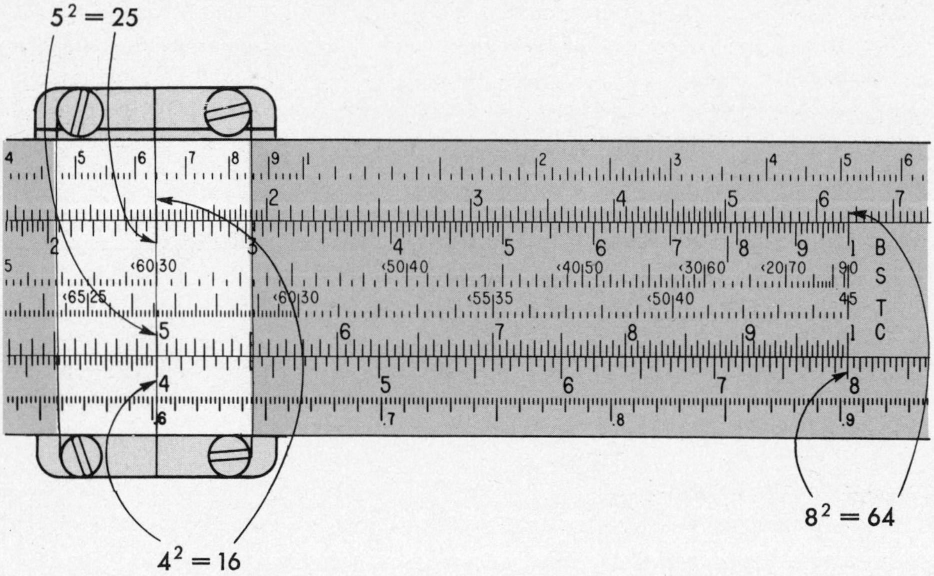

FIGURE 1.4

Example 9. Find $(0.00386)^2$.

On the A scale read 149 directly above the 386 on the D scale. Since $(0.00386)^2 = (3.86 \times 10^{-3})^2$, the answer must be $14.9 \times 10^{-3\times 2} = 14.9 \times 10^{-6} = 0.0000149$.

The process of obtaining square roots is the reverse of that used in calculating squares. Therefore Figs. 1.4 and 1.5 may be used to show that $\sqrt{16} = 4$, $\sqrt{25} = 5$,

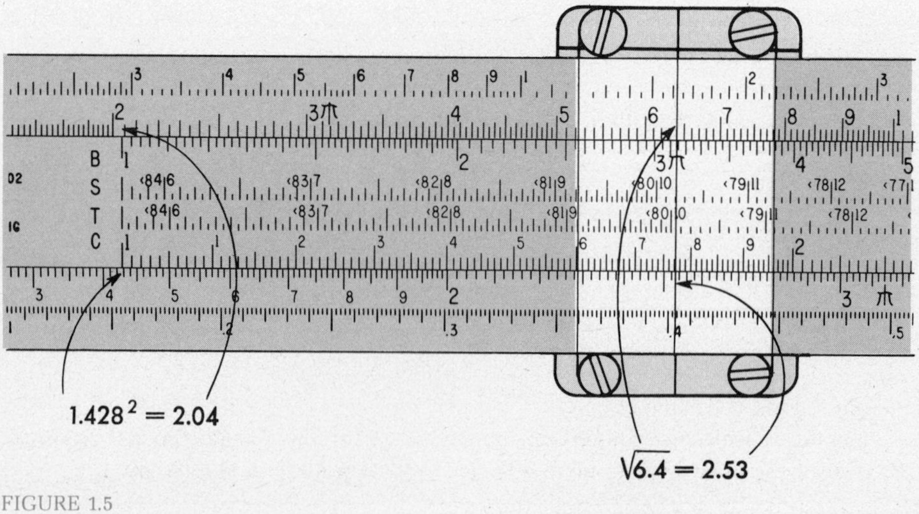

FIGURE 1.5

$\sqrt{64} = 8$, $\sqrt{2.04} = 1{,}428$, and $\sqrt{6.4} = 2.53$. We may indeed use Fig. 1.4 to read $\sqrt{64} = 8$; but if we had not had the operation of squaring 8 to guide us, we might have made an unfortunate choice in working from the 64 on the left half of the A scale; i.e., we might have read 253 directly below on the D scale. A quick check will show that 2.53 is the square root of 6.4. (This procedure is the opposite of squaring 2.53, an operation originally illustrated in Fig. 1.5.)

It is evident that in reversing the procedure for squaring we must first determine which half of the A scale to choose as a starting point. There are a number of ways of making this choice. Perhaps the simplest is that used in the examples in Sec. 1.13. The procedure is as follows: Write down the number whose square root is to be found. Indicate the grouping of the digits as for longhand extraction of square root. Write in their proper positions the decimal point and the first significant digit in the square root. Select that half of the A scale which lies above the first significant figure (just determined) on the D scale.

Example 10. Find $\sqrt{6{,}870{,}000.}$

Indicating the grouping, the decimal point, and the first significant figure, we write

$$\begin{array}{l} \;\;2 \\ \sqrt{6\ 87\ 00\ 00.} \end{array}$$

It is apparent that we read from 687 on the *left* half of the A scale, since we find 2 on the D scale under that half. Accordingly, we read from 687 on the left half of the A scale directly below to 262 on the D scale. This indicates that the square root of 6,870,000 will be written

$$\begin{array}{l} \;\;2\ \ 6\ \ 2\ \ 0. \\ \sqrt{6\ 87\ 00\ 00.} \end{array}$$

Example 11. Find $\sqrt{0.0000687.}$

A rough indication of the answer is found by proceeding as before and writing

$$\begin{array}{l} \;\;0.\ \ 0\ \ 0\ \ 8 \\ \sqrt{0.\ 00\ 00\ 68\ 7} \end{array}$$

In this case we evidently read down from the 687 on the *right* half of the A scale. We read 829 on the D scale, and the answer is clearly 0.00829.

1.10 Cubes and Cube Roots

To find the cube of a number, set the hairline over that number on the D scale and read its cube on the K scale under the hairline.

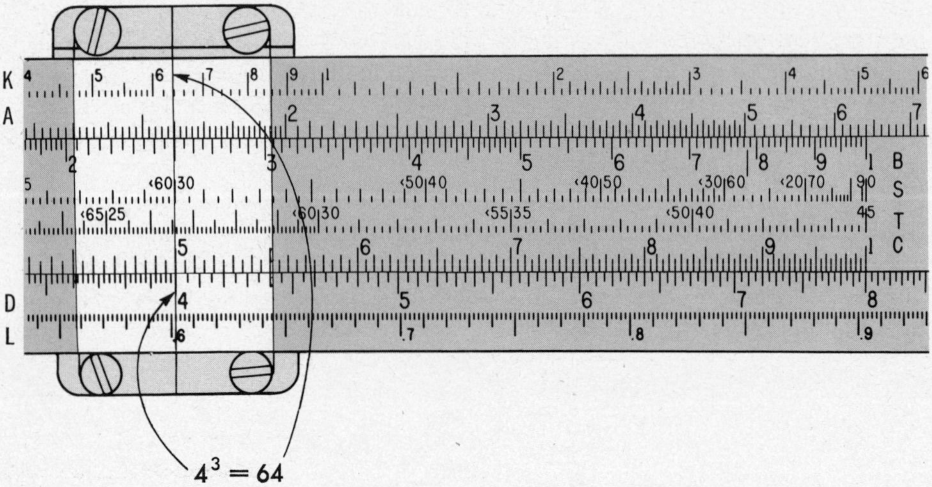

FIGURE 1.6

Example 12. Find $(6.35)^3$.

Set the hairline over 6.35 on the D scale. Read 256 under the hairline on the K scale.

Example 13. Find $(0.0439)^3$.

Read 846 on the K scale directly opposite 439 on the D scale. Since $(0.0439)^3 = (4.39 \times 10^{-2})^3$, the answer must be $84.6 \times 10^{-2\times3} = 84.6 \times 10^{-6} = 0.0000846$.

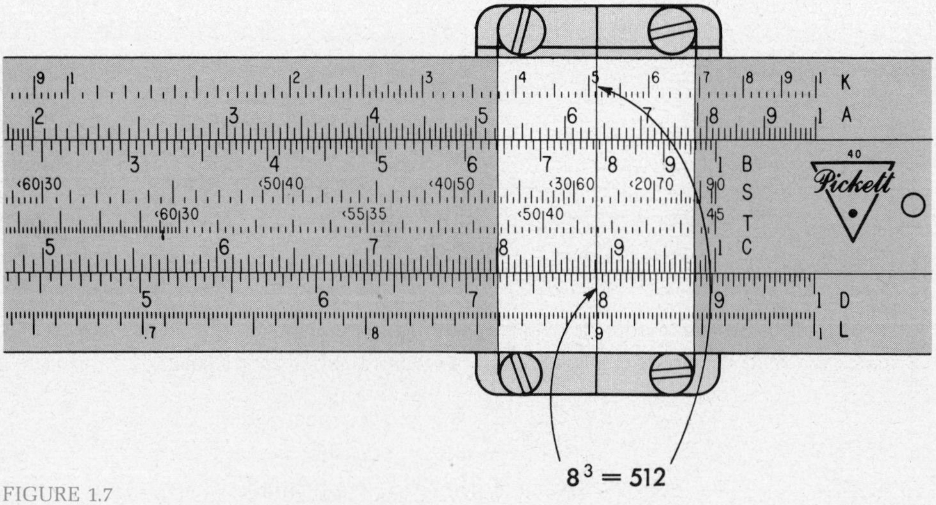

FIGURE 1.7

To find a cube root, we reverse the procedure for cubing and work from the K scale to the D scale. When working from the A scale to the D scale, we had to choose between two sections. On the K scale we must choose the proper section out of three. The process is exactly comparable with that used in finding a square root. Figures 1.6 to 1.8 show the settings for 4^3, 8^3, and 16^3, and therefore the settings for $\sqrt[3]{64}$, $\sqrt[3]{512}$, and $\sqrt[3]{4{,}100}$.

Example 14. Find $\sqrt[3]{0.0000048}$.

Indicating the grouping, the decimal point, and the first significant figure, we write

$$\begin{array}{l} 0.\ 0\quad 1 \\ \sqrt[3]{0.000\ 004\ 8} \end{array}$$

Evidently we work from the *left* third of the K scale, since it lies opposite the 1+ on the D scale. Therefore we read from 48 on the left third of the K scale directly to 1,687 on the D scale. This indicates that the cube root of 0.0000048 will be written

$$\begin{array}{l} 0.\ 0\quad 1\ 6\ 8\ 7 \\ \sqrt[3]{0.000\ 004\ 8} \end{array}$$

Example 15. Find $\sqrt[3]{58{,}500{,}000}$.

Proceeding as before, we write

$$\begin{array}{l} \quad 3 \\ \sqrt[3]{58\ 500\ 000.} \end{array}$$

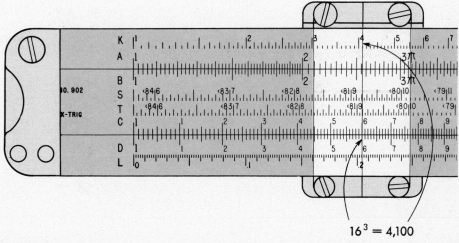

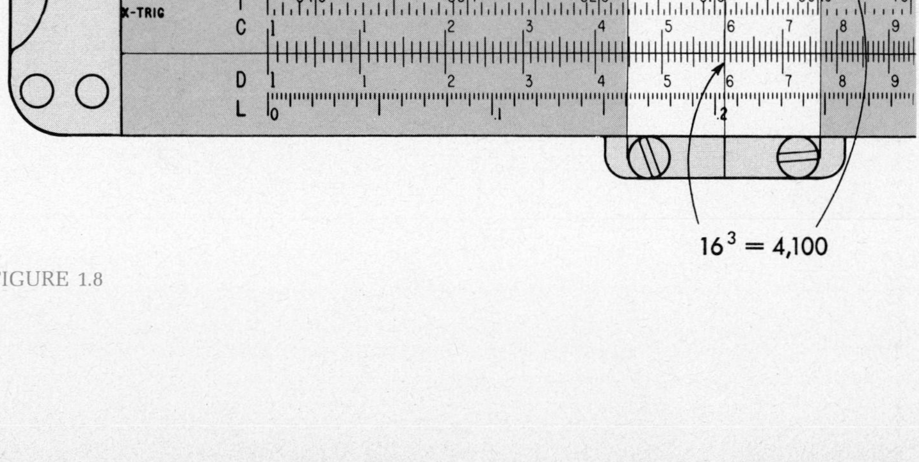

FIGURE 1.8

and find that the *middle* third of the K scale lies opposite the 3 on the D scale. Reading, therefore, from 585 in the middle section of the K scale, we find 388 on the D scale directly opposite. Hence the answer must be 388.

EXERCISE 6

Evaluate the following as accurately as the slide rule will allow:

1. $(18.00)^2$
2. $(2{,}730)^2$
3. $(6.05)^2$
4. $(34.5)^2$
5. $(167.8)^2$
6. $(0.854)^2$
7. $(0.1054)^2$
8. $(0.00782)^2$
9. $(517.23)^2$
10. $(0.030448)^2$
11. $(63 \times 426)^2$
12. $(9.1 \times 0.0119)^2$
13. $(0.027 \times 1.72 \times 7.95)^2$
14. $(5.1 \times 0.438 \times 14.12)^2$
15. $\left(\frac{1{,}647}{658}\right)^2$
16. $\left(\frac{69.8}{858}\right)^2$
17. $\left(\frac{852}{658}\right)^2$
18. $\left(\frac{61.4 \times 0.673}{2.16}\right)^2$
19. $\left(\frac{582 \times 1.104}{37.2 \times 8}\right)^2$
20. $\sqrt{49.2}$
21. $\sqrt{0.00702}$
22. $\sqrt{2{,}980}$
23. $\sqrt{0.837}$
24. $\sqrt{17{,}840}$
25. $\sqrt{0.0542}$
26. $\sqrt{0.000347}$
27. $\sqrt{45{,}897}$
28. $\sqrt{103.6}$
29. $\sqrt{7{,}080{,}000}$
30. $\sqrt{\frac{1.316}{0.016}}$
31. $\sqrt{\frac{1{,}127 \times 5.47}{21 \times 0.0025}}$
32. $\sqrt{\frac{11.26}{0.787 \times 24.8}}$
33. $(11.9)^3$
34. $(1.33)^3$
35. $(0.157)^3$
36. $(118.5)^3$
37. $(23.19)^3$
38. $(0.0342)^3$
39. $(478)^3$
40. $(6.375)^3$
41. $(783)^3$
42. $(0.0876)^3$
43. $(15.45 \times 0.132)^3$
44. $(8.75 \times 0.037)^3$
45. $\left(\frac{10.12}{17.58}\right)^3$
46. $\left(\frac{48.8}{4.21}\right)^3$
47. $\sqrt[3]{13.5}$
48. $\sqrt[3]{0.0474}$
49. $\sqrt[3]{76{,}215}$
50. $\sqrt[3]{2.85}$

51. $\sqrt[3]{9{,}384{,}260}$ 52. $\sqrt[3]{0.00625}$

53. $\sqrt[3]{652 \times 0.725}$ 54. $\sqrt[3]{1.447 \times 0.0298}$

55. $\sqrt[3]{\dfrac{8{,}747}{0.212}}$ 56. $\sqrt[3]{\dfrac{158.5}{255}}$

1.11 Circumference and Area of a Circle

Because the problem of finding the circumference of a circle is simply one of finding the product of a given diameter and 3.14, we follow the regular procedure for multiplication.

To find the area of a circle when the radius is given, set the index of C opposite the radius on the D scale. Place the hairline over π on the B scale. The answer is found under the hairline on the A scale. Figure 1.9 shows that the area of a circle of radius 17.44 in is about 956 in^2.

To find the area of a circle when the diameter is given, set the index of C opposite the diameter on the D scale. Place the hairline over $\pi/4$, or 0.785 on the B scale. The area is found under the hairline on the A scale. Figure 1.10 shows that the area of a 9.03-in-diameter circle is 64.0 in^2.

EXERCISE 7

Make a copy of the following table of circles and fill in the blanks:

	Radius	*Diameter*	*Circumference*	*Area*
1.	6.3 mi	______	______	______
2.	$5\frac{1}{4}$ in	______	______	______
3.	78 ft	______	______	______
4.	$\frac{9}{16}$ in	______	______	______
5.	______	11.2 yd	______	______
6.	______	31.6 ft	______	______
7.	______	$\frac{7}{8}$ in	______	______
8.	______	$14\frac{1}{2}$ in	______	______
9.	______	______	8.43 in	______
10.	______	______	26.7 ft	______
11.	______	______	______	10.00 in^2
12.	______	______	______	63.8 ft^2

1.12 General Suggestions for Slide-rule Operation

As the student becomes skillful in the use of the slide rule, he will acquire various tricks of the trade which will make this tool even more effective. A few suggestions are outlined in the following paragraphs.

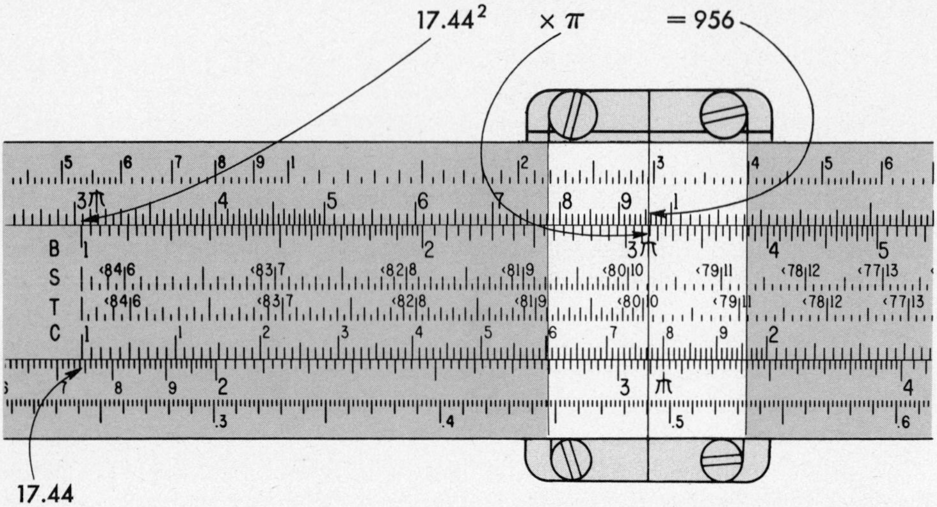

FIGURE 1.9

Before setting numbers on the slide rule, cancel or combine simple numbers to reduce the number of moves required.

Example 16. $\dfrac{2 \times 43 \times 3}{17 \times 61} = \dfrac{6 \times 43}{17 \times 61}$

A move is saved.

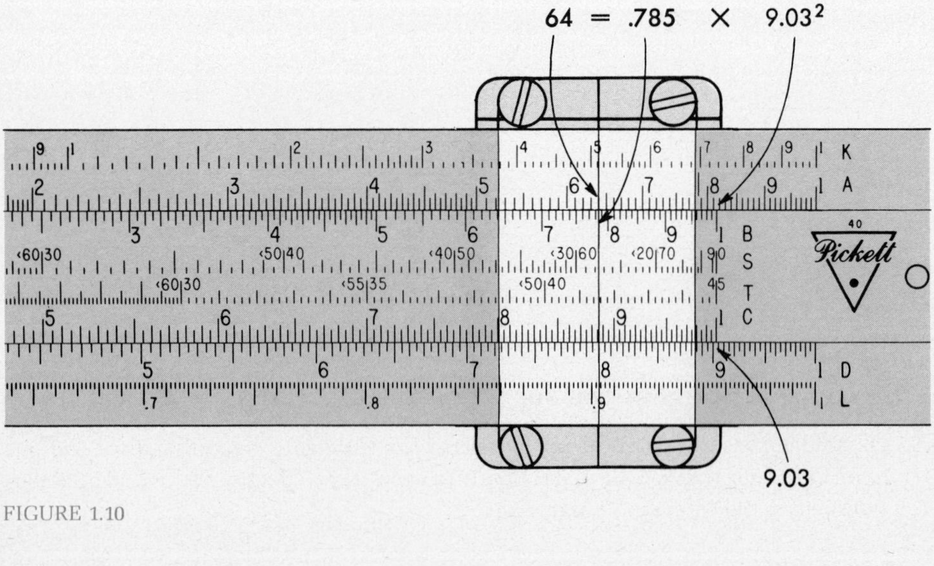

FIGURE 1.10

Example 17. $\dfrac{60 \times 105}{5 \times 2 \times 97} = \dfrac{6 \times 105}{97}$

Two moves are saved.

Increased accuracy in slide-rule division is possible through the calculation of the first few significant figures by long division.

Example 18. Divide 483 by 617, obtaining five significant figures in the quotient.

We may obtain the first two significant figures by long division and the next three by slide rule.

```
        .78
617 )483.00
     431 9
     -----
      51 10
      49 36
      -----
       1 74
```

By slide rule 174 ÷ 617 yields the digits 282. Hence our answer is 0.78282.

In cases in which the dividend differs but little from the divisor, greatly improved accuracy may be obtained, as indicated by the following example.

Example 19. Divide 732.00 by 741.00.

$$\frac{732}{741} = \frac{741 - 9}{741} = 1 - \frac{9}{741}$$

By slide rule, 9 ÷ 741 = 0.01215. Hence

$$\frac{732.00}{741.00} = 1 - 0.01215 = 0.98785$$

A similar device is useful when multiplying by a number having a value near unity.

Example 20. Multiply 0.99756 by 610.95.

$$(0.99756)(610.95) = (1 - 0.00244)(610.95) = 610.95 - 1.49 = 609.46$$

Preliminary rearrangement of formulas is often helpful, as in logarithmic computation (Sec. 8.26).

As an alternative to the factoring method, it is suggested that the familiar

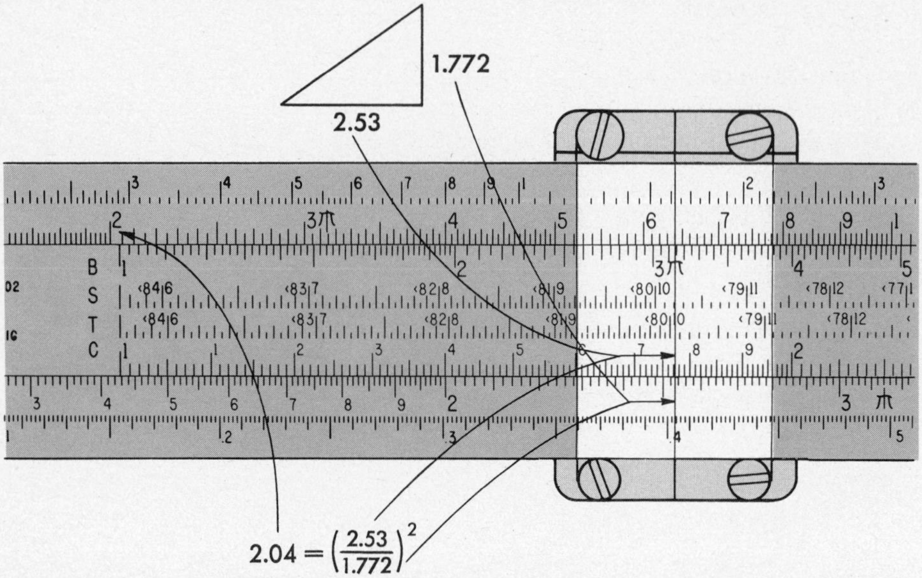

FIGURE 1.11

formulas of the Pythagorean theorem be modified before use on the slide rule, as indicated:

$a = \sqrt{c^2 - b^2}$	becomes	$a = b\sqrt{(c/b)^2 - 1}$	
$b = \sqrt{c^2 - a^2}$	becomes	$b = a\sqrt{(c/a)^2 - 1}$	
$c = \sqrt{a^2 + b^2}$	becomes	$c = b\sqrt{(a/b)^2 + 1}$	$(a > b)$
		$c = a\sqrt{(b/a)^2 + 1}$	$(b > a)$

With the subtraction or addition of 1 done mentally, a minimum of moves is required.

Example 21. Find the hypotenuse of a right triangle whose sides are 2.53 and 1.772.

Letting 2.53, the larger side, be represented by a, and 1.772 by b, and referring to Fig. 1.11, we have the setting for obtaining $(2.53/1.772)^2$, which is seen to be 2.04. Adding 1 mentally to obtain 3.04, or $(a/b)^2 + 1$, we then refer to Fig. 1.12, showing the setting for $1.772\sqrt{3.04}$, which we read on the D scale as approximately 3.09.

EXERCISE 8

Compute the missing sides in the following right triangles in which c is the hypotenuse:

	a	b	c
1.	38	47	______
2.	7.52	10.36	______

3.	523	408	______
4.	$1\frac{7}{8}$ in	$2\frac{3}{4}$ in	______
5.	9.85	25.6	______
6.	______	0.0645	0.0892
7.	______	12.33	20.7
8.	______	$3\frac{1}{8}$ in	$4\frac{1}{4}$ in
9.	5,670	______	7,030
10.	0.1525	______	0.291
11.	$4\frac{7}{8}$ in	______	$5\frac{1}{2}$ in

In finding the hypotenuse of a right triangle containing a small acute angle, the approximation $c \approx a + [b^2/(2a)]$, where b is the smallest side, is useful. The smaller b becomes in relation to a, the closer the approximation. If b is as large as $0.2a$, then c, as calculated by the approximation, will be about 0.02 percent too large.

EXERCISE 9

Find c, evaluating $b^2/(2a)$ to three significant figures by slide rule.

	a	b
1.	52	3
2.	109	4
3.	15 in	$\frac{3}{8}$ in
4.	213	7
5.	1.75	0.08

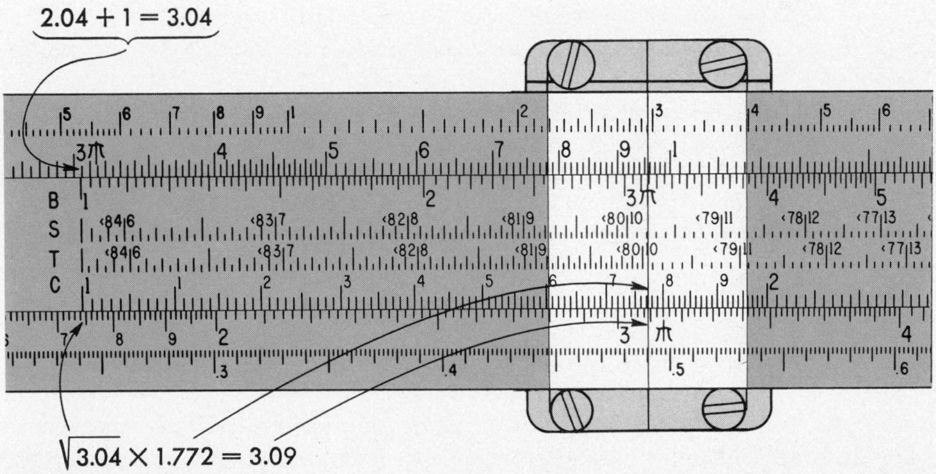

FIGURE 1.12

In the following sections we show how the usefulness of the tables can be extended by appropriate shifting of decimal points and by interpolation.

1.13 Extending the Range of the Tables

The table of squares may be extended beyond the given range by shifting the decimal point twice as many places in the square of the number as in the number itself, for $[x(10)^n]^2 = x^2(10)^{2n}$.

Example 22. Find $(7{,}650)^2$.

In most tables we shall have to use 765, since 7,650 is beyond the scope of the table. Looking up $(765)^2$, we find 585,225. Therefore $(7{,}650)^2 = 58{,}522{,}500$.

Example 23. Find $(1.38)^2$.

Looking up $(138)^2$, we find 19,044. Therefore $(1.38)^2 = 1.9044$.

Note. *The same method applies to finding the areas of circles, since the area varies as the square of the diameter.*

Example 24. Find the area of a $2\frac{3}{4}$-in circle.

Looking up the area of a circle of diameter 275, we find 59,396. Therefore the area of a 2.75-in circle is 5.9396 in^2.

The table of cubes may be extended by shifting the decimal point 3 times as many places in the cube of the number as in the number itself, for $[x(10)^n]^3 = x^3[10]^{3n}$.

Example 25. Find $(3.17)^3$.

Looking up $(317)^3$, we find 31,855,013. Therefore $(3.17)^3 = 31.855013$.

Example 26. Find $(0.431)^3$.

Looking up $(431)^3$, we find 80,062,991. Therefore $(0.431)^3 = 0.080062991$.

The use of the square-root table is governed by a rule similar to those just given. That is, we move the decimal point half as many places in the square root of the number as in the number itself. This is shown by the identity $\sqrt{x(10)^{2n}} = \sqrt{x}(10)^n$. For example,

$$\sqrt{5{,}090{,}000} = \sqrt{(509)(10{,}000)} = 100\sqrt{509}$$

The operation of this rule will be better understood by the following procedure:

Indicate the grouping of the digits of the number as for longhand extraction of square root. Write in their proper positions the decimal point and the first significant digit in the square root. Determine the subsequent digits as found in the square root of the tabulated number having the same grouping as the original number. Fill in these digits in proper sequence after the first significant digit already located.

Example 27. Find $\sqrt{5{,}090{,}000}$

Indicating the grouping and the decimal point and first significant digit in the answer, we write

$$\begin{array}{l} \;\;2 \\ \sqrt{5\ 09\ 00\ 00.} \end{array}$$

The first group, or "key group," is 5, whose square root is 2+. It is apparent that the tabulated number having the same digits and grouping is 509, of which the square root is 22.56103. This indicates that $\sqrt{5{,}090{,}000}$ will be written as follows:

$$\begin{array}{l} \;\;2\ \ 2\ \ 5\ \ 6.\ 103 \\ \sqrt{5\ 09\ 00\ 00.} \end{array}$$

Example 28. Find $\sqrt{0.00509}$.

Our first indication of the answer is given by the grouping

$$\begin{array}{l} \;\;0.\ 0\ \ 7 \\ \sqrt{0.00\ 50\ 90} \end{array}$$

In this example, the first group containing significant figures is 50, whose square root is 7+. Thus the grouping is seen to correspond to that of 5,090, of which the square root is 71.34424. Hence the square root of 0.00509 must be 0.07134424.

The procedure for extending the range of the cube-root table is analogous to that used with the square-root table. That is, we move the decimal point one-third as many places in the cube root of the number as in the number itself. This is shown by the identity $\sqrt[3]{x(10)^{3n}} = \sqrt[3]{x}\,(10)^n$.

Example 29. Find $\sqrt[3]{356{,}000}$.

Indicating the grouping, the decimal point, and the first significant digit in the answer, we write

$$\begin{array}{l} \;\;\;7\ \ \ \ \ . \\ \sqrt[3]{356\ 000.} \end{array}$$

The tabulated number having the same digits and grouping as 356,000 is 356, of which the cube root is 7.087341. Thus the cube root of 356,000 will be

$$\begin{array}{l} \;\;\;7\ \ 0\ .87341 \\ \sqrt[3]{356\ 000.} \end{array}$$

Example 30. Find $\sqrt[3]{0.0356}$.

Grouping, we get

$$\begin{array}{l} 0.\ \ \ 3 \\ \sqrt[3]{0.035\ 600} \end{array}$$

and the corresponding tabulated number is 35,600, of which the cube root is 32.89652. Hence we find

$$\begin{array}{l} 0.\ 3\ \ \ \ 2\ \ \ 8\ 9\ 6\ 5\ 2 \\ \sqrt[3]{0.035\ 6000} \end{array}$$

Example 31. Find $\sqrt[3]{0.00000356}$.

Grouping, we get

$$\begin{array}{l} 0.\ 0\ \ \ \ 1 \\ \sqrt[3]{0.000\ 003\ 560} \end{array}$$

Since the corresponding tabulated number is 3,560, of which the cube root is 15.26921, the desired cube root is

$$\begin{array}{l} 0.\ 0\ \ \ \ 1\ \ 5\ 2\ 6\ 9\ 2\ 1 \\ \sqrt{0.000\ 003\ 560} \end{array}$$

which may be rounded off as desired.

1.14 Other Helpful Devices

Frequently interpolation may be avoided by judicious use of factoring; for example, $\sqrt{1,328} = \sqrt{4(332)} = 2\sqrt{332} = 2(18.2209) = 36.4418$.

The student should not overlook the advantages of rationalization in extracting roots of fractions. For example, $\sqrt{2/3}$ is much more conveniently found by evaluating $\frac{1}{3}\sqrt{6} = \frac{1}{3}(2.4495) = 0.8165$ than by finding $\sqrt{0.666667}$. These operations with radicals are explained in Chap. 2.

Square roots, for instance, may at times be found with increased accuracy by working backward from the table of squares. This is true if the table of square roots is given only to four or five significant figures or so.

Example 32. Find the square root of 174,126.

From the square-root table:

$$
\begin{array}{ccc}
 & x & y\,(=\sqrt{x}) \\
1{,}000\left\{\begin{array}{l} 126\left\{\begin{array}{l}174{,}000\\174{,}126\end{array}\right. \\ \quad 175{,}000\end{array}\right. & & \left.\begin{array}{r}\left.\begin{array}{r}417.13\\?\end{array}\right\} \\ 418.33\end{array}\right\} 120
\end{array}
$$

Interpolation in the usual way gives us $\sqrt{174{,}126} = 417.13 + (126/1{,}000)(120) = 417.13 + 0.15 = 417.28$ (precision to the nearest 0.01).

Using the table of squares:

$$
\begin{array}{cccc}
\Delta x & x\dagger & y\,(=x^2)\dagger & \Delta y \\
1 & \left\{\begin{array}{c}417.000\\?\\418.000\end{array}\right. & \left.\begin{array}{r}\left.\begin{array}{r}173{,}889\\174{,}126\end{array}\right\}237\\174{,}724\end{array}\right\} & 835
\end{array}
$$

† These values are exact.

(Δx and Δy, read "delta x" and "delta y," represent *changes* in x and y.) Interpolating, we obtain

$$417 + \left(\frac{237}{835}\right)1 = 417.284$$

Circumferences by Addition of Parts

Since $\pi(a + b) = \pi a + \pi b$, we may consider that the sum of the circumferences of two circles is equal to the circumference of a circle whose diameter is equal to the sum of the diameters of the first two circles.

Example 33. Find the circumference of a $5\frac{7}{16}$-in circle.

Divide 5.4375 into groups of not more than three significant figures each, to avoid interpolation.

N	πN
5.4	16.96460
0.0375	0.11781
5.4375	17.08241

In most cases two or more superfluous digits will have to be rounded off to be consistent with the accuracy of the data of the problem, but interpolation will have been avoided.

It should be noted in passing that the method of "addition of parts" is applicable to any linear relation between two variables having a common zero, e.g., degrees to radians and inches to centimeters.

The use of the table of multiples of π is by no means limited to circumferences. For example, the area of an ellipse whose semiaxes are 6 and 8 is found by looking up the circumference of a circle of diameter 48. The circumference table is also useful in the calculation of surface speeds of drills, grinding wheels, pulleys, etc. In electrical engineering, multiples of π are involved in calculations of electromagnetic effects, capacitance, and inductance.

The reciprocal table may be used to evaluate fractions.

Example 34. What decimal part of a foot is $^7/_{16}$ in?

$$^7/_{16} \div 12 = {}^7/_{16} \times {}^1/_{12} = {}^7/_{192} = 7({}^1/_{192}) = 7(0.0052083) = 0.03646$$

2 review algebra

It is assumed that the student using this text has successfully completed a thorough course in elementary algebra. However, the following exercises are included as a basis for remedial work if such is needed.

2.1 Elementary Operations

EXERCISE 1

1. Find the sum of each of the following pairs of numbers:
   (*a*) $+8, +5$ (*b*) $+7, -2$ (*c*) $+4, +10$ (*d*) $+6, -9$
   (*e*) $-3, -11$ (*f*) $-12, -8$ (*g*) $-9, +13$ (*h*) $-11, +4$
2. Subtract the second number from the first in each pair of numbers in Prob. 1.
3. Find the algebraic sums of the following:
   (*a*) $8 + 2 - 3 - 4 + 6 - 1 - 9 + 5$
   (*b*) $-3 + 7 + 2 - 6 - 5 + 1 - 8$
   (*c*) $4 + 10 - 3 + 7 - 6 - 9 + 2$
4. Find each of the following products:
   (*a*) $(8)(5)$ (*b*) $(-6)(7)$ (*c*) $(-12)(-4)$
   (*d*) $(9)(-6)$ (*e*) $(2)(-3)(4)$ (*f*) $(-5)(3)(-4)$
   (*g*) $(-3)(-6)(2)(-1)$

5. Perform the indicated operations:

(a) $20 \div 5$ (b) $24 \div (-8)$ (c) $(-30) \div 6$

(d) $(-35) \div (-7)$ (e) $\dfrac{-28}{(-7)(3)}$ (f) $\dfrac{(36)(15)}{-81}$

EXERCISE 2

Write the expressions in Probs. 1 to 8 in the most concise form possible by using coefficients and exponents.

1. $a + a + a - a + a$
2. $x - x - x + x - x - x$
3. $y \cdot y \cdot y \cdot y$
4. $a \cdot a \cdot b \cdot b \cdot b$
5. $4x \cdot y \cdot y \cdot z \cdot z \cdot z$
6. $(a + c)(a + c)(a + c)$
7. $w(xw)w(xw)$
8. $a(ab)(abc)(bc)c$

Find the numerical values in Probs. 9 to 30 if $a = 3$, $b = 4$, $c = -5$, and $x = 1$.

9. $a + b$
10. $2c - a$
11. $7(2a - c)$
12. $3a^2bc$
13. $4a^2 - b^2$
14. $(a + c)^2$
15. $b^2 - x^2$
16. $(3a - b)^3$
17. $(a + b)(a + b)$
18. $a + b(a + b)$
19. $(a + b)a + b$
20. $a + ba + b$
21. $(2a - b + c)^2$
22. $(c + b)^3x$
23. $\sqrt{a^2 + b^2}$
24. $\sqrt{(3a)^2 - b^2 - x^2}$
25. $\dfrac{4a + b}{c + 3x}$
26. $\dfrac{4a}{c} + \dfrac{b}{3x}$
27. $(4b + 3c - x)^4$
28. $\left(\dfrac{4a + 2b}{3x - c}\right)^2$
29. $3abc^2$
30. $(3abc)^2$

Perform the indicated additions in Probs. 31 to 42.

31. $\begin{array}{r} 7x \\ 5x \\ -\ x \\ \hline \end{array}$

32. $\begin{array}{r} -11ab \\ 4ab \\ ab \\ -\ 2ab \\ 8ab \\ \hline \end{array}$

33. $\begin{array}{r} 9mn \\ -2mn \\ -\ mn \\ 7mn \\ \hline \end{array}$

34. $\begin{array}{r} 6cd \\ -4cd \\ 7cd \\ -8cd \\ \hline \end{array}$

35. $\begin{array}{r} 5x + 4y \\ x + 5y \\ \hline \end{array}$

36. $\begin{array}{r} -3a + 2c \\ 4a - 3c \\ \hline \end{array}$

37. $\begin{array}{l} 6m + 10p \\ \underline{6m - 2p} \end{array}$

38. $\begin{array}{l} 4x^2 - 2xy + y^2 \\ \underline{5x^2 + 3xy - 2y^2} \end{array}$

39. $\begin{array}{l} 3k^2 - 2km + m^2 \\ \underline{k^2 \qquad\qquad + 4m^2} \end{array}$

40. $\begin{array}{l} 2p^2 \qquad\quad - 3q^2 \\ \underline{5p^2 + 4pq - 2q^2} \end{array}$

41. $\begin{array}{l} 4x - 2y \\ \underline{5x \qquad\quad - 3z} \end{array}$

42. $\begin{array}{l} 10c^2 + cm - 3m^2 \\ \underline{3c^2 + cm - 4m^2} \end{array}$

43–50. In Probs. 35 to 42 subtract the second expression from the first.

2.2 Symbols of Grouping

Parentheses, ( ), brackets, [ ], or braces, { }, and the less frequently used vinculum, $\overline{\qquad}$, written over an expression are known as *symbols of grouping*. Certain of their uses are illustrated in the examples below.

Example 1. $5 + (2 + 7) = 5 + 9 = 14$

Example 2. $8 - (3 + 10) = 8 - 13 = -5$

Example 3. $6 - \overline{7 - 2} = 6 - 5 = 1$

Example 4. $4(5 + 2) = 4(7) = 28$. Note that we might write (by the distributive law)

$$4(5 + 2) = 4(5) + 4(2) = 20 + 8 = 28$$

Example 5. $5(-4)$ means 5 times -4, or -20.

Example 6. $(14 - 6)/2 = 8/2 = 4$

Example 7. $8 + (3 - 4) = 8 + 3 - 4 = 7$

Example 8. $11 - (7 - 2) = 11 - 7 + 2 = 6$

Example 9. Perform the indicated operations and apply the commutative and distributive laws in the following expression: $3x + 2 - [2y + 5 - (6y - 2x + 3)]$.

Beginning with the inner group and performing the indicated multiplications with due attention to signs, we obtain

$$\begin{aligned} & 3x + 2 - [2y + 5 - (6y - 2x + 3)] \\ = {} & 3x + 2 - [2y + 5 - 6y + 2x - 3] \\ = {} & 3x + 2 - 2y - 5 + 6y - 2x + 3 = x + 4y \end{aligned}$$

EXERCISE 3

In Probs. 1 to 10, simplify by removing the symbols of grouping as was done in Example 9.

1. $3a + 4b + (2a - b)$
2. $5a - 3c - (2a - 4c)$
3. $4x - 7y - (3x - 4y) + x + 3y$
4. $6u + 5 - (3v + 4w - 2) - 2u + 4v$
5. $8m - [4n - (-3m + 3n) + m]$
6. $a - \{2x + [3a - 5x - (4a + x)] - 2a\}$
7. $-7b + \{6c - [2b - c + (8c - 4b) + b]\}$
8. $[8c + 3k - (5c + 2k)] - \{3c + k - [7c - (c - 4k)]\}$
9. $11ab - 3a^2b - [5ab^2 - (6ab + 2a^2b) + ab] + 3ab^2$
10. $[4x^2 - xy + (y^2 - 2xy) - x^2] - \{3x^2 - [y^2 - (2xy + x^2) + xy]\}$

In Probs. 11 to 13 enclose the last three terms in parentheses preceded by (*a*) first a minus sign and (*b*) then a plus sign.

11. $5a + 2b - 4c + m - x$
12. $2a^2 + 3ab - 7b^2 + 4b$
13. $7mn + 3m^2 - 4n^2 - 8m + 5n + 2mn$

2.3 Some Fundamental Rules of Exponents

Definition 1. If n is a positive integer and a is any number, then

$$a^n = a \cdot a \cdot a \cdot a \cdot \cdots \cdot a \qquad \text{(to } n \text{ factors of } a\text{)}$$

Observe that a is one of n equal factors of a^n. The symbol a^n is read "the nth power of a," or "a to the nth power." The symbol a is called the *base*, and n is called the *exponent*.

The following laws relate to positive integral exponents, but in Sec. 2.17 it will be shown that they are valid for fractional and negative exponents as well.

I. *Products* $a^m \cdot a^n = a^{m+n}$ **(1)**

Example 10. $c^2 \cdot c^3 = c^{2+3} = c^5$ because

$$c^2 \cdot c^3 = (c \cdot c)(c \cdot c \cdot c) = c \cdot c \cdot c \cdot c \cdot c = c^5$$

Example 11. $a \cdot a^2 \cdot a^5 = a^1 \cdot a^2 \cdot a^5 = a^{1+2+5} = a^8$

IIa. Powers $(a^m)^n = a^{mn}$ **(2)**

Example 12. $(y^2)^3 = y^{2\times 3} = y^6$ because

$$(y^2)^3 = y^2 \cdot y^2 \cdot y^2 = (y \cdot y)(y \cdot y)(y \cdot y) = y \cdot y \cdot y \cdot y \cdot y \cdot y = y^6$$

IIb. $(ab)^n = a^n b^n$ **(3)**

Example 13. $(ab)^5 = (ab)(ab)(ab)(ab)(ab)$
$= (a \cdot a \cdot a \cdot a \cdot a)(b \cdot b \cdot b \cdot b \cdot b) = a^5 b^5$

IIc. $\left(\frac{a}{b}\right)^n = \frac{a^n}{b^n} \qquad b \neq 0$ **(4)**

Example 14. $\left(\frac{a}{b}\right)^4 = \left(\frac{a}{b}\right)\left(\frac{a}{b}\right)\left(\frac{a}{b}\right)\left(\frac{a}{b}\right) = \frac{a \cdot a \cdot a \cdot a}{b \cdot b \cdot b \cdot b} = \frac{a^4}{b^4}$

IId. $\left(\frac{1}{b}\right)^n = \frac{1}{b^n} \qquad b \neq 0$ **(5)**

Example 15. $\left(\frac{1}{x}\right)^3 = \frac{1}{x^3}$

III. Quotients

$$\frac{a^m}{a^n} = \begin{cases} a^{(m-n)} & \text{if } m > n \text{ and } a \neq 0 \\ \dfrac{1}{a^{(n-m)}} & \text{if } m < n \text{ and } a \neq 0 \end{cases} \qquad \textbf{(6)}$$

The restrictions on Eq. (6) are necessary at this point since we are considering positive integral exponents only, in addition to the obvious requirement that $a \neq 0$.

Example 16. $x^5 \div x^3 = x^{5-3} = x^2$ because

$$x^5 \div x^3 = \frac{\cancel{x} \cdot \cancel{x} \cdot \cancel{x} \cdot x \cdot x}{\cancel{x} \cdot \cancel{x} \cdot \cancel{x}} = x \cdot x = x^2$$

Example 17. $\frac{3^2}{3^7} = \frac{1}{3^{(7-2)}} = \frac{1}{3^5}$

EXERCISE 4

Carry out the indicated operations according to the laws of exponents.

1. $x^4 \cdot x^2$
2. $3^2 \cdot 3^3$
3. $(-1)(-4)^2$
4. $-(-2x)^3$
5. $(a^n)^2$
6. $(5/3)^2$
7. $(0.2x)^3$
8. $(4x^2y^n)^n$
9. $b^x \cdot b^3$
10. $a^{2y} \cdot a^{3y}$
11. $(-2x)^3$
12. $(y^3)^4$
13. $(a^n)^n$
14. $(2/3x)^5$
15. $(a^nb^2)^3$
16. $xy^4(xy)^4$
17. $\dfrac{a^5}{a^3}$
18. $\dfrac{a}{a^5}$
19. $\dfrac{(6x^3)^2}{(4x^2)^3}$
20. $\dfrac{10ab^3}{15(ab)^3}$
21. $\dfrac{y^2}{y^6}$
22. $\dfrac{x^3y^3}{x^2y^4}$
23. $\dfrac{(xy^2)^n}{(x^ny)^2}$
24. $\dfrac{(ab^2c^3)^n}{(a^nb^nc^n)^2}$

2.4 Multiplying by a Monomial

To multiply a monomial by a monomial, multiply the product of the numerical coefficients by the product of the literal factors, making use of the law of exponents where it applies. Determine and apply the proper sign.

Example 18. Find the indicated product:

$(-3axy^2)(5a^3x^2)$ ANS.: $-15a^4x^3y^2$

To multiply a polynomial by a monomial, multiply each term of the polynomial by the monomial and write the sum of the products.

Example 19. $4x^2y(5a^2x - 7b^2y) = 20a^2x^3y - 28b^2x^2y^2$ (by the distributive law)

EXERCISE 5

Perform the following multiplications:

1. $(8mn)(4mx)$
2. $(-3h^2x)(6hx^2)$
3. $(9abc)(-4bcd)$
4. $(-2ck^2x)(-7c^2x^5)$
5. $(a^2m)(m^2x)(ax^2)$
6. $(3ac^2d)(-4cd^3)(-2a^4cd^2)$
7. $(-9a^2b^3c^4)(-4a^3b^4m^5)(-2b^4c^5m^6)$
8. $5(4h - 6k)$
9. $-3y(6m - 5t)$
10. $4ax(5ay + 9mx)$
11. $6a^2b(5a^2 - 7ab - 9b^2)$
12. $-2xy^2(1 - 2x + 3x^2 - 4x^3)$
13. $(-3hk)(-2hk^3)(4a^3h^2 - 11bk)$
14. $\frac{2}{3}ab^2c^3(12ax - 21by)$

2.5 Multiplying One Polynomial by Another Polynomial

To multiply one polynomial by another, arrange the terms in descending powers of one of the letters involved. Multiply the first polynomial by the successive terms of the second, arranging like terms of the product in columns, and add.

Example 20. Multiply $10x - 2x^3 + x^4 - 1$ by $x^2 + 2 + 6x^3$.

Arranging in descending powers of x,

$$\begin{array}{rrrrrrrrl}
 & & & x^4 & -\ 2x^3 & & +\ 10x & -\ 1 & \\
 & & & & 6x^3 & +\ x^2 & & +\ 2 & \\
\hline
6x^7 & -\ 12x^6 & & +\ 60x^4 & -\ 6x^3 & & & & \text{(multiplying by } 6x^3\text{)} \\
 & +\ x^6 & -\ 2x^5 & & +\ 10x^3 & -\ x^2 & & & \text{(multiplying by } x^2\text{)} \\
 & & & +\ 2x^4 & -\ 4x^3 & & +\ 20x & -\ 2 & \text{(multiplying by 2)} \\
\hline
6x^7 & -\ 11x^6 & -\ 2x^5 & +\ 62x^4 & & -\ x^2 & +\ 20x & -\ 2 &
\end{array}$$

EXERCISE 6

1. $(a + b)(c + d)$
2. $(m + x)(m - y)$
3. $(h + k)(h - k)$
4. $(y^4 - y^2)(y^5 + y^3)$
5. $(2m + 5w)(3m - 7w)$
6. $(4x - 6y)(6x + 9y)$
7. $(4x - 2y - 13)(6x + 3y)$
8. $(3p^2 + 4pq + 5q^2)(2p - 3q)$
9. $(b - x - y)(b + x + y)$
10. $(c + d - 5)(c - d + 4)$

2.6 Removing Parentheses Used to Indicate Multiplication

Example 21.

$$\begin{aligned}
& 3 + 2[5 - 4x(1 - 6x - 12)] \\
&= 3 + 2[5 - 4x + 24x^2 + 48x] \\
&= 3 + 10 - 8x + 48x^2 + 96x = 13 + 88x + 48x^2
\end{aligned}$$

EXERCISE 7

Simplify the following expressions:

1. $1 - 2\{1 + 3[1 - 4(1 - 5x)]\}$
2. $a - \{(b - c) - [a + b - c - 2(a - b + c)]\}$
3. $5\{4[3(2 + x)]\} - 5\{-4[-3(2 - x)]\}$
4. $y^2 - y\{y + z[x(y - z) + y(z - x) + z(x - y)]\}$

2.7 Dividing by a Monomial

Example 22. Divide $-20x^3yz^2$ by $-5xyz$.

By dividing like factors out of numerator and denominator, we write

$$\frac{-\overset{4}{\cancel{20x}}\cdot x\cdot x\cdot \cancel{y}\cdot z\cdot \cancel{z}}{-\cancel{5x}\qquad \cancel{y}\quad \cancel{z}} = 4x^2z$$

EXERCISE 8

Obtain the following quotients:

1. $15c^2 \div 5c^2$
2. $-24h^3 \div 8h$
3. $35c^3d^2 \div (-7cd^2)$
4. $-42ab^2c^3 \div (-3ac^2)$
5. $12x^{12} \div 3x^3$
6. $-12ab^2m^3 \div 18a^3bm^2$
7. $40x^2y^3z \div 5wxz^3$
8. $-28a^4h^2k^3 \div (-20a^3h^3n^3)$
9. $(6ab - 8ac) \div 2a$
10. $(12c^2y + 20cw) \div 4c$
11. $(16km^2 - 24k^2m) \div (-8km)$
12. $(6xy - 30x^2y - 6xy^2) \div 6xy$
13. $(\pi r^2h + 2\pi rh) \div \pi rh$
14. $(35xy^4 - 20x^2y^3) \div 10xy^4$

2.8 Dividing by a Polynomial

Example 23. Divide $36x^4 - 25x^2 + 4$ by $3x - 2$.

It will be noted that there are no x^3 and x terms in the dividend. Hence we arrange as follows:

$$
\begin{array}{r|rrrrr}
\multicolumn{1}{r}{} & & 12x^3 & +\ 8x^2 & -\ 3x & -\ 2 \\
\cline{2-6}
3x - 2 & 36x^4 & & -\ 25x^2 & & +\ 4 \\
\multicolumn{1}{r}{} & 36x^4 & -\ 24x^3 & & & \\
\cline{2-3}
\multicolumn{1}{r}{} & & +\ 24x^3 & -\ 25x^2 & & \\
\multicolumn{1}{r}{} & & 24x^3 & -\ 16x^2 & & \\
\cline{3-4}
\multicolumn{1}{r}{} & & & -\ 9x^2 & & \\
\multicolumn{1}{r}{} & & & -\ 9x^2 & +\ 6x & \\
\cline{4-5}
\multicolumn{1}{r}{} & & & & -\ 6x & +\ 4 \\
\multicolumn{1}{r}{} & & & & -\ 6x & +\ 4 \\
\cline{5-6}
\end{array}
$$

EXERCISE 9

Divide:

1. $a^2 + 11a + 24$ by $a + 3$
2. $c^3 - 2c^2 - 2c + 1$ by $1 + c$
3. $8m^2 - 22mw + 15w^2$ by $2m - 3w$
4. $16z^4 - 1$ by $2z - 1$
5. $6k^6 - 48$ by $3k^2 - 6$
6. $8q^2 - q - 19q^3 + 15q^4 - 1$ by $5q^2 - 3q - 1$
7. $h^6 - 2h^3 + 1$ by $h^2 + h + 1$
8. $y^5 - 2y^4 - 13y^2 + 17y + 5$ by $3y + 1 + y^3 - 4y^2$
9. 1 by $1 + x$ (to four terms) $(|x| < 1)$
10. 1 by $x + 1$ (to four terms) $(|x| > 1)$

Note. $|x|$ *denotes absolute value (magnitude without regard to sign).*

2.9 Special Products and Factoring

The following special products are commonly used. Others arise too infrequently to be appropriate in this review.

$a(x + y + z) = ax + ay + az$ (distributive law) (7)

For example: $3ab^2(5ax - 8b) = 15a^2b^2x - 24ab^3$

$(x + y)(x - y) = x^2 - y^2$ (8)

For example: $(3cm^2 + 4x)(3cm^2 - 4x) = 9c^2m^4 - 16x^2$

$(x + y)^2 = x^2 + 2xy + y^2$ (9)

For example: $(5ab + 4w)^2 = 25a^2b^2 + 40abw + 16w^2$

$(x - y)^2 = x^2 - 2xy + y^2$ (10)

For example: $(2ax - 7x^2y)^2 = 4a^2x^2 - 28ax^3y + 49x^4y^2$

$(x + a)(x + b) = x^2 + (a + b)x + ab$ (11)

For example: $(x + 5)(x - 2) = x^2 + (5 - 2)x - 10$
$= x^2 + 3x - 10$

$(ax + b)(cx + d) = acx^2 + (ad + bc)x + bd$ (12)

For example: $(3x + 8)(2x - 7) = 6x^2 + (-21 + 16)x - 56$
$= 6x^2 - 5x - 56$

$(a + b)(c + d) = ac + ad + bc + bd$ (13)

For example: $(3e - 2k)(2m + 5n) = 3e(2m + 5n) - 2k(2m + 5n)$
$= 6em + 15en - 4km - 10kn$

$(x - y)(x^2 + xy + y^2) = x^3 - y^3$ (14)

For example: $(a - 3b)(a^2 + 3ab + 9b^2) = a^3 - 27b^3$

EXERCISE 10

Factor out the common monomial factor from each of the following:

1. $15x - 18y$
2. $16x + 40y$
3. $30ab - 42km$
4. $ax + ay$
5. $a^2 - ac$
6. $12xy - 20x^2$
7. $abc + bcm + cmx$
8. $a^2b^2 + a^2b + ab^2$
9. $42ax^2y - 24bx^3y^2 + 18cx^4y$
10. $15ab^2c^2 - 12a^2bc^2 + 8a^2b^2c$
11. $10a^2x^2 - 15abxy + 20b^2y^2$
12. $30ax^2y + 48bxy^2 - 36cxyz$
13. The expression $ab - ac$ may be written $a(b - c)$. Make use of this identity to state whether or not 63,549 and 63,574 have any common factors.

EXERCISE 11

Factor completely:

1. $x^2 - 4$
2. $c^2 - 25$
3. $36 - y^2$
4. $16z^2 - 1$
5. $49m^2 - 1$
6. $4a^2 - 9b^2$
7. $25d^2 - 64m^2$
8. $36 - 121a^2b^2$
9. $100y^2z^2 - 49c^2d^2$
10. $121k^4 - 1$
11. $16n^8 - 1$
12. $16 - 81x^{12}$
13. $(25)^2 - (24)^2$
14. $(10\frac{1}{2})^2 - (8\frac{1}{2})^2$
15. Show that the number 391 may be expressed as the difference between two squares and, as such, is factorable. Find the factors.

EXERCISE 12

Find the missing terms needed to make the following expressions take the form of the trinomial squares $x^2 + 2xy + y^2$ or $x^2 - 2xy + y^2$. Insert only positive quantities within the parentheses.

1. $x^2 + (\quad) + 25$
2. $y^2 + (\quad) + 81$
3. $z^2 - (\quad) + 49$
4. $m^2 - (\quad) + 144$
5. $4a^2 + (\quad) + 1$
6. $36c^2 - (\quad) + 1$
7. $9n^2 + (\quad) + 25$
8. $16 - (\quad) + 121k^2$
9. $64b^2 - (\quad) + 25h^2$
10. $d^2 + 8d + (\quad)$
11. $p^2 - 10p + (\quad)$
12. $a^2 + 6ab + (\quad)$
13. $c^2 - 14cq + (\quad)$
14. $4w^2 - 28w + (\quad)$
15. $9m^2 + 30mx + (\quad)$
16. $25t^2 - 50tr + (\quad)$

EXERCISE 13

Factor each of the following trinomial squares:

1. $x^2 - 4x + 4$
2. $b^2 + 10b + 25$
3. $36 - 12m + m^2$
4. $4y^2 - 20y + 25$

5. $9 + 42z + 49z^2$
6. $16c^2 + 24cd + 9d^2$
7. $64a^2 - 80an + 25n^2$
8. $49a^2b^2 - 112abc + 64c^2$
9. $81m^4 - 72m^2p + 16p^2$
10. $121x^2 + 154xyz^2 + 49y^2z^4$

EXERCISE 14

Factor each of the following expressions:

1. $y^2 + 7y + 12$
2. $a^2 + 9a + 20$
3. $m^2 - 12m + 35$
4. $c^2 - 15c + 36$
5. $x^2 + 19x + 48$
6. $b^2 - 2b - 24$
7. $h^2 + h - 30$
8. $w^2 - 11w - 42$
9. $k^4 + k^2 - 72$
10. $z^6 - 3z^3 - 108$
11. $x^2 + 21xy + 54y^2$
12. $y^2 - 25yz + 66z^2$
13. $2a^2 + 3a + 1$
14. $3c^2 + 10c + 3$
15. $4m^2 - 11m + 6$
16. $7k^2 - 16k + 4$
17. $8b^2 + 18b + 9$
18. $17n^2 + 6n - 11$
19. $54h^2 - 15h - 50$
20. $48x^2 + 14x - 45$

2.10 Fractions

To reduce a fraction to its lowest terms, express the numerator and denominator as products of their prime factors. Then divide both numerator and denominator by all prime factors common to both.

Example 24. $$\frac{3a + 6b}{a^2 + 3ab + 2b^2} = \frac{3\cancel{(a + 2b)}}{(a + b)\cancel{(a + 2b)}} = \frac{3}{a + b}$$

EXERCISE 15

Reduce the following fractions to lowest terms where possible (some may already be in lowest terms), using a minimum of negative signs in your answer.

1. $\dfrac{xy}{wx + xz}$
2. $\dfrac{a}{a^2 + a}$
3. $\dfrac{am + an}{ab - ac}$
4. $\dfrac{8a - 12b}{16a + 24b}$
5. $\dfrac{a + b}{a^2 + 2ab + b^2}$
6. $\dfrac{k - m}{k^2 - m^2}$
7. $\dfrac{2a + 4b}{a^2 - 4b^2}$
8. $\dfrac{x^2 - 4x + 4}{x^2 - 4}$
9. $\dfrac{6a + 9b}{4a^2 - 9b^2}$
10. $\dfrac{2m^2 - 4m}{m^2 + 4m - 12}$
11. $\dfrac{9 - a^2}{3a^2 - 9a}$
12. $\dfrac{a^2 - 3a + 2}{a^2 + 2a - 3}$
13. $\dfrac{x^2 - 8x + 16}{x^2 - 4}$
14. $\dfrac{5cm^3 - 20c^3m}{10cm^2 - 10c^2m - 20c^3}$
15. $\dfrac{x^2 - 5x + 6}{x^2 + 5x - 6}$

16. $\dfrac{a^2 - b^2}{(a - b)^2}$ 17. $\dfrac{a^2 + b^2}{(a + b)^2}$ 18. $\dfrac{x - y}{y - x}$

19. $\dfrac{(a - m)^2}{(m - a)^2}$

2.11 Multiplying Two or More Fractions

To multiply two or more fractions involving polynomials, write the indicated product of all the factors of the numerators over the indicated product of all the factors of the denominators. Reduce the product to lowest terms if it is not already in lowest terms.

Example 25. $\dfrac{24a^2 - 54b^2}{35x^2y} \cdot \dfrac{28xy^2}{30a^2 + 15ab - 90b^2}$

$$= \frac{6\cancel{(2a - 3b)}(2a + 3b)}{35x^2y} \cdot \frac{28xy^2}{15\cancel{(2a - 3b)}(a + 2b)}$$

$$= \frac{8y(2a + 3b)}{25x(a + 2b)}$$

2.12 Dividing One Fraction by Another

To divide one fraction by another, multiply the first fraction by the reciprocal of the second and multiply as in Sec. 2.11.

Example 26. $\dfrac{k^2 + 9km + 18m^2}{k^2 - 9km + 20m^2} \div \dfrac{k^2 + 6km + 9m^2}{km^2 - 4m^3}$

$$= \frac{k^2 + 9km + 18m^2}{k^2 - 9km + 20m^2} \cdot \frac{km^2 - 4m^3}{k^2 + 6km + 9m^2}$$

$$= \frac{(k + 6m)\cancel{(k + 3m)}}{\cancel{(k - 4m)}(k - 5m)} \cdot \frac{m^2\cancel{(k - 4m)}}{\cancel{(k + 3m)}(k + 3m)}$$

$$= \frac{m^2(k + 6m)}{(k - 5m)(k + 3m)}$$

EXERCISE 16

Carry out the indicated operations:

1. $\dfrac{a^2 - b^2}{16} \cdot \dfrac{12}{a - b}$ 2. $\dfrac{x^2 + 2x + 1}{18cw^3} \cdot \dfrac{12c^3w}{x^2 - 1}$

3. $\dfrac{x^2 - x + 12}{abc} \cdot \dfrac{bcd}{x^2 + x - 6}$ 4. $\dfrac{6x + 12y}{10a + 5} \cdot \dfrac{100a^2 - 25}{9x^2 - 81y^2}$

5. $\dfrac{a^2 + 2ab + b^2}{a^2 - b^2} \cdot \dfrac{a^2 - 2ab + b^2}{a^2 - b^2}$

6. $\dfrac{x + 3y}{2a + 1} \cdot \dfrac{1 - 4a^2}{x^2 - 9y^2}$

7. $\dfrac{m^2 + 2mn + n^2}{4m^2 + 4mn} \cdot \dfrac{6m^2}{n^2 - m^2}$

8. $\dfrac{x^2 + x - 2}{7b^2x^2 - 14b^2x + 7b^2} \cdot \dfrac{14abx - 28ab}{1 - 2x + x^2}$

9. $\dfrac{a + 2}{15} \div \dfrac{a^2 - 4}{10a}$

10. $\dfrac{a - b}{x + y} \div \dfrac{x - y}{a + b}$

11. $\dfrac{4a - 6x}{9ay} \div \dfrac{9x - 6a}{12y^2}$

12. $\dfrac{15ax^2}{x^2 - 9} \div \dfrac{25a^2bx}{x^2 + x - 12}$

2.13 Addition and Subtraction of Fractions

These operations in algebra are entirely comparable with the corresponding arithmetical procedures.

To add or subtract fractions:

1. *Reduce to lowest terms any fractions which may be so reduced.*
2. *Find the least common denominator, which is the LCM of all the denominators.*
3. *For each fraction, divide the least common denominator (LCD) by its own denominator and multiply both numerator and denominator by this quotient.*
4. *Write the new numerators obtained in step 3 over a single denominator (LCD). Each polynomial numerator is placed in parentheses preceded by the sign of the fraction from which it originated.*
5. *Remove the grouping signs, collect terms, and reduce the resulting fraction to lowest terms.*

Example 27. Simplify

$$\frac{2x^2 - 1}{6x^2} - \frac{2x - 5}{10x} - \frac{2}{15}$$

$$\frac{5(2x^2 - 1)}{30x^2} - \frac{3x(2x - 5)}{30x^2} - \frac{4x^2}{30x^2}$$

$$\frac{5(2x^2 - 1) - 3x(2x - 5) - 4x^2}{30x^2} = \frac{10x^2 - 5 - 6x^2 + 15x - 4x^2}{30x^2}$$

$$= \frac{15x - 5}{30x^2}$$

$$= \frac{3x - 1}{6x^2}$$

Example 28. Add

$$\frac{5x}{2x+4} + \frac{3x-1}{x^2-4}$$

$$\frac{5x(x-2)}{2(x-2)(x+2)} + \frac{2(3x-1)}{2(x-2)(x+2)}$$

$$\frac{5x(x-2)+2(3x-1)}{2(x-2)(x+2)} = \frac{5x^2-10x+6x-2}{2(x-2)(x+2)} = \frac{5x^2-4x-2}{2(x-2)(x+2)}$$

EXERCISE 17

Simplify each of the following:

1. $\frac{7x}{10} - \frac{x}{6}$
2. $\frac{5w}{8y} - \frac{7w}{12y}$
3. $\frac{x}{yz} + \frac{y}{xz} + \frac{z}{xy}$
4. $\frac{3x-2y}{6} - \frac{5x+y}{10}$
5. $\frac{7a+b}{8} + \frac{5a-4b}{12} - \frac{-2a+3b}{9}$
6. $\frac{7x-3a^2y}{6a^2b} - \frac{3x-4by}{8b^2}$
7. $\frac{2a+3b-c}{4ab} - \frac{a-2b+3c}{6bc} + \frac{-3a-b+2c}{8ac}$
8. $\frac{1}{a+b} - \frac{1}{a+c}$
9. $\frac{m+5}{5} - \frac{m+6}{6}$
10. $\frac{x+y}{x-y} - \frac{x-y}{x+y}$
11. $a - \frac{c^2}{a}$
12. $\frac{4}{5a} - 3$
13. $b + 2 + \frac{1}{b}$
14. $\frac{6}{k+3} + k - 2$
15. $\frac{a-2b}{a^2-b^2} + \frac{2}{a-b}$
16. $\frac{k+2m}{k^2-9m^2} + \frac{4}{3m-k}$
17. $\frac{x-5}{x-6} + \frac{2x-8}{x^2-10x+24}$
18. $y^2 + y + 1 + \frac{1}{y-1}$
19. $\frac{2-c}{c^2+c-6} - \frac{5}{9-c^2} - \frac{4-c}{c^2-7c+12}$
20. $\frac{a+b}{(b-c)(c-a)} - \frac{b+c}{(a-c)(a-b)} + \frac{a+c}{(a-b)(b-c)}$
21. $\frac{3}{c-d} + \frac{4d}{(c-d)^2} - \frac{5d^2}{(c-d)^3}$
22. $\frac{1}{a-b} - \frac{2b}{a^2-ab} + \frac{b^2}{a^3-a^2b}$

2.14 Complex Fractions

A complex fraction is a fraction whose numerator or denominator or both contain fractions.

Example 29. $$\frac{\dfrac{a^2}{b^2} - 1}{\dfrac{a}{b} + 1}$$

is a complex fraction. For convenience we shall refer to $a^2/b^2 - 1$ as the primary numerator and $a/b + 1$ as the primary denominator, while b^2 and b will be known as *secondary denominators.*

To simplify a complex fraction, reduce the primary numerator and the primary denominator each to a single fraction and divide the primary numerator by the primary denominator.

Example 30. Simplify

$$\frac{4 - \dfrac{4}{a} + \dfrac{1}{a^2}}{1 - \dfrac{1}{4a^2}}$$

Simplifying the primary numerator, we obtain

$$4 - \frac{4}{a} + \frac{1}{a^2} = \frac{4a^2}{a^2} - \frac{4a}{a^2} + \frac{1}{a^2} = \frac{4a^2 - 4a + 1}{a^2} = \frac{(2a - 1)^2}{a^2}$$

Simplifying the primary denominator, we have

$$1 - \frac{1}{4a^2} = \frac{4a^2}{4a^2} - \frac{1}{4a^2} = \frac{4a^2 - 1}{4a^2} = \frac{(2a + 1)(2a - 1)}{4a^2}$$

Then

$$\frac{(2a - 1)^2}{a^2} \div \frac{(2a + 1)(2a - 1)}{4a^2} = \frac{(2a - 1)(2a - 1)}{a^2} \cdot \frac{4a^2}{(2a + 1)(2a - 1)} = \frac{4(2a - 1)}{2a + 1}$$

This operation can often be performed more easily and quickly by finding the LCM of the *secondary* denominators. Multiply the *primary* numerator and denominator by the LCM just found and reduce to lowest terms.

Using the same complex fraction

$$\frac{4 - \dfrac{4}{a} + \dfrac{1}{a^2}}{1 - \dfrac{1}{4a^2}}$$

as in the preceding illustration, we note the LCM of the secondary denominators is $4a^2$. We then write

$$\frac{4a^2\left(4 - \dfrac{4}{a} + \dfrac{1}{a^2}\right)}{4a^2\left(1 - \dfrac{1}{4a^2}\right)} = \frac{16a^2 - 16a + 4}{4a^2 - 1} = \frac{4(4a^2 - 4a + 1)}{(2a + 1)(2a - 1)}$$

$$= \frac{4(2a - 1)\cancel{(2a - 1)}}{(2a + 1)\cancel{(2a - 1)}} = \frac{4(2a - 1)}{2a + 1}$$

The short method often makes it possible to simplify less involved complex fractions at sight; for example,

$$\frac{x - \dfrac{1}{x}}{1 + \dfrac{1}{x}} = \frac{x\left(x - \dfrac{1}{x}\right)}{x\left(1 + \dfrac{1}{x}\right)} = \frac{x^2 - 1}{x + 1} = x - 1$$

EXERCISE 18

Simplify the following complex fractions:

1. $\dfrac{\dfrac{1}{x} - \dfrac{1}{y}}{\dfrac{1}{x} + \dfrac{1}{y}}$

2. $\dfrac{\dfrac{1}{x} + \dfrac{1}{y}}{\dfrac{1}{z}}$

3. $\dfrac{\dfrac{c}{d} - \dfrac{d}{c}}{c - d}$

4. $\dfrac{m + w}{\dfrac{1}{m} + \dfrac{1}{w}}$

5. $\dfrac{\dfrac{1}{h} - \dfrac{1}{k}}{\dfrac{h - k}{hk}}$

6. $\dfrac{\dfrac{b}{c} + \dfrac{b}{d}}{\dfrac{b}{cd}}$

7. $\dfrac{q - \dfrac{1}{q}}{1 + \dfrac{1}{q}}$

8. $\dfrac{\dfrac{a^2 - x^2}{a}}{\dfrac{a + x}{a^2}}$

9. $\dfrac{1 - \dfrac{1}{r}}{r - 2 + \dfrac{1}{r}}$

10. $\dfrac{b + \dfrac{b}{c - 1}}{\dfrac{c}{c - 1}}$

11. $\dfrac{\dfrac{m}{1 + m} - \dfrac{1 - m}{m}}{\dfrac{m}{1 + m} + \dfrac{1 - m}{m}}$

12. $\dfrac{a - \dfrac{ab}{b - a}}{\dfrac{a^2}{a^2 - b^2} - 1}$

2.15 Roots and Radicals

If $a^n = b$, where n is a positive integer, not only is b equal to the nth power of a, but by definition a is said to be an nth root of b. If $n = 2$, a is called the "second root," or the "square root" of b. When $n = 3$, a is called the "third root," or the "cube root" of b. When $n = 5$, a is called the "fifth root" of b, and so on.

Example 31. Since $2^3 = 8$, 2 is a cube root of 8.

Example 32. Since $(-2)^3 = -8$, -2 is a cube root of -8.

Example 33. Since $(-3)^2 = 9$, and $3^2 = 9$, both -3 and 3 are square roots of 9.

Example 34. Since $2^5 = 32$, 2 is a fifth root of 32.

From the above examples it is apparent that a number may have more than one nth root. On the other hand, we have, at this point, no method at all for finding an *even* root of a *negative* number. For example, we can find the square root of $+25$, and we know that there are two such roots: $+5$ and -5. However, we have, at the moment, no method for finding two *equal* factors which will multiply and give -25.

2.16 Principal Roots

The nth root of the quantity b is written $\sqrt[n]{b}$, except that when $n = 2$, we simply write $\sqrt{b}$.

In this notation $\sqrt[n]{b}$ is called a *radical*, the symbol $\sqrt{\ }$ is called a *radical sign*, n is the *index* of the root, and b is called the *radicand*.

Without further definition the symbol $\sqrt[n]{b}$ would be somewhat ambiguous. For example, does $\sqrt{9}$ mean $+3$ or -3? This ambiguity can be removed by introducing the concept of the *principal* nth *root* of a number.

Definition 2. Let a, b, and n be real numbers, where n is a positive integer. The symbol $\sqrt[n]{a}$ is used to designate the *principal* nth *root* of a.

1. If a is a positive number and n is either an even or an odd number,

$$\sqrt[n]{a} = \text{positive } n\text{th root of } a \qquad (15)$$

Example 35. $\sqrt{36} = 6$, since $6^2 = 36$.

Example 36. $\sqrt[5]{243} = 3$, since $3^5 = 243$.

2. If a is a negative number and n is an odd number,

$$\sqrt[n]{a} = \text{only real } n\text{th root of } a\text{, this root being a negative number} \qquad (16)$$

Example 37. $\sqrt[3]{-125} = -5$, since $(-5)^3 = -125$.

3. If a is a negative number and n is an even number,

$$\sqrt[n]{a} = \text{an imaginary number (to be discussed in Sec. 2.24)} \qquad (17)$$

EXERCISE 19

In Probs. 1 to 8, write in radical form the principal roots of the numbers indicated and find their values.

1. The cube root of -8
2. The cube root of 8
3. The fourth root of 81
4. The fifth root of -32
5. The square root of $\frac{1}{25}$
6. The sixth root of $\frac{1}{64}$
7. The square root of 49
8. The cube root of $\frac{27}{125}$

Find the principal value of each of the following:

9. $\sqrt{25}$
10. $\sqrt{121}$
11. $\sqrt{64}$
12. $\sqrt{225}$
13. $\sqrt[3]{27}$
14. $\sqrt[3]{64}$
15. $\sqrt{144}$
16. $\sqrt[3]{-27}$
17. $\sqrt[4]{16}$
18. $\sqrt[3]{1}$
19. $\sqrt[3]{-1}$
20. $\sqrt[5]{32}$
21. $\sqrt{0.04}$
22. $\sqrt[3]{0.125}$
23. $\sqrt{1600}$
24. $\sqrt{\frac{9}{49}}$
25. $\sqrt[3]{-\frac{27}{125}}$
26. $\sqrt[3]{\frac{1}{8}}$
27. $\sqrt{4a^2b^4c^6}$
28. $\sqrt[3]{8m^6n^9}$

2.17 Fractional, Negative, and Zero Exponents

So far we have been considering only positive integral values of n. We shall now attempt to preserve the laws already established for positive integral exponents (with necessary added restrictions) and apply them to negative, fractional, and zero exponents. Then we shall see what significance we must, as a consequence, attribute to negative, fractional, and zero exponents.

Fractional Exponents

In general, if n is a positive integer,

$$a^{1/n} \cdot a^{1/n} \cdot a^{1/n} \cdots \text{(to } n \text{ factors)} = a^{n/n} = a^1 = a$$

where $a^{1/n}$ is one of n equal factors of a. Thus we are led to make the following definition.

Definition 3. If a is a real number and n is a positive integer, then

$$a^{1/n} = \sqrt[n]{a} \tag{18}$$

where $\sqrt[n]{a}$ designates the *principal* nth root of a. We recall, however, that $\sqrt[n]{a}$ does not exist in the set of real numbers if a is a negative number while n is an even number. However, even roots of negative numbers do have meaning, and are known as *imaginary numbers*. We shall discuss these in Sec. 2.24.

Definition 4. If m and n are both integers with n a positive number, and if $\sqrt[n]{a}$ exists as a real number, then

$$a^{m/n} = (\sqrt[n]{a})^m = \sqrt[n]{a^m} \tag{19}$$

The symbol $\sqrt{a^2}$ deserves special attention. From the laws already established we find that

$$\sqrt{(+3)^2} = \sqrt{+9} = +3$$

and

$$\sqrt{(-3)^2} = \sqrt{+9} = +3$$

Accordingly, we define $\sqrt{a^2}$ to be

$$\sqrt{a^2} = |a| \tag{20}$$

not simply a.

Zero Exponent

If a is any number except zero, we can define the symbol a^0 by writing

$$a^0 = 1 \qquad a \neq 0 \tag{21}$$

This interpretation is entirely consistent, since

$$\frac{a^m}{a^m} = 1$$

But by Eq. (6), Sec. 2.3,

$$\frac{a^m}{a^m} = a^{m-m} = a^0 \qquad a \neq 0$$

Hence the two results must be equivalent.

Negative Exponents

We may define the symbol a^{-n} as follows:

$$a^{-n} = \frac{1}{a^n} \qquad \text{and} \qquad a^n = \frac{1}{a^{-n}} \tag{22}$$

This conclusion follows from Eq. (6), Sec. 2.3,

$$\frac{a^m}{a^n} = a^{m-n}$$

And if $m = 0$,

$$\frac{a^0}{a^n} = \frac{1}{a^n} = a^{0-n} = a^{-n}$$

Note from Eq. (22) that any factor (not any term) of the numerator or denominator of a fraction may be transferred to the denominator or numerator, as the case may be, by reversing the sign of its exponent.

Example 38. $16^{3/4} = \sqrt[4]{16^3}$ or more conveniently, $(\sqrt[4]{16})^3 = 2^3 = 8$

Example 39. $27^{2/3} = \sqrt[3]{27^2}$ or more conveniently, $(\sqrt[3]{27})^2 = 3^2 = 9$

Example 40. $12^0 = 1$

Example 41. $x^0 = 1 \qquad x \neq 0$

Example 42. $(4x - 7)^0 = 1 \qquad x \neq 7/4$

Example 43. $3x^{-2} = \dfrac{3}{x^2} \qquad \left(\text{note that we do not obtain } \dfrac{1}{9x^2}\right)$

Example 44. $(3x)^{-2} = \dfrac{1}{(3x)^2} = \dfrac{1}{9x^2}$

Example 45. $8^{-2/3} = \dfrac{1}{8^{2/3}} = \dfrac{1}{(\sqrt[3]{8})^2} = \dfrac{1}{2^2} = \dfrac{1}{4}$

Example 46. $\dfrac{5x^3y^2}{z^4} = 5x^3y^2z^{-4}$

Example 47. $\dfrac{4a^3c}{by^4} = 4a^3b^{-1}cy^{-4}$

Example 48. $\dfrac{1}{x^{-1} - y^{-1}} = \dfrac{1}{1/x - 1/y} = \dfrac{1}{(y - x)/(xy)} = \dfrac{xy}{y - x}$

(A simple solution at sight depends upon multiplying numerator and denominator by xy. See Sec. 2.14.)

EXERCISE 20

Find the value of each expression.

1. $16^{1/4}$
2. $36^{1/2}$
3. 5^{-2}
4. 7^{-1}
5. $(-3)^{-3}$
6. $(49)^{-1/2}$
7. $(\frac{2}{3})^{-3}$
8. $(\frac{1}{32})^{1/5}$
9. $(-\frac{1}{32})^{-1/5}$
10. $(0.09)^{1/2}$
11. $(0.16)^{-1/2}$
12. $\dfrac{3a^0 - b^0}{a^0 + (3b)^0}$
13. $(-3)^4$
14. $-(-3)^4$
15. $(-3)^{-4}$
16. $-(3)^{-4}$
17. 10^{-3}
18. $(-\frac{1}{6})^{-1}$
19. $4^{-1} + 2^{-2}$
20. $(0.001)^{-1/3}$
21. $(-8)^{5/3}$
22. $(-27)^{4/3}$
23. $(8^{-1} - 4^{-1})^{1/3}$
24. $(-\frac{27}{64})^{-2/3}$

Write each expression without negative or zero exponents and simplify.

25. $x^{2/3} \cdot x^{1/2}$
26. $y^5 \cdot y^{-5}$
27. $(16x^{16})^{1/2}$
28. $(3x^{4/3})^3$
29. $(-5^{1/2}x^{3/4}y)^4$
30. $(2^{1/3}x^{1/4}y^{1/6})^{12}$
31. $-(-3a^{0.4}b^{0.6})^5$
32. $4^{-2}ab^{-3}c$
33. $\dfrac{3x^{-3}y^2}{6^{-1}z^{-2}}$
34. $\dfrac{3^{-1}x^6}{8y^{-3}}$
35. $\dfrac{x^0y^{-1}}{x^2w^{-4}}$
36. $\left(\dfrac{10^{-3}a^6}{90}\right)^{1/2}$
37. $(x^{1/2} - x^{-1/2})^2$
38. $(m^{1/2} + n^{1/2})(m^{1/2} - n^{1/2})$
39. $(a^{1/2} - 3a^{-1/2})(a^{1/2} + 3a^{-1/2})$
40. $(x^{3/2} + x^{1/2})^4$

2.18 Laws of Radicals

The following laws of radicals follow directly from the laws of exponents, where we assume (1) that m and n are positive integers and (2) that the radical represents a real number.

$$\sqrt[n]{ab} = \sqrt[n]{a} \cdot \sqrt[n]{b} \tag{23}$$

$$\sqrt[n]{\frac{a}{b}} = \frac{\sqrt[n]{a}}{\sqrt[n]{b}} \tag{24}$$

Also, see Eq. (19).

Example 49. $(\sqrt[3]{x^2})^3 = x^2$

To remove factors from the radicand, apply Eq. (23) and remove from the radicand any factor which is a perfect nth power.

Example 50. $\sqrt{45} = \sqrt{(3)(3)(5)} = \sqrt{(3)^2(5)} = \sqrt{3^2} \cdot \sqrt{5} = 3\sqrt{5}$

Example 51. $\sqrt{4a^2x^2 - 36a^2y^2} = \sqrt{4a^2(x^2 - 9y^2)} = \sqrt{4a^2} \cdot \sqrt{x^2 - 9y^2}$
$= 2a\sqrt{x^2 - 9y^2}$

Exponential notation is often useful in simplifying certain types of radicals involving literal powers and roots.

Example 52. Rationalize $\sqrt[n-3]{a^{2n-1}}$.

In exponential notation this becomes $a^{(2n-1)/(n-3)}$.

But

$$\frac{2n-1}{n-3} = 2 + \frac{5}{n-3}$$

Therefore

$$a^{(2n-1)/(n-3)} = a^{2+5/(n-3)} = a^2 \cdot a^{5/(n-3)} = a^2 \sqrt[n-3]{a^5}$$

EXERCISE 21

Simplify the following expressions by removing factors from the radicands.

1. $\sqrt{8}$	2. $\sqrt{12}$	3. $\sqrt{40}$	4. $\sqrt{54}$
5. $5\sqrt{18}$	6. $2\sqrt{27}$	7. $3\sqrt{32}$	8. $4\sqrt{63}$
9. $\sqrt[3]{24}$	10. $\sqrt[3]{-32}$	11. $5\sqrt[3]{54}$	12. $7\sqrt[3]{192}$
13. $\sqrt[3]{-250}$	14. $4\sqrt[3]{135}$	15. $5\sqrt[4]{96}$	16. $3\sqrt[5]{96}$

17. $\sqrt{x^7}$ 18. $a^2\sqrt{c^9}$ 19. $\sqrt{x^3y^3}$ 20. $a\sqrt{a^2b}$

21. $\sqrt{12x^3y^5}$ 22. $\sqrt{50a^3b^6c^9}$ 23. $\sqrt{ax^2 + bx^2}$ 24. $\sqrt{a^2b^2 + a^2c^2}$

25. $\sqrt{4m^2 - 16n^2}$ 26. $\sqrt{18x^3 - 27x^2y}$ 27. $\sqrt[n]{a^{n+1}}$ 28. $\sqrt[n-1]{a^n}$

29. $\sqrt[n+1]{a^{n+3}}$ 30. $\sqrt[n-1]{a^{2n}}$ 31. $\sqrt[n+1]{a^{2n+3}}$ 32. $\sqrt[n-2]{a^{2n-3}}$

33. $\sqrt[3]{x^6y^{6+a}}$ 34. $\sqrt[4]{x^9y^{10+a}}$ 35. $\sqrt[3n]{x^{8n}y^{6n}}$ 36. $\sqrt[3k-1]{x^{6k}}$

2.19 Rationalizing the Denominator in a Radical

This term refers to the elimination of fractions within a radical. The procedure is desirable in that it usually simplifies numerical computations.

To rationalize the denominator of a radical having an index n, multiply numerator and denominator of the fraction by the smallest quantity which will make the denominator a perfect nth power. Extract the nth root of the denominator [see Eq. (24)].

Example 53. $$\sqrt{\frac{3}{7}} = \sqrt{\frac{3}{7}\cdot\frac{7}{7}} = \sqrt{\frac{21}{49}} = \frac{\sqrt{21}}{\sqrt{49}} = \frac{\sqrt{21}}{\sqrt{7^2}} = \frac{\sqrt{21}}{7}$$

Example 54. $$\sqrt{\frac{c^3}{x^3}} = \sqrt{\frac{c^3\cdot x}{x^3\cdot x}} = \frac{\sqrt{c^3x}}{\sqrt{x^4}} = \frac{c\sqrt{cx}}{x^2}$$

Example 55. $$\sqrt[3]{\frac{5m^4}{16a^2x^4}} = \sqrt[3]{\frac{5m^4\cdot 4ax^2}{16a^2x^4\cdot 4ax^2}} = \frac{\sqrt[3]{20am^4x^2}}{\sqrt[3]{64a^3x^6}} = \frac{m\sqrt[3]{20amx^2}}{4ax^2}$$

Example 56. $$\sqrt{\frac{xy}{x+y}} = \sqrt{\frac{xy}{x+y}\cdot\frac{x+y}{x+y}} = \frac{\sqrt{xy(x+y)}}{\sqrt{(x+y)^2}} = \frac{\sqrt{xy(x+y)}}{x+y}$$

Example 57. $$\sqrt{\frac{a}{b}-\frac{b}{a}} = \sqrt{\frac{a^2-b^2}{ab}} = \sqrt{\frac{ab(a^2-b^2)}{a^2b^2}} = \frac{\sqrt{ab(a^2-b^2)}}{\sqrt{a^2b^2}}$$
$$= \frac{\sqrt{ab(a^2-b^2)}}{ab}$$

EXERCISE 22

In the following expressions, rationalize the denominators and remove any perfect powers from the radicands. Where possible, use tables to compute the decimal values of Probs. 1 to 17.

1. $\sqrt{1/2}$ 2. $\sqrt{2/3}$ 3. $6\sqrt{1/8}$ 4. $9\sqrt{1/12}$

5. $6\sqrt{1/15}$ 6. $15\sqrt{5/18}$ 7. $\sqrt[3]{1/2}$ 8. $\sqrt[3]{1/4}$

9. $8\sqrt[3]{1/16}$ 10. $10\sqrt[3]{1/25}$ 11. $6\sqrt[4]{1/27}$ 12. $6\sqrt[4]{1/8}$

13. $\frac{1}{2}\sqrt{8/3}$ 14. $\sqrt{25/32}$ 15. $4\sqrt{27/80}$ 16. $\sqrt[3]{16/9}$

17. $\frac{1}{3}\sqrt[3]{36/25}$ 18. $\sqrt{\frac{1}{a}}$ 19. $\sqrt{\frac{1}{x^3}}$ 20. $x\sqrt{\frac{1}{x^5}}$

21. $\sqrt[3]{\frac{1}{a^2}}$ 22. $ab\sqrt[3]{\frac{1}{a^4}}$ 23. $\sqrt[3]{\frac{m}{mx^2}}$ 24. $\sqrt{\frac{3x}{2y}}$

25. $\sqrt{\frac{8a^3b}{27c^3}}$ 26. $\frac{a}{b}\sqrt[3]{\frac{1}{ab}}$ 27. $\sqrt{\frac{a-b}{a+b}}$ 28. $\sqrt{x-2+\frac{1}{x}}$

29. $\sqrt[n]{\frac{1}{x}}$ 30. $\sqrt[n+1]{\frac{1}{c^n}}$ 31. $\sqrt{\frac{1}{a^{2n+1}}}$ 32. $\sqrt[3]{\frac{1}{x^{3n-1}}}$

2.20 Reduction of the Order of a Radical

To reduce the order of a radical:

1. *Express the radicand as a perfect power of some rational number.*
2. *Transform the radical to equivalent fractional-exponent notation.*
3. *Reduce the fractional exponent to lowest terms.*
4. *Convert back to radical form.*

Example 58. Reduce the order of $\sqrt[6]{8a^3b^3}$.

$$\sqrt[6]{8a^3b^3} = \sqrt[6]{(2ab)^3} = (2ab)^{3/6} = (2ab)^{1/2} = \sqrt{2ab}$$

EXERCISE 23

Reduce the order of the following radicals.

1. $\sqrt[4]{25}$ 2. $\sqrt[4]{49}$ 3. $\sqrt[6]{16}$ 4. $\sqrt[6]{36}$

5. $\sqrt[6]{x^3y^3}$ 6. $\sqrt[4]{49x^2y^4}$ 7. $\sqrt[6]{25x^4y^6z^8}$ 8. $\sqrt[10]{x^6y^8}$

9. $\sqrt[2n]{x^n}$ 10. $\sqrt[3n]{b^3}$ 11. $\sqrt[6]{1/4}$ 12. $\sqrt[4]{1/25}$

13. $\sqrt[6]{\frac{1}{c^2}}$ 14. $\sqrt[6]{\frac{1}{x^3}}$

2.21 Addition and Subtraction of Radicals

Two radicals are said to be the *same* if they have the same radicand and the same index. Multiples of the same radical can be added or subtracted by combining their coefficients. To add or subtract expressions containing radicals, simplify each radical and collect and combine all multiples of the same radical. Addition of radicals which remain unlike after simplification can only be indicated. The decimal value of numerical problems can be computed approximately by the use of tables.

Example 59. Add $\sqrt{96} - 3\sqrt{2/3} + \frac{1}{2}\sqrt{150} - 2\sqrt{3/8}$.
Simplifying each radical,

$$4\sqrt{6} - \sqrt{6} + \tfrac{5}{2}\sqrt{6} - \tfrac{1}{2}\sqrt{6}$$

By the distributive law,

$$(4 - 1 + \tfrac{5}{2} - \tfrac{1}{2})\sqrt{6} = 5\sqrt{6}$$

Example 60. Add $\sqrt{5x} - \sqrt{5/x} + 2\sqrt{x/5} - \sqrt[6]{25x^2}$.
Simplifying each radical,

$$\sqrt{5x} - \frac{1}{x}\sqrt{5x} + \frac{2}{5}\sqrt{5x} - \sqrt[3]{5x}$$

Adding coefficients of like radicals,

$$\left(1 - \frac{1}{x} + \frac{2}{5}\right)\sqrt{5x} - \sqrt[3]{5x} = \left(\frac{7x - 5}{5x}\right)\sqrt{5x} - \sqrt[3]{5x}$$

EXERCISE 24

Simplify and combine where possible.

1. $\sqrt{2} + 6\sqrt{2}$
2. $3\sqrt{2} - \sqrt{18}$
3. $3\sqrt{75} - 2\sqrt{27} + \sqrt{48}$
4. $\sqrt{40} - 2\sqrt{90} + \sqrt{2/5}$
5. $\sqrt{98} + \frac{1}{3}\sqrt{72} - 2\sqrt{1/8}$
6. $3\sqrt{20} - \sqrt[4]{25} - \frac{2}{3}\sqrt{180}$
7. $3\sqrt{28} + 4\sqrt{1/7} + \sqrt{112}$
8. $\sqrt{60} - \sqrt{3/5} - \sqrt{5/27}$
9. $\frac{1}{2}\sqrt{24} + 3\sqrt{2/3} - 2\sqrt{3/2}$
10. $3\sqrt[3]{6} + 2\sqrt[3]{48} - 4\sqrt[6]{36}$
11. $2\sqrt{28} - 4\sqrt{63} + 14\sqrt{1/7}$
12. $5\sqrt[3]{108} - 2\sqrt[3]{32} - 4\sqrt[3]{1/2}$
13. $\sqrt{x} + \sqrt{x^3} + \sqrt{x^5}$
14. $\sqrt{12x} - \sqrt{75x^3} + \sqrt{3/x}$

2.22 Multiplication and Division of Radicals

A radical may ordinarily be multiplied or divided by another radical of the same order by using the formulas

$$\sqrt[n]{a} \cdot \sqrt[n]{b} = \sqrt[n]{ab} \qquad \textbf{(25)}$$

and

$$\frac{\sqrt[n]{a}}{\sqrt[n]{b}} = \sqrt[n]{\frac{a}{b}} \tag{26}$$

Example 61. Multiply $\sqrt[3]{4x^2y^2}$ by $\sqrt[3]{12a^2x^2}$.

$$\sqrt[3]{4x^2y^2} \cdot \sqrt[3]{12a^2x^2} = \sqrt[3]{48a^2x^4y^2} = \sqrt[3]{(8x^3)(6a^2xy^2)} = 2x\sqrt[3]{6a^2xy^2}$$

Example 62. Divide $\sqrt[4]{8a^3c^2}$ by $\sqrt[4]{54ac^3}$.

$$\frac{\sqrt[4]{8a^3c^2}}{\sqrt[4]{54ac^3}} = \sqrt[4]{\frac{8a^3c^2}{54ac^3}} = \sqrt[4]{\frac{4a^2}{27c}} = \sqrt[4]{\frac{4a^2}{27c}\cdot\frac{3c^3}{3c^3}} = \frac{1}{3c}\sqrt[4]{12a^2c^3}$$

Example 63. Multiply $2\sqrt{6} - \sqrt{3}$ by $3\sqrt{3} - \sqrt{2}$.

$$\begin{array}{l} 2\sqrt{6} - \sqrt{3} \\ 3\sqrt{3} - \sqrt{2} \\ \hline 6\sqrt{18} - 3(3) - 2\sqrt{12} + \sqrt{6} = 18\sqrt{2} - 9 - 4\sqrt{3} + \sqrt{6} \end{array}$$

When radicals of different orders are multiplied or divided, they must first be reduced to radicals of the same order. (The common index is usually the LCM of the original indices.)

Example 64. Multiply $\sqrt{2}$ by $\sqrt[3]{4}$.

$$\sqrt{2}\cdot\sqrt[3]{4} = \sqrt[6]{8}\cdot\sqrt[6]{16} = \sqrt[6]{128} = 2\sqrt[6]{2}$$

Example 65. Divide $\sqrt[3]{9}$ by $\sqrt{3}$.

$$\sqrt[3]{9} \div \sqrt{3} = \sqrt[6]{81} \div \sqrt[6]{27} = \sqrt[6]{81/27} = \sqrt[6]{3}$$

2.23 Division by an Irrational Binomial

In one important case of division of radicals, the divisor is a binomial in which one or both terms contain a second-degree radical. The division is effected by rationalizing the binomial divisor. This is done by multiplying the numerator and denominator of the fraction by the *conjugate* of the denominator, i.e., the denominator with the sign between its terms reversed. Simplify the new numerator and denominator. Similar methods can be applied to other special forms. This method is extremely important in Sec. 2.26, dealing with complex numbers.

Example 66. Rationalize the denominator of

$$\frac{12}{5 - \sqrt{7}}$$

Multiplying numerator and denominator by the conjugate of $5 - \sqrt{7}$, which is $5 + \sqrt{7}$, we obtain

$$\frac{12}{5 - \sqrt{7}} = \frac{12(5 + \sqrt{7})}{(5 - \sqrt{7})(5 + \sqrt{7})}$$

$$\frac{12(5 + \sqrt{7})}{5^2 - (\sqrt{7})^2} = \frac{12(5 + \sqrt{7})}{25 - 7} = \frac{12(5 + \sqrt{7})}{18} = \frac{2(5 + \sqrt{7})}{3}$$

Example 67. Rationalize the denominator of

$$\frac{\sqrt{6} + 3\sqrt{2}}{3\sqrt{6} + 2\sqrt{3}}$$

Multiplying numerator and denominator by $3\sqrt{6} - 2\sqrt{3}$,

$$\begin{aligned}\frac{\sqrt{6} + 3\sqrt{2}}{3\sqrt{6} + 2\sqrt{3}} &= \frac{(\sqrt{6} + 3\sqrt{2})(3\sqrt{6} - 2\sqrt{3})}{(3\sqrt{6} + 2\sqrt{3})(3\sqrt{6} - 2\sqrt{3})}\\ &= \frac{(3)(6) - 2\sqrt{18} + 9\sqrt{12} - 6\sqrt{6}}{(3\sqrt{6})^2 - (2\sqrt{3})^2}\\ &= \frac{18 - 6\sqrt{2} + 18\sqrt{3} - 6\sqrt{6}}{54 - 12}\\ &= \frac{6(3 - \sqrt{2} + 3\sqrt{3} - \sqrt{6})}{42}\\ &= \frac{3 - \sqrt{2} + 3\sqrt{3} - \sqrt{6}}{7}\end{aligned}$$

Example 68. Rationalize the denominator of

$$\frac{\sqrt{a + 1} - \sqrt{a - 1}}{\sqrt{a + 1} + \sqrt{a - 1}}$$

Multiplying numerator and denominator by $\sqrt{a + 1} - \sqrt{a - 1}$,

$$\begin{aligned}\frac{(\sqrt{a + 1} - \sqrt{a - 1})(\sqrt{a + 1} - \sqrt{a - 1})}{(\sqrt{a + 1} + \sqrt{a - 1})(\sqrt{a + 1} - \sqrt{a - 1})} &= \frac{a + 1 - 2\sqrt{a^2 - 1} + a - 1}{(a + 1) - (a - 1)}\\ &= \frac{2a - 2\sqrt{a^2 - 1}}{2} = a - \sqrt{a^2 - 1}\end{aligned}$$

EXERCISE 25

Perform the indicated operations and simplify the results. Where possible, use tables to compute the decimal values of answers containing no literal expressions.

1. $\sqrt{2}\cdot\sqrt{3}$
2. $\sqrt{3}\cdot\sqrt{6}$
3. $\sqrt{7}\cdot\sqrt{14}$
4. $3\sqrt{2}\cdot\sqrt{10}$
5. $2\sqrt{11}\cdot 3\sqrt{11}$
6. $4\sqrt{15}\cdot\sqrt{21}$
7. $\sqrt{6a}\cdot\sqrt{2ab}$
8. $2\sqrt{xy}\cdot\sqrt{yz}$
9. $\sqrt{abc}\cdot\sqrt{bcd}$
10. $\sqrt[3]{4}\cdot\sqrt[3]{6}$
11. $\sqrt[3]{18}\cdot\sqrt[3]{15}$
12. $\sqrt[3]{xy^2z}\cdot\sqrt[3]{x^2yz}$
13. $\sqrt[3]{4}\cdot\sqrt{6}$
14. $\sqrt[3]{9}\cdot\sqrt{3}$
15. $\sqrt[4]{8}\cdot\sqrt{2}$
16. $\sqrt[4]{27}\cdot\sqrt{3}$
17. $(\sqrt{10}+\sqrt{3})(\sqrt{10}-\sqrt{3})$
18. $(7+\sqrt{5})(7-\sqrt{5})$
19. $(5-3\sqrt{2})(5+3\sqrt{2})$
20. $(5\sqrt{6}-2\sqrt{10})(5\sqrt{6}+2\sqrt{10})$
21. $(\sqrt{6}-\sqrt{3})^2$
22. $(7-2\sqrt{5})^2$
23. $(\sqrt{3}+\sqrt{2})(3\sqrt{3}-2\sqrt{2})$
24. $(2\sqrt{6}-\sqrt{3})(\sqrt{6}+3\sqrt{2})$
25. $(\sqrt{6}+2\sqrt{10})(2\sqrt{15}-\sqrt{6})$
26. $\dfrac{\sqrt{6}}{\sqrt{2}}$
27. $\dfrac{\sqrt{35}}{\sqrt{15}}$
28. $\dfrac{5\sqrt{22}}{\sqrt{11}}$
29. $\dfrac{6\sqrt{3}}{\sqrt{15}}$
30. $\dfrac{\sqrt{ab}}{\sqrt{ac}}$
31. $\dfrac{\sqrt{21xy}}{\sqrt{14yz}}$
32. $\dfrac{\sqrt[3]{4}}{\sqrt{2}}$
33. $\dfrac{\sqrt{6}}{\sqrt[3]{3}}$
34. $\dfrac{\sqrt[4]{a^3}}{\sqrt[4]{a}}$
35. $\dfrac{\sqrt[4]{27}}{\sqrt{3}}$
36. $\dfrac{\sqrt{2}}{\sqrt[4]{8}}$
37. $\dfrac{6}{\sqrt{7}-2}$
38. $\dfrac{10}{\sqrt{13}-3}$
39. $\dfrac{24}{10-\sqrt{28}}$
40. $\dfrac{15}{\sqrt{17}-\sqrt{7}}$
41. $\dfrac{21}{2\sqrt{5}-\sqrt{6}}$
42. $\dfrac{\sqrt{6}}{2\sqrt{3}-\sqrt{2}}$
43. $\dfrac{\sqrt{10}}{3\sqrt{5}+2\sqrt{2}}$
44. $\dfrac{3\sqrt{2}-\sqrt{3}}{2\sqrt{3}+\sqrt{2}}$
45. $\dfrac{4\sqrt{5}+3\sqrt{3}}{3\sqrt{5}-2\sqrt{3}}$
46. $\dfrac{\sqrt{a-b}}{\sqrt{a}-\sqrt{b}}$
47. $\dfrac{\sqrt{xy}+\sqrt{yz}}{\sqrt{xyz}}$
48. $\dfrac{a-x}{\sqrt{a}+\sqrt{x}}$

2.24 Imaginary Numbers

Thus far we have been unable to give meaning to an even root of a negative number. For example, up to this point such symbols as $\sqrt{-4}$, $\sqrt[6]{-64}$, etc., have been quite meaningless.

However, by enlarging our concepts of numbers, we are able to give meaning to even roots of negative numbers. We shall begin by giving particular attention to the symbol $\sqrt{-1}$, which we shall call the *imaginary unit.*

It is customary to assign the same meaning to the letters i or j as to the symbol $\sqrt{-1}$. The letter i is standard nomenclature in strictly mathematical work, while j is more common in electrical technology. We shall follow the technology convention and let

$$j = \sqrt{-1} \qquad \textbf{(27)}$$

or

$$j^2 = -1 \qquad (28)$$

More generally, an imaginary number is represented by the symbol

$$\sqrt[n]{-P}$$

where n is an even number and P is any positive real number. However, we shall limit our discussion of imaginary numbers to cases where n is 2.

From Eq. (3), in which a and b are any numbers, imaginary or otherwise, we may write

$$(j\sqrt{P})^2 = j^2(\sqrt{P})^2$$

By applying Eq. (3),

$$(j\sqrt{P})^2 = j^2P$$

or

$$(j\sqrt{P})^2 = (-1)\cdot P = -P$$

Thus $j\sqrt{P}$ is seen to be one of two equal factors of $-P$ and is therefore a *square root* of $-P$.

Even though it can be shown that $-j\sqrt{P}$ is another square root of $-P$, the symbol $j\sqrt{P}$ is defined by common agreement as

$$j\sqrt{P} = \sqrt{-P} \qquad \textbf{(29)}$$

In Eq. (29) P is any positive real number, and $\sqrt{P}$ designates the *principal* square root of P.

For example,

$$\sqrt{-25} = +j5$$

Powers of j

By definition,

$$j^2 = -1 \tag{30}$$

Then it follows from the basic rules of algebra that

$$\begin{aligned}
j^0 &= 1 \\
j^1 &= j \\
j^2 &= -1 \\
j^3 &= j^2 \times j = -j \\
j^4 &= j^2 \times j^2 = 1 \\
j^5 &= j^4 \times j = j \\
j^6 &= j^4 \times j^2 = -1
\end{aligned}$$

In general, where n is any integer (positive, negative, or zero),

$$j^{4n} = +1 \tag{31}$$
$$j^{4n+1} = +j \tag{32}$$
$$j^{4n+2} = -1 \tag{33}$$
$$j^{4n+3} = -j \tag{34}$$

By use of Eqs. (31) to (34), any power of j may be determined at a glance. Observe that any real, integral power of j must be either unity or j or their negatives.

EXERCISE 26

Find the value of

1. j^{10} 2. j^6 3. j^{15} 4. j^{985} 5. j^{-25}

2.25 Operations with Imaginary Numbers

Addition and Subtraction of Imaginary Numbers

Imaginary numbers may be added and subtracted according to the rules of algebra already discussed.

Example 69. Add $\sqrt{-9}$ and $\sqrt{-49}$.

From Eq. (29) we may write

$$\sqrt{-9} = j\sqrt{9} = j3$$
$$\sqrt{-49} = j\sqrt{49} = j7$$
$$\sqrt{-9} + \sqrt{-49} = j3 + j7 = j10$$

Note: An alternative expression is $3j + 7j = 10j$.

Example 70. Subtract $\sqrt{-25}$ from $\sqrt{-121}$.

From Eq. (29) we may write

$$\sqrt{-25} = j\sqrt{25} = j5$$
$$\sqrt{-121} = j\sqrt{121} = j11$$
$$\sqrt{-121} - \sqrt{-25} = j11 - j5 = j6$$

Multiplication of Imaginary Numbers

Multiplication of imaginary numbers can be accomplished as illustrated below.

Example 71. Multiply $\sqrt{-5}$ by $\sqrt{-7}$.

Both $\sqrt{-5}$ and $\sqrt{-7}$ are imaginary numbers and consequently must be changed to the form $j\sqrt{b}$ before multiplying.

$$\sqrt{-5} = j\sqrt{5}$$
$$\sqrt{-7} = j\sqrt{7}$$

Then

$$\sqrt{-5} \times \sqrt{-7} = j\sqrt{5} \cdot j\sqrt{7}$$

or

$$\sqrt{-5} \times \sqrt{-7} = j^2 \cdot \sqrt{5 \cdot 7} = j^2\sqrt{35} = -\sqrt{35} = -5.916$$

Observe that Eq. (23) does not apply to even roots of negative numbers and

$$\sqrt{-5} \times \sqrt{-7} \neq \sqrt{(-5)(-7)}$$
$$\sqrt{-5} \times \sqrt{-7} \neq \sqrt{+35}$$

Example 72. Evaluate $(\sqrt{-5})^2$.
From Eq. (29)

$$\sqrt{-5} = j\sqrt{5}$$

Then

$$(\sqrt{-5})^2 = (j\sqrt{5})^2 = j^2(\sqrt{5})^2$$

From Eqs. (20) and (28), therefore,

$$-(\sqrt{5})^2 = -|5| = -5$$

Also

$$(\sqrt{-5})^2 = j^2(\sqrt{5})^2 = (j)^2(5) = -5$$

Example 73. Evaluate $\sqrt{(-5)^2}$.
From Definition 1, we may write

$$(-5)(-5) = (-5)^2 = +25$$

Then from Sec. 2.16,

$$\sqrt{(-5)^2} = \sqrt{25} = +5$$

Compare with Example 72.

Example 74. Multiply $\sqrt{-5}$, $\sqrt{-7}$, and $\sqrt{-15}$.

$$\sqrt{-5} = j\sqrt{5}$$
$$\sqrt{-7} = j\sqrt{7}$$
$$\sqrt{-15} = j\sqrt{15}$$
$$\sqrt{-5} \times \sqrt{-7} \times \sqrt{-15} = j\sqrt{5} \times j\sqrt{7} \times j\sqrt{15}$$
$$= j^3\sqrt{5} \times \sqrt{7} \times \sqrt{15} = j^3\sqrt{525} = j^3 5\sqrt{21} = -j5\sqrt{21}$$

Example 75. Multiply $3\sqrt{-6} + 2\sqrt{-5}$ by $3\sqrt{-3} - 7\sqrt{-11}$.

$$3\sqrt{-6} = j3\sqrt{6}$$
$$2\sqrt{-5} = j2\sqrt{5}$$
$$3\sqrt{-3} = j3\sqrt{3}$$
$$7\sqrt{-11} = j7\sqrt{11}$$

$$\begin{array}{l} j3\sqrt{6} + j2\sqrt{5} \\ j3\sqrt{3} - j7\sqrt{11} \\ \hline j^2 9\sqrt{18} + j^2 6\sqrt{15} - j^2 21\sqrt{66} - j^2 14\sqrt{55} \end{array}$$

Substituting for j^2 its numerical value, we obtain

$$-9\sqrt{18} - 6\sqrt{15} + 21\sqrt{66} + 14\sqrt{55}$$

Evaluating the radicals, we obtain

$$(-9 \times 4.243) - (6 \times 3.873) + (21 \times 8.124) + (14 \times 7.416)$$
$$= -38.187 - 23.238 + 170.604 + 103.824 = 213.00$$

Division of Imaginary Numbers

Example 76. Divide $\sqrt{-30}$ by $\sqrt{-15}$.

$$\frac{\sqrt{-30}}{\sqrt{-15}} = \frac{j\sqrt{30}}{j\sqrt{15}} = \frac{\sqrt{30}}{\sqrt{15}} = \sqrt{\frac{30}{15}} = \sqrt{2}$$

EXERCISE 27

Simplify:

1. $\sqrt{-27} + \sqrt{-147} - \sqrt{12}$
2. $\sqrt{-150} - \sqrt{-54} + \sqrt{216}$
3. $\sqrt{-18} + \sqrt{-72} - \sqrt{128} + \sqrt{32}$
4. $\sqrt{-63} - \sqrt{-567} + \sqrt{112}$
5. $\sqrt{-80} + \sqrt{-20} + \sqrt{-320} - \sqrt{-245}$
6. $\sqrt{-128} + \sqrt{-72} - \sqrt{-800} + \sqrt{-392}$
7. $\sqrt{-196} - \sqrt{-64} + \sqrt{-80} + \sqrt{80}$
8. $\sqrt{-192} + \sqrt{-12} - \sqrt{-48} + \sqrt{-256}$
9. $\sqrt{-32} - \sqrt{-392} + \sqrt{-128}$
10. $\sqrt{-3} \times \sqrt{-3}$
11. $\sqrt{-25y^4} \times \sqrt{-9x^2}$
12. $(-4\sqrt{-4})(-3\sqrt{-9})$
13. $-\sqrt{-27a^2} \times \sqrt{-75b^2}$
14. $j\sqrt{3} \times j\sqrt{5}$
15. $-j\sqrt{7} \times j\sqrt{15}$
16. $-j\sqrt{2} \times (-j\sqrt{5})$

17. $j5 \times j8$
18. $j5 \times (-j8)$
19. $(-j2) \times (-j3)$
20. $(2\sqrt{-5} - 3\sqrt{-2})(2\sqrt{-5} + 3\sqrt{-2})$
21. $(\sqrt{-2} + \sqrt{-3})^2$
22. $\sqrt{-5} \times \sqrt{-7} \times \sqrt{-2}$
23. $\sqrt{-3} \times \sqrt{-10} \times \sqrt{-5}$
24. $\sqrt{-15} \times \sqrt{-5} \times \sqrt{-3}$
25. $(\sqrt{-5} + \sqrt{-3})(\sqrt{-6} - \sqrt{-2})$
26. $(\sqrt{-2} + \sqrt{-5})(\sqrt{-7} + \sqrt{-6})(\sqrt{-4} - \sqrt{-9})$
27. $\sqrt{-48} \div \sqrt{-96}$
28. $\sqrt{-144} \div \sqrt{-100}$
29. $\sqrt{-294} \div \sqrt{-54}$
30. $j3 \div j^25$
31. $\sqrt{-160} \div \sqrt{8}$
32. $\sqrt{-320} \div \sqrt{-128}$
33. $\sqrt{-63} \div \sqrt{-18}$
34. $\sqrt{96} \div \sqrt{-32}$
35. $(\sqrt{-392} \div \sqrt{-49}) \times \sqrt{196}$
36. $(\sqrt{-128} \div \sqrt{-80})(\sqrt{32} \div \sqrt{-16})$

2.26 Complex Numbers

A *complex number* is an expression in the form $a + jb$, where a and b are real numbers and $j = \sqrt{-1}$.

Complex numbers are used extensively in the solution of alternating-current-circuit problems.

For the present, we shall concentrate on the purely manipulative techniques involving complex numbers, leaving the applications until we have had a chance to cover more advanced algebra and trigonometry.

Notice that in the general form of a complex number $a + jb$, if $a = 0$, we have a pure imaginary number. If $b = 0$, we have a real number.

Two complex numbers are equal if, and only if, their real and imaginary parts are respectively equal. That is,

$$a + jb = c + jd$$

means that

$$a = c \quad \text{and} \quad b = d$$

Addition of Complex Numbers

Example 77. Add the complex numbers $2 + j6$, $3 - j5$, and $4 + j2$.

$$\begin{array}{l} 2 + j6 \\ 3 - j5 \\ \underline{4 + j2} \\ 9 + j3 \end{array}$$

Subtraction of Complex Numbers

Example 78. Subtract $5 + j9$ from $8 + j4$.

$$\begin{array}{l} 8 + j4 \\ \underline{5 + j9} \\ 3 - j5 \end{array}$$

Example 79. Subtract $8 - j5$ from $3 + j2$.

$$\begin{array}{r} 3 + j2 \\ \underline{8 - j5} \\ -5 + j7 \end{array}$$

Multiplication of Complex Numbers

Complex numbers are multiplied according to procedures already described in Sec. 2.25. After multiplication, any powers of j except the first are replaced by their equivalents (Sec. 2.24).

Example 80. Multiply $2 + j7$ by $3 - j6$.

$$\begin{array}{l} 2 + j7 \\ \underline{3 - j6} \\ 6 + j21 - j12 - j^2 42 \end{array}$$

Since $j^2 = -1$, the product can be written

$$6 + j21 - j12 + 42$$

or

$$48 + j9$$

Example 81. Find the product of the general complex numbers $(a + jb)$ and $(c + jd)$. The multiplication is performed exactly as is the multiplication of any two binomials.

$$\begin{array}{l} a + jb \\ \underline{c + jd} \\ ac + jbc + jad + j^2 bd \end{array} \qquad (35)$$

By definition, $j^2 = -1$; therefore expression (35) becomes

$$ac + jbc + jad - bd \qquad (36)$$

Grouping real and imaginary numbers, expression (36) becomes

$$(ac - bd) + j(bc + ad)$$

Division of Complex Numbers

In division of complex numbers we use the principle of rationalization described in Sec. 2.23.

Example 82. Divide $5 + j8$ by $2 - j7$.

The problem can be arranged as

$$\frac{5 + j8}{2 - j7}$$

If we multiply the denominator by the conjugate of the denominator, i.e., by $2 + j7$ (Sec. 2.23), we obtain

$$(2 - j7)(2 + j7) = 4 + 49 = 53$$

Thus it is a basic principle of complex numbers that *the product of a complex number and its conjugate is a real number.*

In the present problem we can multiply both numerator and denominator by the conjugate of the denominator and obtain a fraction with a complex numerator and a real denominator.

$$\frac{(5 + j8)(2 + j7)}{(2 - j7)(2 + j7)} = \frac{(5 + j8)(2 + j7)}{53}$$

The numerator can now be multiplied in the usual way.

$$\begin{array}{r} 5 + j8 \\ 2 + j7 \\ \hline 10 + j16 + j35 + j^2 56 \\ 10 + j16 + j35 - 56 \\ -46 + j51 \end{array}$$

The original fraction is now

$$\frac{-46 + j51}{53}$$

If it is desired to separate the number into its real and imaginary parts, it can be written

$$-\frac{46}{53} + j\frac{51}{53}$$

or

$$-0.868 + j0.962$$

Example 83. Divide the complex number $a + jb$ by the complex number $c + jd$.

Rewriting the problem in the form of a fraction, we have

$$\frac{a + jb}{c + jd} \tag{37}$$

Multiplying numerator and denominator of expression (37) by $c - jd$, which is called the *complex conjugate* of $c + jd$ (Sec. 2.23),

$$\frac{a + jb}{c + jd} = \frac{(a + jb)(c - jd)}{(c + jd)(c - jd)} \tag{38}$$

Performing the indicated multiplication to obtain the numerator of Eq. (38),

$$\begin{array}{r} a + jb \\ c - jd \\ \hline ac + jbc - jad - j^2bd \end{array}$$

Since by definition $j^2 = -1$, the above product becomes

$$ac + jbc - jad + bd$$

or after simplification, the numerator of Eq. (38) becomes

$$(ac + bd) + j(bc - ad)$$

Performing the indicated multiplication to obtain the denominator of Eq. (38),

$$\begin{array}{r} c + jd \\ c - jd \\ \hline c^2 + jcd - jcd - j^2d^2 \end{array} \tag{39}$$

Simplifying expression (39), we obtain

$c^2 + d^2$

Equation (38) can now be written

$$\frac{a + jb}{c + jd} = \frac{(ac + bd) + j(bc - ad)}{c^2 + d^2}$$

or

$$\frac{a + jb}{c + jd} = \frac{ac + bd}{c^2 + d^2} + j\frac{bc - ad}{c^2 + d^2}$$

EXERCISE 28

Multiply the following:

1. $(2 + j3)(7 + j5)$
2. $(-3 - j6)(2 + j8)$
3. $(2 + j7)(4 - j5)(3 + j10)$
4. $(3 + j5)(3 - j5)$
5. $-(2 + j7)(2 - j7)$
6. $(5 + \sqrt{-6})(3 - \sqrt{-8})(2 + \sqrt{-5})$
7. $(2 + j5)^5$
8. $(1.4 + j3.6)(0.7 + j9.1)$
9. $(-0.42 - j2.7)(0.63 + j4.2)$
10. $(-8.6 + j3.6)(4.7 + j5.1)$
11. $\left(-\frac{1}{2} + j\frac{\sqrt{3}}{2}\right)^3$

Divide the following:

12. $\frac{1}{1 + j}$
13. $\frac{3 + j6}{4 - j8}$
14. $\frac{2 - j9}{3 + j5}$
15. $\frac{1 + j}{2j^5}$
16. $\sqrt{4^{-2}} \div \sqrt{0.625}$
17. $(3 - \sqrt{-5}) \div (3 + \sqrt{-5})$
18. $\frac{1}{4 + 2\sqrt{-3} - \sqrt{-7}}$
19. $\frac{1}{\sqrt{-2} - 1}$
20. $\frac{2\sqrt{-5} + 5\sqrt{-2}}{2\sqrt{-5} - 5\sqrt{-2}}$
21. $\frac{\sqrt{5} - \sqrt{-5}}{\sqrt{2} + \sqrt{-2}}$
22. $\frac{3 + j2}{j}$
23. $\frac{j}{5 - 3j}$
24. $\left(\frac{2 + 6j}{2 - 7j}\right)^2$

Simplify:

25. $\dfrac{(2 + 6j)(3 - 7j)}{(5 - 2j) + (6 - 4j)}$

26. $\dfrac{(1 + 7j)(2 - 3j)}{(4 - 6j) - (3 - 5j)}$

27. $\dfrac{(1.8 - 3.2j)(0.8 + 0.6j)}{(1.8 - 3.2j) + (0.8 + 0.6j)}$

28. $\dfrac{(2 + 3j)(6 - 4j)}{(2 + 3j) + (6 - 4j)}$

3 linear equations

An equation such as

$$3x + 5 = 9x - 7$$

is an algebraic sentence. It asserts that the left member $3x + 5$ and the right member $9x - 7$ both designate the same number. In this case x is said to be an *unknown*.

To solve an equation means to find a value (or values) of the unknown, or the *variable*, which will make this algebraic sentence true. Such values are called *roots* or solutions of the equation.

3.1 Solving Linear Equations

The strategy used in solving an equation consists in obtaining a sequence of equivalent equations, the last of which shows the variable alone as one member, the constants constituting the other member.†

There are definite rules by which we can operate on a given equation in order to be sure of obtaining an equivalent equation. These are called *permissible* operations.

† Two or more equations are equivalent if their respective members become equal when the same value (or values) of the unknown letter is used in each case.

Permissible operations are as follows:

1. Adding the same number to both members of the given equation
2. Subtracting the same number from both members of the given equation
3. Multiplying both members of the given equation by the same *nonzero* number
4. Dividing both members of the given equation by the same *nonzero* number

Example 1. Solve the equation

$$\frac{3x}{4} + \frac{1}{6} = 2x - \frac{7}{3}$$

Multiplying by the LCD, 12, we obtain

$$9x + 2 = 24x - 28 \qquad (1)$$

By subtracting 9x from both members of Eq. (1) and adding 28 to both members of Eq. (1), we obtain

$$2 + 28 = 24x - 9x$$

Combining like terms,

$$30 = 15x$$

Dividing by 15,

$$30/15 = 2 = x$$

To check this solution, we substitute 2 for x in the given equation, obtaining

$$\frac{3(2)}{4} + \frac{1}{6} \stackrel{?}{=} 2(2) - \frac{7}{3}$$

$$\frac{3}{2} + \frac{1}{6} \stackrel{?}{=} 4 - \frac{7}{3}$$

$$\frac{9}{6} + \frac{1}{6} \stackrel{?}{=} \frac{12}{3} - \frac{7}{3}$$

$$\frac{10}{6} \stackrel{?}{=} \frac{5}{3}$$

$$\frac{5}{3} = \frac{5}{3}$$

Example 2. Solve for x the equation

$$3(3x - a) + 2a = a(ax - 3) + 6 \tag{2}$$

(This is called a *literal equation,* since in addition to the variable x it contains a letter a, considered here to represent a constant.)

Removing parentheses,

$$9x - 3a + 2a = a^2x - 3a + 6 \tag{3}$$

By subtracting $9x + 6$ and adding $3a$ to both members of Eq. (3), we obtain

$$-3a + 2a + 3a - 6 = a^2x - 9x$$

Collecting like terms,

$$2a - 6 = x(a^2 - 9)$$

Dividing by $a^2 - 9$, $\quad a \neq \pm 3$

$$\frac{2a - 6}{a^2 - 9} = \frac{2}{a + 3} = x$$

We may check by substituting $2/(a + 3)$ for x in Eq. (2), but such a check in a literal equation is apt to entail more work than the original solution. A reasonably certain check may be obtained by assigning to a some arbitrary simple numerical value. We should avoid using 1 or 0 or any number which will make any denominator equal to zero.

In this illustration, if we let $a = -2$, then $x = 2$. Substituting in the original equation.

$$3[(3)(2) - (-2)] + 2(-2) \stackrel{?}{=} (-2)[(-2)(2) - 3] + 6$$

or

$$3(6 + 2) - 4 \stackrel{?}{=} (-2)(-4 - 3) + 6$$

or

$$20 = 20$$

EXERCISE 1

Solve the following linear equations. When more than one letter appears, consider the last letter (in alphabetical order) as the unknown quantity and all other letters as known quantities.

1. $13x - 8 = 8x + 2$
2. $(x - 2)^3 = x^2(x - 6)$
3. $7x + 4 = x - 8$
4. $(z + 1)(z + 5) = (z + 2)(z + 3)$
5. $2 - 3x + 7 = 8x + 3 - x$
6. $(2w + 1)(3w + 1) = (6w - 1)(w + 2)$
7. $5y - (3y - 2) = 10$
8. $\frac{x}{3} + \frac{x}{4} = \frac{7}{2}$
9. $6(w + 5) - 12 = 3(3w - 1) + 4w$
10. $(r + 1)^2 = r^2 + 9$
11. $\frac{x}{10} + \frac{x}{12} + \frac{x}{15} = x - 6$
12. $\frac{1}{8}(1 - y) - \frac{1}{10}(2 - y) - \frac{1}{12}(3 + y) = 0$
13. $\frac{6y - 3}{3y + 2} = \frac{2y + 1}{y + 2}$
14. $0.2x = 46 - 0.03x$
15. $0.103 - 0.1x = 0.02x - 0.13x + 0.11$
16. $\frac{8}{x - 2} - \frac{5}{x - 11} = \frac{3}{x - 5}$
17. $\frac{2}{x} + \frac{3}{x} = 10$
18. $\frac{2x}{x^2 - 4} - \frac{4}{x^2 - 4} = \frac{2}{2x - 3}$
19. $\frac{1}{4y} - \frac{1}{6y} = \frac{1}{8}$
20. $\frac{2}{1 - 2w} + \frac{2}{7 - 2w} = 1 - \frac{4w^2 - 1}{4w^2 - 16w + 7}$
21. $\frac{8}{x + 4} = \frac{6}{x - 4}$
22. $ax + b = c$
23. $\frac{4}{7z + 3} = \frac{3}{6z + 2}$
24. $6abx = 9a^3b^2c$
25. $b(x + 1) = c$
26. $\frac{b}{y} = \frac{c}{d}$
27. $\frac{x}{a} + \frac{x}{b} = a^2 - b^2$
28. $\frac{c}{x} = a + 1$
29. $\frac{m + n}{x} = m^2 + mn$
30. $mx - h = hx - m$
31. $3ay = 5by + 2$
32. By inspection determine the number of roots in

    (a) the equation $y + \frac{3}{y - 5} = -5 + \frac{3}{y - 5}$

    (b) the equation $y + \frac{3}{y - 5} = 5 + \frac{3}{y - 5}$

3.2 Mathematical Operations with Dimensional Units

In setting up equations derived from physical problems, it must be remembered that each side of the equation must reduce to like dimensions and consistent units.

The word *dimension* as used here refers to the *kind* of a quantity with which we are dealing. For example, the weight w of an object may be measured in *units* of pounds, ounces, tons, grams, etc. However, regardless of the units used, w is said to have the dimension of weight.

The speed v of a moving automobile could be expressed in miles per hour, feet per second, or even furlongs per fortnight. In each case, however, v is said to have the dimension of speed, even though the units used are quite different.

Parenthetically, it is worth mentioning that the word "per" means "for each." That is, if an automobile is traveling at the rate of 20 miles *per* hour, this means that it is traveling at the rate of 20 miles *for each* hour.

Operations with dimensional symbols are subject to the usual laws of algebra. Some common examples are:

Length × length = area	$(\text{ft})(\text{ft}) = \text{ft}^2$
Length × length × length = volume	$(\text{ft})(\text{ft})(\text{ft}) = \text{ft}^3$
Area × length = volume	$\text{ft}^2 \times \text{ft} = \text{ft}^3$
$\dfrac{\text{Weight}}{\text{Volume}} = \text{density}\dagger$	$\text{lb} \div \text{ft}^3 = \dfrac{\text{lb}}{\text{ft}^3}$
$\dfrac{\text{Distance}}{\text{Time}} = \text{average velocity}$	$\text{ft} \div \text{s} = \dfrac{\text{ft}}{\text{s}}$
$\dfrac{\text{Change in velocity}}{\text{Time}} = \text{average acceleration}$	$\dfrac{\text{ft}}{\text{s}} \div \text{s} = \dfrac{\text{ft}}{\text{s}^2}$
$\dfrac{\text{Force}}{\text{Area}} = \text{pressure}\dagger$	$\text{lb} \div \text{ft}^2 = \dfrac{\text{lb}}{\text{ft}^2}$
(Weight density) × height = pressure	$\dfrac{\text{lb}}{\text{ft}^3} \times \text{ft} = \dfrac{\text{lb}}{\text{ft}^2}$
Pressure × volume = work†	$\dfrac{\text{lb}}{\text{ft}^2} \times \text{ft}^3 = (\text{ft})(\text{lb})$
Distance × force = work†	$\text{ft} \times \text{lb} = (\text{ft})(\text{lb})$
Power × time = work†	$\dfrac{(\text{ft})(\text{lb})}{\text{s}} \times \text{s} = (\text{ft})(\text{lb})$
$\dfrac{\text{Work}}{\text{Time}} = \text{power}\dagger$	$(\text{ft})(\text{lb}) \div \text{s} = \dfrac{(\text{ft})(\text{lb})}{\text{s}}$

† Gravitational units (the language of the "man on the street"), rather than absolute units, are used.

3.3 Dimensional Units in Conversions

Dimensional units, properly handled, will not only check the dimensional soundness of a formula, they will also indicate what steps are necessary to make a required conversion.

Example 3. It costs \$30/h to run a boat when sailing at 10 mi/h. Find the operating cost in dollars per mile.

$$\frac{\$30}{1\text{ h}} \div \frac{10\text{ mi}}{1\text{ h}} = \frac{\overset{3}{\cancel{\$30}}}{1\,\cancel{\text{h}}} \times \frac{1\,\cancel{\text{h}}}{\underset{1}{\cancel{10}}\text{ mi}} = \$3/\text{mi}$$

Example 4. The density of mercury is 13.6 g/cm³. Express the density in pounds per cubic inch.

$$\frac{13.6\text{ g}}{\text{cm}^3} = \frac{13.6\,\cancel{\text{g}}}{1\,\cancel{\text{cm}^3}} \times \frac{1\text{ lb}}{454\,\cancel{\text{g}}} \times \frac{(2.54)^3\,\cancel{\text{cm}^3}}{1\text{ in}^3} = 0.492\frac{\text{lb}}{\text{in}^3}$$

3.4 Analysis of a Formula

Whenever a formula is developed or applied for the first time, it is instructive to subject it to a few screening tests. The most common of these are the test for dimensional soundness and the test for applicability to special conditions.

The application of these tests can be illustrated to advantage by referring to a formula such as that given in Fact 94, Chap. 5, for the volume of the frustum of a cone. The formula is

$$V = \tfrac{1}{3}\pi h(r_1^2 + r_1r_2 + r_2^2)$$

If the indicated multiplication is carried out, the terms will be hr_1^2, hr_1r_2, and hr_2^2—all third-degree terms in a length unit. Such terms are therefore expressions of volume (Sec. 3.2), and the formula is dimensionally sound.

If we assume $r_1 = r_2$, as would be the case in a cylinder, we obtain

$$V = \tfrac{1}{3}\pi h(r_1^2 + r_1r_1 + r_1^2)$$

or

$$V = \pi r_1^2 h$$

the formula for the volume of a cylinder.

If we assume $r_1 = 0$, as in a cone, we obtain

$$V = \tfrac{1}{3}\pi h r_2^2$$

the formula for the volume of a cone.

If we take $h = 0$, the entire expression assumes the value zero, as is to be expected.

EXERCISE 2

Solve the following formulas for the letter indicated. Leave your answer in the most convenient form for computation, and be prepared to justify your choice. The formulas are identified in the right-hand column.

	Solve for	*Description of formula*
1. $Q = \dfrac{WL}{T}$	T	Latent heat of vaporization
2. $X = \dfrac{1}{2\pi fC}$	C	Reactance of a capacitor
3. $I = \dfrac{E - e}{R}$	e	Current flowing through armature of generator
4. $V = \dfrac{V_t + V_0}{2}$	V_0	Average speed of uniformly accelerating body
5. $\dfrac{E}{e} = \dfrac{R + r}{r}$	r	Voltage drop
6. $T = \dfrac{1}{a} + t$ $\left(\text{first solve for } \dfrac{1}{a}\right)$	a	Temperature-conversion formula
7. $C = \dfrac{Kab}{b - a}$	a	Magnetic potential
8. $S = \dfrac{rl - a}{r - 1}$	a, r	Geometric progression
9. $\rho = \dfrac{m}{d - L} - \dfrac{m}{d + L}$	m	
10. $\dfrac{e}{x} = C(e - b) + \dfrac{b}{x}$	x	
11. $Q = 0.000477EIT$	T	Electrical equivalent of heat
12. $d = \tfrac{1}{2}at^2 - \tfrac{1}{2}a(t - 1)^2$	t	Distance covered by falling body
13. $C = \tfrac{5}{9}(F - 32)$	F	Celsius-Fahrenheit temperature conversion

14. $A = \frac{m}{t}(p + t)$	t	Thickness of pipe
15. $H = \frac{0.4\pi NI}{L}$	I	Magnetic intensity
16. $M = 10.5C + 35.2\left(W - \frac{C}{8}\right)$	C	Theoretical amount of air required to burn solid fuel
17. $\frac{1}{x} + \frac{1}{nx} = \frac{1}{f}$	x	Photographic enlargement
18. $S = \left(\frac{\pi d^2}{2} + \frac{\pi dl}{r}\right) \div \frac{\pi d^2 l}{4rc}$	r	Exposed surface of cylinders
19. $S = T - \frac{1.299}{N}$	N	Tap-size drill for U.S. standard thread
20. $W = \frac{2PR}{R - r}$	R	Differential pulley
21. $\frac{1}{R} = \frac{1}{r_1} + \frac{1}{r_2}$	R	Parallel resistances
22. $I = \frac{E}{r + (R/n)}$	n	Current produced by cells in parallel
23. $T = T_1\left(1 - \frac{n-1}{n} \cdot \frac{h}{h_0}\right)$	n	Adiabatic cooling
24. $x - y = xy$	y	Hyperbola
25. $V = \frac{h}{6}(B + 4M + b)$	M	Prismoidal formula
26. $wf = \left(\frac{w}{k} - 1\right)\frac{1}{k}$	w	
27. $V_1 = V_0(1 + 0.00366t)$	t	Expansion of gases

3.5 Suggestions for the Solution of Applied Problems Involving Linear Equations

There is no pat formula for the solution of "word" problems. One should not feel discouraged if this section of the work seems difficult, for this is a common reaction. This situation is due largely to the fact that the translation of a verbal or descriptive problem (commonly called a word problem) involves a minimum of dependence on mechanical rules. Such translation requires some exercise of ingenuity and of the skill that comes only with experience. If this seems a bleak outlook, it should be remembered that these remarks apply equally well to carpentry, machine design, music, painting, etc. The feeling of accomplishment in solving the more interesting applied problems is not experienced by those who are content merely to follow mechanical procedures.

While a rigid, ironclad procedure cannot be offered, a few general suggestions which have proved helpful can be outlined.

1. *Read the problem through once to get the general idea.*
2. *Carefully reread the problem, noting what is given and what is wanted.*
3. *A rough graphical representation will often suggest relationships leading to a solution (see Sec. 7.8).*
4. *Represent the unknown quantity by some appropriate symbol, such as* v *for velocity,* t *for time,* w *for weight.*

The symbol should be quantitative: it should refer to the number of units in the unknown; e.g., "Let t represent the time for the trip in hours"; "Let w represent the weight of copper in pounds." Be explicit.

All related quantities should be expressed in consistent units. For example, if it has been decided to express a velocity in miles per hour, all distances must be expressed in miles and all times must be expressed in hours.

If you consider your data to be inadequate, make an approximation by any reasonable means.

1. *Try to discover two expressions which are equal. Form them into an equation and check dimensionality.*
2. *Solve the equation and check the solution against the original worded statement, not the equation you derived from it.*

Numerous laws of mathematics, natural sciences, etc., such as the following, may serve as the basis of equality:

The sum of the parts equals the whole.
Distance equals rate times time.
Weight equals volume times density.
Number of units times the unit cost equals the total cost.
Principal times the rate of interest times the time equals the interest.
Amount of material times the fraction of a particular ingredient equals the amount of ingredient.
The square of the hypotenuse of a right triangle equals the sum of the squares of the legs.

3. *Make a quick "commonsense" check to see if your answer seems reasonable.*

Example 4. A tourist having $4\frac{1}{2}$ h at his disposal rides out into the country on a bus at a rate of 19 mi/h. He plans to walk back at a rate of $3\frac{1}{2}$ mi/h. How far can he ride without arriving late at his starting point?

The one-way distance is required. The total time and the outgoing and return rates are given. Let d = number of miles one way. We know that distance = rate × time, or distance/rate = time. We can set up an equation:

$$\text{Outbound time} + \text{return time} = \text{total time} \tag{4}$$

Equation (4) is dimensionally correct since it is expressed as

A time + a time = a time

Now, since

$$\text{Time} = \frac{\text{distance}}{\text{rate}}$$

we may write

$$\underset{\text{(outbound)}}{\frac{\text{Distance}}{\text{Rate}}} + \underset{\text{(return)}}{\frac{\text{distance}}{\text{rate}}} = \text{total time}$$

$$\frac{d}{19} + \frac{d}{3\frac{1}{2}} = 4\frac{1}{2} \tag{5}$$

Equation (5) is consistent with respect to the units used since both distances are in units of miles, both rates are in units of miles per hour, and time is expressed in hours.

Then

$$3\tfrac{1}{2}d + 19d = (19)(3\tfrac{1}{2})(4\tfrac{1}{2})$$
$$22\tfrac{1}{2}d = 299\tfrac{1}{4}$$
$$d = 13.3 \text{ mi}$$

Checking against the original statement,

$$\frac{13.3}{19} = 0.7 \text{ h outbound}$$

$$\frac{13.3}{3.5} = 3.8 \text{ h return}$$

4.5 *total*

Alternatively,

$$\underset{\text{(outbound)}}{\text{Distance}} = \underset{\text{(return)}}{\text{distance}}$$

or

$$\underset{\text{(outbound)}}{\text{Rate} \times \text{time}} = \underset{\text{(return)}}{\text{rate} \times \text{time}}$$

If t is the number of hours outbound, this equation becomes

$$(19)(t) = 3\tfrac{1}{2}(4\tfrac{1}{2} - t)$$

or

$$19t = 15.75 - 3.5t$$

and $t = 0.7$ h outbound and $(0.7)(19) = 13.3$ mi one-way distance.

Example 5. How much 80% by volume antifreeze (alcohol) must be added to 5 qt of 30% antifreeze to raise the strength to 65%?

We wish to know the amount of 80% antifreeze needed. We are given the concentrations of the initial solutions and the final mixture and the amount of the weaker solution. Let n = number of quarts of 80% solution required. Then $n + 5$ = number of quarts of mixture finally obtained. We can set up an equation saying that quarts of pure alcohol in 5 qt of 30% solution plus the quarts of pure alcohol in n qt of 80% solution taken equals the quarts of pure alcohol in $(n + 5)$ qt of 65% final mixture. Hence

$$\begin{aligned}(0.30)(5) + 0.80n &= 0.65(n + 5)\\ 1.5 + 0.8n &= 0.65n + 3.25\\ 0.15n &= 1.75\\ n &= \frac{1.75}{0.15} = 11\tfrac{2}{3} \text{ qt of 80\% antifreeze required}\end{aligned}$$

Check:

$$\begin{aligned}0.80 \times 11\tfrac{2}{3} &= 9\tfrac{1}{3} \text{ qt pure alcohol in 80\% solution}\\ 0.30 \times 5 &= 1\tfrac{1}{2} \text{ qt pure alcohol in 30\% solution}\\ \text{Total} &= 10\tfrac{5}{6} \text{ qt pure alcohol in mixture}\\ 0.65 \times 16\tfrac{2}{3} &= 10\tfrac{5}{6} \text{ qt pure alcohol in mixture (check)}\end{aligned}$$

It may be helpful to set up a table such as the following:

	Volume, qt	**Active ingredient, qt**
80% solution	n	$0.80n$
30% solution	5	$(0.30)(5) = 1.5$
Total	$n + 5$	$0.80n + 1.5$

But $0.80n + 1.5 = 0.65(n + 5)$, as above.

EXERCISE 3

Set up and solve linear equations in terms of one unknown† for the following problems. Check against the original statement.

1. The length of a rectangle exceeds the width by 14 ft. The perimeter is 160 ft. Find the dimensions.
2. The perimeter of an isosceles triangle is 50 in. The base is 11 in longer than one of the equal sides. Find the sides of the triangle.
3. How much solder containing 50 percent tin and how much type metal containing 15 percent tin must be mixed to make 80 lb of solder containing 40 percent tin?

   If t = lb of type metal, then $80 - t$ = lb of 50 percent solder. It follows that lb of tin in original solder + lb of tin in type metal = total tin, or

   $$0.50(80 - t) + 0.15t = (0.40)(80)$$

   (See also Prob. 14, Exercise 5, Chap. 7.)
4. A 12-qt cooling system is filled with 25 percent antifreeze. How many quarts must be drawn off and replaced with pure antifreeze to raise the strength to 45 percent? (See Prob. 15, Exercise 5, Chap. 7.)
5. Two trains leave opposite terminals of a 200-mi line at the same time. If the rates are 40 and 35 mi/h, respectively, when will they meet?
6. A group of bicyclists maintains an average rate of 12 mi/h. One hour and 45 min after they leave, a motorist sets out to overtake them. If his rate is 40 mi/h, how long will he take?
7. A pile of dimes and quarters has a value of $4.60. There are three more quarters than dimes. How many quarters are there?

   We may set up a table as follows:

	Number of coins	Value of coins (cents)
Quarters	q	$25q$
Dimes	$q - 3$	$10(q - 3)$
Total		$25q + 10(q - 3) = 460$ cents

8. A tank can be filled by two pipes in 6 min, while the first pipe alone would require 10 min. How long would it take the second pipe alone to fill the tank?
9. How much time would be required to fill the tank in Prob. 8 if the first pipe operated as an inlet and the second pipe as an outlet? The tank is being used for leaching purposes.

†A few of these problems are repeated in Chap. 9, where two unknowns are used. In many cases the choice between one and two unknowns is a matter of individual preference.

10. A job can be completed by A in $22\frac{1}{2}$ h, by B in $16\frac{2}{3}$ h, and by C in 18 h. Find the time required when all are working together.
11. How many liters of water must be mixed with 500 l of 96 percent (by volume) sulfuric acid to reduce the strength to 80 percent?
12. At a high-school game the price of admission was \$0.25 for each adult and \$0.10 for each child. If the turnstile showed 397 persons at the game and the gate receipts were \$56.80, how many adults attended? (See Prob. 17, Exercise 5, Chap. 7.)
13. A bar of metal contains 20 percent silver, and a second bar 12 percent. How many ounces of each must be taken to make a 40-oz bar containing $14\frac{1}{2}$ percent silver?
14. Of \$8,000, some is invested at $6\frac{1}{2}$ and the rest at $4\frac{1}{2}$ percent. How much must be invested at $6\frac{1}{2}$ percent to ensure a total annual income of \$420?
15. How much high-speed tool steel containing 18 percent tungsten and how much steel containing 12 percent tungsten should be mixed to make 3,000 lb containing 14.6 percent tungsten? (See Prob. 18, Exercise 5, Chap. 7.)
16. What will be the final temperature when 42 lb of water at 135°F is mixed with 70 lb of water at 60°F? In problems of heat exchange involving no change of state, weight × specific heat × temperature change for the warm body = weight × specific heat × temperature change for the cooler body.
17. A bookrack is to be 44 in high overall. The stock is $\frac{7}{8}$ in thick. There are to be five shelf spaces, each one having $\frac{3}{4}$ in more vertical space than the one above it. Find the height of each shelf space. (There are to be six thicknesses of stock.)
18. If the equation $C = \frac{5}{9}(F - 32)$ represents the relationship between the Celsius and Fahrenheit readings for any temperature, find the temperature at which the two will be equal.
19. A machine having an initial value of \$1,450 depreciates in value each year \$50 less than during the preceding year. At the end of the sixth year it has a value of \$190. What is its value at the end of the first year?

    Let d = first year's depreciation, then $d - 50$ = second year's depreciation, etc., and we obtain the equation

$$1{,}450 - 190 = d + (d - 50) + (d - 100) + (d - 150) + (d - 200) + (d - 250)$$

20. In a class election 432 votes were cast. There were two candidates, A and B. If A won by 66 votes, how many votes did each receive?
21. A poorly compensated watch, when carried vertically in the pocket, gains 11 s in 9 h and, when laid down horizontally, loses 28 s in 13 h. How many hours out of 24 in the horizontal position would result in no net gain or loss in a 24-h period?
22. Fifty pounds of high-grade solder spatters containing 50 percent lead and 50 percent tin are to be melted with some type metal containing 90 percent lead and 10 percent tin. The resulting alloy is to be a low-grade solder containing 75 percent lead and 25 percent tin. How many pounds of type metal will be needed?

    A table based on tin would appear as follows:

	Lb metal	Lb tin
Type metal	w	$0.10w$
Solder	50	$(0.50)(50) = 25$
Total	$w + 50$	$0.10w + 25$

from which $0.10w + 25 = (0.25)(w + 50)$.

Or we could set up a table based on lead:

	Lb metal	Lb lead
Type metal	w	$0.90w$
Solder	50	$(0.50)(50) = 25$
Total	$w + 50$	$0.90w + 25$

from which $0.90w + 25 = (0.75)(w + 50)$.

23. A utility company petitioned to change its rate on electrical energy from a straight $5\frac{1}{2}$ cents/kWh to $4\frac{1}{4}$ cents/kWh plus 75 cents/month service charge. What monthly cost would be unaffected by the change in rate?
24. A man pays an income tax of \$118.06 on an income which is taxed as follows: 1 percent on all income over \$1,500, plus 3 percent on all income over \$2,500, plus 5 percent on all income over \$4,000. What is his income?
25. How many gallons of 35 percent antifreeze solution must be added to 3 gal of 80 percent antifreeze solution to reduce the strength to 60 percent?
26. A dairyman has 1,000 qt of milk containing 4.8 percent butterfat, but the city in which he sells his milk requires only 4 percent butterfat. How many quarts of cream testing 20 percent butterfat may be separated from the milk and still satisfy the legal minimum requirement?
27. The outbound trip of a bus was made at 24 mi/h, while the return trip was made at 30 mi/h. Find the one-way distance if the total running time was $4\frac{1}{2}$ h.
28. The indicated airspeed of a Piper Cub plane is 120 mi/h. If a 40-mi/h west wind is blowing, how far west can the plane fly and still return to the airport $2\frac{1}{4}$ h after taking off?
29. A man has $3\frac{1}{4}$ h at his disposal. He can ride out on a bus at 16 mi/h and walk back at $3\frac{1}{2}$ mi/h. How far can he ride and still be able to return to his starting point within the allotted time?
30. At two stations A and B on a railroad line, the prices of soft coal are \$25.50/ton and \$27/ton, respectively. If the distance between A and B is 180 mi and coal can be shipped for $1\frac{1}{2}$ cents/(ton)(mi), find the location on the line between A and B at which it will be immaterial to a consumer whether he buys from A or B.

31. A plane has an airspeed of 300 mi/h. It flies directly into a head wind for 48 min and returns along the same route in 42 min. Find the wind speed.
32. The explosion of a floating mine was heard 8 s sooner through the water than through the air. If the speed of sound is 4,800 ft/s through the water and 1,125 ft/s through the air, how far away was the explosion?
33. To measure the flow of chlorine which would corrode an ordinary mechanical meter, pure oxygen is "bled" into the stream of chlorine gas at the rate of 5.3 ft^3/min. If the chlorine, before dilution, contained 2.8 percent oxygen, and afterward contained 12.1 percent oxygen, find the original flow of chlorine gas in cubic feet per minute.

    Let v = original gas flow (ft^3/min). Then, using an oxygen balance,

$$0.028v + 5.3 = 0.121(v + 5.3)$$

34. In the gambrel roof in Fig. 3.1 the upper set of rafters has a ½ pitch and the lower set a pitch of 2. Find the lengths of AB and BC.

    Hint: Let $AD = h$. Then $DB = 2h$ (why?). EC will then equal $18 - 2h$, and BE will equal $2(18 - 2h)$ (why?).
35. A manufacturer wishes to make a competitive line of copper-coated iron wire which he can sell for \$0.27/lb and make a gross profit of 50 percent above the cost of materials. If copper costs \$0.32/lb and iron costs \$0.12/lb, find the percentage of copper in the wire.
36. A man earning \$180/week goes out on strike for 24 weeks. During the strike he receives \$50/week unemployment benefit. Upon returning to work he receives \$210/week. How many weeks after returning to work will it take to recover the loss incurred by going out on strike?
37. In order to weigh a uniform bar of iron 96 cm long, a 500-g weight was hung 8 cm from one end, whereupon the bar was found to balance 45½ cm from that end. Find the weight of the bar.
38. A planer has a ratio of cutting speed to return speed of 1:2.75. Find the cutting speed in feet per second for a 5-ft stroke when the planer is making 15 cycles every 2 min.

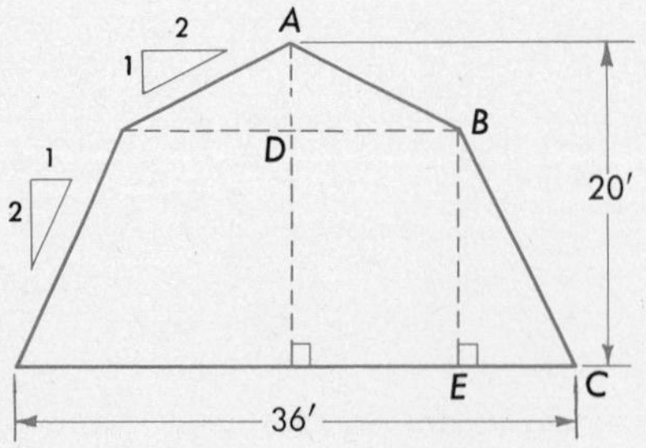

FIGURE 3.1

39. A valve operates off a camshaft turning at a speed of 1,200 r/min. What is the travel of the valve if it opens at the rate of 2 ft/s and closes at the rate of 10 ft/s?
40. A man aged 50 has savings, etc., valued at $24,500. He considers that this amount will increase by $1,000 each year while he is employed. After retirement he will be obliged to reduce the principal by $1,800 each year. At what age can he retire so that the principal will not be exhausted before he reaches age 85?
41. A contractor must finish a job in 35 days. Only one power shovel can be used on the job at a time. The contractor owns a shovel that can do the job in 40 days and can rent, for $50/day, a second shovel that can do the job in 20 days. What is the smallest amount the contractor will have to pay for renting the shovel?
42. A man may retire at age 62 with social security benefits of $250/month for the rest of his life, or he may retire at age 65 with benefits of $325/month. At what age will the total benefits from each plan be equal?
43. A number is composed of six digits, of which the first is 1. When the number is multiplied by 3, the order of digits remains the same except that the 1 is transposed to the units place. What is the number?
44. A closed manometer tube is shown in Fig. 3.2. A length of air column AB is sealed off at atmospheric pressure with mercury. More mercury is then poured into the open arm at D, with new levels at C and D. Find, to the nearest 0.1 in of mercury, the original atmospheric pressure.
45. A man pays 33 cents/gal for gasoline. He gets 15 mi/gal from his car. He can have his engine overhauled for $150, after which he can expect to get 22 mi/gal of gasoline and save 50 cents per 100 mi on oil. After how many miles will he recover the cost of overhauling?

Let m equal the number of miles driven to recover the overhaul cost. Without the overhaul 33 cents/gal $\div$ 15 mi/gal $=$ 33 cents/gal $\times$ $\frac{1}{15}$ gal/mi $=$ $\frac{33}{15}$ cents/mi, or $\frac{33}{15}m$ cents for m miles.

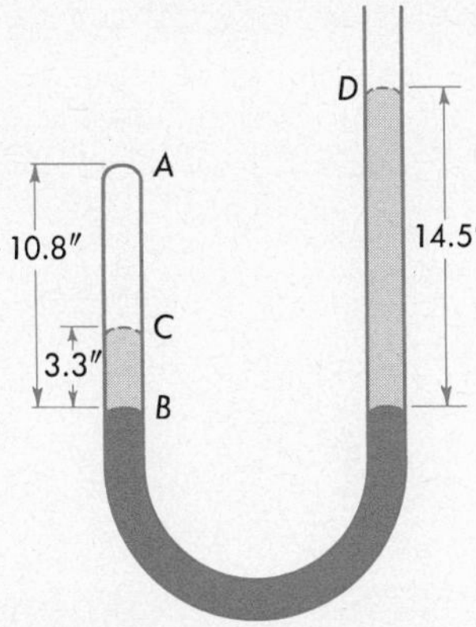

FIGURE 3.2

With overhaul the gas cost will be $^{33}/_{22}m$ cents for m mi. Extra cost of oil without overhaul will be $0.5m$ cents for m mi. Since the cost of gas without overhaul + extra cost of oil equals the cost of gas after overhaul + \$150 (or 15,000 cents) cost of overhaul, we may write

$$^{33}/_{15}m + 0.5m = {}^{33}/_{22}m + 15{,}000$$

4 ratio, proportion, and variation

The comparison of quantities, often indicated by their ratio, is a common occurrence. In business it often takes the form of percentage (e.g., profit, loss, discount, interest rate). In engineering, physics, and other sciences, we find it in such characteristics as specific gravity, specific heat, and atomic weight.

4.1 Ratio

Quantities of the same kind may be compared (1) by stating the difference in magnitude of the two quantities or (2) by finding the quotient of the two quantities when expressed in the same units.

Thus, in a group consisting of 100 men and 20 women, we may say that (1) there are 80 more men than women or (2) there are 5 times as many men as women.

The second type of comparison is called the *ratio* of the quantities. It is expressed as a fraction, in this illustration $^{100}/_{20}$, which is then reduced to lowest terms, $^{5}/_{1}$. We may say that the number of men is to the number of women as 5 is to 1.

If the numbers are prime to each other, the division indicated by the fraction is often carried out; e.g., the rate of 56 to 39 is 1.436 to 1 (to four significant figures).

Note that the comparison must be made between like dimensions, e.g., between a length and a length—not between, say, a length and a weight. The dimensions must be expressed in the same units; e.g., the ratio between 2 lb and 12 oz is $^{32}/_{12}$, or $^{8}/_{3}$.

Occasionally, although incorrectly, we do sometimes apply the word *ratio* to comparisons between unlike quantities. For example, we sometimes speak of the economy ratio of an automobile expressed as the ratio of miles traveled to gallons of gasoline consumed. If the automobile will travel 100 mi on 5 gal of gasoline, the economy ratio is said to be 20 mi/gal.

Such comparisons might more properly be termed *rates* (e.g., miles per hour, dollars per cubic foot, etc.).

As another example, the scale ratio of a certain map may be indicated as 500 ft to 1.5 in. This means that if the distance between two points on the ground is 500 ft, then the corresponding points on the map are 1.5 in apart. Sometimes, with rather loose usage of the equality sign, this information is expressed as 500 ft = 1.5 in.

Since 500 ft is equivalent to $500 \times 12 = 6{,}000$ in, we can express the scale ratio as 6,000 in to 1.5 in. The scale ratio can then be expressed as

$$6{,}000:1.5 \qquad \text{or} \qquad 4{,}000:1$$

The latter form is much preferred.

It will be seen that percentage simply expresses the ratio between a given number of units and 100 units of the same kind.

It should be noted also that the ratio of two like quantities has no units of its own—it is said to be dimensionless. A good illustration of this is π, the ratio between the circumference and diameter of any circle.

EXERCISE 1

Express each of the following ratios in the simplest form:

1. 4 h to 40 min
2. 5 lb to 10 oz
3. 8 in to 2 yd
4. 330 ft to 1 mi
5. 480 in^2 to 1 ft^2
6. 6 ft^3 to 1 yd^3
7. 13,200 ft^2 to 1 acre
8. $1°7'30''$ to 360° (angular measurement)
9. Circumference of a 9-in circle to circumference of a 2-ft circle
10. Area of an 8-in square to area of a 12-in square
11. $6ax^2$ to $8a^2x$
12. $6xy - 4y^2$ to $9x^2 - 6xy$
13. $^{5}/_{8}$ to $^{15}/_{32}$
14. $3\frac{1}{3}$ to $6\frac{1}{4}$

4.2 Proportions

A statement of equality between two ratios is called a *proportion*. Thus $\$3/\$2 = 84$ mi/56 mi is a proportion and is read "\$3 is to \$2 as 84 mi is to 56 mi." The four quantities are called the *terms* of the proportion. The first and fourth terms are called the *extremes*, and the second and third terms are called the *means*, of a proportion.

Among the properties of proportions, perhaps the most important may be listed in terms of the proportion

$$\frac{a}{b} = \frac{c}{d}$$

1. *The product of the extremes is equal to the product of the means. Thus* $ad = bc$.
2. *The terms are in proportion by inversion. Thus* $b/a = d/c$.
3. *The terms are in proportion by alternation. Thus* $a/c = b/d$.

Each of these statements may be confirmed by the ordinary operations of equations.

If the means of a proportion are equal, as in the proportion $m/x = x/n$, it is called a mean proportion, and x is said to be the *mean proportional* between m and n. Strictly speaking, $x = \pm\sqrt{mn}$. However, we shall confine ourselves to the positive root.

A *continued proportion* between six or more quantities is illustrated by the expression $a:b:c = x:y:z$. This is a compact notation for expressing the simultaneous proportions

$$\frac{a}{b} = \frac{x}{y} \qquad \frac{a}{c} = \frac{x}{z} \qquad \frac{b}{c} = \frac{y}{z} \qquad \text{or} \qquad \frac{a}{x} = \frac{b}{y} = \frac{c}{z}$$

Example 1. The sum of \$4,628.20, representing the profits of a venture, is to be divided among three partners in the ratio of 2:3:7. How much does each receive?

We may represent the amounts by 2x, 3x, and 7x, since

$$2x:3x:7x = 2:3:7$$

Therefore

$$\begin{aligned} 2x + 3x + 7x &= \$4{,}628.20 \\ 12x &= 4{,}628.20 \\ x &= 385.683 \\ 2x &= 771.37 \\ 3x &= 1{,}157.05 \\ 7x &= 2{,}699.78 \end{aligned}$$

EXERCISE 2

In Probs. 1 to 10 solve the proportions for x.

1. $\frac{3}{4} = \frac{x}{14 - x}$
2. $\frac{5}{3} = \frac{20 - x}{x}$
3. $\frac{x + 3}{x - 3} = \frac{4}{3}$
4. $\frac{x - 5}{x + 5} = \frac{2}{7}$

5. $\frac{a}{b} = \frac{x}{c}$ 6. $\frac{m}{n} = \frac{k}{x}$ 7. $\frac{a}{b} = \frac{c - x}{x}$ 8. $\frac{h}{k} = \frac{x}{k - x}$

9. $\frac{x + a}{x + b} = \frac{x - c}{x - d}$ 10. $\frac{x - a}{x + b} = \frac{x + a}{x - k}$

In Probs. 11 to 20 find the mean proportional between the given quantities.

11. 6 and 24
12. 8 and 50
13. $2\frac{1}{2}$ and $\frac{5}{8}$
14. $8\frac{1}{3}$ and 12
15. $2a^2x$ and $8b^2x$
16. x/y and y/x
17. $x^2 - y^2$ and $\frac{4(x + y)}{x - y}$
18. $x^2 - 2xy + y^2$ and $x^2 + 2xy + y^2$
19. $\frac{18ab^3}{c}$ and $\frac{2ac}{b}$
20. $x + a$ and $x - a$ (Find the approximate value if a is very small relative to x.)

4.3 Variation

If two variables x and y are related so that $y = kx$, where k is a constant, we say that y *varies directly* as x, or simply y *varies* as x, or y is *proportional* to x. The constant k is called the *constant of proportionality,* or the constant of variation.

An equivalent notation is $y \propto x$, in which the symbol $\propto$ is read "varies as" or "is proportional to." This is *not* an equation but can be converted to the notation of an equation $y = kx$ by introducing the proportionality constant k.

For example, we say that the circumference of a circle varies as the diameter, or $C \propto D$, or $C = kD$. In this instance the proportionality constant k is π.

We note that the relation between y and x is a mutual one. That is, if y varies as x, then $y = kx$; but x is also proportional to y, or $x = (1/k)y$. Therefore, if y varies as x with the constant of proportionality equal to k, then x varies as y with the constant of proportionality equal to $1/k$.

Inverse Variation

If one variable varies directly as the reciprocal of a second, then the first is said to *vary inversely* as the second, or the first is said to be *inversely proportional* to the second. Thus $y = k \cdot 1/x$, or $y = k/x$. Since it is evident that $xy = k$, it follows that if the product of two variables is constant, either variable varies inversely as the other.

A common example of inverse variation is found in the inverse relationship between rate and time when a fixed distance is being covered. Here $rt = d$, or $t = d/r$. The constant of proportionality here is d.

The number of days needed to complete a job is inversely related to the number of men on the job. Here $mt = k$, or $t = k/m$. The constant of proportionality k is the size of the job in man-days. (m = number of men, t = number of days.)

Joint Variation

If a variable x varies directly as the product of y and z, that is, if $x = kyz$, we say that x varies jointly as y and z.

If $x = ky \cdot 1/z = ky/z$, it may be said that x varies directly as y and inversely as z.

Types of variation can be combined. For example, the electrical resistance of a wire varies directly as the length and inversely as the square of the diameter. Translated into algebraic notation, this may be written $R = kl/d^2$.

Solution of Variation Problems

Usually we know the type of variation involved and a set of corresponding values of the variables. From these data we can determine the proportionality constant k and any one missing value in a second set of values of the variables.

Example 2. We are given the relation that x is directly proportional to the square root of y and inversely proportional to z. Further, it is known that $x = 4$ when $y = 9$ and $z = 15$. Find the formula for x, and find x when $y = 25$ and $z = 40$.

Expressing the relationship in algebraic notation, we have the equation of variation:

$$x = \frac{k\sqrt{y}}{z} \tag{1}$$

Substituting in Eq. (1) $x = 4$, $y = 9$, and $z = 15$, we have

$$4 = \frac{k\sqrt{9}}{15} = \frac{3k}{15}$$

or

$$k = 20 \tag{2}$$

From Eqs. (1) and (2) we write the formula

$$x = \frac{20\sqrt{y}}{z} \tag{3}$$

To solve the last part of our problem, we substitute $y = 25$ and $z = 40$ in Eq. (3), obtaining

$$x = \frac{20\sqrt{25}}{40} = \frac{(20)(5)}{40} = 2.5 \qquad (4)$$

The illustration points up the following rules:

1. *Translate the statement of variation into an equation involving an unknown constant of proportionality.*
2. *Solve for the proportionality constant by substituting given data.*
3. *Substitute the value of the constant of proportionality in the equation of variation.*
4. *Use the formula or equation in step 3 to obtain the missing value of a variable when a second set of values of the other variables is given.*

There will be occasions when there are insufficient data to evaluate k or when we are not interested in determining k. To continue with the illustration just given, we represent the first set of values by x_1, y_1, and z_1, and the second set by x_2, y_2, and z_2. Hence we obtain

$$x_1 = \frac{k\sqrt{y_1}}{z_1} \qquad (5)$$

and

$$x_2 = \frac{k\sqrt{y_2}}{z_2} \qquad (6)$$

Dividing Eq. (5) by Eq. (6),

$$\frac{x_1}{x_2} = \frac{z_2\sqrt{y_1}}{z_1\sqrt{y_2}} \qquad (7)$$

Substituting values in Eq. (7),

$$\frac{4}{x_2} = \frac{40\sqrt{9}}{15\sqrt{25}}$$

$$\frac{4}{x_2} = \frac{120}{75}$$

$$x_2 = 2.5$$

It should be noted that the computation in Eq. (7) will often be facilitated if we write it in the form

$$\frac{x_1}{x_2} = \frac{z_2}{z_1}\sqrt{\frac{y_1}{y_2}}$$

If, for example, $y_1 = 63$ and $y_2 = 28$, the preference is obvious when we write

$$\frac{\sqrt{63}}{\sqrt{28}} = \sqrt{\frac{63}{28}} = \sqrt{\frac{9}{4}} = \frac{3}{2}$$

Similarly, if the equation includes the expression $w_1{}^2/w_2{}^2$, the alternative form $(w_1/w_2)^2$ is often preferable. For example, suppose $w_1 = {}^{15}\!/_{32}$ and $w_2 = {}^{9}\!/_{16}$. Then

$$\frac{({}^{15}\!/_{32})^2}{({}^{9}\!/_{16})^2} = \left(\frac{{}^{15}\!/_{32}}{{}^{9}\!/_{16}}\right)^2 = ({}^{15}\!/_{32} \times {}^{16}\!/_{9})^2 = ({}^{5}\!/_{6})^2 = {}^{25}\!/_{36}$$

The process of eliminating the proportionality constant may be used to demonstrate that variation and proportion are equivalent ideas. In general, for repeated application of the same operation, it is convenient to evaluate k. However, for occasional application, the actual value of k is seldom required, and a simpler solution results from its elimination.

Given

$$y_1 = kx_1 \tag{8}$$

and

$$y_2 = kx_2 \tag{9}$$

(y varies directly as x), dividing Eq. (8) by Eq. (9),

$$\frac{y_1}{y_2} = \frac{x_1}{x_2} \tag{10}$$

(y is directly proportional to x.)

Given

$$y_1 = \frac{k}{x_1} \tag{11}$$

and

$$y_2 = \frac{k}{x_2} \tag{12}$$

(y varies inversely as x), dividing Eq. (11) by Eq. (12),

$$\frac{y_1}{y_2} = \frac{x_2}{x_1} \qquad \text{or} \qquad x_1y_1 = x_2y_2 \tag{13}$$

(y is inversely proportional to x.)

Common examples of this relation are:

1. Boyle's law: $P_1V_1 = P_2V_2$, temperature remaining constant.
2. Time required to complete a certain job (constant number of man-hours); e.g., if 10 men can do a given job in 6 h, 4 men can finish the same job in 15 h. That is, $m_1h_1 = m_2h_2$.

There is no substitute for common sense in solving a proportion. For example, it is required to reduce 950 ml of oxygen at 450 K and 840 mm to standard temperature and pressure (273 K and 760 mm). We know that cooling the gas from 450 to 273 K will cause it to contract and that lowering the pressure from 840 to 760 mm will make it expand; therefore we apply the fractions $^{273}/_{450}$ for shrinkage and $^{840}/_{760}$ for expansion. As a result we write

$$V_{\text{stp}} = 950\left(\frac{273}{450}\right)\left(\frac{840}{760}\right) = 637 \text{ ml}$$

4.4 Dimensionality of the Proportionality Constant

It is frequently instructive to determine the dimensionality of k or the units in which k is expressed.

Example 3. It is known that the weight of a rectangular block of wood varies jointly with the thickness, width, and length. If the weight is expressed in pounds and the dimensions are in inches, determine in what units k is expressed.

The equation of variation is

$$W = ktwl$$

Solving for k,

$$\frac{W}{twl} = k$$

Substituting units,

$$\frac{\text{lb}}{(\text{in})(\text{in})(\text{in})} = \frac{\text{lb}}{(\text{in})^3}$$

Hence k is expressed in pounds per cubic inch—a density figure.

Example 4. The volume of a given quantity of a gas varies inversely as the pressure (temperature remaining constant). Determine the units of k if volume is expressed in cubic inches and pressure in pounds per square inch.

The equation of variation is

$$V = \frac{k}{P} \qquad \text{or} \qquad PV = k$$

Substituting units,

$$\frac{\text{lb}}{\text{in}^2}\,\text{in}^3 = \text{in} \cdot \text{lb}$$

Hence k is expressed in inch-pounds—a work unit.

EXERCISE 3

Express each of the relations in Probs. 1 to 5 as an equation containing an unknown constant of proportionality.

1. W varies jointly as x and y.
2. Q varies directly as x and inversely as y.
3. V varies directly as the cube of x and inversely as d.
4. M varies directly as b and inversely as the square root of c.
5. R varies directly as w and the square root of x and inversely as the cube of h.

In Probs. 6 to 10 write the formula for the first variable in terms of the other variables and the computed value of k.

6. H varies directly as x. $H = 8$ when $x = 20$.
7. N varies inversely as y. $N = 20$ when $y = 0.35$.
8. Q varies jointly as a, b, and c. $Q = 300$ when $a = 3$, $b = 7.5$, and $c = 8$.
9. V varies directly as m and inversely as the square of t. $V = 2$ when $m = 15$ and $t = 6$.
10. R varies directly as the fourth power of T and inversely as the square root of x. $R = \frac{1}{3}$ when $T = 2$ and $x = 36$.

EXERCISE 4

In Probs. 1 to 7 determine the numerical value and the units of k that refer to the units in which the first set of values of the variables is expressed. Solve for the unknown value of the variable in the second set of values.

1. P varies inversely as V. If $V = 30$ in^3 when $P = 84$ lb/in^2, find V when $P = 63$ lb/in^2.
2. R varies directly as l. If $R = 6.8\ \Omega$ when $l = 23.5$ ft, find R when $l = 31.8$ ft.
3. v varies directly as t. If $v = 45$ ft/s when $t = 25$ s, find v when $t = 1$ min.
4. W varies directly as d^2. If $W = 12$ oz when $d = 8$ in, find W when $d = 1$ ft.
5. N varies inversely as d^2. If $N = 10{,}890$ plants/acre when set d (= 2 ft) apart, find N when $d = 5\frac{1}{2}$ ft.
6. m varies inversely as d. If $m = 12$ men when $d = 10$ days, find m when $d = 8$ days.
7. v varies jointly as the square root of g and the square root of h. If $v = 3.8$ ft/s when $g = 32$ ft/s^2 and $h = 0.17$ ft, find v when $g = 30$ ft/s^2 and $h = 8$ in.

In Probs. 8 to 12 determine the unknown quantity without solving for k.

8. C varies directly as d^2. If $C = 80$ when $d = 12$, find C when $d = 15$.
9. v varies directly as $\sqrt{h}$. If $v = 28$ when $h = 3$, find v when $h = 12$.
10. R varies directly as l and inversely as d^2. If $R = 35$ when $l = 110$ and $d = 0.006$, find R when $l = 75$ and $d = 0.004$.
11. V varies directly as r^4 and p and inversely as l. If $V = 120$ when $r = 0.012$, $p = 20$, and $l = 30$, find V when $r = 0.016$, $p = 36$, and $l = 25$.
12. a varies directly as v^2 and inversely as r. If $a = 540$ when $v = 84$ and $r = 5$, find a when $v = 119$ and $r = 4$.

4.5 Applications

A few of the more common principles of mathematics and the physical sciences that may be expressed as variations are as follows:

Areas of similar figures vary as the squares of corresponding dimensions.

Volumes of similar solids vary as the cubes of corresponding dimensions. (Note that a 1-in square and a 2-in square, each cut from a $\frac{1}{4}$-in sheet of steel, are not similar solids, since not all three dimensions are doubled. Weights are as $1^2:2^2$, *not* $1^3:2^3$.)

Volumes of gases vary inversely as the absolute pressure and directly as the absolute temperature.

In any given chemical reaction between substances A and B, the reacting amount of A varies directly as the reacting amount of B.

The time required to finish a given job varies inversely as the number of men working on the job.

The rate of energy reception (heat, light, magnetism, etc.) varies inversely as the square of the distance from the source of energy (the *inverse-square* law).

The revolutions per minute of two pulleys belted together vary inversely as their diameters.

The revolutions per minute of two gears in mesh vary inversely as the number of teeth.

Rate of heat conduction through a flat plate varies jointly as the area of one face of the plate and the difference between the temperatures of the opposite faces and inversely as the thickness of the plate.

Electrical resistance of a conductor varies directly as the length and inversely as the cross-section area.

In order to reduce drudgery, it is suggested that the slide rule be used whenever accuracy of three significant figures is sufficient.

EXERCISE 5

1. Hydrogen used for inflation of balloons may be made by passing steam over red-hot scrap iron. If 77 kg of iron will make 44.2 m^3 of hydrogen, how much iron would be needed to make 100 m^3 of hydrogen?
2. Seven men take eighteen 8-h days to finish a job. How large is this job in man-hours? How many men will be needed to finish a like job in twelve $7\frac{1}{2}$-h days?
3. A train usually makes its run in 2 h 25 min at an average speed of 63 mi/h. How long would it take if the speed were reduced to 51 mi/h?
4. The weight of 195 machine screws is $8\frac{1}{2}$ oz. Find the number in 2 lb 7 oz.
5. If 75 iron washers weigh 95 g, how many washers are there in a batch weighing 640 g?
6. The resistance of a spool of enameled magnet wire was 955 Ω. A piece 1 ft $9\frac{1}{2}$ in long was cut off and found to have a resistance of 5.37 Ω. Find the length of wire originally on the spool.
7. A 16-in disk cut from a piece of sheet steel weighs 5.65 lb. What will be the diameter of a disk weighing 2.08 lb cut from the same piece of stock?
8. A formula calls for 15 ml of a 24 percent solution. How many milliliters of a 20 percent solution would be equivalent to this?
9. The profits of a partnership amount to $1,283.67. This is to be divided among four partners in proportion to their investments. Johnson, Miller, Spencer, and Weston invested $842, $1,363, $1,759, and $1,876, respectively. Find each man's share of the profits to the nearest cent.
10. Given two solids of the same volume, the weights are proportional to the density. What is the weight of a bronze casting formed by a pine pattern weighing $4\frac{1}{4}$ lb? Density of pine = 28 lb/ft^3; density of bronze = 550 lb/ft^3.
11. If 117 g of salt (sodium chloride) produces 22.4 l of chlorine, how much salt is needed to produce 8 l of chlorine?
12. If 3800 lb of coke is needed to reduce 7.6 tons of iron ore to pig iron, how much coke will be needed to reduce 4.4 tons of iron ore?

13. If 24 ft^3 of natural gas requires 317 ft^3 of air for complete combustion, how much air will be needed to burn 41 ft^3 of gas?
14. The density of aluminum is 168 lb/ft^3. What is its density expressed in g/cm^3?
15. A property owner pays a \$1385.27 real estate tax bill when the tax rate is \$64.90/M (M = \$1,000). How much more will he have to pay if the tax rate is increased to \$67.25/M?
16. 23.0 lb of potassium hydroxide contained in 100 gal of solution is equivalent to how many g of KOH in a liter of the same concentration?
17. A motor draws 12 kW from the line. If it is 92 percent efficient, what horsepower does it deliver?
18. If 50 sheets of paper form a pile $\frac{9}{32}$ in thick, approximately how many sheets are contained in a pile $2\frac{3}{8}$ in thick?
19. The analysis of a paint shows 46 percent vehicle and 54 percent pigment. The analysis of the pigment shows 15 percent zinc oxide, 60 percent titanium dioxide, and 25 percent lithopone. What is the percentage of each pigment in the ready-mixed paint?
20. Given the formula $x = m\sqrt{f}/[W(a + b^2/k)]$, indicate, quantitatively where possible, the effect on x of doubling each of the other letters, one at a time.
21. What is the area of a room scaling $5\frac{1}{2} \times 7\frac{1}{4}$ in on a floor plan if the scale is $\frac{3}{8}$ in = 1 ft?
22. From a 1:2:3 mixture of cement, sand, and gravel, 84 yd^3 of concrete is to be made. How many cubic yards of each will be needed, allowing for a 20 percent shrinkage on mixing?
23. A "pie chart" is often used to show how the tax dollar is spent (Fig. 4.1). If \$1,190,000 is allocated to the street department, \$860,000 to the police and fire departments, and \$1,870,000 to schools, compute to the nearest degree the size of each section of the "pie."

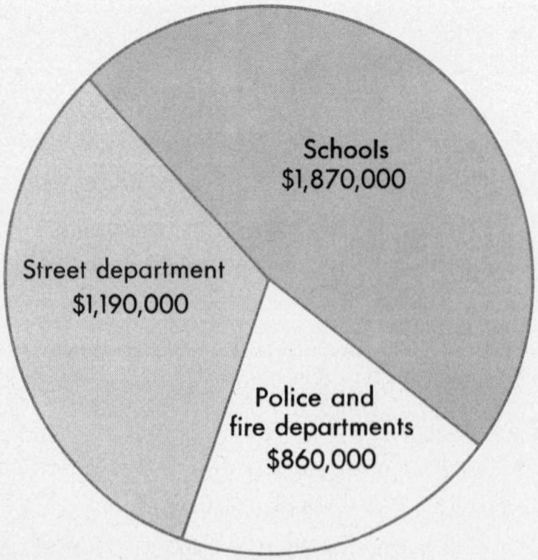

FIGURE 4.1

24. The outline of an estate is cut out from a map and found to weigh 42.78 g. A rectangular section 12 × 20 cm was cut from the same sheet and found to weigh 5.31 g. If the scale of the map is 1 cm to 20 m, find the number of hectares in the estate.
25. The gravity rate of flow of water from the bottom of a tank varies directly as the square root of the depth h of the water in the tank. The rate of flow v was 20 gal/min when the water was 9 ft deep.
(a) Derive a formula for v in terms of h.
(b) Find v when $h = 15$ ft.
(c) Find h when $v = 12$ gal/min.
26. The odometer (mileage indicator) of a car correctly registers a 500-mi trip when the car is equipped with tires measuring 27-in diameter at the tread. What mileage would be indicated for the same trip when using 28-in-diameter tires?
27. In a fish-and-game survey 400 fish were taken from a pond, tagged by coloring with a harmless dye, and released. A few days later 5 tagged fish were counted among 62 that were taken from the pond. Approximately how many fish were in the pond originally?
28. If $3\frac{3}{4}$ in on a road map corresponds to 5 h traveling time, what traveling time corresponds to $4\frac{1}{2}$ in on the map?
29. A motorist gets 18 mi/gal of gasoline on his car. He spends $90/year for gasoline. What would be his annual gasoline bill if he were to get 20 mi/gal?
30. The braking distance of a car is proportional to the square of the speed. This is illustrated in the following table:

$V_{mi/h}$	20	40	60
d_{ft}	100	400	900

Find the braking, or stopping, distance from a speed of 30 mi/h.
31. If the "1940 dollar" will buy only 64 cents worth of goods today, what should a man earning $5,600 in 1940 receive now merely to break even?
32. Compute the missing quantities, where gear A drives gear B.

	Number of teeth in gear A	*Number of teeth in gear B*	*r/min gear A*	*r/min gear B*
(a)	42	96	56	—
(b)	60	—	150	125
(c)	48	84	—	112
(d)	—	36	45	105
(e)	66	—	350	550

33. Referring to Table 4.1, which is an excerpt from Appendix F, we wish to set up a scale model of the solar system in which a $\frac{1}{4}$-in-diameter pellet represents Earth. Confirm (*a*) the model distances of Earth, Venus, Mars, Jupiter, and α Centauri from the sun; (*b*) the model distance of the moon from Earth; (*c*) the model diameters of the moon, Venus, Mars, Jupiter, and the sun.

TABLE 4.1

	Relative mass†	Actual diameter, mi	Scale diameter, in	Actual distance, mi	Scale distance
Earth	1	7,920	$\frac{1}{4}$	9.3×10^7	244 ft
Moon	0.0120	2,160	0.068	2.4×10^5‡	$7\frac{1}{2}$ in
Venus	0.81	7,700	0.24	6.73×10^7	$176\frac{1}{2}$ in
Mars	0.107	4,200	0.132	1.42×10^8	373 ft
Jupiter	318	88,700	2.80	4.84×10^8	1,272 ft
Sun	332,000	864,000	27.2		
α Centauri				4.31 light-years	12,580 mi

†Data for Probs. 34 and 36.
‡Distance from Earth.

34. The acceleration of gravity (g) is proportional to M/r^2, where M is the relative mass of the attracting body and r is the distance from its center. It is 32.2 ft/s^2 on the surface of the earth, whose relative mass = 1 and whose radius = 3,960 mi. Refer to the table of Prob. 33 to determine the value of g on the surface of (*a*) the moon, (*b*) Venus, (*c*) Mars, (*d*) Jupiter, (*e*) the sun. Confirm your answers as found in Appendix F.
35. Find the value of g 1,500 mi above the earth's surface.
36. Assume the earth-moon distance = 240,000 mi center to center. At a point on the earth-moon line 20,000 mi from the center of the moon, calculate the net gravitational pull and its direction.

Most of the essential data needed in the solution of Probs. 37 to 39 will be found in Appendix F.

37. Neglecting air friction, the escape velocity $v_e = \sqrt{2gr}$, where r is the distance from the center of the attracting body, and g is the gravitational constant at that point. Using values of g listed in the table in Appendix F and employing consistent units, verify the escape velocity as given in the same table for (*a*) Earth, (*b*) the moon, (*c*) Mars, (*d*) Venus.
38. Calculate the velocity of escape from a point 1,000 mi above the earth's surface.
39. The weight of an object at any point is proportional to the gravitational acceleration at that point. What would be the weight of a 150-lb astronaut on the surface of (*a*) the moon, (*b*) Mars, (*c*) Jupiter?
40. A man 5 ft 4 in tall weighs 140 lb. Another man, of about the same build, is just 6 ft tall. How much would you expect the taller man to weigh?

41. The distance of the horizon at sea varies directly as the square root of the elevation of the observer above sea level. If the horizon is $4\frac{1}{2}$ mi distant at $13\frac{1}{2}$ ft elevation, find the distance at 380 ft elevation.
42. In Prob. 41 how high above sea level must a lighthouse be to be visible 15 mi out to sea?
43. The horsepower required to drive a motorboat varies as the cube of the speed through the water. If 5 hp drives a boat at 10 mi/h, what size motor is needed to maintain a speed of 14 mi/h?
44. The braking distance of a car is proportional to the square of the velocity. If a car traveling 35 mi/h requires 115 ft to stop, what distance must be allowed when traveling 45 mi/h (assuming constant operating conditions)?
45. The tensile strength of a round bar is proportional to the square of the diameter. If a $\frac{3}{8}$-in-diameter rod supports 40,000 lb, how much will a $\frac{5}{16}$-in-diameter rod support?
46. A ball, starting from rest, rolls 80 cm down an incline during the first 4 s. How far will it roll during the fifth second? Distance is proportional to the square of the time.
47. A cone of slant height 12 cm holds 300 ml of water. How far from the vertex should marks be placed on the slant height to indicate 100 ml? 200 ml?
48. A lot of soda ash containing 52 percent by weight water of crystallization is bought at $17\frac{1}{2}$ cents/lb. When the material is sold at retail, the moisture content is found to have dropped in storage to 37 percent. What should be the retail price per pound to realize a 40 percent profit based on the cost? [*Note:* Comparable purchase price after drying would be $17.5\left(\frac{63}{48}\right) = 23.0$ cents/lb. Why?]
49. A formula calls for $22\frac{1}{2}$ lb of soda ash as originally bought in Prob. 48. Find the proper amount of the material to use after partial drying in storage.
50. It has been stated that 90 percent of the capital in a certain country is held by 8 percent of the population. What is the ratio of the capital of a more affluent citizen to that of a "disadvantaged" one?
51. Ten men are working on a job which must be completed in 18 days. After 8 days the work is only one-third done. How many *extra* men must be hired if the time limit is to be met?
52. The velocity of sound in air is independent of the density and pressure of the air and varies directly as the square root of the absolute temperature. An experimental unit carried on a rocket indicated a sound velocity of 977 ft/s at an altitude of 20 mi. What was the Fahrenheit temperature at that altitude if at 70°F the speed of sound in the air is 1,130 ft/s?
53. The frequency (Hz) of a piano wire varies directly as the square root of the tension and inversely as the length. If a wire 50 cm long under 25-kg tension vibrates at 256 Hz, find the frequency of a like wire 80 cm long under 41-kg tension.

5 applications in geometry

A working knowledge of geometry is essential for solving many practical problems. When data are unavailable, the engineer, technician, or machinist is compelled to obtain his information indirectly. The word *geometry* means earth measurement—a science in which many dimensions are either inaccessible or too large for direct measurement. We assume that you have already learned some geometry; so in this chapter we are dealing chiefly with applications. A list of some of the more important facts in geometry appears on pages 111–120, and in the problems below, reference is made to them in brackets. For additional theorems or formulas, see any standard geometry text or mathematical tables.

A glance at the problems in this chapter might lead to the impression that many different theorems and formulas are involved in their solution. However, in the majority of cases, one uses essentially only such familiar relationships as those dealing with similar figures, properties of the circle, and the Pythagorean theorem. It might be added that it is usually a good idea to draw a radius to any point of tangency on a circle. If two or more circles are involved, it is often helpful to draw their lines of center.

Many times it is a good idea to construct a scale drawing. The drawing will emphasize the relationships among the data and indicate the approximate answer. If the problem can be laid out to scale, it can be solved.

You should watch for situations involving parallel lines cut by a transversal.

You should also be alert for possible angle bisectors. Equal angles so formed may suggest the construction of either congruent or similar triangles.

It is suggested that you solve the problems in this chapter by slide rule as far as possible. You will gain skill in its use, and the drudgery of longhand computation will be reduced.

It is not expected that any particular class will attempt all or even most of the problems in this chapter. The problems are arranged roughly in order of difficulty, and selections may be made accordingly.

The material is divided into three sections:

I. Probs. 1 to 61: basic.
II. Probs. 62 to 76: somewhat less elementary.
III. Probs. 77 to 88: many of these are challenging and nonroutine.

Examine each problem critically. Are the given data of the type considered reliable? Are any unreasonable or unwarranted assumptions involved? Answers should be calculated to a point deemed consistent with data given.

EXERCISE 1 (GROUP I)

1. Find angles *a*, *b*, *c*, and *d* in Fig. 5.1. [5, 16]
2. Find x and *y* in Fig. 5.2. [17, 65]
3. Find angles *a* and *b* in Fig. 5.3. [22]
4. Find to the nearest 0.1 cm^2 the area of a triangle whose sides are 19, 28, and 39 cm. [47]
5. (*a*) Find the area of a 51°24′ sector of a 15-in circle. [54]
   (*b*) Find the length of the arc of the sector. [55]
6. A circle is inscribed in a triangle whose vertex angle is 48°14′. Find the angle formed at the center of the circle by lines drawn to the extremities of the base. [23, 58]
7. What diameter hole should be drilled clear through a ⅜-in plate of cast iron to remove 2 oz? The density of cast iron is 0.26 lb/in^3. [96]
8. A circular coil of wire is approximately 20 in in average diameter and contains 63 turns. About how many feet of wire are there in the coil? [50]

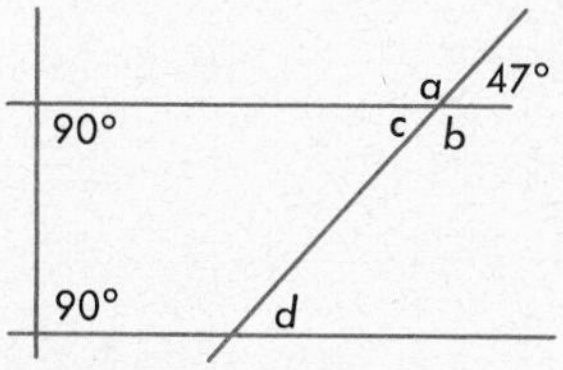

FIGURE 5.1

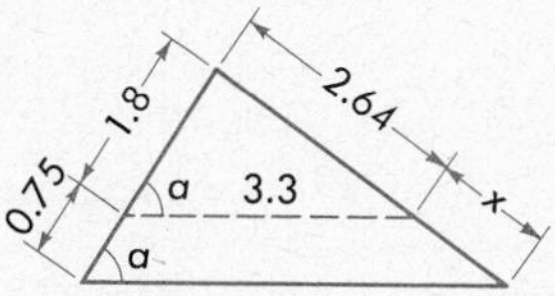

FIGURE 5.2

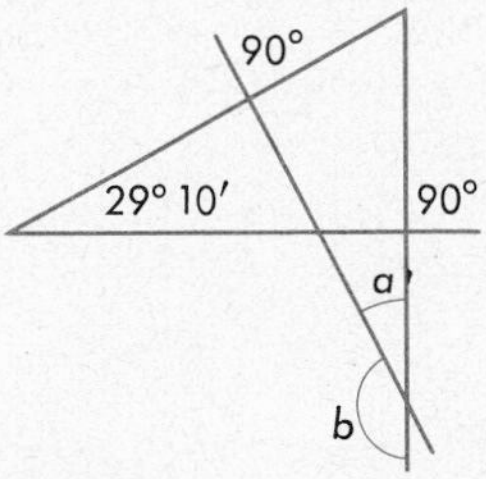

FIGURE 5.3

9. Find the area of the three-cornered section enclosed by three mutually tangent 15-in circles. [54, 80]
10. Find the angle between the bisectors of the two angles of a trapezoid which are formed by the bases and one nonparallel side. [18, 23]
11. Find the angle between the bisectors of the acute angles of a right triangle. [23]
12. Two consecutive angles of a quadrilateral are 83° and 105°. Find the angle between the bisectors of the other two angles. [35]
13. Find the angles a and b in Fig. 5.4. [61, 62]
14. In an isosceles trapezoid the parallel sides are 11 and 19 in long, and the diagonals are each 17 in long. Find its area. [48, 75]
15. Find the area of a segment $3\frac{1}{2}$ in high in a circle 18 in in diameter. The area A of a segment is given closely by $A = \frac{4}{3}h^2 \sqrt{2r/h - 0.608}$ (Fig. 5.5). The smaller h is in relation to r, the closer is the approximation.
16. A horizontal cylindrical tank 30 in in diameter contains 400 gal when full. How many gallons remain when the depth of liquid is 8 in? (See Prob. 15 above.) (The wet area of the end is proportional to the volume of liquid in the tank.)
17. A pyramid is 5 in square on the base and 7 in high. Find the volume, total area, and lateral edge. [91, 92]
18. Two 12-cm circles have their centers 6 cm apart. What is the area of the portion common to both? [54, 80]
19. You are given the following figures, each having a perimeter of 30 in: (a) a right triangle having sides 5, 12, and 13 in; (b) an isosceles triangle whose sides are 11, 11, and 8 in; (c) a 10-in equilateral triangle; (d) a rectangle 4×11 in; (e) a $7\frac{1}{2}$-in square; (f) a regular hexagon 5 in on a side; (g) a circle whose circumference is 30 in. Compare their areas.
20. Find the area of the end of the gable roof shown in Fig. 5.6. [46, 48]
21. What is the total force acting on a $5\frac{1}{2}$-cm-diameter piston if the pressure is 120 kg/cm^2?
22. Find the weight of an open-top sheet-iron cylinder 28 in high and 22 in in diameter. One square foot of sheet iron weighs $10\frac{1}{2}$ oz. Find the capacity of the cylinder in gallons.
23. Find the weight of a 12-ft length of cast-iron pipe 10 in inside diameter, $\frac{3}{4}$ in wall thickness, at 450 lb/ft^3.

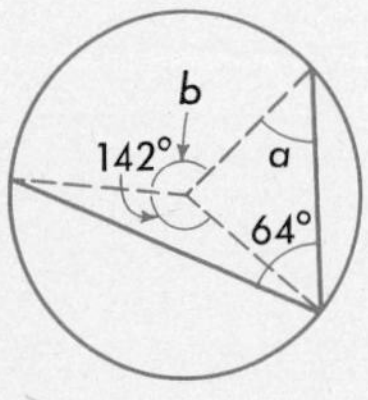

FIGURE 5.4

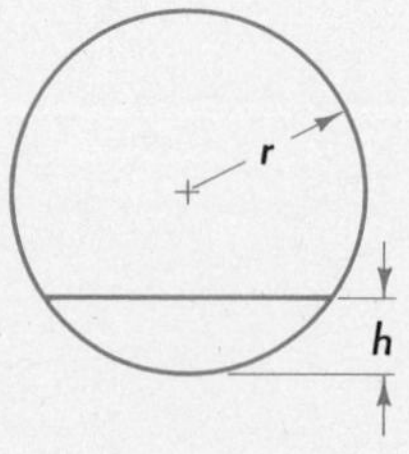

FIGURE 5.5

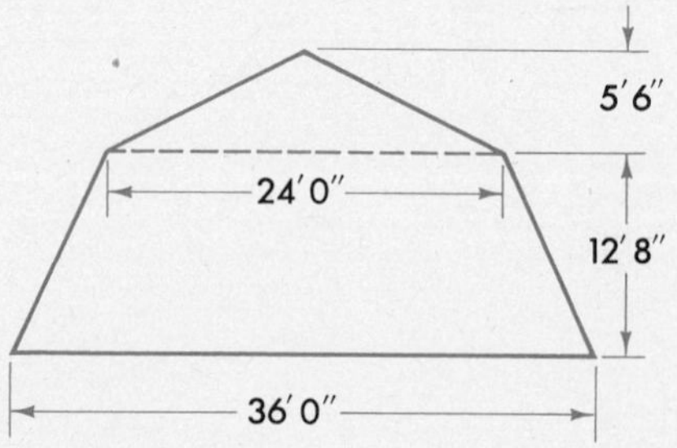

FIGURE 5.6

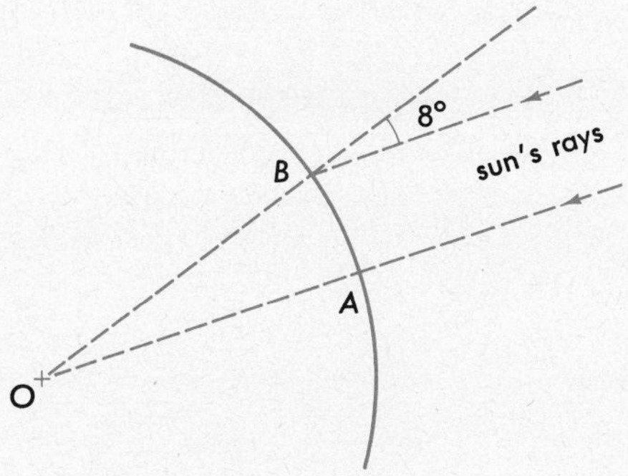

FIGURE 5.7

24. Find the lateral surface of the frustum of a right pyramid whose height is 12 in, lower base 28 in square, and upper base 18 in square. (*Hint:* Can you use the principle of Prob. 83?)
25. In Fig. 5.7 the sun is directly overhead at point A on the earth. At the same time at a point B 550 mi away the sun is 8° from the vertical. Estimate the diameter of the earth. (The sun and points A, B, and O are in the same plane.) [55]
26. Apollo 8 traveled at 3,625 mi/h in a circular orbit 70 mi above the moon's surface. If the diameter of the moon is 2,160 mi, what was the period of Apollo 8? (The period is the time required to make one revolution.)
27. Find the total surface and volume of a cone whose height and base diameter are 17 and 20 in, respectively. See Prob. 83.
28. Find the volume and lateral surface of the frustum of a cone having base diameters of 13 and 22 in and a height of 20 in.
29. The scale ratio of a certain aerial photograph is 1:25,000. What is the area in acres of a town if the area in the photograph is 34.23 in^2?
30. In Fig. 5.8 find the length of a cross brace ab and the distance aw of the rivet from one end. [67, 75]
31. A pumping station at O on a river is to deliver water to A and to B. When angle KOB equals angle AOM, the total length of piping is a minimum. Find this length in Fig. 5.9. [67]

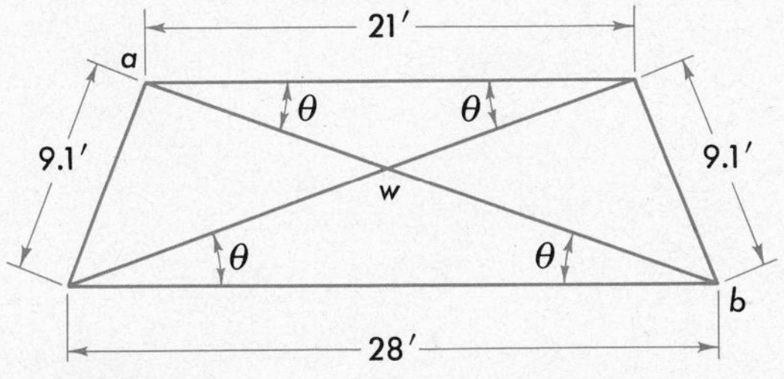

FIGURE 5.8

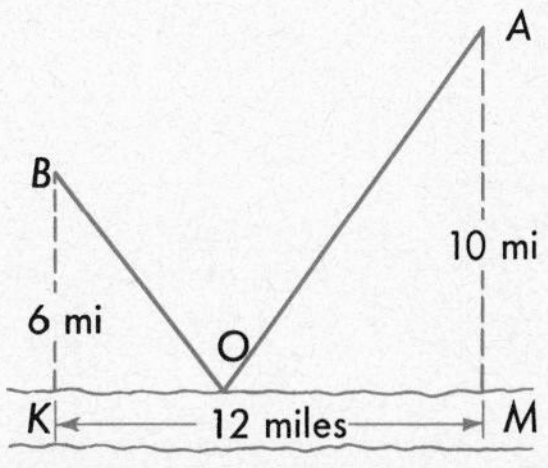

FIGURE 5.9

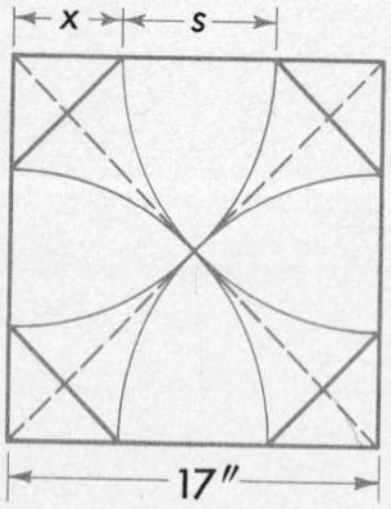

FIGURE 5.10

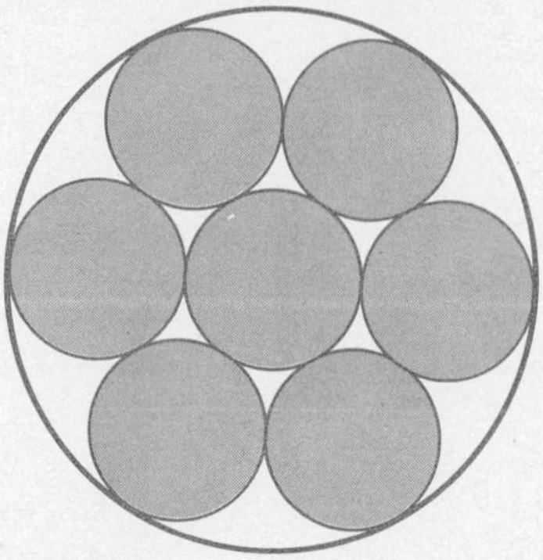
FIGURE 5.11

32. A regular octagon may be cut from a square by the method shown in Fig. 5.10. Find x and s. What percent of the material is wasted?
33. Find the fraction of the large circle occupied by the seven small circles in Fig. 5.11. [53]
34. In Fig. 5.12 the centers of a 6-in and a 12-in circle are 15 in apart. How long is AB?
35. Find the length of stock needed for the piece shown in Fig. 5.13. (Find the length of the centerline.) [55]
36. A 12,000-gal cylindrical tank is to be installed in a factory. Because of headroom the height is restricted to 15 ft. What should be the diameter of the tank to the nearest inch?
37. If water is flowing through an 8-in pipe with an average linear rate of 0.35 ft/s, find the rate of flow in gallons per minute.
38. Find the area in acres of the lot illustrated in Fig. 5.14. [48]
39. Find, in terms of s, the area of the regular dodecagon shown in Fig. 5.15. [80]
40. Find the percentage error in taking the area of the square as equal to that of the circle in Fig. 5.16. Line segment AB is divided into five equal parts.

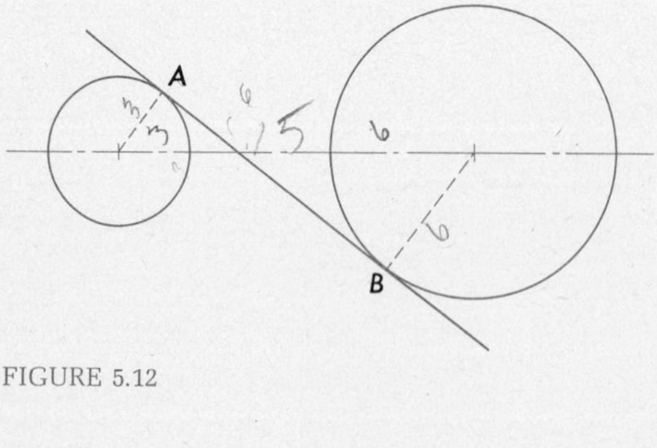

FIGURE 5.12

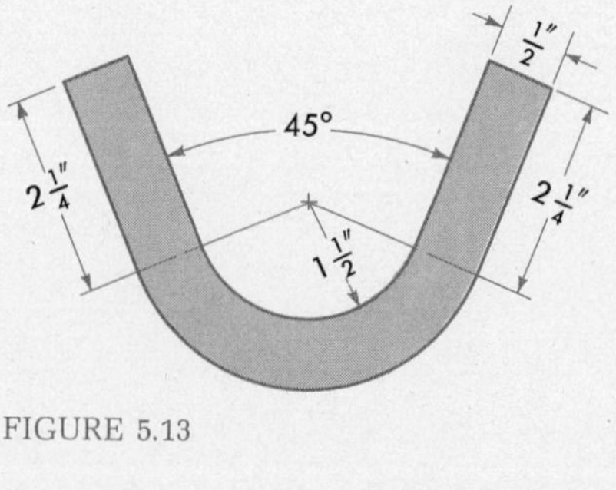

FIGURE 5.13

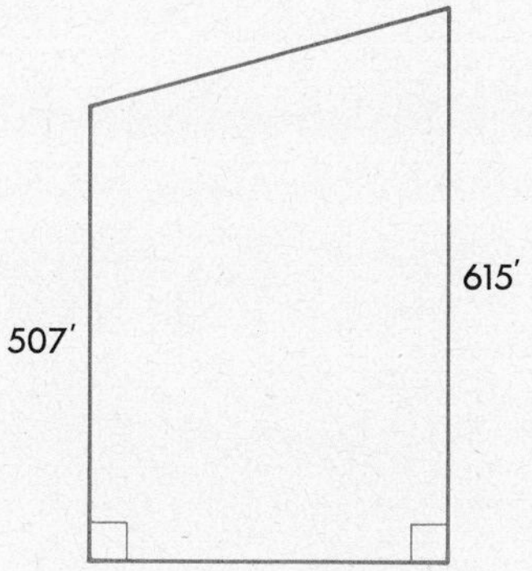

FIGURE 5.14

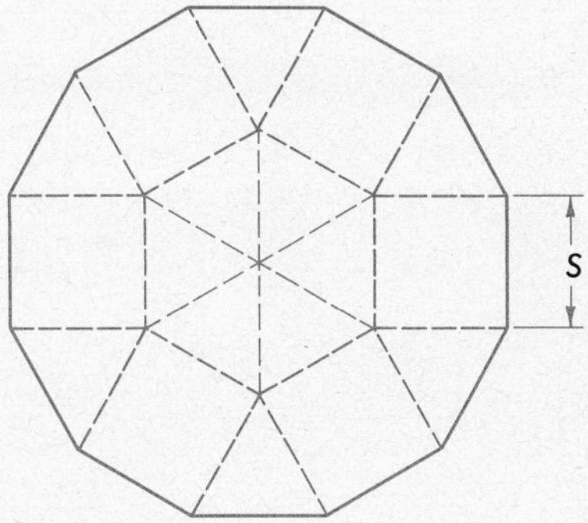

FIGURE 5.15

41. Find the volume of a square pyramid with edges 7 in long. [92]
42. Using 3,960 mi as the radius of the earth, find the length in miles of 1′ longitude (*a*) at the equator; (*b*) at 45°N; (*c*) at 60°N.
43. The circumference of a circle exceeds its diameter by 13. Find the diameter.
44. The hypotenuse of a 45° right triangle exceeds one of the equal sides by 9. Find one of the equal sides. (*Hint:* If side = S, hypotenuse = $S\sqrt{2}$.) [79]
45. The side of an equilateral triangle exceeds the altitude by 5. Find a side of the triangle. [81]
46. Using the three-wire system for determining the root diameter r of a 60° sharp-V thread, develop a formula for r in terms of c and w (Fig. 5.17).
47. Show that the annular area in Fig. 5.18 equals the length of the centerline times the width w.
48. The volume of a prismoid is given by $V = \frac{1}{6}h(b + 4M + B)$, where h = height and b, M, and B are the areas of the upper base, midsection, and lower base, respectively.

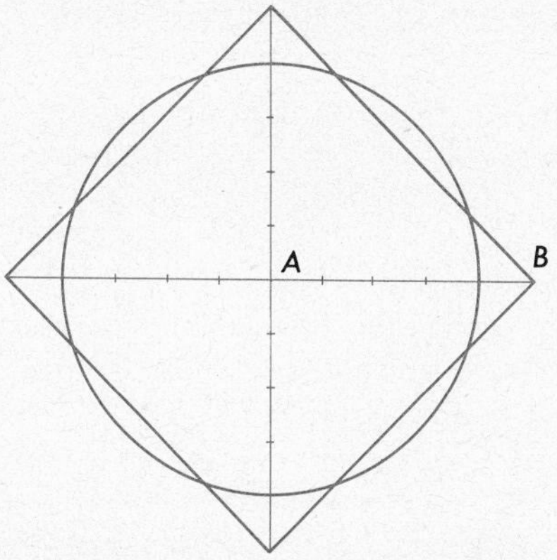

FIGURE 5.16

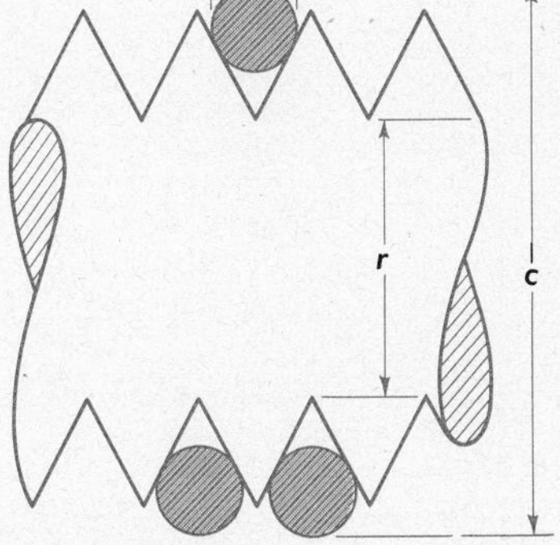

FIGURE 5.17

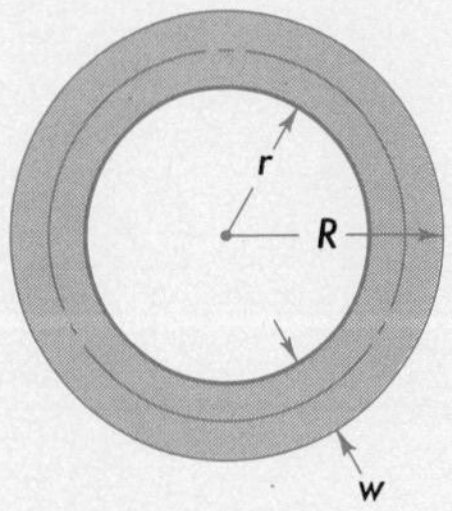

FIGURE 5.18

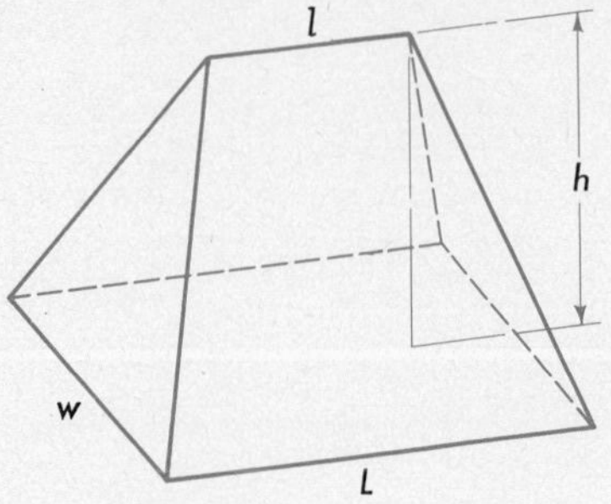

FIGURE 5.19

Applying this formula to the wedge in Fig. 5.19, develop a formula for V in terms of w, h, l, and L.

49. A cone of base diameter d and slant height S is developed from a sector of central angle θ. Derive a formula for θ (in degrees) in terms of d and S.

50. Figure 5.20 illustrates a nomogram for solving equations of the type $1/a + 1/b = 1/c$. To solve this equation for c where a and b are given, draw a 45° line from the origin.

    Draw another line connecting A on one scale with B on the other. The location of the point of intersection of these two lines, which is C, may be referred to either axis.

    With reference to Fig. 5.20, it can be shown that right triangles AMC and

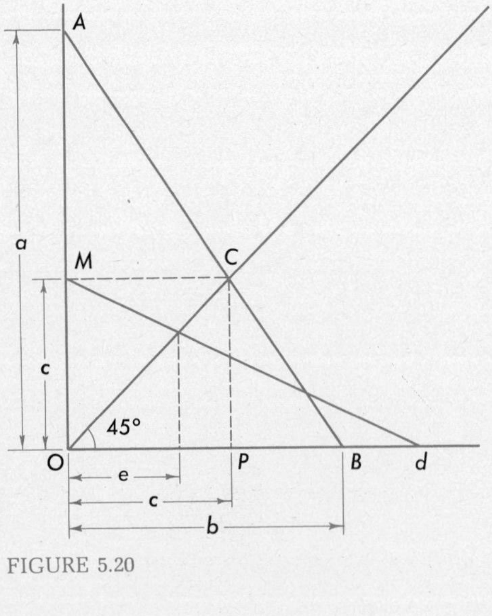

FIGURE 5.20

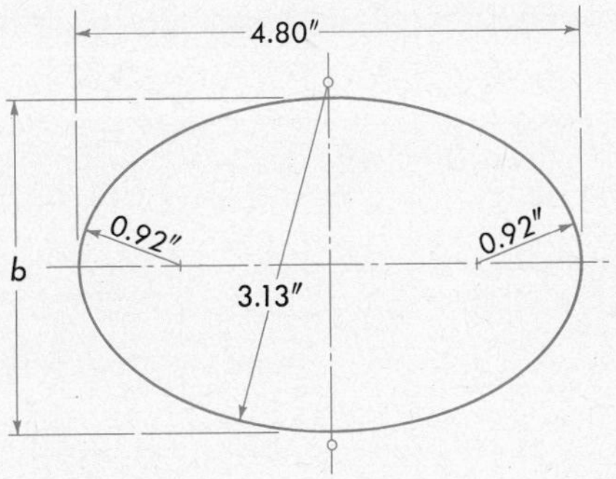

FIGURE 5.21

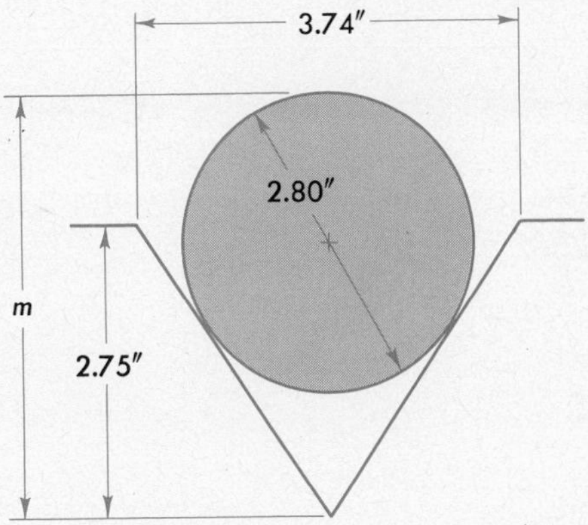

FIGURE 5.22

CPB are similar, and that therefore we may write the equation

$$\frac{a-c}{c}=\frac{c}{b-c}$$

We wish to show that $1/a + 1/b = 1/c$. Can you supply the missing steps?

If three or more reciprocals are to be added, as in the equation $1/a + 1/b + 1/d = 1/e$, the value of c as found above is connected with that of d on the opposite axis, and the value e obtained. This process can be continued for the addition of any number of reciprocals.

The problem $1/a = 1/c - 1/b$ can, of course, be solved by reversing the process. (Connect the points B and C to find A.)

If the student finds much occasion to use this method, he would do well to have the 45° line already drawn and to locate point c by laying a straightedge over points a and b, rather than drawing an actual line on the paper.

Applications of this nomogram† which immediately come to mind are work problems, parallel resistances, and focal length of lenses.

51. Find the short diameter b in the approximate ellipse in Fig. 5.21. [60]
52. Two 15-in pulleys connected by an open belt are 10 ft apart (center to center). If the belt splice passes a given point 125 times per minute, find the speed (revolutions per minute) of one of the pulleys.
53. Find m in Fig. 5.22.
54. A slab of granite is being moved on logs 6 in in diameter. How far will the slab advance when a log revolves once?
55. As an auto traveled at constant speed, a point P on the tread of the tire traveled

† The terms "nomogram," "nomograph," and "alignment chart" are synonymous.

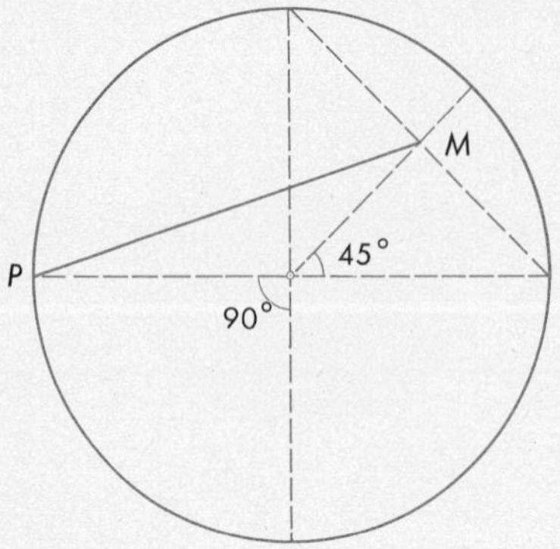

FIGURE 5.23

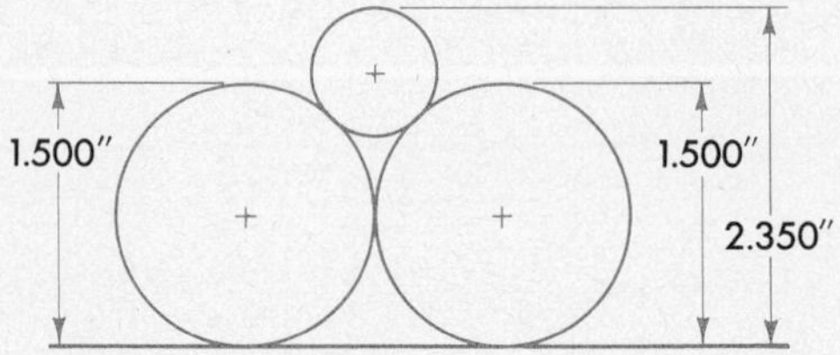

FIGURE 5.24

through space with varying speed, as shown by values taken at intervals during one revolution of the wheel.

Time, s	0	0.02	0.04	0.06	0.08	0.10	0.12	0.14	0.16
Speed, ft/s	0	38	69.5	91.5	99	91.5	69.5	38	0

Find the speed of the car and the diameter of the wheel. (See Prob. 54.)

56. Find the percentage error in taking $4PM$ as equal to the circumference of the circle in Fig. 5.23. Assume the radius is 1. Would the final answer be affected by assuming a different value for the radius?
57. In Fig. 5.24 find the diameter of the smaller circle. [60]
58. An artificial earth satellite is 5,000 mi above the earth's surface. If the radius of the earth is 3,960 mi, what fraction of the earth's surface can the satellite "see"? (Area of curved surface of spherical segment or zone $= 2\pi Rh$, where $R =$ radius of sphere and $h =$ height of segment or zone.) (Fig. 5.25) [49]

    Show that $1/h = 1/h_1 + 1/R$.
59. If three satellites having equatorial orbits are evenly spaced, what must be their altitude so that a satellite is visible from any part of the equator? (Fig. 5.26)
60. Assuming the earth to be a perfect sphere exactly 7,920 mi in diameter, how many significant figures would be needed in the value of π to calculate the length of the equator to the nearest foot?
61. If a right triangle is constructed with legs QR and PR equal to 1 and 2, respectively, and arcs drawn as indicated (Fig. 5.27), show that $a = \sqrt{5} - 1$ and $b = 3 - \sqrt{5}$. Show also that the ratio $a/b = (\sqrt{5} - 1)/(3 - \sqrt{5}) = (1 + \sqrt{5})/2 \approx 1.618$.

    We say that the line segment PR has been divided into extreme and mean ratio, that is, $b/a = a/(a + b)$.

    The constant 1.618 has been variously referred to as ϕ or τ. It has been called

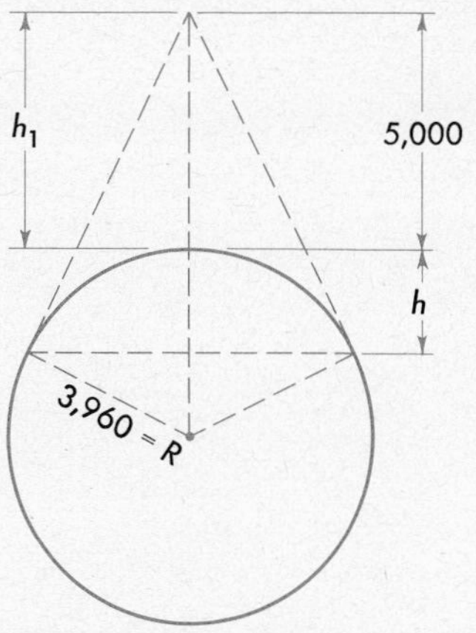

FIGURE 5.25

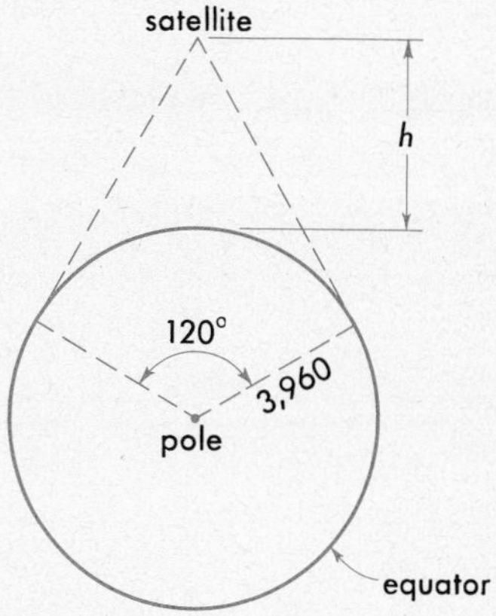

FIGURE 5.26

the "golden mean." The most pleasing shape of a rectangular picture is commonly considered to be about 1.618:1.

The intriguing Fibonacci sequence 1, 1, 2, 3, 5, 8, 13, 21, 34, etc., in which each term is formed from the sum of the two preceding terms, crops up not only in art but in plant life.

Furthermore, as we take the ratio between two successive terms, we obtain values ever closer to 1.618 (for example, $5/3 = 1.667$, $8/5 = 1.600$, $13/8 = 1.625$, $21/13 = 1.615$, $34/21 = 1.619$, etc.).

(GROUP II)

62. (a) How many 2-in-diameter disks may be stamped out of the rectangular sheet shown in Fig. 5.28? (Circles are tangent.)
(b) What is the percent waste?

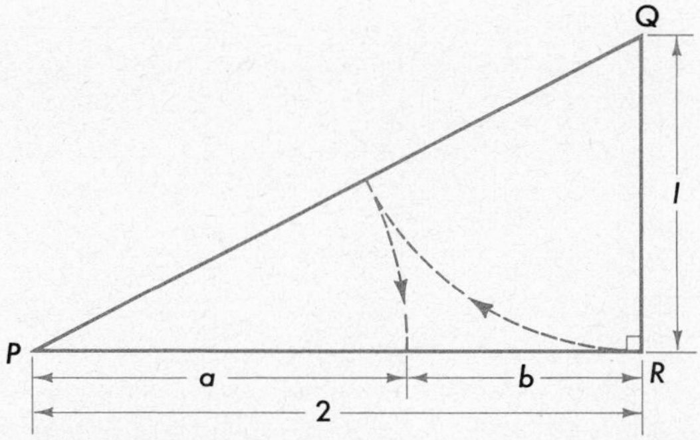

FIGURE 5.27

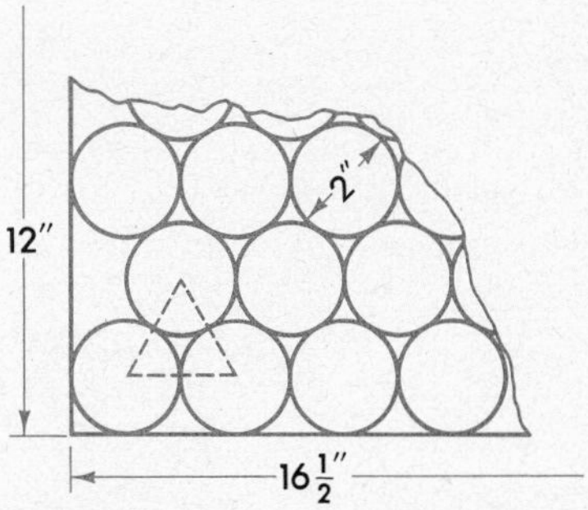

FIGURE 5.28

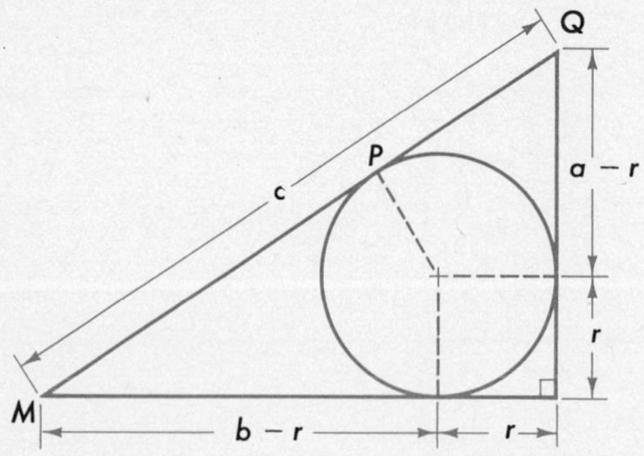

FIGURE 5.29

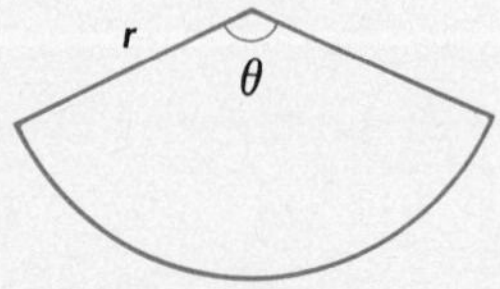

FIGURE 5.30

(c) As the dimensions of the rectangular sheet are increased indefinitely, the scrap metal approaches an irreducible minimum percentage. What is this percentage? [80]

63. In a right triangle whose legs are a and b and hypotenuse c, show that the diameter of the inscribed circle $D = a + b - c$ (Fig. 5.29). [58]
64. The flat sector-shaped sheet in Fig. 5.30 when rolled up will form the cone described in Prob. 27. Find the radius and central angle of this "development."
65. A strip of metal 12 in wide is bent along the centerline to form a V trough. What angle between the sides would correspond to the maximum water capacity of the trough?
66. An empty rectangular swimming pool is 2 ft deep at one end, and the bottom slopes uniformly to a depth of 10 ft at the other end. After cleaning, the pool is being refilled at a constant rate. If after $2\frac{1}{2}$ h the water is 2 ft deep at the deep end, how much longer will it take to fill the pool?
67. Find angle β in Fig. 5.31.
68. An oval running track has semicircular ends and straight sides. The overall length is 3 times the width. If one lap is 600 ft, find the length and width of the oval.

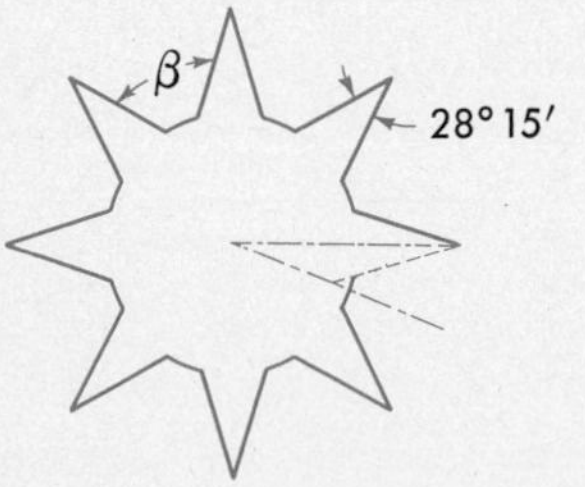

FIGURE 5.31

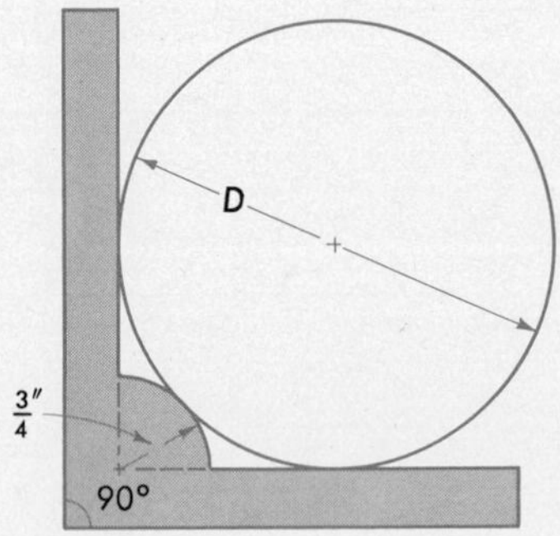

FIGURE 5.32

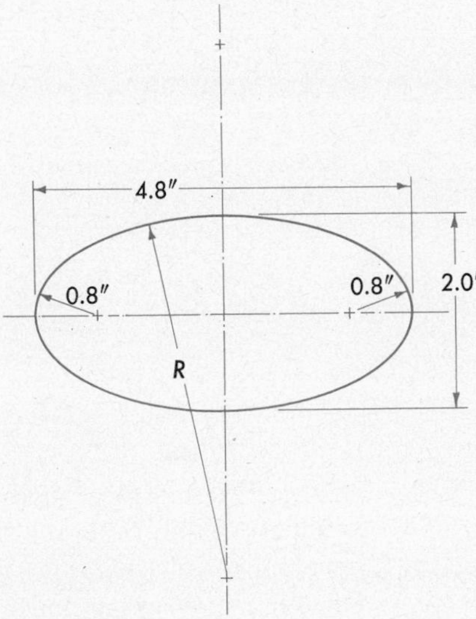

FIGURE 5.33

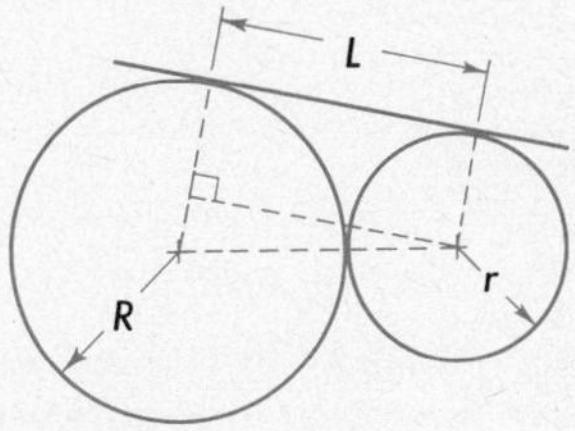

FIGURE 5.34

69. Find the diameter of the circle shown in Fig. 5.32. [60, 75]
70. Find the radius R used in the construction of the approximate ellipse shown in Fig. 5.33.
71. In Fig. 5.34 show that $L = 2\sqrt{Rr}$.
72. In Fig. 5.35 derive an expression for h in terms of the other dimensions.
73. In Fig. 5.36 derive an expression for w in terms of the other dimensions.
74. A 6-ft offset in a pipeline consists of two equal reverse arcs. If the offset is accomplished in a distance of 10 ft (measured parallel to the straight pipe), find the radius of curvature of an arc (Fig. 5.37). [60]
75. A picture AB on a vertical wall (Fig. 5.38) is viewed from eye level CE. Find the distance CD corresponding to the maximum subtended angle ADB (best angle for viewing).

    Can you show that $CD = \sqrt{(AC)(BC)}$? [62]

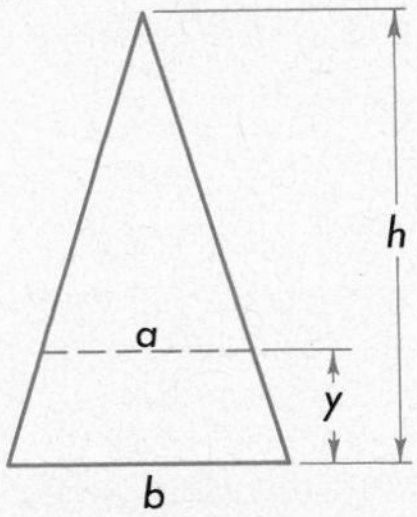

FIGURE 5.35

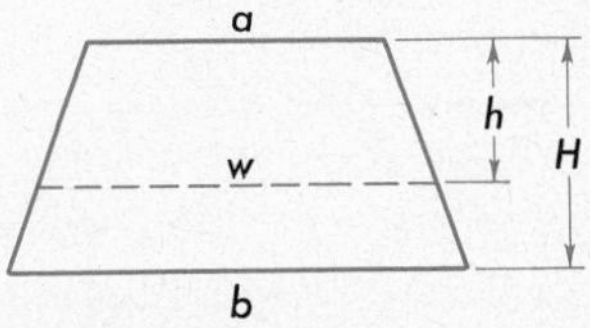

FIGURE 5.36

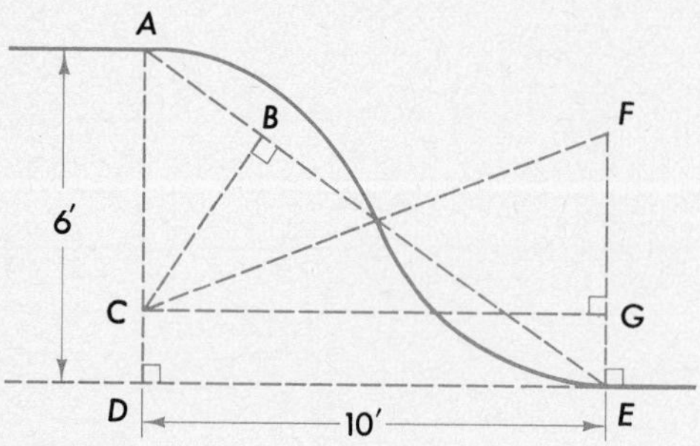

FIGURE 5.37

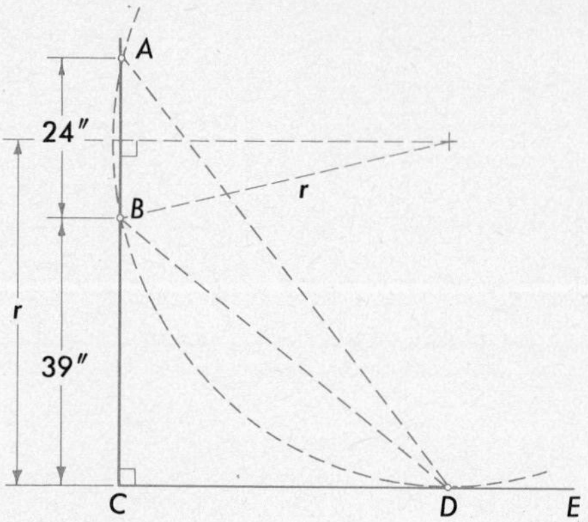

FIGURE 5.38

76. Show algebraically that the volume of a spherical shell is approximately the product of the outer surface times the wall thickness. Volume of a sphere = $(4/3)\pi(\text{radius})^3$, R and r are the outer and inner radii, respectively, and $r \gg R - r$. ($\gg$ means "much greater than.")

(GROUP III)

77. A length of rope hangs from the top of a flagpole to the ground. Six feet of rope lies coiled up on the ground. It is found that the free end of the rope can be brought out 30 ft from the base of the pole and yet be touched to the ground. How high is the flagpole?
78. Assume three mirrors to be arranged at right angles, each to the other two, like the inside corner of a cube. Show that an incident ray, directed to reflect from each of the three faces in succession, will ultimately be reflected back on a path parallel to itself. This would ensure that the reflected ray (from a satellite) would always be beamed back to the station without excessive scattering.
79. In Fig. 5.39 two mirrors form an "optical square." Show that the incident and reflected rays intersect at right angles. (All rays lie in a plane perpendicular to the intersection of the two mirrors.)
80. On one side of a river is a rectangular playground 100 ft wide measured back from the riverbank. An observer on the opposite bank notices that the fence posts of the sides parallel to the riverbank line up at A and B, as illustrated in Fig. 5.40. Assuming the fence posts to be uniformly spaced, find the width of the river.
81. The following data were obtained in finding the diameter of the bore in a capillary glass tube: weight of empty tube, 14.603 g; weight of tube containing a thread of mercury 28.5 cm long, 16.385 g. Find the diameter of the bore to the nearest 0.01 mm if 1 cm^3 mercury weighs 13.6 g.
82. A farmer traced the map of his farm on a sheet of No. 4 zinc and cut out the outline of his map. Then, to the same scale (1 in = 50 ft), he cut out a 4-in square. The

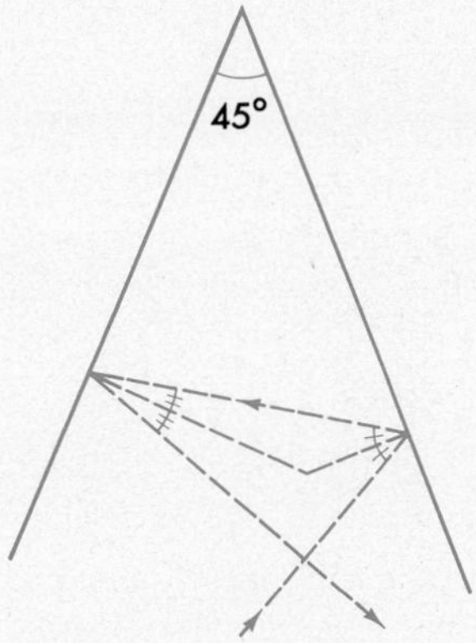

FIGURE 5.39

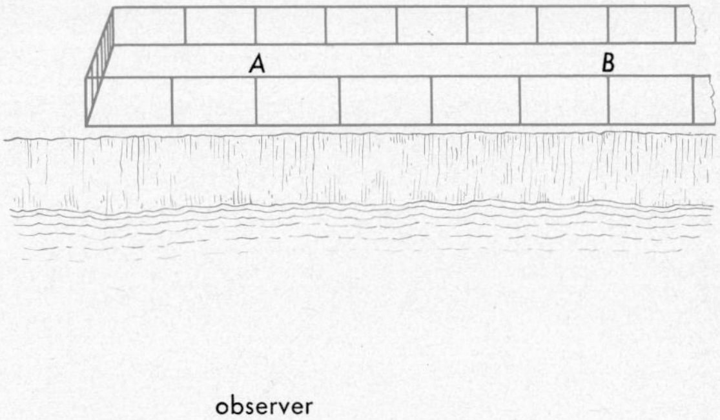

FIGURE 5.40

4-in square weighed ½ oz, while the zinc map weighed 3 lb 10½ oz. How many acres were there in the farm?

83. Find the roof area, the top view of which is given in Fig. 5.41, if all parts of the roof have a ¾ pitch (3-in rise in every 4 in taken horizontally). Area of plane figure outlined by eaves = ⅘ × roof area. Why? Note that the principle involved here may be applied to the computation of the lateral surface of any cone, pyramid, or frustum having "uniform pitch."

84. The profile AB of the nose of an experimental rocket in Figs. 5.42 and 5.43 is an arc of a circle whose center C is on the line BC. If AD is 24 ft and BD is 2½ ft, find the radius r of the cross section at distance x from the nose tip, making x successively 6, 12, and 18 ft. Let R = radius of curvature (ft). Then, since $AC = R$, $DC = R - 2.5$, and $AD = 24$, we have $R^2 = (R - 2.5)^2 + (24)^2$, or $R = 116.45$ ft, and

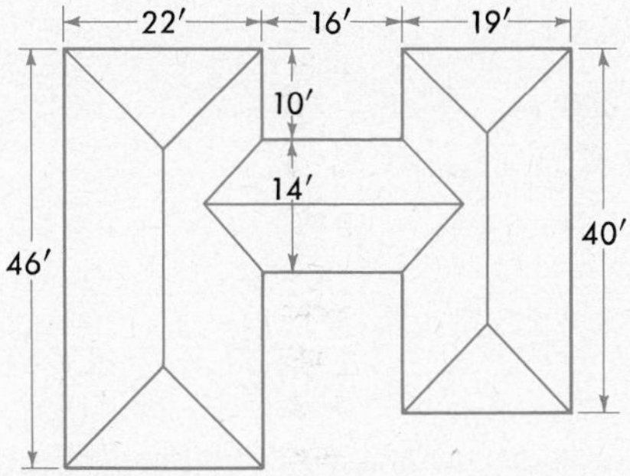

FIGURE 5.41

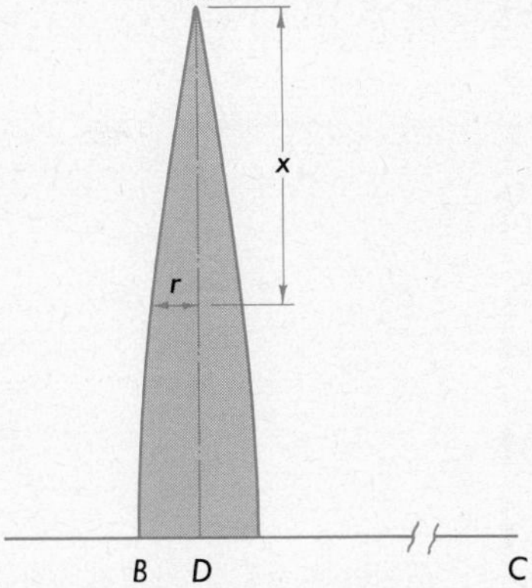

FIGURE 5.42

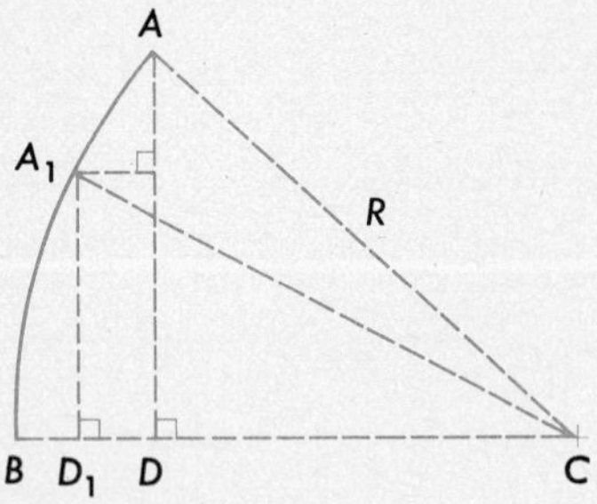

FIGURE 5.43

FIGURE 5.44

$DC = 113.95$ ft. At the 6-ft station $A_1C = 116.45$, $A_1D_1 = 18$, and $D_1C = \sqrt{(116.45)^2 - (18)^2} = 115.05$. $D_1D = 115.05 - 113.95 = 1.10$ ft radius cross section at the 6-ft station.

Repeat this procedure to find D_2C at the 12-ft station and D_3C at the 18-ft station.

85. In Fig. 5.44 the stars photograph as traces (arcs) in a time exposure of the night sky. Estimate the length of exposure by scaling any measurements you think necessary. Polaris is beyond the lower right-hand corner of the photo.
86. A roll of paper 4 ft 6 in in diameter is wound on a 6-in hub. Find the length of the paper in the roll if the sheet is 0.0080 in thick. What assumption is made here?
87. In Fig. 5.45 the speed of the upper pulley is 450 r/min. Find the speed of the lower pulley when the idler belt is in the position shown. What is the extreme range of speeds possible in the lower pulley?†

†The idler belt is the only point of contact between the pulleys.

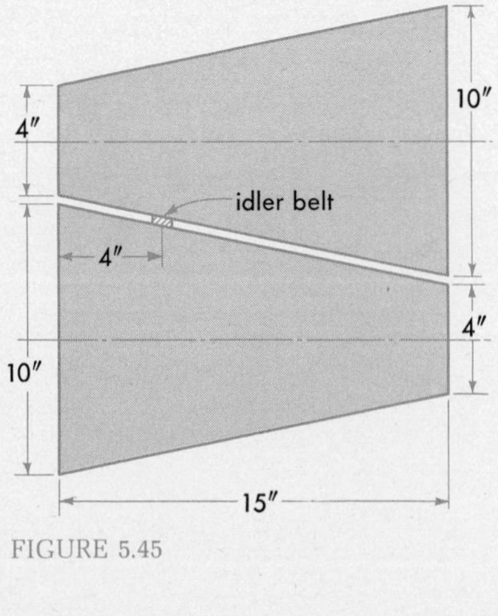

FIGURE 5.45

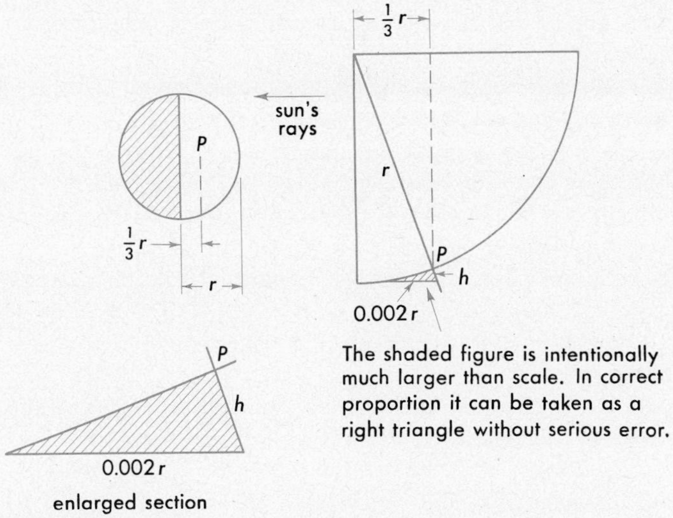

FIGURE 5.46

88. The shadow of a mountain on the moon at first quarter is observed at point P, located at about one-third of a radius from the center of the disk. The length of the shadow is approximately 0.002 times the radius of the moon. What is the height of the mountain if the moon's diameter is 2,160 mi? (Fig. 5.46)

Facts in Geometry

Angles, Straight Lines, Rectilinear Figures

1. Two angles are complementary when their sum is a right angle.
2. Two angles are supplementary when their sum is a straight angle.
3. The sum of all the angles about a point in a plane is two straight angles.
4. The sum of all successive adjacent angles around a point on one side of a straight line is a straight angle.
5. If one straight line intersects another straight line, the opposite or vertical angles are equal. $\angle a = \angle c$ (Fig. I)
6. Two triangles are congruent if two sides and the included angle of one are equal, respectively, to two sides and the included angle of the other.
7. Two triangles are congruent if two angles and the included side of one are equal, respectively, to two angles and the included side of the other.
8. Two triangles are congruent if the three sides of one are equal, respectively, to the three sides of the other.
9. Two right triangles are congruent if the hypotenuse and an acute angle of one are equal to the hypotenuse and an acute angle of the other.

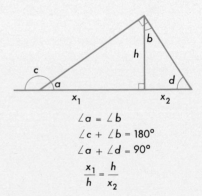

10. Two right triangles are congruent if the hypotenuse and a leg of one are equal to the hypotenuse and a leg of the other.
11. In an isosceles triangle the angles opposite the equal sides are equal.
12. An equilateral triangle is equiangular, and conversely.
13. If one side of a triangle is greater than a second side, the angle opposite the first side is greater than the angle opposite the second side, and conversely.
14. The perpendicular bisector of a line segment is the locus of all points equidistant from the extremities of the segment.
15. The bisector of an angle is the locus of all points equidistant from the sides of the angle.
16. If two parallel straight lines are cut by a transversal, the alternate interior angles are equal. $\angle a = \angle b$ (Fig. I)
17. If two parallel lines are cut by a transversal, the exterior-interior angles on the same side of the transversal are equal. $\angle b = \angle c$ (Fig. I)
18. If two parallels are cut by a transversal, the two interior angles on the same side of the transversal are supplementary, and conversely. $\angle b + \angle d = 180°$ (Fig. I)
19. Two lines parallel to a third line are parallel.
20. Two lines perpendicular to a third line are parallel.
21. If two angles have their sides respectively parallel, they are equal provided both pairs of parallels extend (*a*) in the same direction from their vertices or (*b*) in opposite directions. Otherwise they are supplementary. $\angle c = \angle e$, $\angle a = \angle e$, $\angle d + \angle e = 180°$ (Fig. I)
22. Two angles whose sides are perpendicular, each to each, are either equal or supplementary. $\angle a = \angle b$, $\angle c + \angle b = 180°$ (Fig. II)
23. The sum of the angles of a triangle is equal to 180°.
24. An exterior angle of a triangle is equal to the sum of the two opposite interior angles.

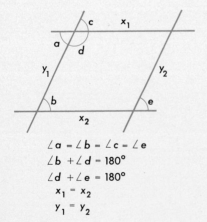

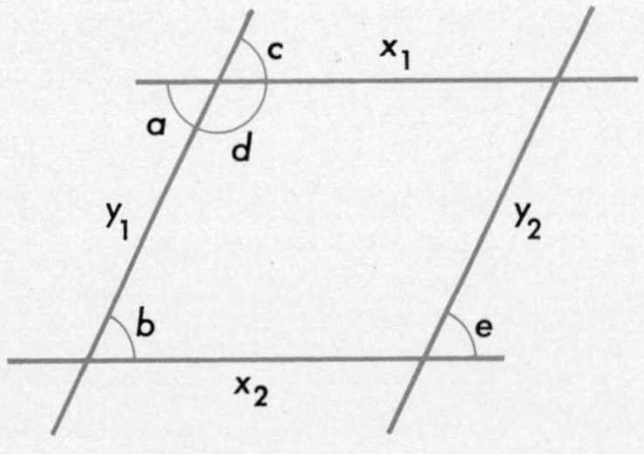

$\angle a = \angle b = \angle c = \angle e$

$\angle b + \angle d = 180°$

$\angle d + \angle e = 180°$

$x_1 = x_2$

$y_1 = y_2$

FIGURE I

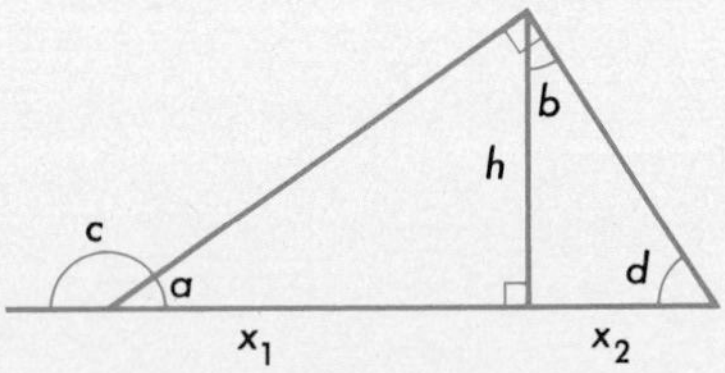

$\angle a = \angle b$

$\angle c + \angle b = 180°$

$\angle a + \angle d = 90°$

$\frac{x_1}{h} = \frac{h}{x_2}$

FIGURE II

25. In a right triangle the sum of the two acute angles equals 90°. $\angle a + \angle d = 90°$ (Fig. II)
26. Two triangles are congruent if two angles and a side of one are equal to two angles and the corresponding side of the second.
27. Two right triangles are congruent if a leg and an acute angle of one are equal to the corresponding leg and acute angle of the other.
28. If two right triangles have the two legs of one equal, respectively, to the two legs of the other, the triangles are congruent.
29. The area of a parallelogram is equal to the product of its base and altitude.
30. A diagonal of a parallelogram divides it into two congruent triangles.
31. Any two consecutive angles of a parallelogram are supplementary.
32. If two sides of a quadrilateral are equal and parallel, the figure is a parallelogram.
33. The opposite sides of a parallelogram are equal; the opposite angles are also equal.
34. The diagonals of a parallelogram bisect each other.
35. The sum of the interior angles of a polygon of n sides is equal to $(n - 2)180°$.
36. Each interior angle of a regular polygon of n sides is equal to $[(n - 2)/n]180°$.
37. Each exterior angle of a regular polygon of n sides is equal to $360°/n$.
38. The central angle of a regular polygon of n sides contains $360/n°$.
39. A regular polygon is a polygon which is both equilateral and equiangular.
40. If three or more parallels intercept equal parts on one transversal, they intercept equal parts on every transversal. Given $a = b = c$, then $d = e = f$. (Fig. III)
41. The line which joins the midpoints of two sides of a triangle is parallel to the third side and is equal to one-half the third side. Given $b = c$ and $e = f$, then $x_1 = \frac{1}{2}x_2$. (Fig. III)
42. The line which joins the midpoints of the legs of a trapezoid is parallel to the bases and equal to their arithmetic mean. $x_2 = (x_1 + x_3)/2$. (Fig. III)
43. The intersection of the bisectors of the angles of a triangle determines the center of the inscribed circle. (Fig. IV)

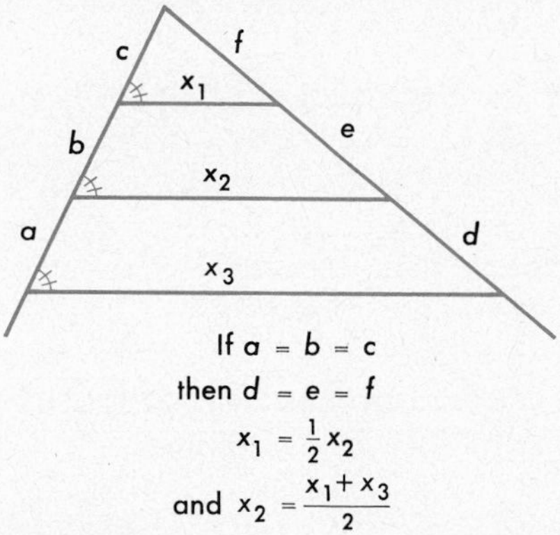

FIGURE III

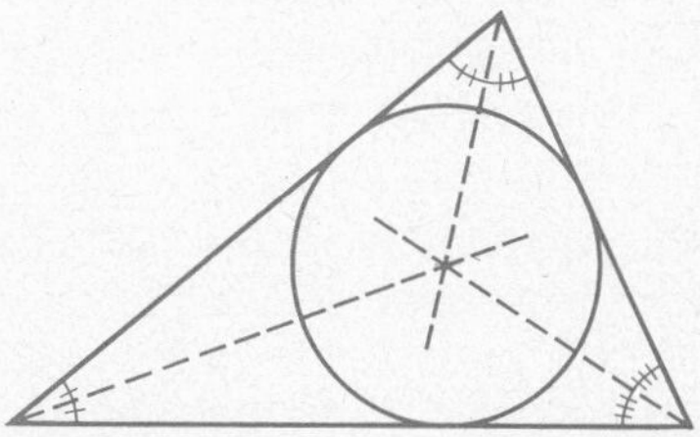

FIGURE IV

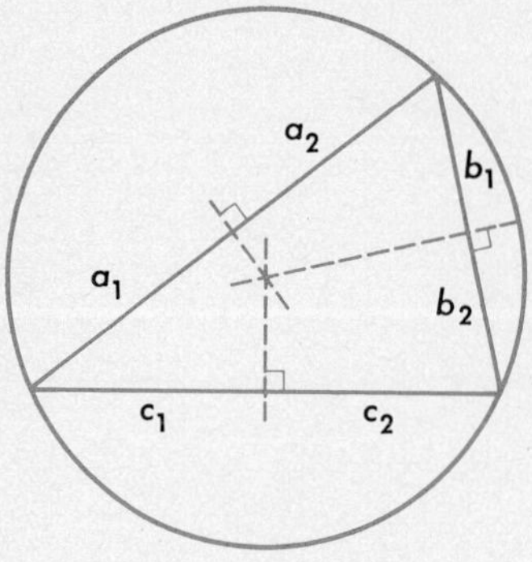

FIGURE V

44. The intersection of the perpendicular bisectors of the sides of a triangle determines the center of the circumscribed circle. $a_1 = a_2$, $b_1 = b_2$, $c_1 = c_2$ (Fig. V)
45. The medians of a triangle intersect at a point (called the *centroid*) which cuts off two-thirds of each median from its vertex.
46. The area of a triangle is equal to one-half the product of its base and its altitude.
47. The area of a triangle equals $\sqrt{s(s-a)(s-b)(s-c)}$, where a, b, and c are the sides and $s = \frac{1}{2}(a + b + c)$.
48. The area of a trapezoid is equal to the altitude multiplied by the average of the bases.

Circles

49. A tangent to a circle is perpendicular to the radius drawn to the point of contact. Tangent at $M \perp MO$ (Fig. VI)
50. The circumference of a circle is expressed by the formula $c = \pi d$, or $c = 2\pi r$. $\pi = c/d = 3.1416$, approximately.
51. The circumferences of two circles have the same ratio as their radii or as their diameters.
52. The area of a circle is given by $A = \pi r^2$, or $A = (\pi/4)d^2$.
53. The areas of two circles have the same ratio as the squares of their radii, or as the squares of their diameters, or as the squares of their circumferences.
54. The area of a sector of a circle is to the area of the circle as the angle of the sector is to 360°.

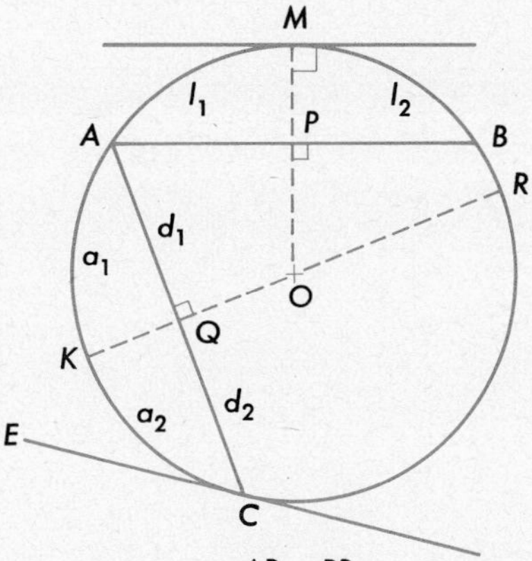

$AP = PB$
and $\widehat{l}_1 = \widehat{l}_2$
$AQ = QC$
and $\widehat{a}_1 = \widehat{a}_2$, $d_1 = d_2$
If $AB = AC$ then $PO = QO$
$\angle ACE = \frac{1}{2}(\widehat{a}_1 + \widehat{a}_2)$ (degrees)
$\frac{KQ}{d_1} = \frac{d_1}{QR}$

FIGURE VI

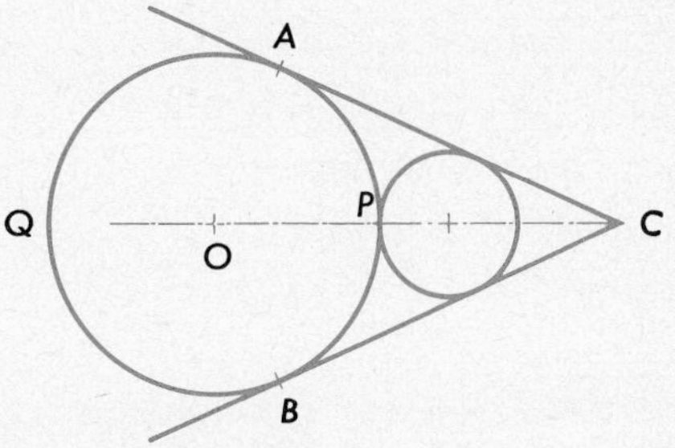

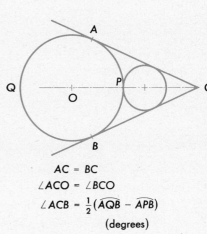

$AC = BC$
$\angle ACO = \angle BCO$
$\angle ACB = \frac{1}{2}(\widehat{AQB} - \widehat{APB})$
(degrees)

FIGURE VII

55. The length of an arc of a circle is to the circumference of the circle as the central angle of the arc is to 360°.
56. A diameter perpendicular to a chord bisects the chord and the arc subtended by the chord. $d_1 = d_2$, $a_1 = a_2$ (Fig. VI)
57. Through three points not in the same straight line, one circle, and only one can be drawn.
58. The two tangents drawn to a circle from an outside point are equal and make equal angles with a line drawn from the point to the center of the circle. $\overline{AC} = \overline{BC}$, $\angle ACO = \angle BCO$ (Fig. VII)
59. If two circles intersect, their line of centers is perpendicular to their common chord at its midpoint.
60. If two circles are tangent to each other, the line of centers passes through the point of contact. (Fig. VII)
61. The number of degrees in a central angle equals the number of degrees in its intercepted arc.
62. An inscribed angle is measured by one-half its intercepted arc. (Fig. VIII)
63. An angle inscribed in a semicircle is a right angle. $\angle ABC = 90°$ (Fig. VIII)
64. Inscribed angles which intercept the same or equal arcs are equal. (Fig. VIII)

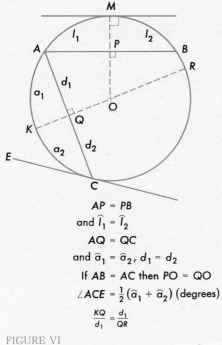

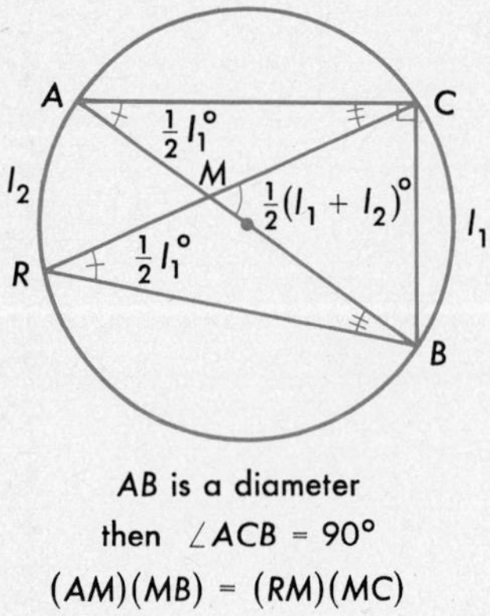

FIGURE VIII

Proportion; Similar Figures

65. A line parallel to one side of a triangle and meeting the other two sides divides these sides proportionally. $a_1/a_2 = b_1/b_2$ (Fig. IX)
66. If two lines are cut by a number of parallels, the corresponding segments are proportional. (Fig. IX)
67. If two triangles are similar, their corresponding sides are in proportion and their corresponding angles are equal, and conversely. (Fig. IX)
68. Similar polygons are polygons whose corresponding angles are equal and whose corresponding sides are proportional.
69. Corresponding sides of congruent polygons are equal.
70. Corresponding angles of congruent polygons are equal.
71. If two triangles are similar to a third triangle, they are similar to each other.
72. If two triangles have an angle of one equal to an angle of the other and the including sides proportional, the triangles are similar.

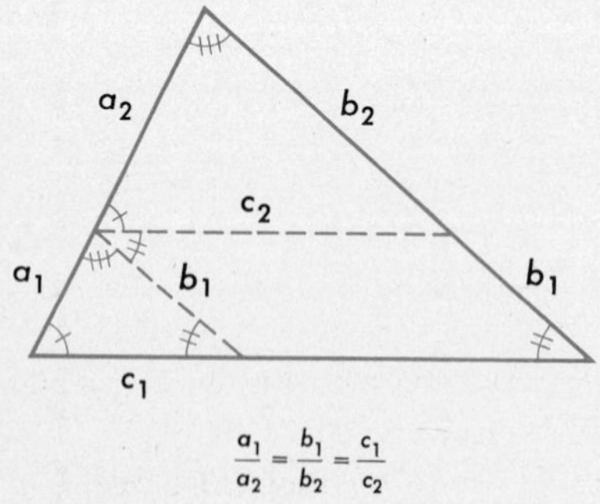

FIGURE IX

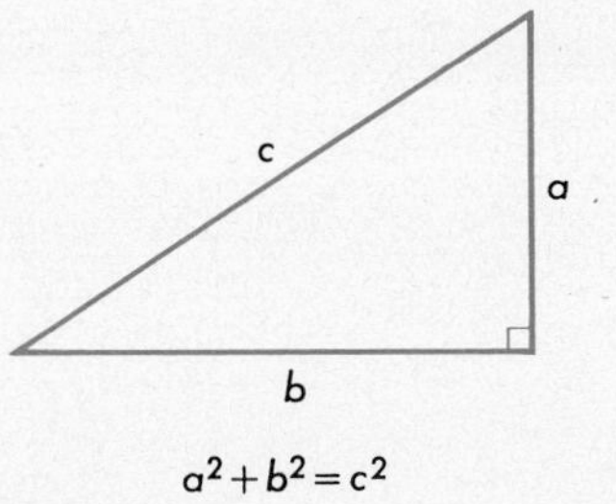

FIGURE X

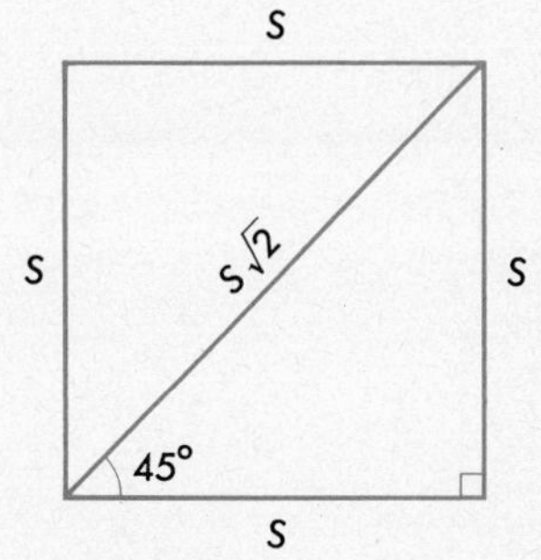

FIGURE XI

73. If two triangles have their sides respectively proportional, they are similar. (Fig. IX)
74. In two similar polygons any two corresponding dimensions are to each other as any other two corresponding dimensions; also the perimeters are to each other as any two corresponding dimensions.
75. In a right triangle the square of the hypotenuse is equal to the sum of the squares of the legs. (Fig. X)
76. The perpendicular from any point on a circle to a diameter of the circle is the mean proportional between the segments of the diameter. $KQ/d_1 = d_1/(QR)$ (Fig. VI)
77. The areas of two similar polygons are to each other as the squares of any two corresponding dimensions.

Regular Polygons

78. The diagonal of a square is equal to one side multiplied by $\sqrt{2}$.
79. The hypotenuse of a 45° right triangle is equal to $\sqrt{2}$ times a leg. (Fig. XI)
80. The area of an equilateral triangle having a side S is given by the formula $A = (S^2/4)\sqrt{3}$. (Fig. XII)
81. In a 30°–60° right triangle the longer leg is $\sqrt{3}$ times the shorter leg, and the hypotenuse is twice the shorter leg. (Fig. XII)
82. A circle may be circumscribed about, and a circle may be inscribed in, any regular polygon.
83. The area of a regular polygon is equal to one-half the product of its perimeter and its apothem (a). (Fig. XIII)
84. Of isoperimetric polygons having the same number of sides, the regular polygon has the greatest area. ("Isoperimetric" means "having the same perimeter.")
85. Of all polygons equivalent in area and having the same number of sides, the regular polygon has the smallest perimeter.

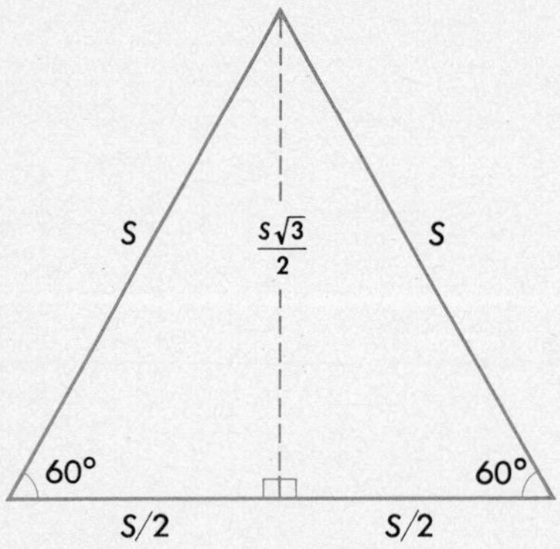

FIGURE XII

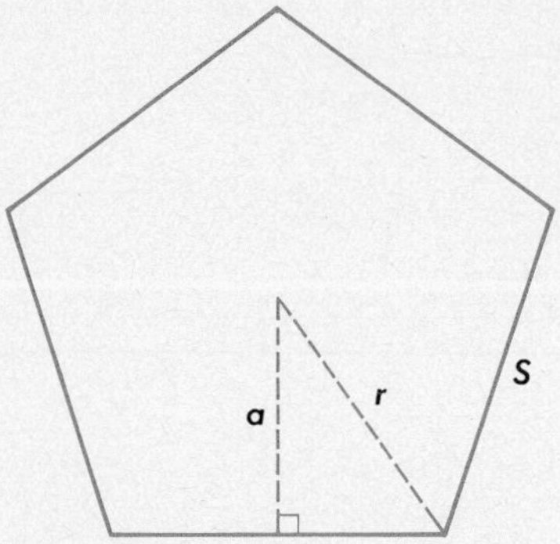

FIGURE XIII

Solid Figures

86. The volumes of two similar solid figures are to each other as the cubes of corresponding dimensions.
87. The surfaces of two similar solid figures are to each other as the squares of corresponding dimensions.
88. Pyramidal or conic sections parallel to the base are figures similar to the base. Corresponding dimensions in two sections are proportional to the distances of the sections from the vertex, and corresponding sectional areas are proportional to the squares of these distances.

Statements 89 to 96 refer to *right* prisms, cylinders, cones, and pyramids.

89. The lateral area of a prism is equal to the product of a lateral edge by the perimeter of the base of any right section.
90. The volume of a prism is equal to the product of the base by the altitude.
91. The lateral area of a regular pyramid or cone is equal to half the product of the slant height by the perimeter of the base. (Fig. XIV)
92. The volume of a cone or pyramid is equal to one-third the product of the base by the altitude.
93. The volume of the frustum of a cone or pyramid is equal to $(\frac{1}{3})(h)(b + \sqrt{bB} + B) = (\frac{1}{6})(h)(b + 4M + B)$. (Fig. XV)
94. The volume of the frustum of a cone is equal to $(\frac{1}{3})(\pi h)(r^2 + rR + R^2)$. (Fig. XVI)
95. The lateral area of a right circular cylinder is equal to the product of the altitude by the circumference of the base.
96. The volume of a right circular cylinder is equal to the product of the base by the altitude.
97. The surface of a sphere is given by $A = 4\pi r^2$.

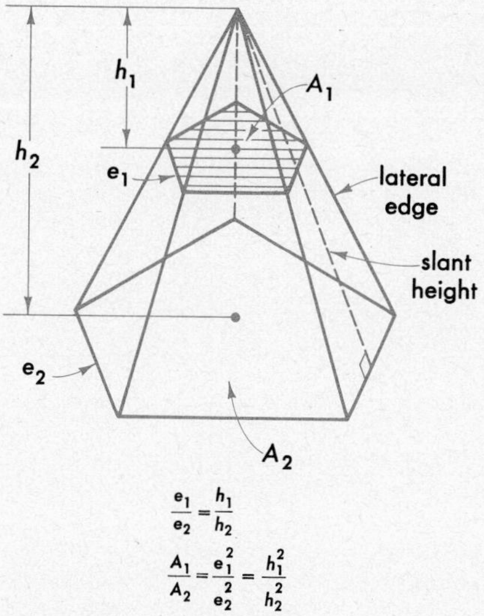

FIGURE XIV

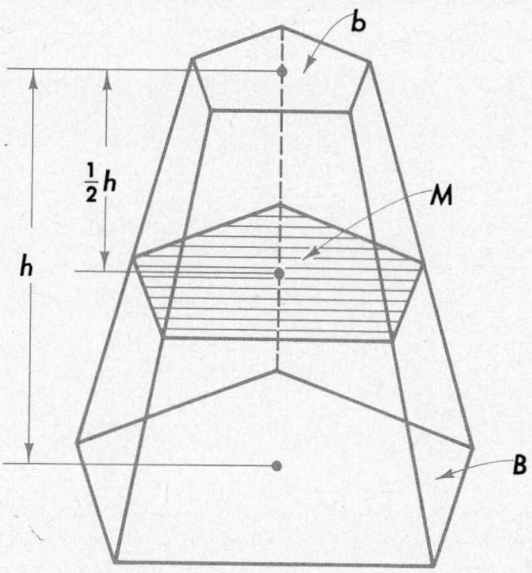

FIGURE XV

98. The volume of a sphere is given by $V = \frac{4}{3}\pi r^3 = \frac{1}{6}\pi d^3$.
99. The intersection of a plane with the surface of a sphere is a circle. If the plane passes through the center of the sphere, the intersection with the spherical surface is called a *great circle*.
100. The shortest distance between two points on a spherical surface is along the great circle connecting the points. (The arc must be $\leq 180°$.)

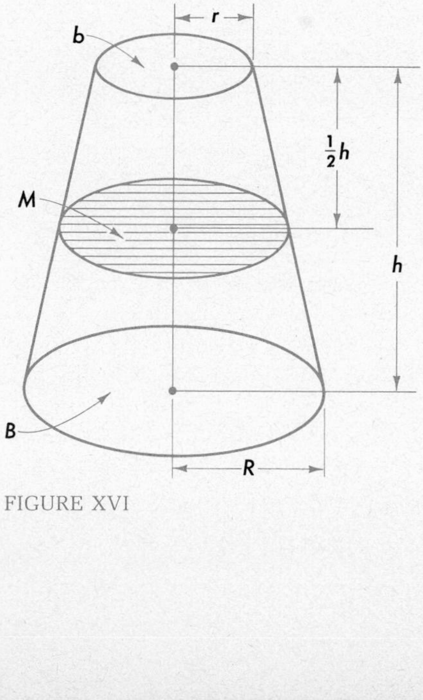

FIGURE XVI

101. The area (curved surface) of a spherical segment or zone is equal to $2\pi Rh$, where R is the radius of the sphere and h is the height of the segment or zone.
102. Through the ends of a diameter of a sphere any number of great circles may be drawn.
103. Through two points on a spherical surface which are not ends of a diameter, only one great circle can be drawn.
104. Through three points on a spherical surface, one and only one circle can be drawn.

6 linear functions

In this chapter we shall briefly introduce the basic idea of a function. Then we shall discuss the graphs of linear functions. This is commonly known as the analytic geometry of the straight line.

6.1 Ordered Pairs of Numbers

If we wish to convert the temperature of a room expressed in degrees Celsius to the corresponding temperature expressed in degrees Fahrenheit, the following equation applies.

$$F = 1.8C + 32 \tag{1}$$

where F = temperature in degrees Fahrenheit
C = temperature in degrees Celsius

By substituting a value of the variable C in Eq. (1), the corresponding value of the variable F may be calculated.

In this approach, the variable F is appropriately called the *dependent* variable and the variable C is called the *independent* variable.

Observe that for each value of the independent variable C there is a unique (only one) corresponding value for the dependent variable F. For example, if we substitute successive values for C, such as -20, -10, 0, $+10$, and $+20$, we find that

TABLE 6.1

Independent variable	Dependent variable
-20	-4
-10	$+14$
0	$+32$
$+10$	$+50$
$+20$	$+68$

corresponding values of F are -4, $+14$, $+32$, $+50$, and $+68$, respectively. These are tabulated in Table 6.1.

Here we have five pairs of numbers. Each pair consists of a value of the independent variable and the corresponding value of the dependent variable. By convention such pairs of numbers are often written in the form $(-20,-4)$, $(-10,+14)$, $(0,+32)$, $(+10,+50)$, and $(+20,+68)$. Observe that the value of the independent variable is written first, followed by the value of the dependent variable. Since the order in which these numbers are written is critical, they are called *ordered pairs* of numbers.

6.2 Functions

When we use the word "function" we shall refer to a set of ordered pairs of numbers, for example (x,y), such that for each value of the first variable x, there corresponds a unique value of the second variable y. Since the value of the variable y is considered to depend upon the value of the variable x, we refer to y as the dependent variable, and to x as the independent variable.

We also sometimes refer to y as the "value" of a function of x.

The *domain* of the function is the set of numbers from which specific values of the independent variable x may be chosen. The *range* of the function is the set of numbers among which are found the corresponding values of the dependent variable y.

Unless otherwise expressed or implied, both the range and the domain of the function involved will be the largest possible set of real numbers.

We observe that there are three important aspects of the discussion of functions so far.

1. The set of x values, or the *domain* of the function
2. The set of y values, or the *range* of the function
3. Some type of association between y and x such that a unique value of y can be determined if x is given

There are four ways by which the type of association between the independent and dependent variables can be described:

1. By a worded statement: The circumference of a circle is the product of π and the diameter.
2. By an equation: $y = 5x^2$.
3. By a table of values enumerating convenient, corresponding values for the variables involved in an equation.
4. By a graph of the function. The graph of a function is the set of points whose coordinates represent, respectively, the set of ordered pairs of numbers which constitutes the function. This is discussed in greater detail in Sec. 6.5.

In physical problems involving the function idea, we often attempt to distinguish between *cause* and *effect* even though by doing so we may arrive at some quite arbitrary distinctions. Even so, it is often convenient to try to represent the cause by the independent variable and the effect by the dependent variable.

In each of the following illustrations it will be noted that the dependent variable is mentioned before the independent variable.

Rate of growth of vegetation depends upon the temperature.
Time of high tide depends upon the position of the moon.
Price of an article depends upon supply and demand.
Flow of electric current through a fixed resistance depends upon the voltage.
Postage to a given destination depends upon the weight of the package.

The primary meaning of the word "function" was given above. However, it is commonly used in a slightly different sense. Thus if

$$A = \pi r^2$$

we often say that A is a function of r. In this sense the word "function" is identified with the dependent variable rather than with an ordered pair of numbers.

6.3 Functional Notation

When, for any reason, the exact relation between variables is not to be expressed, a general form is used. Thus, instead of writing $A = \pi r^2$, we might use the more general form $A = f(r)$, which states that A is a function of r without giving the exact relation. It is read, "A is a function of r," or more simply, "A equals f of r."

If we let y represent the value of some function of x, we may write $y = f(x)$. Then $f(6)$ is the value of y when $x = 6$; likewise $f(-1)$ is the value y assumes when $x = -1$; and so on. In general, $f(a)$ is the value of y which results when a is substituted for x in the expression for $f(x)$.

It should be remembered that $f(x)$ does not mean f times x; in fact, f does not represent a number. In the expression $y = f(x)$, f simply indicates that a functional relationship exists between y and x.

In the present context it is quite common to use y and $f(x)$ interchangeably. Thus we may let either y or $f(x)$ designate the dependent variable.

Example 1. Suppose that $y = x^2 - 3x - 4$. We may then write

$$y = f(x) = x^2 - 3x - 4$$

Then, when $x = 5$,

$$y = f(5) = (5)^2 - 3(5) - 4 = 6$$

Also, when $x = -6$,

$$y = f(-6) = (-6)^2 - 3(-6) - 4 = 50$$

EXERCISE 1

If $y = f(x) = 3x^2 - 2x - 5$, find

1. $f(0)$ 2. $f(-1)$ 3. $f(\frac{2}{3})$ 4. $f(a + 1)$ 5. $f(4) - f(-2)$

If $y = f(x) = 12x/(16 - x^2)$, find

6. $f(-2)$ 7. $f(5)$ 8. $f(\frac{1}{2})$ 9. $f(3a - 4)$ 10. $f(2a) - f(a)$

6.4 Rectangular Coordinates

To form a *rectangular system of coordinates,* we draw a horizontal line $X'X$ and a vertical line $Y'Y$. Their point of intersection O is called the *origin*. $X'X$ is called the X axis, and $Y'Y$ is called the Y axis.

The location of any point in the plane of the coordinate axes may be expressed by stating its distance and direction from each of the two axes. Distances above $X'X$ and distances to the right of $Y'Y$ are positive, whereas distances below $X'X$ and distances to the left of $Y'Y$ are negative.

The distance of a point measured to the right or left of the Y axis is called the *abscissa,* or X coordinate, of the point. The distance of a point from the X axis (upward or downward) is called the *ordinate,* or Y coordinate, of the point. In Fig. 6.1, point P is said to have the *coordinates* (x,y) and may be referred to as the point (x,y). In Fig. 6.1 the points $(3,4)$, $(4,-2)$, $(0,-3)$, $(-5,-1)$, and $(-2,3)$ are also designated. It should be noted that the coordinates are enclosed in parentheses and separated by a comma and that the abscissa is always written first (hence the term "ordered pair"). It will also be seen that the axes divide the plane into four quadrants, numbered as shown.

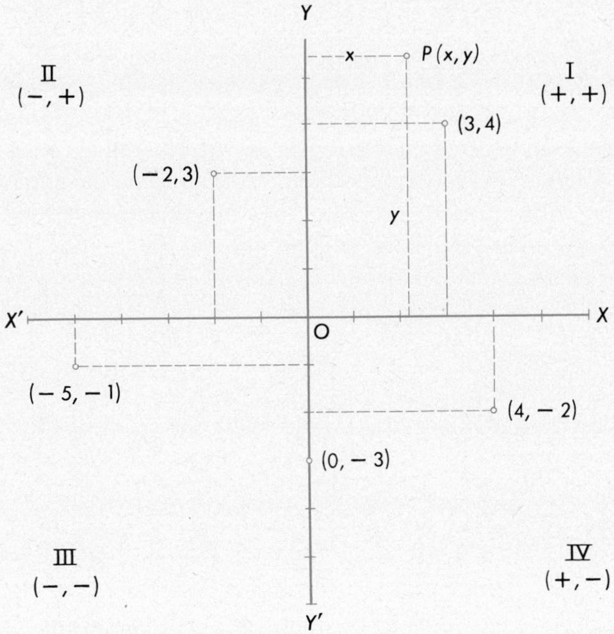

FIGURE 6.1

The signs of the coordinates of points in each quadrant are also indicated.

The position of any point can be determined if its coordinates are known, and conversely, the coordinates of a point appearing on the coordinate plane can be determined by measurement.

EXERCISE 2

Locate the points having the coordinates given below.

1. $(2,5)$	2. $(4,\sqrt{3})$	3. $(-2,6)$	4. $(-\sqrt{2},3)$
5. $(8,-3)$	6. $(7,-4)$	7. $(-3,-5)$	8. $(-6,-2)$
9. $(0,5)$	10. $(-5/2,0)$	11. $(0,0)$	12. $(11/2,-2/3)$

EXERCISE 3

Identify the closed figures formed by plotting the given points and joining in order with straight lines.

1. $(5,2)$, $(5,-4)$, $(-1,-4)$, $(-1,2)$
2. $(0,4)$, $(7,4)$, $(7,-1)$, $(0,-1)$
3. $(3,2)$, $(8,0)$, $(0,-9)$
4. $(2,4)$, $(5,-3)$, $(-1,-3)$
5. $(-1,6)$, $(5,2)$, $(-1,2)$
6. $(5,5)$, $(7,-3)$, $(-4,-3)$, $(-6,5)$
7. $(1,3)$, $(4,2)$, $(6,8)$
8. $(5,3)$, $(12,4)$, $(7,9)$, $(0,8)$

6.5 Graph of a Function

When we sketch the graph of a function, we say that we "graph the function."

Suppose that we are given some function $y = f(x)$. The first step in graphing the function is to make a table listing a number of different values of x and opposite them to write the corresponding values of y. We take these pairs of corresponding values of x and y as the coordinates of points which we plot. These points all lie on the graph of $y = f(x)$. Accordingly, we may define the *graph*, or *locus*, of a function as consisting of a system of points whose coordinates satisfy the relation $y = f(x)$.

A *linear function* of x is a first-degree polynomial in x having the form $mx + b$, where m and b are constants. The graph of such a function is always a straight line; hence the name "linear function."

Example 2. Graph the function $y = f(x) = \frac{2}{3}x - 4$.

Form a table of arbitrarily chosen values of x together with the corresponding values of $f(x)$, that is, of y.

x	−6	−3	0	$1\frac{1}{2}$	3	5	8	12
y	−8	−6	−4	−3	−2	$-\frac{2}{3}$	$1\frac{1}{3}$	4

In Fig. 6.2 the points (−6,−8), (−3,−6), etc., are plotted, and a smooth line is drawn through these points.

It is evident that we might plot any number of points whose coordinates satisfy the equation $y = \frac{2}{3}x - 4$. We infer, then, that we have a straight line which may be extended indefinitely in either direction. Theoretically, two points are sufficient to determine a straight line. However, in graphing any linear function, we should compute a minimum of three values of the function. For the sake of accuracy, these points should be located some distance apart. Any points not lying on the same straight line should be checked for errors.

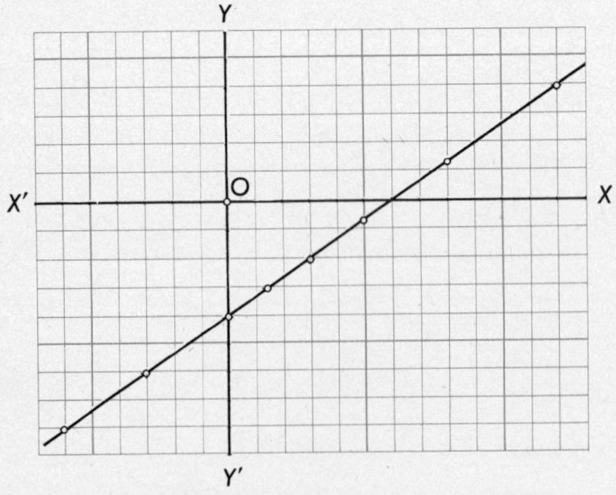

FIGURE 6.2

For a given section of coordinate paper the position of the axes and the number of units assigned to a division on the paper should be chosen so as to make the desired portion of the graph as large as possible.

In general, if a function of x is defined by a formula, its graph is a smooth curve or, in some cases, two or more disconnected smooth curves. The term "smooth curve" is used in a broad sense to denote a line which may be straight or curved but which does not show any abrupt change in direction. For greater clarity it may be desirable to use different scales on the X and Y axes. Perhaps the most common example of an independent variable is time. Time units, with rare exceptions, are scaled horizontally.

It is good practice to see that each division on the axes corresponds to 1, 2, or 5 times an integral power of 10, as is the case with the scales of a slide rule.

Example 3. Graph the function $y = f(x) = -\frac{3}{2}x$.

Form a table listing arbitrary values of x and corresponding values of y:

x	8	5	2	0	−2	−5	−8
y	−12	$-7\frac{1}{2}$	−3	0	3	$7\frac{1}{2}$	12

In Fig. 6.3 the points $(8, -12)$, $(5, -7\frac{1}{2})$, etc., are plotted. They will be seen to lie in one straight line which is drawn through them.

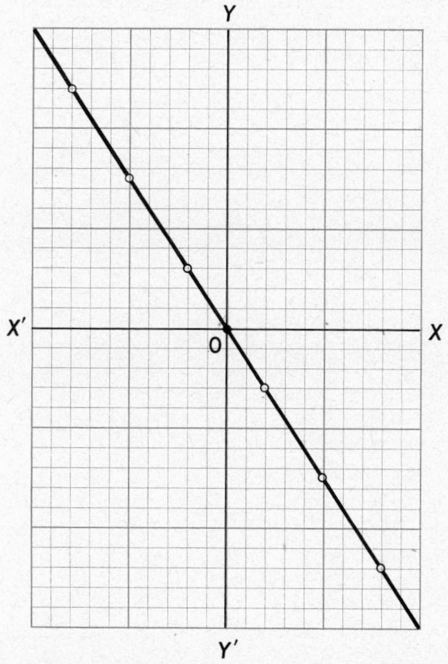

FIGURE 6.3

EXERCISE 4

Plot the graphs of the following equations in which $y = f(x)$, indicating any intersections with the axes:

1. $y = x$
2. $y = 3x$
3. $y = \frac{1}{2}x$
4. $y = -x$
5. $y = -2x$
6. $y = -\frac{1}{3}x$
7. $y = 2$
8. $x = -4$
9. $y = x + 3$
10. $y = 2x - 1$
11. $y = \frac{1}{2}x + 2$
12. $y = -x + 4$
13. $y = -\frac{1}{2}x - 2$
14. $x = 0$
15. $y = 0$

6.6 Slope of a Straight Line

Referring to Fig. 6.4, draw any straight line not parallel to the axes. Let P and Q be any two points on the line; denote the coordinates of P by (x_1,y_1) and the coordinates of Q by (x_2,y_2).

The steepness or slope of the line is then expressed by the equation

$$m = \frac{y_2 - y_1}{x_2 - x_1} \tag{2}$$

provided $x_2 - x_1 \neq 0$ or $x_2 \neq x_1$. Hence the *slope* of the straight line passing through two given points is equal to the difference of the ordinates of the points divided by the difference of their abscissas taken in the same order.

It is apparent from the rule just stated that the slope of a line could also be expressed by the fraction $(y_1 - y_2)/(x_1 - x_2)$. This is, of course, in agreement with the law of signs as applied to fractions.

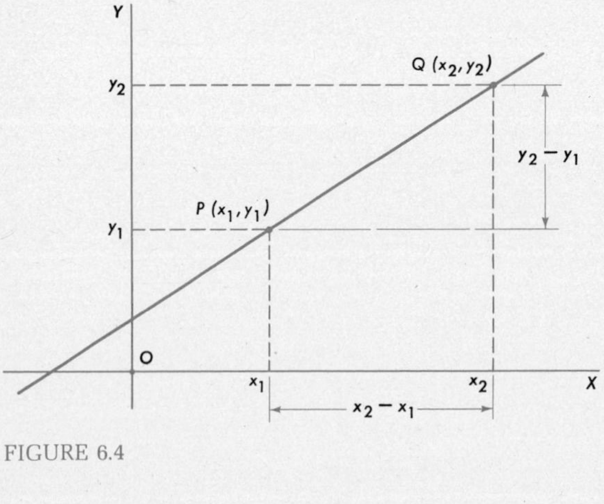

FIGURE 6.4

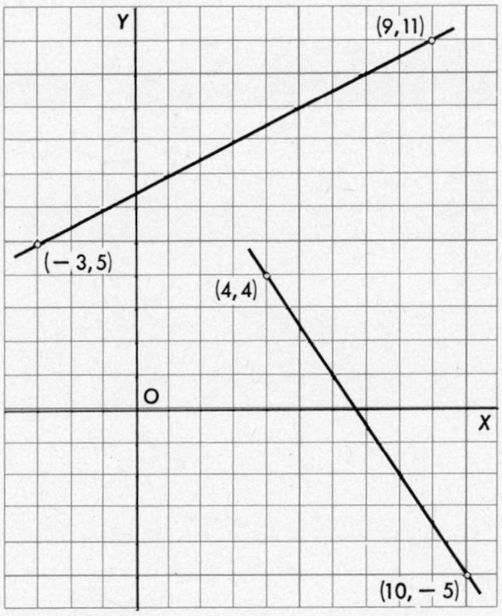

FIGURE 6.5

Example 4. Find the slope of the line passing through (−3,5) and (9,11) (Fig. 6.5).

Referring to Eq. (2), we may consider $x_1 = -3$, $x_2 = 9$, $y_1 = 5$, $y_2 = 11$. The slope is therefore

$$\frac{11 - 5}{9 - (-3)} = \frac{6}{12} = \frac{1}{2}$$

Example 5. Find the slope of the line passing through (4,4) and (10,−5) (Fig. 6.5).

Taking $x_1 = 4$, $x_2 = 10$, $y_1 = 4$, and $y_2 = -5$, we have

$$\text{Slope} = \frac{-5 - 4}{10 - 4} = \frac{-9}{6} = -\frac{3}{2}$$

The following characteristics of slope may be cited:

1. *A line sloping upward to the right has a positive slope; a line sloping downward to the right has a negative slope.*
2. *The slope of a horizontal line is zero.*
3. *The slope of a vertical line is undefined* (since $x_2 - x_1 = 0$ and division by zero is undefined).
4. *If we move a point to the right along a straight line, the slope corresponds to the progress made in a vertical direction when the point has advanced one unit horizontally.* Thus, if the point rises $1\frac{1}{2}$ units while at the same time moving one unit to the right, the slope of the line is $1\frac{1}{2}$; if the point falls $\frac{4}{5}$ of a unit while advancing one unit to the right, the slope is $-\frac{4}{5}$. Scale units are to be used in all cases.

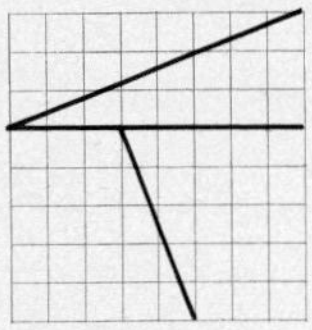

FIGURE 6.6a

FIGURE 6.6b

EXERCISE 5

Find the slope of the straight line passing through the following points:

1. $(-2,1)$ and $(4,3)$
2. $(1,-3)$ and $(4,3)$
3. $(0,4)$ and $(8,-2)$
4. $(-2,5)$ and $(3,0)$
5. Origin and $(4,10)$
6. $(-3,-1)$ and $(5,-1)$
7. What is the slope of (a) a 30° line, (b) a 45° line, (c) a 60° line, (d) a 120° line, (e) a 135° line, and (f) a 150° line? Assume equal X and Y scales. (The angle in question is measured counterclockwise from the x axis to the given line. See Fig. 6.15.)
8. An 8 × 8 square is cut up into four sections which are apparently reassembled to form a 5 × 13 rectangle. Where did the extra unit of area come from? (See Fig. 6.6.)

If three points $P(x_1, y_1)$, $Q(x_2, y_2)$, and $R(x_3, y_3)$ lie in a straight line (Fig. 6.7), the slope of PQ must be equal to that of QR. Hence, by Eq. (2), for three points lying in a straight line,

$$\frac{y_3 - y_2}{x_3 - x_2} = \frac{y_2 - y_1}{x_2 - x_1} \tag{3}$$

The student will recognize that this is the type of straight-line equation which forms the basis of interpolation.

Example 6. The following data are thought to represent a straight line. Confirm this algebraically.

x	y	Δx	Δy	$\frac{\Delta y}{\Delta x}$
5	1			
		4	6	1.5
9	7			
		6	9	1.5
15	16			
		2	3	1.5
17	19			
		8	12	1.5
25	31			

In this table Δx represents the change in x from the preceding value. Thus the first value in the Δx column is found by writing $9 - 5 = 4$. Likewise the first value

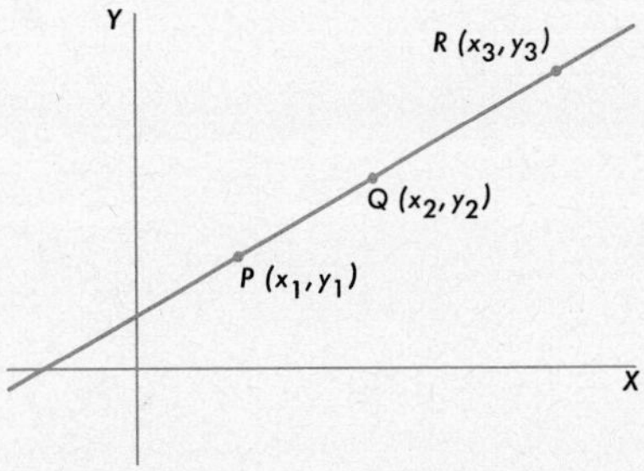

FIGURE 6.7

in the Δy column is found by writing $7 - 1 = 6$. The $\Delta y/\Delta x$ column (read "delta y over delta x") indicates the ratio of Δy to the corresponding Δx, and therefore represents the slopes of straight-line segments connecting consecutive pairs of points. Since these ratios are equal, all the points must be *collinear* (lie in the same straight line).

This test is routinely used to check against errors in data expected to be represented by a straight line.

6.7 Rate of Change of Linear Functions

It will be noted that Eq. (2) for slope expresses the *ratio* of the *change in* y to the *change in* x. We may then extend Eq. (2) to read

$$m = \frac{y_2 - y_1}{x_2 - x_1} = \frac{\Delta y}{\Delta x}$$

The delta concept of rates of change (representing the slope of the function) is of utmost importance in the study of calculus.

To express the concepts of Sec. 6.6 in functional notation, we shall find the rate of change in the value of a linear function by starting with a definite value of the independent variable, for example x, to which we shall assign the value x_1 and let x change by a certain amount Δx (Fig. 6.8*a*). Then the rate of change in the value of this function is

$$\text{Rate of change in } f(x) = \frac{f(x_1 + \Delta x) - f(x_1)}{\Delta x}$$

We shall agree that $+\Delta x$ denotes an increase in the value of x and that $-\Delta x$ denotes a decrease in the value of x.

If we let

$$\Delta y = f(x_1 + \Delta x) - f(x_1)$$

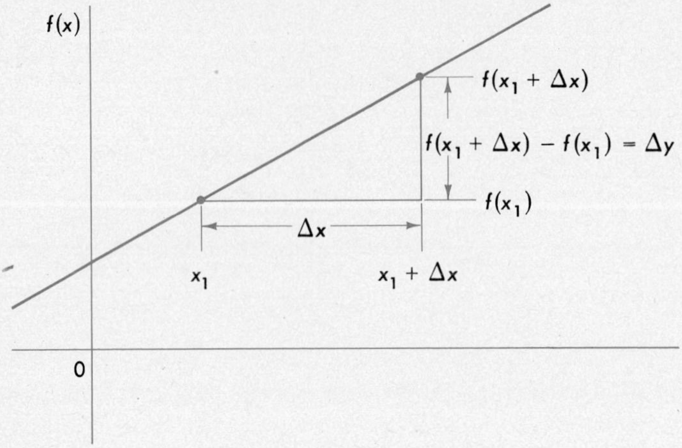

FIGURE 6.8*a*

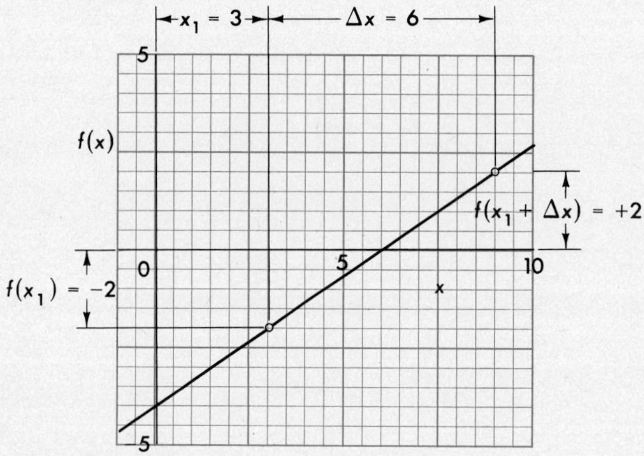

FIGURE 6.8*b*

then the rate of change in $f(x)$ with respect to x, or what amounts to the same thing, the rate of change in y with respect to x, is

$$\frac{\Delta y}{\Delta x} = \frac{f(x_1 + \Delta x) - f(x_1)}{\Delta x} \tag{4}$$

By comparing Eq. (4) above with Eq. (2) in Sec. 6.6, we note that the rate of change in the value of a linear function is numerically equal to the slope of the graph of that linear function.

Example 7. For the linear function represented in Fig. 6.8*b* find $f(x_1)$ and $f(x_1 + \Delta x)$ by direct reading of the graph when $x_1 = 3$ and $\Delta x = 6$. Also find the rate of change of this function.

By reading the graph, $f(x_1) = f(3) = -2$ and $f(x_1 + \Delta x) = f(3 + 6) = +2$.

$$\frac{f(x_1 + \Delta x) - f(x_1)}{\Delta x} = \frac{\Delta y}{\Delta x} = \frac{2 - (-2)}{6} = \frac{2}{3}$$

In this example we could, with equal logic, have reasoned that as x decreases by 6 units, then y decreases by 4 units and $\Delta y/\Delta x = -4/-6 = \frac{2}{3}$. However, it is usually more convenient to deal consistently with increasing abscissas.

Example 8. If a straight line passes through the points $(-5,-16)$ and $(+10,+20)$, how much does y change when x increases by 0.005?

$$\text{Slope} = m = \frac{20 - (-16)}{10 - (-5)} = \frac{20 + 16}{10 + 5} = \frac{36}{15} = \frac{12}{5} = +2.4$$

In other words,

$$\frac{\Delta y}{\Delta x} = +\frac{12}{5} = +2.4$$

In this example Δx is given to be 0.005, and we are required to find Δy. Therefore

$$\frac{\Delta y}{0.005} = 2.4$$

$$\Delta y = 2.4 \times 0.005 = 0.012$$

EXERCISE 6

1. For the linear function displayed in Fig. 6.9 find $f(x_1 + \Delta x)$ by direct reading of the graph. Also calculate the rate of change of $f(x)$ per unit increase of x when (*a*) $x_1 = 9$, $\Delta x = 6$; (*b*) $x_1 = 21$, $\Delta x = 12$; (*c*) $x_1 = 27$, $\Delta x = 15$. (*d*) How much does y change when x increases by 0.012? (This graph shows the expansion at constant pressure of a gas occupying 91 ml at 0°C and warming to 45°C. Can you attribute any physical significance to the value of the slope?) [*Note:* $y = f(x)$.]
2. As in Prob. 1, find the rate of change of the function in Fig. 6.10. (*a*) $x_1 = 4$, $\Delta x = 3$; (*b*) $x_1 = 12$, $\Delta x = 5$; (*c*) $x_1 = 20$, $\Delta x = 8$. (*d*) How much does y change when x increases by 0.04? (Figure 6.10 represents the "straight-line" depreciation of a machine over a period of 30 years.) [*Note:* $y = f(x)$.]
3. A straight line passes through the points $(-2,7)$ and $(6,1)$. Determine the ordinate of a point on the line whose abscissa is 6.2.

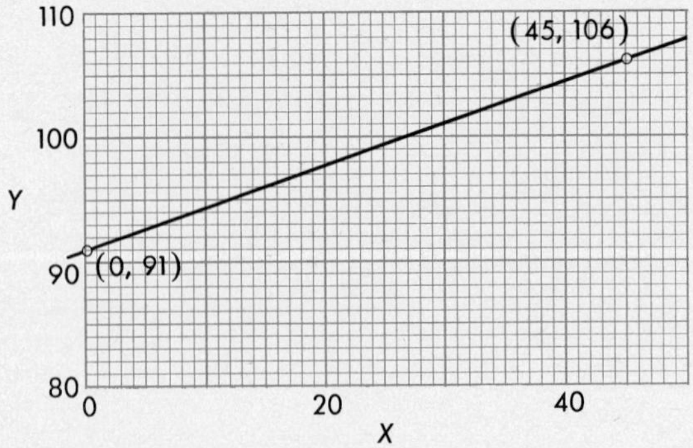

FIGURE 6.9

6.8 Determination of a Straight Line

The equation of a particular straight line may be determined (1) if the slope of the line and the coordinates of a point on the line are known or (2) if the coordinates of two points on the line are known.

Observe that in Fig. 6.11 the straight-line graph intersects the Y axis at the point whose coordinates are $(0,b)$. The ordinate b is called the *y intercept*.

According to Sec. 6.6, the slope of the graph in Fig. 6.11 is given by

$$m = \frac{y - b}{x - 0} \tag{5}$$

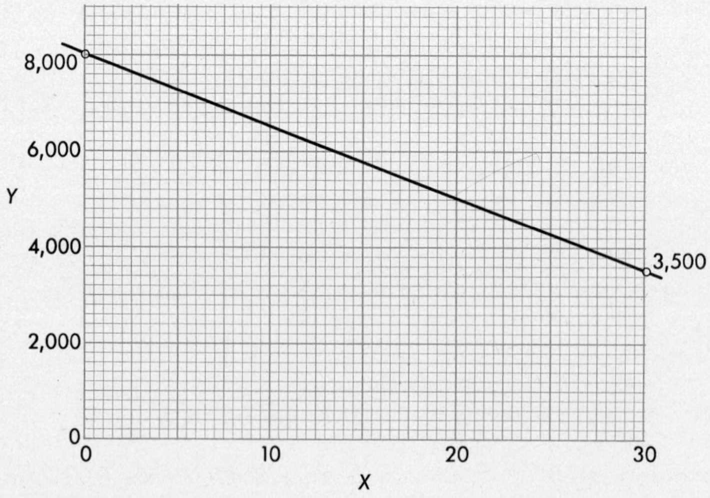

FIGURE 6.10

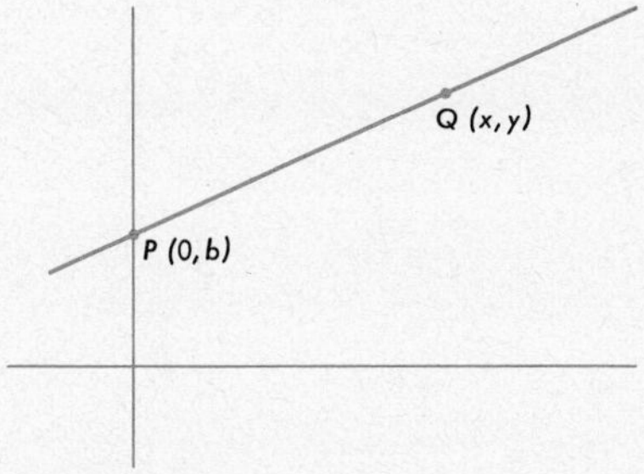

FIGURE 6.11

By solving Eq. (5) for y, we obtain

$$mx = y - b$$

or

$$y = mx + b \tag{6}$$

where m = slope

b = y intercept

The y intercept is the value of y when x = 0. Similarly, the x *intercept* is the value of x when y = 0.

Equation (6) is called the *slope-intercept form* of a linear equation because both the slope and the y intercept are explicitly evident.

The slope m is the coefficient of the independent variable x, and the y intercept is the constant term b. Equation (6) is the most widely used of the various straight-line equations.

Knowing the y intercept and the slope of the line enables us to visualize the line at once.

6.9 Graphical Evaluation of m and b

We can find the equation for the line segment $\overline{AB}$ in Fig. 6.12 directly from the graph.

By inspection we would select two arbitrary points on the line, such as $C(4,2)$ and $D(16,-1)$. It can be seen that

$$m = \frac{-1 - 2}{16 - 4} = -\frac{1}{4}$$

If the line is extended to cut the y axis, we read the y intercept = 3. Therefore the equation is $y = -\frac{1}{4}x + 3$. (Does the x intercept confirm this equation?)

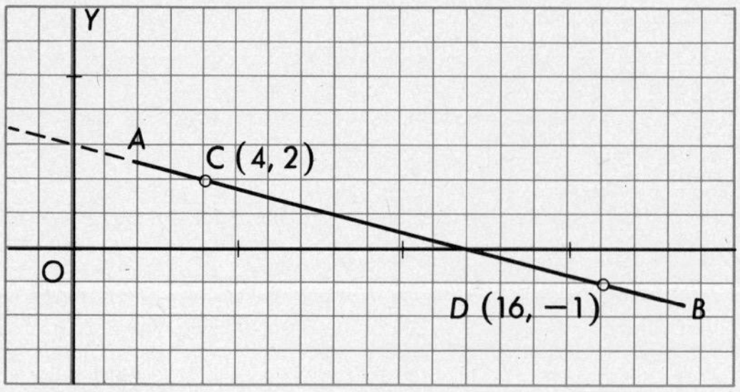

FIGURE 6.12

EXERCISE 7

Determine the equation for each line in Fig. 6.13 in the form $y = mx + b$. Where possible, confirm your answer by determining the x intercept by inspection.

1. Line A 2. Line B 3. Line C 4. Line D
5. Line E 6. Line F 7. Line G

Note: Try to devise your own method of solving Probs. 6 and 7.

6.10 Algebraic Evaluation of m and b

The slope-intercept form of a linear equation is probably the most generally useful form for our purpose. However, there are other forms, and we shall mention two of them briefly.

For example, consider the linear equation

$$y = -\tfrac{2}{3}x + 18 \qquad (7)$$

By multiplying both members of Eq. (7) by 3, we obtain

$$3y = -2x + 54$$

Then we may write

$$2x + 3y = 54 \qquad (8)$$

which is a form equivalent to Eq. (7). Note that all coefficients and constants are integers having no common factor. This type equation is often referred to as the integral form. By dividing Eq. (8) by 54, we obtain the *intercept form*

$$\frac{x}{27} + \frac{y}{18} = 1 \qquad (9)$$

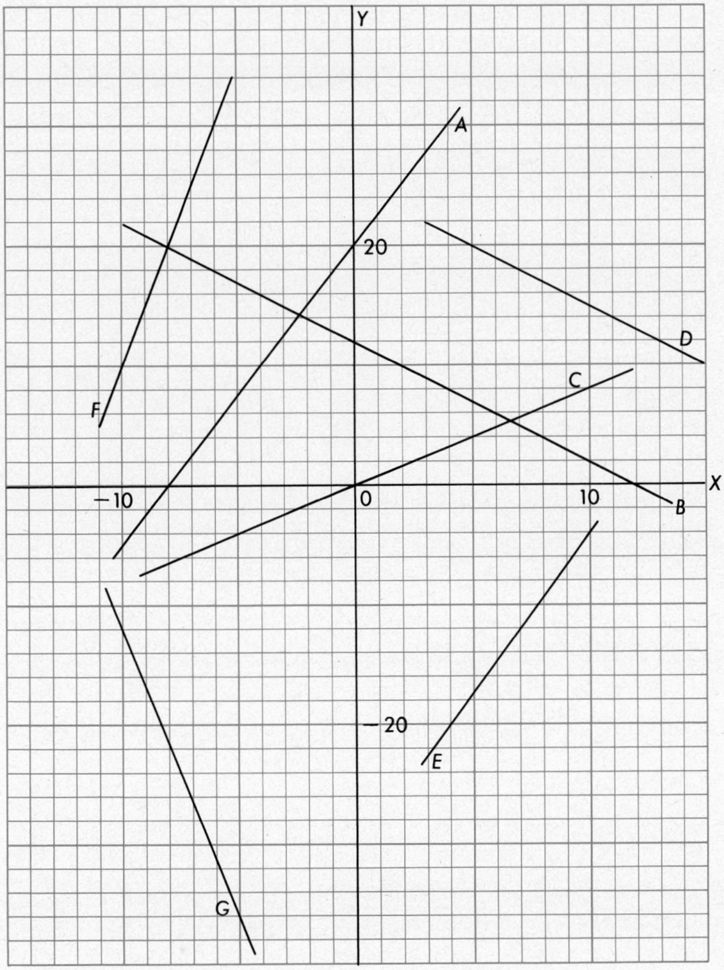

FIGURE 6.13

which is still another form equivalent to the slope-intercept form shown as Eq. (7).

When satisfactory graphical data are not available (as in Sec. 6.9), we apply algebraic methods of evaluating m and b.

Example 9. Find the equation of the straight line having a slope of $\frac{2}{3}$ and passing through point (4,5).

By substituting $\frac{2}{3}$, which is the given slope, in Eq. (6), we have

$$y = \tfrac{2}{3}x + b$$

We also know from the data given in the statement of the problem that when $x = 4$, $y = 5$. Thus we may write

$$5 = \tfrac{2}{3} \cdot 4 + b$$

Solving for b, we obtain

$$5 = \tfrac{8}{3} + b$$

or

$$b = 5 - \frac{8}{3} = \frac{15 - 8}{3} = \frac{7}{3}$$

and

$$y = \tfrac{2}{3}x + \tfrac{7}{3}$$

which is the equation of the straight line having a slope of $\tfrac{2}{3}$ and passing through the point (4,5).

Example 10. Find the slope and y intercept of the line whose equation is

$$3x + 2y = 8$$

Solving the equation for y, we obtain

$$y = -\tfrac{3}{2}x + 4$$

Hence the line has a slope of $-\tfrac{3}{2}$ and a y intercept of 4.

A common example of the slope-intercept form occurs in the equation $l_1 = kW + l$, which states that in a spring balance the length of the relaxed spring is extended by k length units per W units of weight applied, producing a length l_1 under tension.

If the student has any doubt that the graph of $y = mx + b$ is a straight line, he may be reassured by noting the similarity to a flight of stairs. If we tabulate a series of values as in plotting a graph, we obtain the following table:

Δx		1	1	1	1	1	
x	0	1	2	3	4	5	. . .
y	b	$m + b$	$2m + b$	$3m + b$	$4m + b$	$5m + b$	. . .
Δy		m	m	m	m	m	

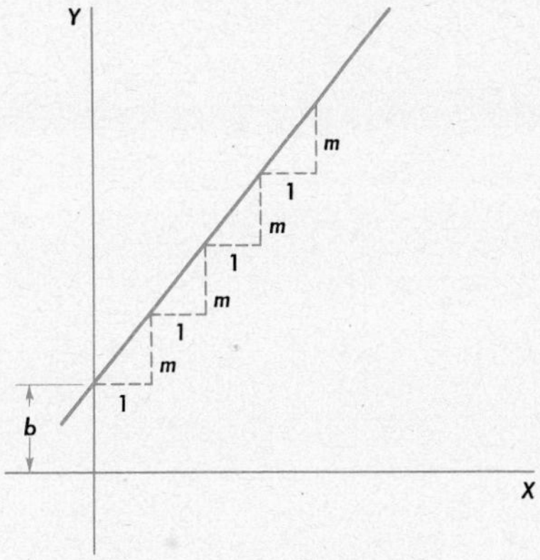

FIGURE 6.14

The change in x from point to point has been represented by Δx. The change in y from point to point has been represented by Δy.

It will be noted that when x increases uniformly in steps of 1, y also increases uniformly, but in steps of m. The ratio of vertical progress to horizontal progress is therefore uniform, and the slope is everywhere equal to m. Referring to Fig. 6.14, we may draw an analogy to a flight of steps, each tread being equal to 1, and each riser equal to m.

Example 11. Find the equation of the straight line passing through the points (−2,3) and (6,9).

From Eq. (2) the slope m is given by

$$m = \frac{9-3}{6-(-2)} = \frac{9-3}{6+2} = \frac{6}{8} = 0.75$$

From Eq. (6) we may now write

$$y = 0.75x + b$$

From the given conditions of the problem we know that when $x = 6$, then $y = 9$. Substituting these values in the above equation, we obtain

$$9 = 0.75 \times 6 + b$$

or

$$b = 9 - 0.75 \times 6 = 9 - 4.5 = 4.5$$

Then

$$y = 0.75x + 4.5$$

We could also have used the point $(-2,3)$. Then we would have written

$$3 = 0.75 \times (-2) + b = -1.5 + b$$

and

$$b = 3 + 1.5 = 4.5$$

Alternatively we could have used Eq. (6) to set up the simultaneous equations

$$3 = (m)(-2) + b$$

and

$$9 = (m)(6) + b$$

solving for m and b by the methods of Sec. 7.3.

Example 12. Find the equation of the line having an x intercept of -4 and a y intercept of 10.

The coordinates of the x intercept are $(-4,0)$. The coordinates of the y intercept are $(0,10)$. Therefore, from Eq. (2), the slope m is given by

$$m = \frac{10 - 0}{0 - (-4)} = \frac{10}{4} = +2.5$$

From Eq. (6) we may write

$$y = 2.5 \cdot x + b$$

The y intercept b is given directly. Thus

$$y = 2.5x + 10$$

Example 13. Find the intercepts of the straight line whose equation is $3x - 4y = 12$.

Since the y intercept is the value of y when $x = 0$ and the x intercept is the value of x when $y = 0$, we may solve for these intercepts by replacing x and y in turn by zero.

When $x = 0$: $-4y = 12$ or $y = -3$ (y intercept)
When $y = 0$: $3x = 12$ or $x = 4$ (x intercept)

6.11 Lines Parallel to the Axes

If a line is parallel to the X axis, its slope m is equal to zero, for by Eq. (1), $m = (y_2 - y_1)/(x_2 - x_1)$, or $m = 0/(x_2 - x_1) = 0$ (since $y_2 = y_1$). Substituting $m = 0$ in $y = mx + b$, we obtain $y = b$. This is reasonable, for it indicates that everywhere on the line the ordinate is b. Hence the line is parallel to the X axis and b units above it or below it, according to the sign of b.

Since a line parallel to the Y axis is vertical, it has no finite slope, and the form $y = mx + b$ does not apply, for $x_2 = x_1$ and by Eq. (1), $m = (y_2 - y_1)/(x_2 - x_1)$, or $m = (y_2 - y_1)/0$; since division by zero is undefined, m is undefined. Moreover, it should be clear that a vertical line a units to the right or left of the Y axis must have the equation $x = a$, where a may be either positive or negative.

It follows that every line constituting the grid of a sheet of graph paper has a unique equation (e.g., each horizontal line and each vertical line in Fig. 6.13 is represented by its own distinct equation).

6.12 Lines Passing through the Origin

If the line $y = mx + b$ passes through the origin, the y intercept b must equal zero, and the equation cannot have a constant term.

Example 14. Show that the line passing through the points (12,8) and (9,6) also passes through the origin.

From Eq. (2) the slope m is given by

$$m = \frac{6 - 8}{9 - 12} = \frac{-2}{-3} = \frac{2}{3}$$

and the equation for this straight line can be written

$$y = \tfrac{2}{3}x + b$$

However, when $x = 12$, $y = 8$, and by substituting these values in the above equation, we find

$$8 = \tfrac{2}{3}(12) + b$$

or

$$8 = 8 + b$$

and $b = 0$.

Thus the y intercept is 0, and the graph therefore does pass through the origin, and the equation is

$$y = \frac{2}{3}x$$

EXERCISE 8

Write the equations for lines passing through the given point P and having the slope indicated. (See Fig. 6.15, where $\angle A$ is given in degrees. See also Sec. 6.6.)

In Probs. 5 to 8, assume equal x and y scale moduli.

1. $P(4,6)$; $m = \frac{1}{2}$
2. $P(-2,3)$; $m = 1$
3. $P(5,-1)$; $m = 2$
4. $P(-3,-2)$; $m = -\frac{2}{3}$
5. $P(3,7)$; $\angle A = 45°$
6. $P(-3,6)$; $\angle A = 30°$
7. $P(2,-5)$; $\angle A = 60°$
8. $P(0,0)$; $\angle A = 135°$
9. $P(2,7)$; horizontal
10. $P(4,-3)$; vertical

Convert each of the following equations to the slope-intercept form $y = mx + b$, finding the slope and y intercept in each case.

11. $x + y = 8$
12. $2x - y = 6$
13. $x - 3y = 12$
14. $2x + 3y = 6$
15. $4y - x = 10$
16. $3x - 4y - 6 = 0$
17. $7x - 5y + 14 = 0$
18. $\frac{1}{2}x - \frac{1}{3}y = 1$
19. $4y = 6$
20. $3x = 2y$
21. $3y + 2x = 0$

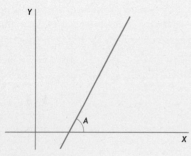

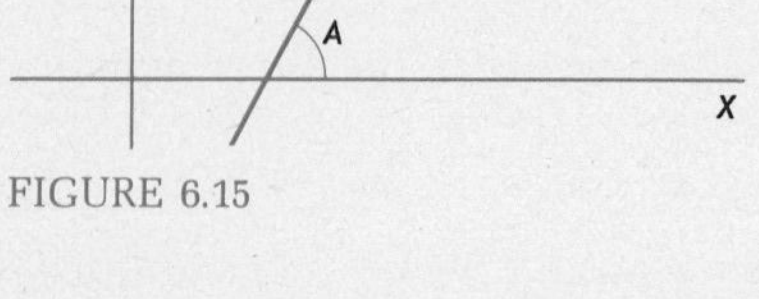

FIGURE 6.15

Find the equation of the line passing through each of the following given pairs of points, leaving the answer in the form $Ax + By = C$, where A, B, and C are integers containing no common factor.

22. (3,1), (5,3)
23. (3,2), (6,3)
24. (1,−1), (3,3)
25. (2,−4), (−6,2)
26. (0,0), (−4,−6)
27. (3,0), (−5,2)
28. (6,3), (−4,−2)
29. (−2,5), (4,5)

Find the equations of the lines having the following given intercepts:

30. x intercept: 3; y intercept: −6
31. x intercept: −4; y intercept: 2
32. x intercept: 10; y intercept: 4
33. x intercept: −9; y intercept: −6
34. x intercept: 6; y intercept: −10
35. x intercept: −8; y intercept: 6
36. x intercept: 8; y intercept: 14
37. x intercept: −15; y intercept: −10
38. Problem 23, page 77, is repeated below. Express the current and proposed schedules in the form $y = mx + b$.

A utility company petitioned to change its rate on electrical energy from a straight $5\frac{1}{2}$ cents/kWh to $4\frac{1}{4}$ cents/kWh plus 75 cents/month service charge. What monthly cost would be unaffected by the change in rate?

6.13 Parallel Lines

If two lines are parallel, their slopes are equal.

The comparison is most conveniently made by reducing both equations to the slope-intercept form, $y = mx + b$ [Eq. (6)].

6.14 Perpendicular Lines

In Fig. 6.16 let AC and CD be two perpendicular lines, where $C(b,c)$ is their common point and $A(a,0)$ and $D(d,0)$ are their x intercepts. Let $B(b,0)$ be the foot of the perpendicular CB drawn from C to AD.

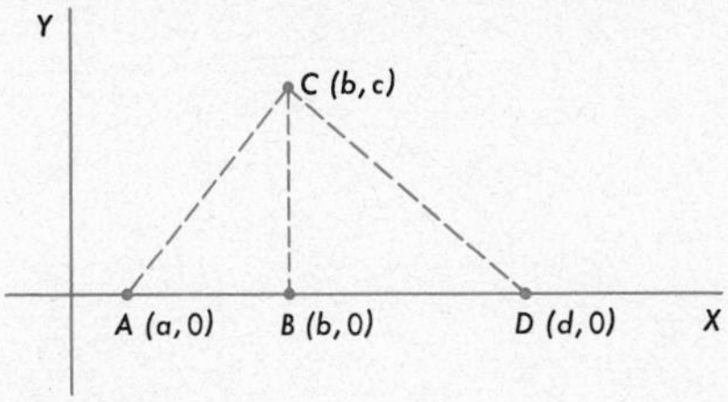

FIGURE 6.16

Since the triangles ABC and BCD in Fig. 6.16 are similar (why?), we may write

$$\frac{\overline{CB}}{\overline{BD}} = \frac{\overline{AB}}{\overline{CB}}$$

or

$$\overline{CB}^2 = \overline{AB} \cdot \overline{BD}$$

Expressed in terms of the coordinates, this relationship becomes

$$c^2 = (b - a)(d - b) \tag{10}$$

The slope m_1 of AC is $(c - 0)/(b - a)$, or

$$m_1 = \frac{c}{b - a}$$

The slope m_2 of CD is $(c - 0)/(b - d)$, or

$$m_2 = \frac{c}{b - d}$$

Multiplying the values of the two slopes together, we obtain

$$m_1 m_2 = \frac{c^2}{(b - a)(b - d)} = -\frac{c^2}{(b - a)(d - b)}$$

Since from Eq. (10)

$$c^2 = (b - a)(d - b)$$

we may write

$$m_1 m_2 = -\frac{c^2}{c^2} = -1$$

or

$$m_1 = -\frac{1}{m_2} \tag{11}$$

Hence *the slopes of perpendicular lines are negative reciprocals.*

6.15 The Midpoint Formula

In Fig. 6.17 the point Q is midway between points P and R and lies on the line segment $\overline{PR}$. Thus

$$\overline{PQ} = \overline{QR}$$

Since the triangles PQa and QRb are congruent (Fact 9, Chap. 5), we may write

$$x_2 - x_1 = x_3 - x_2$$

Then

$$2x_2 = x_3 + x_1$$

or

$$\text{Abscissa of midpoint} = x_2 = (1/2)(x_3 + x_1) \tag{12}$$

The student should verify the fact that

$$\text{Ordinate of midpoint} = y_2 = (1/2)(y_3 + y_1) \tag{13}$$

It is intuitively evident that x_2 must be the arithmetic average of x_1 and x_3 and that y_2 must be the average of y_1 and y_3.

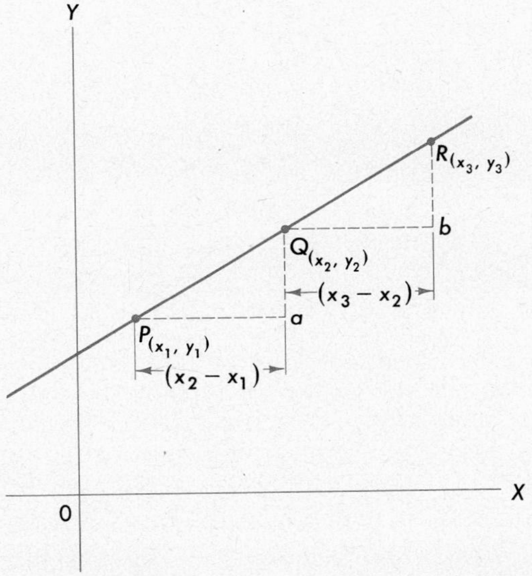

FIGURE 6.17

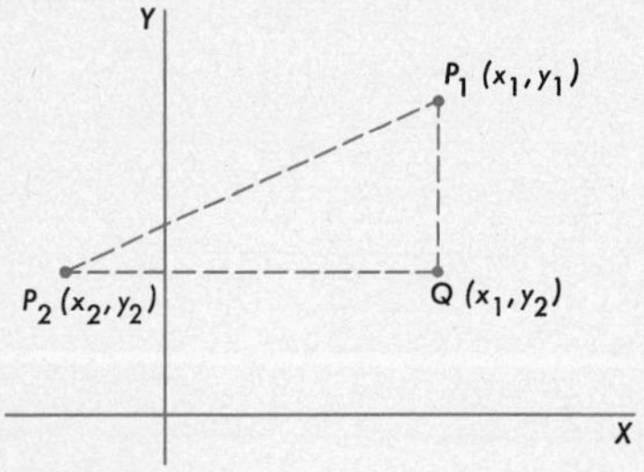

FIGURE 6.18

6.16 Distance between Two Points

Given the points $P_1(x_1,y_1)$ and $P_2(x_2,y_2)$ in Fig. 6.18, locate the point $Q(x_1,y_2)$ and draw lines $\overline{P_1P_2}$, $\overline{P_1Q}$, and $\overline{P_2Q}$. Then in right triangle P_1P_2Q,

$$\overline{P_1P_2}^2 = \overline{P_1Q}^2 + \overline{P_2Q}^2$$

In terms of the coordinates, this becomes

$$\overline{P_1P_2}^2 = (y_1 - y_2)^2 + (x_1 - x_2)^2$$

The distance between P_1 and P_2 is then

$$\overline{P_1P_2} = \sqrt{(y_1 - y_2)^2 + (x_1 - x_2)^2} \qquad \textbf{(14)}$$

This rule is valid regardless of the quadrants in which P_1 and P_2 are located, provided only that due regard is paid to signs when evaluating $y_1 - y_2$ and $x_1 - x_2$.

In short, we find the absolute values of $\overline{P_1Q}$ and $\overline{P_2Q}$ and determine the hypotenuse $\overline{P_2P_1}$ of the triangle in the usual way.

Obviously, in cases where $y_1 = y_2$ or $x_1 = x_2$, we have a horizontal line or a vertical line, respectively, and the answer follows by inspection.

EXERCISE 9

1. Given the equation $3x - 4y = 24$, corresponding to the general equation $Ax + By = C$, modify only one quantity at a time (A, B, or C) to make the line (*a*) pass through the origin; (*b*) vertical; (*c*) horizontal; (*d*) parallel to $6x - y = 11$; and (*e*) perpendicular to $8x - 12y = 13$.
2. Given the equation $5x + 8y = 20$, proceed as in Prob. 1 to make the line (*a*) pass through the origin; (*b*) vertical; (*c*) horizontal; (*d*) parallel to $15x - 10y = 23$; and (*e*) perpendicular to $4x - 15y = 17$.

Find the distance between P_1 and P_2 in Probs. 3 to 10.

3. $P_1(2,5)$; $P_2(2,11)$
4. $P_1(3,-4)$; $P_2(3,3)$
5. $P_1(-4,7)$; $P_2(5,7)$
6. $P_1(6,1)$; $P_2(0,9)$
7. $P_1(1,5)$; $P_2(4,9)$
8. $P_1(-2,6)$; $P_2(3,9)$
9. $P_1(8,-4)$; $P_2(-1,-6)$
10. $P_1(7,-8)$; $P_2(3,-5)$

11. Find the coordinates of the point midway between the given points. (*a*) (2,7) and (8,3); (*b*) (−6,5) and (9,−5)
12. Without plotting, determine what kind of figure is enclosed by the lines $x + y = -3$, $x - y = 3$, and $y = 3$.
13. What points on the line $2x + 3y = 6$ are equidistant from the axes?
14. Write the equation for the line passing through the origin and perpendicular to the line $y = \frac{3}{2}x - 4$.
15. Write the equation for the line parallel to the line $2x + 3y = 9$ and having its x intercept = 7.
16. Find the distance between the lines $y = 2x + 3$ and $y = 2x + 8$.
17. Given points $A(2,7)$ and $B(14,3)$, what is the equation for the perpendicular bisector of the line segment AB?
18. Find the distance from the point (6,7) to the line $3x + 4y = 30$.
19. A tangent is drawn to the circle $x^2 + y^2 = 40$ at point (6,2) (Fig. 6.19). The slope

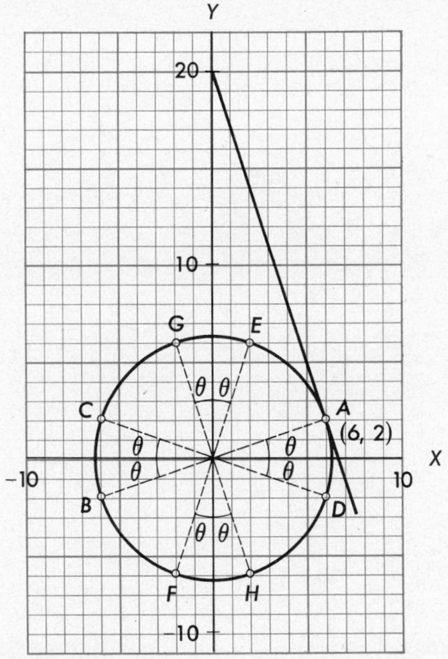

FIGURE 6.19

of the tangent is -3. (Why?) Show that the equation of the tangent is

$$y = -3x + 20$$

Using the properties of symmetry, rather than developing independent solutions, determine the equations of lines tangent at the points indicated.

20. Locate the point on the Y axis which is equidistant from the points $(-4,3)$ and $(8,11)$.

6.17 Area of a Triangle

The area of the triangle *PQR* (Fig. 6.20) is evidently equal to the area of the triangle *PQM* plus the area of the trapezoid *MQRN* minus the area of the triangle *PRN*.

In terms of the coordinates we have

$$\text{Area of } PQM = \tfrac{1}{2}(x_3 - x_1)(y_3 - y_1)$$

$$\text{Area of } MQRN = \tfrac{1}{2}(x_2 - x_3)[(y_2 - y_1) + (y_3 - y_1)]$$

$$\text{Area of } PRN = \tfrac{1}{2}(x_2 - x_1)(y_2 - y_1)$$

(The order of points must be counterclockwise.) Therefore

$$\begin{aligned}\text{Area of } PRQ &= PQM + MQRN - PRN \\ &= \tfrac{1}{2}(x_3 - x_1)(y_3 - y_1) + \tfrac{1}{2}(x_2 - x_3)[(y_2 - y_1) + (y_3 - y_1)] \\ &\qquad - \tfrac{1}{2}(x_2 - x_1)(y_2 - y_1) \\ &= \tfrac{1}{2}(x_3y_3 - x_1y_3 - x_3y_1 + x_1y_1 + x_2y_2 - x_3y_2 - 2x_2y_1 \\ &\qquad + 2x_3y_1 + x_2y_3 - x_3y_3 - x_2y_2 + x_1y_2 + x_2y_1 - x_1y_1) \\ &= \tfrac{1}{2}(-x_1y_3 - x_3y_2 - x_2y_1 + x_3y_1 + x_2y_3 + x_1y_2) \\ &= \tfrac{1}{2}[x_1(y_2 - y_3) + x_2(y_3 - y_1) + x_3(y_1 - y_2)] \qquad \textbf{(15)}\end{aligned}$$

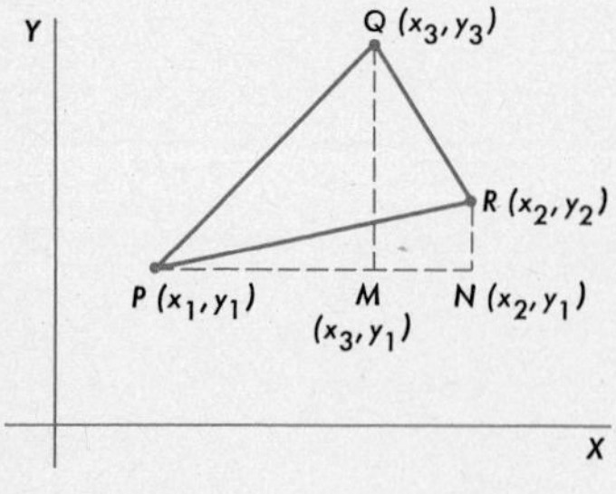

FIGURE 6.20

If any of the vertices lie outside the first quadrant, proper attention must be paid to signs.

Example 15. Find the area of the triangle in Fig. 6.21.

From the figure we write

$x_1 = -3 \qquad y_1 = -5 \qquad x_2 = 17 \qquad y_2 = 2 \qquad x_3 = 3 \qquad y_3 = 8$

Substituting in Eq. (15),

$$\begin{aligned}\text{Area of } \Delta PQR &= \tfrac{1}{2}\{(-3)(2-8) + 17[8-(-5)] + 3(-5-2)\}\\ &= \tfrac{1}{2}(18 + 221 - 21)\\ &= 109\end{aligned}$$

A simple method of computing the area of the triangle in Example 15 without memorizing a formula consists of enclosing the triangle in a rectangle and subtracting from the area of the rectangle the combined area of the three smaller right triangles that are formed. From Fig. 6.21 the dimensions may be shown as in Fig. 6.22.

$$\begin{aligned}\text{Area of triangle I} &= \text{area of rectangle} - (\text{area of triangles II + III + IV})\\ &= (13)(20) - \tfrac{1}{2}[(6)(13) + (14)(6) + (7)(20)]\\ &= 260 - \tfrac{1}{2}(302)\\ &= 109\end{aligned}$$

The area of a polygon of n sides may be found in like manner by first dividing by diagonals into $n - 2$ triangles.

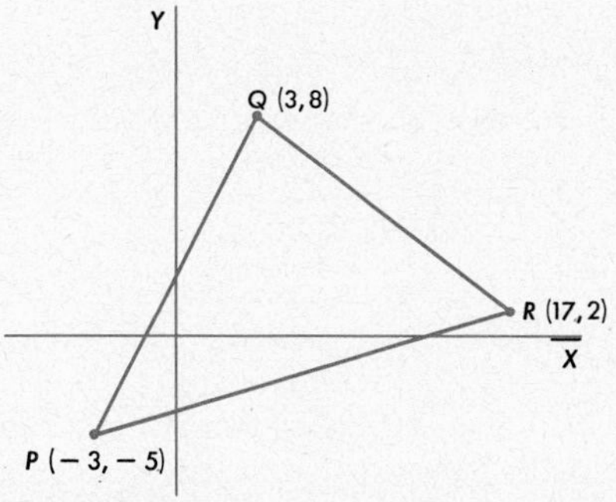

FIGURE 6.21

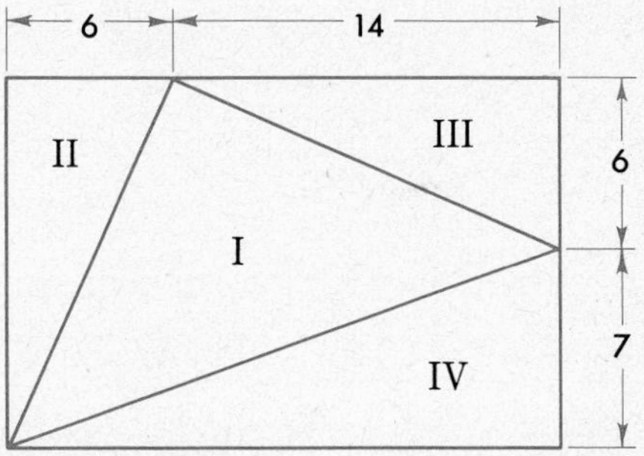

FIGURE 6.22

EXERCISE 10

Find the area of the triangles represented by the following vertices:

1. (0,0), (0,8), (12,0)
2. (−2,−5), (−4,4), (7,1)
3. (−5,−3), (2,3), (9,−7)
4. (−5,6), (3,8), (4,−4)
5. (−5,0), (0,7), (8,−4)
6. (1,4), (10,5), (3,−4)
7. Prove that the triangle in Prob. 5 is isosceles.

Find the areas of the polygons formed by joining the following points in the order given:

8. (−2,2), (2,6), (8,3), (5,−3)
9. (0,−4), (3,4), (12,0), (10,−3)
10. (−3,−1), (0,8), (12,4), (9,−5)
11. (−2,−4), (−3,3), (4,6), (7,2), (4,−3)
12. Prove that the figure in Prob. 10 is a rectangle.

6.18 Area under a Straight-line Graph

The phrase "area under a graph" refers to the area between the graph and the X axis (see Figs. 6.23 and 6.24).

The region C in Fig. 6.23 is the area under the graph between $x = +15$ and $x = +35$. The region D in Fig. 6.24 is the area "under" the graph between $x = +2.5$ and $x = +10$. The region E in Fig. 6.25 is the area "under" the graph between $x = +5$ and $x = +20$.

In the case of a straight line (and in this case only), the area under the graph is either a triangle, a trapezoid, or a rectangle.

In Fig. 6.23

$$A_C = \frac{y_2 + y_1}{2}(x_2 - x_1) \tag{16}$$

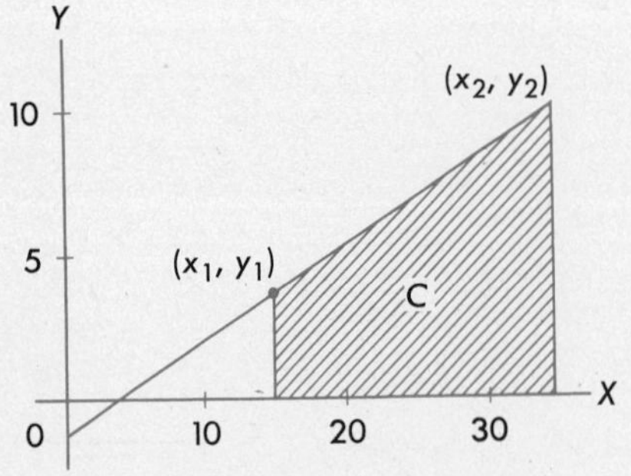

FIGURE 6.23

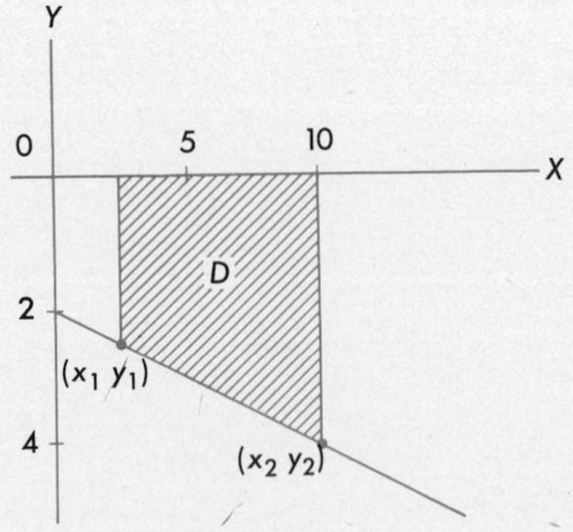

FIGURE 6.24

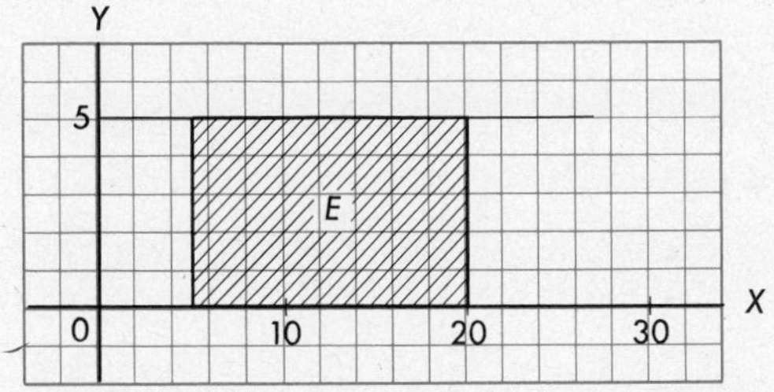

FIGURE 6.25

In Fig. 6.24 the area under the graph is also

$$A_D = \frac{y_2 + y_1}{2}(x_2 - x_1) \tag{17}$$

(See Fact 48, page 114.) By reading the graph,

$$A_C = \frac{10.0 + 3.5}{2}(35 - 15) = 135.0$$

It is important to observe that we use the scale of the graph in calculating the area:

$$A_D = \frac{-4 + (-2.5)}{2}(10.0 - 2.5) = -24.375$$

In this case the signs of the ordinates lead to a negative area. In the case of a practical problem, the negative sign attached to the area may or may not be significant. We shall retain such negative signs, at least for the present.

The quantity $(y_1 + y_2)/2$ is the arithmetic mean (or average) of y_1 and y_2. The symbol $\bar{y}$ is adopted to mean "average y." It is read "bar y" or "average y" or "mean ordinate." In general

$$\bar{y} = \frac{y_2 + y_1}{2} \tag{18}$$

and

$$A = \bar{y}(x_2 - x_1) \tag{19}$$

where A = area under graph between ordinates erected at x_2 and x_1
$\bar{y}$ = mean ordinate between x_2 and x_1

If we define the quantity $x_2 - x_1$ as the *base* of the area, we can define mean ordinate as "that ordinate which, multiplied by the base, equals the area under the graph."

Dimensionally, the area under the graph is the product of the dimension of the mean ordinate and the dimension of the abscissa.

If the dimension of the mean ordinate is *force* and the dimension of the abscissa is *distance*, then the dimension of the area under the graph is

$$\text{Force} \times \text{distance} = \text{work}$$

provided the force is in the direction of motion.

If the dimension of the mean ordinate is *speed* and the dimension of the abscissa is *time*, then the dimension of the area under the graph is

$$\text{Speed} \times \text{time} = \text{distance}$$

If the dimension of the mean ordinate is *area* and the dimension of the abscissa is *length*, then the dimension of the area under the graph is

$$\text{Area} \times \text{length} = \text{volume}$$

For example, let us consider a coiled spring elongated by a variable force F.

Let the elongation caused by the force be e. We shall let F be measured in pounds and e in inches. A graph of the elongation related to F is shown in Fig. 6.26. Actually F is the independent variable, and e is the dependent variable. Nevertheless, it will be more convenient to plot F vertically and e horizontally.

The slope of this line is

$$m = \frac{35 - 0}{40 - 0} = 0.875 \frac{\text{lb}}{\text{in}}$$

It follows that the equation for this line is $F = 0.875e$ (Sec. 6.12).

Example 16. Find the work done in elongating the spring from 30 to 40 in (see Fig. 6.26).

The force exerted for a 30-in elongation is read from the graph to be 26.25 lb. The force exerted for a 40-in elongation is read from the graph to be 35 lb. The *average* force is

$$\bar{F} = \frac{35 + 26.25}{2} = \frac{61.25}{2} = 30.625 \text{ lb}$$

Note that more simply $\bar{F}$ = the ordinate at $(e_1 + e_2)/2$ (at $e = 35$).

$$\text{Work} = 30.625 \times 10 = 306.25 \text{ in-lb}$$

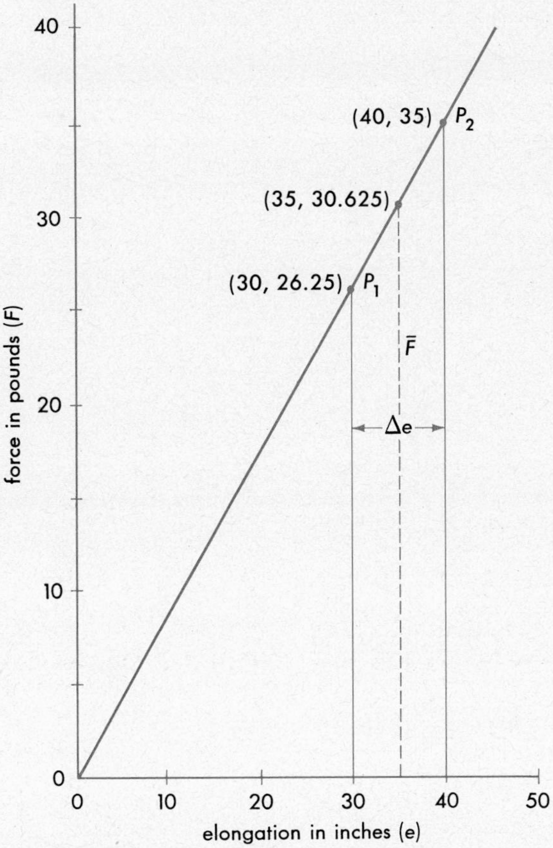

FIGURE 6.26

This is precisely the area under the quadrilateral $P_2P_1(30,0)$ $(40,0)$ in terms of the scale of the graph (see Fig. 6.26).

Suppose we are required to plot a curve of the work done to reach any elongation between 0 and 40 in (see Fig. 6.27). We can proceed as follows.

By direct reading of the graph in Fig. 6.26, we find that the average force between $e = 0$ and $e = 10$ is

$\bar{F}_{0\text{-}10} = 4.38$ lb $\qquad$ ($\bar{F}$ = force at $e = 5$)

It might be argued that we cannot read F this closely, but knowing that $F = 0.875e$, it follows that $\bar{F} = 0.875(5) = 4.38$ lb.

The elongation over this interval is 10 in. The work done over this interval is therefore

$$W_{0\text{-}10} = 4.38 \times 10 = 43.8 \text{ in-lb}$$

Similarly, by direct reading of the graph, we find that the average force between $e = 0$ and $e = 20$ is

$$\bar{F}_{0\text{-}20} = 8.75 \text{ lb} \qquad (\bar{F} = \text{force at } e = 10)$$

The elongation over this interval is 20 in. The work done in this interval is therefore

$$W_{0\text{-}20} = 8.75 \times 20 = 175 \text{ in-lb}$$

In the same way additional data could be calculated for plotting the work versus elongation graph shown in Fig. 6.27.

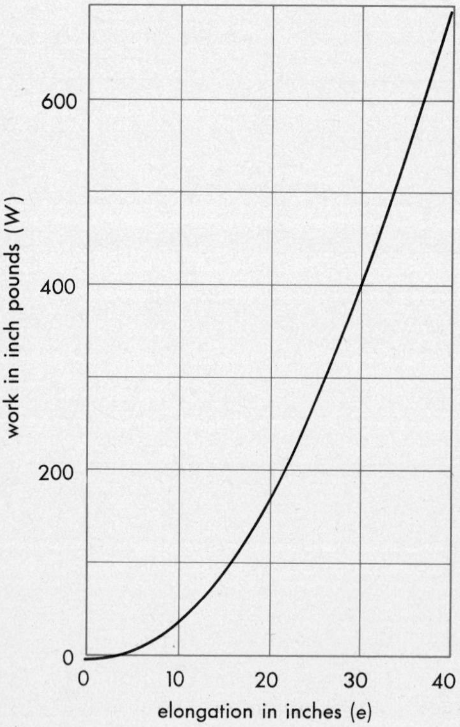

FIGURE 6.27

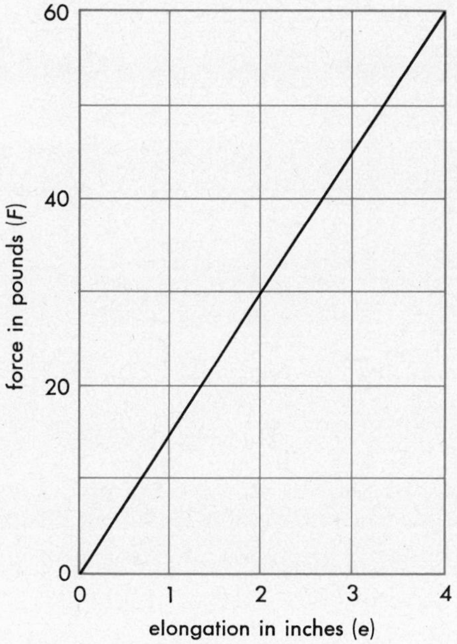

FIGURE 6.28

EXERCISE 11

The relation between the force and the corresponding elongation of a spring is illustrated by Fig. 6.28.

1. (*a*) Find the average force over the interval between $e = 1$ and $e = 3$.
   (*b*) Find the work done in elongating the spring over this interval.
2. Plot a curve of work done versus elongation between $e = 0$ in and $e = 4$ in.
3. The pressure on a certain piston is related to the volume between the piston and cylinder head by the equation

   $$p = 900V + 3{,}000 \text{ lb/ft}^2$$

   The work done in compressing the volume from 1 to 0.5 ft^3 is equal to the area between the given curve, the V axis, from $V = 0.5$ to $V = 1$. Determine this area.
4. The specific heat of mercury c at a temperature of T°C is given by $c = 0.03346 - 0.000{,}009{,}2T$ cal per degree Celsius (at constant pressure). Sketch and determine the area between the straight line, the horizontal T axis, and $T = 0°$ to $T = 50°$. This area is equivalent to the heat required to raise the temperature of 1 g of mercury from 0 to 50°C.

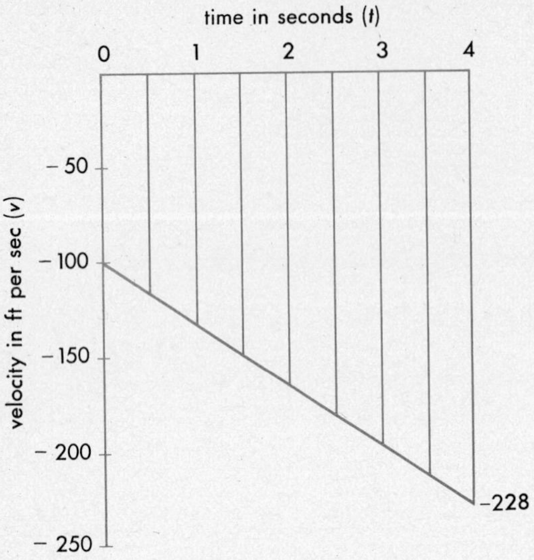

FIGURE 6.29

6.19 Calculation of Distance from a Speed-Time Graph

If we have given a graph of the speed versus time for a moving object, we can calculate the distance covered in a way exactly analogous to the calculation of work from a force-distance plot (see Sec. 6.18).

Figure 6.29 shows the graph of speed for a freely falling body with an initial downward velocity of 100 ft/s.

The area between the graph and the t axis is proportional to the distance covered.

It will be noted that this area carries a negative sign. The reason is that velocities in a downward direction are conventionally negative.

The area under this graph is the product of a negative velocity and a positive time interval. This product is a negative distance (see Fig. 6.24 and Sec. 6.18).

EXERCISE 12

1. Find the distance the object falls for each strip in Fig. 6.29.
2. Plot the distance the object falls versus time.
3. Plot a curve of altitude versus time. The object was thrown downward from a height of 600 ft.
4. When does the object hit the ground?

7 simultaneous linear equations

In this chapter we shall develop methods (including determinants) for the solution of simultaneous linear equations. These principles will be applied to the solution of "word" problems. This entails a translation from the English language to the language of algebra, and is often quite frustrating to the student.

An effective aid in this process is the use of freehand, dimensioned graphs in the setting up of algebraic equations.

7.1 Graphical Solution of a System of Two Equations

If in a system of two or more equations, all the equations have a common solution, they are called *simultaneous equations.* A solution of two simultaneous equations in two variables, x and y, is a pair of corresponding values of x and y which simultaneously satisfies both equations.

Example 1. Solve graphically

$$x + y = 1 \qquad (1)$$
$$x - 2y = 7 \qquad (2)$$

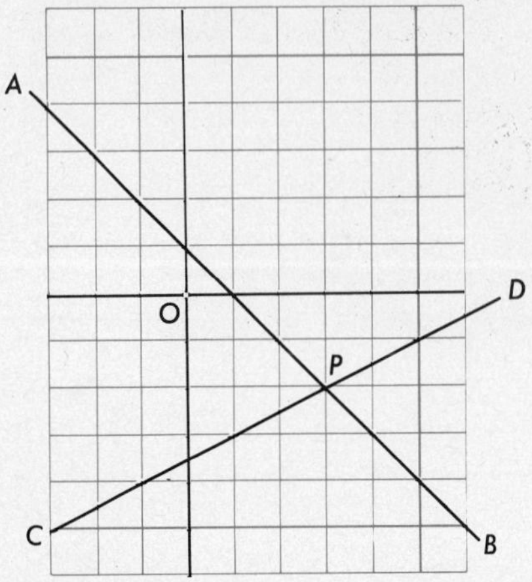

FIGURE 7.1

In Fig. 7.1, AB is the graph of Eq. (1) and CD is the graph of Eq. (2). All points of AB have coordinates satisfying Eq. (1), and all points on CD have coordinates satisfying Eq. (2); therefore the intersection point P has coordinates satisfying the two equations *simultaneously*. Since two straight lines can intersect in but one point, P is the only point having the property of a common solution. In this example the coordinates of P are $(3, -2)$; therefore $(x = 3, y = -2)$ is the only solution of this system of equations.

If the graphs of the equations are parallel lines, there is no solution and the equations are termed *inconsistent*.

Example 2. We are given the system of equations

$$3x - 5y = 6 \tag{3}$$
$$6x - 10y = 10 \tag{4}$$

The graphs of these two equations are parallel lines (Fig. 7.2), each having a slope of $3/5$; since the lines cannot intersect, the equations have no common solution. This

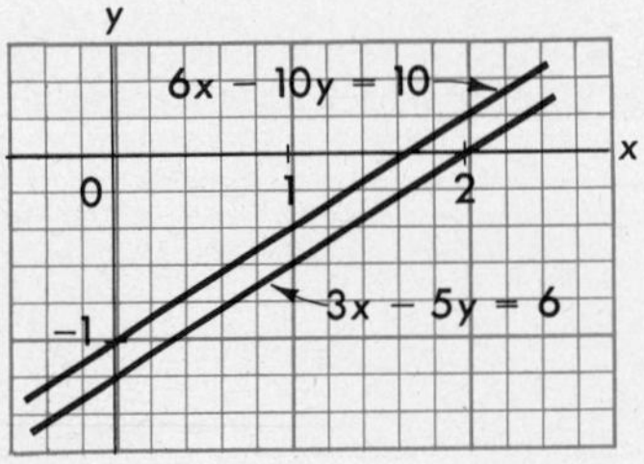

FIGURE 7.2

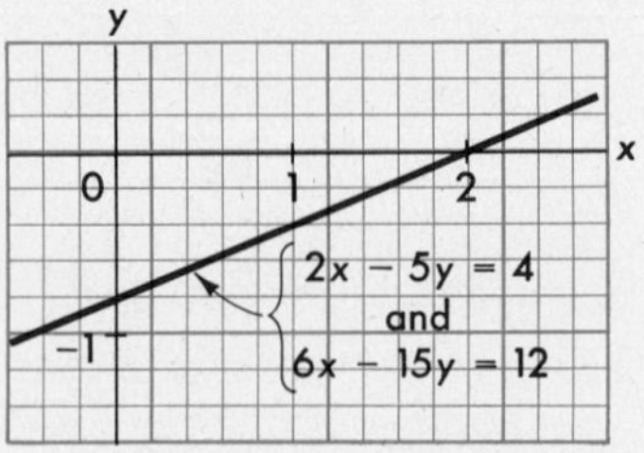

FIGURE 7.3

conclusion might have been reached without plotting since, on dividing Eq. (4) by 2, we have $3x - 5y = 5$. Since the expression $3x - 5y$ cannot, at the same time, be equal to 6 and to 5, there are no values of x and y satisfying both equations simultaneously.

If the graphs of the two equations are the same line, any solution of one equation is also a solution of the other, and the system has an unlimited number of solutions. Such equations are known as *dependent,* or equivalent, equations.

Example 3. Given the system

$$2x - 5y = 4 \tag{5}$$
$$6x - 15y = 12 \tag{6}$$

solve for x and y (see Fig. 7.3).

Since Eq. (6) is reducible to Eq. (5) by division by 3, the equations are not independent but are equivalent.

It will be appreciated that graphical solutions are only approximate; when we have to estimate fractional scale divisions, the approximation is rougher.

EXERCISE 1

In the following problems determine, by inspection if possible, whether each pair of equations is inconsistent or dependent or possesses one common solution. In the last case solve graphically, estimating fractional answers to the nearest 0.1. It is suggested that the x and y intercepts and one or two other well-spaced points be used in the plotting.

1. $x + y = 8$, $x - y = 2$
2. $x + y = -4$, $x - y = 8$
3. $2x - y = 3$, $2x - 3y = 11$
4. $3x - y = 4$, $2y - 6x = -8$
5. $2x + 5y = 8$, $3x - 2y = -7$
6. $4x - 6y = 8$, $6x - 9y = 14$
7. $2x = 7y$, $6x - 5y = 16$
8. $3x + 2y = 12$, $3y - 2x = 4$
9. $4x - 3y = 10$, $6y - 8x = -20$
10. $5x - 8y = 0$, $7y - 4x = 3$
11. $2x - y = 5$, $x + y = 2$
12. $8x - 12y = 10$, $18y - 12x = 15$
13. $12x + 5y = 0$, $8x - 10y = 8$
14. $2x - 7y + 9 = 0$, $5x + 3y - 6 = 0$

7.2 Algebraic Methods of Solution

Algebraic methods of solving systems of simultaneous equations depend on eliminating one of the variables. There are three common methods of solution: addition or subtraction, substitution, and determinants.

7.3 Elimination by Addition or Subtraction

Example 4. Solve for x and y:

$$4x - 7y = 29 \qquad (7)$$
$$6x + 5y = -3 \qquad (8)$$

Multiplying Eq. (7) by 3,

$$12x - 21y = 87 \qquad (9)$$

Multiplying Eq. (8) by 2,

$$12x + 10y = -6 \qquad (10)$$

Subtracting Eq. (10) from Eq. (9),

$$-31y = 93 \qquad (11)$$

Dividing Eq. (11) by -31,

$$y = -3 \qquad (12)$$

Substituting -3 for y in Eq. (7),

$$4x + 21 = 29$$

or

$$x = 2 \qquad (13)$$

Check by substituting $x = 2$ and $y = -3$ in Eq. (8):

$$12 - 15 = -3 \qquad \text{(check)}$$

The above procedure may be summarized as follows:

To solve a system of linear equations by elimination by addition or subtraction:

1. *Multiply both members of both equations, if necessary, by nonzero numbers, which will cause the coefficients of one of the variables to have the same absolute value in both equations.*

2. *To eliminate this variable, the two equations obtained in step 1 are added if the matched coefficients have opposite signs. They are subtracted if they have like signs.*
3. *Solve the equation formed in step 2 for the variable contained in it. Substitute the result in one of the original equations to obtain the other variable.*
4. *Check by substituting the values of the variables in the original equation not used in step 3.*

Note: If both members of an equation contain a common factor, it may be advisable to divide through by that factor.
Clear of any fractions before eliminating a variable (see exception, Sec. 7.6).

It will usually be preferable to eliminate the variable whose coefficients have the smaller LCM.

Example 5. Referring to Fig. 7.2, we see the graphical appearance of two inconsistent equations.

If we were to attempt an algebraic solution by the method of Example 4, we would arrive at an absurd result such as $0 = 2$. This would be the algebraic indication of inconsistency.

Example 6. Figure 7.3 shows the graphical appearance of two equivalent, or dependent, equations. An attempt to apply the algebraic method of Example 4 would lead to the unrewarding result $0 = 0$. This, then, would indicate that the two equations are equivalent.

7.4 Elimination by Substitution

Example 7. Solve for x and y:

$$7x - 3y = 10 \tag{14}$$
$$5x - 2y = 8 \tag{15}$$

Solve Eq. (15) for y:

$$5x - 8 = 2y \tag{16}$$

or

$$y = \frac{5x - 8}{2} \tag{17}$$

Substitute $(5x - 8)/2$ for y in Eq. (14):

$$7x - 3\left(\frac{5x - 8}{2}\right) = 10 \tag{18}$$

Solve Eq. (18) for x, first eliminating fractions:

$$14x - 3(5x - 8) = 20$$
$$14x - 15x + 24 = 20$$
$$x = 4$$

Substitute $x = 4$ in Eq. (17):

$$y = \frac{(5)(4) - 8}{2}$$

or

$$y = 6$$

Hence the solution of the system is $x = 4$, $y = 6$.

Check by substituting $x = 4$ and $y = 6$ in Eq. (14):

$$(7)(4) - (3)(6) = 10 \qquad 28 - 18 = 10$$

To solve a system of two linear equations by elimination by substitution:

1. *Solve one equation for one variable (preferably the variable having the simplest coefficient) in terms of the other.*
2. *The expression obtained in step 1 is to be substituted for the equivalent variable in the other equation.*
3. *Solve the equation obtained in step 2 for the second variable.*
4. *Substitute the value of the second variable in the expression obtained in step 1, and solve for the first variable.*
5. *Check by substituting values of both variables in the original equation not used in step 1.*

Note. *The method of addition or subtraction is the most generally useful, especially when the coefficients of one variable have the same absolute value in both equations.*

The method of substitution is most convenient to apply when the variable which is to be expressed in terms of the other has a coefficient of 1.

EXERCISE 2

Solve the following systems of equations by the most convenient method:

1. $3x - 2y = 4$, $x = y$
2. $9x - 5y = 42$, $x + y = 0$
3. $8y - 5x = 18$, $x - y = 0$

4. $7x - 5y = 161$, $x = 4y$

5. $9x + 8y = 77$, $x - y = 1$

6. $3x - 2y = 10$, $x - y = 1$

7. $8x - 5y = 58$, $x + y = 4$

8. $6x - 10y = 4$, $x + y = 14$

9. $2x + y = 5$, $x + 2y = 19$

10. $4x + 5y = 30$, $6x + y = 19$

11. $x + y = 13$, $x - y = 5$

12. $5x + 2z = 61$, $3x - 2z = 43$

13. $11y - 4z = 41$, $7y + 2z = 42$

14. $5w + 6y = 17$, $3w - 2y = 27$

15. $9x - 13w = -3$, $6x - 7w = 3$

16. $12x - 11z = -5$, $9x + 4z = 33$

17. $7x - 3y = 41$, $4x + 5y = 10$

18. $9w + 8z = 15$, $5w + 7z = 16$

19. $11x - 3y + 34 = 0$, $8x + 10y - 24 = 0$

20. $13y + 5z - 33 = 0$, $7y - 9z - 47 = 0$

21. $3(x + y) = 33$, $5(x - y) = 25$

22. $4(x + z) = 22$, $6(x - z) = 15$

23. $0.5x + 0.4w = 0.26$, $0.7x + 0.3w = 0.26$

24. $0.3x + 0.4y = 14.5$, $0.4x + 0.3y = 13.5$

25. $\frac{x}{4} + 4y = 28$, $7x - \frac{y}{5} = 36$

26. $\frac{x}{3} - 4y = -58$, $5x - \frac{y}{6} = 27\frac{1}{2}$

27. $\frac{w + 3}{2} + 5z = 9$, $\frac{z + 9}{10} - \frac{w - 2}{3} = 0$

28. $\frac{x - 2}{10} + 3y = 8$, $\frac{x + 2}{6} - \frac{y - 7}{9} = 2$

Solve Probs. 29 and 30 by slide rule to whatever degree of accuracy is possible.

29. $0.103x + 0.950y = 10.47$, $1.068x - 2.74y = 19.63$

30. $5.95x + 5.17y = 3.39$, $4.62x - 12.3y = 5.56$

Note. *In the slide-rule solution of Prob. 30, instead of finding the LCM of 5.95 and 4.62, we would usually prefer to eliminate a variable, say x, by dividing the first equation through by 5.95 and the second by 4.62. (Prob. 29 is similar.)*

7.5 Literal Linear Equations

A system involving letters other than the *variables* is usually best solved by finding each variable independently by elimination by addition or subtraction.

Example 8. Solve for x and y:

$$mx + ny = 2(m^2 - n^2) \tag{19}$$
$$x - y = m + n \tag{20}$$

Multiply Eq. (20) by n:

$$nx - ny = mn + n^2 \tag{21}$$

Add Eqs. (19) and (21):

$$\begin{array}{l} mx + ny = 2m^2 \qquad\quad - 2n^2 \\ \underline{nx - ny = \qquad\quad mn + \ n^2} \\ mx + nx = 2m^2 + mn - n^2 \end{array} \tag{22}$$

Factor Eq. (22):

$$x(m + n) = (m + n)(2m - n) \tag{23}$$

Divide Eq. (23) through by $m + n$:

$$x = 2m - n \qquad (m \neq -n)$$

Multiply Eq. (20) by m:

$$mx - my = m^2 + mn \tag{24}$$

Subtract Eq. (24) from Eq. (19):

$$\begin{array}{l} mx + \ ny = 2m^2 \qquad\quad - 2n^2 \\ \underline{mx - my = \ m^2 + mn \qquad\qquad} \\ ny + my = \ m^2 - mn - 2n^2 \end{array} \tag{25}$$

Factor Eq. (25):

$$y(n + m) = (m + n)(m - 2n) \tag{26}$$

Divide Eq. (26) through by $m + n$:

$$y = m - 2n$$

But note that y is more easily found here by substitution. Rewriting Eq. (20) as $x - m - n = y$ and substituting $x = 2m - n$, we find at once that $2m - n - m - n = m - 2n = y$.

If answers are at all involved, checking may best be done by numerical substitution.

Referring to the above example, if we arbitrarily replace m by 3 and n by 2, $x = 2(3) - 2 = 4$, and $y = 3 - 2(2) = -1$. If, then, we substitute these numerical values in Eq. (19), we obtain $(3)(4) + (2)(-1) = 2(3^2 - 2^2)$ or $12 - 2 = 2(5)$ or $10 = 10$.

7.6 Equations Linear in the Reciprocals of the Variables

Equations of the type $a/x + b/y = c$ are usually best solved without removing the variables from the denominators.

Example 9. Solve the system

$$\frac{9}{x} - \frac{15}{y} = 1 \qquad (27)$$

$$\frac{14}{x} + \frac{20}{y} = 3 \qquad (28)$$

Multiply Eq. (27) by 4:

$$\frac{36}{x} - \frac{60}{y} = 4 \qquad (29)$$

Multiply Eq. (28) by 3:

$$\frac{42}{x} + \frac{60}{y} = 9 \qquad (30)$$

Add Eqs. (29) and (30):

$$\frac{78}{x} = 13$$

$$78 = 13x$$

or

$$x = 6$$

Substitute $x = 6$ in Eq. (27):

$$\frac{9}{6} - \frac{15}{y} = 1$$

$$-\frac{15}{y} = -\frac{1}{2}$$

$$y = 30$$

The solution of the system is $x = 6$, $y = 30$.

Example 10. Solve the system

$$\frac{3}{8x} - \frac{1}{2y} = 2 \tag{31}$$

$$\frac{5}{6x} - \frac{5}{3y} = -8\tfrac{1}{3} \tag{32}$$

Multiply Eq. (31) by 10:

$$\frac{15}{4x} - \frac{5}{y} = 20 \tag{33}$$

Multiply Eq. (32) by 3:

$$\frac{5}{2x} + \frac{5}{y} = +25 \tag{34}$$

Subtract Eq. (34) from Eq. (33):

$$\frac{15}{4x} - \frac{5}{2x} = 45 \tag{35}$$

Multiply Eq. (35) by 4x:

$$15 - 10 = 180x$$
$$x = \tfrac{1}{36}$$

Substitute $x = \frac{1}{36}$ in Eq. (31):

$$\frac{3}{8(\frac{1}{36})} - \frac{1}{2y} = 2$$
$$\frac{27}{2} - \frac{1}{2y} = 2$$
$$-\frac{1}{2y} = -\frac{23}{2}$$
$$y = \frac{1}{23}$$

Hence the solution of the system is $x = \frac{1}{36}$, $y = \frac{1}{23}$.

EXERCISE 3

Solve the following systems for x, y, z, or w, as the case may be.

1. $3x + y = 4c$
   $x - y = 4d$
2. $x + y = 5a$
   $2x - 3y = 5b$
3. $2x - 3y = a + 4b$
   $x + 2y = 4a - 5b$
4. $5x - 4y = 6c - 15d$
   $3x + y = 7c - 9d$
5. $ax + 2by = 4$
   $2ax - 6by = 3$
6. $12ax - 5by = -16$
   $6ax + 7by = 30$
7. $2ax + by = 10c$
   $ax - 3by = -9c$
8. $3ax - 4by = 18ab$
   $2ax + by = ab$
9. $bx + cy = 2bc$
   $cx + by = b^2 + c^2$
10. $ax - by = 2a^2 - 6ab + 2b^2$
    $bx + ay = 3a^2 - 3b^2$
11. $2nx + 2my = m^2 + n^2$
    $4nx - mx + my = mn + 2n^2$
12. $ax + 2cy = 5ac$
    $\dfrac{2x}{c} - \dfrac{y}{a} = \dfrac{-5}{ac}$
13. $\dfrac{1}{x} + \dfrac{1}{y} = 6$
    $\dfrac{1}{x} - \dfrac{1}{y} = 4$
14. $\dfrac{3}{x} - \dfrac{2}{y} = 10$
    $\dfrac{4}{x} + \dfrac{1}{y} = 28$
15. $\dfrac{10}{x} + \dfrac{6}{y} = 7$
    $\dfrac{14}{x} - \dfrac{9}{y} = 4$
16. $\dfrac{15}{x} + \dfrac{14}{w} = 5$
    $\dfrac{25}{x} - \dfrac{6}{w} = 1$
17. $\dfrac{1}{2x} + \dfrac{1}{3y} = 12$
    $\dfrac{1}{4x} + \dfrac{1}{9y} = 5$
18. $\dfrac{5}{6x} - \dfrac{3}{4z} = 6$
    $\dfrac{7}{9x} + \dfrac{1}{6z} = 7\frac{1}{3}$

7.7 Linear Equations in More Than Two Variables

Like a system in two variables, a system of linear equations in more than two variables may have a solution or may be dependent or inconsistent. Only the first case will be considered here. For a system to have a unique solution, it must have as many independent equations as variables.

Example 11. Solve for x, y, and z:

$$6x - 5y - 2z = 2 \tag{36}$$
$$4x + y + 3z = 10 \tag{37}$$
$$5x + 3y + 7z = 13 \tag{38}$$

Multiply Eq. (37) by 5:

$$\begin{array}{lrrrl} & 20x & +\ 5y & +\ 15z & = 50 \\ \text{Add Eq. (36):} & 6x & -\ 5y & -\ 2z & = 2 \\ \hline & 26x & & +\ 13z & = 52 \end{array} \qquad (39)$$

Multiply Eq. (37) by 3:

$$\begin{array}{lrrrl} & 12x & +\ 3y & +\ 9z & = 30 \\ \text{Subtract Eq. (38):} & 5x & +\ 3y & +\ 7z & = 13 \\ \hline & 7x & & +\ 2z & = 17 \end{array} \qquad (40)$$

Note that Eq. (39) may be divided throughout by 13. Therefore we will obtain smaller coefficients in Eq. (41) by multiplying by $\frac{2}{13}$ rather than by 2.

$$\begin{array}{lrrl} & 4x & +\ 2z & = 8 \qquad (41) \\ \text{Subtract Eq. (40):} & 7x & +\ 2z & = 17 \\ \hline & -3x & & = -9 \\ & & x & = 3 \end{array}$$

Substitute $x = 3$ in Eq. (40):

$$(7)(3) + 2z = 17$$
$$z = -2$$

Substitute $x = 3$ and $z = -2$ in Eq. (37):

$$(4)(3) + y + 3(-2) = 10$$
$$y = 4$$

Check the solution by substituting the values of x, y, and z in Eq. (36) and (38).

The procedure for solving a system of three linear equations in three variables may be summarized as follows:

1. *Select the variable most easily eliminated and eliminate this variable from one pair of equations.*
2. *Eliminate the same variable from one of the equations just used and the third equation.*
3. *Solve the two equations so obtained as in Sec. 7.3.*
4. *Substitute the two values found in step 3 in the simplest of the original equations and solve for the third variable.*

5. *Check by substituting the values of the variables in each of the two original equations not used in step 4.*

Simultaneous linear equations in more than three variables may be solved by an extension of the above method.

EXERCISE 4

Solve the following systems of equations:

1. $x + y = 7$
   $x + z = 8$
   $y + z = 9$
2. $x + y = 4$
   $x + z = 7$
   $y + z = 1$
3. $x + y + z = 8$
   $x - y + z = 2$
   $x + y - z = 12$
4. $x - y - z = 1$
   $x + y - z = 6$
   $x - y + z = -1$

Suggestion for Probs. 5 and 6: Add the equations and divide the sum through by the common factor.

5. $2x + y + z = 7$
   $x + 2y + z = 15$
   $x + y + 2z = 18$
6. $x + y + 3z = 9$
   $x + 3y + z = 7/3$
   $3x + y + z = 7$
7. $2x + 3y - 4z = 11$
   $3x - 5y + z = -3$
   $6x + 2y - 7z = 18$
8. $7x + 4y - 3z = -15$
   $5x - 6y + 2z = 41$
   $x - 10y - 9z = -8$
9. $6x - 8y + 3z = -5$
   $9x + 20y - 4z = 25$
   $15x + 12y + 7z = 12$
10. $10x + 9y + 7z = 32$
    $11x - 6y - 8z = 20$
    $-9x + 12y + 10z = -22$

7.8 The Graph As an Aid to Setting Up Algebraic Equations

Rough graphical representation is often a powerful way of setting up an equation for algebraic solution. Perhaps the reader's first reaction is that we have here a means of scaling an answer from a graph drawn accurately to scale. Although this is true, the objective is the setting up of equations, based on dimensions and relations appearing in a rough freehand sketch.

The problems illustrated below have been selected from Exercise 3, Chap. 3, as typical examples.

Prob. 21, page 76 (Fig. 7.4). Draw a line OA with a slope of $11/9$ s/h. Draw from the point (24,0) the line BC with a slope of $-28/13$ s/h. Drop the perpendicular DE, dividing the 24 h into $24 - h$ vertical hours and h horizontal hours.

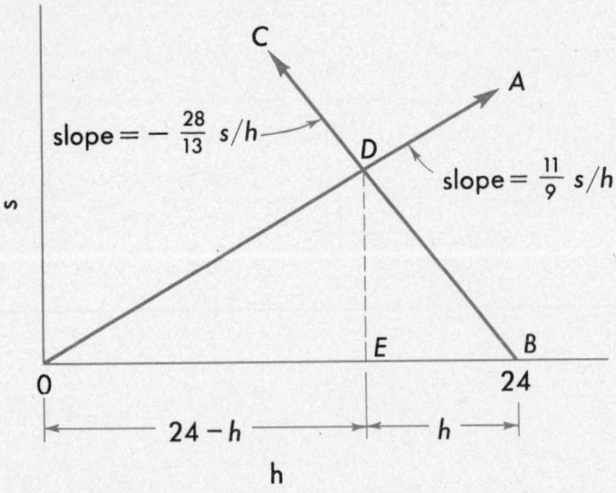

FIGURE 7.4

Algebraically, since $\Delta y = m\,\Delta x$, the gain in $24 - h$ h in the vertical position is $ED = {}^{11}\!/_{9}(24 - h)$. The loss in h h in a horizontal position is $DE = -{}^{28}\!/_{13}h$. (Here, again using the relation $\Delta y = m\,\Delta x$, or $DE = -{}^{28}\!/_{13}h$.) Since the net gain or loss is zero, we have ${}^{11}\!/_{9}(24 - h) + (-{}^{28}\!/_{13})h = 0$. ANS.: $h = 8.7$ h

Prob. 22, page 76 (Fig. 7.5). Locate point A at (50,25). Draw line OA. From A draw line AB with a slope of 0.1 lb tin/lb metal. Draw line OC with a slope of 0.25 lb tin/lb metal. From the intersection point D of lines AB and OC drop the perpendicular DE. Since D is on the 25 percent line, it must represent an alloy containing 25 percent tin. Drop the perpendicular AG. This length represents 25 lb, which is the weight of tin in 50 lb of solder. DF is the weight of tin in w lb of type metal, or

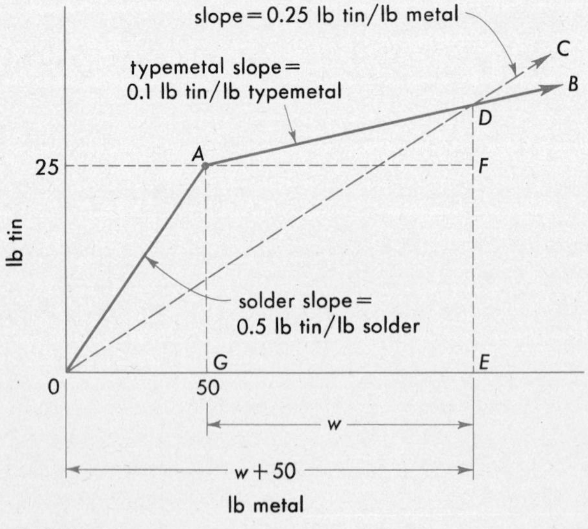

FIGURE 7.5

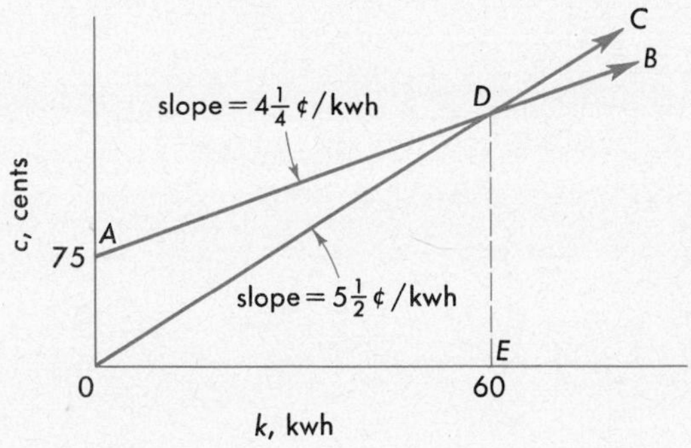

FIGURE 7.6

$DF = 0.1w$. Total tin $= AG + DF = 25 + 0.1w$ (since $\Delta y = m\,\Delta x$). Total tin also $= DE = 0.25(w + 50)$. Therefore $25 + 0.1w = 0.25(w + 50)$. ANS.: $w = 83\frac{1}{3}$ lb

Prob. 23, page 77 (Fig. 7.6). From point $A = 75$ draw line AB with a slope of $4\frac{1}{4}$ cents/kWh. From the slope-intercept equation (6) the equation for this line must be $c = 4\frac{1}{4}k + 75$. Draw line OC with a slope of $5\frac{1}{2}$ cents/kWh. The equation for this line is evidently $c = 5\frac{1}{2}k$. At the intersection point D we have $c = 4\frac{1}{4}k + 75 = 5\frac{1}{2}k$. ANS.: $k = 60$ kWh

7.9 Applications of Simultaneous Linear Equations

EXERCISE 5

Solve the following problems as directed. A few of these problems are repeated from Chap. 3, where one variable was used. In this exercise they are to be solved using two variables for comparison.

1. The sum of two numbers is 53 and their difference is 7. Find the numbers.
2. A fraction reduces to $\frac{2}{3}$ if 2 is added to its numerator. It reduces to $\frac{1}{2}$ if 1 is added to its denominator. What is the fraction?
3. A boat travels 60 mi upstream in 10 h, making the return trip downstream in 8 h. Find the rate of the current and of the boat in still water.
4. Two planes are 60 mi apart. If they are flying toward each other, they will pass in 5 min. If they are headed in the same direction, the faster plane will overtake the slower in 45 min. What are their speeds?
5. If the width of a rectangle is increased by 2 ft and the length by 12 ft, the area will be increased by 480 ft^2. If the width is increased by 12 ft and the length by 2 ft, the area will be increased by 660 ft^2. Find the dimensions of the original rectangle.
6. A plumber and his helper together receive \$69.60, the plumber working 5 h and

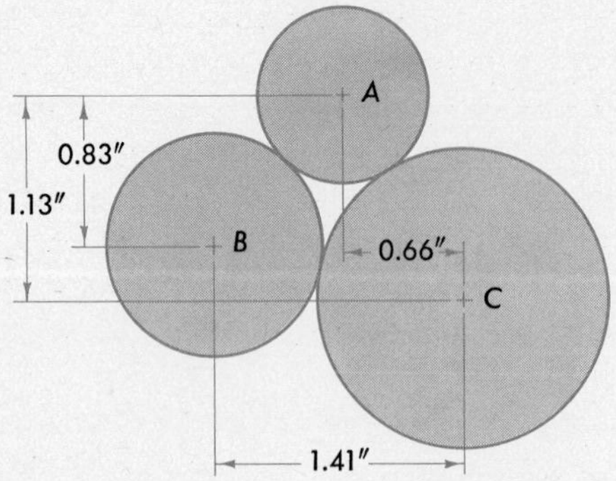

FIGURE 7.7

the helper 6 h. At another time the plumber works 8 h and the helper $7\frac{1}{2}$ h, and they receive together \$99.60. What are the hourly wages of each?

7. Three men and 6 boys can do in 2 days what 1 man and 8 boys can do in 3 days. Find the time required for 1 man alone and for 1 boy alone to do the work.
8. Six men and 5 boys take 2 days to do what 9 men and 15 boys can do in 1 day. If the labor cost for the job is \$504, find the daily wage for a man and for a boy.
9. Three disks A, B, and C are externally tangent each to each. If the center-to-center distances AB, AC, and BC are $6\frac{3}{4}$, $6\frac{1}{4}$, and $8\frac{1}{2}$ in, respectively, find the diameters.
10. Find the diameters of the disks in Fig. 7.7.
11. Mr. Warner and his son Phil agree to paint a house for \$600. After working together for 10 days, the job is $\frac{5}{8}$ finished, and Mr. Warner leaves Phil to finish the job alone, which he does in 18 more days. How should the \$600 be divided between father and son?
12. The reduced value of a fraction is $\frac{4}{5}$. If 21 is deducted from both numerator and denominator, the reduced value of the new fraction is $\frac{1}{3}$. Find the original fraction.

    If $n =$ the numerator and $d =$ the denominator, we have $n/d = \frac{4}{5}$ and $(n - 21)/(d - 21) = \frac{1}{3}$.
13. A pile of dimes and quarters has a value of \$4.60. There are three more quarters than dimes. How many quarters are there?
14. How much solder containing 50 percent tin and how much type metal containing 15 percent tin must be mixed to make 80 lb of solder containing 40 percent tin?

    We may set up a table as follows:

	Lb original material	*Tin content, lb*
Solder	s	$0.50s$
Type metal	t	$0.15t$
Total	$s + t = 80$	$0.50s + 0.15t = (0.40)(80) = 32$

The two equations may be solved simultaneously for s and t.

15. A 12-qt cooling system is filled with 25 percent antifreeze. How many quarts must be drawn off and replaced with pure antifreeze to raise the strength to 45 percent?
16. A popular airline advertises a nonstop flight time of 1.2 h from Boston to Buffalo and 1.0 h for the return trip. Assuming the prevailing wind to blow from the west, what airspeed of the plane and what windspeed do these figures imply? (Boston to Buffalo distance is 400 mi.)
17. At a high school game the price of admission was \$0.25 for each adult and \$0.10 for each child. If the turnstile showed that 397 persons attended the game and the gate receipts were \$56.80, how many adults attended?
18. How much high-speed tool steel containing 18 percent tungsten and how much steel containing 12 percent tungsten should be mixed to make 3,000 lb containing 14.6 percent tungsten?
19. A stick of wood is to be cut into four equal sections for braces, as shown in Fig. 7.8. Find x and y, making no allowance for saw kerfs.
20. The resistance R_t of a nickel wire at any Celsius temperature t is equal to $R_0(1 + at)$, where R_0 is the resistance at 0°C and a is the temperature coefficient of resistance. If the resistance at 20°C is 26.82 Ω, and at 32°C is 28.10 Ω, find a and R_0.
21. Express the area of the ring in Fig. 7.9 in terms of AB. Given a regular 6-in pentagon, find the difference between the areas of the circumscribed and inscribed circles. How does your answer compare with that obtained by taking a 6-in heptagon?
22. Two stations A and B on the same railroad line are on opposite sides of a mountain pass. A is 10 mi east of the divide, and B is 15 mi west of the divide. The grade is the same on both sides. If the running time from A to B is 44 min and the running time from B to A is 50 min, find the upgrade and downgrade speeds.
23. A gas company charges \$$a$ service charge plus \$$b$/1,000 ft³. Find a and b if 12,000 ft³ of gas costs \$6.40 and 20,000 ft³ costs \$10.00.

Example 12. A small firm has a taxable income of \$390,000. The state tax is 10 percent of that portion remaining after the federal tax is paid. The federal tax is 25 percent of that portion remaining after the state tax is paid. What are the state and federal taxes?

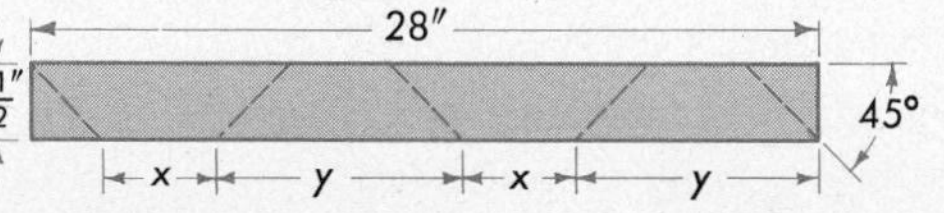

FIGURE 7.8

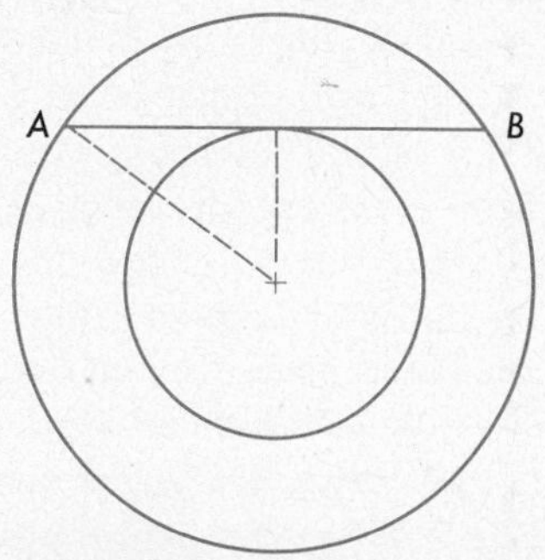

FIGURE 7.9

Let s = state tax (\$) and f = federal tax (\$); then

$$s = 0.10(390{,}000 - f)$$
$$f = 0.25(390{,}000 - s)$$

These equations can be rearranged as follows:

$$10s + f = 390{,}000$$
$$0.25s + f = 97{,}500$$

Subtraction yields

$$9.75s = 292{,}500 \qquad \text{or} \qquad s = \$30{,}000 \qquad \text{and} \qquad f = \$90{,}000$$

Checking,

$$\text{State tax} = 0.10(390{,}000 - 90{,}000) = \$30{,}000$$
$$\text{Federal tax} = 0.25(390{,}000 - 30{,}000) = \$90{,}000$$

24. A man ordered a number of pamphlets from a job printer. The printer made a fixed charge for each order plus a certain amount for each pamphlet. The total cost amounted to \$42. Several months later the customer placed a somewhat larger order for additional pamphlets. This order cost \$54. Had the customer been able to anticipate his needs and ordered all the pamphlets at one time, they would have cost only \$84. How much was the fixed charge? If the second order contained 80 more pamphlets than the first, find the number of pamphlets in each order and the unit cost.
25. The difference between two quantities equals their product. Their sum less their product equals the smaller divided by the larger. What are the numbers?
26. The product of two quantities equals their difference. Their product plus their sum equals the larger divided by 3 times the smaller. Find the numbers.
27. In a race of 100 yd, A beats B by $\frac{1}{5}$ s. In the second trial, A gives B a start of 4 yd and B wins by $\frac{1}{5}$ s. Find the time required for A and B each to run 100 yd.
28. Two cars are traveling in the same direction around a 1-mi circular racetrack. The faster car overtakes the slower car every 3 min. When the cars are traveling in opposite directions, they pass each other every 18 s. Find their speeds.
29. Two runners A and B run around a 1-mi circular track at 18 and 22 ft/s, respectively. If they start simultaneously at the same point:
(*a*) How often will B overtake A going in the same direction?
(*b*) How often will B pass A going in the opposite direction?

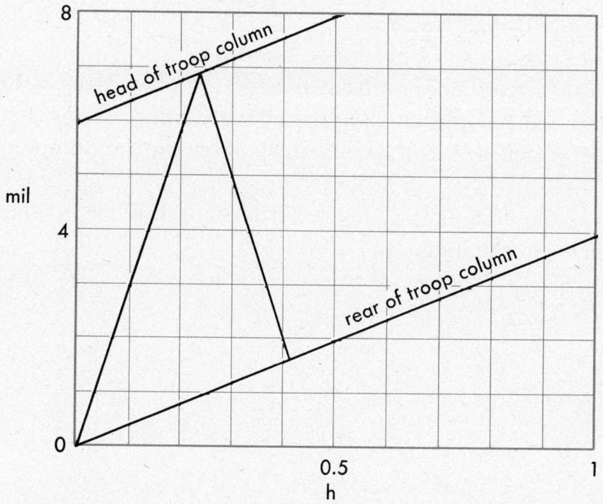

FIGURE 7.10

Example 13. A time-honored problem is that of the motorcycle courier who starts from the rear of a troop column, rides to the head of the column, and immediately returns to the rear. How far did the courier ride if the column is 6 mi long and marching at 4 mi/h? The speed of the motorcycle is 30 mi/h. How long was the courier riding?

According to Fig. 7.10, the courier traveled about 12.2 mi (6.9 mi to the head of the column and 5.3 mi to the rear). The total time was about 0.4 h, or 24 min.

This problem is a good example of the opportunity offered by maintaining the proper relative values while changing other conditions.

In this illustration let us consider rates of the cyclist relative to that of the troop column. It is evident that the cyclist is riding at 30 − 4, or 26, mi/h relative to the troop column while riding to the head of the column, and 30 + 4, or 34, mi/h relative to the column while riding to the rear. If the 6-mi column were stationary, then our problem would be to find the total time for the cyclist to advance 6 mi at 26 mi/h and return at 34 mi/h. The solution follows readily:

$$\frac{6}{34} + \frac{6}{26} = 0.1765 + 0.231, \text{ or } 0.408 \text{ h}$$

and confirms the answer already obtained by graphical means.

30. A bicyclist rides at a steady 20 mi/h parallel to a double-track rapid-transit line on which trains are running in both directions at regular intervals. Every 11 min 40 s a train overtakes him going in the same direction. Every 5 min a train passes him going in the opposite direction.

(*a*) What is the speed of a rapid-transit train?
(*b*) What is the headway between trains in miles? In minutes?

31. A bus and a hiker start at the same time, one from *A* to *B*, the other from *B* to *A*. If they arrive at their destinations 5 min and 3 h, respectively, after passing one another, compare their rates of speed. What other information can be obtained from these data?
32. In balancing the equation for the combustion of methyl alcohol, the coefficients *a*, *b*, and *c* must be determined in the equation

$$aCH_3OH + bO_2 \longrightarrow cH_2O + aCO_2$$

According to a hydrogen balance,

$$4a = 2c$$

An oxygen balance requires that

$$a + 2b = c + 2a$$

Find the smallest integral values of *a*, *b*, and *c* satisfying the above equations.
33. The solution of copper in nitric acid proceeds according to the equation

$$aCu + 2bHNO_3 \longrightarrow aCu(NO_3)_2 + cNO + bH_2O$$

The nitrogen balance requires that

$$2b = 2a + c$$

The oxygen balance requires that

$$6b = 6a + c + b$$

Find the smallest integral values of *a*, *b*, and *c* satisfying the above equations.
34. In how many ways may a bill of \$1.37 be paid using only 5-cent and 8-cent stamps? You will develop an equation containing two variables. Ordinarily there would be an infinite number of solutions. In this case roots must be integral (Diophantine equations). They must also be positive. Often there may be many solutions, sometimes none (for example, $2x + 4y = 15$). Plot your equation. Can you see any pattern in your answers?

7.10 Matrices

Rectangular arrays of numbers such as

$$\begin{bmatrix} a_1 & b_1 & c_1 \\ a_2 & b_2 & c_2 \\ a_3 & b_3 & c_3 \end{bmatrix} \qquad \begin{bmatrix} a_1 & b_1 & c_1 \\ a_2 & b_2 & c_2 \end{bmatrix} \qquad \begin{bmatrix} a_1 \\ a_2 \\ a_3 \end{bmatrix}$$

are called *matrices*. Any one of them is called a *matrix*. The numbers a_1, a_2, a_3, b_1, b_2, b_3, and so on, are called *elements* of the matrix. In the present text, all the elements will be real numbers.

Horizontal lines of numbers such as a_1, b_1, c_1, etc., are called *rows*. Vertical lines of numbers such as a_1, a_2, a_3, etc., are called *columns*.

In this text we shall be interested only in *square* matrices. These are matrices having the same number of rows as columns.

A square matrix having two rows and two columns is said to be a 2-by-2 (sometimes written 2×2), or a *second-order*, matrix. A square matrix having six rows and six columns is said to be a 6-by-6, or a sixth-order, matrix, and so on.

7.11 Determinants

With each square matrix we may associate a unique number, to be defined presently, called the *determinant* of the matrix.

For example, the determinant of the square matrix

$$\begin{bmatrix} a_1 & b_1 \\ a_2 & b_2 \end{bmatrix} \quad \text{is symbolized by} \quad \begin{vmatrix} a_1 & b_1 \\ a_2 & b_2 \end{vmatrix}$$

The value of this number is defined to be

$$\begin{vmatrix} a_1 & b_1 \\ a_2 & b_2 \end{vmatrix} = a_1b_2 - a_2b_1$$

As a convenience we do often refer to the symbol

$$\begin{vmatrix} a_1 & b_1 \\ a_2 & b_2 \end{vmatrix}$$

for example, as a "determinant" in the sense that this symbol represents the number which is the determinant of the matrix

$$\begin{bmatrix} a_1 & b_1 \\ a_2 & b_2 \end{bmatrix}$$

Example 14. Find the value of $\begin{vmatrix} 4 & 5 \\ 3 & 7 \end{vmatrix}$

$$\begin{vmatrix} 4 & 5 \\ 3 & 7 \end{vmatrix} = (4)(7) - (3)(5) = 28 - 15 = 13$$

Example 15. Evaluate $\begin{vmatrix} 6 & 3 \\ -2 & 5 \end{vmatrix}$

$$\begin{vmatrix} 6 & 3 \\ -2 & 5 \end{vmatrix} = (6)(5) - (-2)(3) = 30 + 6 = 36$$

Example 16. Evaluate $\begin{vmatrix} 7 & x \\ 5 & -y \end{vmatrix}$

$$\begin{vmatrix} 7 & x \\ 5 & -y \end{vmatrix} = (7)(-y) - (5)(x) = -7y - 5x$$

EXERCISE 6

Evaluate the following determinants:

1. $\begin{vmatrix} 3 & 5 \\ 5 & 8 \end{vmatrix}$
2. $\begin{vmatrix} 3 & a \\ 4 & b \end{vmatrix}$
3. $\begin{vmatrix} 4 & -6 \\ 2 & 5 \end{vmatrix}$
4. $\begin{vmatrix} 7 & -x \\ 6 & y \end{vmatrix}$
5. $\begin{vmatrix} 9a & 5b \\ 4b & a \end{vmatrix}$
6. $\begin{vmatrix} 6x & -7x \\ 5y & -6y \end{vmatrix}$

7.12 Solution of Simultaneous Linear Equations by Determinants

A system of linear equations is said to be in *standard form* if, as in the equations below [Eq. (42)], the terms containing the variables are in the left-hand members and in the same order in all equations. The right-hand members contain only constants.

$$\begin{aligned} a_1x + b_1y &= k_1 \\ a_2x + b_2y &= k_2 \end{aligned} \tag{42}$$

Given such a system of equations in x and y, the solution can be shown to be

$$x = \frac{k_1b_2 - k_2b_1}{a_1b_2 - a_2b_1} \qquad y = \frac{a_1k_2 - a_2k_1}{a_1b_2 - a_2b_1} \tag{43}$$

provided $a_1b_2 - a_2b_1$ is not equal to zero.

In determinant notation we can write

$$k_1b_2 - k_2b_1 = \begin{vmatrix} k_1 & b_1 \\ k_2 & b_2 \end{vmatrix} \qquad a_1k_2 - a_2k_1 = \begin{vmatrix} a_1 & k_1 \\ a_2 & k_2 \end{vmatrix}$$

and

$$a_1b_2 - a_2b_1 = \begin{vmatrix} a_1 & b_1 \\ a_2 & b_2 \end{vmatrix}$$

We can therefore write the solution [Eq. (43)] in the form

$$x = \frac{\begin{vmatrix} k_1 & b_1 \\ k_2 & b_2 \end{vmatrix}}{\begin{vmatrix} a_1 & b_1 \\ a_2 & b_2 \end{vmatrix}} \qquad y = \frac{\begin{vmatrix} a_1 & k_1 \\ a_2 & k_2 \end{vmatrix}}{\begin{vmatrix} a_1 & b_1 \\ a_2 & b_2 \end{vmatrix}} \qquad \text{if} \qquad \begin{vmatrix} a_1 & b_1 \\ a_2 & b_2 \end{vmatrix} \neq 0 \tag{44}$$

The solution [Eq. (44)] is therefore a general formula applicable to any system of two simultaneous linear equations in two variables when arranged in standard form. It will be noted that both denominators of Eqs. (44) are the same. This determinant

$$\begin{vmatrix} a_1 & b_1 \\ a_2 & b_2 \end{vmatrix}$$

is called the *determinant of the system*. Its elements are the coefficients of the variable quantities arranged in the same relative position as in the system of equations when the equations are arranged in standard form.

The numerator of the fraction which expresses the value of x differs from the denominator in that the constants k_1 and k_2 replace a_1 and a_2, the coefficients of x; and the numerator of the fraction which expresses the value of y differs from the denominator in that the constants k_1 and k_2 replace b_1 and b_2, the coefficients of y. This procedure may be summarized in *Cramer's rule:*

Arrange the given equations in standard form. In the solution, the value of a variable is given by a fraction whose denominator is the determinant of the system and whose numerator is the same determinant except that the coefficients of the variable have been replaced by the constants k_1 and k_2.

Example 17. Solve by determinants

$$4x + 7y = -19$$
$$5x - 3y = 35$$

We have

$$\begin{array}{lll} a_1 = 4 & b_1 = 7 & k_1 = -19 \\ a_2 = 5 & b_2 = -3 & k_2 = 35 \end{array}$$

Hence

$$x = \frac{\begin{vmatrix} -19 & 7 \\ 35 & -3 \end{vmatrix}}{\begin{vmatrix} 4 & 7 \\ 5 & -3 \end{vmatrix}} = \frac{57 - 245}{-12 - 35} = \frac{-188}{-47} = 4$$

$$y = \frac{\begin{vmatrix} 4 & -19 \\ 5 & 35 \end{vmatrix}}{\begin{vmatrix} 4 & 7 \\ 5 & -3 \end{vmatrix}} = \frac{140 + 95}{-12 - 35} = \frac{235}{-47} = -5$$

Example 18. Solve by determinants

$$\begin{aligned} x - y &= m - n \\ mx - ny &= 2m^2 - 2n^2 \end{aligned}$$

Here

$$\begin{array}{lll} a_1 = 1 & b_1 = -1 & k_1 = m - n \\ a_2 = m & b_2 = -n & k_2 = 2m^2 - 2n^2 \end{array}$$

Hence

$$x = \frac{\begin{vmatrix} m - n & -1 \\ 2m^2 - 2n^2 & -n \end{vmatrix}}{\begin{vmatrix} 1 & -1 \\ m & -n \end{vmatrix}} = \frac{-mn + n^2 + 2m^2 - 2n^2}{-n + m}$$

$$= \frac{2m^2 - mn - n^2}{m - n} = 2m + n$$

$$y = \frac{\begin{vmatrix} 1 & m - n \\ m & 2m^2 - 2n^2 \end{vmatrix}}{\begin{vmatrix} 1 & -1 \\ m & -n \end{vmatrix}} = \frac{2m^2 - 2n^2 - m^2 + mn}{-n + m}$$

$$= \frac{m^2 + mn - 2n^2}{m - n} = m + 2n$$

If the equations $a_1x + b_1y = k_1$ and $a_2x + b_2y = k_2$ have no unique simultaneous solution, they are either inconsistent or dependent. Graphically, this means that the lines are either parallel or coincident. In either case the slopes are equal, and $-(a_1/b_1) = -(a_2/b_2)$, or $a_1b_2 - a_2b_1 = 0$. If the two lines coincide, their y intercepts are equal, or $k_1/b_1 = k_2/b_2$; that is, $k_1b_2 - k_2b_1 = 0$.

These facts may be summarized as follows:

If $a_1b_2 - a_2b_1 \neq 0$: *The equations have a unique simultaneous solution.*

If $a_1b_2 - a_2b_1 = 0$
and $k_1b_2 - k_2b_1 \neq 0$: *The equations are inconsistent and have no solution.*

If $a_1b_2 - a_2b_1 = 0$
and $k_1b_2 - k_2b_1 = 0$: *The equations are dependent and have an infinite number of solutions.*

EXERCISE 7

In the following systems, use determinants to ascertain whether the equations are inconsistent, dependent, or have a unique common solution. Determine any common solutions.

1. $2x - 3y = 5$
   $4x - 6y = 8$
2. $3x - 7y = 1$
   $6x + 5y = 40$
3. $6x + 9y = 15$
   $8x + 12y = 20$
4. $3x - 4y - 15 = 0$
   $7x + 2y - 52 = 0$
5. $4x + 15y = 7a$
   $10x - 9y = 2a$
6. $\dfrac{2x - y}{3} = 5$
   $\dfrac{11x + 2y}{5} = 6$
7. $ax + by = (a - b)^2$
   $ax - by = a^2 - b^2$
8. $bx + ay = 2ab$
   $ax + by = a^2 + b^2$
9. $17x + 11y = 13$
   $7x - 9y = 73$

7.13 Determinants of the Third Order

A third-order determinant is the determinant of a third-order matrix and may be symbolized as

$$\begin{vmatrix} a_1 & b_1 & c_1 \\ a_2 & b_2 & c_2 \\ a_3 & b_3 & c_3 \end{vmatrix}$$

By definition its value may be written

$$\begin{vmatrix} a_1 & b_1 & c_1 \\ a_2 & b_2 & c_2 \\ a_3 & b_3 & c_3 \end{vmatrix} = a_1b_2c_3 + a_2b_3c_1 + a_3b_1c_2 - a_3b_2c_1 - a_2b_1c_3 - a_1b_3c_2$$

There are various ways of evaluating a determinant of the third order. If the student does not expect to use determinants of higher order than the third, the following is an easily remembered rule:

1. *Repeat the first and second columns of the determinant at the right of the determinant.*
2. *Form the products of the numbers in each full diagonal running downward to the right.*
3. *Form the products of the numbers in each full diagonal running upward to the right.*
4. *Subtract the algebraic sum of the products in step 3 from the algebraic sum of the products in step 2.*

This method is valid for a determinant of the third order, *but not for one of any higher order.*

The arrangement is illustrated as follows:

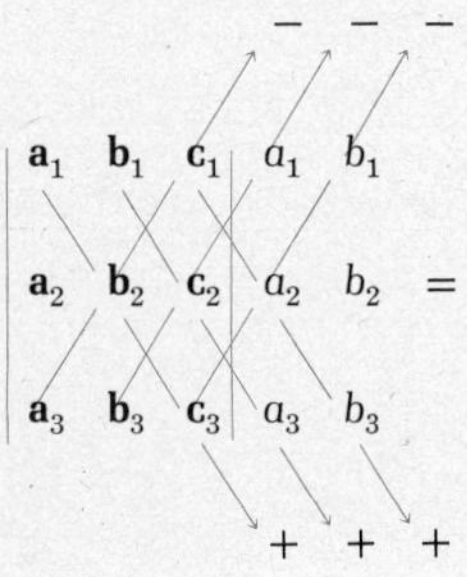

$$= a_1b_2c_3 + a_2b_3c_1 + a_3b_1c_2 - a_3b_2c_1 - a_2b_1c_3 - a_1b_3c_2$$

Example 19. Evaluate the third-order determinant

$$\begin{vmatrix} 8 & -2 & 3 \\ 5 & -4 & 1 \\ -6 & 7 & 2 \end{vmatrix}$$

Arranging as described, we write

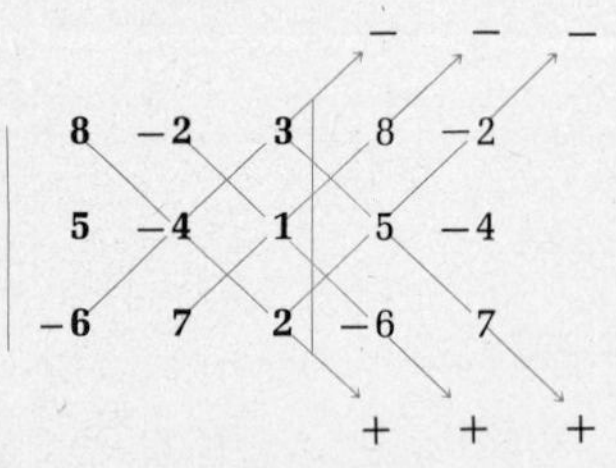

and obtain

$$(8)(-4)(2) + (-2)(1)(-6) + (3)(5)(7) - (-6)(-4)(3) - (7)(1)(8) - (2)(5)(-2)$$
$$= -64 + 12 + 105 - 72 - 56 + 20$$
$$= -55$$

7.14 Minors and Cofactors

The definitions given in this section are of great importance in preparation for the study of Sec. 7.15.

Figure 7.11 shows a third-order determinant in which the row and column containing a_1 have been deleted.

The second-order determinant

$$\begin{vmatrix} b_2 & c_2 \\ b_3 & c_3 \end{vmatrix}$$

remains. This second-order determinant is called the *minor* of the element a_1.

In general, if one row and one column are deleted from a determinant of order n (where n is an integer), the remaining array forms a determinant of order $(n - 1)$. This determinant is called the *minor* of the element common to the deleted row and column.

For example, Fig. 7.12 shows a fourth-order determinant for which, of course, $n = 4$. If we delete a column and a row, then a determinant of order

$$4 - 1 = 3$$

remains.

In particular, if we delete the second row and the third column as shown in Fig. 7.12, the third-order determinant

$$\begin{vmatrix} a_1 & b_1 & d_1 \\ a_3 & b_3 & d_3 \\ a_4 & b_4 & d_4 \end{vmatrix}$$

remains. This determinant is said to be the *minor* of c_2.

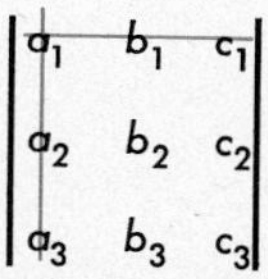

FIGURE 7.11

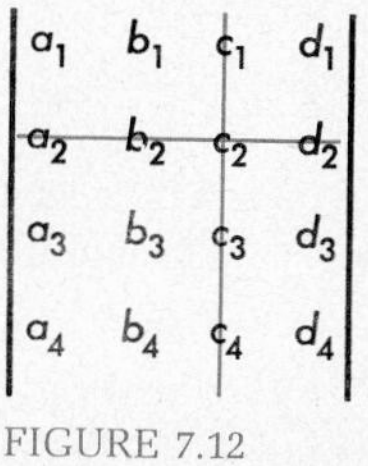

FIGURE 7.12

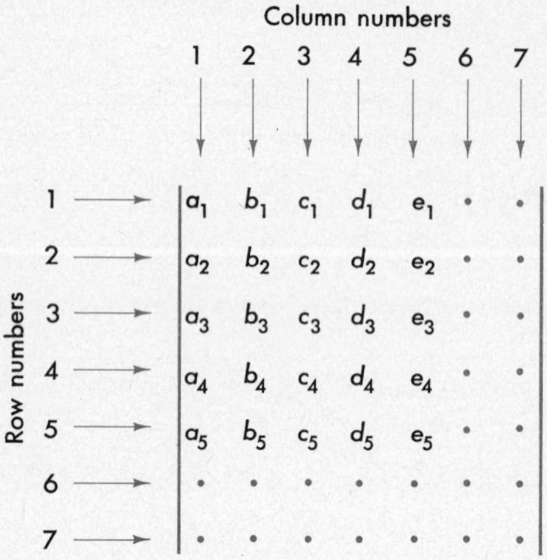

FIGURE 7.13

For purposes of discussion and explanation, it is convenient to identify by number the row and column in which a given element lies (Fig. 7.13). Here, for example, the element d_2 is located in the second row and the fourth column. Its row number is therefore 2, and its column number is 4.

The element c_4 is located in the fourth row and the third column. Its row number is therefore 4, and its column number is 3.

An element is called an *even* element if the sum of its row number and its column number is an even number. An element is called an *odd* element if the sum of its row number and its column number is an odd number.

The element d_2 in Fig. 7.12 is therefore an even element since the sum of its row and column number is $2 + 4 = 6$, which is an even number.

The element c_4 in Fig. 7.12 is an odd element since the sum of its row and column number is $4 + 3 = 7$, which is an odd number.

The *cofactor* of an *even* element is defined to be its own minor. The *cofactor* of an *odd* element is defined to be the *negative* of its own minor.

The cofactor of the element d_2 in Fig. 7.12 is therefore

$$\begin{vmatrix} a_1 & b_1 & c_1 \\ a_3 & b_3 & c_3 \\ a_4 & b_4 & c_4 \end{vmatrix}$$

The cofactor of the element c_4 in Fig. 7.12 is

$$-\begin{vmatrix} a_1 & b_1 & d_1 \\ a_2 & b_2 & d_2 \\ a_3 & b_3 & d_3 \end{vmatrix}$$

7.15 Evaluation of Determinants by Cofactors

The diagonal method described in Sec. 7.13 may be used to evaluate third-order determinants but none of higher order. The method of cofactors about to be discussed may be used for evaluating both third- and higher-order determinants.

The evaluation of third- and higher-order determinants may be accomplished by the application of the following theorem, which is stated without proof.

Theorem. *The value of any third- or higher-order determinant is equal to the algebraic sum of the products formed by multiplying each element of a row (or column) by its own cofactor.*

Example 20. Evaluate the third-order determinant

$$\begin{vmatrix} a_1 & b_1 & c_1 \\ a_2 & b_2 & c_2 \\ a_3 & b_3 & c_3 \end{vmatrix}$$

by the method of cofactors.

This evaluation is illustrated by the equation

$$\begin{vmatrix} a_1 & b_1 & c_1 \\ a_2 & b_2 & c_2 \\ a_3 & b_3 & c_3 \end{vmatrix} = a_1\begin{vmatrix} b_2 & c_2 \\ b_3 & c_3 \end{vmatrix} - a_2\begin{vmatrix} b_1 & c_1 \\ b_3 & c_3 \end{vmatrix} + a_3\begin{vmatrix} b_1 & c_1 \\ b_2 & c_2 \end{vmatrix} \qquad \textbf{(45)}$$

Here we chose to use the elements of column 1. These elements are a_1, a_2, and a_3. We observe that a_1 and a_3 are even elements. Hence the signs associated with the first and third terms are positive. The element a_2 is an odd element. Therefore the algebraic sign associated with the second term is negative.

The cofactor of a_1 is $\begin{vmatrix} b_2 & c_2 \\ b_3 & c_3 \end{vmatrix}$, the cofactor of a_2 is $-\begin{vmatrix} b_1 & c_1 \\ b_3 & c_3 \end{vmatrix}$, and the cofactor of a_3 is $\begin{vmatrix} b_1 & c_1 \\ b_2 & c_2 \end{vmatrix}$.

The following display may be helpful as a memory aid for determining the signs of the various terms involved in evaluating a given determinant.

In this diagram each $-$ sign occupies the same relative position as an odd element. Each $+$ sign occupies the same relative position as an even element.

$$\begin{vmatrix} + & - & + & - & \cdot & \cdot \\ - & + & - & + & \cdot & \cdot \\ + & - & + & - & \cdot & \cdot \\ - & + & - & + & \cdot & \cdot \\ \cdot & \cdot & \cdot & \cdot & \cdot & \cdot \\ \cdot & \cdot & \cdot & \cdot & \cdot & \cdot \end{vmatrix}$$

The general procedure of expansion by minors is applicable to determinants of fourth or higher order. Thus a fourth-order determinant will have as minors of its elements four determinants of the third order. Each of these third-order determinants will expand into three second-order determinants. In this way a fourth-order determinant expands into 12 second-order determinants, a fifth-order determinant into 60 of the second order, and so on.

If one of the elements of a determinant is zero, the work may be simplified by using minors of the elements in the same row or column (see Example 22).

Example 21. Evaluate the determinant

$$\begin{vmatrix} 8 & -2 & 3 \\ 5 & -4 & 1 \\ -6 & 7 & 2 \end{vmatrix}$$

Expanding by elements of the third column (we might have chosen any column or any row), we obtain

$$\begin{vmatrix} 8 & -2 & 3 \\ 5 & -4 & 1 \\ -6 & 7 & 2 \end{vmatrix} = 3\begin{vmatrix} 5 & -4 \\ -6 & 7 \end{vmatrix} - 1\begin{vmatrix} 8 & -2 \\ -6 & 7 \end{vmatrix} + 2\begin{vmatrix} 8 & -2 \\ 5 & -4 \end{vmatrix}$$

$$= 3[(5)(7) - (-6)(-4)] - 1[(8)(7) - (-6)(-2)] + 2[(8)(-4) - (5)(-2)]$$
$$= 3(35 - 24) - 1(56 - 12) + 2(-32 + 10) = 33 - 44 - 44 = -55$$

Example 22. Evaluate the determinant

$$\begin{vmatrix} 3 & 0 & -2 & 1 \\ 4 & -5 & 2 & -3 \\ -1 & 6 & 0 & -4 \\ 7 & 1 & -6 & 5 \end{vmatrix}$$

Expanding by elements of the first row (since it contains a zero),

$$3\begin{vmatrix} -5 & 2 & -3 \\ 6 & 0 & -4 \\ 1 & -6 & 5 \end{vmatrix} - 0\begin{vmatrix} 4 & 2 & -3 \\ -1 & 0 & -4 \\ 7 & -6 & 5 \end{vmatrix} + (-2)\begin{vmatrix} 4 & -5 & -3 \\ -1 & 6 & -4 \\ 7 & 1 & 5 \end{vmatrix} - 1\begin{vmatrix} 4 & -5 & 2 \\ -1 & 6 & 0 \\ 7 & 1 & -6 \end{vmatrix}$$

Taking elements of the second row of the first determinant, since it contains a zero, the first term equals

$$3\left[-6\begin{vmatrix} 2 & -3 \\ -6 & 5 \end{vmatrix} + 0\begin{vmatrix} -5 & -3 \\ 1 & 5 \end{vmatrix} - (-4)\begin{vmatrix} -5 & 2 \\ 1 & -6 \end{vmatrix}\right]$$

$$= 3[-6(10 - 18) + 0 + 4(30 - 2)] = 3(48 + 112) = 480$$

The value of the second term is zero.

Taking elements of the first row, the third term equals

$$-2\left[4\begin{vmatrix}6 & -4\\1 & 5\end{vmatrix} - (-5)\begin{vmatrix}-1 & -4\\7 & 5\end{vmatrix} + (-3)\begin{vmatrix}-1 & 6\\7 & 1\end{vmatrix}\right]$$

$$= -2[4(30 + 4) + 5(-5 + 28) - 3(-1 - 42)]$$
$$= -2(136 + 115 + 129) = -760$$

Taking elements of the second row, the fourth term equals

$$-1\left[-(-1)\begin{vmatrix}-5 & 2\\1 & -6\end{vmatrix} + 6\begin{vmatrix}4 & 2\\7 & -6\end{vmatrix} - 0\begin{vmatrix}4 & -5\\7 & 1\end{vmatrix}\right]$$

$$= -1[30 - 2 + 6(-24 - 14) - 0] = -1(28 - 228) = 200$$

Hence the value of the fourth-order determinant is

$$480 - 0 - 760 + 200 = -80$$

7.16 Simplifying Determinants

The following theorem is of considerable importance in reducing the labor of evaluating determinants.

Theorem 1. *The value of a determinant is not changed if all the elements in any column or row are multiplied by the same number and either added to or subtracted from the corresponding elements in another column or row.*

The proof of this theorem may be found in texts on college algebra. We shall not prove it formally, but we shall illustrate its use.

By reference to Eq. (45), it is evident that if one of the elements a_1, a_2, or a_3 is zero, then the product of it and its associated cofactor will also be zero, and no particular arithmetical work is involved in evaluating the product.

Frequently we can, by the use of the above theorem, take a given determinant and from it write an equal determinant in which one or more elements in a row or column are zero. If we then choose our elements from this row or column, we know without further calculation that the products of these zero elements and their associated cofactors are zero.

By this method let us evaluate the third-order determinant

$$\begin{vmatrix}8 & -2 & 3\\5 & -4 & 1\\-6 & 7 & 2\end{vmatrix}$$

given in Example 21.

Multiply the third column by 5 and subtract from the first column, obtaining

$$\begin{vmatrix} -7 & -2 & 3 \\ 0 & -4 & 1 \\ -16 & 7 & 2 \end{vmatrix}$$

Multiply the third column by 4 and add to the second column, obtaining

$$\begin{vmatrix} -7 & 10 & 3 \\ 0 & 0 & 1 \\ -16 & 15 & 2 \end{vmatrix}$$

This determinant may be expressed as

$$-1\begin{vmatrix} -7 & 10 \\ -16 & 15 \end{vmatrix} = -1(-105 + 160) = -55$$

Note that in this problem we were fortunately able to retain the element 1, which reduced the arithmetical labor also.

As another example let us simplify the fourth-order determinant

$$\begin{vmatrix} 3 & 0 & -2 & 1 \\ 4 & -5 & 2 & -3 \\ -1 & 6 & 0 & -4 \\ 7 & 1 & -6 & 5 \end{vmatrix}$$

given in Example 22.

Multiply the fourth column by 3 and subtract from the first column, obtaining

$$\begin{vmatrix} 0 & 0 & -2 & 1 \\ 13 & -5 & 2 & -3 \\ 11 & 6 & 0 & -4 \\ -8 & 1 & -6 & 5 \end{vmatrix}$$

Multiply the fourth column by 2 and add to the third column, obtaining

$$\begin{vmatrix} 0 & 0 & 0 & 1 \\ 13 & -5 & -4 & -3 \\ 11 & 6 & -8 & -4 \\ -8 & 1 & 4 & 5 \end{vmatrix}$$

This reduces to

$$-1\begin{vmatrix} 13 & -5 & -4 \\ 11 & 6 & -8 \\ -8 & 1 & 4 \end{vmatrix}$$

Multiply the second column of the above third-order determinant by 8 and add to the first column, obtaining

$$-1\begin{vmatrix} -27 & -5 & -4 \\ 59 & 6 & -8 \\ 0 & 1 & 4 \end{vmatrix}$$

Multiply the second column of the above third-order determinant by 4 and subtract from the third column, obtaining

$$-1\begin{vmatrix} -27 & -5 & 16 \\ 59 & 6 & -32 \\ 0 & 1 & 0 \end{vmatrix}$$

This reduces to

$$(-1)(-1)\begin{vmatrix} -27 & 16 \\ 59 & -32 \end{vmatrix} = (-27)(-32) - (59)(16) = -80$$

EXERCISE 8

Evaluate each of the following determinants as directed by the instructor:

1. $\begin{vmatrix} 2 & -1 & 3 \\ 4 & 5 & -2 \\ 1 & -3 & 1 \end{vmatrix}$

2. $\begin{vmatrix} 5 & 4 & 3 \\ 0 & 6 & 2 \\ 1 & 1 & 7 \end{vmatrix}$

3. $\begin{vmatrix} 4 & 0 & -2 \\ 7 & 8 & 3 \\ -5 & 0 & 1 \end{vmatrix}$

4. $\begin{vmatrix} 8 & 7 & -6 \\ 2 & 1 & 4 \\ 3 & -1 & 0 \end{vmatrix}$

5. $\begin{vmatrix} 6 & 2 & 1 \\ -3 & 4 & -5 \\ 3 & -1 & 2 \end{vmatrix}$

6. $\begin{vmatrix} 7 & 0 & -2 \\ -3 & 1 & 4 \\ 6 & 3 & 5 \end{vmatrix}$

7. $\begin{vmatrix} 4 & -4 & a \\ 3 & 5 & a \\ 2 & -1 & a \end{vmatrix}$

8. $\begin{vmatrix} 11 & 2 & -3 \\ -10 & 1 & 4 \\ 9 & 5 & 3 \end{vmatrix}$

9. $\begin{vmatrix} 2 & 3 & a+b \\ 1 & -4 & b+c \\ 5 & -1 & a+c \end{vmatrix}$ 10. $\begin{vmatrix} m & -2 & 3 \\ 4 & 2 & 5 \\ 1 & -1 & m \end{vmatrix}$

11. $\begin{vmatrix} 1 & 2 & 0 & 5 \\ 3 & 0 & 7 & 4 \\ 0 & -6 & 1 & -1 \\ 4 & 3 & 0 & -2 \end{vmatrix}$ 12. $\begin{vmatrix} 7 & 2 & 5 & -1 \\ 4 & 3 & 6 & 1 \\ 8 & 0 & 9 & -2 \\ -3 & 4 & 2 & 1 \end{vmatrix}$

13. $\begin{vmatrix} 5 & 2 & -3 & 8 \\ 4 & -1 & 0 & -2 \\ 0 & 3 & -4 & 1 \\ 6 & 0 & 3 & 5 \end{vmatrix}$ 14. $\begin{vmatrix} 6 & 4 & 0 & -1 \\ 1 & 3 & -5 & m \\ 2 & 0 & -4 & 0 \\ 7 & -3 & 1 & -2m \end{vmatrix}$

15. Show that the equivalent of Eq. (15), page 148, in determinant form is

$$A = \frac{1}{2}\begin{vmatrix} x_1 & y_1 & 1 \\ x_2 & y_2 & 1 \\ x_3 & y_3 & 1 \end{vmatrix}$$

In addition to Theorem 1 set forth at the beginning of this section we state without proof the following:

Theorem 2. *If the rows of a given determinant correspond to the columns of a second, then the two determinants are equal.*

Theorem 3. *If two rows or two columns of a determinant are identical, the value of the determinant is equal to zero.*

Theorem 4. *If each element of a row or column of a determinant is multiplied by the same constant k, the determinant is multiplied by k.*

Theorem 5. *If the elements of any row or any column are all zero, the value of the determinant is zero.*

Theorem 6. *If two rows or two columns of a determinant are interchanged, the determinant so formed is the negative of the original determinant.*

7.17 Determinant Formulas for the Solution of Linear Equations in Three Variables

The application of Cramer's rule to the solution of a system of three linear equations in three variables is entirely comparable with that used in the solution of two simultaneous equations in two variables.

In solving the system

$$a_1x + b_1y + c_1z = k_1$$
$$a_2x + b_2y + c_2z = k_2$$
$$a_3x + b_3y + c_3z = k_3$$

we obtain, by a method entirely analogous to that used in Sec. 7.12,

$$x = \frac{\begin{vmatrix} k_1 & b_1 & c_1 \\ k_2 & b_2 & c_2 \\ k_3 & b_3 & c_3 \end{vmatrix}}{\begin{vmatrix} a_1 & b_1 & c_1 \\ a_2 & b_2 & c_2 \\ a_3 & b_3 & c_3 \end{vmatrix}} \qquad y = \frac{\begin{vmatrix} a_1 & k_1 & c_1 \\ a_2 & k_2 & c_2 \\ a_3 & k_3 & c_3 \end{vmatrix}}{\begin{vmatrix} a_1 & b_1 & c_1 \\ a_2 & b_2 & c_2 \\ a_3 & b_3 & c_3 \end{vmatrix}} \qquad z = \frac{\begin{vmatrix} a_1 & b_1 & k_1 \\ a_2 & b_2 & k_2 \\ a_3 & b_3 & k_3 \end{vmatrix}}{\begin{vmatrix} a_1 & b_1 & c_1 \\ a_2 & b_2 & c_2 \\ a_3 & b_3 & c_3 \end{vmatrix}} \tag{46}$$

As in second-order determinants, the common denominator is called the *determinant of the system.*

As in the case of two equations in two variables, if the determinant of the system equals zero, the equations are either inconsistent, with no solution, or dependent, with infinitely many solutions.

Example 23. Use determinants to solve the system

$$10x + 3y - 6z = -9$$
$$7x + 5y + 4z = 12$$
$$8x - 2y - 9z = -2$$

We note the following values:

$$\begin{array}{llll} a_1 = 10 & b_1 = 3 & c_1 = -6 & k_1 = -9 \\ a_2 = 7 & b_2 = 5 & c_2 = 4 & k_2 = 12 \\ a_3 = 8 & b_3 = -2 & c_3 = -9 & k_3 = -2 \end{array}$$

Hence

$$x = \frac{\begin{vmatrix} -9 & 3 & -6 \\ 12 & 5 & 4 \\ -2 & -2 & -9 \end{vmatrix}}{\begin{vmatrix} 10 & 3 & -6 \\ 7 & 5 & 4 \\ 8 & -2 & -9 \end{vmatrix}}$$

Expanding each determinant by elements of the first row,

$$x = \frac{(-9)\begin{vmatrix} 5 & 4 \\ -2 & -9 \end{vmatrix} - (3)\begin{vmatrix} 12 & 4 \\ -2 & -9 \end{vmatrix} + (-6)\begin{vmatrix} 12 & 5 \\ -2 & -2 \end{vmatrix}}{(10)\begin{vmatrix} 5 & 4 \\ -2 & -9 \end{vmatrix} - (3)\begin{vmatrix} 7 & 4 \\ 8 & -9 \end{vmatrix} + (-6)\begin{vmatrix} 7 & 5 \\ 8 & -2 \end{vmatrix}}$$

$$= \frac{-9[(5)(-9) - (-2)(4)] - 3[(12)(-9) - (-2)(4)] - 6[(12)(-2) - (-2)(5)]}{10[(5)(-9) - (-2)(4)] - 3[(7)(-9) - (8)(4)] - 6[(7)(-2) - (8)(5)]}$$

$$= \frac{-9(-45 + 8) - 3(-108 + 8) - 6(-24 + 10)}{10(-45 + 8) - 3(-63 - 32) - 6(-14 - 40)}$$

$$= \frac{333 + 300 + 84}{-370 + 285 + 324} = \frac{717}{239} = 3$$

By a similar method y and z can be calculated, giving

$$y = \frac{\begin{vmatrix} 10 & -9 & -6 \\ 7 & 12 & 4 \\ 8 & -2 & -9 \end{vmatrix}}{\begin{vmatrix} 10 & 3 & -6 \\ 7 & 5 & 4 \\ 8 & -2 & -9 \end{vmatrix}} = -5 \qquad z = \frac{\begin{vmatrix} 10 & 3 & -9 \\ 7 & 5 & 12 \\ 8 & -2 & -2 \end{vmatrix}}{\begin{vmatrix} 10 & 3 & -6 \\ 7 & 5 & 4 \\ 8 & -2 & -9 \end{vmatrix}} = 4$$

EXERCISE 9

Solve the following systems of simultaneous linear equations by determinants:

1. $x + 2y + z = 20$
   $3x - y + 2z = 22$
   $2x + y - 4z = 7$

2. $4x + 7y + 2z = 21$
   $5x + 8y - 3z = 16$
   $-3x - 5y + 9z = 5$

Suggestion for Prob. 3: Missing variables must be included using coefficient = 0; the first equation would read $5x + 2y + 0z = -17$.

3. $5x + 2y = -17$
   $3x + 7z = 23$
   $4y + 6z = 36$

4. $3x + 5y - 4z = 9a$
   $2x - 3y + 4z = 7b$
   $-6x + y + 3z = b - a$

Suggestion for Prob. 6: Let $a = 1/x$, $b = 1/y$, $c = 1/z$, and solve for a, b, and c.

5. $-7x + y + 4z = -16a$
   $x + y - 4z = -8b$
   $-x + 7y - 4z = 16c$

6. $\frac{1}{x} - \frac{1}{y} + \frac{2}{z} = 7$
   $\frac{2}{x} + \frac{2}{y} - \frac{3}{z} = -2$
   $-\frac{3}{x} + \frac{1}{y} + \frac{1}{z} = 1$

7. $x - 2y - 3z + 4w = -4$
$3x - z + 2w = 16$
$5y + 2z - 3w = 20$
$4x + y - 7w = 10$

8. $x + 2y + 3z = 11$
$-x + 2z + 3w = 9$
$2x - 3y - w = -23$
$y - z + 2w = -1$

Problems in Exercises 2, 3, 4, and 5 may be worked by determinants as directed by the instructor.

7.18 Application of Simultaneous Linear Equations to Kirchhoff's Law

Figure 7.14 is an idealized diagram of considerable importance if batteries are operated in parallel. Ordinarily, in such problems the given circuit parameters are the resistances R_1, R_2, and R_3 and the battery voltages E_1 and E_2. The problem is to solve for the currents I_1 and I_2. The arrows next to the resistors indicate the direction in which the current is assumed to flow. Should either I_1 or I_2 come out negative, it simply means that the assumed direction of current flow was wrong, but if the solution is otherwise correct, the absolute value of the current will be correct.

The basic equations for the solution of this and similar problems are

$$E_1 = R_1I_1 + R_3(I_1 + I_2) \tag{47}$$
$$E_2 = R_2I_2 + R_3(I_1 + I_2) \tag{48}$$

EXERCISE 10

1. Find I_1 and I_2 when the circuit parameters are as follows:

	R_1	R_2	R_3	E_1	E_2
(a)	0.05	0.10	0.75	4.5	5.2
(b)	1.50	2.30	0.50	32.0	35.5
(c)	0.10	0.01	5.00	6.0	7.5

2. (a) Solve Eq. (47) for I_1 and find under what conditions I_1 must be negative.
(b) Solve Eq. (48) for I_2 and find under what conditions I_2 must be negative.

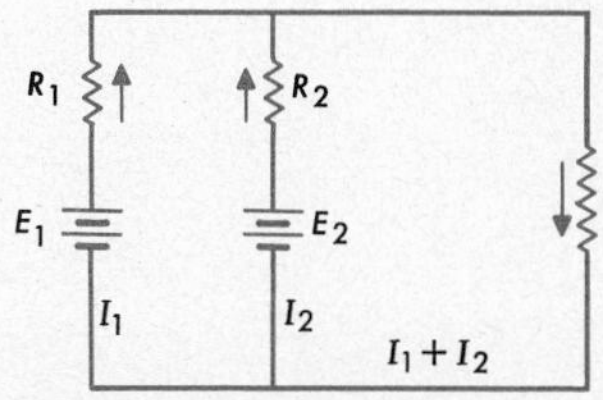

FIGURE 7.14

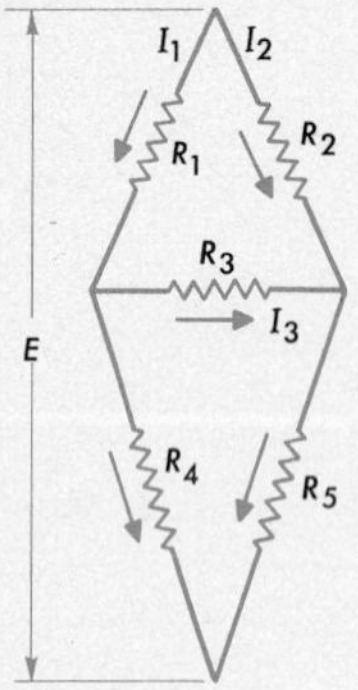

FIGURE 7.15

3. If $E_1 = 5$, $E_2 = 6$, and $R_3 = 10$, find the value of R_2 so that $I_1 = 0$.
4. Show that if

$$\frac{R_2}{R_3} + 1 = \frac{E_2}{E_1}$$

then $I_1 = 0$. [Refer to Eqs. (47) and (48).]

Figure 7.15 illustrates a "bridge" circuit which is widely used for electrical measurements as well as other applications.

We shall assume that the known quantities are E, R_1, R_2, R_3, R_4, and R_5. Having been given these quantities, we shall solve for I_1, I_2, and I_3. As in the previous group of problems, the arrows next to the resistors indicate the assumed direction of current flow. Should either I_1, I_2, or I_3 come out to be negative, it means that the actual direction of current flow is exactly opposite to the assumed direction. This will not affect the absolute value of the current.

The basic equations involved are the following:

$$E = R_1I_1 + R_4(I_1 - I_3)$$
$$E = R_2I_2 + R_5(I_2 + I_3)$$
$$E = R_1I_1 + R_3I_3 + R_5(I_3 + I_2)$$

EXERCISE 11

1. Find I_1, I_2, and I_3 from the following data:

	E	R_1	R_2	R_3	R_4	R_5
(a)	10	2	3	4	5	6
(b)	5	1	5	3	8	4
(c)	1	2	6	9	5	3

(d)	2	5	9	5	3	8
(e)	25	6	9	2	5	8

2. If $I_3 = 0$, show that $R_1/R_4 = R_2/R_5$.

EXERCISE 12

Solve the following problems, using determinants.

1. Three bars of metal A, B, and C have the following weight composition: A contains 6 parts gold, 2 parts silver, and 1 part copper; B, 3 parts gold, 4 parts silver, and 2 parts copper; C, 1 part gold, 3 parts silver, and 5 parts copper. How many ounces of each must be taken to make 28 oz of alloy containing equal parts of gold, silver, and copper?
2. The following table gives the weight composition of three alloys A, B, and C.

	Copper, %	*Tin, %*	*Zinc, %*
A	80	10	10
B	20	40	40
C	50	. . .	50

How many pounds each of A, B, and C must be mixed to produce 600 lb of an alloy containing 60 percent copper, 10 percent tin, and 30 percent zinc?
3. A man wishes to apply to his garden 50 kg of a fertilizer containing 5 percent phosphorus and 12 percent nitrogen. He has available brand A containing 4 percent phosphorus and 10 percent nitrogen, brand B containing 7 percent phosphorus and 11 percent nitrogen, and brand C containing negligible phosphorus and 18 percent nitrogen. How much of each brand should be taken?
4. A waste mixed acid left over from nitrating is composed of 61.8 percent sulfuric acid, 20.1 percent nitric acid, and 18.1 percent water. It is required to make a mixture of 1,000 lb containing 60 percent sulfuric acid, 23 percent nitric acid, and 17 percent water. Solutions of sulfuric acid (98 percent) and nitric acid (90 percent) are available. How many pounds each of waste acid, sulfuric acid, and nitric acid must be taken if no additional water is used?
5. A beam AF weighing 400 lb/ft is supported at points A, B, C, D, E, and F. $AB = 5$ ft, $BC = 6$ ft, $CD = 7$ ft, $DE = 5$ ft, and $EF = 4$ ft. To determine the load carried by each support, the following equations must be solved for W_2, W_3, W_4, and W_5:

$$
\begin{aligned}
11W_2 + 3W_3 &= -\ 34{,}100 \\
6W_2 + 26W_3 + 7W_4 &= -118{,}000 \\
7W_3 + 24W_4 + 5W_5 &= -\ 93{,}600 \\
5W_4 + 16W_5 &= -\ 37{,}800
\end{aligned}
$$

6. A girder AE weighing p lb/ft is supported at five equally spaced points A, B, C, D, and E. $AB = d$ ft. To determine how much of the load each support bears, solve the following equations for W_2, W_3, and W_4 in terms of p and d. ($W_1 = W_5 = 0$.)

$$W_1 + 4W_2 + W_3 = -\frac{pd^2}{2}$$

$$W_2 + 4W_3 + W_4 = -\frac{pd^2}{2}$$

$$W_3 + 4W_4 + W_5 = -\frac{pd^2}{2}$$

7. Fifty people wish to reach a place $27\frac{1}{2}$ mi away. The only available transportation is a bus having a capacity of 30 people and a speed of 35 mi/h. The party is divided into two roughly equal groups, which start at the same time. The first group starts on foot, walking at an average rate of 4 mi/h. The second group rides on the bus a certain distance and then walks the rest of the way at an average rate of 3 mi/h. The bus returns to meet the first group and to carry it the rest of the way. How far should each group walk in order that all may arrive at their destination at the same time? How many hours are required for the transfer?

7.19 Linear Empirical Equations

The underlying relationship between the variables in a set of experimental data is often more clearly revealed if expressed in the form of an equation. Because of the limitations of measured data, such an equation is called empirical. An *empirical formula* is one whose reliability is based upon a limited number of observations and is not necessarily supported by any established theory or law. It is based upon immediate experience rather than logical or mathematical conclusions. The term is not applied in a derogatory sense since many currently accepted scientific laws have been the outgrowth of empirical equations.

A vast amount of work in this area is done, not to discover or verify fundamental scientific laws but to discover and exhibit the performance characteristics of various equipment such as automobile engines, electronic gear, air conditioners, and the like.

It is common observation that experimentally obtained data rarely fall on a straight line when plotted, even though the general relationship appears to be linear. In such cases the constants of the most suitable linear equation may be derived by a variety of methods. One method consists in simply drawing a straight line through two representative points visually selected. This is done when the data are so rough that extreme refinements would be a waste of time and might even be misleading. The method of least squares is indicated when the data are sufficiently refined to warrant expenditure of considerable time. The method of averages represents a fair compromise between these two extremes. In this chapter we shall limit our discussion of derivation of constants to the method of averages.

Example 24. The following data were obtained on the amount of fuel oil (G gal/24 h) required to heat a house at various outdoor temperatures ($T°$ = 24 h average). To avoid complicating factors, only clear, relatively calm days were chosen.

ΔT	$T°$	G	ΔG	$\Delta G/\Delta T$
	9	13.0		
9			−2.0	−0.22
	18	11.0		
7			−1.8	−0.26
	25	9.2		
10			−2.2	−0.22
	35	7.0		
11			−2.5	−0.23
	46	4.5		
13			−2.8	−0.22
	59	1.7		

To satisfy ourselves as to the degree of linearity, we may plot these data or determine the constancy of the ratio $\Delta G/\Delta T$. These ratios have been tabulated above and indicate a fairly close, but not exact, correspondence to linearity. Figure 7.16 indicates the same thing.

In view of the approximate nature of the relationship, we shall use the *method of averages*. This method requires that the data be divided into two groups as nearly equal as possible and the values averaged. Hence we obtain

$$T_1 = \text{average of first three } T\text{'s} = \frac{9 + 18 + 25}{3} = 17.3$$

$$T_2 = \text{average of last three } T\text{'s} = \frac{35 + 46 + 59}{3} = 46.7$$

$$G_1 = \text{average of first three } G\text{'s} = \frac{13.0 + 11.0 + 9.2}{3} = 11.1$$

$$G_2 = \text{average of last three } G\text{'s} = \frac{7.0 + 4.5 + 1.7}{3} = 4.4$$

We shall now obtain the equation of the straight line through the points whose coordinates are (T_1,G_1) and (T_2,G_2).

This equation will be in the slope-intercept form

$$G = mT + b \tag{49}$$

Let the point P_1 (Fig. 7.17) be the point whose coordinates are (T_1,G_1), or (17.3,11.1). Let the point P_2 be the point whose coordinates are (T_2,G_2), or (46.7,4.4). The slope m

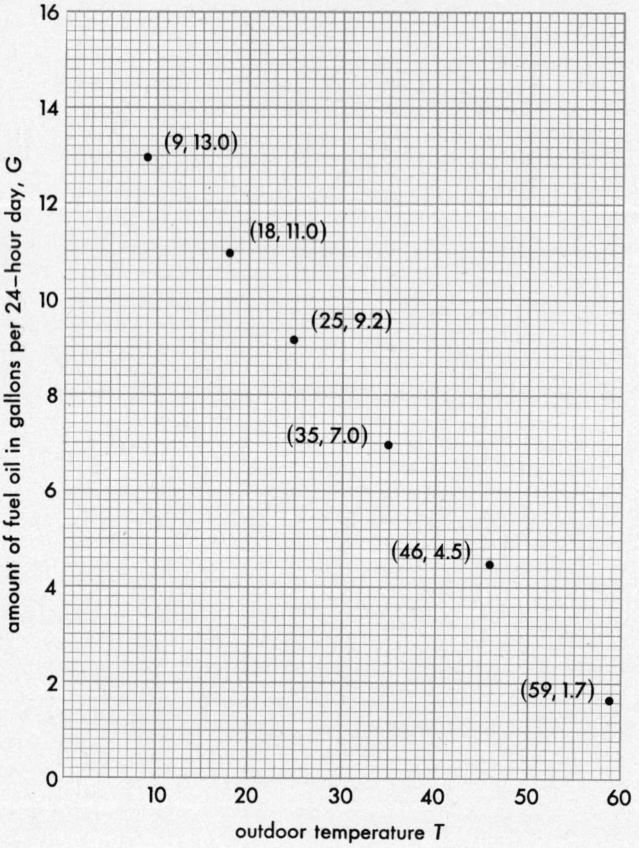

FIGURE 7.16

of this line is

$$m = \frac{G_2 - G_1}{T_2 - T_1} = \frac{4.4 - 11.1}{46.7 - 17.3} = -\frac{6.7}{29.4} = -0.228$$

By substituting this value of slope in Eq. (49), we obtain

$$G = -0.228T + b \tag{50}$$

The coordinates of point P_1 in Fig. 7.17 are (17.3,11.1). (Observe that we could have chosen the point P_2 just as well.)

By substituting 17.3 for T and 11.1 for G in Eq. (50), we obtain

$$11.1 = (-0.228 \times 17.3) + b \tag{50a}$$

from which

$$11.1 = -3.94 + b$$

or

$$b = 11.1 + 3.94 = 15.04$$

or

$$b = 15.0 \qquad \text{(to three significant digits)}$$

The linear equation for G in terms of T in this instance is therefore

$$G = -0.228T + 15.0 \tag{51}$$

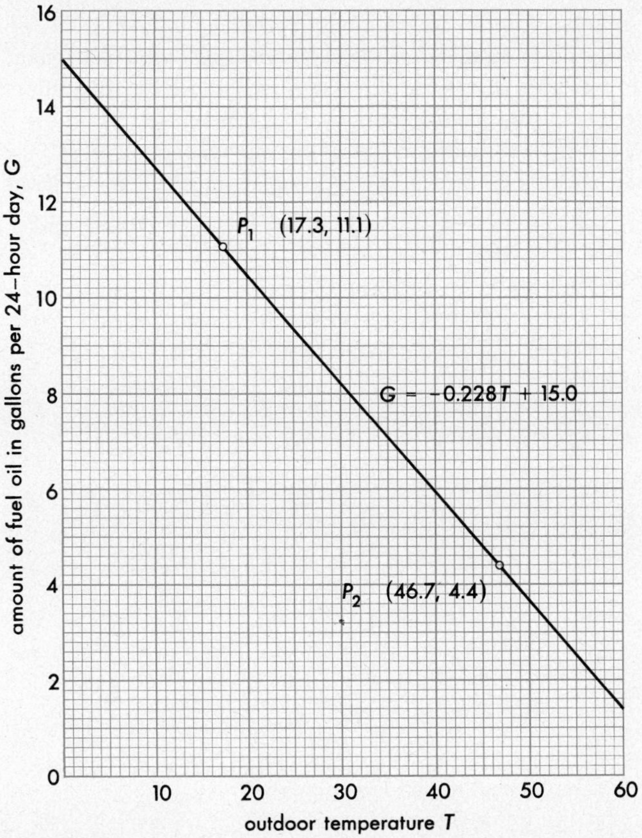

FIGURE 7.17

Some students might prefer to substitute the values (17.3,11.1) and (46.7,4.4) in the equation $G = mT + b$, obtaining the simultaneous equations

$$11.1 = m(17.3) + b$$
$$4.4 = m(46.7) + b$$

Subtracting, we have $6.7 = -29.4m$, or $m = -0.228$. Completing the solution as in Eq. (50*a*), $b = 15.0$, or

$$G = -0.228T + 15.0$$

as above.

According to Eq. (51), when the outdoor temperature is 0°F, the fuel consumption is 15.0 gal/24 h and decreases by 0.228 gal for each degree rise in temperature.

It will be noted in the above examples that we have solved for the dependent variable in terms of the independent variable. Although this is the usual practice, it is occasionally preferable to solve for the independent variable. Problem 9 in the following exercise illustrates this point. In this case the initial reading of the instrument is in terms of the dependent variable (temperature). Then we proceed to determine the corresponding independent variable (concentration of alcohol).

Other examples of this reversal of common procedure are conversion of voltage reading to temperature when checking a thermocouple; conversion of a manometer reading of pressure difference to rate of fluid flow; computation of wind speed from rpm of an anemometer; etc. (see Sec. 6.2).

Incidentally, wherever the time element is involved, it is almost without exception the independent variable.

EXERCISE 13

1. Show, without plotting, that the points in the following table fall exactly in a straight line. (See Example 6, page 130.)

x	20	28	34	44	48
y	50	38	29	14	8

(*a*) Derive the equation for y in terms of x.
(*b*) Find y when $x = 100$.
(*c*) Find x when $y = -13$.
(*d*) At what value is $x = y$?
(*e*) How could your answer in (*d*) be obtained graphically?

2. Show, without plotting, that the following points fall exactly in a straight line.

x	−10	15	65	165	240
y	−5	−3	1	9	15

(*a*) Derive the equation for y in terms of x.
(*b*) Find the x intercept.
(*c*) Find y when $x = 40$.

3. Calculate, by the method of averages, the empirical linear equation best fitting the following data:

x	8	18	29	37	48	51	62	68
y	18	25	32	36	44	45	52	56

When $x = 55$ what is the probable value of y?

4. The overall cost of owning and operating a popular car is given in the following table:

A, mi/year	*B, overall cost, cents/mi*	*C, total cost, \$/year*
5,000	25.0	___
10,000	14.5	___
15,000	11.0	___
20,000	9.25	___

Complete the column for value of C (\$/year). Set up an equation of the type $C = kA + b$, where k and b are constants.

Plot A as abscissas versus C as ordinates. Do the points lie exactly in a straight line? What is the physical significance of the constants k and b?

5. Find the empirical equation, as in Prob. 3, for the following data:

x	−11	1	9	12	19	25	34	45
y	−3	5	10	12	17	22	28	35

In Prob. 6–12, derive the empirical linear equations best representing the data in the tables below. Indicate whether the linear relationship is exact or approximate. If approximate, use the method of averages.

6. The following readings were taken in calibrating a spring where W is the load in pounds and d is the extension in inches. Derive an equation expressing W as a function of d.

W	3.0	5.0	7.0	8.5	11.0	12.0
d	0.20	0.45	0.80	1.0	1.3	1.5

7. The barometer reading (P) in inches of mercury varies with the altitude above sea level (h) in feet as follows:

h	200	500	1,200	1,800	2,500	3,200
P	29.72	29.36	28.58	27.93	27.20	26.48

What linear equation best describes h as a function of P within the range of the data? What is the sea-level pressure?

8. The following prices were quoted for printing a quantity of booklets, where N is the number of booklets and C is the cost (dollars) of the lot.

N	100	250	500	800	1,200
C	30	45	70	100	140

Derive a formula for C in terms of N. What is the significance of the constants?

9. The boiling point (t°C) of dilute alcohol solutions is related to the weight percent concentration of alcohol (p) as shown in the following table:

p	0	2	4	7	10
t	100	97.2	95.2	92.5	90.3

What formula will indicate approximately the alcoholic content when the boiling point is known? It is required that the values $p = 0$, $t = 100$ satisfy the equation. (Base your equation on two points, the first being $p = 0$, $t = 100$, the other point being the average of the other four.)

10. The boiling point of water (t°C) is related to the atmospheric pressure (P mm) as follows:

P	777	766	760	750	740.4	731.4	723.3
t	100.62	100.22	100.00	99.63	99.27	98.93	98.62

It is required that the equation shall be satisfied by the values $P = 760$, $t = 100$ and that it shall represent the best fit for the remaining data.

Derive an equation for P in terms of t.

Derive an equation for t in terms of P.

11. The speed of revolution of an anemometer (R r/min) was checked against the wind speed (V mi/h) to yield the following calibration data:

V	5.0	11.0	17.0	20.0	25.0	30.0	33.0	37.0
R	50	120	190	230	300	360	410	470

Derive a linear equation for V in terms of R. What is the significance of the constants?

12. The resistance R_t of a nickel wire at various Celsius temperatures (t) is shown in the following table:

t	10	25	45	70
R_t	50.4	55.2	61.6	69.6

Derive an equation of the form $R_t = R_{20}[1 + a(t - 20)]$, where R_{20} is the resistance at 20°C.

What is the nature of a?

13. The velocity of sound in air (meters per second) at any Celsius temperature (t) is given by the formula

$$V = 331.7\sqrt{1 + \frac{t}{273}}$$

Evaluate V at $t = -30, -20, -10, 0, 10, 20, 30, 40$ and derive a linear formula for V in terms of t to best fit these points.

8 Logarithms

One of the most effective devices for saving time and effort in mathematical computations when a desk calculator is not available is the logarithm. By means of logarithms, processes of multiplication and division are replaced by addition and subtraction, and those of raising to a power and extracting a root are replaced by multiplication and division. In fact, some mathematical operations, previously difficult, admit of ready solution by logarithms.

8.1 The Concept of a Logarithm

Given the equation $x = b^y$, the following assertions may be made:

1. If b is any positive real number other than unity, then for every real value of y there exists one and only one positive number x, defined by the equation $x = b^y$.
2. Conversely, for every positive value of x there exists a unique real number y such that $x = b^y$.

If

$$x = b^y \qquad (b > 0 \text{ and } b \neq 1) \tag{1}$$

then y is called the logarithm of x to the base b and is written

$$y = \log_b x \tag{2}$$

For example,

$3^2 = 9$ is equivalent to $\log_3 9 = 2$
$5^3 = 125$ is equivalent to $\log_5 125 = 3$
$4^{-1} = 1/4$ is equivalent to $\log_4 1/4 = -1$
$5^{-2} = 1/25$ is equivalent to $\log_5 1/25 = -2$
$49^{1/2} = 7$ is equivalent to $\log_{49} 7 = 1/2$
$15^0 = 1$ is equivalent to $\log_{15} 1 = 0$

Substituting $\log_b x$ for y in the equation $x = b^y$, we have $x = b^{\log_b x}$, from which it follows that

The logarithm of a number is the exponent indicating the power to which it is necessary to raise the base to equal the given number.

The above assertions imply that:

1. For any given logarithm y to a given base there exists a unique number x corresponding to that logarithm.
2. Every positive number x has a unique logarithm for any given positive base other than unity.

Since any number other than zero raised to the zero power equals 1, it follows that the logarithm of 1 to any base equals zero.

EXERCISE 1

In Probs. 1 to 9 write each exponential expression in logarithmic notation.

1. (a) $2^3 = 8$ (b) $2^{-6} = 1/64$ (c) $7^{-2} = 1/49$
2. (a) $3^5 = 243$ (b) $10^{-2} = 0.01$ (c) $(1/6)^2 = 1/36$
3. (a) $5^4 = 625$ (b) $3^{-3} = 1/27$ (c) $(2/3)^3 = 8/27$
4. (a) $2^5 = 32$ (b) $7^0 = 1$ (c) $b^0 = 1$
5. (a) $3^{-4} = 1/81$ (b) $6^2 = 36$ (c) $(1/5)^{-2} = 25$
6. (a) $4^{1/2} = 2$ (b) $8^{1/3} = 2$ (c) $9^{3/2} = 27$
7. (a) $16^{3/4} = 8$ (b) $25^{1/2} = 5$ (c) $27^{2/3} = 9$
8. (a) $125^{2/3} = 25$ (b) $32^{3/5} = 8$ (c) $b^1 = b$
9. (a) $27^{-1/3} = 1/3$ (b) $16^{-5/4} = 1/32$ (c) $36^{-3/2} = 1/216$

Let it be required to find the value of $\log_7 49$. Setting $\log_7 49 = y$, we paraphrase the question by asking ourselves what power of 7 equals 49. Since $7^2 = 49$, it is apparent that $\log_7 49 = 2$.

EXERCISE 2

Find the values of the following logarithms:

1. (a) $\log_5 25$ (b) $\log_2 8$ (c) $\log_3 81$
2. (a) $\log_4 8$ (b) $\log_8 16$ (c) $\log_{16} 8$
3. (a) $\log_9 27$ (b) $\log_{27} 81$ (c) $\log_{125} 25$
4. (a) $\log_7 \sqrt{7}$ (b) $\log_{12} 1$ (c) $\log_3 \frac{1}{3}$
5. (a) $\log_2 \frac{1}{8}$ (b) $\log_{10} 0.001$ (c) $\log_4 \frac{1}{32}$
6. (a) $\log_{125} 5$ (b) $\log_{16} 4$ (c) $\log_{16} \sqrt{4}$

Another version of the logarithmic relationship is exemplified by the equation $\log_5 x = 3$. Here we wish to know what number is equal to the third power of 5. Since $5^3 = 125$, we have $\log_5 125 = 3$.

It may be required to find the base of a logarithmic equation. For example, $\log_b 16 = 4$. This is read "log 16 to what base equals 4?" In other words, what number b raised to the fourth power equals 16? The answer is evidently 2. Hence $\log_2 16 = 4$.

EXERCISE 3

Find the value of x in Probs. 1 to 4.

1. (a) $\log_2 x = 3$ (b) $\log_5 x = 2$ (c) $\log_3 x = 4$
2. (a) $\log_5 x = 0$ (b) $\log_6 x = -1$ (c) $\log_8 x = \frac{4}{3}$
3. (a) $\log_{10} x = 2$ (b) $\log_3 x = -2$ (c) $\log_{27} x = \frac{2}{3}$
4. (a) $\log_{16} x = \frac{3}{4}$ (b) $\log_8 x = -\frac{2}{3}$ (c) $\log_{25} x = -\frac{1}{2}$

In Probs. 5 to 10 find the value of the base b.

5. (a) $\log_b 9 = 2$ (b) $\log_b 8 = 3$ (c) $\log_b 4 = \frac{2}{3}$
6. (a) $\log_b 1{,}000 = 3$ (b) $\log_b 25 = 2$ (c) $\log_b 3 = \frac{1}{2}$
7. (a) $\log_b 15 = 1$ (b) $\log_b 1 = 0$ (c) $\log_b \frac{1}{4} = -2$
8. (a) $\log_b \frac{1}{27} = -\frac{3}{2}$ (b) $\log_b \frac{1}{25} = -\frac{2}{3}$ (c) $\log_b 7 = -\frac{1}{2}$
9. (a) $\log_b 9 = -\frac{2}{3}$ (b) $\log_b 0.01 = 2$ (c) $\log_b \frac{1}{16} = -\frac{4}{3}$
10. (a) $\log_b 1{,}000 = \frac{3}{2}$ (b) $\log_b 6 = -\frac{1}{2}$ (c) $\log_b \frac{1}{64} = -6$

8.2 Properties of Logarithms

Since logarithms are exponents, the rules relating to the use of logarithms resemble the laws of exponents.

The most common relationships are the following:

$$\log_b (PQ) = \log_b P + \log_b Q \quad (3)$$

$$\log_b \frac{P}{Q} = \log_b P - \log_b Q \quad (4)$$

$$\log_b P^n = n \log_b P \quad (5)$$

$$\log_b \sqrt[n]{P} = \frac{1}{n} \log_b P \quad (6)$$

$$\log_b 1 = 0 \quad (7)$$

$$\log_b \frac{1}{P} = -\log_b P \quad (8)$$

These rules will be derived in Secs. 8.3 to 8.8.

8.3 Multiplication

Let

$$P = b^c \qquad \text{or} \qquad \log_b P = c$$

and

$$Q = b^d \qquad \text{or} \qquad \log_b Q = d$$

Then

$$PQ = b^c \cdot b^d = b^{c+d}$$

In logarithmic notation, this becomes

$$\log_b (PQ) = c + d$$

But

$$c + d = \log_b P + \log_b Q$$

Therefore

$$\log_b (PQ) = \log_b P + \log_b Q \qquad \text{[Eq. (3)]}$$

The logarithm of a product is equal to the sum of the logarithms of the separate factors.

8.4 Division

Let

$P = b^c \qquad \text{or} \qquad \log_b P = c$

and

$Q = b^d \qquad \text{or} \qquad \log_b Q = d$

Then

$$\frac{P}{Q} = \frac{b^c}{b^d} = b^{c-d}$$

In logarithmic notation, this becomes

$$\log_b \frac{P}{Q} = c - d$$

But

$$c - d = \log_b P - \log_b Q$$

Therefore

$$\log_b \frac{P}{Q} = \log_b P - \log_b Q \qquad \text{[Eq. (4)]}$$

The logarithm of a quotient is equal to the logarithm of the numerator minus the logarithm of the denominator.

8.5 Powers

If

$$P = b^c$$

then

$$\log_b P = c$$

Also

$$P^n = b^{cn}$$

which in logarithmic notation is

$$\log_b P^n = cn$$

But

$$c = \log_b P$$

Therefore

$$\log_b P^n = n \log_b P \qquad \text{[Eq. (5)]}$$

This is a form of the product rule. If we let $P = Q$ in Eq. (3), then $\log_b P^2 = 2 \log_b P$, or in general, $\log_b P^n = n \log_b P$.

The logarithm of a power of a number is equal to the exponent times the logarithm of the number.

8.6 Roots

This is a form of the power rule, for if we write

$$\log_b \sqrt[n]{P} \qquad \text{as } \log_b P^{1/n}$$

we obtain

$$\log_b P^{1/n} = \frac{1}{n} \log_b P$$

Therefore

$$\log_b \sqrt[n]{P} = \frac{1}{n} \log_b P \qquad \text{[Eq. (6)]}$$

The logarithm of a root of a number is the logarithm of that number divided by the index of the root.

8.7 Logarithm of Unity

This is also a special case of the power rule in which $n = 0$.

$$\log_b 1 = \log_b P^0 = 0 \log_b P = 0 \qquad \text{[see Eq. (7)]}$$

The logarithm of unity to any base is zero.

8.8 Reciprocal

This is another variation of the power law. In this case $n = -1$.

$$\log_b \frac{1}{P} = \log_b P^{-1} = (-1) \log_b P = -\log_b P \qquad \text{[see Eq. (8)]}$$

The logarithm of the reciprocal of a number is the negative of the logarithm of that number.

8.9 Logarithm of the Base

If in Eq. (1) we let

$$x = b$$

then

$$b = b^y$$

Following Sec. 2.3, it is evident that

$$y = 1$$

From Eq. (2) of this chapter,

$$1 = \log_b b \qquad \textbf{(9)}$$

Thus *the logarithm of the base in any system is 1.*

8.10 Systems of Logarithms

From the problems in Exercises 1 to 3 it is evident that any positive number, except 1, can be used as a base for a system of logarithms. The number 1 cannot be used as a base because 1, when raised to any power whatever, is still equal to 1.

There are two systems of logarithms in general use: the system of common logarithms to the base 10 and the system of natural logarithms to the base *e*, or 2.71828· · ·. Natural logarithms will be discussed in the next chapter.

The system of common logarithms is most convenient for general computation because it is best suited to the decimal system. Hereafter, unless otherwise indicated, the word *logarithm* will be understood to mean common logarithm. When the base is not expressed, the base 10 is understood. Thus $\log 3 = 0.47712$ means $\log_{10} 3 = 0.47712$.

From the laws of exponents we know that $10^0 = 1$, $10^1 = 10$, $10^2 = 100$, $10^3 = 1{,}000$, $10^4 = 10{,}000$, $10^5 = 100{,}000$, etc.

In logarithmic notation the above equations become $\log_{10} 1 = 0$, $\log_{10} 10 = 1$, $\log_{10} 100 = 2$, $\log_{10} 1{,}000 = 3$, $\log_{10} 10{,}000 = 4$, $\log_{10} 100{,}000 = 5$, etc.

8.11 Change of Base

At times it is necessary to change from one base to another, especially when dealing with sound levels, mechanical shock, and transient electric currents. The formula is

$$\log_a Q = (\log_a b)(\log_b Q) \qquad \textbf{(10)}$$

Since *a* and *b* are both constants, $\log_a b$ is also a constant. Hence, if only a table to the base *b* is available, the logarithm of a number to the base *b* can be converted to the logarithm of the same number to the base *a* by multiplying the former by the constant $\log_a b$.† See Eq. (16) below.

The proof of the statement follows:

Let

$$Q = b^x$$

so that

$$\log_b Q = x \qquad (11)$$

Also if

$$Q = b^x$$

† $\log_a b$ has the advantage of being a multiplying (rather than a dividing) constant, especially in repetitive calculations. Since $\log_a b$ may be obtained by evaluating $1/(\log_b a)$, Eq. (16), we can still operate entirely within the system of logarithms to the base *b*.

then

$$\log_a Q = \log_a b^x = x \log_a b \tag{12}$$

but

$$x = \log_b Q$$

Then from Eqs. (11) and (12)

$$\log_a Q = (\log_b Q)(\log_a b)$$

or better,

$$\log_a Q = (\log_a b)(\log_b Q)$$

Also let

$$Q = a^y$$

Then

$$\log_a Q = y \tag{13}$$

Also if

$$Q = a^y$$

$$\log_b Q = \log_b a^y = y \log_b a \tag{14}$$

but

$$y = \log_a Q$$

Then from Eqs. (13) and (14)

$$\log_b Q = (\log_a Q)(\log_b a)$$

or better,

$$\log_b Q = (\log_b a)(\log_a Q) \tag{15}$$

From Eq. (10)

$$\frac{\log_a Q}{\log_b Q} = \log_a b$$

and, from Eq. (15)

$$\frac{\log_a Q}{\log_b Q} = \frac{1}{\log_b a}$$

Therefore

$$\log_a b = \frac{1}{\log_b a} \qquad \textbf{(16)}$$

or

$$(\log_a b)(\log_b a) = 1 \qquad \textbf{(17)}$$

Eq. (17) may be readily confirmed by the following illustration.

Given $4^{3/2} = 8$ then $\log_4 4^{3/2} = \log_4 8$ or $\frac{3}{2} = \log_4 8$

but $8^{2/3} = 4$ then $\log_8 8^{2/3} = \log_8 4$ or $\frac{2}{3} = \log_8 4$

therefore

$$(\log_4 8)(\log_8 4) = 1$$

8.12 Graphical Derivation of Table

If we use 10 for the base instead of the general value b, we obtain the graph shown in Fig. 8.1. This, then, is the graph of $x = 10^y$, or $y = \log_{10} x$. It is apparent that when $y = 0$, $x = 1$. When $y = \frac{1}{3}$, $x = 10^{1/3}$, or $\sqrt[3]{10}$, or 2.154. When $y = \frac{1}{2}$, $x = 10^{1/2}$, or $\sqrt{10}$, or 3.162. When $y = 1$, $x = 10$, etc.

For any given value of y, there is only one value of x; and conversely, for any given positive value of x, there is only one value of y (Sec. 8.1). Thus any positive number x may be expressed as a power of 10, just as we have considered 2.154 as the 0.333 power of 10 and 3.162 as the 0.500 power of 10.

If this curve were drawn to a large enough scale, we should be able to read

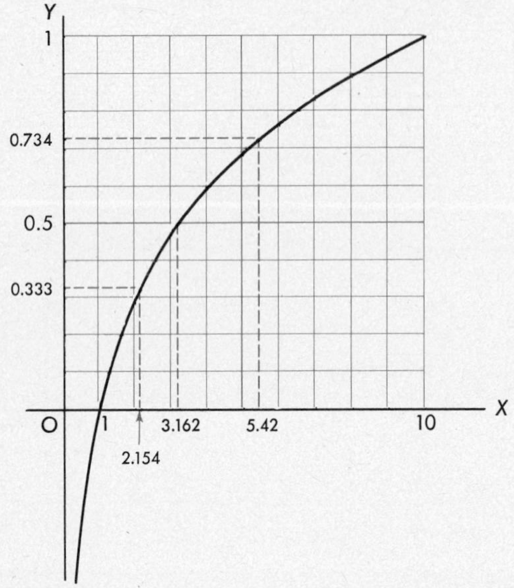

FIGURE 8.1

that when $x = 5.42$, $y = 0.734$ (approximately). Evidently, then, $10^{0.734} = 5.42$, or $\log_{10} 5.42 = 0.734$.

8.13 Characteristics and Mantissas

If we know that $10^{0.734} = 5.42$, then from Eqs. (1) and (2) we may write

$$\log_{10} 5.42 = 0.734$$

Now it is a simple matter to find the logarithm of 54.2, 542, 5,420, 0.00542, or any number with this particular sequence of digits, regardless of the position of the decimal point. The student should study the following examples carefully.

$$\log 54.2 = \log (10 \times 5.42) = \log 10 + \log 5.42 = 1 + 0.734$$
$$\log 542 = \log (100 \times 5.42) = \log 100 + \log 5.42 = 2 + 0.734$$
$$\log 5{,}420 = \log (1{,}000 \times 5.42) = \log 1{,}000 + \log 5.42 = 3 + 0.734$$
$$\log 0.542 = \log (0.1 \times 5.42) = \log 0.1 + \log 5.42 = -1 + 0.734$$
$$\log 0.0542 = \log (0.01 \times 5.42) = \log 0.01 + \log 5.42 = -2 + 0.734$$
$$\log 0.00542 = \log (0.001 \times 5.42) = \log 0.001 + \log 5.42 = -3 + 0.734$$

Each logarithm will be seen to consist of an integer (positive, negative, or zero) and a decimal which is a positive number or zero and less than 1.

The integral part is called the *characteristic*, and the decimal part is called the *mantissa*. The mantissa is usually an unending decimal which, by more advanced mathematics, may be computed to as many places as desired.

It will be noted that the mantissa depends only on a given sequence of digits, in this case 542. All numbers having a given sequence of digits will have the same mantissa. On the other hand, the characteristic is seen to be related to the position of the decimal point.

The relationships set forth in the beginning of this section are summarized in Table 8.1.

TABLE 8.1

		Characteristic		Mantissa	Common method of writing logarithm
log 5,420	=	3	+	0.734	3.734
log 542	=	2	+	0.734	2.734
log 54.2	=	1	+	0.734	1.734
log 5.42	=	0	+	0.734	0.734
log 0.542	=	−1	+	0.734	0.734 − 1
log 0.0542	=	−2	+	0.734	0.734 − 2
log 0.00542	=	−3	+	0.734	0.734 − 3

From Table 8.1 it will be evident that

For numbers larger than 1 the characteristic of the logarithm is zero or a positive number and one less than the number of digits at the left of the decimal point in the number. If the number is smaller than 1, the characteristic is negative and corresponds to the position of the first significant figure.

For example, in the number 0.00542 the first significant digit is in the third place to the right of the decimal point; therefore the characteristic of the logarithm is −3.

By common agreement the mantissa in a logarithm table (and elsewhere except as noted below) is always considered to be positive.

Alternative conventions of writing logarithms containing negative characteristics are illustrated below. For the most part we shall confine ourselves in this text to the form shown in the left-hand column.

0.734 − 1	9.734 − 10	$\bar{1}.734$	−0.266
0.734 − 2	8.734 − 10	$\bar{2}.734$	−1.266
0.734 − 3	7.734 − 10	$\bar{3}.734$	−2.266

The notation in the extreme right-hand column is used only under special conditions (Sec. 8.28).

TABLE 8.2

Number	Scientific notation	Logarithm
5,420	5.42×10^3	3.734
542	5.42×10^2	2.734
54.2	5.42×10^1	1.734
5.42	5.42×10^0	0.734
0.542	5.42×10^{-1}	$0.734 - 1$
0.0542	5.42×10^{-2}	$0.734 - 2$
0.00542	5.42×10^{-3}	$0.734 - 3$

If the number is expressed in scientific notation, the characteristic corresponds to the power of 10, as illustrated in Table 8.2.

A table of mantissas, or logarithms of numbers between 1 and 10, will be seen to be sufficient to determine the logarithm of any positive number, the proper positive or negative characteristic being supplied by inspection.

8.14 The Antilogarithm of a Number

A number N is called the *antilogarithm* (or *antilog*) of another number y if

$$y = \log N$$

For example, we see from Table 8.2 that

$$1.734 = \log 54.2$$

Therefore 54.2 is the antilogarithm of 1.734.

EXERCISE 4

1. Complete the following table:

	Number	*Scientific notation*	*Logarithm*
(*a*)	8.61	$8.61\ (\times 10^0)$	0.935
(*b*)	861	8.61×10^2	2.935
(*c*)	0.0861	8.61×10^{-2}	$0.935 - 2$
(*d*)	8,610	———	———
(*e*)	———	8.61×10^5	———
(*f*)	———	———	4.935
(*g*)	0.00861	———	———

(h)	———	8.61×10^{-1}	———
(i)	———	———	0.935 − 4
(j)	8,610,000	———	———
(k)	———	8.61×10^{8}	———
(l)	———	———	0.935 − 3

Given log 3.54 = 0.549 and log 7.98 = 0.902 in Probs. 2 to 4, find the logarithms of the given numbers. In Probs. 5 to 7 find the antilogarithms of the given logarithms.

2. (a) 35.4	(b) 798	(c) 79,800
3. (a) 0.0354	(b) 0.354	(c) 7,980
4. (a) 0.00798	(b) 3,540,000	(c) 0.000354
5. (a) 2.549	(b) 1.902	(c) 8.902 − 10
6. (a) 0.902 − 3	(b) 4.549	(c) 0.549 − 1
7. (a) 6.549 − 10	(b) 3.902	(c) 0.549 − 3

8.15 Using a Table of Logarithms

A portion of a five-place table of logarithms is reproduced in Table 8.3. (Since this table shows mantissas only, it would be more precise to refer to it as a table of mantissas. However, in ordinary usage such tables are referred to as "log tables." Therefore we shall continue to refer to them in this way.)

From this table we find that the mantissa of the logarithm of 3,124 is 0.49471. We have obtained this value by reading in from the number representing the first three digits, 312, and under the fourth digit, 4. Two space-saving conventions will be noted: the decimal point is not shown; neither are the first two digits, 49, of the mantissa shown.

Another space-saving device is revealed if it is required to look up the mantissa of the logarithm of 3,168. Reading opposite 316 and under 8, we find *079. The asterisk tells us that we have moved from mantissas 0.49··· to mantissas 0.50···. Therefore this particular mantissa is 0.50079.

Since $3{,}168 = 3.168 \times 10^3$, the characteristic of the logarithm is seen to be 3, and the complete logarithm of 3,168 is 3.50079.

EXERCISE 5

Referring to Table 8.3, determine the complete logarithms (characteristic and mantissa) of the following numbers:

1. 3,103	2. 313.6	3. 310	4. 3.190
5. 31,160	6. 318,200	7. 3.152	8. 3,167
9. 3,100,000	10. 31.63	11. 31	12. 3.1

TABLE 8.3

N	0	1	2	3	4	5	6	7	8	9
310	49136	150	164	178	192	206	220	234	248	262
311	276	290	304	318	332	346	360	374	388	402
312	415	429	443	457	471	485	499	513	527	541
313	554	568	582	596	610	624	638	651	665	679
314	693	707	721	734	748	762	776	790	803	817
315	831	845	859	872	886	900	914	927	941	955
316	969	982	996	*010	*024	*037	*051	*065	*079	*092
317	50106	120	133	147	161	174	188	202	215	229
318	243	256	270	284	297	311	325	338	352	365
319	379	393	406	420	433	447	461	474	488	501
320	515	529	542	556	569	583	596	610	623	637

In looking up the logarithm of a number smaller than unity, we may first express the number in scientific notation and then determine the mantissa and characteristic from the respective first and second parts of that number.

Example 1. Use Table 8.3 to read the logarithm of 0.003148. In scientific notation this becomes 3.148×10^{-3}. Therefore by inspection the characteristic is -3, and from the table, the mantissa is 0.49803. Hence the logarithm of 0.003148 is $0.49803 - 3$.

EXERCISE 6

Referring to Table 8.3, determine the logarithms of the numbers in Probs. 1 to 12.

1. 0.003122 2. 0.03196 3. 0.3144 4. 0.00031
5. 0.03167 6. 0.0000315 7. 0.3171 8. 0.003185
9. 0.00000319 10. 0.3111 11. 0.03105 12. 0.003162

Referring to Table 8.3, determine the numbers corresponding to the logarithms (i.e., find the antilogarithms) in Probs. 13 to 24.

13. 1.49178 14. 2.49374 15. 3.50065
16. $0.50092 - 2$ 17. $0.50515 - 3$ 18. $0.50284 - 1$
19. 4.50569 20. 0.50243 21. 5.49290
22. $0.50325 - 4$ 23. 1.50010 24. $0.49996 - 1$

EXERCISE 7

Referring to a five-place log table, find the logarithms of the numbers in Probs. 1 to 3.

1. (*a*) 1,234 (*b*) 100.3 (*c*) 0.01234 (*d*) 37.05 (*e*) 398.4

2. (*a*) 79,020 (*b*) 0.3076 (*c*) 3,000 (*d*) 0.005006 (*e*) 1,003,000
3. (*a*) 179.7 (*b*) 0.1042 (*c*) 0.01090 (*d*) 709.3 (*e*) 0.0007065

Find the numbers corresponding to the logarithms in Probs. 4 to 6.

4. (*a*) 3.75051 (*b*) 0.56038 − 2 (*c*) 1.55096
   (*d*) 0.00043 (*e*) 0.93997 − 1
5. (*a*) 7.93475 − 10 (*b*) 0.06333 (*c*) 5.60206
   (*d*) 2.96440 (*e*) 4.76005
6. (*a*) 1.21537 (*b*) 3.61794 (*c*) 0.27161 − 4
   (*d*) 5.99502 (*e*) 2.47012

8.16 Interpolation

It is often necessary to find the logarithm of a number which does not exactly appear in the table. If we are satisfied to use the logarithm of the nearest number, we reduce the accuracy of a five-place table to that of a four-place table. It is not necessary to sacrifice this extra degree of accuracy if we resort to interpolation. In a five-place table interpolation will determine for us the fifth digit in the mantissa, but not a sixth.

Example 2. Find by interpolation log 25.813.

The characteristic of the required logarithm is found by inspection. In this case the characteristic is 1. For the present, therefore, we shall give our entire attention to the problem of finding the required mantissa.

From Sec. 8.12 we recall that the mantissa of the logarithm of a number depends only on the sequence of digits in that number, and not on the position of the decimal point in it. For example, the mantissa of the logarithm of 25.813 is exactly the same as the mantissa of the logarithm of 25,813, and we shall proceed to use this equivalence in the discussion to follow, not from necessity but as a matter of convenience.

First find the mantissas of 25,810 and 25,820. These are 41179 and 41196, respectively (decimal points are disregarded for the time being). The *tabular difference* between the mantissas is 17, whereas the difference between 25,810 and 25,820 is 10. It is evident that the given number 25,813 is 0.3 of the way from 25,810 to 25,820. Therefore the desired mantissa must be about 0.3 of the way from 41179 to 41196. Three-tenths of 17 is 5.1, which is rounded off to 5. Adding 5 to 41179 we get 41184. Therefore the mantissa is 0.41184, and by inspection the characteristic is 1. Hence log 25.813 = 1.41184.

The interpolation may be arranged as follows:

Write down the bracketing numbers and their mantissas, leaving space for the intermediate number and its mantissa. Annex a cipher as a fifth digit to each bracketing number and write in the given number. Indicate the differences or proportional parts. By proportion, $3/10 = x/17$, or $x = (3/10)(17) = 5.1$, by mental calculation or slide rule.

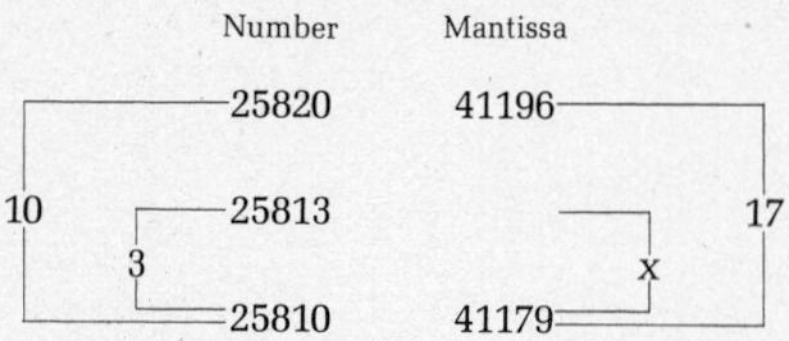

Observe that since the mantissas are unending decimals and are rounded off to five digits, there would be no point in adding 41179 and 5.1 and calling the result 41184.1. Hence we calculate x only to the nearest whole number.

Most tables include tables of proportional parts in which x in the above proportion may be found. This is simply a table of tenths of the tabular difference, which is 17 in this example. Usually, mental computation is the quickest way to determine the proportional part x.

	17
1	1.7
2	3.4
3	5.1
⋮	⋮

Example 3. Find log 232.464973.

If, as in this example, the given number contains more than five significant figures and the tabular difference is 15 or more, round off to six significant figures and proceed as in the following example.

Rounding off to six digits, we get 232.465.

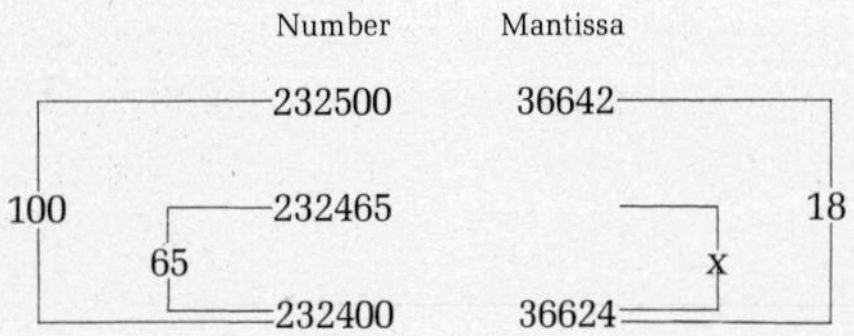

By proportion, $65/100 = x/18$, or $x = (^{65}/_{100})(18) = 11.7$, which we call 12. Therefore the mantissa is $36624 + 12$, or 0.36636. The complete logarithm is 2.36636.

The process of interpolation as applied to antilogarithms is simply the reverse of that used in looking up logarithms.

Example 4. Find antilog 3.54859.

We do not find 54859 in the table of mantissas, but we do find the bracketing mantissas 54851 and 54864. These correspond to the numbers 3,536 and 3,537, respectively. The operation is illustrated as follows:

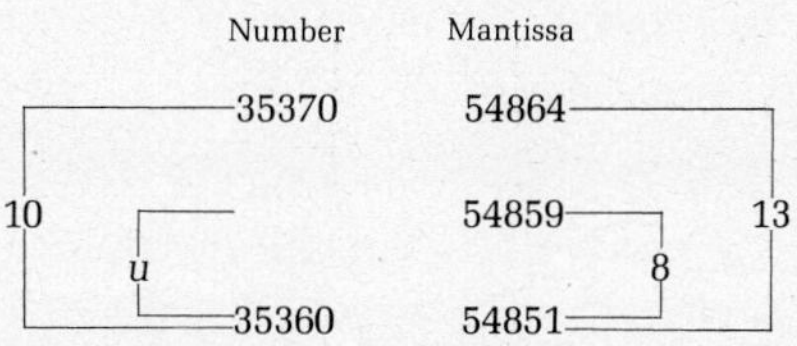

By proportion, $u/10 = 8/13$, or $u = (8/13)(10) = 6.2$, which we call 6. Therefore the digits of the number are 35,360 + 6, or 35,366. The characteristic 3 determines the number to be 3,536.6.

If we choose to use the proportional-parts table, we scan the values listed under 13 until we come to the value nearest 8. This is 7.8, which corresponds to 6 (0.6 of 13).

	13
—	—
5	6.5
6	7.8
7	9.1
—	—

Note that if the difference x is less than 1 part out of 20, interpolation is omitted, since if $x < 1$, $(x/20)(10) < 0.5$, or less than 5 in the sixth place.

In this case, simply the nearest mantissa is taken.

Example 5. Find the antilogarithm of 1.21565.

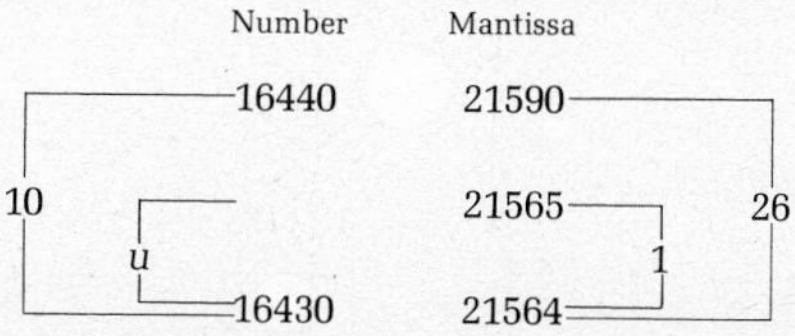

$u/10 = 1/26$, or $u = (1/26)(10) = 0.4$, which is less than 0.5; $21564 + 0.4 = 21564$. Therefore we ignore interpolation and take the nearest mantissa, 21564. Thus we get antilog $1.21565 = 16.430$.

Interpolation may sometimes be facilitated by approaching our answer from the upper value instead of the lower.

Example 6. Find log 0.012148.

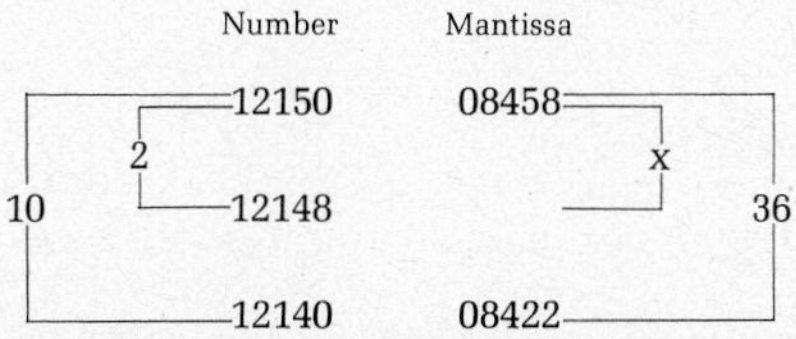

Here we write $x/36 = 2/10$, or $x = (^2/_{10})(36) = 7.2$, or 7; $08458 - 7 = 08451$.

This is somewhat easier than the equivalent operation:

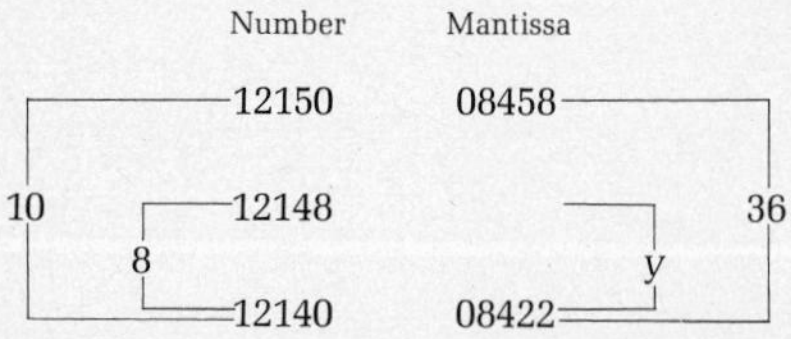

$y/36 = 8/10$; $y = 28.8$ or 29; $08422 + 29 = 08451$.

In either case the complete logarithm is $0.08451 - 2$.

EXERCISE 8

Using a five-place log table, look up the logarithms of the numbers in Probs. 1 to 3, obtaining the last digit by interpolation.

1. (*a*) 268.18 (*b*) 0.0043356 (*c*) 21.355
   (*d*) 9.2354 (*e*) 4.1497
2. (*a*) 68.173 (*b*) 0.030689 (*c*) 55,071
   (*d*) 0.13309 (*e*) 8,585.4
3. (*a*) 11,958 (*b*) 37.596 (*c*) 0.00079364
   (*d*) 2,090.2 (*e*) 118,210,000

Find to five significant figures the numbers whose logarithms are given in Probs. 4 to 6. Obtain the fifth significant figure by interpolation.

4. (*a*) 3.20756 (*b*) $0.29577 - 1$ (*c*) 1.79652
   (*d*) 4.38896 (*e*) 2.59460
5. (*a*) $0.00309 - 3$ (*b*) 0.47562 (*c*) $0.89964 - 4$
   (*d*) $0.69250 - 2$ (*e*) 5.14521
6. (*a*) $0.01997 - 4$ (*b*) 1.27461 (*c*) 5.93376
   (*d*) 2.00215 (*e*) $0.37965 - 1$

8.17 Computation Using Logarithms

In carrying out computations involving logarithms, we shall make use of the equations set forth in Sec. 8.2.

8.18 Multiplication by the Use of Logarithms

According to Eq. (3), the logarithm of a product equals the sum of the logarithms of the separate factors.

Example 7. Find the product (238.24)(0.072495)(9.5668) = N.

From Eq. (3), log 238.24 + log 0.072495 + log 9.5668 = log N.

From the tables,

$$
\begin{aligned}
\log 238.24 &= 2.37701 \\
\log 0.072495 &= 0.86031 - 2 \\
\log 9.5668 &= \underline{0.98077} \\
\log N &= 4.21809 - 2 \\
&= 2.21809 \\
N &= 165.23
\end{aligned}
$$

If a computation involves negative quantities, they should be treated as though they were positive, since a negative number does not have a logarithm in the set of real numbers.

The sign of the answer can be determined by inspection after completion of the computation.

EXERCISE 9

Using logarithms, perform the following computations to five significant figures:

1. 47.690 × 32.410 × 76.480 × 1.9320
2. 3.7596 × 159.06
3. 10.365 × 0.42659
4. (2,586.0)(−169.20)(1.4230)(−0.96000)
5. 73.650 × 9.9000 × 0.99990 × 1.0010 × 0.013090
6. (70.603)(0.55146)(0.00021300)(1.4020)(40.326)(−743.01)
7. 25.726 × 5.0789 × 2,188.5 × 5.2525 × 4,660.1
8. 2,208.6 × 0.043680 × 2,781,200,000 × 0.000016976
9. 0.0018746 × 15.856 × 2,650.0 × 2.0460 × 50,620,000
10. 3.6492 × 1,006.4 × 0.00037964 × 0.0017960 × 36.592

8.19 Division by the Use of Logarithms

From Eq. (4) we find that the logarithm of a quotient equals the logarithm of the numerator minus the logarithm of the denominator.

Example 8. Evaluate 845.67/0.68332 = N.

$$
\begin{aligned}
\log 845.67 &= 2.92720 \\
\log 0.68332 &= \underline{0.83462 - 1} \\
\log N &= 2.09258 + 1 \\
&= 3.09258 \\
N &= 1237.6
\end{aligned}
$$

Example 9. Evaluate $37.844/510.26 = N$.

If we attempt to perform this subtraction directly, we write

$$\begin{aligned} \log 37.844 &= 1.57800 \\ \log 510.36 &= \underline{2.70788} \\ \log N &= -1.12988 \end{aligned}$$

Although the logarithm of the product is algebraically correct, we are unable to look up the antilogarithm because the ordinary tables do not contain negative mantissas. To avoid this impasse, we may write the logarithm of the numerator in the equivalent form

$$\log 37.844 = 1.57800 = 1.57800 + 2 - 2$$

or

$$\log 37.844 = 3.57800 - 2$$

Then the logarithmic subtraction would appear as

$$\begin{aligned} \log 37.844 &= 3.57800 - 2 \\ \log 510.36 &= \underline{2.70788 } \\ \log N &= 0.87012 - 2 \end{aligned}$$

and $N = 0.074152$.

This device can be used whenever it is necessary to subtract a larger logarithm from a smaller one in the process of calculating the logarithm of a quotient. In general, we add and subtract an integer which is large enough to yield a positive mantissa in the difference.

EXERCISE 10

Use logarithms to compute the following quotients to five significant figures:

1. $(3{,}796.0) \div (-472.00)$	2. $7{,}943.2 \div 25.793$
3. $7.5437 \div 97.604$	4. $0.047920 \div 6.3951$
5. $4{,}605.2 \div 56{,}517$	6. $99.976 \div 10.532$
7. $1{,}000.1 \div 3{,}576.5$	8. $0.37960 \div 0.020710$
9. $12.147 \div 0.00049630$	10. $-5{,}076.0 \div 0.043297$
11. $1 \div 53.827$	12. $1 \div 0.082941$

8.20 Combined Multiplication and Division

This is simply a combination of Eqs. (3) and (4) for multiplication and division.

Example 10. Evaluate $75.282\pi/[(6.754)(0.38949)(0.01217)] = N$.

$$
\begin{aligned}
\log 75.282 &= 1.87669 \\
\log 3.1416 &= \underline{0.49715} \\
\log \text{num.} &= 2.37384 \qquad \longrightarrow \quad 2.37384 \\
\log 6.754 &= 0.82956 \\
\log 0.38949 &= 0.59050 - 1 \\
\log 0.01217 &= \underline{0.08529 - 2} \\
\log \text{den.} &= 1.50535 - 3 \longrightarrow \underline{1.50535 - 3} \\
\log \text{num.} - \log \text{den.} &= \qquad\qquad \longrightarrow 0.86849 + 3 \\
\log N &= 3.86849
\end{aligned}
$$

$N = 7387.3$ or better $N = 7387$ (This is limited to four significant figures of accuracy. See Sec. 8.25)

8.21 Cologarithms

The *cologarithm* of a number is the logarithm of the reciprocal of the number. It is therefore equal to the negative of the logarithm of the number.

$$\operatorname{colog} N = \log \frac{1}{N} = -\log N \tag{18}$$

Since division by N is equivalent to multiplication by $1/N$, it follows that division by a given number may be accomplished by adding the cologarithm instead of subtracting the logarithm. A combined multiplication and division problem may therefore be evaluated by adding up only one column of logarithms.

For convenience, we wish to avoid becoming involved with negative mantissas when using cologs in calculations. To accomplish this, we often resort to the same sort of a device as we used in Example 9. For example, following Eq. (18), we may write

$$
\begin{aligned}
\operatorname{colog} N &= -\log N \\
&= -\log N + 10 - 10
\end{aligned} \tag{19}
$$

(It is usually more convenient to add and subtract 10 or some integral multiple of 10.)

We may write Eq. (19) as

$$\operatorname{colog} N = (10 - \log N) - 10 \tag{20}$$

Example 11. Find the cologarithm of N if $N = 66.32$.

First let us evaluate the quantity $(10 - \log 66.32)$ in Eq. (20). From a five-place log table we find that

$$\log 66.32 = 1.82164$$

Then

$$\begin{aligned} 10 - \log N &= 10.00000 - 1.82164 \\ &= 8.17836 \end{aligned}$$

and from Eq. (20)

$$\operatorname{colog} 66.32 = 8.17836 - 10 = 0.17836 - 2$$

As a practical matter, we usually evaluate the quantity $(10 - \log N)$ mentally as we read the value of $\log N$ directly from the table. Beginning at the left, we subtract each digit in the logarithm of N from 9 until we reach the last *significant* digit, which we subtract from 10. The result is the cologarithm of N.

Example 12. Find the colog of N if $N = 0.7042$.

$$\begin{aligned} \operatorname{colog} 0.7042 &= (10 - \log 0.7042) - 10 \\ &= [10 - (0.84770 - 1)] - 10 \\ &= 10 - 0.84770 + 1 - 10 \\ &= 9.15230 + 1 - 10 \\ &= 9.15230 - 9 = 0.15230 \end{aligned}$$

Example 13. Evaluate N in Example 10 by using cologs.

$$\begin{aligned} \log 75.282 &= 1.87669 \\ \log 3.1416 &= 0.49715 \\ \operatorname{colog} 6.754 &= 0.17044 - 1 \\ \operatorname{colog} 0.38949 &= 0.40950 \\ \operatorname{colog} 0.01217 &= \underline{1.91471} \\ & \quad 4.86849 - 1 \\ \log N &= 3.86849 \\ N &= 7387.3 \end{aligned}$$

EXERCISE 11

Evaluate the following to five significant figures.

1. $\dfrac{576.43 \times 976.52 \times 1.4962}{3.7425 \times 0.0096520 \times 0.017360}$

2. $\dfrac{57.040 \times 25.936 \times 0.48352}{764.32 \times 97.630 \times 0.0079860}$

3. $\dfrac{601.47 \times 93.276 \times 2.5037 \times 79.631}{927.43 \times 26.485 \times 0.0017930 \times 62.000}$

4. $\dfrac{10.243 \times 1.5006 \times 0.96016 \times 9.1207}{59.329 \times 3.8421 \times 0.027532 \times 0.50008}$

8.22 Raising to a Power

According to Eq. (5), the logarithm of the power of a number is found by multiplying the logarithm of the number by the exponent.

Example 14. Evaluate $(1.8653)^8 = N$.
From Eq. (5) we may write

$$\log N = 8 \log 1.8653$$

From a table of five-place logarithms we find that

$$\log 1.8653 = 0.27075$$

Then

$$\log N = 8 \times 0.27075 = 2.16600$$

and

$$N = 146.56$$

Example 15. Evaluate $(5.167)^{-2.8} = N$.
From Eq. (5) we may write

$$\log N = -2.8 \log 5.167$$

From a table of five-place logarithms we find

$$\log 5.167 = 0.71324$$

Then

$$\log N = -2.8 \times 0.71324 = -1.99707$$

Observe that the negative sign in the foregoing equation affects the entire logarithm, both characteristic and mantissa. To obtain a logarithm of equal value but with a positive mantissa, we again resort to the device used in Example 9, and we write

$$\begin{aligned} \log N &= -1.99707 = (10 - 1.99707) - 10 \\ &= 8.00293 - 10 \\ &= 0.00293 - 2 \end{aligned}$$

Then we find

$$N = 0.010068$$

Alternative solution.

$$(5.167)^{-2.8} = \frac{1}{(5.167)^{2.8}} \qquad \text{(law of exponents)}$$

$$\begin{array}{rl} \log 5.167 = & 0.71324 \\ & \underline{2.8} \\ & 570592 \\ & \underline{142648} \\ \log (5.167)^{2.8} = & 1.997072 \end{array}$$

$$\begin{aligned} \log 1 &= 2.00000 - 2 \\ \log (5.167)^{2.8} &= \underline{1.99707} \\ \log N &= 0.00293 - 2 \qquad \text{(subtracting)} \\ N &= 0.010068 \end{aligned}$$

Example 16. Evaluate $(0.17528)^{1.75} = N$.

$$\begin{aligned} \log 0.17528 &= 0.24373 - 1 \\ \log N &= 1.75 \log 0.17528 \\ &= 1.75(0.24373 - 1) \\ &= 0.42653 - 1.75 \end{aligned}$$

Now add zero in a form to make the characteristic a whole number. In this case we add zero in the form of $(0.25 - 0.25)$ as follows:

$$\begin{array}{rl} & 0.42653 - 1.75 \\ & +0.25 \quad\; - 0.25 \quad (=0) \\ \hline \log N = & 0.67653 - 2 \\ N = & 0.047482 \end{array}$$

Example 17. Evaluate $(0.4627)^{-3.2} = N$.

$$\begin{aligned} \log N &= -3.2 \log 0.4627 \\ &= -3.2(0.66530 - 1) \end{aligned}$$

where $\log 0.4627 = 0.66530 - 1$

$$\log N = -2.12896 + 3.20000 = +1.07104$$
$$N = 11.777$$

Alternative solution.

$$(0.4627)^{-3.2} = \frac{1}{(0.4627)^{3.2}} = \left(\frac{1}{0.4627}\right)^{3.2}$$

$$\begin{array}{rll} \log 1 = & 1.00000 - 1 & \\ \log 0.4627 = & 0.66530 - 1 & \text{(subtracting)} \\ \hline & 0.33470 & \\ & 3.2 & \\ \hline & 66940 & \\ & 100410 & \\ \hline \log N = & 1.07104 & \\ N = & 11.777 & \end{array}$$

EXERCISE 12

Use logarithms to evaluate the following to five significant figures. Consider all values good to five significant figures.

1. (*a*) $(4.875)^5$ (*b*) $(-11.83)^3$ (*c*) $(0.6432)^4$
2. (*a*) $(0.09458)^3$ (*b*) $(0.14732)^2$ (*c*) $(-0.25713)^4$
3. (*a*) $(23.805)^{-1}$ (*b*) $(7.432)^{-2}$ (*c*) $(16.031)^{-3}$
4. (*a*) $(17.584)^{3/2}$ (*b*) $(405.76)^{2/3}$ (*c*) $(1807.4)^{2/5}$
5. (*a*) $(0.6432)^{2.2}$ (*b*) $(0.09473)^{-1.8}$ (*c*) $(2.75)^{2.75}$
6. (*a*) $(0.16223)^{3/4}$ (*b*) $(0.074962)^{4/5}$ (*c*) $(0.25814)^{5/2}$
7. (*a*) $(70.58)^{0.2}$ (*b*) $(13.625)^{1.3}$ (*c*) $(48.461)^{-0.3}$
8. (*a*) $(14.83)^{-1.62}$ (*b*) $(0.3447)^{-2.22}$ (*c*) $(0.0962)^{3.15}$

8.23 Extracting Roots

Referring to Eq. (6), Sec. 8.2, we read that the logarithm of the root of a number equals the logarithm of that number divided by the index of the root.

Example 18. Evaluate $\sqrt[4]{737.12} = N$.

$$\log 737.12 = 2.86754$$

$$\log N = \frac{2.86754}{4}$$

$$= 0.71688$$

$$N = 5.2106$$

Example 19. Evaluate $\sqrt[3]{0.00028864} = N$.

$$\log 0.00028864 = 0.46036 - 4$$

If we were to divide the entire logarithm by 3 as it stands, the characteristic -4 would give us the awkward -1.33333. To avoid this, we add at the left, and subtract at the right, a quantity which will make the characteristic divisible by 3. The simplest such number is 2.

$$\begin{aligned}
\log 0.00028864 &= 0.46036 - 4 \\
&\ \ +2 \qquad\quad\ \ - 2 \\
&\ \ 3\,\underline{/2.46036 - 6} \\
\log N &= 0.82012 - 2 \\
N &= 0.066087
\end{aligned}$$

EXERCISE 13

Evaluate the following expressions, assuming all values accurate to five significant figures:

1. (*a*) $\sqrt[3]{972}$ (*b*) $\sqrt[3]{97.2}$ (*c*) $\sqrt[3]{9.72}$
2. (*a*) $\sqrt[3]{0.972}$ (*b*) $\sqrt[3]{0.0972}$ (*c*) $\sqrt[3]{0.00972}$
3. (*a*) $\sqrt{73.464}$ (*b*) $\sqrt[3]{168.15}$ (*c*) $\sqrt[4]{3051.8}$
4. (*a*) $\sqrt{0.082167}$ (*b*) $\sqrt[3]{0.22469}$ (*c*) $\sqrt[4]{0.000058274}$
5. $(8.527)^3 \times (0.7161)^2$
6. $\sqrt{58.43} \times (6.710)^2$
7. $(185.2 \times 0.071828)^3$
8. $\sqrt{97.422 \times 4.7881}$
9. $\sqrt{\dfrac{219.6}{0.005733}}$
10. $\sqrt[3]{\dfrac{52.482}{371.05 \times 0.18061}}$

11. $\sqrt[3]{\dfrac{3 \times 0.28617}{4\pi}}$

12. $[\pi(0.07112)(8.859)]^2$

13. $\sqrt[3]{\dfrac{(427.5)^2}{(13.482)^5}}$

14. $\sqrt[6]{\left(\dfrac{27.42}{0.03966}\right)^5}$

15. $\sqrt[5]{-381.72}$

16. $\sqrt[3]{\dfrac{-17.477}{(-0.84991)^2}}$

17. $\left(\dfrac{64.66}{-1{,}009}\right)^{2/3}$

18. $\sqrt[4]{\dfrac{1}{8.3567}}$

8.24 Logarithmic Computation of Expressions Involving Addition and Subtraction

Since numbers cannot be added or subtracted by logarithms, we must convert to antilogarithms before performing such an operation.

Example 20. Evaluate $\sqrt{(a^5 + 1)/(a^5 - 1)} = N$, where $a = 1.0037$.

$$\begin{aligned}
\log 1.0037 &= 0.0016039 \qquad \text{(seven-place table)}\\
&\quad \underline{\qquad\qquad 5}\\
\log (1.0037)^5 &= 0.0080195\\
(1.0037)^5 &= 1.01864 \qquad \text{(seven-place table)}\\
\sqrt{\frac{1.01864 + 1}{1.01864 - 1}} &= \sqrt{\frac{2.01864}{0.01864}}\\
\log 2.0186 &= 0.30505\\
\text{Subtract:}\quad \log 0.01864 &= \underline{0.27045 - 2}\\
&\quad 0.03460 + 2\\
&\quad 2\underline{/2.03460}\\
\log N &= 1.01730\\
N &= 10.41
\end{aligned}$$

Note that although we have been able to find $(1.0037)^5$ to six figures using a seven-place table, after we subtract 1 we get a denominator 0.01864 having only four significant figures. Therefore we can retain only four significant figures in our answer. This situation points up the need of extra accuracy in reading logarithms of numbers near unity. The mantissas of such numbers may have only two or three significant figures when taken from a five-place table.

EXERCISE 14

Use logarithms to compute the value of the following to five significant figures.

1. $\sqrt{(8.3150)^2 - (5.0240)^2}$ (see Sec. 8.26)
2. $\sqrt{(11.964)^2 + (4.4857)^2}$
3. $\sqrt[3]{(4.1150)^3 + (6.3820)^3}$
4. $\sqrt[5]{(1.4860)^7 - 20.000}$
5. $\sqrt[3]{\dfrac{(1.3890)^3 + 1}{(1.3890)^3 - 1}}$

The short problems in Exercises 15 and 16 may be used to test the student's understanding of the properties of logarithms without spending the time usually required in consulting tables.

EXERCISE 15

Transform the equations in probs. 1 to 4 into exponential form.

1. $\log_b (a - x) = c$
2. $\log_b (x^2 + 3) - \log_b (2x + 1) = k$
3. $2 \log_b (3x - 2) = a + c$
4. $\log_b y = \sqrt{2x + 5}$
5. If $\log \sqrt{x} = 0.35$, find $\log x^2$.
6. If $\log_b bx = 5$, find $\log_b x$.
7. If $\log 1/x = 1/4$, find $\log x$.
8. If $\log x^2 = 16$, find $\log x$.
9. If $\log (x^2 - 9) - \log (x + 3) = 0$, find x.

Rewrite the expressions in Probs. 10 to 12 without exponents or radicals.

10. (a) $\log x^5$ (b) $\log 3x^2$ (c) $\log (5/x^2)$
11. (a) $\log \sqrt[3]{x}$ (b) $\log \dfrac{1}{x^3}$ (c) $\log \dfrac{1}{2\sqrt{x}}$
12. (a) $\log \dfrac{x^5}{8}$ (b) $\log_b bx^2$ (c) $\log_b \dfrac{2x^3}{b^2}$

Convert the expressions in Probs. 13 and 14 to single positive logarithms whose coefficient is 1.

13. (a) $6 \log x$ (b) $2 \log x - \log 3$ (c) $(\log_b x)/2 + 1$
14. (a) $3 - \log_b x$ (b) $\frac{1}{2}(\log x + \log 2)$ (c) $-10 \log x$

15. A student wrote $\log (N + 2) + \log N = \log (2N + 2)$. This is true only for what positive value of N?
16. What is the value of $\log_5 0.04$?
17. If $\log (p/q) + \log (q/r) - \log (r/p) - 2 \log (p/r) = \log x$, what is x?
18. If $S = P(1 + r)^{-n}$, solve for n.
19. If $\log_b y = 2 - 3 \log_b x$, solve for y.

EXERCISE 16

Given only that $\log 2 = 0.301$ and $\log 3 = 0.477$, find the following without using tables:

1. (a) log 2,000 (b) log 0.03 (c) $\log \sqrt{30}$
2. (a) $\log \frac{1}{16}$ (b) $\log (3)^7$ (c) log 6
3. (a) log 1 (b) log 20 (c) log 5
4. (a) log 1.5 (b) log 8 (c) log 0.0003
5. (a) $\log \sqrt{15}$ (b) $\log \sqrt[3]{60}$ (c) $\log 3\frac{1}{3}$
6. (a) log 39 − log 13 (b) $\log (\frac{1}{3})^4$ (c) $\log \sqrt[5]{\frac{1}{2}}$
7. (a) $\log \sqrt[4]{\frac{1}{3}}$ (b) $\log \sqrt[3]{0.0002}$ (c) $\log (24)^{1.65}$
8. (a) log 46 − log 23 (b) antilog 3.477 (c) antilog 0.301 − 3
9. (a) antilog 2.301 (b) antilog 0.176 − 2 (c) antilog 3.01
10. (a) antilog 1.778 (b) antilog 7.778 − 10 (c) antilog 0.0477

8.25 Accuracy in Logarithmic Computations

The student should bear in mind that in multiplication and division the accuracy of the result is determined by the least accurate individual factor. If several six-digit numbers are to be multiplied by a number of four significant figures, all the individual factors should be rounded off to four significant figures, since the answer will be limited to this degree of accuracy. Consequently, a four-place table of logarithms will suffice. By the same token, if the utmost accuracy is to be secured from a combination of numbers of seven significant figures, a table to at least seven places must be used.

8.26 Aids to Logarithmic Computation

Computation involving logarithms may be expedited by observing a few details of technique, of which the following are representative:

1. Follow some orderly plan of development, such as that set forth in Example 10, Sec. 8.20.
2. Cancel or combine simple numbers where possible to reduce the number of logarithms to be handled.
3. Improve the arrangement for logarithmic computation, e.g.,
   (a) $2\pi r^2 + 2\pi rh = 2\pi r(r + h)$. Once r and h are added, there will be no further obstacle to logarithmic computation.
   (b) $\sqrt{c^2 - a^2} = \sqrt{(c + a)(c - a)}$. Here we enter a "straightaway" as soon as $c + a$ and $c - a$ are evaluated.
4. Negative characteristics and mantissas can often be avoided in a division problem by multiplying numerator and denominator by some integral power of 10, for example, 0.03152/0.00567 = 31.52/5.67.
5. Another device to circumvent negative logarithms is multiplication by a^n. For example, the equation $47.59 = (1.52)^{-3}N$ may be multiplied throughout by $(1.52)^3$; thus we get $(47.59)(1.52)^3 = N$.

8.27 Power Function vs. Exponential Function

Thus far our discussion of calculation of powers and roots by means of logarithms has been limited to cases of the type $x = b^c$, where x is a variable and c is a constant. (See particularly Probs. 1 and 2, Exercise 13, page 230.)

An expression such as x^3, in which a variable is raised to a fixed power, is called a *power function*. We shall now consider *exponential functions,* that is, expressions in which the variable occurs in the exponent. Table 8.4 contrasts these functions.

TABLE 8.4

	x	0	1	2	3	4	5	6	7
Power function	x^3	0	1	8	27	64	125	216	343
Exponential function	3^x	1	3	9	27	81	243	729	2,187

In this table we note that values of x, which are evenly spaced, are in arithmetic progression because there is a constant difference between successive values. If we examine the values of 3^x, we see that they are in geometric progression because there is a constant ratio between two successive values. This is a most important property of exponential functions.

8.28 Exponential Equations

An equation in which the unknown appears in the exponent is called an *exponential equation*. An example of the simplest of this type is $3^x = 9$. Here x is obviously equal to 2, since $3^2 = 9$.

In equations in which the result cannot be determined by inspection, we must take logarithms of both sides of the equation and obtain the final solution by ordinary algebraic methods.

Example 21. Solve the following equation for x:

$$32^x = 512$$

Since we might have written $(2^5)^x = 2^9$, it is quite obvious from inspection that $5x = 9$ and that $x = 1.8$. However, we wish to assure ourselves that the logarithmic method is valid. Therefore we shall take the logarithm of each member, obtaining

$$\log 32^x = \log 512$$

Then

$$x \log 32 = \log 512$$
$$1.50515x = 2.70927$$

To avoid confusion, it is suggested that the student consider this equation as an ordinary linear equation, which it is. Had this equation appeared in the section of elementary algebra devoted to linear equations in one variable, there would be no doubt as to the method of solving for x. The possible origin of the equation did not affect the procedure there; neither does it in this case. Accordingly,

$$x = \frac{2.70927}{1.50515} = 1.8000$$

If only two- or three-place accuracy is desired, this division may be performed on the slide rule.

Example 22. Solve the equation $9^{2x-7} = 27^{x-3}$ for x.

Since in this example both 9 and 27 are powers of the same number, 3, we might proceed by inspection without tables:

$$9^{2x-7} = 27^{x-3}$$

But

$$9 = 3^2 \qquad \text{and} \qquad 27 = 3^3$$

Therefore

$$(3^2)^{2x-7} = (3^3)^{x-3}$$
$$3^{4x-14} = 3^{3x-9}$$

It is evident that $4x - 14$ must equal $3x - 9$; therefore $x = 5$.

Alternative solution. Taking logarithms of each member, we obtain

$$\log 9^{2x-7} = \log 27^{x-3}$$
$$(2x - 7) \log 9 = (x - 3) \log 27$$
$$(2x - 7)(0.95424) = (x - 3)(1.43136)$$

Here again we have an ordinary linear equation and proceed accordingly. Carrying out the indicated multiplication,

$$1.90848x - 6.67968 = 1.43136x - 4.29408$$

$$0.47712x = 2.38560$$

$$x = \frac{2.38560}{0.47712} = 5.0000$$

In some cases a few preliminary steps are necessary to obtain one term on each side of the equation before taking logarithms.

In Examples 23 and 25 below we cannot solve by inspection, and we must use the general logarithmic method.

Example 23. Solve for x the equation $\frac{(1.05)^x - 1}{0.05} = 18.$

$$(1.05)^x - 1 = (0.05)(18) = 0.9$$
$$(1.05)^x = 1.9$$

Proceed as before.

Example 24. Given the equation $y = 10(1.065)^t$, evaluate y to 0.01 when $t = 0, 11, 22, 33, 44$. Using the principles of Sec. 8.22, we can relate y and t in the following table:

t	0	11	22	33	44
y	10.00	19.99	39.97	79.90	159.73

This is actually a table of the growth of \$10 at $6\frac{1}{2}$ percent compound interest. The compound amount y is seen to approximately double in the first 11 years and predictably doubles again in each successive 11 years. We shall deal with this property at some length in Sec. 8.29.

Some equations in which the value of the exponent ultimately proves to be negative depend for their solution upon the deliberate conversion of the mantissa of a logarithm to the negative form (Sec. 8.13).

Example 25. Solve for x the equation $6^x = 0.0208$.

Taking logarithms of both sides,

$$x \log 6 = \log 0.0208$$

Then

$$x(0.77815) = 0.31806 - 2$$

Treating this as an ordinary linear equation, we obtain

$$0.77815x = 0.31806 - 2.00000$$

$$0.77815x = -1.68194$$

$$x = \frac{-1.68194}{0.77815}$$

$$= -2.1615$$

Example 26. Solve the equation $0.05 = (\frac{2}{3})^x$ for x.

In equations of this type we can avoid negative characteristics, thereby simplifying our computation by taking reciprocals of both sides. Thus we obtain $1/0.05 = [1/(\frac{2}{3})]^x$, or $20 = (\frac{3}{2})^x$. Then, as in Example 25, $\log 20 = x \log 1.5$, or $1.30103 = 0.17609x$ and $x = 7.3884$.

EXERCISE 17

Solve for x in the following exponential equations:

1. $2^x = 75$
2. $(1.07)^x = 3$
3. $125^x = 48(5)^x$
4. $5^x = 1{,}000$
5. $(1.05)^{-x} = 0.36$
6. $3^{x+1} = 5^{x-1}$
7. $4^{x+2} = 8^{2x-1}$
8. $6^{-x} = 0.02$
9. $(1.04)^{-x} = 0.75$
10. $\dfrac{(1.06)^x - 1}{0.06} = 12$
11. $8^x = \dfrac{8}{2^{x-3}}$
12. $5^x = 20^{1/x}$

8.29 Compound Interest Law (CIL), or Exponential Law of Growth and Decay

Many quantities in nature grow in much the same way as a sum of money at compound interest; i.e., the rate of growth is a fixed percentage of the amount on hand at the beginning of the interest period in question. Many chemical reactions conform to this type.

The growth of money occurs stepwise at the end of each interest-conversion period, whereas growth (and decay) in nature usually appears to be a smooth, continuous process. This simply means that the "interest" is converted exceedingly often, and the analogy to compound interest remains close.

If a chemical substance is reacting, it is reacting one molecule at a time. An electrical condenser discharges one electron at a time, and a hot body is radiating its energy one quantum at a time.

As indicated above, one of the best-known examples of exponential equations is found in the growth of money at compound interest. The equation is

$$S = P(1 + r)^n \qquad \textbf{(21)}$$

where P = original principal invested
n = number of interest periods
r = rate of interest (expressed as a decimal) applied to one interest period
S = compound amount of original principal plus accrued interest

Example 27. Make a table of compound amounts for the first 5 years if \$100 is invested at 6 percent compounded annually.

Substituting in Eq. (21), we have $S = 100(1 + 0.06)^t$. Since we have one period per year, we may replace n by t.

Year, t	*Principal at beginning of year*	*Common multiplier*	*Compound amount at end of year, S*
1	\$100.00	1.06	$100(1.06) =$ \$106.00
2	106.00	1.06	$100(1.06)^2 =$ 112.36
3	112.36	1.06	$100(1.06)^3 =$ 119.10
4	119.10	1.06	$100(1.06)^4 =$ 126.25
5	126.25	1.06	$100(1.06)^5 =$ 133.82
⋮	⋮	⋮	⋮

Example 28. Repeat Example 27 except that interest is to be compounded (or converted) semiannually. Here we have two periods a year at 3 percent per period, which requires that we replace n by $2t$ and set $r = 0.03$ (3 percent per half-year).

Thus we have $S = 100(1 + 0.03)^{2t}$, and the principal will grow according to the following table.

Year, t	*Periods, n = 2t*	*Principal at beginning of year*	*Common multiplier*	*Compound amount at end of year, S*
1	2	\$100.00	$(1.03)^2$	$100(1.03)^2 =$ \$106.09
2	4	106.09	$(1.03)^2$	$100(1.03)^4 =$ 112.55
3	6	112.55	$(1.03)^2$	$100(1.03)^6 =$ 119.41
4	8	119.41	$(1.03)^2$	$100(1.03)^8 =$ 126.68
5	10	126.68	$(1.03)^2$	$100(1.03)^{10} =$ 134.39
⋮	⋮	⋮	⋮	⋮

Example 29. A machine worth \$1,280 new depreciates in value by a constant 25 percent annually of its value at the beginning of any given year. In this example $r = -0.25$, and the equation might be expressed

$$V = V_0(1 - 0.25)^t = V_0(0.75)^t$$

where t = time in years dating from time of purchase (= number of periods)
V_0 = original purchase price (= \$1,280)
V = book value after t years

A table of book values would appear as follows:

Year, t	*Book value at beginning of year*	*Common multiplier*	*Book value at end of year, V*
1	\$1,280	0.75	$1{,}280(0.75) = \$960$
2	960	0.75	$1{,}280(0.75)^2 = 720$
3	720	0.75	$1{,}280(0.75)^3 = 540$
4	540	0.75	$1{,}280(0.75)^4 = 405$
⋮	⋮	⋮	⋮

There are many physical laws which obey the CIL concept. A number of these laws are concerned with a depreciating value, as in Example 29. A few typical examples are found in radioactive decay, cooling of a warm object, attenuation of light in an absorbing medium, discharge of an electrical condenser, etc. In all these cases r is negative, and the common multiplier, $1 + r$, while positive, is smaller than unity.

Example 30. The temperature of a warm body surrounded by a cooler medium is given by the equation

$T = T_0(1 + r)^n$ Newton's law of cooling

where T_0 = initial temperature difference between temperatures of body and its surroundings
T = temperature difference after any number of periods (n)
r = rate of decay per period (a negative rate of growth)

Assume that an object initially 50° warmer than its surroundings cools by 20 percent per period of the temperature difference at the beginning of the period. Referring to the general equation above, we may write

$$T = 50(1 - 0.20)^n = 50(0.80)^n$$

If the period is 10 min, then

$$T = 50(0.80)^{t/10}$$

where t is the elapsed time in minutes. A table would appear as follows;

Minutes, t	*Periods, n = t/10*	*Temperature difference at beginning of period*	*Common multiplier*	*Temperature difference at end of period = T*
10	1	50	0.80	$50(0.80) = 40$
20	2	40	0.80	$50(0.80)^2 = 32$
30	3	32	0.80	$50(0.80)^3 = 25.6$
40	4	25.6	0.80	$50(0.80)^4 = 20.48$
⋮	⋮	⋮	⋮	⋮

Example 31. A radioactive sample has a half-life of 18 h; i.e., after any 18-h period, the radioactive weight is one-half its value at the beginning of that period. The appropriate equation could be written $W = W_0(0.50)^{t/18}$. This is equivalent to writing $W = W_0(2)^{-t/18}$. Why? If the initial weight $W_0 = 12$ mg, the following table would apply:

Hours, t	*Periods, n = t/18*	*Radioactive weight at beginning of period, mg*	*Common multiplier*	*Radioactive weight at end of period, mg*
18	1	12	0.5	$12(0.5) = 6$
36	2	6	0.5	$12(0.5)^2 = 3$
54	3	3	0.5	$12(0.5)^3 = 1.5$
72	4	1.5	0.5	$12(0.5)^4 = 0.75$
⋮	⋮	⋮	⋮	⋮

A most important conclusion can be drawn from the above CIL examples: When the values of the independent variable (in these cases, time) are evenly spaced, the successive values of the dependent variable are obtained by multiplying by a constant ratio.

EXERCISE 18

Apply the compound interest law to the solution of the following problems:

1. To what amount (nearest cent) will $100 grow in 1 year at 12 percent interest compounded (*a*) annually, (*b*) quarterly, (*c*) monthly, (*d*)† daily?
2. If $900 grows to $3,200 in 26 years with interest compounded annually, find the rate.
3. How long will it take for a principal to double at $6\frac{1}{2}$ percent compounded annually?
4. If $100 grows to $200 in 12 years with interest compounded annually, can you determine the amount (*a*) after 6 years, (*b*) after 4 years, without using logs?

† We are given $\log\left(1 + \frac{0.12}{365}\right) = 0.00014278$. Why is this much precision necessary?

5. A chemical decomposition follows the CIL. The weights of undecomposed chemical remaining at various times are given by the table

t, hr	0	1	2	3
W, g	54	36	24	—

(a) Predict at sight W at $t = 3$ h.
(b) If the equation is $W = W_0C^t$, find the values of W_0 and C.
(c) Find W at $t = 2.3$ h.
(d) What is the period of half-life?

6. The population of a small city in 1960 was 27,000; in 1970 it was 38,500. Find the annual percentage rate of increase, assuming it to be uniform. What was the probable population in 1967?
7. The speed of a chemical reaction doubles for each 18°F rise in temperature. What temperature rise will be needed to produce a 20-fold increase in the velocity of the reaction? (*Hint:* If \$1.00 at compound interest grows to \$2.00 in 18 years, what will it amount to after the first year? When will it amount to \$20?)
8. When light passes through a transparent medium, its intensity is reduced according to the equation

$$I = I_0c^{d/k}$$

where I_0 = initial light intensity
I = intensity after passing through a medium of thickness d
c, k = constants depending upon nature of light and of medium

If the intensity of sunlight is reduced to half its original value after penetrating water to a depth of 4 ft: (a) Evaluate c and k. (b) At what depth will the light intensity be 10 percent of that at the surface?

9. The temperature of a body surrounded by a medium at a different temperature is given by the equation

$$T = T_0c^n = T_0c^{t/3}$$

where T_0 = initial difference between temperatures of body and surroundings
T = temperature difference at any time t
c = a constant multiplier depending upon various physical conditions
n = number of periods

(See Example 30.)

If, during a power failure, a home freezer warms up from -10 to $+2°F$ after standing for 3 h in a room at 50°F, how much longer will it take to warm up to 32°F?

10. If a machine costs $8,700 new and depreciates 17 percent a year, find its value after 9 years.
11. A pump cost $740 new and after 6 years is worth $110 as scrap. Assuming constant percent rate of depreciation, find the annual rate of depreciation and the value at the end of 1 year.
12. If $1 is invested at 8 percent compounded quarterly, determine (to the nearest quarter year) how long it will take to grow to (*a*) $2, (*b*) $4, (*c*) $8.
13. Show that a valid formula is $S = (1)(2)^{t/k}$, where t is the time in years and k is the answer obtained in part *a* of the preceding problem.
14. In radioactive-carbon dating, the half-life of C^{14} is estimated to be 5,500 years. If so, the equation $W_t = W_0(2)^{-t/5,500}$ would apply, where W_0 is the original amount of C^{14} and W_t is the amount of C^{14} remaining after t years. Estimate the age of a relic containing 60 percent of its original C^{14}.
15. A machine worth $10,000 new depreciates at a constant 6.7 percent per year. It can be calculated that its value drops to half, or $5,000, at the end of 10 years, approximately.

    Show that equivalent formulas for the book value V at the end of t years are (*a*) $V = 10,000(0.933)^t$, (*b*) $V = 10,000(0.5)^{t/10}$, (*c*) $V = 10,000(2)^{-t/10}$.
16. The magnitude, or brightness, of a star is given by the equation

$$M = 2.5 \log \frac{I_0}{I}$$

where M = magnitude of star whose light intensity is I
I_0 = light intensity of star of zero magnitude

Determine the ratio of the light intensities I/I_0 for a star of the fourth magnitude ($M = 4$). (Note that the brighter the star, the lower the magnitude; in fact, for the brighter planets M is negative.)

It can be shown that each time we multiply I by 0.1, M will increase by 2.5. Since M is the observed value of sensation and I is the stimulus producing that sensation. Fechner's law applies (see Prob. 8, Exercise 19).

As a matter of interest, in connection with the foregoing, the magnitudes of the sun, full moon, and Venus (at its brightest) are -26.5, -12.5, and -4.0, respectively. The naked-eye limit is about $+6.5$, and the 6-in telescope is $+13$.

17. The Richter scale of representing the intensity of an earthquake is exponential. An earthquake of magnitude 7 is 10 times as strong as one of magnitude 6. A quake of magnitude 8 is 10 times as strong as one of magnitude 7, etc. Thus we may state that $I \propto 10^R$, where I is the relative intensity of the shock and R is the Richter scale number.

An equivalent relation would be $I_1/I_2 = 10^{R_1-R_2}$.

How did the San Francisco quake in 1906 (Richter scale 8.4) compare with the Los Angeles quake in 1971 (Richter scale 6.7)?

8.30 Applications from Technology

EXERCISE 19

The following problems are drawn from various fields of technology. In each case compute the answer to the degree of accuracy you think is warranted by the data.

1. A solid cast-iron sphere $4\frac{3}{4}$ in in diameter weighs 14.6 lb. Find to the nearest 0.01 in the diameter of a cast-iron sphere weighing 32 lb.
2. By the use of logarithms find the radius r of a circle inscribed in a triangle whose sides are a, b, and c if

$$r = \sqrt{\frac{(s-a)(s-b)(s-c)}{s}}$$

where s is half of the perimeter and the sides are 53.60, 41.90, and 38.40.

3. Find the diameter of a circle inscribed in a triangle whose sides are 287.6, 303.1, and 365.9.
4. The electrical resistance of a wire doubles (approximately) as the B & S gauge number increases 3 units. If the resistance of No. 10 copper wire is 1 Ω/1,000 ft, find the resistances of No. 13 and No. 4 wire.
5. What is the resistance ratio between two successive B & S wire sizes?
6. Find the resistance of No. 5 copper wire.
7. What is the diameter ratio between two successive B & S wire sizes?
8. In public address systems the decibel gain $D = 10 \log (P_A/P_B)$, where P_A and P_B are the power levels of the two sounds A and B, and D is the difference in loudness (in decibels) between the sounds A and B. Show that $10^{D/10} = P_A/P_B$; also show that the following table is valid:

P_A/P_B	1	10	100	1,000
D	0	10	20	30

Thus, while D, the intensity of the sensation, is in arithmetic progression, P_A/P_B, the stimulus producing the sensation, is in geometric progression. This is known as Fechner's law. It applied also in Prob. 16, Exercise 18.

Restated, the response to any stimulus is proportional to the logarithm of that stimulus; that is, $\log (P_A/P_B) = D/10$.

9. Find the decibel gain in an electric circuit if the input is 2 W and the output is 5 W.

10. What is the decibel loss in a circuit if the output is 0.07 W and the input is 0.10 W?
11. If the power ratio between input and output of an amplifier is $\frac{1}{3}$, what is the decibel gain?
12. A loudspeaker requires 1.2 W to produce the proper volume of sound. If we assign to this sound level an arbitrary value of 1, calculate the volume range within which the speaker operates if the power varies between 1.0 and 1.5 W.
13. If the sound output of an amplifier varies from 4 dB above to 3 dB below the normal value, between what power levels does the amplifier operate?
14. The ratio of sound volume in speech may range as high as 250:1. What is the range in decibels?
15. The normal power rating of an amplifier is 1.6 W. To what should this be increased to produce a perceptible (that is, 1-dB) increase in sound level?

For radio and public address work, etc., 0.006 W is a common reference level from which to figure sound-energy levels. If the output of an amplifier is 0.24 W, the decibel difference between this level and 0.006 W is

$$L_{dB} = 10 \log \frac{0.24}{0.006} = 10 \log 40 = 10 \times 1.60206 = 16 \text{ dB}$$

where L_{dB} is the so-called power level at the amplifier. For convenience, the power level of this amplifier is said to be 16 dB. We understand, however, that we really should say that the power level of the amplifier output is 16 dB above 0.006 W.

16. What is the decibel level equivalent to 0.0005 W?
17. What is the decibel level equivalent to 0.46 W?
18. What is the difference between the decibel levels in Probs. 16 and 17?

Problems having to do with air conditioning, refrigeration, internal-combustion engines, air compressors, etc., often use formulas based on the following fundamental types of equations:

$$V = \frac{KT}{P} \tag{22}$$

(By Charles' and Boyle's laws, the volume V of a given weight of gas varies directly as the absolute temperature T and inversely as the absolute pressure P.)

$$\frac{PV}{T} = K \tag{23}$$

Under two separate sets of conditions of pressure, volume, and temperature for the *same weight* of gas we may write

$$\frac{P_1V_1}{T_1} = K \tag{24}$$

for the first set of conditions and

$$\frac{P_2V_2}{T_2} = K \tag{25}$$

for the second set of conditions. Any consistent set of units may be used as long as P and T are expressed on an absolute scale. Usually, P is expressed in pounds per square inch absolute (equals pounds per square inch gauge + 14.7), and T is expressed in Rankine or Fahrenheit absolute (equals Fahrenheit + 460).

From Eqs. (24) and (25) we obtain

$$\frac{P_1V_1}{T_1} = \frac{P_2V_2}{T_2} \tag{26}$$

If we wish to express the pressure-volume relationship of a given weight of gas undergoing adiabatic (with no gain or loss of heat from the system) compression or expansion without being concerned about any accompanying temperature change, we could write, for thermodynamic considerations,

$$PV^n = C \tag{27}$$

where n and C are constants.

Then for two distinct sets of conditions for the same weight of gas we may write

$$P_1V_1^n = C \tag{28}$$

and

$$P_2V_2^n = C \tag{29}$$

From Eqs. (28) and (29) we obtain

$$P_1V_1^n = P_2V_2^n \tag{30}$$

In Probs. 19 and 20 we develop formulas to be used when we are not interested in pressure changes involved or when the pressure is unknown.

19. From Eqs. (26) and (30) show that

$$\frac{T_1}{T_2} = \left(\frac{V_2}{V_1}\right)^{n-1}$$

20. From Prob. 19 show that

$$\frac{V_2}{V_1} = \left(\frac{T_1}{T_2}\right)^{1/(n-1)}$$

Formulas in Probs. 21 and 22 are used when we are not concerned with changes in volume or when data are unavailable.

21. From Eq. (30) and Prob. 20 show that

$$\frac{T_1}{T_2} = \left(\frac{P_1}{P_2}\right)^{(n-1)/n}$$

22. From Prob. 21 show that

$$\frac{P_1}{P_2} = \left(\frac{T_1}{T_2}\right)^{n/(n-1)}$$

23. Find the final gauge pressure of a quantity of gas if the volume is compressed from 220 to 150 ft^3. P_1 is atmospheric pressure and $n = 1.39$.
24. Show that if $n = 0$, the pressure is constant, that if $n = 1$, the temperature is constant, and that if $n = \infty$, the volume is constant (see formulas in Probs. 19 to 22).
25. If $n = 1.64$, find the final volume of 6.8 l of gas when, under compression, the temperature rises from 29 to 62°C.
26. A gas is compressed from 4.32 to 2.09 ft^3. Find the final temperature if the original temperature was 30°F and $n = 1.4$.
27. When 10 ft^3 of a vapor expanded to 32 ft^3, the temperature fell from 191 to 0°F. Find n to 0.01.
28. The pressure on 220 ml of a gas is increased from 1 to 2 atm, while the volume decreases to 127 ml. Find n.
29. Following is a formula for the velocity of air being discharged through an orifice to the atmosphere:

$$V = 108.9\sqrt{T\left[1 - \left(\frac{14.7}{P}\right)^{n}\right]}$$

Find n if the air is being discharged at the rate of 323 ft^3/min through a $1\frac{5}{8}$-in-diameter orifice. The pressure in the tank is 1.2 (lb/in^2 gauge), and the temperature in the tank is 65°F.

V = linear airflow, ft/s
T = air temperature in tank, °R (Fahrenheit absolute)
P = absolute air pressure in tank, lb/in^2

30. 1,000 ml of a salt solution contains a suspended sludge. The sludge is washed by allowing it to settle; part of the clear, overlying salt solution is poured off, replaced by an equal volume of pure water, stirred, and allowed to settle. This cycle is to be repeated until the necessary amount of salt is washed out. The required equation is

$$C_n = \left(\frac{1{,}000 - w}{1{,}000}\right)^n C_0$$

where C_0 = original concentration of salt = 15.8 g/l
C_n = final concentration of salt
w = milliliters of solution removed and replaced by water, each cycle = 400 ml
n = number of washings

(a) If $n = 8$, find C_n.
(b) Find n to reduce C_n to less than 0.085 g/l.

31. In the measurement of heat flow through pipe insulation, the log mean diameter of the insulation is computed. This is

$$D_{av} = \frac{D_2 - D_1}{2.3 \log (D_2/D_1)}$$

where D_1 = outer diameter of pipe
D_2 = outer diameter of insulation

Find D_{av} when the outer pipe diameter is $2\frac{5}{8}$ in and the insulation if $2\frac{5}{16}$ in thick. Compare with the arithmetic mean.

32. A snow-making apparatus is being used to condition a ski slope. If the initial air pressure P_1 = 50 lb/in^2 gauge, P_2 = atmospheric pressure = 14.7 lb/in^2 abs, and the initial air temperature T_1 = 30°F, find T_2 (before the air has been warmed by contact with the water spray). Assume $n = 1.4$. (See Prob. 22.)

33. The equation $H = 60{,}470 \log (B_2/B_1)$ is used in the determination of altitudes by the use of barometer readings, where H is the difference in elevation (in feet) between two points at which the respective barometer readings are B_1 and B_2.

If B_2 = 29.33 in at the base station and B_1 = 26.14 in on the mountainside, find (to the nearest foot) the difference in altitude between the two stations.

34. Under certain conditions the drying of sheets of wallboard may be expressed by the equation

$$\log \frac{T_0 - E}{T - E} = K\theta$$

where T_0 = grams of moisture per gram of bone-dry stock before drying
T = amount of moisture remaining (same basis) after θ h
E = grams of moisture per gram of bone-dry stock remaining in stock after coming to equilibrium with air used for drying; that is, E represents limit to drying possible under given conditions
K = constant

If the moisture content drops from 1.2 to 0.8 g/g in 3 h, with a further drop to 0.64 g/g in another 6 h, find the amount of moisture remaining in the stock after a drying period of indefinitely great length.

The two equations are

$$\log \frac{1.2 - E}{0.8 - E} = 3K \tag{31}$$

and

$$\log \frac{0.8 - E}{0.64 - E} = 6K = 2(3K) \tag{32}$$

Replacing 3K in Eq. (32) by its equivalent, we obtain

$$\log \frac{0.8 - E}{0.64 - E} = 2 \log \frac{1.2 - E}{0.8 - E}$$

or

$$\frac{0.8 - E}{0.64 - E} = \left(\frac{1.2 - E}{0.8 - E}\right)^2 \tag{33}$$

Since E^3 terms cancel, Eq. (33) is actually a quadratic which is readily solved.

35. The resistance of a tungsten-lamp filament is given by the relationship

$$\frac{R_1}{R_2} = \left(\frac{T_1}{T_2}\right)^{1.2}$$

where R_1 = resistance at room temperature T_1
R_2 = resistance at operating temperature T_2

Temperatures are either both Kelvin (Celsius absolute) or both Rankine (Fahrenheit absolute). If the resistance at 20°C is 16 Ω and the operating resistance is 232 Ω, find the operating temperature in degrees Celsius.

36. A tungsten lamp is rated at 60 W at 115 V. If the resistance measured at 75°F is 15.2 Ω, find the operating temperature in degrees Fahrenheit. Ohms = $(\text{volts})^2/\text{watt}$ (see Prob. 35).

The following space problems 37 to 43 require the use of data in Appendix F.

37. Referring to Eq. (3), Appendix F, determine the period of a satellite traveling in a circular orbit 870 mi above the earth's surface. (*Note:* $M_b = M_e$ and $R = 3{,}960 + 870 = 4{,}830$ mi.)
38. Calculate the period for a satellite orbiting 22,300 mi above the earth's surface. Has this answer any special significance?
39. Repeat Prob. 38 for the moon if the average altitude is 237,000 mi above the earth's surface.
40. Use Eq. (3), Appendix F, to confirm the period of the earth's revolution about the sun.
41. Apollo 8 orbited around the moon at a constant altitude of 160 mi. Find its velocity and period.
42. Calculate the period of an AES traveling at an altitude of 1,200 mi above the earth's surface.
43. Confirm the velocity of escape from the moon's surface as given in the table in Appendix F. [Use Eq. (4).]

8.31 Relation of Logarithms to the Slide Rule

An arrangement of uniform scales similar to those illustrated in Fig. 8.2 could be used for mechanically adding or subtracting numbers.

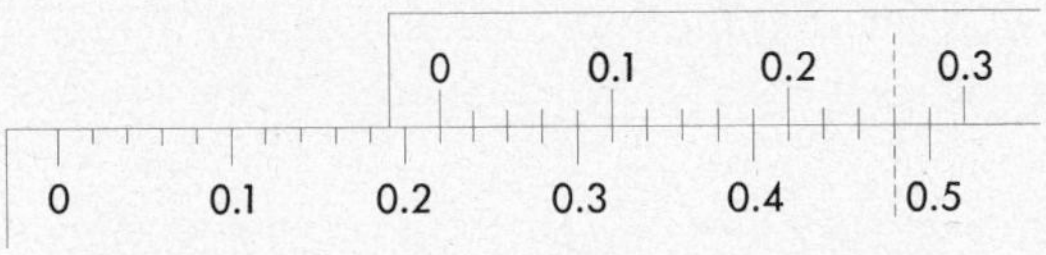

FIGURE 8.2

This figure illustrates the addition $0.22 + 0.26 = 0.48$. It also illustrates the subtraction $0.48 - 0.26 = 0.22$.

As an example of multiplication, multiply 1.66 by 1.82. Looking up three-place logarithms, we find 0.220 and 0.260 to be the respective mantissas. We may use the scales to add 0.220 and 0.260, obtaining 0.480, as in Fig. 8.2. Looking up the antilogarithm of 0.480, we obtain 3.02.

The slide rule of Fig. 8.2 would not be of much help to us. However, if we replace the uniform scales which we have been using to represent mantissas by scales bearing the numbers to which these mantissas correspond, we will have eliminated the necessity of looking up logarithms and antilogarithms (Fig. 8.3). Thus the scheme for mechanically

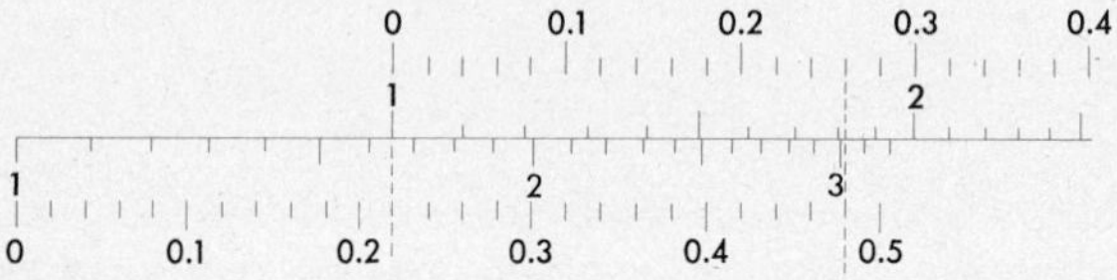

FIGURE 8.3

adding 0.22 and 0.26 becomes a means of multiplying the antilogarithms 1.66 and 1.82 to get 3.02. Evidently, by reversal of the procedure, $0.48 - 0.26 = 0.22$ corresponds to $3.02 \div 1.82 = 1.66$.

In Fig. 8.4, it will be observed that opposite any given number n on the D scale we read $2n$ on the A scale.

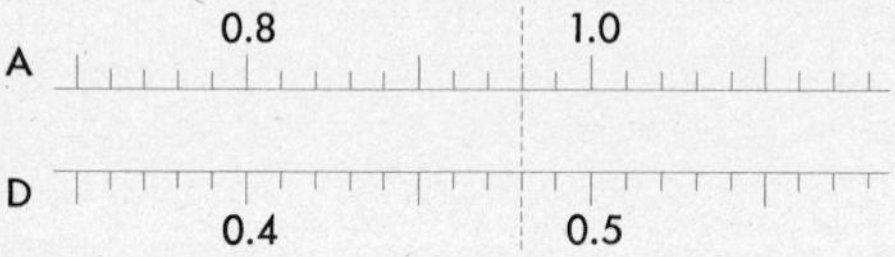

FIGURE 8.4

If we wished to square 3.02, we could look up the (three-place) mantissa, 0.480, double by the arrangement in Fig. 8.4, and look up the antilogarithm of 0.96, obtaining 9.12. Obviously, we stand to gain here also by placing the antilogarithms in the place of the corresponding mantissas. Thus the process of mechanically multiplying 0.48 by 2 to get 0.96 becomes the operation of squaring 3.02 to obtain 9.12. Likewise, the operation $0.96/2 = 0.48$ is replaced by $\sqrt{9.12} = 3.02$ (Fig. 8.5).

These illustrations will serve to indicate that the slide rule is basically a device to add or subtract quantities (mantissas) mechanically. A knowledge of the laws of

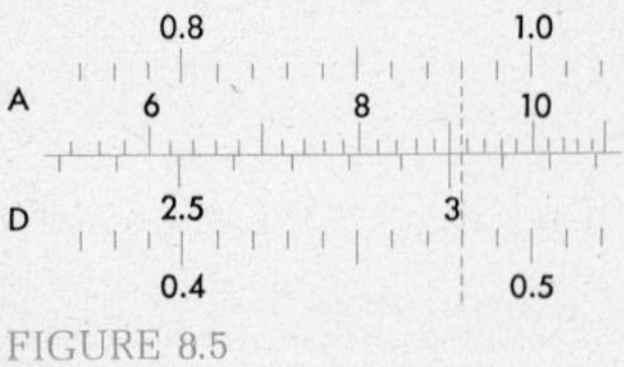

FIGURE 8.5

logarithms (Sec. 8.2) will be naturally helpful in developing facility in the use of the slide rule.

8.32 Logarithmic Computations on the Slide Rule

It will be noticed that the uniform scale we discussed in Sec. 8.31 is engraved on the slide rule as the L scale. If we set the hairline over a given number on the D scale, we shall at the same time find under the hairline on the L scale the mantissa of the logarithm of that number. Thus in Fig. 8.6, we find illustrated log 4 = 0.602; in Fig. 8.7, log 8 = 0.903; in Fig. 8.8, the mantissa of log 16 = 0.204, or log 16 = 1.204.

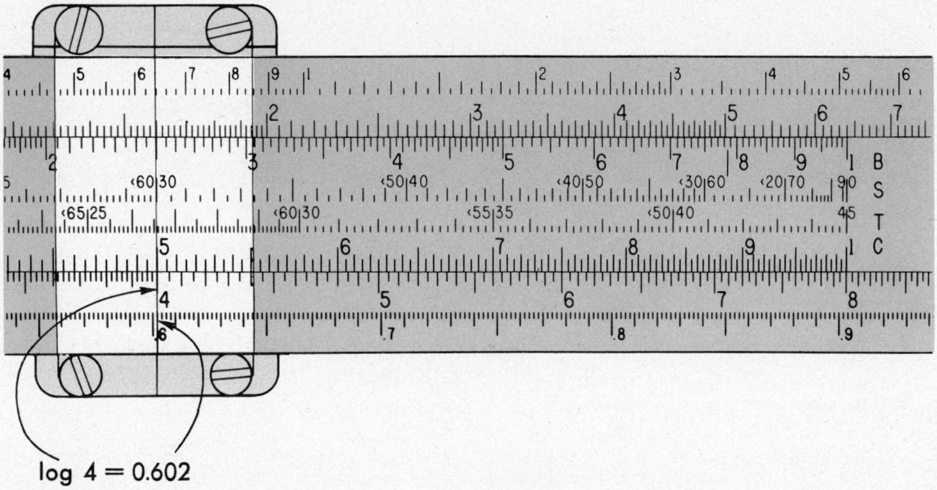

FIGURE 8.6

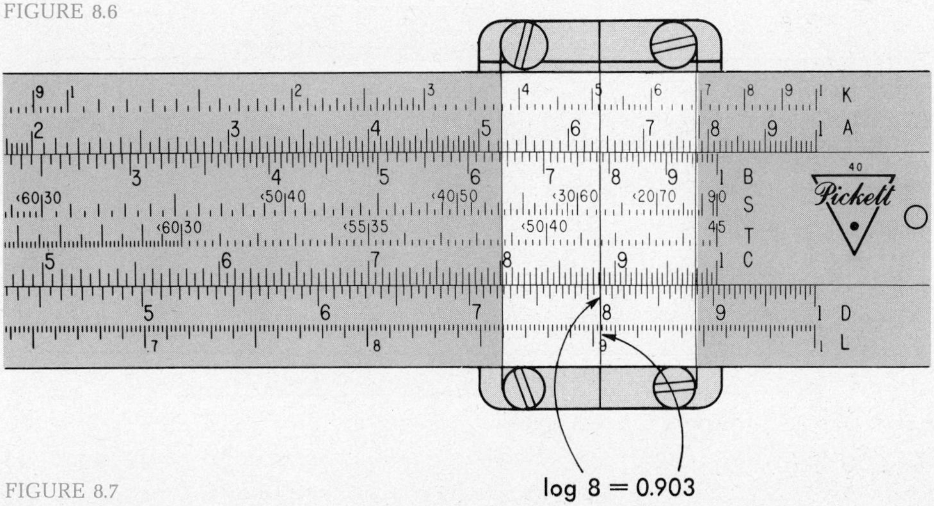

FIGURE 8.7

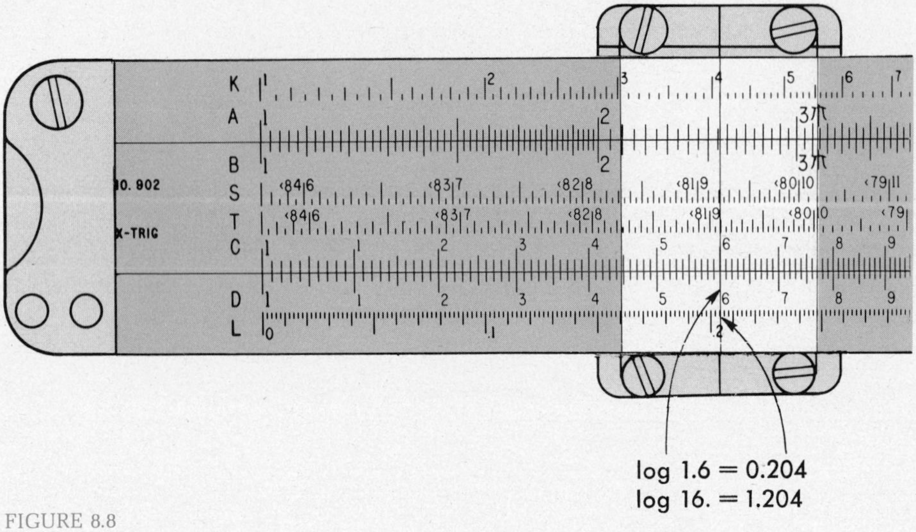

FIGURE 8.8

Let us illustrate the use of the L scale in certain logarithmic computations.

Example 32. Solve the equation $4^{3/2} = x$.

Taking logarithms, we have $1.5 \log 4 = \log x$ (Sec. 8.22). In Fig. 8.6, we have shown that $\log 4 = 0.602$. Figure 8.9 shows that $1.5 \times 0.602 = 0.903$. If $\log x = 0.903$, then $\text{antilog}\, 0.903 = x = 8$. This step is illustrated in Fig. 8.7.

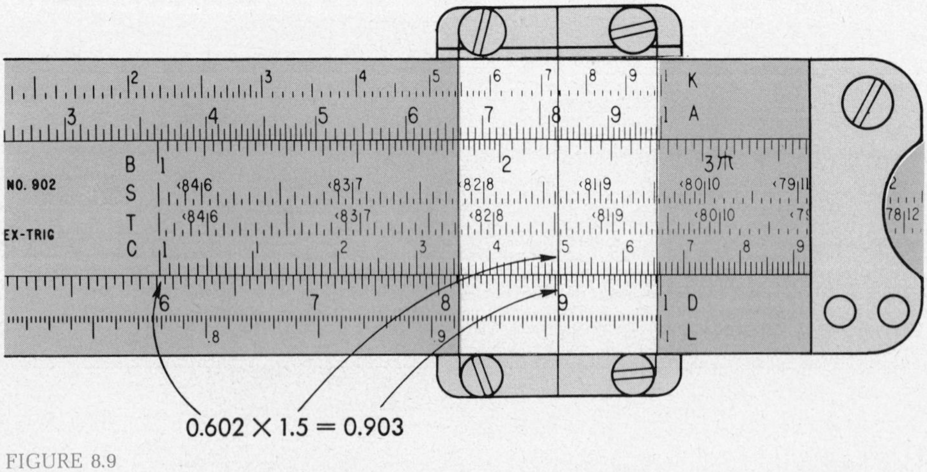

FIGURE 8.9

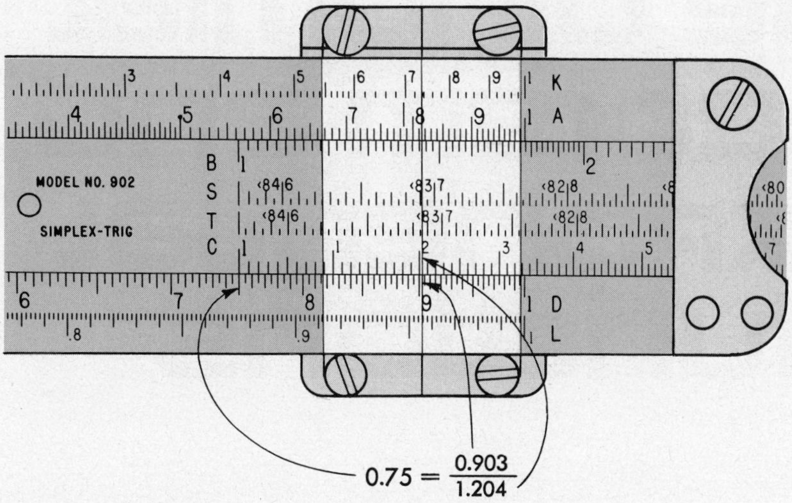

FIGURE 8.10

Example 33. Solve the equation $16^x = 8$.

Taking logs of both sides, we have $x \log 16 = \log 8$. Since the settings in Figs. 8.7 and 8.8 show that $\log 16 = 1.204$ and $\log 8 = 0.903$, we may write $1.204x = 0.903$. Finally, Fig. 8.10 illustrates the division $0.903 \div 1.204 = 0.75 = x$.

9 the binomial theorem and exponential functions

The binomial theorem finds application in the ready calculation of any power or root of a number and serves as the basis of derivation of many approximation formulas. It is at the very foundation of probability and statistics, for the normal curve of distribution is based on this theorem. Finally we shall see that the binomial theorem is the means by which we evaluate e, the base of natural logarithms.

9.1 The Binomial Theorem

The binomial theorem enables us to expand any power of a binomial into a series of terms. Powers of binomials occur frequently, and the application of the theorem can effect a substantial saving in time and labor. An important application of the binomial expansion will be made in Chap. 17, in which we shall use it to develop equations occurring in alternating-current theory.

9.2 Expansion of a Positive Integral Power of a Binomial

By actual multiplication the student may verify that

$$(a + b)^0 = 1$$
$$(a + b)^1 = a + b$$

$(a + b)^2 = a^2 + 2ab + b^2$
$(a + b)^3 = a^3 + 3a^2b + 3ab^2 + b^3$
$(a + b)^4 = a^4 + 4a^3b + 6a^2b^2 + 4ab^3 + b^4$

We see from the foregoing that the expansion of the general expression $(a + b)^n$ has the following properties:

1. *The expansion contains $n + 1$ terms.*
2. *The first term is a^n, and in each successive term the exponent of a decreases by 1.*
3. *The second term is $na^{n-1}b$, and in each successive term the exponent of b increases by 1, making the last term b^n.*
4. *In any term the sum of the exponents of a and b is n.*
5. *The coefficients of terms equidistant from the ends are equal.*
6. *If the coefficient of any term is multiplied by the exponent of a in that term, and the product divided by the number of that term, the result is the coefficient of the next term.*

Application of the above rules leads to the following formula:

$$(a + b)^n = a^n + na^{n-1}b + \frac{n(n-1)}{2!}a^{n-2}b^2 + \frac{n(n-1)(n-2)}{3!}a^{n-3}b^3 + \cdots + b^n \qquad \textbf{(1)}$$

The notation $r!$ is read "factorial r" and denotes the product of the first r integers. Thus $3! = 1 \cdot 2 \cdot 3$; $5! = 1 \cdot 2 \cdot 3 \cdot 4 \cdot 5$; etc.

In this text we shall assume without proof that the theorem holds not only for all positive integers but also for all rational numbers, negative as well as fractional. When n is negative or fractional, we obtain an unending, or infinite, series, of which we compute as many terms as desired.

If we arrange in rows the coefficients of the expansion of a positive integral power of a binomial, we obtain the following arrangement, known as *Pascal's triangle.*

		Sum of coefficients
$n = 0$	1	$1 = 2^0$
$n = 1$	1 1	$2 = 2^1$
$n = 2$	1 2 1	$4 = 2^2$
$n = 3$	1 3 3 1	$8 = 2^3$
$n = 4$	1 4 6 4 1	$16 = 2^4$
$n = 5$	1 5 10 10 5 1	$32 = 2^5$
$n = 6$	1 6 15 20 15 6 1	$64 = 2^6$

It will be seen that the first and last coefficient in each row is 1 and that the second and next-to-last coefficients equal n. Any other coefficients may be obtained by adding the two nearest coefficients in the row above.

Example 1. Expand $(2x + 3y)^4$.

Substituting $2x$ for a, $3y$ for b, and 4 for n in Eq. (1), we obtain

$$(2x + 3y)^4 = (2x)^4 + 4(2x)^3(3y) + \frac{4 \cdot 3}{2!}(2x)^2(3y)^2 + \frac{4 \cdot 3 \cdot 2}{3!}(2x)(3y)^3 + \frac{4 \cdot 3 \cdot 2 \cdot 1}{4!}(3y)^4 \qquad (2)$$

$$\begin{aligned}(2x + 3y)^4 &= (2x)^4 + 4(2x)^3(3y) + 6(2x)^2(3y)^2 + 4(2x)(3y)^3 + (3y)^4 \\ &= 16x^4 + 96x^3y + 216x^2y^2 + 216xy^3 + 81y^4 \qquad (3)\end{aligned}$$

Note that if we had referred to Pascal's triangle, we could have written Eq. (3) directly. However, Pascal's triangle is not applicable to expansions of negative and fractional powers.

Example 2. Expand $\left(3x - \dfrac{1}{2x^2}\right)^6$.

Substituting $3x$ for a, $-\dfrac{1}{2x^2}$ for b, and 6 for n in Eq. (1), we obtain

$$\begin{aligned}\left[3x + \left(-\frac{1}{2x^2}\right)\right]^6 &= (3x)^6 + 6(3x)^5\left(-\frac{1}{2x^2}\right) + \frac{6 \cdot 5}{2!}(3x)^4\left(-\frac{1}{2x^2}\right)^2 \\ &+ \frac{6 \cdot 5 \cdot 4}{3!}(3x)^3\left(-\frac{1}{2x^2}\right)^3 + \frac{6 \cdot 5 \cdot 4 \cdot 3}{4!}(3x)^2\left(-\frac{1}{2x^2}\right)^4 \\ &+ \frac{6 \cdot 5 \cdot 4 \cdot 3 \cdot 2}{5!}(3x)\left(-\frac{1}{2x^2}\right)^5 + \frac{6 \cdot 5 \cdot 4 \cdot 3 \cdot 2 \cdot 1}{6!}\left(-\frac{1}{2x^2}\right)^6 \\ &= 729x^6 - 729x^3 + \frac{1{,}215}{4} - \frac{135}{2x^3} + \frac{135}{16x^6} - \frac{9}{16x^9} + \frac{1}{64x^{12}}\end{aligned}$$

Two significant points are brought out by Example 2. (1) If the terms of the binomial are at all complicated, each term should be enclosed in parentheses, with the proper coefficients and exponents as required by the binomial rule, after which the expansion may be computed. (2) If the terms of the binomial are opposite in sign and n is a positive integer, the terms of the expansion will alternate in sign, since odd powers of a negative quantity are negative, and even powers are positive.

EXERCISE 1

Expand each expression in Probs. 1 to 9 by the binomial theorem.

1. $(x + 3y)^4$
2. $(2m + k)^3$
3. $(w^2 + \frac{1}{2}x)^4$
4. $(\frac{2}{3}x - 6)^4$
5. $\left(4x + \frac{1}{2x}\right)^5$
6. $(\frac{2}{3}x - \frac{3}{4}y)^4$
7. $\left(\frac{x}{y} + \frac{y}{z}\right)^6$
8. $\left(\sqrt{x} - \frac{1}{\sqrt{x}}\right)^6$
9. $(100 - 2)^3$
10. Using the identity $1^n \equiv (\frac{1}{2} + \frac{1}{2})^n$, show that the sum of the coefficients of the terms in the expansion of $(a + b)^n = 2^n$. See Pascal's triangle, Sec. 9.2.

9.3 Computation of Powers and Roots

Many powers and roots may be found by calculating as many terms in the series as needed to give the required accuracy. The smaller the second term in the binomial relative to the first, the fewer terms will be required. In computing a root, i.e., a fractional power, the first term of the bionomial should be a perfect power of the order corresponding to the index of the root.

Example 3. Find $\sqrt[6]{1.04}$ to six significant figures.

Arranging in a form suitable for expansion, we have $(1 + 0.04)^{1/6}$. Substituting in the formula $a = 1$, $b = 0.04$, and $n = \frac{1}{6}$, we obtain

$$(1)^{1/6} + \frac{1}{6}(1)^{-5/6}(0.04) + \frac{(\frac{1}{6})(-\frac{5}{6})(1)^{-11/6}(0.04)^2}{2!} + \frac{(\frac{1}{6})(-\frac{5}{6})(-\frac{11}{6})(1)^{-17/6}(0.04)^3}{3!} + \cdots$$

$$= 1 + 0.006667 - 0.000111 + 0.000003 \cdots \text{(negligible terms)} = 1.00656$$

We note that the terms in the foregoing series become rapidly smaller. The series is said to converge rapidly, and relatively few terms are needed.

Example 4. Find $1/(0.985)^3$ to six significant figures.

Our problem is evidently to expand $(1 - 0.015)^{-3}$. Substituting in the formula $a = 1$, $b = -0.015$, and $n = -3$, we write

$$(1)^{-3} + (-3)(1)^{-4}(-0.015) + \frac{(-3)(-4)(1)^{-5}(-0.015)^2}{2!} + \frac{(-3)(-4)(-5)(1)^{-6}(-0.015)^3}{3!} + \cdots$$

$$= 1 + 0.045 + 0.00135 + 0.00003375 + \cdots \text{(negligible terms)} = 1.04638$$

Example 5. Find $\sqrt[3]{200}$ correct to six significant figures.

Since the perfect cube nearest to 200 is 216, our problem is to evaluate $(216-16)^{1/3}$. The expansion will be

$$(216)^{1/3} + \frac{1}{3}(216)^{-2/3}(-16) + \frac{(\frac{1}{3})(-\frac{2}{3})(216)^{-5/3}(-16)^2}{2!} + \frac{(\frac{1}{3})(-\frac{2}{3})(-\frac{5}{3})(216)^{-8/3}(-16)^3}{3!} + \cdots$$
$$= 6 - 0.14815 - 0.00366 - 0.00015 - \cdots = 5.84804$$

EXERCISE 2

In Probs. 1 to 6 compute the first four terms in each expansion. (Confirm answers to Probs. 1 and 6 by division.)

1. $(1+y)^{-1}$
2. $(a^2+b)^{1/2}$
3. $(1-x)^{-1/4}$
4. $(x^2+2)^{-1/2}$
5. $(a^3+b)^{1/3}$
6. $(2w+5)^{-2}$

In Probs. 7 to 15 compute each value to five significant figures, using no tables.

7. $\sqrt{50}$
8. $\sqrt{35}$
9. $\sqrt{1.5}$
10. $\sqrt[3]{9}$
11. $\sqrt[3]{60}$
12. $\sqrt[3]{120}$
13. $\sqrt[5]{35}$
14. $1/\sqrt{5}$
15. $(25)^{2/3}$

9.4 Exponential Functions—Rate of Growth

Many phenomena of the physical sciences obey the compound interest law (CIL) with interest in effect compounded continuously. This brings us to the discussion of e, the base of natural logarithms. It develops in calculus that this is indeed a "natural" logarithm.

The natural logarithm is the logical outgrowth of the situation in which the rate of growth or depreciation of a variable at any time is proportional to the amount of the variable itself at that time. To cite some fields in which e commonly occurs, we might mention heat transfer, radioactive materials, rate of chemical reaction, thermodynamics, transient electric currents, and characteristic impedance of transmission lines.

9.5 Significance of e

A common formula used in compound-interest problems is given in Eq. (21), Sec. 8.29. We shall now modify Eq. (21) to read $S = P(1+i/m)^{mn}$, in which P is the amount invested, i is the stated rate of interest, m is the number of times interest is compounded in a year, n is the number of years, and S is the total amount of original principal plus accrued interest.

If we consider the growth of \$1 at 100 percent interest compounded m times a year for 1 year, P, i, and n each become equal to 1, and we obtain the equation $S = (1 + 1/m)^m$.

It is apparent that for semiannual compounding $m = 2$ and $S = 2.441$. If it were possible to compound 100 times a year, S would equal 2.705, and when $m = 10{,}000$, $S = 2.718$. Evidently S is approaching a limit of some kind as m becomes extremely large.

To arrive at a more accurate value of this limit, we shall expand $(1 + 1/m)^m$ by the binomial theorem and allow m to increase indefinitely in the result. Thus we obtain

$$\begin{aligned}\left(1+\frac{1}{m}\right)^m &= 1 + m\frac{1}{m} + \frac{m(m-1)}{2!}\frac{1}{m^2} + \frac{m(m-1)(m-2)}{3!}\frac{1}{m^3} \\ &\quad + \frac{m(m-1)(m-2)(m-3)}{4!}\frac{1}{m^4} + \cdots \\ &= 1 + 1 + \frac{1}{2!}\left(1-\frac{1}{m}\right) + \frac{1}{3!}\left(1-\frac{1}{m}\right)\left(1-\frac{2}{m}\right) \\ &\quad + \frac{1}{4!}\left(1-\frac{1}{m}\right)\left(1-\frac{2}{m}\right)\left(1-\frac{3}{m}\right) + \cdots\end{aligned}$$

As m increases indefinitely, $1/m$, $2/m$, $3/m$, etc., approach zero, and we have

$$e = \lim_{m\to\infty}\left(1+\frac{1}{m}\right)^m = 1 + 1 + \frac{1}{2!} + \frac{1}{3!} + \frac{1}{4!} + \cdots = 2.7183 \text{ approx} \tag{4}$$

which is the base of natural logarithms and occurs frequently in problems concerned with natural growth or decay, e.g., speed of chemical reactions, decrease of atmospheric pressure with increasing altitude, radioactive decay, and rate of cooling of a warm object.

A compact arrangement for calculating e to six figures is shown below:

$$\begin{array}{rl} 1.000000 & \\ 2\underline{/1.000000} & \\ 3\underline{/0.500000} & \\ 4\underline{/0.166667} & \\ 5\underline{/0.041667} & \\ 6\underline{/0.008333} & \\ 7\underline{/0.001389} & \\ 8\underline{/0.000198} & \\ 9\underline{/0.000025} & \\ 0.000003 & \\ \hline\hline 2.718282 & \text{Total} \end{array}$$

Or $e = 2.71828$, to six significant figures.

A value for any power of e may be found by evaluating

$$\left[\left(1 + \frac{1}{m}\right)^m\right]^x = \left(1 + \frac{1}{m}\right)^{mx}$$

as above. Thus we obtain

$$\left(1 + \frac{1}{m}\right)^{mx} = 1 + mx\frac{1}{m} + \frac{mx(mx - 1)}{2!}\frac{1}{m^2} + \frac{mx(mx - 1)(mx - 2)}{3!}\frac{1}{m^3} + \cdots$$

$$= 1 + x + \frac{x^2}{2!}\left(1 - \frac{1}{mx}\right) + \frac{x^3}{3!}\left(1 - \frac{1}{mx}\right)\left(1 - \frac{2}{mx}\right) + \cdots$$

As m increases without limit, $1/(mx)$, $2/(mx)$, etc., approach zero, and we obtain the series for e^x:

$$e^x = \lim_{m\to\infty}\left(1 + \frac{1}{m}\right)^{mx} = 1 + x + \frac{x^2}{2!} + \frac{x^3}{3!} + \frac{x^4}{4!} + \cdots \qquad \textbf{(5)}$$

In using Eq. (4) or (5) for computation, enough terms should be used so that the first term omitted is less than half the allowable error.

9.6 Natural Logarithms

Common logarithms are based upon the fact that every positive number can be expressed as a power of 10. Similarly, it is true that every such number may be expressed as a power of e. For example, $3.8 = e^{1.335}$, and we say that the logarithm of 3.8 to the base e is 1.335. This is written $\log_e 3.8 = 1.335$ or $\ln 3.8 = 1.335$.

Natural logarithms (ln), or logarithms to the base e, follow the same rules of computation that apply to common logarithms, as set forth in Sec. 8.2.

9.7 Use of the Table

Part of a table of natural, or Napierian, logarithms is reproduced as Table 9.1.

TABLE 9.1

N	0	1	2	3	4	5	6	7	8	9
7.0	1.9459	473	488	502	516	530	544	559	573	587
7.1	601	615	629	643	657	671	685	699	713	727
10.0	2.3026	036	046	056	066	076	086	096	106	115

From this table we read that

$$\ln 7.16 = 1.9685 \quad \text{or} \quad 7.16 = e^{1.9685}$$
$$\ln 10 = 2.3026 \quad \text{or} \quad 10 = e^{2.3026}$$

In order to find the natural logarithm of a number which lies outside the limits of the table, we cannot simply change the characteristic as in common logs. The common logarithm of 716 is $\log 7.16 + \log 100$, or $0.8549 + 2$; but since e^2 is not 100, the natural logarithm of 100 is not 2. However, we can make use of scientific notation to carry out much the same idea.

Hence we write

$$716 = 7.16 \times 10^2$$

and

$$\ln 716 = \ln 7.16 + 2 \ln 10 = 1.9685 + 2(2.3026) = 6.5737$$

Conversely, to find anti-ln 6.5737 (or the value of $e^{6.5737}$), we would subtract from 6.5737 as many 2.3026's as necessary to work within the scope of the table, which would be two. Therefore we would write $6.5737 - 2(2.3026) = 1.9685$ or $\ln N - 2 \ln 10 = \ln \dfrac{N}{100} = 1.9685$. Hence the anti-ln $1.9685 = 7.16 = N/100$, and $N = 716$.

If we wish to find ln 0.703, we write $0.703 = 7.03 \times 10^{-1}$ and $\ln 0.703 = \ln 7.03 - \ln 10 = 1.9502 - 2.3026 = -0.3524$. Note that with natural logarithms we make no attempt to make the mantissa positive, since the mantissas for, say, ln 70.3, ln 7.03, and ln 0.703 would bear no resemblance to one another.

Let it be required to find anti-ln (-4.9505). We shall add only enough 2.3026's to -4.9505 to make the total positive. We shall need three. Hence we write $-4.9505 + 3(2.3026) = 1.9573$, or $\ln N + 3 \ln 10 = \ln (1{,}000\, N) = 1.9573$. Anti-ln $1.9573 = 7.08 = 1{,}000\, N$. Hence $N = 0.00708$.

EXERCISE 3

1. Look up the natural logarithms of
   (*a*) 6.14 (*b*) 9.08 (*c*) 1.97 (*d*) 33.8
   (*e*) 417 (*f*) 0.216 (*g*) 0.0117
2. Use interpolation to obtain the natural logarithms of
   (*a*) 49.73 (*b*) 0.06492 (*c*) 3,584 (*d*) 0.1856
3. Look up the antilogarithms of
   (*a*) 3.65325 (*b*) 9.06878 (*c*) -3.00376
   (*d*) -4.05705 (*e*) 11.28351

4. Use interpolation where necessary to find the antilogarithms of
   (*a*) 4.08770 (*b*) 10.06228 (*c*) −6.72112 (*d*) −0.12461
   (*e*) 7.58732
5. Using natural logarithms, calculate
   (*a*) $e^{3.8}$ (*b*) $e^{2.6}$ (*c*) $e^{-1.4}$ (*d*) $e^{-0.9}$
   (*e*) $56e^{-2.2}$ (*f*) $452e^{1.85}$ (*g*) $0.087e^{4.732}$ (*h*) $5300e^{-6.185}$
   (*i*) Confirm answers to parts *a* to *d*, inclusive, using a table of e^x.
6. Solve the following for *n*. Note that our task of looking up natural logarithms will be facilitated by first dividing through by (in part *a*) 100, giving us $3.46 = 1.95e^{10n}$.
   (*a*) $346 = 195e^{10n}$ (*b*) $14.7 = 68.3e^{-0.6n}$
   (*c*) $0.0183 = 0.087e^{-0.02n}$ (*d*) $0.0964 = 0.0529e^{1.28n}$
   (*e*) $450 = 2{,}000e^{20n}$ (*f*) $3{,}000 = 11.8e^{-50n}$

9.8 Relation between Common and Natural Logarithms

The general formula for converting the logarithm of a number from one base to another is, from Eq. (10), Sec. 8.11,

$$\log_a N = (\log_a b)(\log_b N) \tag{6}$$

Hence it follows that if $b = 10$ and $a = e$, substitution in Eq. (6) produces the formula for converting common logarithms to natural logarithms:

$$\log_e N = (\log_e 10)(\log_{10} N)$$

or

$$\ln N = (\ln 10)(\log N)$$
$$\ln N = 2.3026 \log N \tag{7}$$

Also substituting $b = 10$ and $a = e$ in Eq. (15), Sec. 8.11,

$$\log_{10} N = (\log_{10} e)(\log_e N)$$

or

$$\log N = 0.43429 \ln N \tag{8}$$

and from Eq. (16), Sec. 8.11,

$$\ln 10 = \frac{1}{\log e} \tag{9}$$

also from Eq. (9)

$$(\ln 10)(\log e) = 1 \tag{10}$$

EXERCISE 4

1. Convert the following to common logarithms.
   (a) $\ln x = 3.0425$ (b) $\ln x = 0.00488$
   (c) $\ln x = -2.0714$ (d) $\ln x = -1.3507$
   (e) $\ln x = -1.7106$ (f) $\ln x = -3.3822$
2. Convert the following to natural logarithms.
   (a) $\log x = 2.1734$ (b) $\log x = 0.01007$
   (c) $\log x = 8.7466 - 10$ (d) $\log x = 0.7843 - 2$
   (e) $\log x = -1.2755$ (f) $\log x = 9.0843 - 10$
3. In Prob. 1 find x, using the values of common logarithms obtained.
4. Using only a table of common logarithms, find
   (a) $\ln 5.828$ (b) $\ln 73.46$ (c) $\ln 10{,}000$
   (d) $\ln 0.08469$ (e) $\ln 0.005497$ (f) $\ln \frac{1}{15}$

9.9 Equivalent Expressions

Because of an occasional lack of a table of natural logarithms or for other reasons, it is desirable to be able to express an equation in the exponential form to any required base or in terms of either system of logarithms. The following typical problem will illustrate the steps involved.

Example 6. Given the equation $y = 8.3e^{1.2x}$:
(a) Convert to the form $y = kb^x$.
(b) Express as a natural logarithmic equation.
(c) Express as a common logarithmic equation.

(a) Since we may write $y = 8.3(e^{1.2})^x$, we can find from tables that $e^{1.2} = 3.3201$. Hence $y = 8.3(3.3201)^x$.
(b) Taking natural logarithms of both sides of the equation,

$$\ln y = \ln (8.3e^{1.2x}) = \ln 8.3 + \ln e^{1.2x}$$

or

$$\ln y = 2.1163 + 1.2x$$

(c) Taking common logarithms of both sides, we obtain

$$\begin{aligned}\log y &= \log(8.3e^{1.2x})\\ &= \log 8.3 + 1.2x \log e\\ &= \log 8.3 + 1.2x(0.43429)\\ &= 0.91908 + 0.52115x\end{aligned}$$

Perhaps the most frequently used of these procedures is (c), in which the equation is immediately expressed in terms of common logs.

Example 7. Referring to Example 30, page 239, (a) use the equation $T = 50(0.80)^{t/10}$ to find T after 28 min and (b) convert the above equation to the form $T = 50\,e^{-kt}$ and again calculate T at $t = 28$.

(a) $T = 50(0.80)^{28/10} = (50)(0.535) = 26.8°$

(b) $(0.80)^{28/10} = e^{-28k}$

$2.8 \ln 0.80 = \ln e^{-28k} = -28k$

$(2.8)(-0.223) = -28k \qquad k = 0.0223$

(Note this indicates a 2.23 percent instantaneous rate of decrease of temperature difference per minute.)

$T = 50(e^{-0.0223})^{28} = 50e^{-0.624} = 50(0.535) = 26.8°$

EXERCISE 5

1. Calculate $\log_2 e$.
2. Express the following in exponential form (solve for y).
   (*a*) $\ln y = x$ (*b*) $\ln y + \ln a = x$ (*c*) $a \ln y = x$
3. Express the following in natural logarithmic form.
   (*a*) $z = e^w$ (*b*) $y = ae^{cx}$ (*c*) $y = 3/\sqrt{e}$
4. Find the value of the following, first using only a table of natural logarithms, then using only a table of common logarithms.
   (*a*) $e^{2.5}$ (*b*) $e^{-3.5}$ (*c*) $0.08552e^{3.52}$
5. Convert the following to the form $y = be^{kx}$.
   (*a*) $y = 5(1.6)^x$ (*b*) $y = 3.2(0.275)^x$
   (*c*) $y = 3(2)^{5x}$ (*d*) $y = e^{(0.94+x)/2}$
6. Convert the following to the form $y = kb^x$.
   (*a*) $y = 0.63e^{2.7x}$ (*b*) $y = 1.62e^{-1.4x}$
7. Solve for x in each of the following.
   (*a*) $T = ae^{-kx}$ (*b*) $\dfrac{c^2}{x^2} = e^{-1.44t^2}$ (*c*) $y = \ln \dfrac{1}{x^n}$ (*d*) $2.5 = 5e^{-0.3x}$
8. (*a*) If $\ln \sqrt{x} = 2$, find $\ln x^3$. (*b*) If $\ln ex = 4$, find $\ln x$.
   (*c*) If $\ln x^3 = 27$, find $\ln x$.
9. Solve for x in terms of e: (*a*) $\ln e/x + \frac{1}{2} = 0$, (*b*) $2 \ln x = 6 - \ln 16$,
   (*c*) $\ln(x^2 - e^2) - \ln(x + e) = 1$.

In the following problems, given only that $e = 2.718$, $\ln 10 = 2.303$, $\ln 7 = 1.946$, $\ln 17 = 2.833$, $\log 8 = 0.903$, and $\log 9 = 0.954$, calculate without tables or slide rule the values of

10. $\log e$
11. $\ln 8$
12. $\ln 9$
13. $\ln 3$
14. $\ln 0.008$
15. $\ln 90$
16. $\ln \frac{1}{8}$
17. $\ln 4$
18. $\ln 27.18$
19. $\log 0.2718$
20. $\log 170$
21. anti-ln 2.946
22. anti-ln 1.833
23. anti-ln (-1.946)
24. t if $8 = \dfrac{1}{e^{3t}}$

EXERCISE 6

1. In a dc circuit containing a capacitor C and a resistance R in series, the instantaneous value of the current i at any time t after the circuit has been closed is given by the equation

$$\ln i = -\frac{t}{RC} + \ln E - \ln R$$

Convert this equation to the exponential form (i.e., solve for i rather than $\ln i$).

2. Use the answer obtained in Prob. 1 to find the current 0.00002 s after the circuit has been closed, if $E = 24$ V, $R = 9.5\ \Omega$, and $C = 0.000029$ F.
3. Find i in Prob. 1 when $E = 100$, $R = 250$, $C = 25 \times 10^{-6}$, and $t = 3 \times 10^{-5}$.
4. Find i in Prob. 1 when $t = 0$.
5. In Prob. 1 what is the approximate value of i when t is very large?
6. In Prob. 1 what percentage is i of E/R when $t = RC$?
7. (a) The emission current for a heated filament is given by the equation

$$i = AT^2e^{-B/T}$$

where i is expressed in amperes, A is a constant equal to 60, B is a constant equal to 5.24×10^4 for a tungsten filament, and T is the temperature in degrees Kelvin. Find i when $T = 2400°$K.

(b) How would you proceed to solve an equation of the type in (a) in which T is the unknown?

8. In a simple steam engine the equation for the mean effective pressure is

$$P_m = P\left(\frac{1 + \ln r}{r}\right) - p$$

Determine P_m if $P = 100\ \text{lb/in}^2$, $p = 14.7$, and $r = 3.54$.

9. When light passes through a transparent medium, its intensity is reduced according to the equation

$$I = I_0 e^{-ad}$$

where I_0 = initial light intensity
I = intensity after passing through a medium of thickness d
a = a constant depending upon nature of light and medium

If the intensity of sunlight is reduced to half its original value after penetrating water to depth of 4 ft: (*a*) Evaluate a. (*b*) At what depth will the light intensity be 10 percent of that at the surface? Compare with Prob. 8, page 241.

10. The temperature of a body surrounded by a medium at a different temperature is given by the equation

$$T = T_0 e^{-kt}$$

where T_0 is the initial difference between the temperatures of body and surroundings, T is the temperature difference at any time t, and k is a heat-transfer constant dependent upon various physical conditions and the units involved. If, during a power failure, a home freezer warms up from $-10°$ to $+2°$F after standing for 3 h in a room at 50°F, how much longer will it take to warm up to 32°F?

11. A radioactive material disintegrates according to the relation

$$A = A_0 e^{-kt}$$

where A_0 is the original amount of active material, A is the amount of active material remaining at time t, and k is a constant characteristic of the given material. It is frequently desirable to determine the period of half-life, i.e., that time at which half of the original material still remains.

(*a*) Show that the period of half-life is equal to $0.6932/k$.

(*b*) If 3 percent of a certain radioactive material disintegrates in 1 h, find the period of half-life.

12. A problem in electrical engineering required the solution of the following system of simultaneous equations:

$$E_m(1 - e^{-3n}) = 13$$
$$E_m(1 - e^{-n}) = 8$$

Solve for E_m and n to four significant figures. (*Hint:* Divide the first equation by the second.)

13. If

$$i = \frac{E}{R}(1 - e^{-Rt/L})$$

find i when $E = 10$, $L = 0.9$, $R = 12$, and $t = 0.005$.

14. Find i in Prob. 13 if $t = 0$.
15. Approximately what is the value of i in Prob. 13 when t is very large?
16. If you were given i, E, L, and t, how would you go about solving for R in Prob. 13?
17. When $t = L/R$, what percentage is i of E/R? Is this percentage independent of the actual values of the variables?
18. If $x = y$, refer to the principles relating e and natural logarithms to show that $x = e^{\ln y}$.
19. (a) Referring to Prob. 14, page 242, if we replace the factor $2^{-t/5,500}$ by e^{-kt}, solve for the constant k.
    (b) Referring to Prob. 15, page 242, if we replace the factor 0.933^t by e^{-kt}, solve for the constant k.
20. In the formula $P = 29.92e^{-h/5}$, P is the barometer reading in inches of mercury and h is the altitude in miles.
    (a) Show that equivalent formulas are $P = 29.92(0.8187)^h$ and $P = 29.92(2)^{-h/3.47}$.
    (b) What will the pressure be at 28,000 ft?
    (c) What altitude in feet corresponds to a pressure of 19.50 in?
    (d) What is the sea-level pressure?
21. In Fig. 9.1 a weight W is suspended by a rope over a round beam. The rope is prevented from slipping by a force F at the other end.

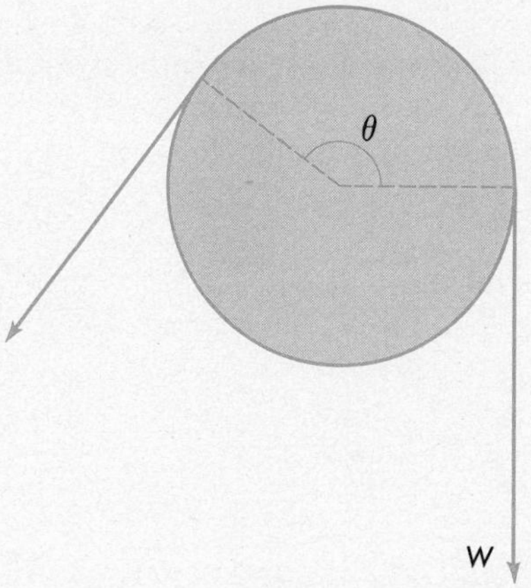

FIGURE 9.1

(a) Using the formula $F = We^{-a\theta}$, where θ is the angle of contact of the rope on the beam (expressed in turns), find a to 0.01 if 170 lb supports 200 lb when $\theta = 150°$.

(b) What force is needed to support 200 lb, using two complete turns of rope?

(c) How many turns would be required for 50 lb to support 200 lb?

22. The current flowing in a series circuit (with inductance L henrys, resistance $R\ \Omega$ and voltage E V) is given by

$$I = \frac{E}{R}(1 - e^{-RT/L}) \qquad \text{A}$$

and the power going into the magnetic field is given by

$$P = \frac{E^2}{R}(e^{-Rt/L} - e^{-2Rt/L})$$

(a) If $R = 10\ \Omega$, $L = 0.0001$ henry, and $E = 15$ V, sketch graphs of P and I as functions of the time t.

(b) Sketch graphs of RI/E and RP/E^2 as functions of Rt/L. These are dimensionless groups.

23. The following is taken from an article in *Chemical Engineering* on gasoline cracking. Sketch graphs of x and y as functions of the time t if

$$x = 100(1 - e^{-kt}) \qquad \text{and} \qquad y = 100e^{-kt}$$

where $k = 0.01076$.

9.10 General Formula

In order to determine the effect of continuous compounding at any rate for any length of time, we shall again refer to the formula $S = P(1 + i/m)^{mn}$, expand by the binomial theorem, and allow m to increase without limit in the result. Thus we obtain the expansion

$$\left(1 + \frac{i}{m}\right)^{mn} = 1 + mn\frac{i}{m} + \frac{mn(mn-1)}{2!}\frac{i^2}{m^2} + \frac{mn(mn-1)(mn-2)}{3!}\frac{i^3}{m^3} + \cdots$$

$$= 1 + ni + \frac{n^2i^2}{2!}\left(1 - \frac{1}{mn}\right) + \frac{n^3i^3}{3!}\left(1 - \frac{1}{mn}\right)\left(1 - \frac{2}{mn}\right) + \cdots$$

and

$$\lim_{m\to\infty}\left(1 + \frac{i}{m}\right)^{mn} = 1 + ni + \frac{n^2i^2}{2!} + \frac{n^3i^3}{3!} + \cdots$$

However it can be shown by analogy to Eq. (5) that

$$e^{ni} = \lim_{m\to\infty}\left(1+\frac{1}{m}\right)^{mni}$$

also equals

$$1 + ni + \frac{n^2i^2}{2!} + \frac{n^3i^3}{3!} + \cdots$$

Hence we may write

$$\lim_{m\to\infty}\left(1+\frac{i}{m}\right)^{mn} = e^{ni}$$

or

$$S = \lim_{m\to\infty} P\left(1+\frac{i}{m}\right)^{mn} = Pe^{ni} \qquad \text{(growth)} \tag{11}$$

Observe that in computations of continuous depreciation or decay instead of growth, i will be negative and

$$S = \lim_{m\to\infty} P\left(1-\frac{i}{m}\right)^{mn} = Pe^{-ni} \qquad \text{(depreciation)} \tag{12}$$

The proof of Eq. (12) is left as an exercise for the student.

Example 8. A radioactive material decays according to the equation $W = 200e^{-0.2t}$, where W is in mg and t is in days.
(*a*) Find the instantaneous rate of decay at any time as a percent.
(*b*) Find the percent loss in 1 day.
(*c*) Find the period of half-life.
(*d*) Find the instantaneous rate of decay in mg/day at $t = 5$.

(*a*) The constant -0.2 indicates directly that the instantaneous rate of decay is 20 percent per day.
(*b*) Since $t = 1$, we evaluate $e^{(-0.2)(1)} = e^{-0.2}$ from tables of e^x and find $e^{-0.2}$ to be 0.8187. That is, at the end of a day the weight of undecomposed material will be 0.8187 times the active weight at the beginning of the day, or the percent loss in 1 day is 18.13 percent.
(*c*) To find the period of half-life we replace W by 100, obtaining the equation $100 = 200e^{-0.2t}$. Dividing both sides by 200 and taking natural logarithms of both

sides, we obtain

$$\ln 0.5 = \ln e^{-0.2t} = -0.2t$$

or

$$-0.6932 = -0.2t$$

from which

$$t = 3.466 \text{ days, the period of half-life}$$

(*d*) At $t = 5$, $W = 200e^{(-0.2)(5)} = (200)(0.3679) = 73.58$ g remaining. Since the instantaneous rate of decay is 20 percent of the weight of active material remaining at the moment, we have (0.20)(73.58) or 14.72 mg/day instantaneous rate of decay at $t = 5$ days.

Example 9. The number of bacteria in a colony increased at an instantaneous rate (per hour) continuously equal to 20 percent of the number at that time.
(*a*) Starting from a colony of 1,000 bacteria, how many would there be in 6 h?

Substituting, in Eq. (11), $P = 1{,}000$, $n = 6$, and $i = 0.2$, we have

$$S = 1{,}000e^{1.2}$$

From tables of e^x,

$$e^{1.2} = 3.320$$

Hence

$$S = 1{,}000(3.320) = 3{,}320$$

(*b*) Find the percent increase from hour to hour.

The amount to which one unit would grow in 1 h is given by $S = e^i = 1 + r$, where r is the nominal hourly rate of increase.

Here

$$e^i = e^{0.20} = 1.221$$

Therefore

$$1 + r = 1.221 \qquad \text{or} \qquad r = 0.221 = 22.1 \text{ percent}$$

Example 10. Radium decomposes at an instantaneous rate (per century) continuously equal to 4.1 percent of the amount remaining at that time. If 25 mg is present at the start, how much will be left after 2,000 years?

Substituting, in Eq. (12), $P = 25$, $n = 20$, and $i = 0.041$, we have

$$S = 25e^{-0.82}$$

From tables of e^{-x},

$$e^{-0.82} = 0.44043$$

Hence

$$S = 25(0.44043) = 11.011 \text{ mg}$$

EXERCISE 7

1. Using the series, calculate the value of $e^{0.2}$ to five significant figures. Check your answer by the table.
2. Repeat Prob. 1 for $e^{-0.5}$.
3. The speed of a given chemical reaction depends upon the temperature t according to the formula $V = 0.8e^{0.15t}$. Find V (*a*) when $t = 20°$; (*b*) when $t = 60°$. (*c*) Determine the temperature at which $V = 100$. (*d*) Determine what temperature rise is required to double V.
4. The curve which a chain or rope assumes when hanging under its own weight is called a *catenary*. The equation for the catenary is $y = (a/2)(e^{x/a} + e^{-x/a})$. If $a = 1$, plot the graph from $x = 2$ to $x = -2$.
5. According to Halley's law, the atmospheric pressure P in inches is related to the height above sea level by the following equation: $P = 29.92e^{-h/5}$, where h is the altitude in miles. What is the barometer reading at (*a*) sea level; (*b*) 2,640 ft; (*c*) 3 mi; (*d*) what is the elevation in feet if the barometer reads 23.62 in?
6. The speed V of a rotating wheel after the power was cut off decreased at a rate (per minute) which at every instant was 35 percent of V itself. If the original value of V was 1,500 r/min, find its value after (*a*) 5 min; (*b*) 10 min; (*c*) 15 min. (*d*) How long will it take for the speed to drop to one-tenth of its original value?
7. If 80 g of cane sugar is inverted by acid so that the inversion rate is constantly 13.5 percent (per hour) of the remaining cane sugar, find the amount of cane sugar remaining after 12 h.
8. The temperature of a warm object initially 150° warmer than the surroundings is falling at an instantaneous rate of 60 percent (per hour) of the temperature differ-

ence at the time. Find the temperature difference remaining after (*a*) 40 min; (*b*) 2 h. (*c*) Find the percent decrease in differential over any 1-h interval.

9. If a plant is growing so that its rate of growth is constantly 40 percent (per week) of its weight, find the actual percentage increase in weight in a week.
10. In Example 10, page 271, what is the period of half-life; i.e., when will the radium be 50 percent disintegrated?

10 quadratic equations in one variable

In Chap. 3 we discussed linear equations (or first-degree equations) in one variable.

In this chapter we shall be particularly concerned with second-degree equations in one variable in the form

$$ax^2 + bx + c = 0 \qquad a \neq 0 \tag{1}$$

10.1 Quadratic Equations

An equation equivalent to Eq. (1) is called a *quadratic equation*.

If either b or $c = 0$ (note that a cannot be zero), the equations

$$ax^2 + c = 0$$

and

$$ax^2 + bx = 0$$

are known as *incomplete quadratic equations*.

10.2 Solution of Incomplete Quadratics

Both types of incomplete quadratic equations are easily solved.

Example 1. Solve the equation $4x^2 - 9 = 0$.

Adding 9 to both sides and dividing by 4,

$$x^2 = 9/4$$

Extracting the square root,

$$x = \pm 3/2$$

That is,

$$x = +3/2 \qquad \text{and} \qquad x = -3/2$$

Note that both $+3/2$ and $-3/2$ are actually roots of the given equation, since by substitution in the given equation we find that

$$4\left(+\frac{3}{2}\right)^2 = 9$$

and

$$4\left(-\frac{3}{2}\right)^2 = 9$$

The same example might have been solved by the factoring method as follows:

$$4x^2 - 9 = 0$$
$$(2x + 3)(2x - 3) = 0$$

We recall that if the product of two or more factors is zero, then at least one of these factors must be zero.

$$2x + 3 = 0$$

or

$$x = -3/2$$

$$2x - 3 = 0$$

or

$$x = 3/2$$

as above.

Example 2. Solve the equation $2x^2 + 6x = 0$.

Factoring,

$$2x(x + 3) = 0$$

Setting each factor equal to zero,

$$2x = 0 \quad \text{or} \quad x = 0$$
$$x + 3 = 0 \quad \text{or} \quad x = -3$$

EXERCISE 1

Solve the following incomplete quadratic equations, regarding x, y, z, and w as unknown quantities.

1. $y^2 - 9 = 0$
2. $z^2 - 16z = 0$
3. $x^2 = 49$
4. $144 - w^2 = 0$
5. $y^2 = 121$
6. $x^2 - 81 = 0$
7. $z^2 = 8$
8. $12 - w^2 = 0$
9. $x^2 - 30 = 0$
10. $z^2 = c^2$
11. $y^2 = 9a^2$
12. $x^2 - 16b^2 = 0$
13. $w^2 = aw$
14. $y^2 = a^2 + b^2$
15. $z^2 = 1/c^2$
16. $a^2/b^2 - y^2 = 0$
17. $16x^2 = 1$
18. $9y^2 - 25 = 0$
19. $12w^2 = 1$
20. $9z^2 = 8$
21. $w^2 + 121 = 5w^2$
22. $3y^2 - 17 = 8 - y^2$
23. $x^2/3 = 48$
24. $z^2/b = 4b$
25. $4/y^2 = 49$
26. $1/y^2 = 36$
27. $m^2/x^2 = 25$
28. $\dfrac{1}{20y^2} = 5$
29. $\dfrac{1}{z^2} = \dfrac{1}{16}$
30. $\dfrac{a^2}{c^2} = \dfrac{1}{w^2}$
31. $\dfrac{4}{x} = \dfrac{x}{9}$
32. $\dfrac{1}{2x} = \dfrac{8x}{9}$
33. $\dfrac{3w}{4} - \dfrac{9}{2w} = \dfrac{5w}{8}$
34. $\dfrac{x^2 - 1}{6} - \dfrac{x^2 + 2}{9} = 1$

10.3 Solution of the Quadratic $ax^2 + bx + c = 0$

The solution of the equation $ax^2 + bx + c = 0$ may be accomplished by the following means:

1. Plotting (approximate solutions—limited by accuracy of reading)
2. Factoring
3. Completing the square
4. Quadratic formula

10.4 Solution by Plotting

While exact answers can be obtained by plotting if they are integers, fractional values are apt to be approximated, and irrational answers will always be approximations. Imaginary roots cannot normally be found by plotting. However, by a suitable shift in the relative positions of the curve on the X axis, such roots may be approximated.

Example 3. Solve the equation $x^2 - 2x - 11 = 0$ by plotting.

Set $x^2 - 2x - 11 = y$. Substitute various values of x, and determine the corresponding values of y. For instance, if $x = 7$, then

$$y = (7)^2 - 2(7) - 11 = 49 - 14 - 11 = 24$$

In like manner make out a table, continuing to substitute various values of x until it becomes evident that y is receding from zero at an increasing rate.

x	6	5	4	3	2	1	0	−1	−2	−3	−4	. . .
y	13	4	−3	−8	−11	−12	−11	−8	−3	4	13	. . .

Plot these values on coordinate paper. Answers correspond to the intersection of the curve and the X axis. This is reasonable because, in effect, we are solving for the simultaneous equations $y = x^2 - 2x - 11$ and $y = 0$.

Figure 10.1 shows the result obtained by plotting these data. The indicated answers are roughly $x = 4.5$ and $x = -2.5$. We say that we have found the zeros of the equation $y = x^2 - 2x - 11$.

Tabulation may be facilitated if we take uniformly spaced values of x and list increments in y (represented by Δy) and also increments in Δy [that is, $\Delta(\Delta y)$], which we abbreviate to $\Delta^2 y$.

Δx		−1		−1		−1		−1		−1		−1		−1		−1		−1		−1	
x	6		5		4		3		2		1		0		−1		−2		−3		−4
y	13		4		−3		−8		−11		−12		−11		−8		−3		4		13
Δy		−9		−7		−5		−3		−1		1		3		5		7		9	
$\Delta^2 y$			2		2		2		2		2		2		2		2		2		

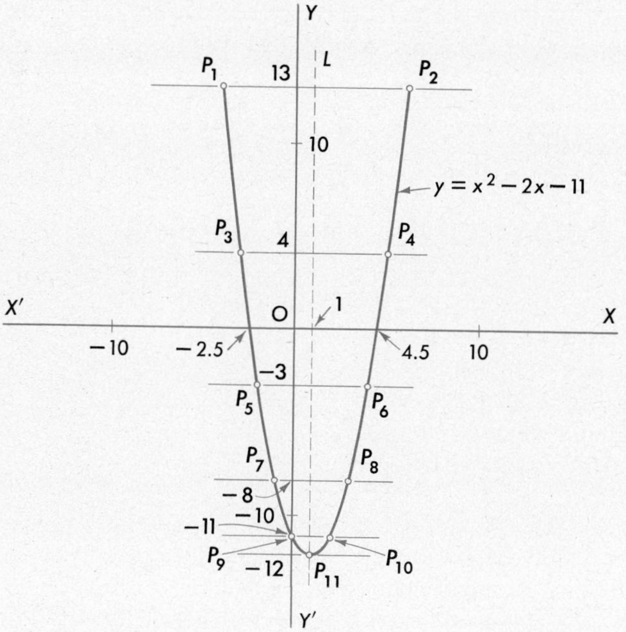

FIGURE 10.1

The table may be extended quite rapidly by taking advantage of the fact that $\Delta^2 y$ constantly equals 2.

By using the word "symmetry" in the ordinary meaning it seems quite appropriate to say that the graph in Fig. 10.1 is symmetrical with respect to the dashed line L. In this context L is said to be the *axis of symmetry*. If a series of points has been plotted on one side of the axis of symmetry, corresponding points may be located on the opposite side, as in a mirror image. The edge of the mirror rests on the axis of symmetry.

From another view, if we fold the paper on which the graph is plotted along the axis of symmetry and press it flat, we find that one branch of the curve lies exactly over the other branch.

In general, two points P_1 and P_2 (Fig. 10.1) are said to be symmetric with respect to a line L if the line L is the perpendicular bisector of the line segment P_1P_2.

Observe the lines whose equations are $y = 13, 4, -3, -8, -11$, and -12.

What are the coordinates of the midpoints on the line segments P_1P_2, P_3P_4, etc.?

If we rewrite the equation $x^2 - 2x - 11 = y$ to read $x^2 - 2x + 1 - 12 = y$ or $(x - 1)^2 - 12 = y$, it is apparent that the smallest possible value of $(x - 1)^2$ is zero. This occurs at $x = 1$. Thus y has a minimum value of -12 at $x = 1$. Note that for $x = 2$ or 0, $(x - 1)^2 = 1$ and $y = -11$. For $x = 3$ or -1, $(x - 1)^2 = 4$ and $y = -8$, etc., thus indicating a symmetry about the line $x = 1$.

If accurate plotting is not required, the parabola may be sketched rapidly by means of the intercepts and the axis of symmetry as indicated above.

EXERCISE 2

Plot as directed, labeling all curves.

1. Plot on a common area.
   (*a*) $y = x^2$ (*b*) $y = -x^2$ (*c*) $y = \frac{1}{4}x^2$ (*d*) $y = \frac{1}{2}x^2$
2. Plot on a common area.
   (*a*) $y = 2x^2$ (*b*) $x = y^2$ (*c*) $x = -y^2$ (*d*) $y = x^2 - 4$
3. Plot on a common area. Find x when $y = 0$.
   (*a*) $y = (x - 3)^2$ (*b*) $y = (x - 3)^2 - 4$
   (*c*) $y = (x + 3)^2$ (*d*) $y = x^2 - 6x + 5$
4. Plot on a common area. Find x when $y = 0$.
   (*a*) $y = 2(x - 4)^2$ (*b*) $y = 2x^2 - 16x + 14$
   (*c*) $y = 2(x - 4)^2 - 18$
5. Plot on a common area.
   (*a*) $y = -3x^2 - 12x + 15$ (*b*) $y = -3(x + 2)^2 + 27$
6. Plot $y = x^2 - 4x - 5$. Determine its intersection with the lines
   (*a*) $y = 16$ (*b*) $y = 7$ (*c*) $y = 0$ (*d*) $y = -5$
   (*e*) $y = -8$ (*f*) $y = -9$

EXERCISE 3

Solve the following quadratic equations by sketching the curve $y = f(x)$ as above and plotting in greater detail in the vicinity of the x intercepts.

1. $x^2 - 2x - 3 = 0$
2. $x^2 + x - 6 = 0$
3. $x^2 + x = 56$
*4. $x^2 + 4 = -4x$
5. $x(x + 5) = 24$
6. $2x^2 - 3x + 1 = 0$
7. $3x^2 - x - 2 = 0$
8. $5x^2 - 11x + 2 = 0$
9. $(x - 2)(x - 5) = x - 5$
10. $(x - 5)(x + 8) = x - 16$

10.5 Solution by Factoring

This method is useful when factors of an expression are fairly obvious. See Example 1. However, the student should not spend too much time looking for factors that may not exist.

Example 4. Solve the equation $x(2x - 1) = 15$ by factoring.

*Note that Prob. 4 has two identical solutions.

Carrying out the indicated multiplication,

$2x^2 - x = 15$

Subtracting 15 from both members of the equation,

$2x^2 - x - 15 = 0$

Inspection will show that the factored form is

$(2x + 5)(x - 3) = 0$

Therefore

$2x + 5 = 0$ and $x = -5/2$
$x - 3 = 0$ and $x = 3$

Note that, if the equation had been written $12x^2 - 6x - 90 = 0$, our first step would be the division by a common monomial factor—in this case, by 6.

Example 5. Using the factoring method, confirm the answers obtained to Prob. 6*a*, Exercise 2.

Since we wish to locate the intersections of the lines $y = x^2 - 4x - 5$ and $y = 16$, we shall replace y by 16 in the first equation and write

$16 = x^2 - 4x - 5$ or $0 = x^2 - 4x - 21 = (x - 7)(x + 3)$

Therefore

$x - 7 = 0$ or $x = 7$

and

$x + 3 = 0$ or $x = -3$

EXERCISE 4

Solve the following quadratic equations by the method of factoring:

1. $x^2 - 4x + 4 = 0$
2. $x^2 - x - 30 = 0$
3. $x^2 + x = 72$
4. $x^2 - 2x = 15$
5. $x^2 + 7x = -12$
6. $x^2 - 33 = 8x$

7. $x^2 - 48 = 2x$
8. $x(x - 5) = 36$
9. $x(x + 3) = 40$
10. $x^2 + 3(x - 18) = 0$
11. $2x^2 + 3x + 1 = 0$
12. $5x^2 - 2x - 3 = 0$
13. $8x^2 + 10x - 12 = 0$
14. $21x^2 - 12x - 9 = 0$
15. $(x - 4)(x - 7) = x - 4$
16. $(x + 6)(x - 6) = 5x$
17. $\frac{1}{y + 4} = \frac{3}{y^2 + 12}$
18. $\frac{2}{w - 3} = \frac{w + 3}{8}$

10.6 Solution by Completing the Square

Under certain special conditions this method offers a ready solution. It will be used in Sec. 10.7 to derive the quadratic formula. It is also useful in sketching the parabola (Sec. 10.4).

Example 6. Solve the equation $x^2 + 8x - 48 = 0$ by completing the square.

Rearranging so that all terms containing the variable are on one side of the equation and all constant terms are on the other, we have

$$x^2 + 8x = +48$$

Making the left side a perfect square by adding 16 to both sides (see Prob. 10, Exercise 12, Chap. 2).

$$x^2 + 8x + 16 = 48 + 16 = 64$$

from which

$$(x + 4)^2 = 64$$

Then

$$x + 4 = \pm\sqrt{64} = \pm 8$$

Therefore

$$x + 4 = +8 \qquad x = +4$$

and

$$x + 4 = -8 \qquad x = -12$$

The selection of the quantity to be added to both sides before extracting the square root is governed by considering the identity

$$(x + k)^2 = x^2 + (2k)x + k^2$$

This identity can be verified directly by multiplication.

$$\begin{array}{l} x + k \\ x + k \\ \hline x^2 + kx \\ \qquad kx + k^2 \\ \hline x^2 + (2k)x + k^2 \end{array}$$

where the coefficient of x is $2k$. Observe that the constant term k^2 is the square of one-half the coefficient of x.

Thus, in our example, we square one-half the coefficient of x to obtain $(8/2)^2 = 16$.

Example 7. Solve, by completing the square, the equation $3x(x - 3) = 2(1 - 2x)$.

Carrying out indicated multiplications,

$$3x^2 - 9x = 2 - 4x \tag{2}$$

Adding 4x to both members, leaving the constant term on the right,

$$3x^2 - 5x = 2 \tag{3}$$

Note. *In Example 5 the coefficient of the x^2 term in the given equation is 1. Before proceeding with this example, we shall have to write an equation which is equivalent to Eq. (3), in which the coefficient of the x^2 is also 1.*

We obtain such an equation by dividing both members of Eq. (3) by 3. Thus

$$x^2 - \frac{5x}{3} = \frac{2}{3} \tag{4}$$

The term to be added to both sides will be the square of half the coefficient of the x term,

$$\left(\frac{-5/3}{2}\right)^2 = \frac{25}{36}$$

Adding $^{25}/_{36}$ to both sides of Eq. (4),

$$x^2 - \frac{5x}{3} + \frac{25}{36} = \frac{2}{3} + \frac{25}{36} = \frac{49}{36} \tag{5}$$

Extracting the square root,

$$x - \tfrac{5}{6} = \pm\tfrac{7}{6}$$
$$x = \tfrac{5}{6} + \tfrac{7}{6} \qquad \text{or} \qquad x = 2$$
$$x = \tfrac{5}{6} - \tfrac{7}{6} \qquad \text{or} \qquad x = -\tfrac{1}{3} \tag{6}$$

Example 8. Solve, by the method of completing the square, the equation

$$x^2 - 6cx = 4a^2 - 12ac \tag{7}$$

In this example the terms not containing x have already been separated from those containing x. The missing quantity which will make the left side a perfect square is $(-6c/2)^2 = 9c^2$. Adding $9c^2$ to both sides of Eq. (7), we obtain

$$x^2 - 6cx + 9c^2 = 4a^2 - 12ac + 9c^2 \tag{8}$$

or

$$(x - 3c)^2 = (2a - 3c)^2$$

Extracting the square root of both members,

$$x - 3c = \pm(2a - 3c) \tag{9}$$

Hence

$$x = 3c + (2a - 3c) = 2a$$

Also

$$x = 3c - (2a - 3c) = 6c - 2a$$

Each of these answers will be found to check the original equation.

It is evident that the method of completing the square can be used to the greatest advantage when the coefficient of the second-degree term is unity and that of the first-degree term contains 2 as a factor.

To summarize, the solution of a quadratic by the method of completing the square consists in the following steps:

1. *Write an equivalent equation if necessary so that the constant term is on one side of the equation, and terms containing the variable are on the other side.*
2. *Make the coefficient of x^2 equal to unity by dividing by the coefficient of x^2 unless it is already equal to 1. The equation now has the form $x^2 + px = q$.*
3. *Add to both sides of the equation the square of half the coefficient of x. This transforms the left side of the equation to $x^2 + px + p^2/4$, a perfect square.*
4. *Extract the square roots of both sides, remembering to place a $\pm$ sign before the square root of the right-hand number.*
5. *Solve the two equations so formed for the variable.*
6. *Check the results in the original equation.*

EXERCISE 5

Solve the following equations by means of completing the square, leaving any irrational answers in radical form.

1. $x^2 + 2x - 3 = 0$
2. $x^2 - 4x - 21 = 0$
3. $x^2 + 6x - 7 = 0$
4. $x^2 - 8x - 20 = 0$
5. $x^2 + 10x - 24 = 0$
6. $y^2 - 12y + 27 = 0$
7. $x(x - 10) = 39$
8. $z(z + 8) = 48$
9. $x^2 + 2bx = a^2 - b^2$
10. $x^2 - 2dx = c^2 + 2cd$
11. $x^2 + 2ax = -6ab + 9b^2$
12. $x^2 - 4cx = 9b^2 + 12bc$
13. $9x^2 + 6x - 8 = 0$
14. $5y^2 - 4y = 9$
15. $y^2 - 20y + 105 = 0$
16. $5x^2 - 6x = 8$
17. $w^2 - 4w = 8$
18. $x^2 + 10x = 55$
19. $2z^2 + z - 6 = 0$
20. $x^2 - 8x + 27 = 0$
21. $x^2 + 8x = 32$
22. $12w - w^2 = 16$
23. $14x - x^2 = 59$
24. $3u^2 - 4u = 55$

10.7 Solution by the Quadratic Formula

The most generally applicable method of solving a quadratic equation is that employing the *quadratic formula*. The derivation of this formula begins with the general quadratic

$$ax^2 + bx + c = 0$$

Subtracting c from both members of the above equation,

$$ax^2 + bx = -c \tag{10}$$

Dividing by the coefficient of x^2,

$$x^2 + \frac{bx}{a} = -\frac{c}{a} \tag{11}$$

Adding the square of half the coefficient of x to both members,

$$x^2 + \frac{bx}{a} + \frac{b^2}{4a^2} = \frac{b^2}{4a^2} - \frac{c}{a} \tag{12}$$

Combining fractions on the right,

$$x^2 + \frac{bx}{a} + \frac{b^2}{4a^2} = \frac{b^2 - 4ac}{4a^2} \tag{13}$$

Taking square roots of both members,

$$x + \frac{b}{2a} = \pm\frac{\sqrt{b^2 - 4ac}}{2a} \tag{14}$$

Subtracting $b/(2a)$ from both members of Eq. (14),

$$x = -\frac{b}{2a} \pm \frac{\sqrt{b^2 - 4ac}}{2a} \tag{15}$$

Combining fractions,

$$x = \frac{-b \pm \sqrt{b^2 - 4ac}}{2a} \tag{16}$$

Equation (16) is commonly known as the *quadratic formula*. This formula has the advantage of being applicable to any quadratic equation. Under special conditions, the methods of factoring or completing the square may be more convenient. With practice, there should be no difficulty in selecting the shortest method for the equation at hand.

It should be remembered that a is the coefficient of the second-degree term, b is the coefficient of the first-degree term, and c includes all terms not containing the unknown.

Example 9. Use the quadratic formula to solve the quadratic equation

$$2x(4x - 1) = 15$$

Performing the indicated multiplication,

$$8x^2 - 2x = 15$$

Subtracting 15 from both members,

$$8x^2 - 2x - 15 = 0$$

According to Eq. (1), $a = 8$, $b = -2$, and $c = -15$. Then

$$x = \frac{-(-2) \pm \sqrt{(-2)^2 - 4(8)(-15)}}{(2)(8)}$$

$$= \frac{2 \pm \sqrt{4 + 480}}{16} = \frac{2 \pm 22}{16}$$

Hence

$$x = \frac{2 + 22}{16} = \frac{3}{2}$$

Also

$$x = \frac{2 - 22}{16} = -\frac{5}{4}$$

EXERCISE 6

Solve the following equations by the quadratic formula, leaving any irrational answers in the radical form:

1. $x^2 - 17x + 60 = 0$
2. $x^2 + x - 156 = 0$
3. $x^2 - 4x = 165$
4. $3x^2 + 7x = 6$
5. $5y - 6y^2 + 1 = 0$
6. $12z^2 + 24z = -9$
7. $x^2 + x + 1 = 0$
*8. $1/x = x/(x + 1)$
9. $3w^2 - 6w + 5 = 0$
10. $5x^2 - 55x - 5 = 0$
11. $3x^2 - 1 = 11x/12$
12. $30y^2 + 76y + 48 = 0$
13. $w^2 + 5w + 7 = 0$
14. $7y^2 + 12y + 4 = 0$
15. $5p^2 - 3p + 1 = 0$
16. $\dfrac{1}{y-1} + \dfrac{2}{y+2} = \dfrac{1}{y+1}$

*See Prob. 61, page 104, "Golden Mean."

10.8 Literal Quadratic Equations

In a *literal* quadratic equation some or all of the constants are literal numbers. These constants are usually represented by the first several letters of the alphabet or may involve π. In some cases it is preferable not to substitute the numerical value of π until a later stage of the solution.

The formula usually offers the easiest means of solution in the long run.

Example 10. Solve the equation $2(x^2 + p^2) + q(x + p - q) = 5px$.

Carrying out the indicated multiplication,

$$2x^2 + 2p^2 + qx + qp - q^2 = 5px$$

By subtracting $5px$ from both members of this equation and arranging in descending powers of x, we obtain

$$2x^2 + qx - 5px + 2p^2 + pq - q^2 = 0$$

Grouping and factoring x^2 and x terms,

$$2x^2 + (q - 5p)x + 2p^2 + qp - q^2 = 0$$

Tabulate the values a, b, and c of the quadratic formula [Eq. (16)], remembering that all terms not containing the variable, no matter how many there may be, are grouped under c. Thus $a = 2$, $b = q - 5p$, $c = 2p^2 + pq - q^2$. Then

$$\begin{aligned} x &= \frac{-(q - 5p) \pm \sqrt{(q - 5p)^2 - 8(2p^2 + pq - q^2)}}{2(2)} \\ &= \frac{-q + 5p \pm \sqrt{q^2 - 10qp + 25p^2 - 16p^2 - 8pq + 8q^2}}{4} \\ &= \frac{-q + 5p \pm \sqrt{9q^2 - 18pq + 9p^2}}{4} \\ &= \frac{-q + 5p \pm (3q - 3p)}{4} \end{aligned}$$

Hence

$$x = \frac{-q + 5p + (3q - 3p)}{4} = \frac{2q + 2p}{4} = \frac{q + p}{2}$$

and

$$x = \frac{-q + 5p - (3q - 3p)}{4} = \frac{-4q + 8p}{4} = 2p - q$$

In cases in which the equation or the roots are more involved, checking by direct substitution may entail as much time and effort as the original solution. The process may be facilitated by assigning numerical values to the literal constants. Avoid assigning numerical values which will make a denominator equal to zero. See Sec. 7.5.

Example 11. Check the equation $(n - k)x^2 + (k - m)x + m - n = 0$, whose roots are $x = (m - n)/(n - k)$ and $x = 1$. (*Note:* Only the first root requires discussion.) Assigning arbitrary simple numerical values (other than 0 and 1) to m, n, and k such that x will also be a simple integer, we might select $m = 10$, $n = 4$, and $k = 2$; therefore

$$x = \frac{10 - 4}{4 - 2} = 3$$

Substituting in the original equation,

$$(4 - 2)(3)^2 + (2 - 10)(3) + 10 - 4 \stackrel{?}{=} 0$$

or

$$(2)(9) + (-8)(3) + 6 \stackrel{?}{=} 0$$

or

$$\begin{aligned} 18 - 24 + 6 &= 0 \\ 0 &= 0 \end{aligned}$$

EXERCISE 7

Solve the following literal quadratic equations for w, x, y, or z as the case may be:

1. $15x^2 - mx - 2m^2 = 0$
2. $4x^2 + (x + 3a)^2 = 17a^2$
3. $w^2 + aw + bw - cw = c(a + b)$
4. $abcx^2 + b^2cx + ac^2x + bc^2 = 0$
5. $(b - c)y^2 + (c - a)y + a - b = 0$
6. $w^2 - \left(\frac{a}{b} + \frac{b}{a}\right)w + 1 = 0$
7. $3z^2 - hz - 5 = 0$
8. $\frac{c^2}{x^2} = \frac{c + 1}{x + 1}$

9. $(x - k)^2 + (x - h)^2 = k^2 + h^2$
10. $a = \pi x(x + 2h)$
11. Given the equation $(x - 2)/(m - 1) = 2m/(2x - 3m)$, which is to be solved for x, write the expressions for a, b, and c of the quadratic formula [Eq. (16)], but do not solve.

10.9 Precautions Regarding Roots

At this point it is important to guard against two common errors resulting from apparently legitimate operations. These pitfalls are vanishing roots and extraneous roots. *Extraneous roots* are values which are created in the process of solving an equation but which do not check the original equation.

10.10 Vanishing Roots

It is not advisable to divide an equation through by an expression containing the variable. By such division a root may be lost.

Example 12. Solve the equation $x^2 - 5x = 0$.
Dividing through by x,

$$x - 5 = 0$$

or

$$x = 5$$

It is evident that another root, $x = 0$, has been lost in this process. Clearly, we should have factored and set each factor equal to zero. Thus we obtain the equation $x(x - 5) = 0$ and the roots $x = 0$ and $x = 5$.

Example 13. Solve the equation $2x^2 + 3x - 2 = x^2 - 4$.
Dividing through by $x + 2$,

$$2x - 1 = x - 2$$

Adding $1 - x$ to both members,

$$x = -1$$

In this case, by dividing by $x + 2$, we have lost the root $x = -2$.

10.11 Extraneous Roots

If both members of a given equation are multiplied by an expression involving the variable, the resulting equation may have solutions (or roots) which are not solutions (or roots) of the given equation. These are called *extraneous solutions,* or *extraneous roots.*

Because of the possibility of obtaining such extraneous values, it is absolutely necessary that all roots or solutions be checked by substitution in the given equation.

Example 14. Solve the equation

$$3 + \frac{4}{x + 2} = \frac{x^2}{x + 2} - 1$$

Multiplying by $x + 2$,

$$3(x + 2) + 4 = x^2 - (x + 2)$$

Clearing of parentheses,

$$3x + 6 + 4 = x^2 - x - 2$$

By collecting terms after subtracting $3x + 10$ from both members of the above equation, we obtain

$$0 = x^2 - 4x - 12$$

Factoring;

$$0 = (x - 6)(x + 2)$$

$$x - 6 = 0 \quad \text{or} \quad x = 6$$

$$x + 2 = 0 \quad \text{or} \quad x = -2$$

The root $x = 6$ satisfies the equation, but the root $x = -2$ does not. (If we replace x by -2 in the original equation, both denominators become zero, but division by zero is impossible.)

Note that this situation could have been avoided by writing

$$3 + 1 = \frac{x^2}{x + 2} - \frac{4}{x + 2}$$

Combining fractions and reducing,

$$4 = \frac{x^2 - 4}{x + 2} = x - 2$$

or

$$x = 6$$

10.12 Checking

Checking is usually accomplished by direct substitution of the answers, or roots, in the original equation. However, if the original equation is in the type form for the general quadratic, a shorter method is available, especially if one or both roots are fractions. It depends upon the fact that if m and n are roots of a given equation, we may write $(x - m)(x - n) = 0$. [The *factor theorem* states that if r is a root of the equation $f(x) = 0$, then $x - r$ is a factor of the polynomial $f(x)$.] Referring back to Example 7 and the equation $3x^2 - 5x = 2$ whose roots are 2 and $-\frac{1}{3}$, we may check by writing

$$(x - 2)[x - (-\tfrac{1}{3})] = 0$$

Multiplying by 3,

$$(x - 2)(3x + 1) = 0$$
$$3x^2 - 5x - 2 = 0$$

which checks all but the preliminary multiplication and transposition.

Note. *The alert student will appreciate that we have here an aid to factoring expressions of the type* $acx^2 + (ad + bc)x + bd$ *(expansion 12, Sec. 2.9). If necessary, first factor the expression to free it of monomial factors. Set the resulting expression, such as* $3x^2 - 5x - 2$*, equal to zero, determine the roots by Eq. (16), the quadratic formula, and derive the factored form of the expression* $(x - 2)(3x + 1)$ *as above.*

10.13 Summary of Procedure for Solving Quadratic Equations

1. *Simplify any reducible fractions and combine any fractions having a common denominator.*
2. *Clear of fractions.*

3. *If there is a factor (not containing the variable) common to all terms, divide through by that factor.*
4. *The choice of the method of solution might well be based upon consideration of the following suggestions in the order given:*
   a. *Use the factoring method if the factors are readily discernible.*
   b. *Use the method of completing the square if the coefficient of the second-degree term is unity and that of the first-degree term is divisible by 2.*
   c. *If neither (a) nor (b) is applicable, use the quadratic formula. This is somewhat longer but has general application to all cases.*
5. *Check all answers, discarding any extraneous roots.*

EXERCISE 8

Solve the following equations by the most convenient method, rejecting any extraneous roots and leaving any irrational answers in the radical form.

1. $\dfrac{y}{y+1} = \dfrac{y+2}{3y}$
2. $(w+2)^3 - w^3 = 56$
3. $\dfrac{1}{z-3} + \dfrac{1}{z+4} = \dfrac{1}{12}$
4. $x + \dfrac{1}{5} = 5 + \dfrac{1}{x}$
5. $y + \dfrac{mn}{y} = m + n$
6. $\dfrac{1}{r} + r = 3 + \dfrac{3}{r}$
7. $11d^2 + 7d + 1 = 0$
8. $\dfrac{10}{x} - \dfrac{9}{x+1} - \dfrac{8}{x+2} = 0$
9. $\dfrac{h}{5} - \dfrac{5}{6} = \dfrac{6}{5} - \dfrac{5}{h}$
10. $\dfrac{1}{x} - \dfrac{1}{d} = \dfrac{1}{x+d}$
11. $\dfrac{1}{c} + \dfrac{1}{8-c} = \dfrac{1}{8}$
12. $x(2x-c) + x(x-c) = bx$
13. $2y(7y-a) = (a+y)(a-y)$
14. $\dfrac{1}{x+3} + \dfrac{1}{x+2} - \dfrac{1}{x+1} = 0$
15. $\pi x^2 + 2\pi nx - A = 0$
16. $8w = -3(1 + 4w^2)$
17. $\dfrac{2}{m+5} - \dfrac{m+3}{(m+4)(m+5)} = \dfrac{1}{4(m-8)}$
18. $\dfrac{a}{x-b} + \dfrac{b}{x-a} = 2$
19. $c(x^2-1) = (ax+b)(x-1)$
20. $\dfrac{1}{w-2} + 1 = \dfrac{6-w}{w^2-4} + \dfrac{1}{w+2}$
21. $\dfrac{a}{x} + \dfrac{x}{a} = \dfrac{33a^2 - x^2}{ax}$
22. $\dfrac{1}{c+d+x} = \dfrac{1}{c} + \dfrac{1}{d} + \dfrac{1}{x}$
23. $9x^2 - hx + h^2 = 0$
24. The roots of a quadratic equation are $2/3$ and $-5/2$. Write the original equation cleared of fractions.

10.14 Discriminant

In the quadratic formula

$$x = \frac{-b \pm \sqrt{b^2 - 4ac}}{2a}$$

the expression $b^2 - 4ac$ is called the *discriminant*. The value of the discriminant may usually be determined by inspection and indicates the nature of the roots of the equation $ax^2 + bx + c = 0$. The relationships are summarized in Table 10.1.

TABLE 10.1

Discriminant	Positive and a perfect square	Positive but not a perfect square	Zero	Negative
Character of the roots	Real, rational, and unequal	Real, irrational, and unequal	Real, rational, and equal	Complex and unequal if $b \neq 0$; imaginary if $b = 0$
Graph of $ax^2 + bx + c = y$	Cuts X axis in two points		Tangent to X axis	Does not intersect X axis

Example 15. Determine the nature of the roots of the equation $2x^2 - 7x - 5 = 0$.

Here $b^2 - 4ac = (-7)^2 - 4(2)(-5) = 49 + 40 = 89$. Since 89 is positive but not a perfect square, the roots are real, irrational, and unequal.

Example 16. Determine the nature of the roots of the equation $25x^2 - 30x + 9 = 0$.

In this example, $b^2 - 4ac = (-30)^2 - 4(25)(9) = 0$. Hence the roots are real, rational, and equal.

EXERCISE 9

Calculate the discriminant and describe the character of the roots without solving:

1. $x^2 + 4x - 12 = 0$
2. $x^2 - x - 20 = 0$
3. $x^2 - 6x + 9 = 0$
4. $x^2 - 3x - 5 = 0$
5. $2x^2 + 5x - 3 = 0$
6. $4x^2 + 20x + 25 = 0$
7. $6x^2 - x - 2 = 0$
8. $x^2 + 7x + 18 = 0$
9. $3x^2 - 18x + 27 = 0$
10. $2x^2 + 7x + 9 = 0$
11. $5x^2 - x - 10 = 0$
12. $28x^2 + 84x + 63 = 0$
13. $20x^2 - 7x - 3 = 0$
14. $14x^2 + 13x - 12 = 0$

10.15 Axis of Symmetry—Extreme Value

An equation in the form

$$ax^2 + bx + c = y$$

where a is a positive number, is plotted in Fig. 10.2a. Observe that this graph intersects the X axis at the two points

$$x = \frac{-b + \sqrt{b^2 - 4ac}}{2a}$$

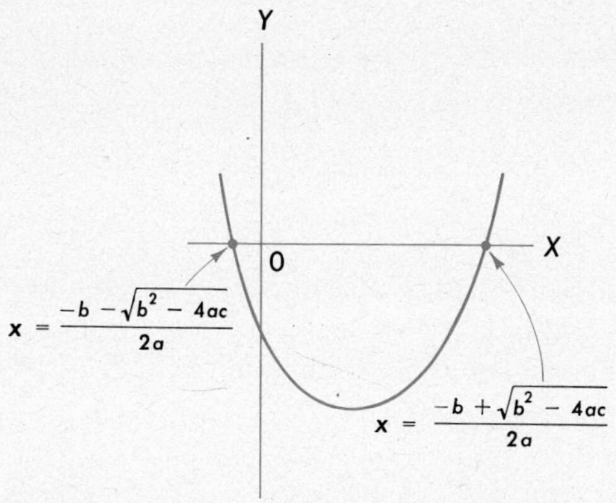

FIGURE 10.2a

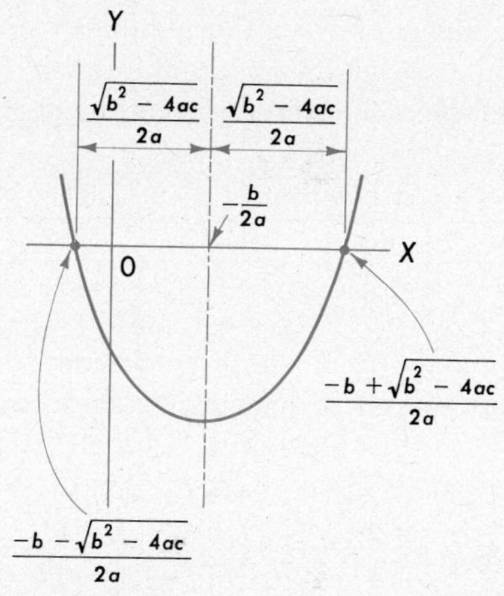

FIGURE 10.2b

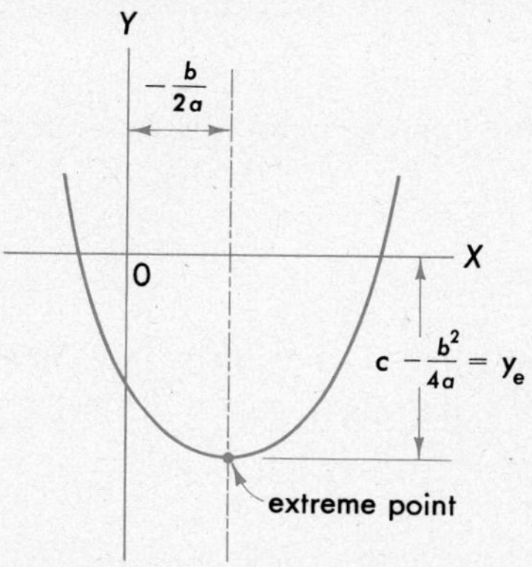

FIGURE 10.2c

and

$$x = \frac{-b - \sqrt{b^2 - 4ac}}{2a}$$

From Eq. (16) it is evident that these two values of x are the roots of the equation

$$ax^2 + bx + c = 0$$

That is, they are the values of x for which $y = 0$.

We recall from Sec. 10.4 that the graph of the equation $ax^2 + bx + c = y$ has a vertical axis of symmetry,† and that the extreme value of y, or the turning point of the curve, lies on this axis. The axis of symmetry intersects the X axis at a point midway between the x intercepts of the graph.

From the midpoint formula (Sec. 6.15) the axis of symmetry intersects the X axis at the point whose x coordinate is given by

$$\frac{\dfrac{-b + \sqrt{b^2 - 4ac}}{2a} + \dfrac{-b - \sqrt{b^2 - 4ac}}{2a}}{2}$$

or at the point whose x coordinate is $-b/(2a)$. See Fig. 10.2b; also Fig. 10.1. The equation of the axis of symmetry is therefore $x = -b/(2a)$.

By substituting $-b/(2a)$ for x in the given equation, we obtain

$$y_e = a\left(\frac{b^2}{4a^2}\right) - b\left(\frac{b}{2a}\right) + c = \frac{b^2}{4a} - \frac{b^2}{2a} + c$$
$$= c - \frac{b^2}{4a}$$

where y_e is the ordinate of the graph at the extreme point, or the turning point (Fig. 10.2c). The coordinates of the extreme point are therefore

$$\left(-\frac{b}{2a}, c - \frac{b^2}{4a}\right) \qquad \textbf{(17)}$$

A brief check will show that if a is positive, the curve opens upward, $\smile$, and the extreme is a minimum. On the other hand, if a is negative, the curve opens downward, $\frown$, and the extreme is a maximum.

†In this instance a was equal to unity, but the symmetry still exists for any $a \neq 0$.

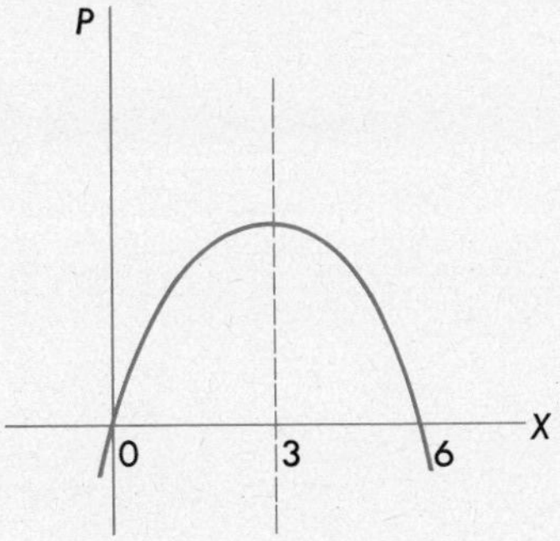

FIGURE 10.3

Example 17. Divide 6 into two parts such that their product is a maximum.

If x and 6 − x represent the two parts, we have

$$P = x(6 - x) = -x^2 + 6x$$

where *P* is the product.

By Eq. (17), x for a maximum *P* is

$$x = -\frac{6}{(2)(-1)} = 3$$

and the maximum product is also given by Eq. (17):

$$P_{max} = 0 - \frac{(6)^2}{(4)(-1)} = 9$$

Actually, no formal rule is necessary. If the graph of the given equation is sketched as in Fig. 10.3, the x intercepts appear at $x = 0$ and $x = 6$. The axis of symmetry intersects the X axis at

$$x = \frac{0 + 6}{2} = +3$$

As we found above, this leads to a maximum product of 9.

EXERCISE 10

In Probs. 1 to 10, determine the nature (max or min) and coordinates of the extreme point of the graphs of the following equations and the equation of the axis of symmetry.

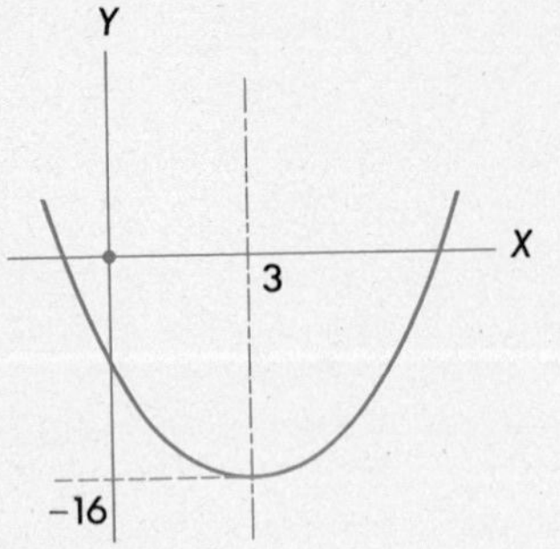

FIGURE 10.4

1. $x^2 - 2x - 15 = y$
2. $-x^2 - 4x + 12 = y$
3. $x^2 + 7x + 6 = y$
4. $2x^2 + 5x - 3 = y$
5. $-x^2 + 6x = y$
6. $5x^2 - 6x - 8 = y$
7. $-6x^2 + 7x - 2 = y$
8. $3x^2 - x - 10 = y$
9. $-4x^2 - 4x + 15 = y$
10. $-2x^2 + x + 28 = y$
11. The equation of a certain parabola is of the type $y + b = (x + a)^2$. Evaluate a and b by inspection. Find the x and y intercepts. See Fig. 10.4.
12. Divide 17 into two parts such that their product will be a maximum.
13. Find the dimensions of the largest possible rectangular area that may be enclosed by 140 ft of fencing.
14. The work done by exploding a mixture of 1 ft^3 of water gas and v ft^3 of air is $w = 84v - 3.15v^2$. What value of v will lead to the maximum value of w? What is the maximum value of w?
15. A ball is thrown upward with a speed of 144 ft/s from a building 340 ft high. If the height of the ball h in feet at any time t s after throwing is given by the equation $h = 340 + 144t - 16t^2$, find the maximum height reached.
16. The power delivered to an external circuit by a 32-V generator whose internal resistance is 2 Ω is $32a - 2a^2$ W, where a is the current in amperes. At what current will this generator deliver the maximum power?
17. A long sheet of copper 22 in wide is to be made into a gutter by turning strips up vertically along the two sides. How many inches should be turned up at each side to obtain the greatest carrying capacity?
18. A transit authority charges 35 cents per ride and carries an average of 2,100 passengers daily. It proposes to reduce an operating deficit by raising the fares. However, it has good reason to believe that for each 5-cent increase in the fare, 200 riders will seek other means of transportation. What fare would result in the maximum return?

    (It follows that if n is the number of 5-cent increases, there will be $2{,}100 - 200n$ riders, each paying a fare of $35 + 5n$ cents.)

10.16 Applications Leading to Quadratic Equations in One Variable

In Sec. 10.11 we learned that an *extraneous* solution to a quadratic equation in one variable is a solution which is introduced in the process of solving the problem but which is not a solution to the given equation.

Many of the problems in Exercise 11 are problems in which a quadratic equation is used as a mathematical model of a certain physical situation. Very often in such cases a pair of solutions are found which do check when substituted in the basic equation but which are inconsistent with the physical restrictions imposed by the statement of the problem. Since such solutions do in fact check out in the original equation, they cannot be considered mathematically extraneous. Nevertheless, they may at times violate some of the physical conditions of the problem and are appropriately called *secondary solutions.*

Example 18. Figure 10.5 illustrates a block of concrete resting on the floor of a room and in contact with a vertical wall of the room. The concrete block is 2 ft wide and 1 ft high. The problem is to find the radius of a wheel whose circumference rests on the floor, in contact with the wall and the edge of the concrete block at point A.

We construct the right triangle ABC in which the hypotenuse is R, the vertical side is $R - 1$, and the horizontal side is $R - 2$. Then, by the Pythagorean theorem,

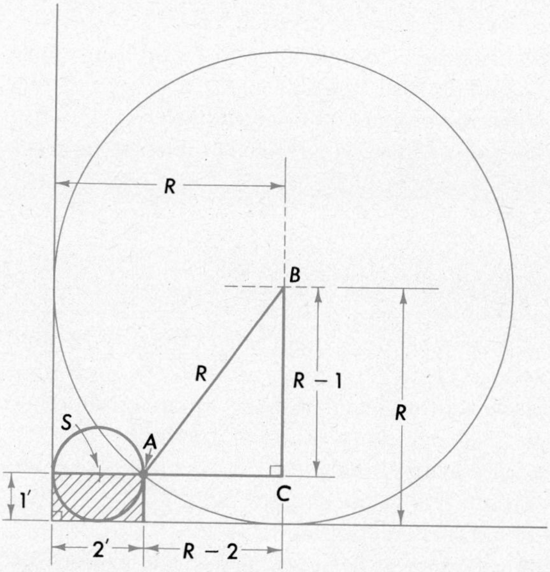

FIGURE 10.5

$$R^2 = (R - 1)^2 + (R - 2)^2$$

or

$$R^2 = R^2 - 2R + 1 + R^2 - 4R + 4$$

or

$$0 = R^2 - 6R + 5$$

Then

$$0 = (R - 5)(R - 1)$$

from which

$$R = 5 \text{ ft} \qquad \text{and} \qquad R = 1 \text{ ft}$$

Both of these roots are found to check in the original equation. Hence neither of them is extraneous. However, the 5-ft radius is the only one which is consistent with the physical conditions of the problem.

The circle with a 1-ft radius whose center is at point S would be an absurdity since it would require a wheel to occupy space already occupied by a block of concrete.

Therefore the solution $R = 1$ ft is called a *secondary* solution.

It is frequently interesting and instructive to determine the significance of a secondary solution. (See Probs. 13, 14, and 28; also Example 19.) It may suggest that the scope of the problem is broader than the original question indicates.

Remember that a "check," unless made on the original stated problem, is no check at all.

EXERCISE 11

1. Find two numbers whose sum is 23 and whose product is 126.
2. Separate 19 into two parts whose product is 84.
3. The difference between two positive numbers is 7 and their product is 78. Find the numbers.
4. Separate 132 into two positive parts such that one part is the square of the other.
5. The sum of a positive number and its square is 72. Find the number.
6. Find two consecutive positive integers whose product is 156.
7. Find two consecutive positive even integers whose product is 224.
8. Find two consecutive positive odd integers whose product is 195.
9. Find a positive number whose square exceeds 36 by as much as 36 exceeds the number.

10. What number added to its reciprocal equals 2.9?
11. A ball is thrown downward from a building 380 ft high with a speed of 112 ft/s. Under these conditions the height h of the ball in feet at any time t s after throwing the ball is given by the equation $h = -16t^2 - 112t + 380$. When will the ball strike the ground?
12. Repeat Prob. 11 for the time at which the ball is 252 ft above the ground. Can you explain the secondary (negative) answer?
13. A model rocket is fired upward from a building 60 ft high with a speed of 112 ft/s. The height h (in feet) above the ground level at any time t (in seconds) after firing is given by the equation

$$h = -16t^2 + 112t + 60$$

(a) Calculate h at $t = -1$, 0, 1, 2, 3, 4, 5, 6, 7, and 8 s.
(b) Plot the graph of this equation (h vertically and t horizontally).
(c) When did the maximum height occur? What was the height?
(d) When did $h = 0$? What is the significance of each of the two answers?

14. A strip of metal 8 in wide is to be bent into a trough of rectangular cross section (open top) whose cross-sectional area is to be $7\frac{1}{2}$ in^2. Find the depth and width of the trough. How many answers?
15. The hypotenuse of a right triangle is 10 cm longer than the shorter side and 5 cm longer than the longer side. Find the sides of the triangle.
16. If the cross-sectional area of the angle beam in Fig. 10.6 is $6\frac{1}{4}$ in^2, find the thickness x.

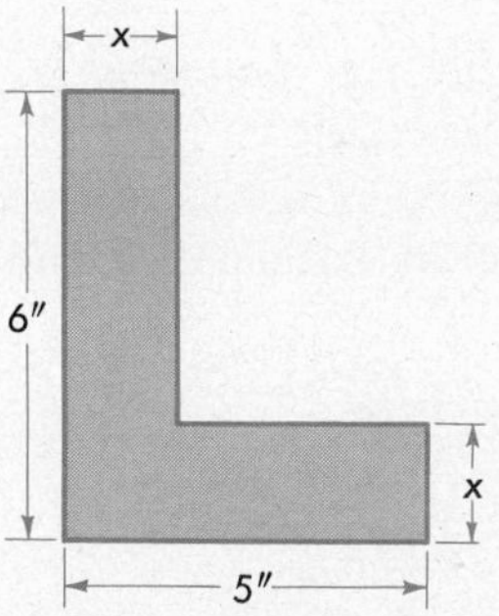

FIGURE 10.6

17. A group of boys bought a canoe for $70, planning to divide the expense equally. However, two boys dropped out, increasing the share of each boy by $1.75. How many boys were there in the original group?
18. Find the radius R in Fig. 10.7. (*Hint:* Draw the construction lines AB, BC, and CA as in Fig. 10.8. Then form the right triangle ABC. Find the missing dimensions in

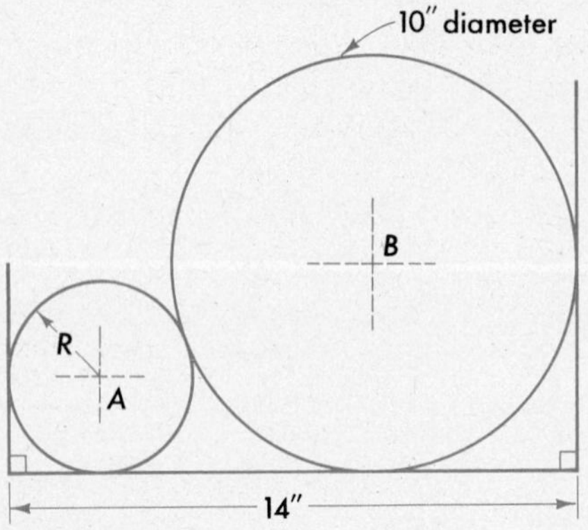

FIGURE 10.7

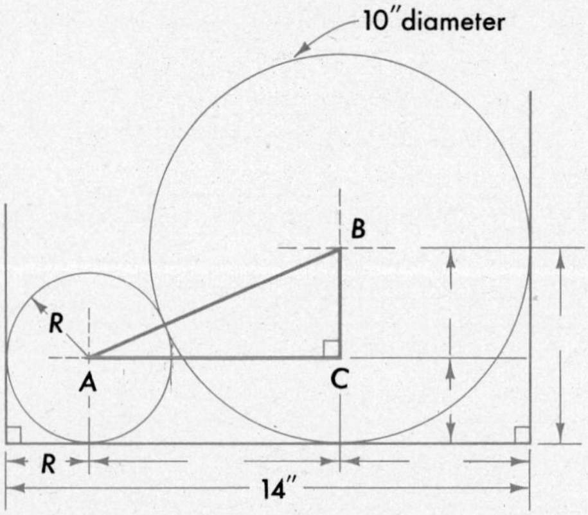

FIGURE 10.8

Fig. 10.8 in terms of R and the given constants. By means of the Pythagorean theorem relate the sides of the right triangle ABC and solve for R.)

19. Find the radius R in Fig. 10.9.
20. Find the diameter of the circle in Fig. 10.10.
21. Two resistances in parallel have a joint resistance of 4.2 Ω. The same two resistances in series have a resistance of 20 Ω. Find the value of each resistance.
22. A park is 480 yd long by 320 yd wide. It is decided to double its area, retaining the rectangular shape, by adding strips of equal width to one end and one side. Find the width of the strips.
23. The perimeter of a rectangular field is 274 m, and the diagonal is 97 m. Find its dimensions.
24. The sum of the areas of the two inner circles in Fig. 10.11 is three-quarters the area of the outer circle. Find the diameter of the smallest circle.
25. The outer portion of a garden 22 by 30 ft is to be occupied by a walk of uniform width. If the garden is to be reduced to three-quarters of its original area, find the width of the walk.

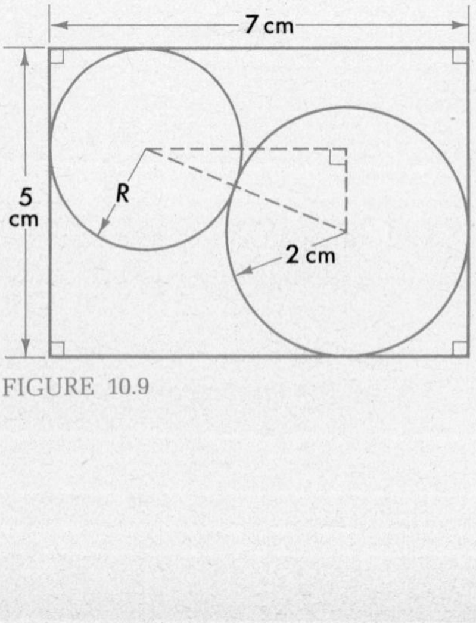

FIGURE 10.9

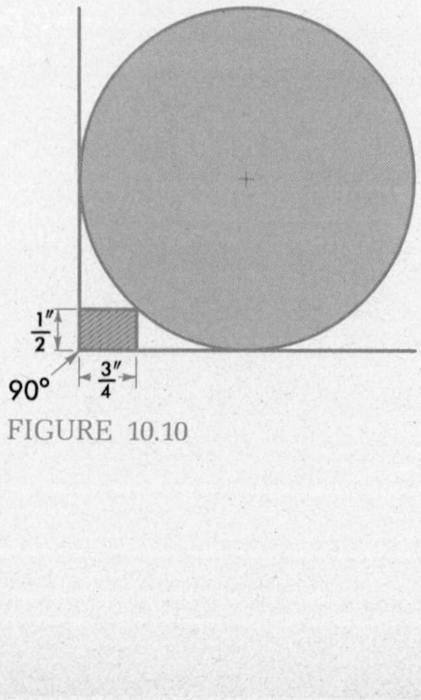

FIGURE 10.10

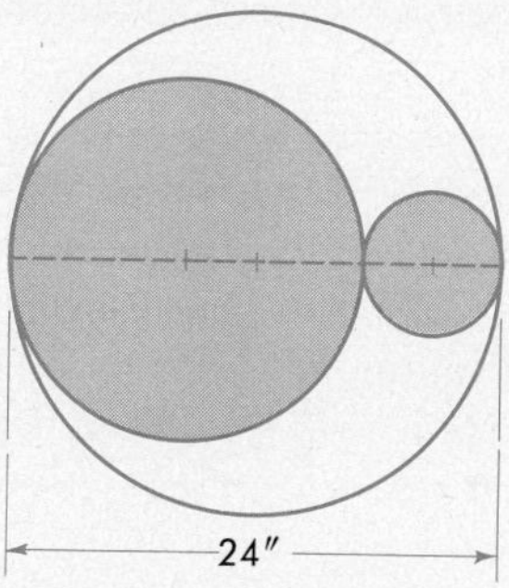

FIGURE 10.11

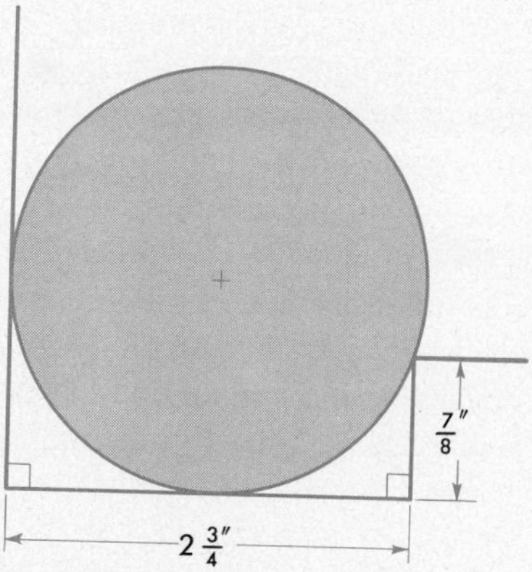

FIGURE 10.12

26. A motorboat takes 2 h 8 min longer to make a trip of 48 mi up a stream than it takes on the return trip downstream. If the average rate of the current is 4 mi/h, find the rate of the boat in still water.
27. The sides of a triangle are in the ratio of 5:6:7, and the area is 900 in². Find the shortest side.
28. Find the diameter of the circle in Fig. 10.12.
29. Find the radius R of the cylindrical gauge in Fig. 10.13a. (*Note:* In one respect an equation resembles a slide rule or computer—it will deliver only what you feed into it. In effect we "told" the equation we wanted a circle tangent to the sides of the right angle and also to the semicircle. We had no way of "programming"

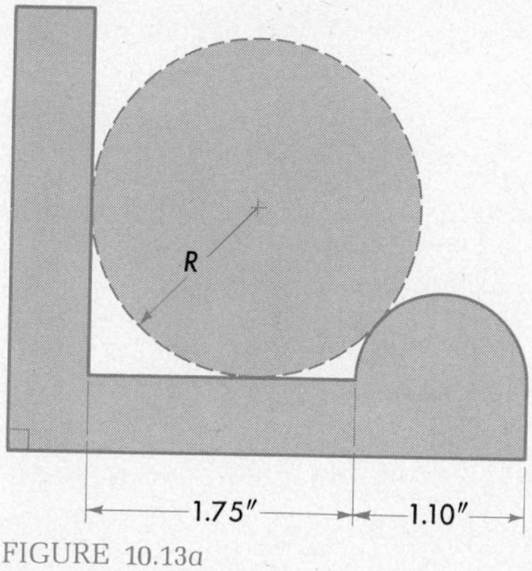

FIGURE 10.13a

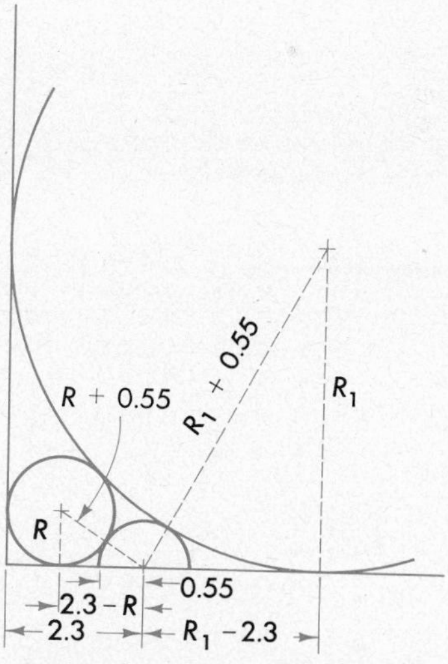

FIGURE 10.13b

the restriction excluding the larger circle; so we find in our "output" both circles meeting the tangency requirement. See. Fig. 10.13*b*.)

30. A 2-ft walk surrounds a circular flower bed. If the area of the walk is one-tenth the area of the flower bed, find the diameter of the bed.
31. Ice on a power-transmission line may be melted off by increasing the voltage. If $E^2/[a(1 + bt)] = K(t - t_0)$, find the temperature t°F of the wire if the voltage E is 580; a is the resistance of the line at 0°F and is equal to 52 Ω; b is the temperature coefficient of resistance of the wire, or 0.003; K is the coefficient of heat transfer by convection and conduction, or 350; t_0 is the air temperature, or 24°F.
32. A triangle has a 12-in altitude and a 20-in base. How wide a strip should be cut off by a line parallel to the base to leave 55 in^2 at the top?

Example 19. A 50-cd lamp and a 120-cd lamp are 30 ft apart. Find the point on a line between them which is equally illuminated by both lights. When an object is equally illuminated by two light sources, the light intensities vary directly as the squares of their respective distances from the object. What significance attaches to the secondary solution of this problem? What can you say about the locus of all such equally illuminated points (a) in the same plane, (b) in three-dimensional space? (The relationship in this problem might have been restated to read that "the intensity of illumination varies inversely as the square of the distance from the light source." A similar relationship holds for other forms of energy or force, e.g., heat, electricity, magnetism, and gravity. These are examples of the *inverse-square law*.)

An advantageous method of approaching the solution consists in setting up the proportion

$$\frac{(30 - x)^2}{x^2} = \frac{120}{50}$$

followed by taking the square root of both sides to obtain

$$\frac{30 - x}{x} = \pm\sqrt{\frac{120}{50}} = \pm 1.549$$

from which $x = 11.8$ and $x = -54.6$. It is true that $18.2/11.8 = \sqrt{120/50}$, but it is also true that

$$\frac{|-54.6| + |30|}{|-54.6|} = \sqrt{\frac{120}{50}}$$

(Fig. 10.14). In fact, $PB/PA = \sqrt{120/50}$, where P is any point on the dotted curve which can be shown to be a circle by analytic geometry. The circle may also represent a spherical surface of the same radius and center.

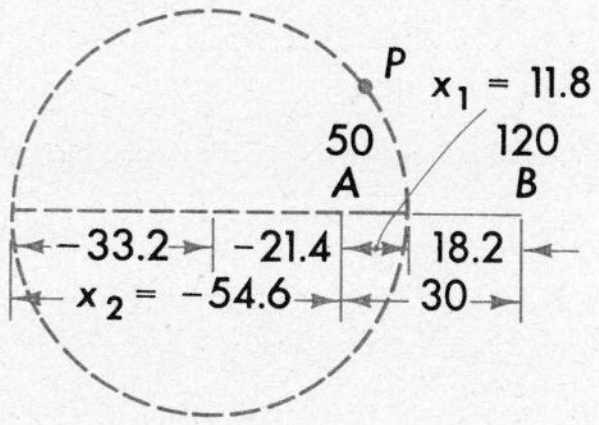

FIGURE 10.14

The moral of this example is: Don't reject a secondary solution out of hand. Perhaps it is trying to tell you something!

33. The solution of the problem of determining the location of the point of *minimum total* illumination between two light sources required that the real root of the equation

$$\frac{(30 - x)^3}{x^3} = \frac{120}{50} = 2.4$$

be found. Calculate x to the nearest 0.1. (*Hint:* Do not expand, but take the cube root of both sides.) It can be shown that this solution will yield the only real root of the equation. Compare your answer with that obtained in Example 19 above.
34. The law of gravitational attraction states that the gravitational force exerted on an object varies inversely as the square of its distance from the attracting body. At what distance x from the surface of the earth (on the earth-moon line) will the gravitational attraction of the earth just balance that of the moon? This is known as the *neutral point* (Fig. 10.15).
35. Mars will be most favorably situated for exploration when it is at its minimum distance, or about 35,000,000 mi from the earth. Locate the neutral point (where Earth's g and Mars' g just balance) under these conditions.

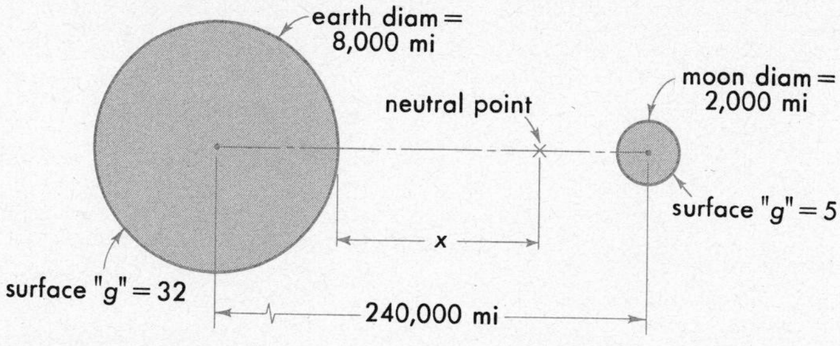

FIGURE 10.15

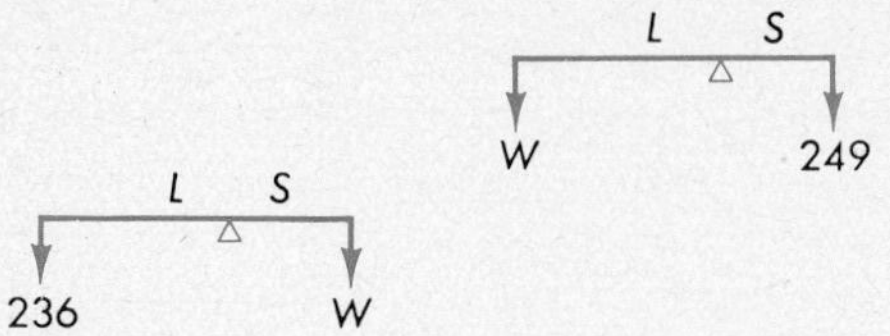

FIGURE 10.16

Example 20. An object is weighed on a platform balance and is found to balance 236.0 g. When the positions of object and weights are reversed, the indicated weight is 249.0 g because of unequal balance arms. Find the true weight correct to 0.1 g. See Fig. 10.16.

Here we find

$$236L = SW$$

and

$$LW = 249S$$

By dividing we find

$$\frac{236L}{LW} = \frac{SW}{249S}$$

or

$$\frac{236}{W} = \frac{W}{249}$$

from which

$$W^2 = 236 \times 249$$

or

$$W = \sqrt{236 \times 249} = 242.4 \text{ g}$$

Note that this answer closely approximates

$$\frac{236 + 249}{2} = 242.5$$

The student may wish to know when the arithmetic mean leads to a close enough answer. The smaller the relative difference between the numbers to be averaged, the better the approximation. This is the basis of a rapid and accurate method of determining square root on a desk calculator or even by longhand.

36. Find a such that the area of the trapezoid shown in Fig. 10.17 is 300 square units if

V = velocity, ft/s
t = time, s
Area = (ft/s)(s) = feet traveled in time t

37. Find the radius of curvature in Fig. 10.18.
38. A man travels 30 mi by bus and returns by a train which runs 15 mi/h faster. If the total running time is 1 h 57 min, find the rates of the bus and the train.
39. A right triangle containing 210 m^2 is roped off by a line 70 m long. Find the three sides of the triangle.
40. Six seconds after a stone is dropped into a mine shaft, the sound of the impact at the bottom reaches the top. If the velocity of sound is 1,120 ft/s and the usual formula for a freely falling body applies to the falling stone, find the depth of the shaft.
41. A flat disk $1\frac{3}{8}$ in in diameter is to be pressed into an open-top cylinder $\frac{5}{8}$ in deep. If the total surface of the metal is unchanged during the operation, find the diameter of the cylinder.
42. A rail-diesel coach has an acceleration of 0.8 ft/s^2 and a braking deceleration of 1.2 ft/s^2. If two stations are $1\frac{1}{4}$ mi apart, what is the maximum speed reached when

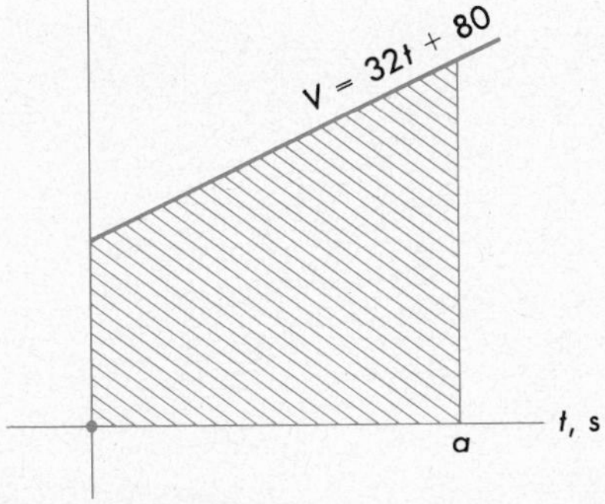

FIGURE 10.17

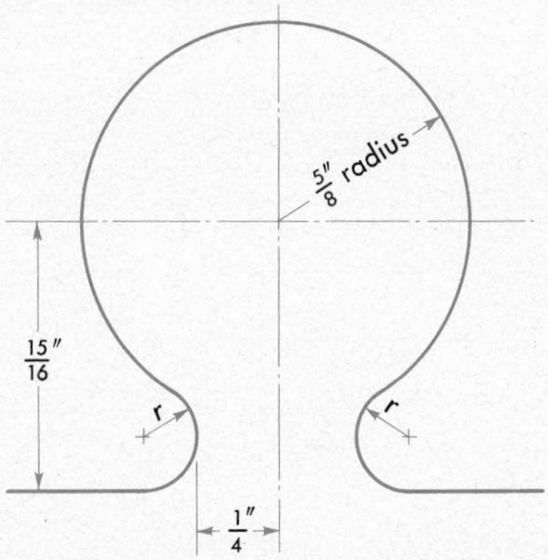

FIGURE 10.18

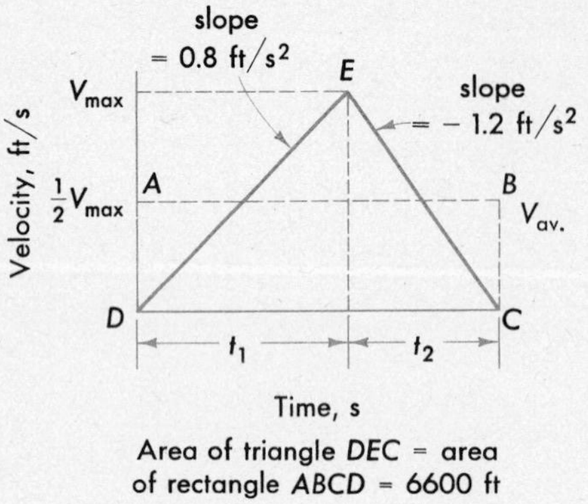

FIGURE 10.19

the power is shut off and the brakes applied? What time is required between the two stops?

To aid in setting up equations, a graph of the speed-time relation is shown in Fig. 10.19.

43. Two boats leave simultaneously from the opposite shores of a bay which is $2\frac{1}{4}$ mi wide and pass each other in 6 min. The faster boat completes the trip $4\frac{1}{2}$ min before the other boat docks. Find the rates of the boats in miles per hour.
44. In the trapezoid shown in Fig. 10.20, find x such that a line drawn parallel to the base shall divide the area in half.
45. A parabola $y = ax^2 + bx + c$ passes through the points $(10, -13)$, $(30,1)$, and $(40,23)$. Substitute the x and y values of the given coordinates successively in the given equation and solve the three simultaneous equations thus formed for a, b, and c.
46. The equation of a circle is $(x - a)^2 + (y - b)^2 = R^2$, where R is the radius. The coordinates of the center of the circle are given by (a,b). The graph passes through the points (3,18), (18,13), and (7,2). Substitute the x and y coordinates of these points

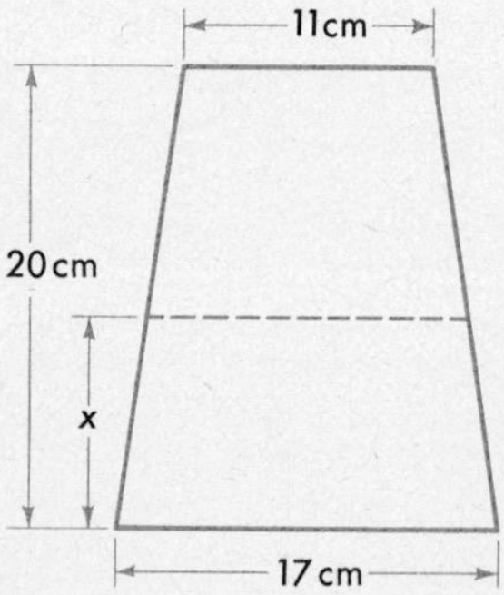

FIGURE 10.20

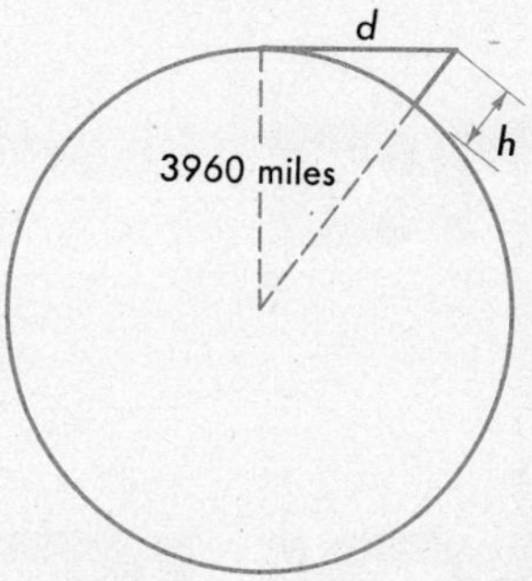

FIGURE 10.21

successively in the given equation and solve the simultaneous equations thus formed for a, b, and R.

47. If the radius of the earth is 3,960 mi, h is the elevation of the observer (feet above sea level), and d is the distance in miles of the horizon at sea, derive an equation for d in terms of h (Fig. 10.21). In this approximation a term is dropped, since its importance is considered to be less than that of light refraction. Show that this assumption is probably justified for such values of h as 100 ft, 1,000 ft, and even 5 mi.
48. Using algebraic methods, confirm the answer to Prob. 4, Exercise 12, Chap. 6.

11 curve sketching and simultaneous quadratic equations

In most cases point-by-point curve plotting will be accomplished more efficiently if it is preceded by curve sketching. In fact, curve sketching is a very effective way of analyzing the properties of a function, whether or not we intend to do any plotting.

11.1 Advantages of Sketching

We learned in Chap. 6 how to draw graphs by plotting a number of points. This is adequate for the straight lines and simple curves encountered there. In this chapter we shall be interested in nonlinear functions and their graphs.

Plotting has several weaknesses when applied to more complicated curves:

1. Too much time is wasted on less significant parts of the curve.
2. The important properties of the curve are not emphasized.
3. It gives no indication of a proper choice of units on the two axes.
4. One cannot be sure when enough points have been plotted to reveal all characteristic properties of the graph.

It is suggested that the curve first be sketched, then plotted in more accurate detail in the vicinity of critical points such as intercepts, extremes, etc.

The most commonly sought properties of a graph include intercepts, symmetry, extent, discontinuities, asymptotes, and excluded regions. Additional properties such as max and min points, singular points, extreme slopes, etc., usually require methods of calculus (see Chap. 20).

11.2 Intercepts

The intercepts of a graph have been discussed in Secs. 6.8 and 10.4. By way of review, the following examples and exercise are included.

Example 1. Find all the intercepts of the curve $y = x^2 - 9$.

When $x = 0$, $y = -9$. When $y = 0$, $x = \pm 3$. Hence the intercepts of the graph of this equation are $(0, -9)$, $(3,0)$, and $(-3,0)$.

Example 2. Determine the intercepts of the curve $x^2 - 4y^2 - x - 6y + 10 = 0$.

When $x = 0$, $y = 1$ or $-5/2$. When $y = 0$, the roots are imaginary. Therefore the graph does not meet the X axis.

EXERCISE 1

Find the intercepts (if any) of the following curves.

1. $y = (x + 10)/(x + 2)$
2. $x^2 - y^2 - 4 = 0$
3. $x^2 + 4y^2 = 36$
4. $y = x^2 + 2x$
5. $y = 8/x$
6. $y = -2x$
7. $y = 9/x^2$
8. $x = y^2 - y - 30$
9. $(x - 2)^2 + (y + 5)^2 = 49$

11.3 Symmetry

The graph of an equation may be symmetric with respect to one or more lines, or to a point.

Symmetry to X Axis

The graph of an equation is symmetric with respect to the X axis if and only if the equation obtained by replacing y with $-y$ is equivalent to the original equation. (That is, the equation contains only even powers of y.)

If a mirror be placed on the X axis, the reflection of the upper (or lower) half coincides with the lower (or upper) half.

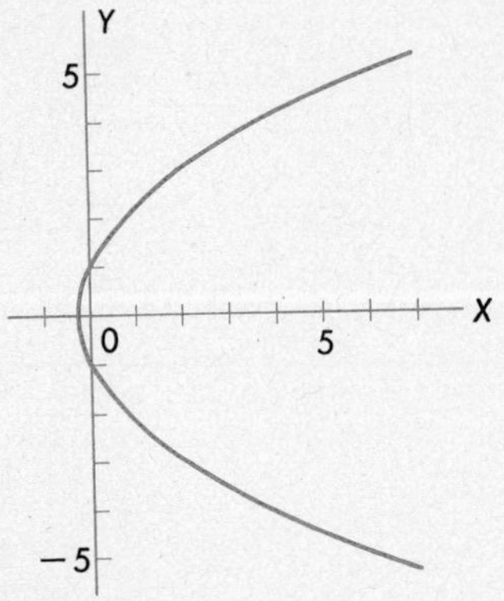

FIGURE 11.1

Example 3. The graph of $y^2 = 4x + 1$ is symmetric with respect to the X axis since $(-y)^2 = 4x + 1$ is equivalent to $y^2 = 4x + 1$ (Fig. 11.1).

Symmetry to Y Axis

The graph is symmetric with respect to the Y axis if and only if the equation obtained by replacing x with $-x$ is equivalent to the original equation. (That is, the equation contains only even powers of x.) Such a function is known as an *even function*. An example is the equation $y = \cos x$. See Fig. 16.1 and Eq. (22), Sec. 17.3.

Symmetry about an axis aids sketching since one half of the curve may be copied from the other half. If there is symmetry about both axes, one quadrant can serve as the pattern for the other three.

Example 4. The graph of $y = 60/(x^2 + 4)$ is symmetric with respect to the y axis (Fig. 11.2). Here the "mirror" is on the Y axis.

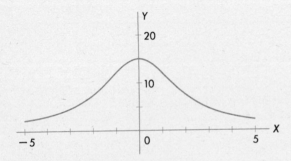

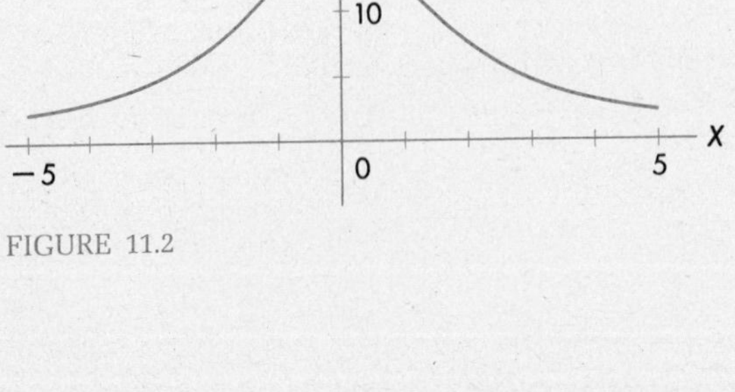

FIGURE 11.2

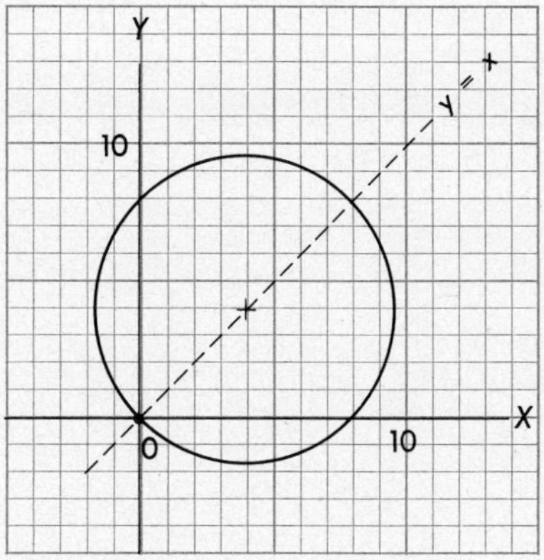

FIGURE 11.3

Symmetry about the Line $y = x$

The graph is symmetric with respect to the line $y = x$ if y may be replaced by x while simultaneously x is replaced by y.

Example 5. In Fig. 11.3 the circle $x^2 - 8x + y^2 - 8y = 0$ meets the test of interchangeability of x and y.

In connection with symmetry about the line $y = x$, if we plot the equations $y = x^2 - 4$ and $x = y^2 - 4$ (Fig. 11.4), we note that one graph is the mirror image of the other if the mirror is placed on the line $y = x$.

Each equation is called the *inverse function* of the other. That is, if we replace the x and y of one equation by y and x, respectively, we obtain the other equation.

Symmetry about Any Line

In general, two distinct points P and P' are symmetric with respect to a line L if L is the perpendicular bisector of the line segment PP'. P and P' are said to be symmetric partners with respect to the line L.

Example 6. The parabola $y = x^2 - 4x - 21$ shows symmetry about the vertical line $x = 2$ (Fig. 11.5). The horizontal line $y = -9$ intersects the curve, making $PP_m = P_mP' = 4$.

Note: *Our equation may be rewritten $y = (x - 2)^2 - 25$. This procedure was suggested in Sec. 10.4.*

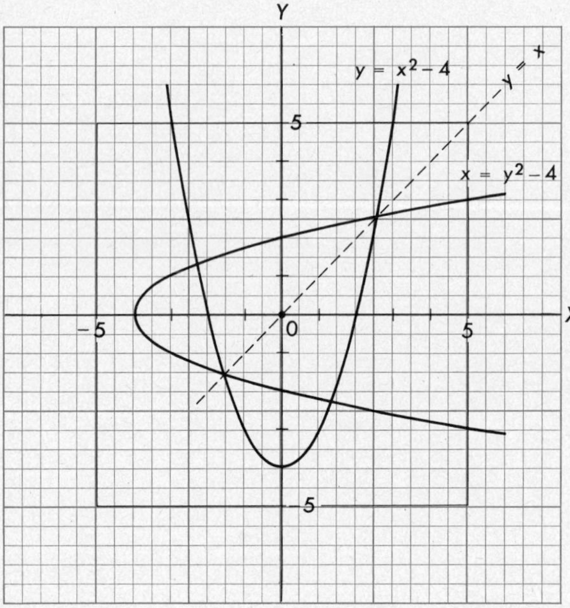

FIGURE 11.4

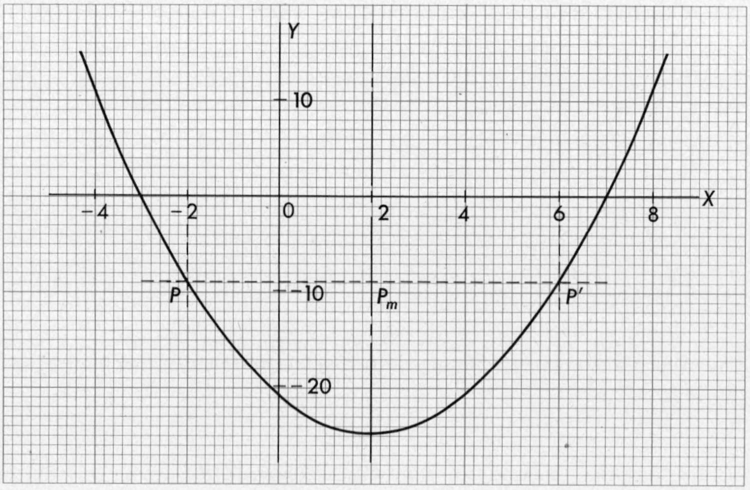

FIGURE 11.5

Symmetry about the Origin

The graph is symmetric with respect to the origin if the equation obtained by replacing x by $-x$ and y by $-y$ is identical with the original equation. Graphically it will be noted that a straight line passing through the origin O intersects the curve at P and P′ such that line segments PO and OP′ are equal. A graph symmetric to the origin is known as an *odd function*. The equation $y = \sin x$ is an example. See Fig. 16.1 and Eq. (23), Sec. 17.3.

Example 7. The graph of $y = x^3$ is symmetric with respect to the origin since the curve $-y = (-x)^3$ is identical with the curve $y = x^3$. In Fig. 11.6 the line $y = 4x$ intersects the curve $y = x^3$ at (2,8), (0,0), and (−2,−8). Thus $PO = P'O = \sqrt{68}$. If a curve is symmetric to both axes, it is also symmetric to the origin.

Another property of symmetry about the origin is that such a curve rotated 180° about the origin will coincide with itself.

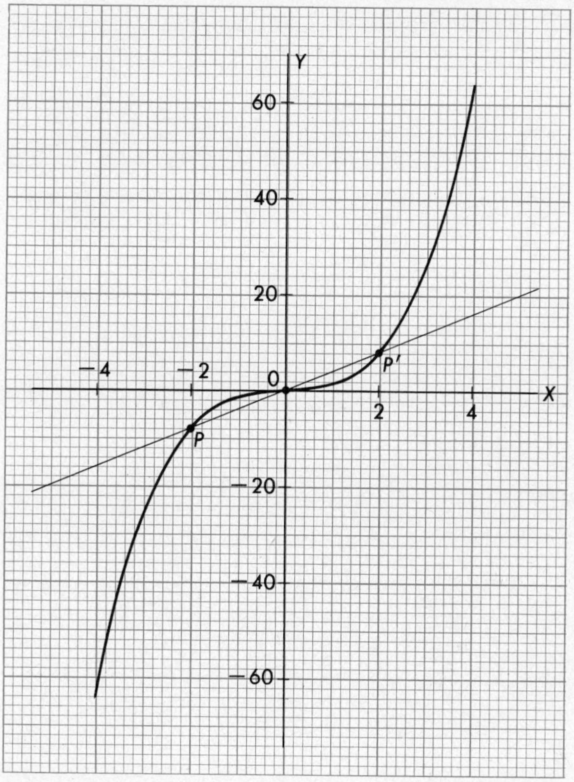

FIGURE 11.6

EXERCISE 2

Discuss the symmetry of the following curves.

1. $x^2 + y^2 = 4$
2. $x^2 - y^2 = 4$
3. $x^2 - 4y = 0$
4. $y = (x - 4)^2$
5. $y = 8/x$
6. $x^2/36 + y^2/9 = 1$
7. $y = x^2 - 8x + 16$
8. $y^2 = x^3$
9. $x^2 + y^2 + 6y = 16$
10. $y = x^3 - x$
11. $x^2y + y - 4x = 0$
12. $x^2 - xy + y^2 = 36$

11.4 Extent

The extent of the graph includes the *domain* (the "spread" of real values of x), and the *range* (the "spread" of real values of y).

Example 8. Determine the extent of the graph of $(y + 15)^2 = 25 - (x - 20)^2$.

From Fig. 11.7 it can be seen that the domain is $15 \leq x \leq 25$ (read "x is equal to or greater than 15 and equal to or less than 25"), and the range is $-20 \leq y \leq -10$ (read "y is equal to or greater than -20 and equal to or less than -10").

11.5 Discontinuities

Occasionally one encounters an equation whose graph may consist of two or more separated sections. In contrast, we think of a function as being *continuous* over a given

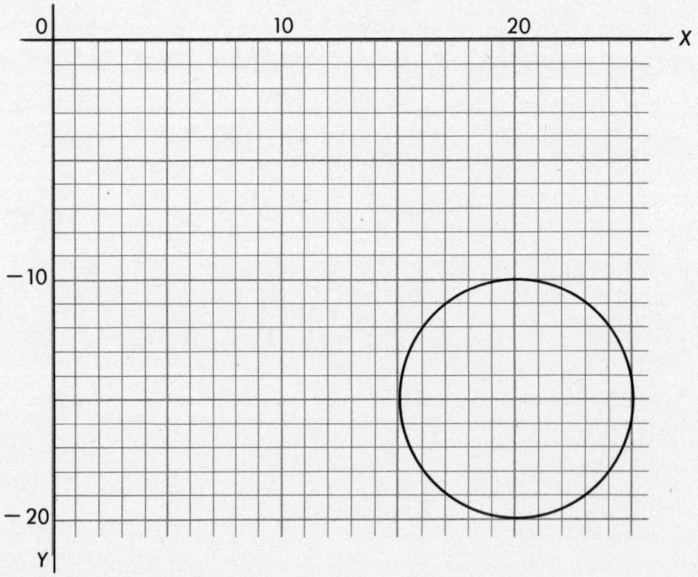

FIGURE 11.7

range if anywhere within that region as we take values of the independent variable closer and closer together, the corresponding values of the dependent variable also become closer and closer together, so that their difference approaches zero.

The matter of continuity, if treated rigorously, is enormously complex. Fortunately, however, the engineering technician is unlikely to encounter situations in which the more subtle aspects of continuity are critical. He usually deals with functions that are continuous over the region of interest or in which discontinuities, if they exist, are easily detected.

Therefore, the intuitive notion of continuity outlined in the first paragraph of this section is usually sufficient. It is admittedly inadequate in certain situations.

As a practical matter, if we plot a function over a given interval, using enough points, and find that the graph appears to be a smooth, unbroken line with no abrupt changes, the function it represents is *probably* continuous in this interval.

Since division by zero is impossible, a discontinuity will occur for a value of the independent variable which leads to an indicated division by zero. This is illustrated in Example 9 below.

Example 9. Graph the function $f(x) = y = 60/x$ (Fig. 11.8).

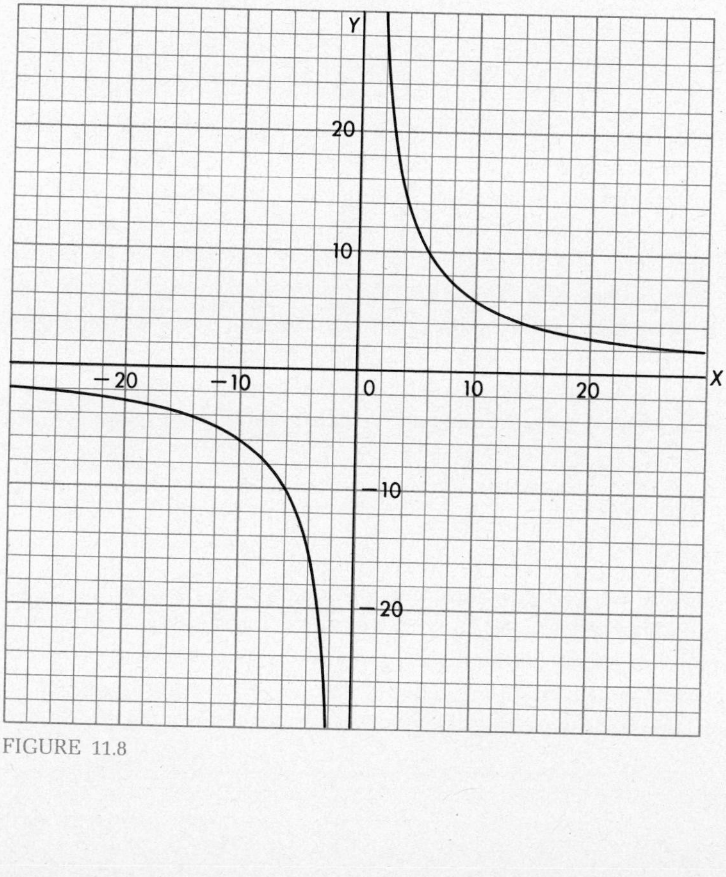

FIGURE 11.8

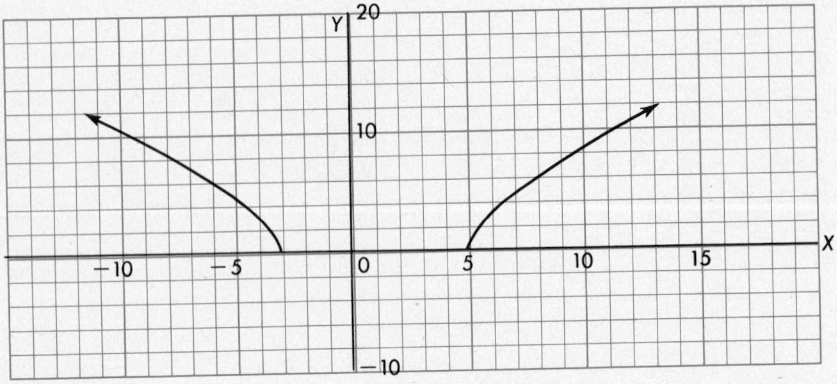

FIGURE 11.9

Observe that the domain of this function is $-\infty < x < 0$ and $0 < x < +\infty$. The range is $\infty > y > 0$ and $0 > y > -\infty$. Also note that since division by zero is undefined, there is a discontinuity at $x = 0$.

Another cause of a discontinuity is the presence of complex quantities, since in the coordinate system with which we are working there is no provision for other than real numbers.

Example 10. Sketch the graph of the equation $y = \sqrt{x^2 - 2x - 15}$ (Fig. 11.9).

If we rearrange this as $y = \sqrt{(x + 3)(x - 5)}$, it is clear that if $x > 5$ (x is greater than 5), both factors in the radicand are positive and the radicand is positive. If $x < -3$ (x is less than -3), both factors in the radicand are negative and again the radicand is positive. But if $-3 < x < +5$ (x is greater than -3 and less than $+5$), the factor $x + 3$ is positive and the factor $x - 5$ is negative; accordingly the radicand is negative, and we obtain imaginary values of y. Therefore such values of x must be excluded from the coordinate system. It follows that the domain is $-\infty < x \leq -3$ and $5 \leq x < +\infty$. [The points $(-3,0)$ and $(5,0)$ are called *end minima*.]

Negative values of y cannot exist, since, by definition, y is the positive square root of $x^2 - 2x - 15$. In other words, the range of y is zero and the set of all positive real numbers.

11.6 Asymptotes

We have noted that discontinuities may result from division by zero. This leads us to the consideration of asymptotes. Returning to Fig. 11.8, we can see that as we scan the graph upward from the origin, the graph continually approaches the Y axis. The same is true as we scan the graph downward from the origin. In fact, as we attempt to reduce $|x|$ further, the graph recedes even more rapidly from the origin and, for $x = 0$, we can assign no finite value for y. We say that y is undefined. The Y axis is said to be an asymptote of the graph.

If we rewrite the equation as $x = 60/y$, inspection indicates that the X axis is also an asymptote.

Although a technically precise definition of an asymptote is not appropriate at this time, we can describe the idea well enough for practical use. A line is an asymptote of a graph if the distance between the line and the graph becomes less and less as the distance moved along the line from some fixed point on it increases without limit. This line is usually vertical or horizontal, but may be inclined, and occasionally even curved (see Fig. 11.12).

Example 11. Consider the graph of the equation $2y = \pm\sqrt{x^2 - 9}$ (Fig. 11.10).

Rearranging, we have $y = \pm(\frac{1}{2})\sqrt{x^2(1 - 9/x^2)} = \pm(x/2)\sqrt{1 - 9/x^2}$.

It will be observed that as $|x|$ increases indefinitely, y approximates more and more closely the value $\pm x/2$ in both the equation and the graph. Therefore the lines $y = x/2$ and $y = -x/2$ are asymptotes of the curve $2y = \pm\sqrt{x^2 - 9}$.

Example 12. Determine the asymptotes of the graph of the equation $y = x^2 + 1/x$ (Fig. 11.11).

As we allow $|x|$ to increase indefinitely, it can be seen that the equation $y = x^2 + 1/x$ approximates more and more closely the equation $y = x^2$. Hence the graph of $y = x^2 + 1/x$ continually gets closer to the asymptotic line $y = x^2$ as $|x|$ increases without limit (see points *A* and *B*). As $|x|$ continually gets closer to zero, the expression

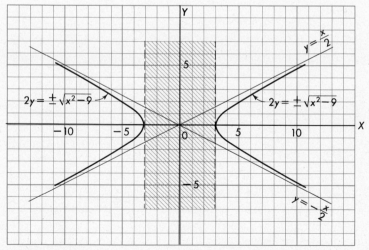

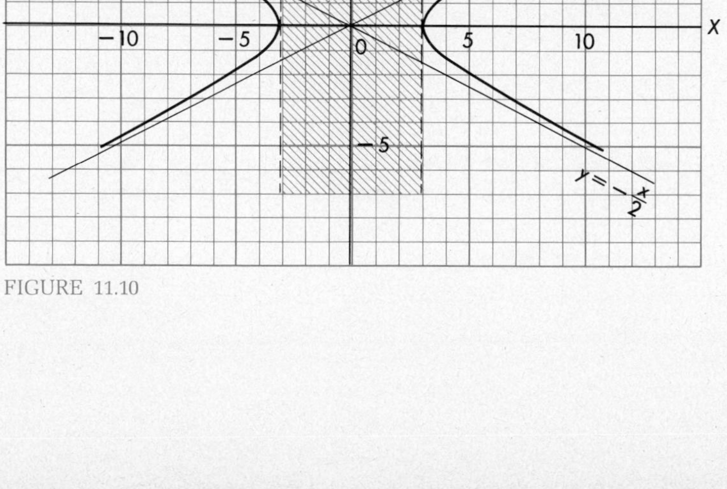

FIGURE 11.10

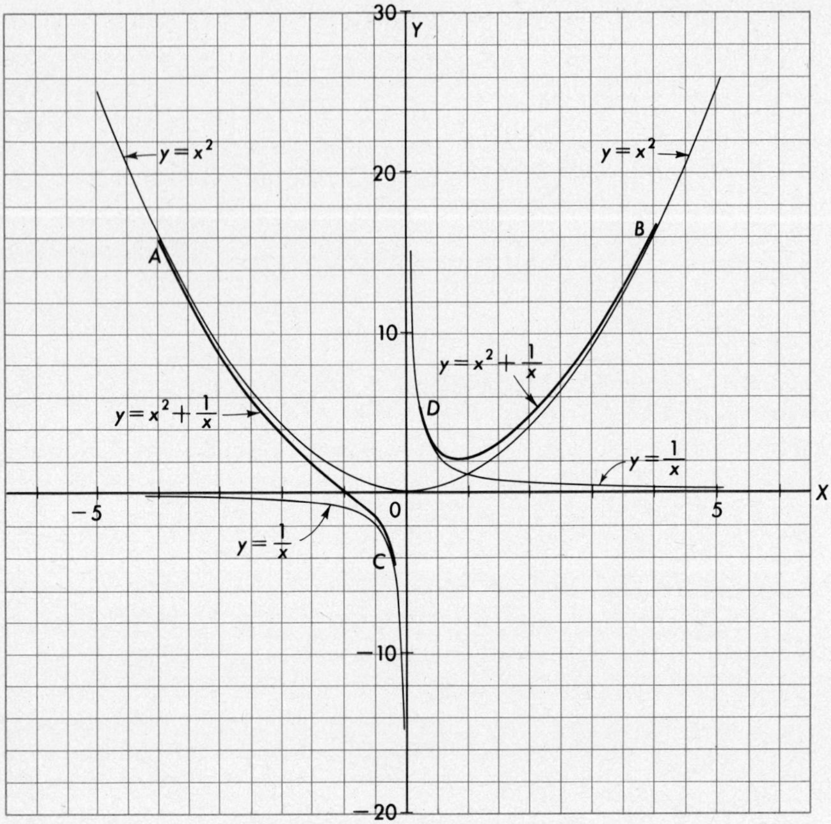

FIGURE 11.11

$x^2 + 1/x$ approximates $1/x$ ever more closely. Therefore the equation $y = 1/x$ is also an asymptote, as suggested by points C and D.

11.7 Excluded Regions

The terms "excluded region" and "extent" are mutually exclusive. Referring to Example 11 and Fig. 11.10, it is evident that for the region $-3 < x < 3$ the radicand is negative and y is imaginary. Hence we say that $-3 < x < 3$ is an excluded region (represented by the shaded area), whereas the domain is $-\infty < x \leq -3$ and $3 \leq x < +\infty$. At this point it will be agreed that we shall delineate excluded regions by vertical or horizontal lines.

If we solve the equation for x, obtaining $x = \pm\sqrt{4y^2 + 9}$, it follows that for all real values of y the radicand is positive and there is an unlimited range of y. Note also that the smallest possible value of $|x|$ is 3, occurring when $y = 0$, confirming the conclusion reached as to domain.

We must be careful not to confuse extent and asymptote. The values $x = 3$ and $x = -3$ are not asymptotes. The curve does not continually approach the lines $x = 3$ and $x = -3$ as y becomes smaller. On the contrary, the curve approaches these lines, touches them, and then recedes.

11.8 Composition of Ordinates

Plotting of a curve can often be simplified by the composition of ordinates. This consists of expressing an equation as the combination of two or more simpler equations. Thus, by separately sketching the ordinates of the component equations on a common area and then adding the ordinates graphically, there will often result an easier method for sketching the curve of an equation than by graphing it as a unit (Example 13).

The sketching of products, reciprocals, squares, or square roots of ordinates of certain equations can also be used to advantage.

Addition of Ordinates

Example 13. Sketch the curve $y = (x^2 + 12)/(2x)$.

Performing the indicated division, we obtain the equation

$$y = \frac{x}{2} + \frac{6}{x}$$

Here we separately sketch (Fig. 11.12)

$$y_1 = \frac{x}{2}$$

$$y_2 = \frac{6}{x}$$

Algebraic addition of ordinates gives us the equation

$$y_1 + y_2 = y = \frac{x}{2} + \frac{6}{x}$$

while by graphical addition we obtain the graph of $y = x/2 + 6/x$, shown as a heavy line.

It will be seen that large absolute values of x make $x/2$ the dominant term, while small absolute values of x make the term $6/x$ dominant.

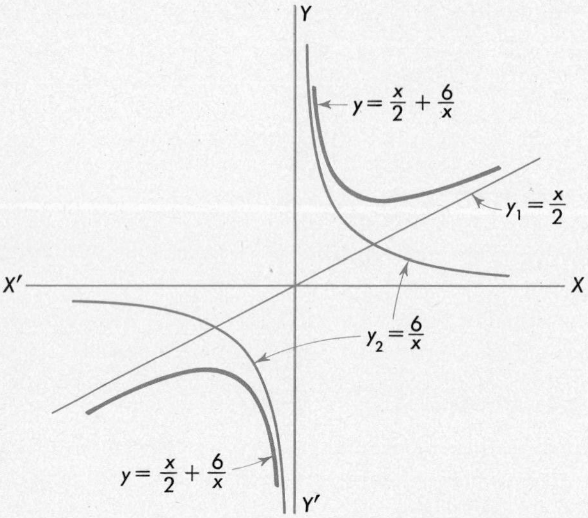

FIGURE 11.12

The graph emphasizes this relationship in a slightly different way. The curves $y = x/2$ and $y = 6/x$ appear as the asymptotes.

The choice of scales will be dictated by the range of the variables to be covered. They may not be equal. In any event one scale division should equal 1, 2, or 5 times some integral power of 10.

11.9 Logarithmic Functions

An equation of the form $y = \log_b x$ is called a logarithmic function. Here b may be any positive real number other than unity. For the sake of simplicity we shall make $b > 1$. (Note that if $b = e$, the equation involves natural logarithms.) Since b has been restricted, we have guaranteed that $x > 0$. This last statement should then suggest that the graph of $y = \log_b x$ will lie to the right of the Y axis. This can be verified by considering values of x between 0 and 1. We note that y is negative in this range. It is also apparent that as $x \to 0$, $y \to -\infty$. (Read "as x approaches zero, y becomes infinitely more negative.") Hence the line $x = 0$ is an asymptote of the curve $y = \log_b x$. At the same time, as x increases, y is also increasing. When x takes on the value of 1, $y = 0$, and hence the x intercept is located. Since this is an increasing function, the shape of the curve is now apparent. It is also obvious that there is no symmetry, as may be confirmed by the usual test (see Fig. 11.13).

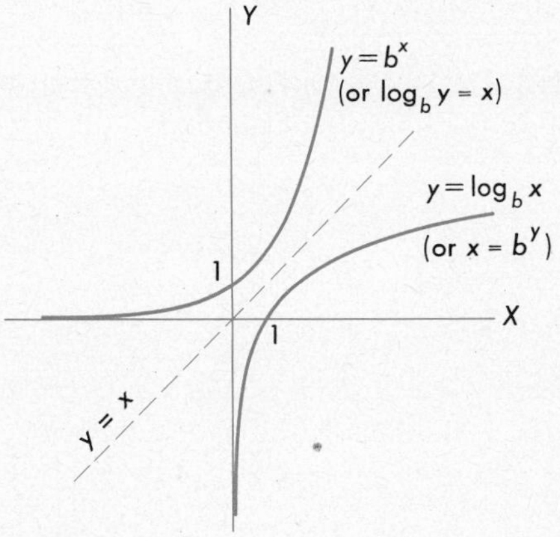

FIGURE 11.13

11.10 Exponential Function

Any function of the form $y = b^x$, where x represents the set of all real numbers and $b \neq 0$, is considered to be an exponential function. It is apparent that if $b = e$ (the base of natural logarithms), we have the familiar exponential function used so frequently in mathematics. In this discussion, we will confine ourselves to the case where $b > 1$.

It would be well worthwhile to try to capitalize on an intuitional approach to sketching the graph of $y = b^x$ (see Fig. 11.13). We have no restrictions on x except that it be real. At the same time, we have agreed to consider only cases where $b > 1$. This, in fact, says that as x increases without limit ($x \rightarrow +\infty$), y also increases very rapidly and does indeed become infinite (hence, as $x \rightarrow +\infty$, $y \rightarrow +\infty$). On the other hand, when $x \rightarrow -\infty$ (meaning x increases negatively without limit), it can be seen that $y \rightarrow 0$ (y approaches zero), since in the equation $y = b^x$ (where $x \rightarrow -\infty$) the term $b^x \rightarrow 0$ and hence the above statement holds. The curve does cross the Y axis as can readily be seen by letting $x = 0$. This condition will produce a value of 1 for y. Hence, the y intercept is at (0,1). As previously mentioned, condition $x \rightarrow -\infty$ shows that the function is approaching zero. However, it actually never does touch the X axis for any finite value of x. Hence, this condition implies that the line $y = 0$ (or the X axis) is the asymptote of the curve. There is no symmetry in the usual sense. Note however, in referring to Fig. 11.13, that a symmetry does exist between the related curves $y = \log_b x$ and $y = b^x$. If we apply the principles of symmetry about the line $x = y$ (Sec. 11.3) and interchange the variables in the equation $y = \log_b x$, we obtain the equation $x = \log_b y$, which is equivalent to writing $y = b^x$. That is, each curve is the *inverse function* of the other.

11.11 Determination of Characteristic Properties

To summarize what we have learned in Secs. 11.2 to 11.7, we shall analyze and sketch the graph of the equation $y = (x^2 - 4)/(x^2 - 1)$ in the following example.

Example 14. Analyze and sketch the function

$$y = \frac{x^2 - 4}{x^2 - 1} \tag{1}$$

Intercepts: It is evident that $y = 0$ when $x^2 - 4 = 0$. That is, the x intercepts are located at $x = 2$ and $x = -2$. When $x = 0$, $y = 4$, which is the only y intercept.

Symmetry: Since the equation contains only even powers of x, the graph is symmetric about the Y axis.

Discontinuities: There are two discontinuities in the graph, one at $x = 1$, the other at $x = -1$, since each of these values leads to an indicated division by zero.

Extent: Since for all real values of x (excepting $+1$ and -1 noted above) there are corresponding real values of y, the domain of x is unlimited.

Before evaluating the range, it would be helpful to solve the original equation for x, obtaining $x = \pm\sqrt{(y - 4)/(y - 1)}$. In order to limit ourselves to real values of x, the radicand cannot be negative. When $y > 4$, both members of the fraction are positive, the radicand is positive, and x is a real number. Likewise when $y < 1$, both members of the fraction are negative, the radicand is again positive, and x is a real number. For $4 > y > 1$, the numerator is negative, the denominator is positive, and the radicand is negative, leading to an imaginary value of x. Therefore the range is $4 \leq y < 1$.

Asymptotes: The asymptotes will be more readily determined if we perform the division indicated in the right-hand member of Eq. (1). Our equation now takes the form $y = 1 - 3/(x^2 - 1)$. As $|x|$ approaches 1 from the high side, y continually decreases, tending to become negative without limit. As $|x|$ approaches 1 from the low side, y continually increases, tending to become positive without limit. Hence the lines $x = 1$ and $x = -1$ are vertical asymptotes. Note also that as $|x|$ increases indefinitely, the value of $1 - 3/(x^2 - 1)$ approaches 1 as a limiting value. That is, the line $y = 1$ is a horizontal asymptote.

To confirm our conclusions and for more accurate representation, a brief table of ordered pairs is shown below. Because of the symmetry of the graph, only positive values of x are shown.

x	0	0.5	0.9	0.95	1.0	1.05	1.1	1.5	2.0	4.0	10	20
y	4.0	5.0	16.8	31.8	—	−28.3	−13.3	−1.4	0	0.8	0.97	0.9925

The graph is shown in Fig. 11.14.

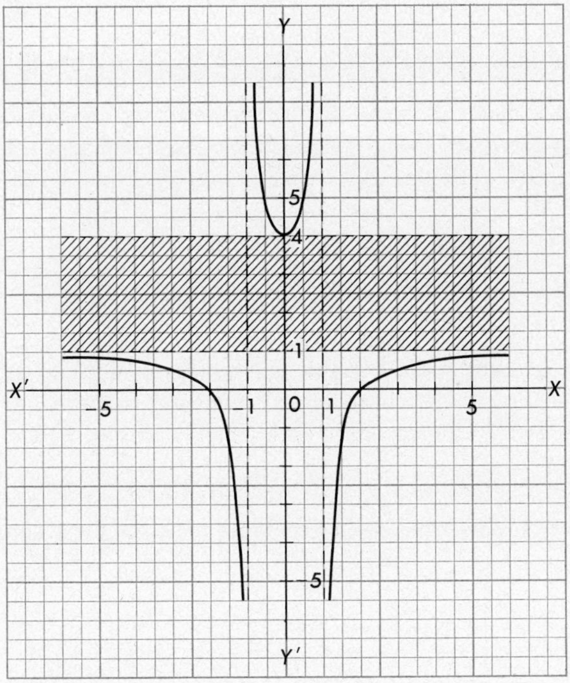

FIGURE 11.14

EXERCISE 3

Determine the properties, as set forth in Secs. 11.2 to 11.7, of each of Probs. 1 to 14.

1. $x^2 + y^2 = 16$
2. $x^2 + 4y^2 = 25$
3. $x^2 - y^2 = -9$
4. $xy = -8$
5. $x = 4y$
6. $y = x^2 - 4x - 21$
7. $y = 60/(x^2 + 4)$
8. $y = -x^2 + 9$
9. $y = (x - 1)/(x + 1)$
10. $y = 4/(x^2 - 16)$
11. $y = \sqrt{25 - x^2}$
12. $y = \log(1/x)$
13. $y = 10e^{-x^2}$
14. $y = e^{1/x^2}$

15. Sketch with reference to a common pair of coordinate axes the graph of the equation $4x^2 - 9y^2 = k$, letting k be successively 36, 16, 4, 0, −4, −16, and −36. Label your graphs.

11.12 Characteristic Types of Quadratic Curves

There is no simple general algebraic solution for two simultaneous quadratic equations of the type

$$Ax^2 + Bxy + Cy^2 + Dx + Ey = F \qquad (2)$$

An approximate graphical solution may be obtained by plotting. This is also useful at any time as a rough check on the algebraic solution. The algebraic solutions will be limited to the simpler cases. In more advanced mathematics it is stated that the graph of any quadratic equation in two variables is always a parabola, ellipse, circle, hyperbola, two straight lines, or occasionally a single point or no graph at all.

The following statements are confirmed in analytic geometry.

Parabola

An equation in x and y that is linear in one variable and quadratic in the other and contains no xy term represents a parabola whose axis of symmetry is parallel to either the X axis or the Y axis (Fig. 11.15). Plotting of the parabola is discussed in Sec. 10.4.

Example 15. To reinforce the concept of Sec. 10.4, let it be required to sketch the graph of the equation

$$-2y^2 - x + 4y = -10$$

According to Fig. 11.15, we have a parabola which is concave to the left since the coefficients of y^2 and x have the same sign.

Since our objective is to write the equation in the form $x = p(y + q)^2 + r$ (where

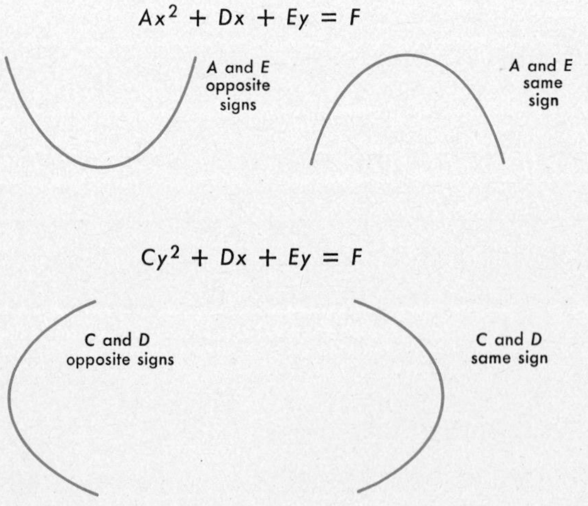

FIGURE 11.15

p, q, and r are constants), we shall rearrange our original equation to read

$$x = -2y^2 + 4y + 10$$

Factoring:

$$x = -2(y^2 - 2y - 5)$$

Isolating the trinomial square:

$$x = -2[(y^2 - 2y + 1) - 6]$$

or

$$x = -2(y^2 - 2y + 1) + 12 = -2(y - 1)^2 + 12$$

By inspection we can see that the axis of symmetry is the line $y = 1$, and the maximum value of x is located at the point (12,1). At $y = 0$, $x = 10$ (x intercept). The y intercepts are most readily found through the following steps:

Setting $x = 0$,

$$0 = -2(y - 1)^2 + 12$$

or

$$(y - 1)^2 = 6 \qquad y - 1 = \pm\sqrt{6} = \pm 2.45$$
$$y = 3.45 \text{ and } -1.45$$

The sketch in Fig. 11.16 reflects these conclusions.

EXERCISE 4

Plot the following parabolas. Each group is referred to its own set of coordinate axes. All the equations in that group are to be plotted on that one area.

(GROUP I)

1. $y = x^2$ 2. $y = -x^2$ 3. $x = y^2$ 4. $x = -y^2$

(GROUP II)

1. $y = x^2$ 2. $y = 2x^2$ 3. $y = \frac{1}{4}x^2$ 4. $y = -\frac{1}{4}x^2$

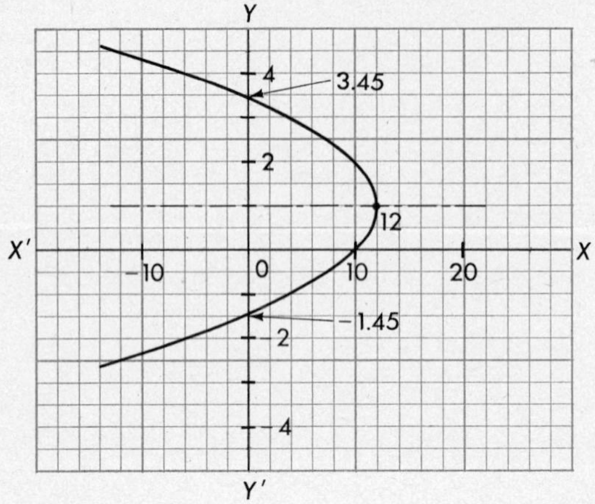

FIGURE 11.16

(GROUP III)

1. $y = x^2$ 2. $y = x^2 + 6$ 3. $y = x^2 - 9$ 4. $y = -\frac{1}{4}x^2 + 9$

(GROUP IV)

1. $y = x^2$ 2. $y = (x + 2)^2$ 3. $y = (x - 4)^2$ 4. $y = (x + 2)^2 - 9$

(GROUP V)

1. $y = x^2 + 4x - 5$ 2. $y = x^2 - 6x + 8$
3. $y = -(x + 5)^2$ 4. $y = -4x^2 + 8x - 3$

(GROUP VI)

1. $x = (y - 3)^2$ 2. $x = -(y - 3)^2 + 4$
3. $x = (y + 4)^2 - 9$ 4. $x = y^2 - 2y - 15$

In this section we shall discuss the basic graphs of the ellipse, circle, and hyperbola. That is, each of these curves will be symmetric about the origin.

Ellipse

An equation of the type

$$Ax^2 + Cy^2 = F$$

where A, C, and F all have the same sign and $A \neq C$, represents an ellipse symmetrical about both axes.

Example 16. Outline the graph of the equation

$$4x^2 + 9y^2 = 100$$

In order to outline the curve roughly (Fig. 11.17*a*), find the intercepts as follows: Substitute $y = 0$, obtaining

$$4x^2 = 100$$

whereby

$$x = \pm 5$$

Substituting $x = 0$ in the original equation, we have

$$9y^2 = 100 \qquad \text{or} \qquad y = \pm 10/3$$

If a more accurate curve is required, other substitutions may be made. For example, if we let $x = \pm 3$, then $y = \pm 8/3$, giving us the four points A, B, C, and D.

Similarly when $A > C$, such as in the equation $9x^2 + 4y^2 = 100$, we obtain x intercepts of $\pm 10/3$ and y intercepts of ± 5 (Fig. 11.17*b*).

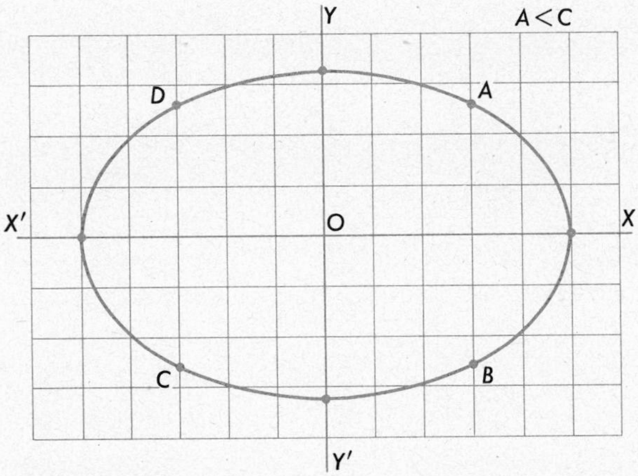

FIGURE 11.17*a*

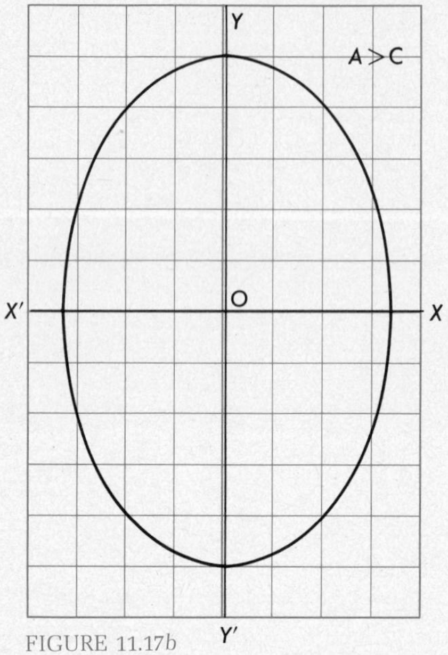

FIGURE 11.17b

Circle

An equation of the type

$$Ax^2 + Cy^2 = F$$

where A, C, and F all have the same sign and $A = C$, represents a circle of radius $\sqrt{F/A}$ with its center at the origin. (*Note:* The circle is a special case of the ellipse.)

Example 17. Outline the graph of the equation (Fig. 11.18)

$$4x^2 + 4y^2 = 81$$

Dividing through by 4, we obtain

$$x^2 + y^2 = 81/4$$

or

$$\sqrt{x^2 + y^2} = 9/2$$

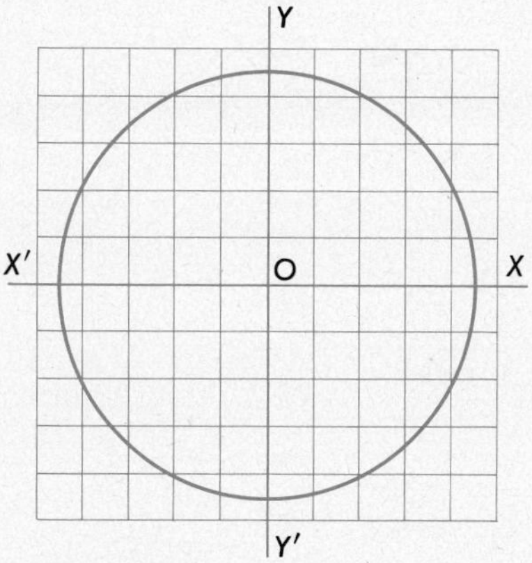

FIGURE 11.18

Since the distance from the origin to any point (x,y) is $\sqrt{x^2 + y^2}$ (Sec. 6.16), the graph is the locus of all points whose distances from the origin are $9/2$. Hence we have a circle of radius $9/2$ with its center at the origin. Obviously this curve is best drawn with a compass.

Two Intersecting Straight Lines

An equation of the type

$$Ax^2 + Cy^2 = 0$$

where A and C have opposite signs, represents a pair of straight lines intersecting at the origin. It is a special case of the hyperbola (see below) in which $F = 0$.

Example 18. Plot the locus of

$$9x^2 - 25y^2 = 0 \tag{3}$$

Factoring Eq. (3), we obtain

$$(3x + 5y)(3x - 5y) = 0 \tag{4}$$

This equation may be transformed into two equations (Example 1, Sec. 10.2).

$$3x + 5y = 0$$
$$3x - 5y = 0$$

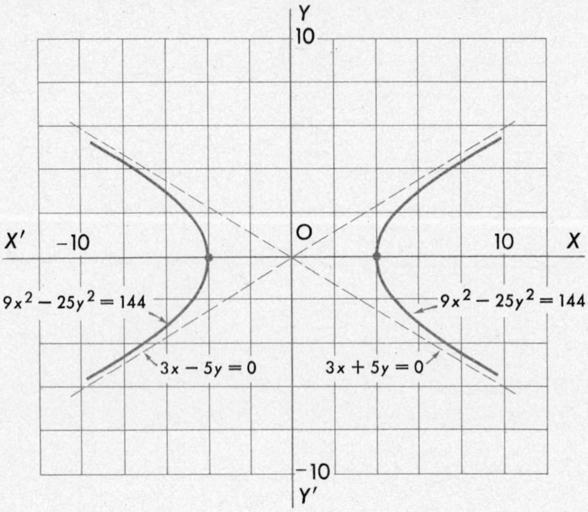

FIGURE 11.19

These straight lines constitute the locus of Eq. (3). They are drawn as dashed lines in Fig. 11.19.

Hyperbola

An equation of the type

$$Ax^2 + Cy^2 = F$$

where A and C have opposite signs and $F \neq 0$, represents a hyperbola symmetric about the coordinate axes.

Example 19. Sketch the graph (Fig. 11.19) of

$$9x^2 - 25y^2 = 144 \tag{5}$$

Substituting $y = 0$, we find $x = \pm 4$.

If we attempt to find the y intercepts by substituting $x = 0$ in Eq. (5), we find $y = \pm {}^{12}\!/_5\sqrt{-1}$, which, being an imaginary quantity, cannot be plotted.

If we solve Eq. (5) for y, we obtain

$$y = \pm {}^{3}\!/_5\sqrt{x^2 - 16}$$

It is apparent that the curve does not occur in the band between the lines $x = 4$ and $x = -4$, and that there is no y intercept.

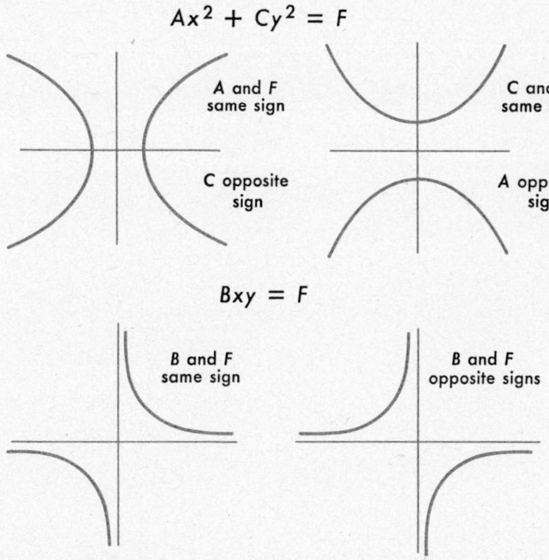

FIGURE 11.20

Replacing the value of the constant F in Eq. (5) by 0, we obtain Eq. (3), discussed above and plotted as dashed lines in Fig. 11.19.

These lines are the *asymptotes* of the graph of Eq. (5). (An *asymptote* of a curve is a line which the curve approaches but never reaches as the absolute numerical value of one of the variables increases without limit. See Sec. 11.6.)

A hyperbola may be sketched roughly by locating x or y intercepts and using the asymptotes as guiding lines. As in our previous discussion, additional points may be obtained by substitution. For this purpose it is suggested that an equation such as Eq. (5) be converted to the form

$$x = \pm \tfrac{1}{3}\sqrt{25y^2 + 144}$$

The advantage of this transformation lies in the fact that all values of y will correspond to real points on the curve.

Simple forms of hyperbola are illustrated in Fig. 11.20.

11.13 Translation of Axes

In most of our graphing so far, the curves have been symmetric with respect to the origin or to an axis. In this section we shall develop methods for relating the equation of an "off-center" curve to the equation of the same curve after it is moved to a position of symmetry.

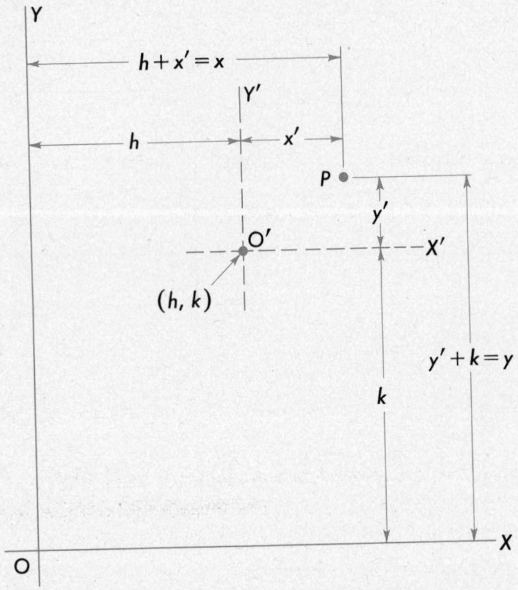

FIGURE 11.21

We shall refer such curves to two different coordinate systems (Fig. 11.21). Referred to the X and Y axes, the coordinates of origin O' are (h,k). Now let $P(x',y')$ be any point referred to the X′ and Y′-axes. Its coordinates with respect to the X and Y axes are $x' + h$ and $y' + k$.

That is,

$$x = x' + h \tag{6}$$

or

$$x' = x - h \tag{7}$$

and

$$y = y' + k \tag{8}$$

or

$$y' = y - k \tag{9}$$

Example 20. Sketch the graph of the equation

$$(x + 20)^2 + (y - 15)^2 = 25 \tag{10}$$

Applying Eqs. (6) through (9), we may write

$$(x - h)^2 + (y - k)^2 = 25 \tag{11}$$

and

$$x'^2 + y'^2 = 25 \tag{12}$$

We note that Eq. (12) (which is our "basic equation") is a decided simplification of Eq. (10).

On comparing Eqs. (10) and (11), we find that $h = -20$ and $k = 15$. Therefore Eq. (10) represents a circle of radius 5 with center located at $(-20, +15)$ (Fig. 11.22*a*).

Figure 11.22 relates the position of the center of the circle to the constants h and k contained in its equation. It will be noted that positive values of h move the curve h units to the right, and vice versa. Positive values of k move the curve k units upward, and vice versa.

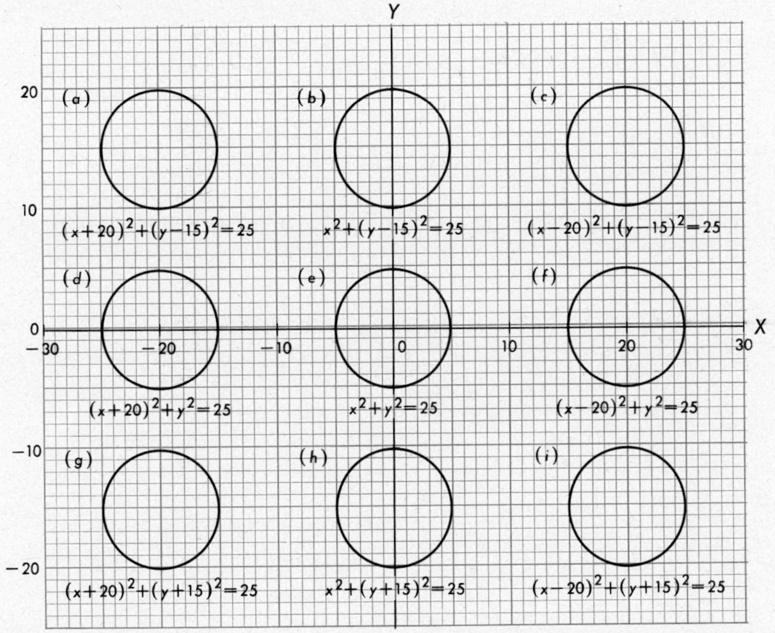

FIGURE 11.22

Usually the equation will appear in the expanded form rather than in the factored form of Eq. (10). The following illustrates how such a curve is moved to new axes.

Example 21. Convert the equation $x^2 + 40x + y^2 - 30y = -600$ to the factored form.

$$\begin{array}{l} x^2 + 40x + y^2 - 30y = -600 \\ + 400 + 225 = 625 \\ \hline x^2 + 40x + 400 + y^2 - 30y + 225 = 25 \end{array} \qquad \text{(completing squares)}$$

or

$$(x + 20)^2 + (y - 15)^2 = 25$$

which we recognize as Eq. (10).

It then follows that replacing x by $x' - 20$ and y by $y' + 15$, we obtain Eq. (12).

Graphically, then, we would draw the circle, radius $= 5$, with center at the origin and then draw a like circle with center moved 20 units to the left and 15 units up. As a practical expedient, it is equivalent and much easier for most curves to locate new axes about a new origin 20 units to the right and 15 units down from the origin of Eq. (10). The X' and Y' axes for Eq. (12) would be drawn lightly or dashed and the X and Y axes for Eq. (10) in heavy solid lines. Let us illustrate the method of shifting axes by the following example.

Example 22. Sketch the curve

$$xy - 3y + x = 9 \tag{13}$$

In order to put this equation into a more tractable form, we solve for y, obtaining the equation

$$y = \frac{-x + 9}{x - 3}$$

Performing the indicated division, we have

$$y = -1 + \frac{6}{x - 3}$$

or

$$y + 1 = \frac{6}{x - 3}$$

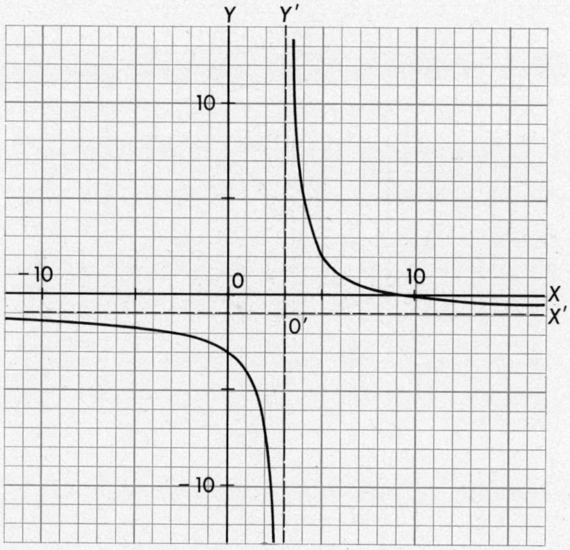

FIGURE 11.23

and

$$(y + 1)(x - 3) = 6 \tag{14}$$

Thus the basic equation is the hyperbola $y'x' = 6$ which we sketch in relation to the dashed X′ and Y′ axes (Fig. 11.23).

Equation (14) indicates that the solid Y and X axes are to be drawn 3 units to the left and 1 unit up, respectively.

Substituting $x = 0$, we obtain $y = -3$, and when $y = 0$, $x = 9$, which agrees with the intercepts indicated on the graph.

Example 23. Sketch the curve

$$2x^2 + 3y^2 - 8x + 6y = 7 \tag{15}$$

Completing squares,

$$\begin{array}{rrrrl} 2x^2 - 8x & & + 3y^2 + 6y & & = 7 \\ & + 8 & & + 3 & = 11 \\ \hline 2x^2 - 8x & + 8 & + 3y^2 + 6y & + 3 & = 18 \end{array}$$

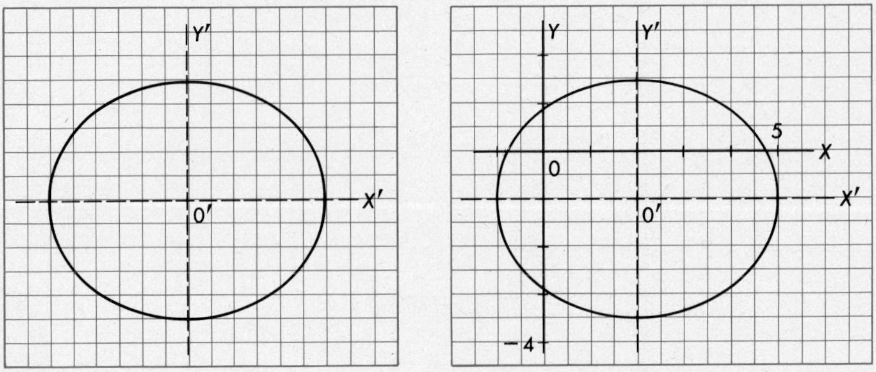

(a) (b)

FIGURE 11.24

or

$$2(x-2)^2 + 3(y+1)^2 = 18 \tag{16}$$

This indicates that our basic equation is $2x'^2 + 3y'^2 = 18$ (an ellipse), which we sketch in relation to the dashed X′ and Y′ axes (Fig. 11.24*a*). We then draw our solid X and Y axes 2 units to the left and 1 unit up, respectively (Fig. 11.24*b*), and check the intercepts for Eq. (16).

The calculation of the x intercepts is shown in detail to emphasize the advantage of using the equation in the form of (16) rather than (15). Substituting $y = 0$,

$$2(x-2)^2 + 3(1)^2 = 18$$
$$(x-2)^2 = (18-3)/2 = 7.5$$
$$x - 2 = \pm\sqrt{7.5} = \pm 2.74$$

Therefore the x intercepts are 4.74 and −0.74.

In similar fashion the y intercepts are found to be 0.82 and −2.82

Summary

1. *Derive the "basic equation."*
2. *Sketch the basic equation referred to the dashed axes X′ and Y′ by the procedure outlined above. The straight line and the parabola will pass through the origin O′. The circle, ellipse, and hyperbola will be symmetric about the origin O′.*
3. *Draw the solid Y axis h units to the right of the Y′ axis if h is negative; to the left if h is positive.*

Draw the solid X axis k units above the X′ axis if k is negative; below if k is positive.

4. *If possible, check the curve by the method of intercepts.*

EXERCISE 5

In Probs. 1 to 12, inclusive, sketch the curves, using the method of translation of axes. Write the basic equation in each case.

1. $y = 1 + 2/x$
2. $(x - 2)^2 + (y + 5)^2 = 49$
3. $y = x^2 - 2x - 15$
4. $y = -2x^2 + 8x + 24$
5. $(y - 1)(x - 2) = 8$
6. $4x^2 + y^2 + 8x - 6y = 36$
7. $y^2 - 4y - 9x - 23 = 0$
8. $3x^2 - 4y^2 + 12x + 8y - 28 = 0$
9. $x^2 + y^2 + 2x - 4y - 31 = 0$
10. $x^2 + 5y^2 - 2x - 20y - 28 = 0$
11. $3x^2 + 3y^2 - 12x + 12y - 1 = 0$
12. $xy - x + 2y = 10$
13. A cable supporting a suspension bridge hangs in the form of a parabola. The tops of the supporting towers are 35 ft above the floor of the bridge, and the lowest point of the cable is 5 ft above the bridge. The distance between the supporting towers is 60 ft. Determine the length of a suspending cable (a vertical cable from the bridge to the parabolic cable) 10 ft from one of the supporting towers.
14. An arch has a cross section, as shown in Fig. 11.25, with the curve a semiellipse.
    (*a*) Determine the lengths of the ordinates to the arch measured from the ground at 2, 4, and 6 ft from the point *A*.
    (*b*) If the arch is 10 ft thick, determine the number of cubic yards of concrete necessary in its construction.
15. Sketch a graph of X as a function of the positive values of f if $X = 2\pi fL - 1/(2\pi fC)$ for the following sets of values for L and C. Determine algebraically and from your graph the value of f that makes X zero.
    (*a*) $L = 0.00025$ henry, $C = 10^{-10}$ F (data for a radio circuit).
    (*b*) $L = 1$ henry, $C = 7(10^{-6})$ F (data for a power circuit).

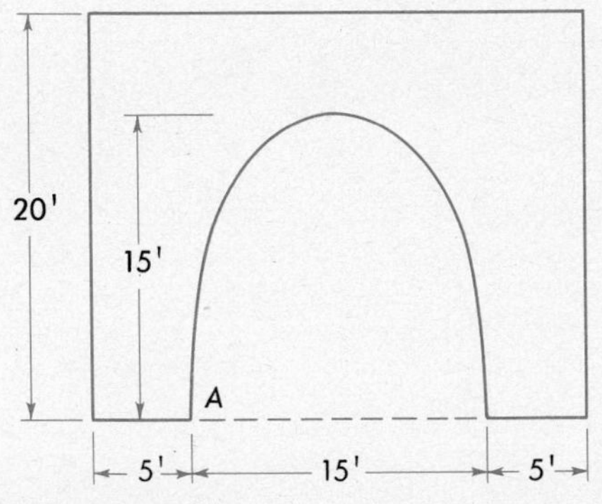

FIGURE 11.25

[*Note:* This equation gives the net "reactance" X in an ac circuit containing inductance L and capacitance C (as well as resistance R) in series with a sinusoidal voltage of frequency f.]

11.14 Graphical Solution

An approximate graphical solution of a system of two quadratic equations (or one quadratic and one linear equation) may be obtained by sketching their loci. Estimate the coordinates of the points of intersection or tangency of the two curves. The coordinates of each such point satisfying both equations constitute a solution.

It is evident that two quadratic curves intersect in at most four points (Fig. 11.26), while a system consisting of one linear and one quadratic curve has at most two real solutions.

Application of the discriminant (Sec. 10.14) at this stage can be related to Fig. 11.27:

Negative discriminant	no intersection	line *a*
Zero discriminant	tangency-identical roots	line *b*
Positive discriminant	two intersections	line *c*

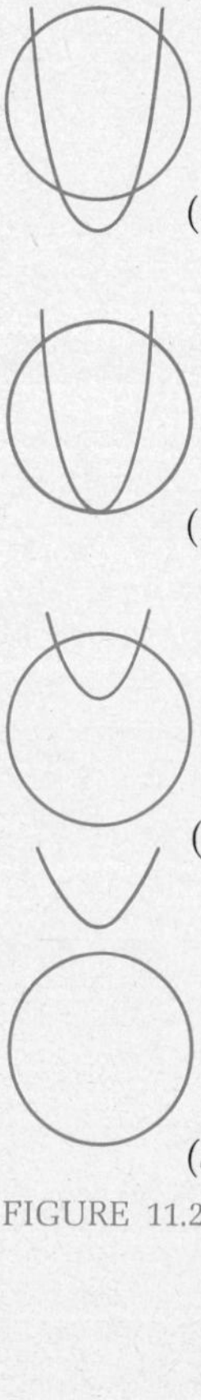

(*a*) (*a*) Four real distinct roots

(*b*) (*b*) Four real roots—two identical

(*c*) (*c*) Two real roots—two imaginary

(*d*) (*d*) Four imaginary roots

FIGURE 11.26

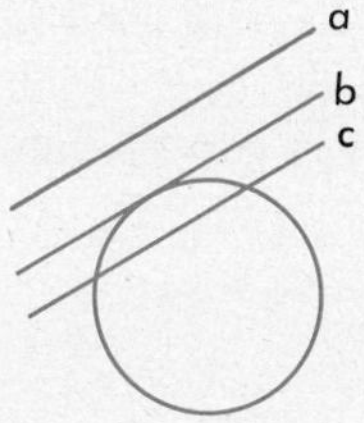

a. Two imaginary roots

b. Two real identical roots

c. Two real distinct roots

FIGURE 11.27

More accurate information may be obtained by plotting more points in the vicinity of the intersection, and often it will be advisable to plot the critical portion to a larger scale.

Example 24. Solve graphically the system

$$x^2 - 4x + y^2 - 4y = 9 \tag{17}$$

$$y = x^2 - 3 \tag{18}$$

Using the methods of Sec. 11.13, we can write Eq. (17) as

$$(x - 2)^2 + (y - 2)^2 = 17 \tag{19}$$

This is sketched in Fig. 11.28*a*, where it appears as a circle of radius $\sqrt{17}$ and center at (2,2). In the same figure is shown the graph of Eq. (18), a parabola shifted 3 units downward. From the sketch it is apparent that we can confine our point-by-point plotting to areas in the vicinity of points *A*, *B*, and *C*.

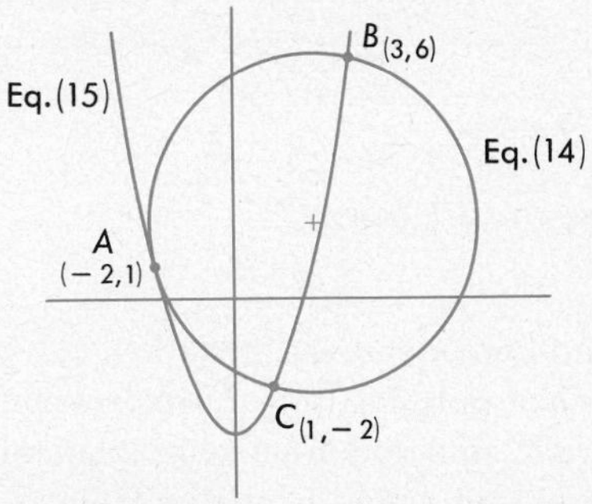

FIGURE 11.28*a*

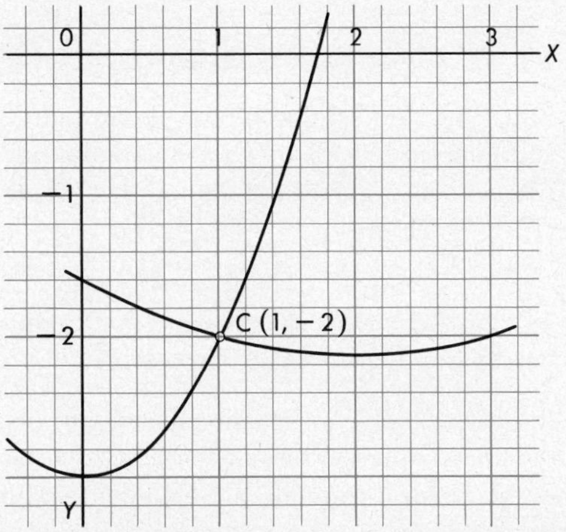

FIGURE 11.28*b*

The detailed plotting is shown in Fig. 11.28*b* for point *C*, with Eq. (19) used to obtain points on the circle, as described in Sec. 11.13. Of course, in the case of the circle, it would be preferable to use a compass. The point of tangency *A* corresponds to two real identical roots. Hence the solution is

A: $x = -2, y = 1$
$x = -2, y = 1$
B: $x = 3, \quad y = 6$
C: $x = 1, \quad y = -2$

EXERCISE 6

Solve the following systems graphically. Sketch the curves, and then plot critical areas in detail estimating any nonintegral answers to two significant figures. Of course any circles that you can identify as such are best drawn with a compass.

1. $xy = 6$
   $3x - y = 7$
2. $x^2 + y^2 = 20$
   $x - y = 6$
3. $y = x^2 - 4x - 1$
   $2x + y = -2$
4. $x^2 + 4y^2 = 36$
   $2x - 3y = 18$
5. $x^2 - y^2 = 9$
   $5x + 4y = -9$
6. $3x^2 + 3y^2 = 40$
   $3x + 2y = -18$
7. $x^2 + y^2 + 6x - 8y = 0$
   $16x^2 + 9y^2 = 144$
8. $xy = -12$
   $x^2 + y^2 = 25$
9. $y = x^2 - 6$
   $x = y^2 - 6$
10. $4x^2 + 9y^2 = 36$
    $9y - x^2 = 0$
11. $4y^2 - x^2 = 25$
    $x^2 + y^2 = 4$
12. $9x^2 + 25y^2 = 144$
    $xy = 6$

11.15 Algebraic Solutions of Quadratic Systems

Since the graphical solution of a quadratic system leads to only approximate real solutions and yields no imaginary solutions at all, we shall require algebraic solutions for more accurate results. Our study of algebraic solutions will be confined to the simple types of systems.

11.16 Solution of Systems Consisting of One Linear and One Quadratic Equation

In order to solve a system consisting of one linear and one quadratic equation, solve the linear equation for one variable in terms of the other and substitute the expression in the quadratic equation. Solve the resulting quadratic equation in one variable and substitute each value in turn in the linear equation to find values of the variable.

Example 25. Solve the system

$$x^2 - 3xy - 2y^2 = 4 \tag{20}$$
$$4x + y = 5 \tag{21}$$

Solve Eq. (21) for y:

$$y = 5 - 4x \tag{22}$$

(Note that we chose y in preference to x because of the simpler resultant expression.) Substituting Eq. (22) in Eq. (20), we obtain

$$x^2 - 3x(5 - 4x) - 2(5 - 4x)^2 = 4$$

Simplifying,

$$19x^2 - 65x + 54 = 0 \tag{23}$$

Solving Eq. (23), we find

$$x = 2 \quad \text{and} \quad x = {}^{27}\!/_{19}$$

Substituting these values successively in Eq. (22), we obtain

$$y = -3 \quad \text{and} \quad y = -{}^{13}\!/_{19}$$

The solutions are therefore

$$x = 2,\ y = -3 \quad \text{and} \quad x = {}^{27}\!/_{19},\ y = -{}^{13}\!/_{19}$$

EXERCISE 7

In each of Probs. 1 to 10, solve for x and y algebraically.

1. $xy = 48$, $3x - y = 0$
2. $xy = -36$, $4y + x = 0$
3. $xy = 80$, $4x - 5y = 0$
4. $xy = -96$, $3x + 2y = 0$
5. $x^2 + y^2 = 25$, $x + y = -1$
6. $x^2 + y^2 = 100$, $x - y = 2$
7. $x^2 - y^2 = 40$, $x + 2y = 13$
8. $x^2 - 2y^2 = -34$, $5x - y = 15$
9. $x^2 + xy + y^2 = 12$, $5x + 2y = 2$
10. $5x^2 - xy = 15$, $3x + 2y = 26$

11. We wish to draw a tangent having a slope of unity to the parabola $y = kx^2$ (k is positive). (*a*) Show that the coordinates of the point of tangency are $(1/(2k), 1/(4k))$. (*b*) Can you show also that $1/(4k)$ is the focal length of the parabola?

11.17 Equations of the Form $ax^2 + by^2 = c$

When both equations have the form $ax^2 + by^2 = c$, the system is linear in x^2 and y^2 and can be solved for them by the usual procedure applicable to systems of linear equations. From the values of x^2 and y^2, usually four solutions will be obtained which, if real, will correspond to four points symmetrically grouped about the origin.

Example 26. Solve the system (Fig. 11.29)

$$5x^2 + 7y^2 = 47 \tag{24}$$
$$6x^2 - 10y^2 = 15 \tag{25}$$

Multiply Eq. (24) by 6:

$$30x^2 + 42y^2 = 282 \tag{26}$$

Multiply Eq. (25) by 5:

$$30x^2 - 50y^2 = 75 \tag{27}$$

Subtract Eq. (27) from Eq. (26):

$$92y^2 = 207$$

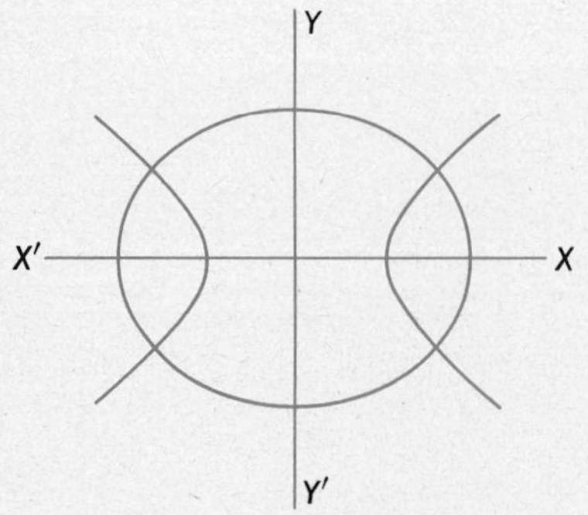

FIGURE 11.29

Solving for y,

$y = \pm 3/2$

Substitute $y^2 = 9/4$ in Eq. (25):

$$6x^2 - 10(9/4) = 15$$
$$x = \pm 5/2$$

There are four solutions:

$x = 5/2, y = 3/2$ $\quad x = 5/2, y = -3/2$
$x = -5/2, y = 3/2$ $\quad x = -5/2, y = -3/2$

EXERCISE 8

Solve algebraically for all values of x and y.

1. $3x^2 + y^2 = 12$, $x^2 + 2y^2 = 19$
2. $2x^2 - 3y^2 = 5$, $4x^2 + y^2 = 17$
3. $5x^2 - 2y^2 = 20$, $x^2 + 3y^2 = 4$
4. $2y^2 - 3x^2 = 18$, $x^2 + y^2 = 9$
5. $4x^2 + 4y^2 = 15$, $6x^2 - 5y^2 = 20$
6. $6x^2 + 6y^2 = 25$, $9y^2 - 5x^2 = 30$
7. $4x^2 - y^2 = 20$, $2y^2 - x^2 = 8$
8. $3x^2 + 8y^2 = 20$, $5x^2 + 5y^2 = 28$

11.18 Elimination of Constants

A quadratic system in two variables in which all terms containing the variables are of the second degree may often be solved by first eliminating the constant terms from the original system. The method is as follows:

1. *Using the method of addition or subtraction, combine the two equations, eliminating the constant terms and obtaining a single equation of the type*

   $$Ax^2 + Bxy + Cy^2 = 0$$

2. *Factor this quadratic equation and express one of the variables as a multiple of the other.*
3. *Substitute the relations in step 2 successively in one of the original equations, and solve the resulting equations in one variable.*
4. *Substitute in step 2 the values obtained in step 3 to determine the other variable.*

Example 27. Solve the system

$$2x^2 - 3xy + 2y^2 = 28 \qquad (28)$$
$$4x^2 + 3xy - y^2 = 21 \qquad (29)$$

Multiplying Eq. (29) by 4 and Eq. (28) by 3, we obtain

$$16x^2 + 12xy - 4y^2 = 84 \qquad (30)$$
$$6x^2 - 9xy + 6y^2 = 84 \qquad (31)$$

Subtracting,

$$10x^2 + 21xy - 10y^2 = 0 \qquad (32)$$

Factoring Eq. (32), we obtain

$$(5x - 2y)(2x + 5y) = 0 \qquad (33)$$

From Eq. (33) we get two solutions:

$$x = \tfrac{2}{5}y \qquad (34)$$
$$x = -\tfrac{5}{2}y \qquad (35)$$

Substituting Eq. (34) in Eq. (28), we obtain

$$2(\tfrac{2}{5}y)^2 - 3y(\tfrac{2}{5}y) + 2y^2 = 28$$
$$8y^2 - 30y^2 + 50y^2 = 700$$

from which

$$y^2 = 25$$
$$y = \pm 5$$

Since $x = \frac{2}{5}y$, the corresponding values of x are ± 2. Substituting Eq. (35) in Eq. (28), we have

$$2(-\tfrac{5}{2}y)^2 - 3y(-\tfrac{5}{2}y) + 2y^2 = 28$$
$$25y^2 + 15y^2 + 4y^2 = 56$$

from which

$$y^2 = \tfrac{14}{11}$$
$$y = \pm \tfrac{1}{11}\sqrt{154}$$

Since $x = -\frac{5}{2}y$, the corresponding values of x are $\mp\frac{5}{22}\sqrt{154}$. Pairing the values of x and y, we obtain

	From $x = \frac{2}{5}y$		From $x = -\frac{5}{2}y$	
x	2	−2	$\frac{5}{22}\sqrt{154}$	$-\frac{5}{22}\sqrt{154}$
y	5	−5	$-\frac{1}{11}\sqrt{154}$	$\frac{1}{11}\sqrt{154}$

EXERCISE 9

Solve Probs. 1 to 8, inclusive, by eliminating the constant terms.

1. $x^2 + xy = 3$
   $xy + y^2 = 10$
2. $4x^2 + 3xy + y^2 = 22$
   $x^2 + xy = 4$
3. $x^2 - 8xy + 17y^2 = 5$
   $x^2 - 5xy + 9y^2 = 15$
4. $2x^2 + 3xy + 2y^2 = 64$
   $x^2 - 6xy + 6y^2 = -8$
5. $(2x - 9y)(x - 2y) = -12$
   $(2x + y)(x - 3y) = 16$
6. $x + y = 20/x$
   $x - y = 3/y$
7. $3x^2 + 3xy + y^2 = 7$
   $x^2 + 11xy + 5y^2 = 19$
8. $4x + 5y = 84/x$
   $3x + 16y = 28/y$

9. In electrical engineering occur the two simultaneous equations

$$\frac{SK}{K^2 - 1} = R \qquad S\frac{K^2 + 1}{K^2 - 1} = D \qquad (K \text{ cannot be } \pm 1)$$

Eliminate S and solve for K in terms of D and R. Also show that the two answers for K are reciprocals.

12 nonlinear empirical equations

In Chaps. 6, 7, and 10 we dealt with the drawing of curves from given data and equations. In Sec. 7.19 we discussed the inverse problem of deriving empirical linear equations from given data and straight lines. We shall now describe how to derive empirical equations to fit curved lines. In order to avail ourselves of the convenient relationships of the straight line, we shall learn how to convert a nonlinear relationship to a linear relationship whenever possible.

12.1 Rectification of Data

If a set of data can be expressed by an equation whose graph is a straight line on some type of coordinate paper, plotting and interpolation will be simplified. The process of conversion to an equation of linear characteristics is called *rectification*.

Extrapolation of a graph beyond the range of the given data is made possible by rectification, but is a risky procedure and should be attempted only as a last resort. In fact, it may prove necessary to represent various portions of the curve by different equations.

Short intervals of a given curve may often be expressed by a variety of equations. These equations may or may not be a rational expression of the law involved. In any event, we should expect our equation to be dimensionally sound with respect to the variables involved; otherwise its utility is likely to be sharply limited.

12.2 Procedure for Rectification of Data

In general, our first step in rectification of data is to plot them on ordinary cross-section paper. This plot will often indicate the relationship involved.

If the graph exhibits only a slight curvature, the *polynomial* relationship $y = a + bx + cx^2 + dx^3 + \cdots$ should be tested first. If a sharp curvature is displayed, the power and exponential types should also be investigated. It is obvious that we must have sufficient data to set up as many equations as there are constants to be determined. If there are more points available than constants to be determined, we shall use the method of averages. However, it should be stressed that the method of averages can be applied only to data which can be represented by a straight line. Occasionally, when but few points are known, they can be shown to fit more than one type of equation.

12.3 Parabolic Relationship

It can be stated that, in general, through any three points not in the same straight line, one, and only one, parabola of the general equation $y = ax^2 + bx + c$ may be passed. The constants a, b, and c are determined by substituting the coordinates of the given points in the general equation and solving simultaneously the three resulting equations.

Example 1. Determine the constants of the equation $y = ax^2 + bx + c$ which passes through the points (5,6); (8,3); (10,−1).

Substituting the pairs of coordinates successively in the general equation, we have

$$6 = a(5)^2 + b(5) + c \qquad \text{or} \qquad 6 = 25a + 5b + c$$
$$3 = a(8)^2 + b(8) + c \qquad \text{or} \qquad 3 = 64a + 8b + c$$
$$-1 = a(10)^2 + b(10) + c \qquad \text{or} \qquad -1 = 100a + 10b + c$$

Solution of this system of equations yields $a = -0.2$, $b = 1.6$, $c = 3$.

Hence the required equation is $y = -0.2x^2 + 1.6x + 3$, which passes through the three given points.

EXERCISE 1

Determine the constants of the equation $y = ax^2 + bx + c$ which passes through the three given points in each case.

1. (3,−5); (5,7); (9,55)
2. (1,−3); (4,30); (7,99)
3. (2,30); (5,18); (7,0)
4. (2,5); (4,17); (6,21)
5. (5,1); (17,10); (26,20)

6. (*a*) Show that a parabola $x = py^2 + qy + r$ may be passed through the points given in Prob. 4.
   (*b*) Sketch both curves between $x = -2$ and $x = +10$ for comparison.

We make no attempt in this text to rectify the polynomial relationship. For this reason we cannot take averages but instead resort to the method of selected points.

12.4 General Polynomial Relationship

If, for evenly spaced values of x, the second, third, or nth differences of y are reasonably constant, a second-, third- or, in general, nth-degree function of x is indicated. If the x values contained in the data are not evenly spaced, the data should be plotted and the ordinates corresponding to evenly spaced abscissas should be read off from the graph.

Example 2. The following data are thought to represent y as a polynomial function of x. Determine the equation best fitting the data.

x	10	20	30	40	50	60	70	80
y	11.55	14.79	18.31	22.55	27.80	34.46	42.88	53.42

Rearranging the data so that successive differences in y may be better shown, we have

x	y	Δy	$\Delta^2 y$	$\Delta^3 y$	$\Delta^4 y$
10	11.55				
		3.24			
20	14.79		0.28		
		3.52		0.44	
30	18.31		0.72		−0.15
		4.24		0.29	
40	22.55		1.01		0.11
		5.25		0.40	
50	27.80		1.41		−0.05
		6.66		0.35	
60	34.46		1.76		0.01
		8.42		0.36	
70	42.88		2.12		
		10.54			
80	53.42				

Since the column of third differences ($\Delta^3 y$) shows the least variation, we shall be dealing with a cubic equation of the form $y = a + bx + cx^2 + dx^3$. We shall need four independent equations in order to determine the four constants a, b, c, and d. In order to cover the range of the data, we shall select the points $x = 20, 40, 60, 80$.

If the data indicate sharp curvature over any range, this range should be well represented; correspondingly selected points can be more widely spaced over a flat portion of the curve.

The equations in this example will therefore be:

$$14.79 = a + 20b + (20)^2c + (20)^3d$$
$$22.55 = a + 40b + (40)^2c + (40)^3d$$
$$34.46 = a + 60b + (60)^2c + (60)^3d$$
$$53.42 = a + 80b + (80)^2c + (80)^3d$$

The solution of this system of equations is

$$a = 8.28 \qquad b = 0.343 \qquad c = -2.06 \times 10^{-3} \qquad d = 6.04 \times 10^{-5}$$

Accordingly, the desired equation is

$$y = 8.28 + 0.343x - 2.06(10)^{-3}x^2 + 6.04(10)^{-5}x^3$$

12.5 Power Functions

Typical of a *power function* is the equation $y = bx^a$, where a and b are constants. In the simplest case where only two points are given and the relation is known to be a power function, we may solve the equations $y_1 = bx_1{}^a$ and $y_2 = bx_2{}^a$ simultaneously.

Example 3. Derive the constants of the equation $y = bx^a$ satisfied by the points (2,6) and (10,2).

Substituting data in the general equation,

$$6 = b(2)^a \qquad (1)$$
$$2 = b(10)^a \qquad (2)$$

Dividing (1) by (2), we obtain $3 = (0.2)^a$. Taking logs,

$$\log 3 = a \log 0.2$$
$$0.47712 = a(0.30103 - 1) = -0.69897a$$
$$a = -0.6826$$

Substituting in (2),

$$2 = b(10)^{-0.6826} = b(0.2077)$$
$$b = 9.629$$

Therefore our equation is

$$y = 9.63x^{-0.683}$$

In order to rectify experimental data represented by a power function, we take logarithms of both sides of the equation $y = bx^a$.

We obtain

$$\log y = \log b + a \log x \tag{3}$$

Substituting Y for log y, B for log b, and X for log x, we obtain

$$Y = B + aX$$

where B is also a constant.

The similarity between this equation and the straight-line equation $y = ax + b$ will at once be apparent.

Let us illustrate this relationship with the pressure-volume relationship for ethane gas $PV^{1.22} = K$. In this instance we shall deal with 40 ft^3 of ethane at 1 atm pressure, for which we obtain

$$1(40)^{1.22} = K = 90$$

In order to do this we shall first rearrange our equation to read $P = 90V^{-1.22}$ and then tabulate values of V, P, and their logarithms.

V	P	log V = X	log P = Y
1	90	0	1.954
2	38.7	0.301	1.587
5	12.6	0.699	1.101
10	5.42	1.000	0.734
20	2.33	1.301	0.367
40	1.00	1.602	0.000

The plot of V against P on ordinary cross-section paper is shown in Fig. 12.1, while the plot of X against Y is illustrated in Fig. 12.2.

Now, if we use logarithmic scales for both variables (log-log paper), we shall retain the linear feature of Fig. 12.2 and yet be able to plot values of V and P directly without looking up logarithms (Fig. 12.3). We note that the y intercept indicates a multiplying factor (that is, $y = b$ when $x = 1$) while the slope a of the line represents

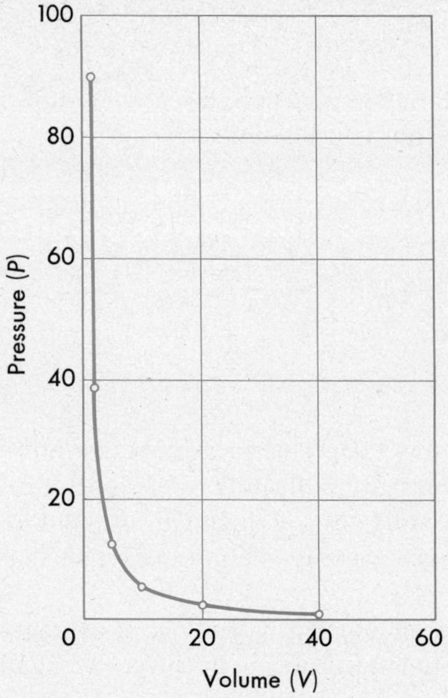

FIGURE 12.1

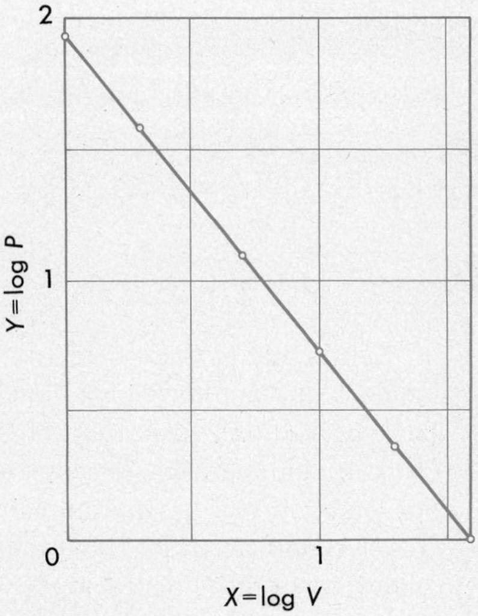

FIGURE 12.2

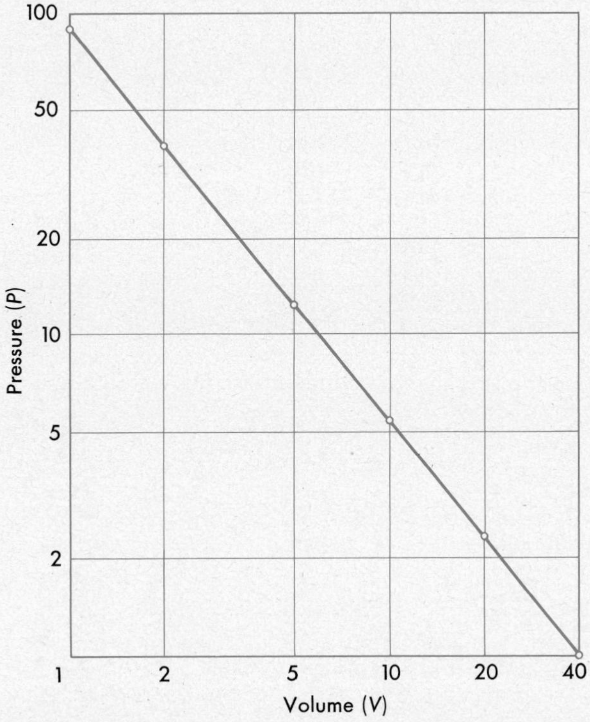

FIGURE 12.3

the power of the independent variable. Note that the slope is determined by measuring vertical and horizontal distances in actual inches, not in scale units.

Example 4. Determine the empirical formula corresponding to the following data:

x	1.5	2.2	3.1	4.4	7.4	12.5
y	9.8	8.0	6.8	5.7	4.4	3.4

The plot of these data on ordinary cross-section paper has a definite curvature whereas the plot on log-log paper is reasonably straight, indicating a relationship of the type $y = bx^a$. Inspection of this straight line indicates a y intercept of about 12 $(=b)$ and an approximate slope of $-\frac{1}{2}$ $(= a)$. Hence we may venture to predict that our equation will be approximately $y = 12/\sqrt{x}$.

A more accurate result may be obtained by employing the method of averages analogous to that illustrated in Sec. 7.19. In this type of problem, however, we shall take averages of the logarithms as indicated in the following procedure: Three-place logarithms will be accurate enough for the data.

x	y	Average log x	log x	log y	Average log y
1.5	9.8		0.176	0.991	
2.2	8.0	0.336	0.342	0.903	0.909
3.1	6.8		0.491	0.833	
4.4	5.7		0.643	0.756	
7.4	4.4	0.870	0.869	0.643	0.644
12.5	3.4		1.097	0.532	

Substituting the average logarithms in Eq. (3), we obtain

$$0.909 = \log b + 0.336a \qquad (4)$$
$$0.644 = \log b + 0.870a \qquad (5)$$

Subtracting (5) from (4),

$$0.265 = -0.534a$$

and solving for a,

$$a = -0.497$$

Substituting $a = -0.497$ in Eq. (5), we have

$$0.644 = \log b + (0.870)(-0.497)$$
$$1.076 = \log b$$
$$b = 11.9$$

Hence the required equation is $y = 11.9x^{-0.497}$, which was closely predicted by inspection of the graph.

EXERCISE 2

1. Plot on a common area of log-log paper the equations (*a*) $y = x$, (*b*) $y = x^2$, (*c*) $y = 1/x$, (*d*) $y = \sqrt{x}$, (*e*) $y = 1/\sqrt{x}$. Label each line with its equation.
2. Do the same as in Prob. 1 for the equations (*a*) $y = 5x^2$, (*b*) $y = \pi x^2$, (*c*) $y = 1.5x^2$, (*d*) $y = x^2/2$.
3. Do the same as in Prob. 1 for the equations (*a*) $y = x^3/4$, (*b*) $y = 4/x^2$, (*c*) $y = x^{3/2}$, (*d*) $y = 2\sqrt{x}$, (*e*) $y = x^{-1/3}$, (*f*) $y = 5\sqrt[3]{x}$.

12.6 Exponential Functions

An exponential function is characterized by a constant to a variable power. It may be represented by the type equation $y = ba^x$, where a and b are constants. In the simplest case, where only two points are given and the relation is known to be exponential, we may solve the equations $y_1 = ba^{x_1}$ and $y_2 = ba^{x_2}$ simultaneously.

Example 5. Derive the constants of the equation $y = ba^x$ satisfied by the points (4,1.5) and (14,6).

Substituting data in the general equation,

$$1.5 = ba^4 \tag{6}$$
$$6 = ba^{14} \tag{7}$$

Dividing (7) by (6), we obtain

$$4 = a^{10}$$

It follows that

$$a = \sqrt[10]{4} = 1.1487$$

Substituting the value of a just found in (6),

$$1.5 = b(1.1487)^4$$
$$b = 0.8615$$

Therefore our equation is

$$y = 0.862(1.149)^x$$

In order to rectify exponential experimental data, we take logs of both sides of the equation $y = ba^x$, obtaining

$$\log y = \log b + x \log a \tag{8}$$

Since $\log b$ and $\log a$ are constants, it follows that a straight line should result if y values are located on a logarithmic scale and x values on a uniform scale.

To confirm this statement, consider the equation $S = 10(1.03)^n$ which represents the amount of \$10 at continuously compounded interest for n years. The rate is equivalent to 3 percent compounded annually. It has been plotted on ordinary graph paper in Fig. 12.4 and on semilogarithmic paper in Fig. 12.5.

Returning to our type equation $y = ba^x$, it will be seen that the constant b corresponds to the y intercept just as it does in the power relationship. Also, while we instinctively realize that the slope of the graph on semilog paper is somehow related

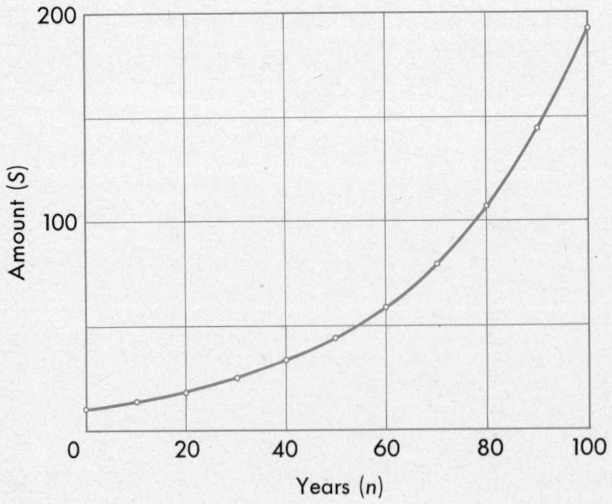

FIGURE 12.4

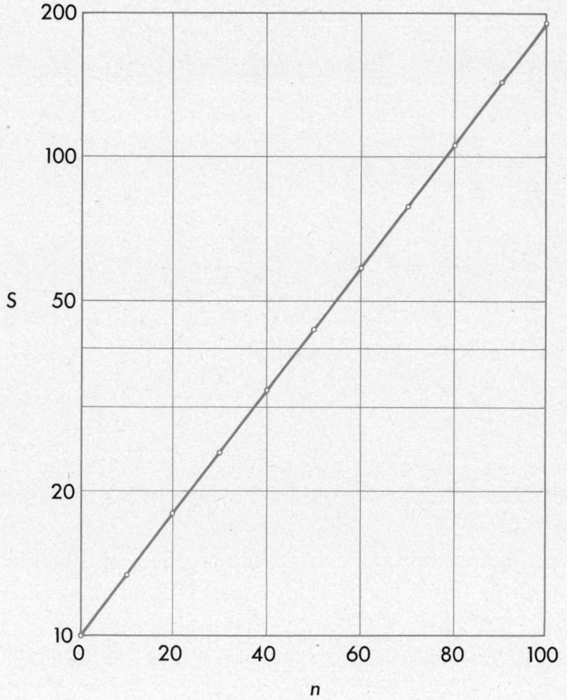

FIGURE 12.5

to the value of the constant a, it is not immediately apparent how a can be determined by measuring the slope of the line.

Referring to Fig. 12.6, let $P(x,y_0)$, $Q(x + 1, y_1)$, and $R(x + n, y_n)$ represent points on the graph $y = ba^x$.

If we substitute the coordinates of Q in the type equation, we obtain

$$y_1 = ba^{x+1} \tag{9}$$

Repeating for point P, we have

$$y_0 = ba^x \tag{10}$$

Dividing (9) by (10),

$$\frac{y_1}{y_0} = \frac{ba^{x+1}}{ba^x} = a \tag{11}$$

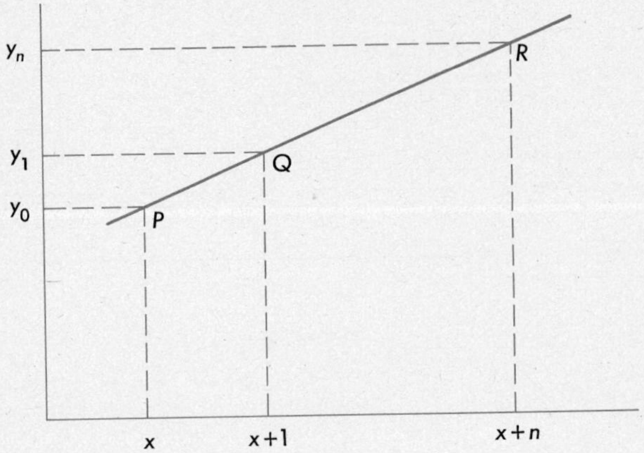

FIGURE 12.6

Hence if $P(x,y_0)$ and $Q(x + 1, y_1)$ represent any two points on the graph whose abscissas differ by 1, the ratio of the ordinates y_1/y_0 (in scale units) will be a measure of a.

If the slope of the line is nearly horizontal, greater accuracy may be obtained by taking the more widely spaced points $P(x,y_0)$ and $R(x + n, y_n)$.

Substituting the coordinates of R in the type equation, we have

$$y_n = ba^{x+n} \tag{12}$$

Dividing (12) by (10),

$$\frac{y_n}{y_0} = \frac{ba^{x+n}}{ba^x} = a^n$$

or

$$a = \sqrt[n]{\frac{y_n}{y_0}} \tag{13}$$

From this we conclude that *if $P(x,y_0)$ and $R(x + n, y_n)$ represent any two points on the graph whose abscissas differ by n, the nth root of the ratio of the ordinates y_n/y_0 will equal the value of a.*

Example 6. Determine the equation of the type $y = ba^x$, which best fits the following data:

x	0.8	2.0	2.75	3.7	5.0	6.45
y	3.5	5.85	8.0	12.0	21.0	39.0

Plotting the ordinates of these points on a logarithmic scale and the abscissas on a uniform scale, we find we have a well-defined linear relationship. Extension of the line indicates a y intercept of about 2.5, the approximate value of b.

Reading the ordinates corresponding to two consecutive values of x, say, 1 and 2, we find 3.8 and 5.85, respectively. The ratio $5.85:3.8 = 1.54$, the approximate value of a. Hence we may predict that our relationship may be roughly represented by the equation

$$y = 2.5(1.54)^x \tag{14}$$

It is often desirable to express an exponential function as $y = be^{kx}$. In this example the equation

$$y = 2.5(1.54)^x \qquad \text{becomes} \qquad y = 2.5e^{0.432x} \tag{15}$$

Note that Eq. (14) indicates a constant rate of growth of y of 54 percent per unit increase in x, where Eq. (15) indicates that the equivalent instantaneous rate is 43.2 percent (Sec. 9.10).

In using the method of averages, a glance at Eq. (8) will show that we should average the logarithms of y and should average x directly.

Average x	x	y	log y	Average log y
	0.8	3.5	0.544	
1.85	2.0	5.85	0.767	0.738
	2.75	8.0	0.903	
	3.7	12.0	1.079	
5.05	5.0	21.0	1.322	1.331
	6.45	39.0	1.591	

Substituting our average values in Eq. (8), we obtain

$$1.331 = \log b + 5.05 \log a \tag{16}$$
$$0.738 = \log b + 1.85 \log a \tag{17}$$

Subtracting (17) from (16),

$$0.593 = 3.20 \log a$$
$$0.1853 = \log a$$
$$a = 1.53$$

Substituting $\log a = 0.1853$ in Eq. (17), we have

$$0.738 = \log b + 1.85(0.1853)$$
$$0.395 = \log b$$
$$b = 2.48$$

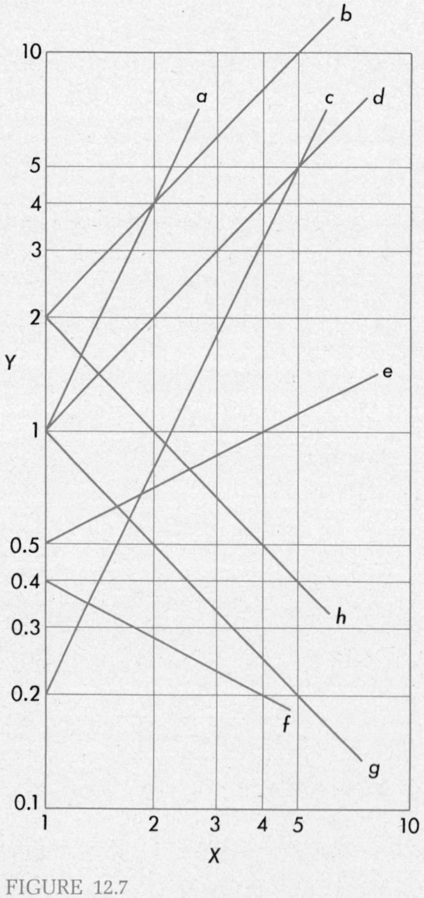

FIGURE 12.7

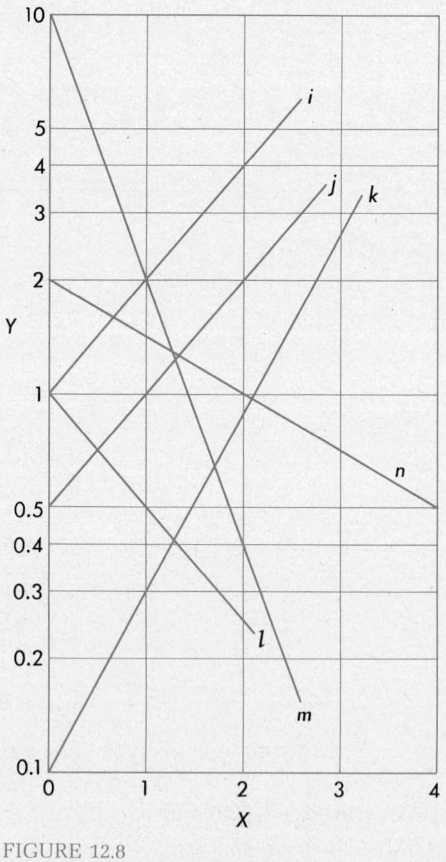

FIGURE 12.8

Therefore the equation is $y = 2.48(1.53)^x$, which agrees well with the result anticipated by inspection.

EXERCISE 3

1. Plot on a common area of semilog paper the equations (*a*) $y = 2^x$, (*b*) $y = 5^x$, (*c*) $y = 1.5^x$, (*d*) $y = 0.5^x$, (*e*) $y = 2^{-x}$, (*f*) $y = e^x$. Label each line with its equation.
2. Do the same as in Prob. 1 for the equations (*a*) $y = 5(1.5)^x$, (*b*) $y = 2(1.5)^x$, (*c*) $y = 0.7(1.5)^x$.
3. Do the same as in Prob. 1 for the equations (*a*) $y = 3(2)^x$, (*b*) $y = 0.2(5)^x$, (*c*) $y = 5(2)^{-x}$, (*d*) $y = 4e^{-x}$, (*e*) $y = 0.5e^x$, (*f*) $y = e^{-0.47x}$. (This is a constant percentage depreciation curve. Instantaneous rate is 47 percent, annual rate is $37\frac{1}{2}$ percent, initial value = 1.)

EXERCISE 4

Referring to Figs. 12.7 and 12.8, write, by inspection, the equation for each line *a* through *n*, inclusive.

12.7 Summary of Suggestions for Determining the Nature of the Relationship between the Variables

1. *Plot the data on ordinary cross-section paper. A straight line indicates the relationship* $y = mx + b$.
2. *If the graph is almost linear, try the polynomial equation* $y = a + bx + cx^2 + \cdots$. *If this fails, try* $x = a + by + cy^2 + \cdots$.
3. *If the graph shows considerable curvature, plot the data on log-log paper. A straight line indicates a power relationship* $y = bx^a$.
4. *Plot the data on semilog paper with y plotted on the log scale. A straight line indicates an equation of the type* $y = ba^x$. *However, it may happen that the curvature is not reduced; it may even be accentuated. In this event reverse the positions of x and y and plot x on the log scale, in which case a straight line indicates the type equation* $x = ba^y$.

This procedure is designed to cover only the simpler cases illustrated. More involved relationships are beyond the scope of this text. They are covered in detail in more specialized works on empirical equations and curve fitting, such as the following:

Davis, D. S.: "Empirical Equations and Nomography," McGraw-Hill Book Company, New York, 1943.

Lipka, J.: "Graphical and Mechanical Computation," John Wiley & Sons, Inc., New York, 1918.

Worthing, Archie G., and J. Geffner: "Treatment of Experimental Data," John Wiley & Sons, Inc., New York, 1943.

EXERCISE 5

In Probs. 1 to 10 the type of equation fitting the data has been indicated. Determine the best values of the constants of the equations.

1. (*a*) Evaluate the constants a and b in the equation $y = ba^x$ if $y = 2$ when $x = 2$ and $y = 50$ when $x = 12$.
   (*b*) Transform your answer in (*a*) to the form $y = be^{kx}$.
2. Repeat Prob. 1 if $y = 10$ when $x = 0.2$ and $y = 0.2$ when $x = 1.1$.
3. Evaluate the constants a and b in the equation $y = bx^a$ if $y = 370$ when $x = 4.4$ and $y = 830$ when $x = 20$.
4. Repeat Prob. 3 if $y = 7$ when $x = 16.5$ and $y = 1.6$ when $x = 38$.
5. The following data give the discharge Q (ft^3/s) over a rectangular weir for a given head H (ft).

H	0.166	0.509	0.989	1.152	1.792	3.970
Q	0.93	5.58	13.85	17.52	34.05	107.0

   The formula for Q is known to be $Q = CLH^n$, where C and n are constants. C is called the mean value of the coefficient of discharge. L is the length of the weir in feet and is 4.26 for these data. Plot on log-log paper to confirm nature of equation. Determine the best values of C and n.
6. A 120-V tungsten lamp was found to have the following voltage-amperage characteristics:

E, V	2	8	25	50	100	150
i, A	0.0368	0.0855	0.1688	0.2572	0.3908	0.4942

   Derive an equation of the type $i = bE^a$. (First confirm nature of relationship.)
7. (*a*) The rpm (N) of a flywheel was noted at various times (t min) after power was shut off.

t	0	0.5	1.0	1.5	2.0	2.5	3.0
N	20	9.94	4.94	2.44	1.22	0.60	0.28

   Determine an equation of the type $N = ba^t$. (First plot on semilog paper to confirm nature of equation.)
   (*b*) Convert your answer in (*a*) to the form $N = be^{kt}$.
8. (*a*) The temperature of an object when placed in cooler surroundings drops according to the equation $T = ba^\theta$ (Newton's law of cooling), where T is the

temperature differential between the object and the room at any time θ since the beginning of observations. Confirm the type of equation and determine the values of a and b.

θ	0	6.9	21.7	38.6	57.6	80.2	107.5	141.9
T	39.9	37.8	33.5	29.8	25.9	22.0	17.6	13.8

(*b*) Convert your answer in (*a*) to the form $T = be^{k\theta}$.

9. A Chromel-Alumel thermocouple generates a certain number of millivolts (E) at various Celsius temperatures (t) according to the following table (cold junction at 0°C):

t	0	100	200	300	400	500	600	700	800	900	1,000	1,100
E	0	4.08	8.19	12.31	16.48	20.74	25.00	29.21	33.28	37.25	41.13	44.85

Confirm a cubic relationship and express in the form of the equation

$$E = a + bt + ct^2 + dt^3$$

10. Barometer reading (p-in mercury) is related to the height above sea level (h ft) as follows:

h	0	500	1,000	1,500	2,000	2,500	3,000	3,500	4,000	4,500	5,000	5,500	6,000
p	29.92	29.36	28.80	28.26	27.72	27.20	26.68	26.18	25.68	25.20	24.72	24.26	23.79

Confirm and derive an equation of the type

$$p = ba^{h/10,000}$$

In Probs. 11 to 18 determine the type of equation fitting the data and compute its constants. (Consider the second variable to be the dependent variable in all cases.)

11.

x	1	3.5	5.5	9
y	4	7	11	24

12.

x	2	10	40	80
y	19	10	5.8	4.2

13. A quantity of saturated steam showed the following pressure-volume relationship:

p	7.35	8.765	10.40	12.27	14.42	16.86	19.62	22.74
V	13.22	11.20	9.54	8.16	7.02	6.06	5.265	4.574

14. An experimental run with a gas engine yielded the following data:

p (lb/in^2)	29.8	35.9	49.0	57.2	75.5	90.5
V (in^3)	14.06	11.3	7.80	6.47	4.70	3.80

15. Rope over a round beam; θ = angle of contact, turns; F = lb force to restrain a dead weight at the free end of the rope:

θ	$\frac{1}{2}$	1	$1\frac{1}{4}$	$1\frac{3}{4}$
F	325	148	100	44.5

What is the significance of the multiplying constant?

16. Pressure required to compress 250 ft^3 of helium originally at atmospheric pressure to various volumes V:

V	26.5	37.5	51	60	80	97	135	250
P	620	350	210	160	100	72	42	15

17. The following data were taken in an ingenious method for estimating the solar energy which the earth's surface would receive if not weakened by atmospheric absorption (see Fig. 12.9).

θ	M, air mass	E, solar energy received, g cal/cm^2 · s
	0	
90°	1	1.66
30°	2	1.42
19°28′	3	1.22
14°29′	4	1.05
11°32′	5	0.90

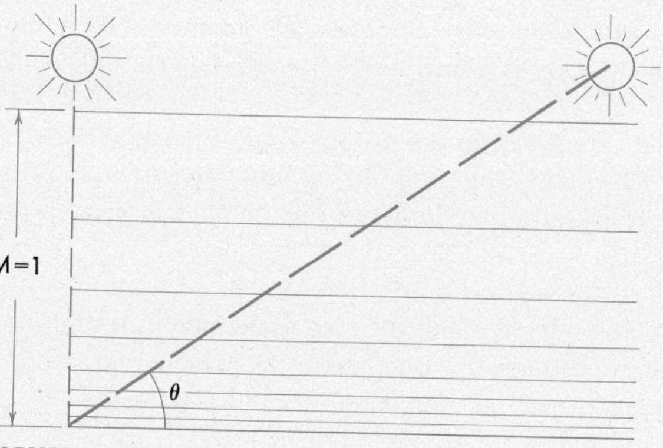

FIGURE 12.9

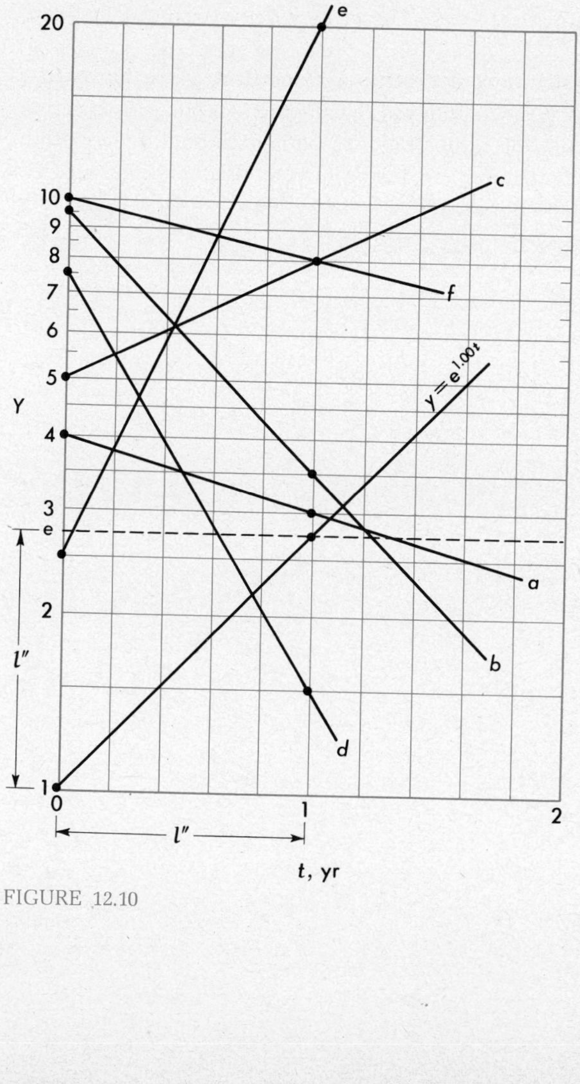

FIGURE 12.10

Taking the air layer as unit thickness (air mass = 1 when $\theta = 90°$), then cosec θ will indicate the relative thickness of air layers traversed at various angles of elevation of the sun.

By plotting these data (E versus M) on the proper kind of paper and extrapolating, we can estimate the solar energy entering the upper atmosphere. In other words, we can climb above our surrounding blanket of air mathematically if not physically.

Estimate the value of E to the nearest 0.01 when $M = 0$.

18. In the semilog chart in Fig. 12.10 we have made the two scale moduli (t and ln y) equal as shown. Under these conditions the line $y = e^{1.00t}$, which represents a constant growth rate of 100 percent, actually appears as a 45° line, or a slope of 1.00.

In general if the slope of the line = m, its equation is $y = ke^{mt}$.

What is the value of y at $t = 0$, at $t = 1$? Therefore what is the annual percent rate of growth?

By inspection we see that line a represents a 25 percent depreciation in 1 yr. By actual measurement in inches, we find that the slope is -0.288. The equation for a may then be written $y = 4(0.75)^t$ indicating a 25 percent annual depreciation rate or $y = 4e^{-0.288t}$ indicating a 28.8 percent instantaneous depreciation rate.

By inspection determine the approximate instantaneous and annual growth (or depreciation) rates for each of the lines b through f.

13 introduction to trigonometry

Historically, trigonometry arose out of the need for calculating the unknown sides and angles in triangles as for example in surveying, navigation, and the like. However, of equal importance is its application to problems involving certain types of periodic motion and electric circuits.

13.1 Angles

For the present purpose an angle will be described in terms of Fig. 13.1. The side r was originally coincident with the side OX. The side OX is called the initial position of r, or the *initial side* of the angle. However, r as shown in the diagram has been revolved about O in the direction of the arrow and has become the *terminal side* of the angle.

13.2 Units of Angular Measure

Angles are commonly measured in either of two systems of units: the degree system or the radian system.

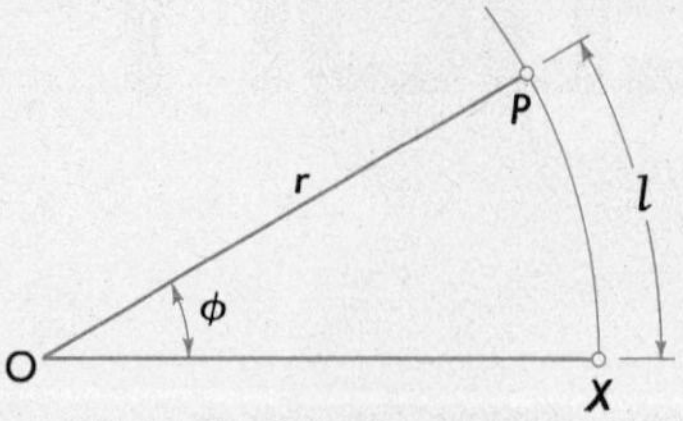

FIGURE 13.1

The Degree System

If r had revolved about O for one complete revolution from the initial position, an angle of 360 degrees would have been generated. By definition, 1 degree is equivalent to $\frac{1}{360}$ revolution. An angle of 90 degrees (written 90°) is equivalent to $\frac{90}{360}$, or $\frac{1}{4}$ revolution. An angle of 180° would be equivalent to $\frac{180}{360}$, or $\frac{1}{2}$ revolution.

Often angles are measured in degrees and a decimal fraction of a degree, as for example 37.594°. Also, they are measured in degrees and subunits of a degree, called minutes and seconds. There are, by definition, 60 minutes in 1 degree and 60 seconds in 1 minute. The angular magnitude 37 degrees 42 minutes and 36 seconds would be written 37°42′36″. Since there are 60 seconds in a minute, it follows that 6″ is equivalent to $\frac{1}{10}$ minute. The angle 37°42′36″ could also have been written 37°42.6′, and indeed angles are frequently measured in degrees, minutes, and tenths of minutes.

Since there are 60′ in a degree,

$$42.6' = \frac{42.6}{60} = 0.71^\circ$$

and the angle 37°42′36″ may be written 37.71° or 37.7° to the nearest 0.1°.

For purposes of numerical calculation in solving triangles etc., the degree system is ordinarily used. In more analytical work the radian system is common.

The Radian System

As the radius r in Fig. 13.1 rotates about point O, generating the angle ϕ, the point P moves in a circular path. If the arc length traversed by P is $\widehat{XP}$ (where $\widehat{XP}$ is measured in the same linear units as r), then ϕ measured in radians is

$$\phi = \frac{\widehat{XP}}{r} \qquad \textbf{(1)}$$

and

$$\widehat{XP} = r \times \phi \qquad (2)$$

or

$$l = r\phi \tag{3}$$

In other words, the quotient of the arc length divided by the radius is the measure of the central angle in radians.

In Fig. 13.2 the arc $\widehat{XP}$ equals the radius r, and ϕ is 1 rad.

If the radius r makes one complete revolution, then the arc length becomes the circumference of the circle, and

$$\phi = \frac{2\pi r}{r} = 2\pi \tag{4}$$

There are 2π rad in one revolution, and 1 rad is $1/(2\pi)$ revolution. Since by definition one revolution of the radius r is equivalent to an angle of 360°, and since by definition one revolution is also equivalent to 2π rad,

$$2\pi \text{ rad} = 360°$$
$$\pi \text{ rad} = 180°$$
$$1 \text{ rad} = \frac{180°}{\pi} = 57.2957795° \tag{5}$$

$$1° = \frac{\pi}{180} = 0.01745329 \text{ rad} \tag{6}$$

For simplicity, we usually choose to write π rad rather than 3.14159 rad, $\pi/2$ rad rather than 1.57080 rad, $3\pi/2$ rad rather than 4.71239 rad, etc. In such cases it is easy to change from radian measure to degree measure by substituting for π rad the

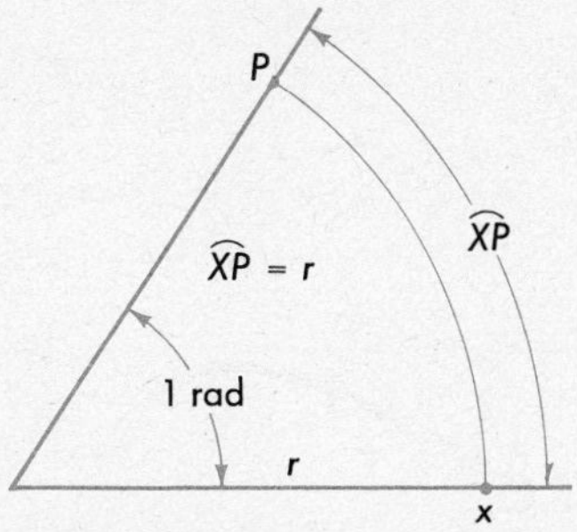

FIGURE 13.2

degree equivalent, 180°.

$$\pi \text{ rad} = 180° \tag{7}$$

$$\frac{\pi}{2} \text{ rad} = \frac{180°}{2} = 90° \tag{8}$$

$$\frac{3\pi}{2} \text{ rad} = \frac{3 \times 180°}{2} = 270° \tag{9}$$

Example 1. Change 56.73° to radians.
Since by Eq. (6)

$$1° = \frac{\pi}{180} \text{ rad}$$

then

$$56.73° = 56.73 \times \frac{\pi}{180} = 0.99013 \text{ rad}$$

Example 2. Change 0.792 rad to degrees. Leave the answer a decimal.
Since by Eq. (5)

$$1 \text{ rad} = \frac{180°}{\pi}$$

then

$$0.792 \text{ rad} = 0.792 \times \frac{180}{\pi} = \frac{0.792 \times 180}{\pi}$$

$$= 45.38°$$

Example 3. How many degrees are there in $7\pi/15$ rad?

$$\pi \text{ rad} = 180°$$

$$\frac{7}{15} \pi \text{ rad} = \frac{7}{15} \times 180° = \frac{1{,}260}{15} = 84°$$

Example 4. How many revolutions are there in an angle of 5π rad?
Since 1 revolution = 2π rad, it follows that

$$5\pi \text{ rad} = \frac{5\pi}{2\pi} = 2.5 \text{ revolutions}$$

Example 5. How many revolutions are there in 2.5 rad?

Since 1 revolution = 2π or 6.2832 rad, it follows that

$$2.5 \text{ rad} = 2.5/6.2832 = 0.40 \text{ revolution}$$

Example 6. Refer to Fig. 13.1. If $l = 5$ in and $r = 3$ in, find the angle ϕ in radians.

Following Eq. (3),

$$l = r\phi_{rad}$$

then

$$5 = 3\phi_{rad}$$

or

$$\phi = 5/3 \text{ rad}$$

Example 7. What is the arc length which subtends a central angle of 2.36 rad in a circle whose radius is 4 in?

Following Eq. (3),

$$l = 4 \times 2.36 = 9.44 \text{ in}$$

Example 8. How many revolutions are equivalent to 4,320°?

Since there are 360° in one revolution, we may write

$$4{,}320/360 = 12 \text{ revolutions}$$

EXERCISE 1

Change the following examples of angular measure from degrees to radians.

1. 27° 2. 137° 3. 251° 4. 322°

Change the following examples of angular measure from radians to degrees.

5. 1.36_{rad} 6. 0.37_{rad} 7. 3.67_{rad} 8. 0.592_{rad}

EXERCISE 2

Referring to Fig. 13.1, find arc length, radius, or central angle as indicated in the following tabulation:

	Arc length, in	Radius, in	Central angle
1.		16	4 rad
2.	12		8 rad
3.	2.4	5	
4.		25	2 revolutions
5.	18		45°
6.	32	8	Find central angle in revolutions

EXERCISE 3

Convert into degrees, radians, and revolutions as indicated in the following tabulation:

	Radians	Degrees	Revolutions
1.	2.5		
2.			0.75
3.		1,000	
4.		2,000	
5.			400
6.	100		
7.	400π		
8.		30	
9.		315	
10.	$3\pi/2$		

13.3 Angles in Standard Position

An angle is said to be drawn in standard position if, as in Fig. 13.3, it has its vertex at the origin of a system of rectangular coordinates and its initial side coincident with the positive side of the X axis. The terminal side of the angle may occupy any position in the coordinate plane, depending on the size of the angle.

13.4 Positive and Negative Angles

A positive angle is an angle generated by a counterclockwise rotation of the radius r as in Fig. 13.3.

A negative angle is an angle generated by a clockwise rotation of the radius r.

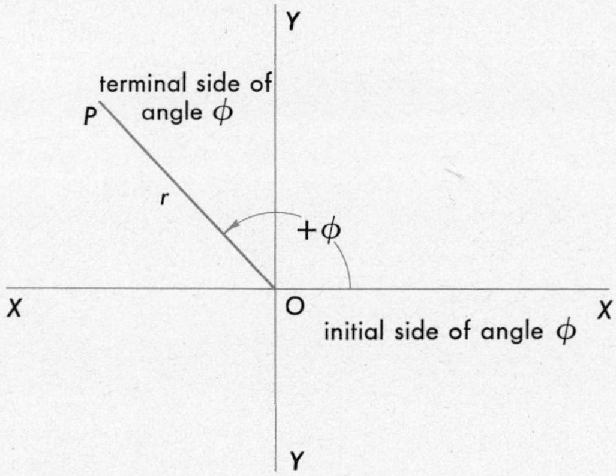

FIGURE 13.3

13.5 Angles of Any Magnitude

In the process of making one complete rotation, the radius r generates all angles in standard position between 0° and 360°. However, r may be made to continue its rotation through the 360° position and go around again, generating angles between 360° and 720°. During another revolution it would generate angles between 720° and 1080°, and so on indefinitely. See Fig. 13.4.

If two angles when placed in standard position have the same terminal side, they are said to be *coterminal* angles. Observe that the angles +30°, +390°, −330°, and −690° are therefore coterminal angles.

13.6 The Quadrants

The coordinate plane is divided into four parts, as shown in Fig. 13.5.

An angle drawn in standard position is said to be a first-, second-, third-, or fourth-quadrant angle as its terminal side lies in the first, second, third, or fourth quadrant, respectively. See Fig. 13.6 in which ϕ_1 is a first-quadrant angle, ϕ_2 is a second-quadrant angle, ϕ_3 is a third-quadrant angle and ϕ_4 is a fourth-quadrant angle.

13.7 The Definitions of the Trigonometric Functions

In Fig. 13.6 we let (x,y) be the coordinates of the point P. This point is on the terminal side of the angle at a distance $r = \sqrt{x^2 + y^2}$ from the origin.

We shall now define six quantities called the *trigonometric functions* of the angle ϕ. They are named the sine of ϕ, the cosine of ϕ, the tangent of ϕ, the cotangent of ϕ, the secant of ϕ, and the cosecant of ϕ. They are usually abbreviated to sin ϕ, cos ϕ,

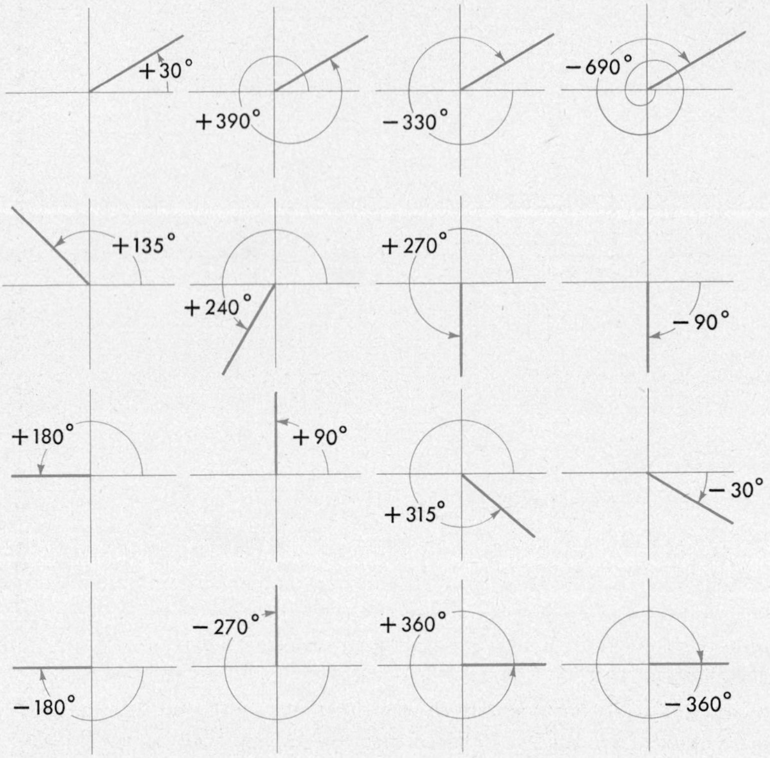

FIGURE 13.4

tan ϕ, cot ϕ, sec ϕ, and cosec ϕ, respectively. These functions of ϕ are defined in Table 13.1 with reference to Fig. 13.6.

13.8 The Signs of the Functions in Any Quadrant

Following the conventions of rectangular coordinates discussed in Sec. 6.4, when P is in the first or second quadrant, its ordinate is a positive number. When it is in the third or fourth quadrant, its ordinate is a negative number. When P is in the first or

TABLE 13.1

$\sin\phi = \frac{y}{r}$	$\cos\phi = \frac{x}{r}$	$\tan\phi = \frac{y}{x}$
$\cot\phi = \frac{x}{y}$	$\sec\phi = \frac{r}{x}$	$\csc\phi = \frac{r}{y}$

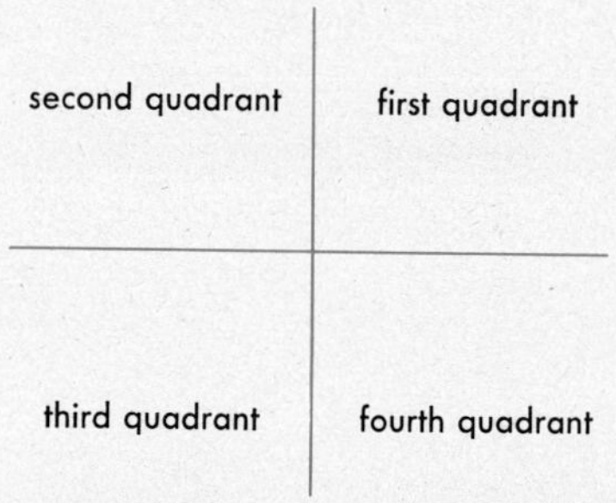

FIGURE 13.5

fourth quadrant, its abscissa is a positive number. When it is in the second or third quadrant, its abscissa is a negative number. These relations are indicated in Fig. 13.6e, where the + or − sign indicates whether the corresponding coordinate is a positive or a negative number, respectively. The length r is always a positive number and is so designated in the drawing.

By recalling the definitions of the functions from Table 13.1 and the sign conventions from Fig. 13.6, we may construct Table 13.2. In Table 13.2 the + and − signs indicate positive and negative numbers, respectively.

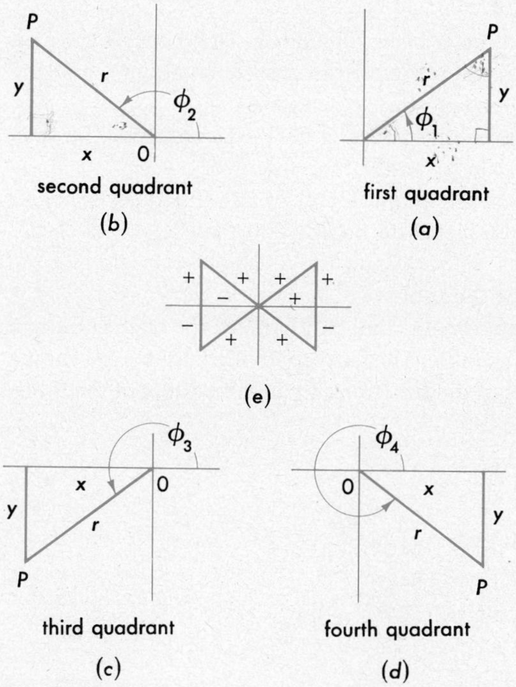

FIGURE 13.6

TABLE 13.2

Function	First quadrant	Second quadrant	Third quadrant	Fourth quadrant
$\sin = \frac{y}{r}$	$\frac{+}{+} = +$	$\frac{+}{+} = +$	$\frac{-}{+} = -$	$\frac{-}{+} = -$
$\cos = \frac{x}{r}$	$\frac{+}{+} = +$	$\frac{-}{+} = -$	$\frac{-}{+} = -$	$\frac{+}{+} = +$
$\tan = \frac{y}{x}$	$\frac{+}{+} = +$	$\frac{+}{-} = -$	$\frac{-}{-} = +$	$\frac{-}{+} = -$
$\cot = \frac{x}{y}$	$\frac{+}{+} = +$	$\frac{-}{+} = -$	$\frac{-}{-} = +$	$\frac{+}{-} = -$
$\sec = \frac{r}{x}$	$\frac{+}{+} = +$	$\frac{+}{-} = -$	$\frac{+}{-} = -$	$\frac{+}{+} = +$
$\csc = \frac{r}{y}$	$\frac{+}{+} = +$	$\frac{+}{+} = +$	$\frac{+}{-} = -$	$\frac{+}{-} = -$

13.9 Trigonometric Tables

The values of all functions of any angle have been calculated. The theory by which these calculations were made is beyond the scope of the present treatment, and the arithmetical work involved is too cumbersome for everyday use.

Table 1, beginning on page 843, gives the values of each trigonometric function to five significant digits for angles between 0° and 90° by minutes.

Table 13.3, shown here, is an excerpt from that table. To find functions of angles between 0° and 45°, look for the degrees shown in boldface at the upper left corner of the table. The corresponding minutes are shown in the left-hand column, and the names of the functions are at the top of the table.

To find the functions of angles between 45° and 90°, look for the degrees shown in boldface at the lower right corner of the table. The corresponding minutes are shown in the right-hand column, and the names of the functions are at the bottom of the table.

EXERCISE 4

From Table 13.3 verify the following.

1. $\sin 40°04' = 0.64368$
2. $\cos 49°56' = 0.64368$
3. $\tan 40°59' = 0.86878$
4. $\cot 49°01' = 0.86878$
5. $\sin 49°50' = 0.76417$
6. $\cos 40°10' = 0.76417$
7. $\cot 40°48' = 1.1585$
8. $\tan 49°12' = 1.1585$
9. $\sec 49°09' = 1.5289$
10. $\text{cosec}\ 40°51' = 1.5289$

Find the values of the six functions of the following acute angles from five-place tables.

11. 20°30′ 12. 40°27′ 13. 44°59′ 14. 45°01′
15. 25°45′ 16. 60°42′ 17. 80°28′ 18. 42°38′
19. 00°10′ 20. 89°30′ 21. 13°25′ 22. 48°05′
23. 55°55′ 24. 81°36′ 25. 01°45′

Find the acute angle whose functions are given below.

26. $\sin A = 0.00582$
27. $\sin A = 0.18052$
28. $\sin A = 0.68179$
29. $\sin A = 0.75414$
30. $\sin A = 0.99986$
31. $\cos A = 0.71873$
32. $\cos A = 0.54708$
33. $\cos A = 0.93190$
34. $\cos A = 0.16906$
35. $\cos A = 0.99854$
36. $\tan A = 0.06993$
37. $\tan A = 1.2124$
38. $\tan A = 0.46312$
39. $\tan A = 1.4596$

TABLE 13.3

40° (220°) (319°) **139°**

′	Sin	Tan	Ctn	Cos	Sec	Csc	′
0	.64279	.83910	1.1918	.76604	1.3054	1.5557	60
1	.64301	.83960	1.1910	.76586	1.3057	1.5552	59
2	.64323	.84009	1.1903	.76567	1.3060	1.5546	58
3	.64346	.84059	1.1896	.76548	1.3064	1.5541	57
4	.64368	.84108	1.1889	.76530	1.3067	1.5536	56
5	.64390	.84158	1.1882	.76511	1.3070	1.5530	55
6	.64412	.84208	1.1875	.76492	1.3073	1.5525	54
7	.64435	.84258	1.1868	.76473	1.3076	1.5520	53
8	.64457	.84307	1.1861	.76455	1.3080	1.5514	52
9	.64479	.84357	1.1854	.76436	1.3083	1.5509	51
10	.64501	.84407	1.1847	.76417	1.3086	1.5504	50
11	.64524	.84457	1.1840	.76398	1.3089	1.5498	49
12	.64546	.84507	1.1833	.76380	1.3093	1.5493	48
13	.64568	.84556	1.1826	.76361	1.3096	1.5488	47
14	.64590	.84606	1.1819	.76342	1.3099	1.5482	46
15	.64612	.84656	1.1812	.76323	1.3102	1.5477	45
42	.65210	.86014	1.1626	.75813	1.3190	1.5335	18
43	.65232	.86064	1.1619	.75794	1.3194	1.5330	17
44	.65254	.86115	1.1612	.75775	1.3197	1.5325	16
45	.65276	.86166	1.1606	.75756	1.3200	1.5320	15
46	.65298	.86216	1.1599	.75738	1.3203	1.5314	14
47	.65320	.86267	1.1592	.75719	1.3207	1.5309	13
48	.65342	.86318	1.1585	.75700	1.3210	1.5304	12
49	.65364	.86368	1.1578	.75680	1.3213	1.5299	11
50	.65386	.86419	1.1571	.75661	1.3217	1.5294	10
51	.65408	.86470	1.1565	.75642	1.3220	1.5289	9
52	.65430	.86521	1.1558	.75623	1.3223	1.5283	8
53	.65452	.86572	1.1551	.75604	1.3227	1.5278	7
54	.65474	.86623	1.1544	.75585	1.3230	1.5273	6
55	.65496	.86674	1.1538	.75566	1.3233	1.5268	5
56	.65518	.86725	1.1531	.75547	1.3237	1.5263	4
57	.65540	.86776	1.1524	.75528	1.3240	1.5258	3
58	.65562	.86827	1.1517	.75509	1.3243	1.5253	2
59	.65584	.86878	1.1510	.75490	1.3247	1.5248	1
60	.65606	.86929	1.1504	.75471	1.3250	1.5243	0
′	Cos	Ctn	Tan	Sin	Csc	Sec	′

130° (310°) (229°) **49°**

40. $\tan A = 0.90251$
41. $\cot A = 0.89883$
42. $\cot A = 1.7917$
43. $\cot A = 2.1364$
44. $\cot A = 0.62487$
45. $\cot A = 5.0658$
46. $\sec A = 1.0193$
47. $\sec A = 2.6040$
48. $\sec A = 1.2265$
49. $\sec A = 1.5601$
50. $\sec A = 1.4755$
51. $\operatorname{cosec} A = 1.5212$
52. $\operatorname{cosec} A = 1.2215$
53. $\operatorname{cosec} A = 2.0466$
54. $\operatorname{cosec} A = 6.1880$
55. $\operatorname{cosec} A = 11.105$

13.10 Evaluating the Functions of Any Angle

Thus far we have used the tables for evaluating functions of acute angles only.

Now we shall see how to use these same tables for evaluating functions of any nonquadrantal† angle, whether acute or not.

In Fig. 13.7, r and the coordinates of P have the specific values shown. By inspection, then, the triangles OPQ are congruent for all four quadrants. Thus the acute angle A is the same for all quadrants.

The acute angle A is called the *associated acute angle* and is associated with the angles ϕ_1, ϕ_2, ϕ_3, and ϕ_4 in the following ways.

In the first quadrant,

$$A = \phi_1 \tag{10}$$

Thus, in the first quadrant, ϕ_1 is its own associated acute angle.

In the second quadrant,

$$A = 180° - \phi_2 \tag{11}$$

In the third quadrant,

$$A = \phi_3 - 180° \tag{12}$$

In the fourth quadrant,

$$A = 360° - \phi_4 \tag{13}$$

In Fig. 13.7, the six functions of angles ϕ_1, ϕ_2, ϕ_3, and ϕ_4 have been calculated and tabulated from the data given in the drawing. Now let us compare these tabulations. First, we note that the absolute values of the same-named functions of ϕ_1, ϕ_2, ϕ_3, and

†Quadrantal angles are the angles 0°, 90°, 180°, 270° and all angles having the same terminal sides as any of these.

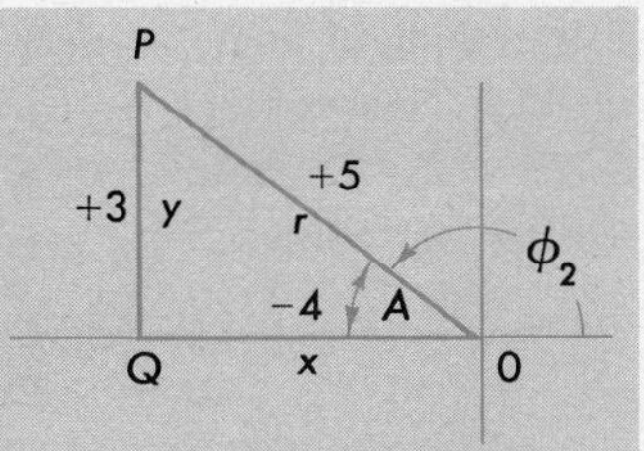

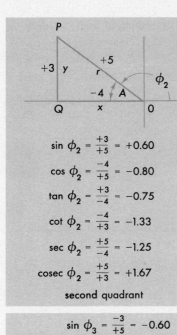

$\sin \phi_2 = \frac{+3}{+5} = +0.60$

$\cos \phi_2 = \frac{-4}{+5} = -0.80$

$\tan \phi_2 = \frac{+3}{-4} = -0.75$

$\cot \phi_2 = \frac{-4}{+3} = -1.33$

$\sec \phi_2 = \frac{+5}{-4} = -1.25$

$\operatorname{cosec} \phi_2 = \frac{+5}{+3} = +1.67$

second quadrant

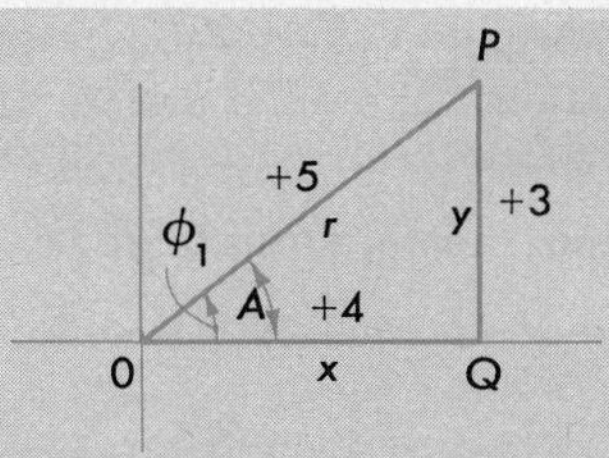

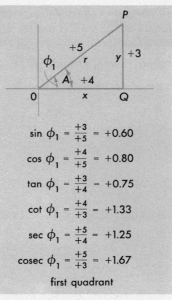

$\sin \phi_1 = \frac{+3}{+5} = +0.60$

$\cos \phi_1 = \frac{+4}{+5} = +0.80$

$\tan \phi_1 = \frac{+3}{+4} = +0.75$

$\cot \phi_1 = \frac{+4}{+3} = +1.33$

$\sec \phi_1 = \frac{+5}{+4} = +1.25$

$\operatorname{cosec} \phi_1 = \frac{+5}{+3} = +1.67$

first quadrant

$\sin \phi_3 = \frac{-3}{+5} = -0.60$

$\cos \phi_3 = \frac{-4}{+5} = -0.80$

$\tan \phi_3 = \frac{-3}{-4} = +0.75$

$\cot \phi_3 = \frac{-4}{-3} = +1.33$

$\sec \phi_3 = \frac{+5}{-4} = -1.25$

$\operatorname{cosec} \phi_3 = \frac{+5}{-3} = -1.67$

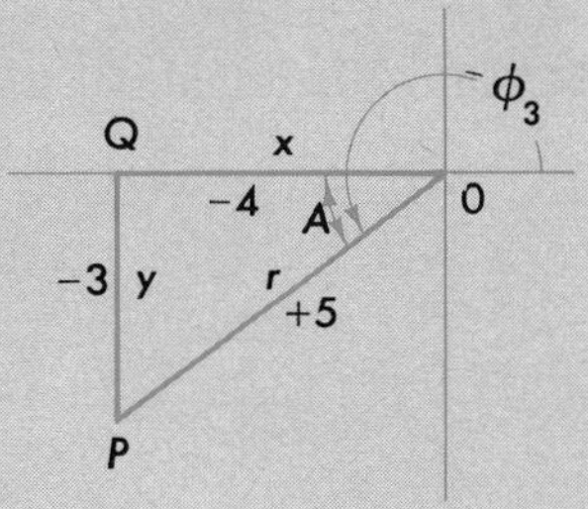

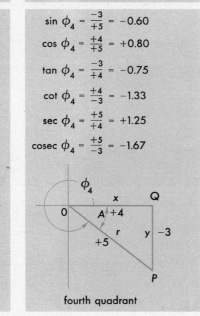

third quadrant

$\sin \phi_4 = \frac{-3}{+5} = -0.60$

$\cos \phi_4 = \frac{+4}{+5} = +0.80$

$\tan \phi_4 = \frac{-3}{+4} = -0.75$

$\cot \phi_4 = \frac{+4}{-3} = -1.33$

$\sec \phi_4 = \frac{+5}{+4} = +1.25$

$\operatorname{cosec} \phi_4 = \frac{+5}{-3} = -1.67$

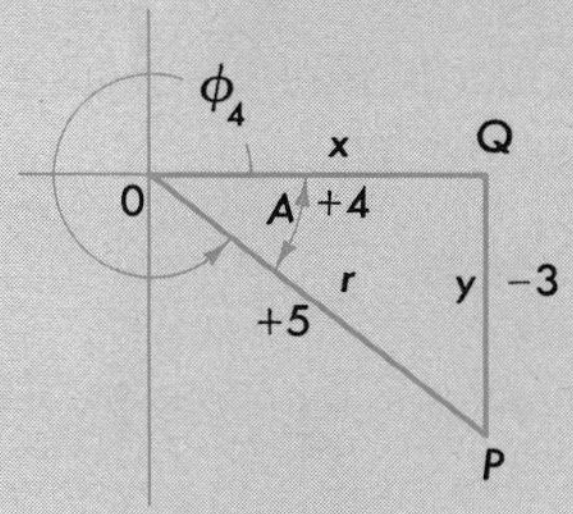

fourth quadrant

FIGURE 13.7

ϕ_4 are identical with absolute values of the respective functions of angle A. Second, the *signs* of these functions follow the pattern of Table 13.2. Therefore

To find a function of any nonquadrantal angle, we proceed as follows:

1. *Find the associated acute angle.*
2. *Find the value of the required function of the associated acute angle from a table of the trigonometric functions.*
3. *Attach the proper algebraic sign.*

Example 9. Find the cosine of 115°.

1. The angle 115° is a second-quadrant angle. From Eq. (11) we find that the associated acute angle A is given by

$$A = 180° - 115° = 65°$$

2. From a table of trigonometric functions we find that

$$\cos 65° = 0.42262$$

3. From Table 13.2 we find that the cosine of a second-quadrant angle is a negative number. Thus

$$\cos 115° = -0.42262$$

Example 10. Find the sine of 295°45′.

1. The angle 295°45′ is a fourth-quadrant angle. From Eq. (13) we find that the associated acute angle A is given by

$$A = 360° - 295°45' = 64°15'$$

2. From a table of trigonometric functions we find that

$$\sin 64°15' = 0.90070$$

3. From Table 13.2 we find that the sine of a fourth-quadrant angle is a negative number. Thus

$$\sin 295°45' = -0.90070$$

Example 11. Find the sine of $244°15'$.

1. The angle $244°15'$ is a third-quadrant angle. From Eq. (12) we find that the associated acute angle A is given by

   $$A = 244°15' - 180° = 64°15'$$

2. From a table of trigonometric functions we find that

   $$\sin 64°15' = 0.90070$$

3. From Table 13.2 we find that the sine of a third-quadrant angle is a negative number. Thus

   $$\sin 244°15' = -0.90070$$

Example 12. Find the tangent of $236°28'$.

1. The angle $236°28'$ is a third-quadrant angle. From Eq. (12) we find that the associated acute angle A is given by

   $$A = 236°28' - 180° = 56°28'$$

2. From a table of trigonometric functions we find that

   $$\tan 56°28' = 1.5089$$

3. From Table 13.2 we find that the tangent of a third-quadrant angle is a positive number. Thus

   $$\tan 236°28' = 1.5089$$

EXERCISE 5

Find the six trigonometric functions of the following angles to five significant digits.

1. $140°$	2. $170°$	3. $95°30'$
4. $234°13'$	5. $246°30'$	6. $194°32'$
7. $355°09'$	8. $280°10'$	9. $359°40'$

13.11 Finding Angles When One of Their Functions Is Given

In general, there are two positive angles less than $360°$, each having the same value of a given trigonometric function. For instance, in Example 10 we found that the sine of 295°45′ is −0.90070. In Example 11 we found that the sine of 244°15′ is also −0.90070. Thus, if $\sin \phi = -0.90070$, then $\phi = 295°45'$, or $\phi = 244°15'$. It is important to note that the same acute angle is associated with both values of ϕ.

If a function of an unknown angle (or angles) is given, we know from Sec. 13.10 that the numerical (absolute) value of that function is equal to the value of the same-named function of the associated acute angle. Thus,

To find the angles having a given function, we proceed as follows:

1. *Find the numerical (absolute) value of the given function.*
2. *From a table of the trigonometric functions find the associated acute angle A.*
3. *From the sign of the given function determine by Table 13.2 the quadrants in which the unknown angles lie.*

Example 13. If $\sin \phi = 0.86310$, find all positive values of ϕ less than 360°.

1. The numerical value of the given function is 0.86310. Thus

$$\sin A = 0.86310$$

2. From a table of trigonometric functions

$$A = 59°40'$$

3. Since the sine of the unknown angles ϕ is positive, one angle must be a first-quadrant angle and the other must be a second-quadrant angle.
4. From Eqs. (10) and (11)

$$\phi_1 = 59°40'$$

and

$$\phi_2 = 180° - 59°40' = 120°20'$$

Example 14. If $\sin \phi = -0.58519$, find all positive values of ϕ less than 360°.

1. The numerical value of the given function is 0.58519. Thus

$$\sin A = 0.58519.$$

2. From a table of trigonometric functions

$$A = 35°49'$$

3. Since the sine of the unknown angles ϕ is negative, one angle must be a third-quadrant angle and the other must be a fourth-quadrant angle.
4. From Eqs. (12) and (13)

$$\phi_3 = 180° + 35°49' = 215°49'$$

and

$$\phi_4 = 360° - 35°49' = 324°11'$$

Example 15. If $\cos \phi = 0.94495$, find all positive values of ϕ less than 360°.

1. The numerical value of the given function is 0.94495. Thus

$$\cos A = 0.94495$$

2. From a table of trigonometric functions

$$A = 19°06'$$

3. Since the cosine of the unknown angles ϕ is positive, one angle must be a first-quadrant angle and the other must be a fourth-quadrant angle.
4. From Eqs. (10) and (13),

$$\phi_1 = 19°06'$$

and

$$\phi_4 = 360° - 19°06' = 340°54'$$

EXERCISE 6

Find two positive angles ϕ less than 360° which have each of the functions listed below.

1. $\sin \phi = 0.00582$
2. $\sin \phi = -0.18052$
3. $\sin \phi = 0.68179$
4. $\sin \phi = 0.75414$
5. $\sin \phi = -0.99986$
6. $\cos \phi = 0.71873$
7. $\cos \phi = 0.54708$
8. $\cos \phi = -0.93190$
9. $\cos \phi = -0.16906$
10. $\cos \phi = 0.99854$
11. $\tan \phi = 0.06993$
12. $\tan \phi = -1.2124$
13. $\tan \phi = 0.46312$
14. $\tan \phi = 1.4596$
15. $\tan \phi = -0.90251$
16. $\cot \phi = 0.89883$

17. $\cot\phi = 1.7917$
18. $\cot\phi = -2.1364$
19. $\cot\phi = -0.62487$
20. $\cot\phi = 5.0658$
21. $\sec\phi = 1.0193$
22. $\sec\phi = 2.6040$
23. $\sec\phi = 1.2265$
24. $\sec\phi = -1.5601$
25. $\sec\phi = -1.4755$
26. $\operatorname{cosec}\phi = 1.5212$
27. $\operatorname{cosec}\phi = 1.2215$
28. $\operatorname{cosec}\phi = -2.0466$
29. $\operatorname{cosec}\phi = -6.1880$
30. $\operatorname{cosec}\phi = 11.105$

13.12 The Functions of 0°

When $\phi = 0°$ as in Fig. 13.8, $y = 0$ and $x = r$; therefore,

$$\sin 0° = \frac{y}{r} = \frac{0}{r} = 0$$

$$\cos 0° = \frac{x}{r} = \frac{r}{r} = +1$$

$$\tan 0° = \frac{y}{x} = \frac{0}{x} = 0$$

$$\sec 0° = \frac{r}{x} = \frac{r}{r} = +1$$

The cotangent and the cosecant of zero degrees do not exist, since a calculation of them involves a division by zero. However, if ϕ is a very small positive angle, then y will be a very small linear dimension, and both the cotangent and cosecant will be large numbers. The smaller ϕ is made while still positive, the larger the cotangent and cosecant become.

13.13 The Functions of 90°

When $\phi = 90°$ as in Fig. 13.9, $x = 0$ and $y = r$. Thus

$$\sin 90° = \frac{y}{r} = \frac{r}{r} = +1$$

$$\cos 90° = \frac{x}{r} = \frac{0}{r} = 0$$

$$\cot 90° = \frac{x}{y} = \frac{0}{y} = 0$$

$$\csc 90° = \frac{r}{y} = \frac{r}{r} = +1$$

Here the tangent and the secant do not exist. But if ϕ is slightly less than 90°, the tangent and secant are enormously large numbers. The closer ϕ approaches 90° while remaining in the first quadrant, the larger the tangent and secant become.

It is important to observe that if ϕ is made ever so slightly greater than 90°, the signs of the tangent and secant change and become negative. The tangent and secant would then be extremely large in absolute value but negative in sign.

If the angle ϕ approaches 90° from the second quadrant, the tangent decreases without limit. If the angle ϕ approaches 90° from the first quadrant, the tangent increases without limit.

13.14 The Functions of 180°

When $\phi = 180°$ as in Fig. 13.10, $y = 0$ and $x = -r$. Thus

$$\sin 180° = \frac{y}{r} = \frac{0}{r} = 0$$

$$\cos 180° = \frac{x}{r} = \frac{-r}{r} = -1$$

$$\tan 180° = \frac{y}{x} = \frac{0}{x} = 0$$

$$\sec 180° = \frac{r}{x} = \frac{r}{-r} = -1$$

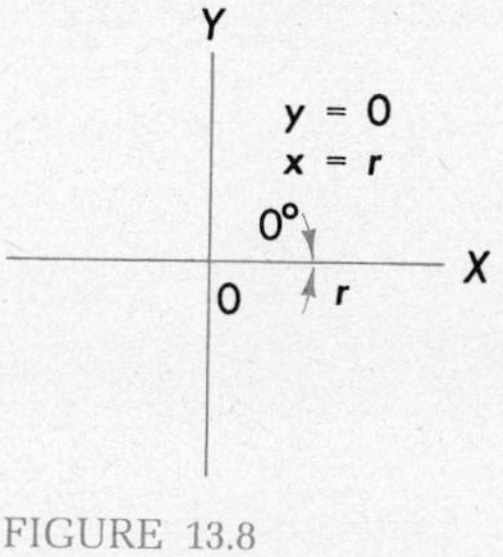

FIGURE 13.8

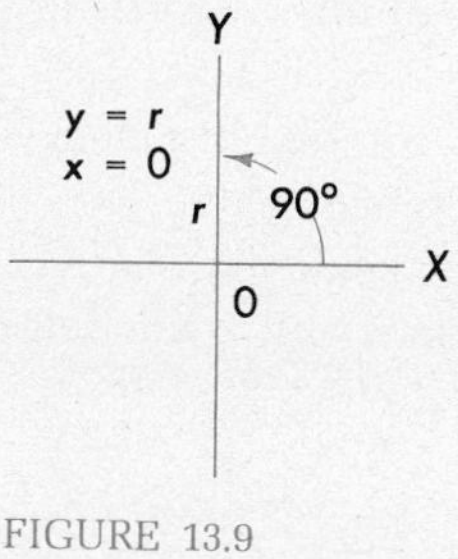

FIGURE 13.9

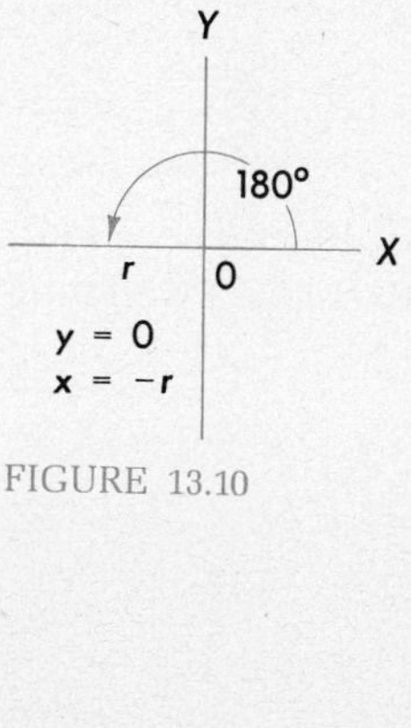

FIGURE 13.10

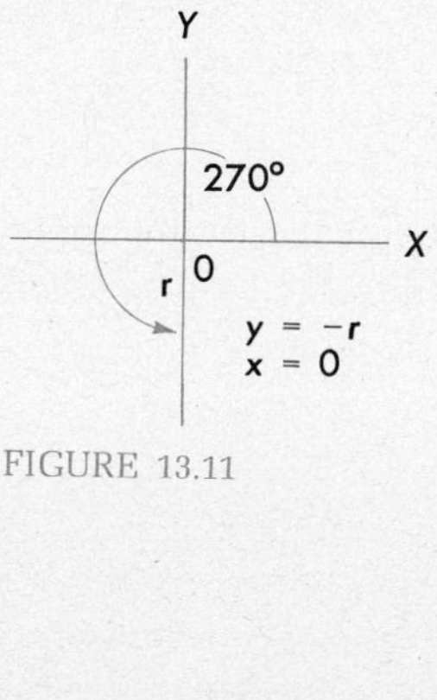

FIGURE 13.11

The cotangent and cosecant of 180° do not exist since each involves a division by zero in this case.

13.15 The Functions of 270° and 360°

It is left to the student to verify the following equations by consulting Figs. 13.8 and 13.11:

$\sin 270^\circ = -1$	$\sin 360^\circ = 0$
$\cos 270^\circ = 0$	$\cos 360^\circ = 1$
$\tan 270^\circ$ does not exist	$\tan 360^\circ = 0$
$\cot 270^\circ = 0$	$\cot 360^\circ$ does not exist
$\sec 270^\circ$ does not exist	$\sec 360^\circ = 1$
$\csc 270^\circ = -1$	$\csc 360^\circ$ does not exist

13.16 The Functions of Angles Greater Than 360° and Less Than 0°

Suppose the radius r were initially at any given position in the coordinate plane. Then let it be rotated an integral multiple of 360° in either direction. It would then come to rest exactly coincident with its original position.

Therefore the values of the functions of the reference angle after this rotation would be exactly the same as the values of the functions of the initial reference angle.

Each 360° rotation in a counterclockwise direction is equivalent to adding 360° to the original reference angle. Each 360° rotation in a clockwise direction is equivalent to subtracting 360° from the initial reference angle.

Now suppose we wish to find the cosine of 2,635°. This angle can be expressed not only in degrees, but also in revolutions and a fraction thereof. Thus

$$2{,}635^\circ = \frac{2{,}635}{360} = 7 + \frac{115}{360} \text{ revolutions}$$

That is,

$$2{,}635^\circ = 7 \text{ revolutions} + 115^\circ$$

and all the functions of 2,635° are identical with the same-named functions of 115°. The cosine of 2,635° is therefore equal to the cosine of 115°. In Example 9 we found that

$$\cos 115^\circ = -0.42262$$

Therefore

$$\cos 2{,}635^\circ = -0.42262$$

Similarly, the angle -605° can be expressed as

$$-605^\circ = \frac{-605}{360} = -1 \text{ revolution} - 245^\circ$$

but an angle of -245° has the same functions as an angle of $360^\circ - 245^\circ = 115^\circ$.
From Example 9 we find that

$$\cos 115^\circ = -0.42262$$

Therefore

$$\cos(-605^\circ) = -0.42262$$

13.17 Variations in the Functions

As the radius r rotates from the initial position through the first quadrant to the 90° position, the sine of the angle ϕ increases from 0 to 1. In the second quadrant the sine decreases from 1 at the 90° position to 0 at the 180° position. In the third quadrant, the sine decreases from 0 to -1, and in the fourth quadrant it increases from -1 to 0.

In a like manner the variations in the other five functions can be traced.

EXERCISE 7

1. Write the sine of 0°, 30°, 45°, 60°, 90°, 120°, 135°, 150°, 180°, 210°, 225°, 240°, 270°, 300°, 315°, 330°, and 360° in decimals, using proper signs.
2. In which quadrants does the sine increase as the radius vector rotates counterclockwise? In which quadrant does the cosine increase? The tangent? The cotangent? The secant? The cosecant?
3. Within what numerical limits can the sine, the cosine, the tangent, the cotangent, the secant, and the cosecant exist?
4. What are the maximum and minimum values of each of the six functions?
5. Sketch a graph of each function with the value of the function plotted vertically against the angle plotted horizontally. Plot the graph between -360° and $+360^\circ$.
6. Find the sine of 15°, 375°, 735°, 1,095°, 1,455°.
7. Find the cosine of 135°, -225°, -585°, -945°.

14 the solution of triangles

In this chapter we shall discuss the application of the topics in Chap. 13 to the numerical solution of right and oblique triangles.

14.1 The Right Triangle

For the solution of right triangles it will be convenient to define the functions of the acute angles in terms of the hypotenuse and the two sides.

Figure 14.1 shows a right triangle whose sides are designated by a, b, and c. The side c designates the hypotenuse, and the angle C designates the right angle. The side a is opposite angle A and adjacent to the angle B. The side b is adjacent to the angle A and opposite the angle B.

Now let us place the triangle ABC in Fig. 14.1 on a rectangular coordinate system (see Fig. 14.2) with the angle A in standard position such that side b is on the X axis. The sides b and a then represent, respectively, the abscissa and the ordinate of the vertex point of angle B. Then from the definitions of the trigonometric functions given in Table 13.1, we may form Table 14.1.

The definitions shown in Table 14.1 are of course independent of any particular coordinate system. Also the designations "opposite side" and "adjacent side" may refer to either acute angle. See Table 14.2 and Fig. 14.3 in which the functions of angle B are explicitly stated.

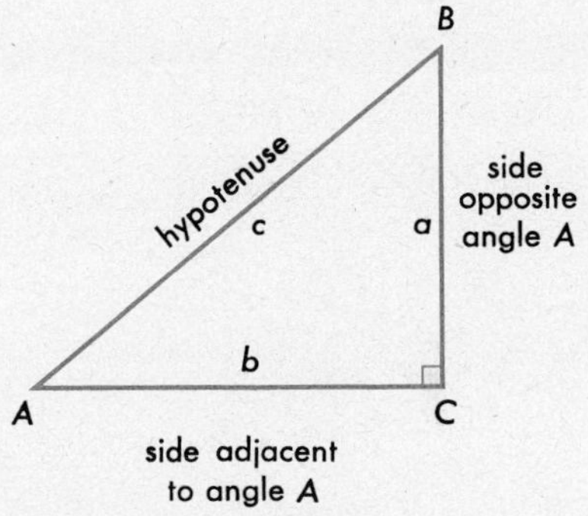

FIGURE 14.1

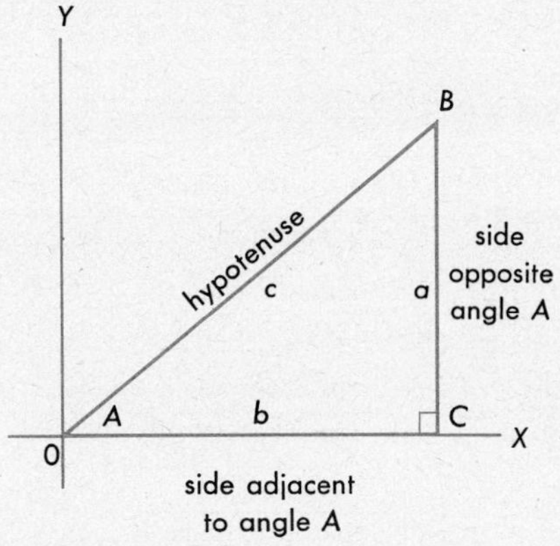

FIGURE 14.2

14.2 The Cofunctions

The word *cosine*, for example, means the sine of the complementary angle. In general, a cofunction is the function of the complementary angle. One angle is said to be the complement of another if their sum is 90°. In a right triangle the two acute angles are always complementary.

From Eqs. (1) through (12) the student should verify the following relations:

$\sin A = \cos B$	$\cot A = \tan B$
$\cos A = \sin B$	$\sec A = \csc B$
$\tan A = \cot B$	$\csc A = \sec B$

TABLE 14.1

$$\sin A = \frac{\text{side opposite angle } A}{\text{hypotenuse}} = \frac{a}{c} \tag{1}$$

$$\cos A = \frac{\text{side adjacent to angle } A}{\text{hypotenuse}} = \frac{b}{c} \tag{2}$$

$$\tan A = \frac{\text{side opposite angle } A}{\text{side adjacent to angle } A} = \frac{a}{b} \tag{3}$$

$$\cot A = \frac{\text{side adjacent to angle } A}{\text{side opposite angle } A} = \frac{b}{a} \tag{4}$$

$$\sec A = \frac{\text{hypotenuse}}{\text{side adjacent to angle } A} = \frac{c}{b} \tag{5}$$

$$\csc A = \frac{\text{hypotenuse}}{\text{side opposite angle } A} = \frac{c}{a} \tag{6}$$

TABLE 14.2

$$\sin B = \frac{\text{side opposite angle } B}{\text{hypotenuse}} = \frac{b}{c} \tag{7}$$

$$\cos B = \frac{\text{side adjacent to angle } B}{\text{hypotenuse}} = \frac{a}{c} \tag{8}$$

$$\tan B = \frac{\text{side opposite angle } B}{\text{side adjacent to angle } B} = \frac{b}{a} \tag{9}$$

$$\cot B = \frac{\text{side adjacent to angle } B}{\text{side opposite angle } B} = \frac{a}{b} \tag{10}$$

$$\sec B = \frac{\text{hypotenuse}}{\text{side adjacent to angle } B} = \frac{c}{a} \tag{11}$$

$$\csc B = \frac{\text{hypotenuse}}{\text{side opposite angle } B} = \frac{c}{b} \tag{12}$$

EXERCISE 1

Express as functions of the complementary angle the following:

1. $\sin 20°$
2. $\cos 45°$
3. $\cos 60°$
4. $\tan 25°$
5. $\cot 17°$
6. $\sec 84°$
7. $\cos 38.5°$
8. $\csc 80°$
9. $\sec 25°$

14.3 Reciprocal Functions

Referring to Sec. 14.1 and Table 14.1,

$$\sin A = \frac{a}{c} \qquad \text{and} \qquad \csc A = \frac{c}{a}$$

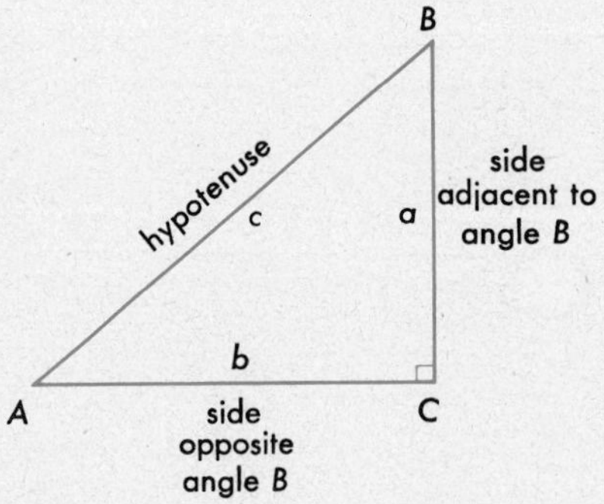

FIGURE 14.3

Therefore

$$\sin A \times \csc A = \frac{a}{c} \times \frac{c}{a} = 1$$

or

$$\sin A = \frac{1}{\csc A} \qquad \text{and} \qquad \csc A = \frac{1}{\sin A}$$

Also

$$\tan A = \frac{a}{b} \qquad \text{and} \qquad \cot A = \frac{b}{a}$$

Therefore

$$\tan A \times \cot A = \frac{a}{b} \times \frac{b}{a} = 1$$

or

$$\tan A = \frac{1}{\cot A} \qquad \text{and} \qquad \cot A = \frac{1}{\tan A}$$

Also

$$\cos A = \frac{b}{c} \qquad \text{and} \qquad \sec A = \frac{c}{b}$$

Therefore

$$\cos A \times \sec A = \frac{b}{c} \times \frac{c}{b} = 1$$

or

$$\cos A = \frac{1}{\sec A} \qquad \text{and} \qquad \sec A = \frac{1}{\cos A}$$

It is apparent, then, that:

1. *The sine of an angle is the reciprocal of the cosecant of the same angle.*
2. *The cosine of an angle is the reciprocal of the secant of the same angle.*
3. *The tangent of an angle is the reciprocal of the cotangent of the same angle.*

14.4 Suggestions for Solving Right Triangles Using Tables of Natural Functions

In Sec. 13.9 we described a table in which we find the values of the trigonometric functions of a given angle. We call this sort of a table a table of *natural functions* to distinguish it from a similar table giving the *logarithms* of the functions. We will discuss these tables in Sec. 14.7.

In the examples given below the student should understand that all given linear dimensions are known to five significant digits and that all given angles are known to the nearest second.

The labor of solving triangles can be reduced considerably by intelligently choosing a method of attack. The student will be well advised to consider the suggestions given.

As a rule, it is better to use the formula in which the unknown side appears in the numerator. For example, suppose we are to solve the triangle in which $c = 15$ and $A = 42°$. First let us find side a. We write the fraction a/c and then check Eqs. (1) to (6), looking for the fraction a/c. We find that $a/c = \sin A$, and we shall use this formula. There is another formula which would, theoretically, be just as good: $c/a = \csc A$. However, in solving for a, the first equation leads to a multiplication, while the second leads to a division. Usually, the one involving a multiplication is easier to use than the one involving a division.

When we have two sides given and wish to find a trigonometric function by division, it is best to choose the formula which places the number with the fewest significant digits in the denominator. This usually leads to an easier division.

It is always well to examine the data to see if a given decimal fraction can profitably be converted to a common fraction.

Suppose that in Fig. 14.4 the data are given as shown and the angle ϕ is to be calculated. There are two choices: either the tangent or the cotangent of ϕ may be calculated. If the tangent of ϕ is calculated, the operation involves the division of a three-figure number (0.625) by a five-figure number (1.3795); if the cotangent is calculated, the operation involves the division of a five-figure number by a three-figure number. The arithmetic will be easier in calculating the cotangent. In this particular problem there is a still easier method if the student recognizes that 0.625 is the decimal equivalent of $\frac{5}{8}$. The arithmetic can now be reduced to a multiplication by 8 and a division by 5, as shown:

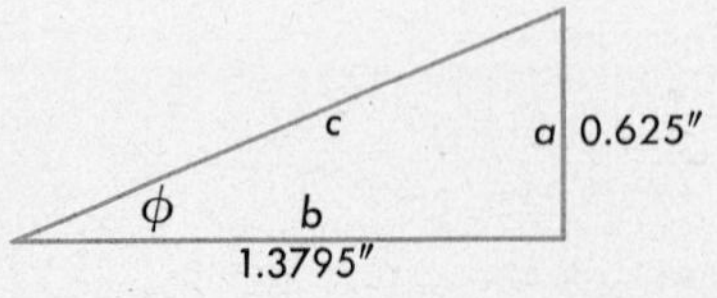

FIGURE 14.4

$$\cot \phi = \frac{1.3795}{5/8} = \frac{1.3795 \times 8}{5} = \frac{11.036}{5} = 2.2072$$

Example 1. Referring to Fig. 14.2, if $c = 22.000'$ and $A = 28°32'$, find B, a, and b.

$$B = 90° - 28°32' = 61°28'$$

According to Eq. (1),

$$a = c \sin A = 22 \sin 28°32'$$
$$= 22 \times 0.47767 = 10.509 \text{ in}$$

Following Eq. (2)

$$b = c \cos A = 22 \cos 28°32'$$
$$= 22 \times 0.87854 = 19.328 \text{ in}$$

Example 2. Referring to Fig. 14.2, if $a = 19.000''$ and $A = 62°27'$, find B, b, and c.

$$B = 90° - 62°27' = 27°33'$$

Following Eq. (6),

$$c = a \csc A = 19 \csc 62°27'$$
$$= 19 \times 1.1279 = 21.430 \text{ in}$$

Following Eq. (4),

$$b = a \cot A = 19 \cot 62°27'$$
$$= 19 \times 0.52168 = 9.9119 \text{ in}$$

Example 3. Referring to Fig. 14.2, if $b = 26.000''$ and $A = 15°48'$, find B, a, and c.

$$B = 90° - 15°48' = 74°12'$$

Following Eq. (3),

$$a = b \tan A = 26 \tan 15°48'$$
$$= 26 \times 0.28297 = 7.3572 \text{ in}$$

Following Eq. (5),

$$c = b \sec A = 26 \sec 15°48'$$
$$= 26 \times 1.0393 = 27.022 \text{ in}$$

Example 4. Referring to Fig. 14.3, if $a = 45.000''$ and $B = 24°00'$, find A, b, and c.

$$A = 90° - 24° = 66°$$

Following Eq. (9),

$$b = a \tan B = 45 \tan 24°$$
$$= 45 \times 0.44523 = 20.035 \text{ in}$$

Following Eq. (11),

$$c = a \sec B = 45 \sec 24°$$
$$= 45 \times 1.0946 = 49.257 \text{ in}$$

Example 5. Referring to Fig. 14.3, if $b = 75.000''$ and $B = 85°00'$, find A, a, and c.

$$A = 90° - 85° = 5°$$

Following Eq. (10),

$$a = b \cot B = 75 \cot 85°$$
$$= 75 \times 0.08749 = 6.5618 \text{ in}$$

Following Eq. (12),

$$c = b \csc B = 75 \csc 85°$$
$$= 75 \times 1.0038 = 75.285 \text{ in}$$

Example 6. Referring to Fig. 14.3, if $c = 65.000''$ and $B = 8°00'$, find A, a, and b.

$$A = 90° - 8° = 82°$$

Following Eq. (8),

$$a = c \cos B = 65 \cos 8°$$
$$= 65 \times 0.99027 = 64.368 \text{ in}$$

Following Eq. (7),

$$b = c \sin B = 65 \sin 8°$$
$$= 65 \times 0.13917 = 9.0460 \text{ in}$$

Example 7. Referring to Fig. 14.2, if $b = 578.00''$ and $a = 483.00''$, find A, B, and c.
Following Eq. (3),

$$\tan A = \frac{a}{b} = \frac{483}{578} = 0.83564 \qquad \text{(to five figures)}$$

and

$$A = 39°53'$$

Following Eq. (5),

$$c = b \sec A = 578 \sec 39°53' = 578 \times 1.3032 = 753.25 \text{ in}$$

or following Eq. (6),

$$c = a \csc A = 483 \csc 39°53' = 483 \times 1.5595 = 753.24 \text{ in}$$

or following Eq. (1),

$$c = \frac{a}{\sin A} = \frac{483}{\sin 39°53'} = \frac{483}{0.64123} = 753.24 \text{ in}$$

or following Eq. (2),

$$c = \frac{b}{\cos A} = \frac{578}{\cos 39°53'} = \frac{578}{0.76735} = 753.24 \text{ in}$$

or using the Pythagorean theorem,

$$c = \sqrt{578^2 + 483^2} = \sqrt{567{,}373} = 753.24 \text{ in}$$

Example 8. Referring to Fig. 14.2, if $c = 1{,}237.0''$ and $a = 333.00''$, find A, B, and b.
Following Eq. (1),

$$\sin A = \frac{a}{c} = \frac{333}{1{,}237} = 0.26920 \qquad \text{(to five figures)}$$

and

$A = 15°37'$

or following Eq. (6),

$$\csc A = \frac{c}{a} = \frac{1{,}237}{333} = 3.7147 \qquad \text{(to five figures)}$$

and

$A = 15°37'$
$B = 90° - 15°37' = 74°23'$
$b = c \cos A = 1{,}237 \times \cos 15°37'$
$= 1{,}237 \times 0.96308 = 1{,}191.3 \text{ in}$

or

$$b = \sqrt{c^2 - a^2} = \sqrt{(1{,}237)^2 - (333)^2} = \sqrt{1{,}419{,}280} = 1{,}191.3 \text{ in}$$

EXERCISE 2

In the following right triangles find the unknown dimensions, using a five-place table. Calculate linear dimensions accurate to five figures and angles accurate to the nearest minute. The class may of course be instructed to round off both the data and the corresponding answers to whatever number of significant figures seems appropriate. In these problems all given linear dimensions are known to five significant digits, and all given angles are known to the nearest second.

1. $A = 36°14'$	$c = 94.309$ ft	2. $A = 38°19'$	$c = 8.125$ in
3. $B = 62°52'$	$c = 132.00$ ft	4. $B = 11°10'$	$c = 89.048$ in
5. $A = 8°8'$	$c = 2.1919$ in	6. $B = 49°44'$	$c = 355.06$ in
7. $A = 68°22'$	$c = 250.00$ in	8. $A = 8°25'$	$c = 12.500$ ft
9. $B = 37°47'$	$c = 64.290$ ft	10. $B = 39°30'$	$c = 9.6354$ in
11. $A = 82°16'$	$a = 40{,}625$ ft	12. $A = 16°4'$	$a = 0.93750$ ft
13. $A = 19°21'$	$a = 47.395$ ft	14. $A = 19°31'$	$a = 31.250$ in
15. $A = 16°18'$	$a = 14.0625$ ft	16. $B = 74°24'$	$b = 93.750$ in
17. $B = 47°35'$	$a = 312.50$ in	18. $B = 50°26'$	$b = 15.625$ in
19. $A = 48°40'$	$b = 8{,}125.0$ in	20. $A = 72°48'$	$b = 718.75$ ft
21. $a = 347$ ft	$b = 167$ ft	22. $a = 199$ ft	$b = 160$ ft
23. $a = 67{,}130$ in	$b = 25{,}210$ in	24. $a = 46.370$ ft	$b = 94.720$ ft
25. $a = 141$ in	$b = 203$ in	26. $c = 3{,}477$ ft	$a = 2{,}638$ ft

27. $c = 2{,}691$ ft	$a = 839.0$ ft	28. $c = 505.0$ ft	$a = 457.0$ ft
29. $c = 43{,}649$ ft	$a = 17{,}962$ ft	30. $c = 248.09$ ft	$a = 218.54$ ft
31. $c = 11{,}223$ ft	$b = 10{,}454$ ft	32. $c = 87.02$ ft	$b = 55.43$ ft
33. $c = 2{,}338$ ft	$b = 1{,}877$ ft	34. $c = 455$ in	$b = 241$ in
35. $c = 1{,}029$ ft	$b = 985.0$ ft		

14.5 Interpolation in the Five-place Tables

It is often necessary to find a function of an angle intermediate between values given in a table of natural trigonometric functions. In such cases we resort to interpolation. In Sec. 8.16 we discussed the principles of interpolation in logarithmic tables. In this section we shall therefore be somewhat brief in our discussion of interpolation applied to tables of natural trigonometric functions.

Example 9. Find the sine of 26°45′12″.

From the tables we find that sin 26°45′ = 0.45010 and sin 26°46′ = 0.45036. In the process of becoming familiar with this interpolation technique, it may be convenient to use the following pattern. See Sec. 8.16.

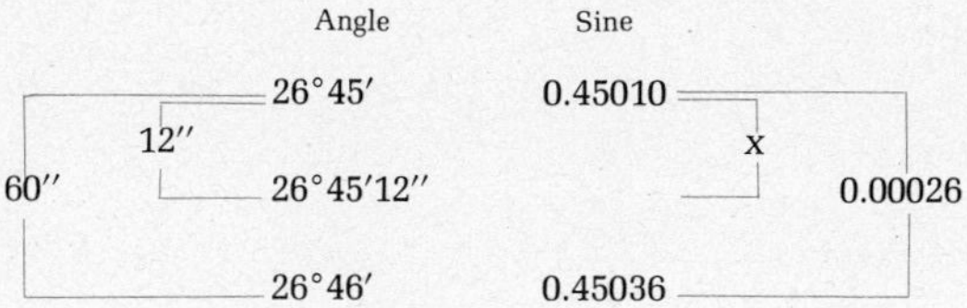

By proportion

$$\frac{x}{0.00026} = \frac{12}{60}$$

or

$$x = {}^{12}\!/_{60} \times 0.00026 = 0.00005$$
$$\sin 26°45'12'' = 0.45010 + 0.00005 = 0.45015$$

In the following examples we shall dispense with the above diagram.

Example 10. Find the sine of 26°15.6′.

$$\sin 26°16' = 0.44255$$
$$\sin 26°15' = \underline{0.44229}$$
$$0.00026 \qquad {}^{6}\!/_{10} \times 0.00026 = 0.000156, \text{ or } 0.00016$$
$$\sin 26°15.6' = 0.44229 + 0.00016 = 0.44245$$

Example 11. Find the cosine of 61°13′52″.

$$\begin{aligned}\cos 61°13' &= 0.48150\\ \cos 61°14' &= \underline{0.48124}\\ & 0.00026 \qquad {}^{52}\!/_{60} \times 0.00026 = 0.00023\end{aligned}$$

$$\cos 61°13'52'' = 0.48150 - 0.00023 = 0.48127$$

Observe in Example 11 that, as the angle increases, its cosine decreases.

The student should confirm from the tables that in the first quadrant, as the angle *increases*, its sine, tangent, and secant all *increase*, while its cosine, cotangent, and cosecant all *decrease*.

Example 12. Find the tangent of 53°27′19″.

$$\begin{aligned}\tan 53°28' &= 1.3498\\ \tan 53°27' &= \underline{1.3490}\\ & 0.0008 \qquad {}^{19}\!/_{60} \times 0.0008 = 0.0003\end{aligned}$$

$$\tan 53°27'19'' = 1.3490 + 0.0003 = 1.3493$$

Example 13. Find the cotangent of 38°41′25″.

$$\begin{aligned}\cot 38°41' &= 1.2489\\ \cot 38°42' &= \underline{1.2482}\\ & 0.0007 \qquad {}^{25}\!/_{60} \times 0.0007 = 0.0003\end{aligned}$$

$$\cot 38°41'25'' = 1.2489 - 0.0003 = 1.2486$$

Example 14. Find ϕ if $\sin \phi = 0.56295$.

$$\begin{aligned}\sin 34°16' &= 0.56305 & \sin \phi &= 0.56295\\ \sin 34°15' &= \underline{0.56280} & \sin 34°15' &= \underline{0.56280}\\ & 0.00025 & & 0.00015\end{aligned}$$

$$\phi = 34°15' + ({}^{15}\!/_{25} \times 60'') = 34°15'36''$$

Example 15. Find ϕ if $\cos \phi = 0.81555$.

$$\begin{aligned}\cos 35°21' &= 0.81563 & \cos 35°21' &= 0.81563\\ \cos 35°22' &= \underline{0.81546} & \cos \phi &= \underline{0.81555}\\ & 0.00017 & & 0.00008\end{aligned}$$

$$\phi = 35°21' + ({}^{8}\!/_{17} \times 60'') = 35°21'28''$$

If we are dealing in angular measure to the nearest second, we are in effect recognizing 60 angles between adjacent tabular entries in the angle column. However, there may be less or more than 60 five-digit numbers between corresponding tabular entries in the function column.

Therefore, if the tabular difference in the function column is small, there may be several closely grouped angles measured to the nearest second which will have the same function to five digits. If the tabular difference in the function column is large, a single angle measured to the nearest second may correspond to a range of five-figure numbers in the function column.

Refer to Example 12 above. Here, the difference between tabular entries in the tangent column is 8 in the last decimal place used. The difference in the angle is 60″. Therefore in this range of this table a difference of one unit in the last place in the tangent column corresponds to a difference of $^{60}/_{8} = 7.5''$ in the angle column. Consequently, in this portion of the five-place tables, the tangent may not be sensitive to angular changes of less than 7.5″.

If we were looking up the angle whose tangent is 1.3493, we probably should write the angle as $53°27'22'' \pm 4''$.

While we ordinarily do not go to this extreme in indicating the precision of interpolated angles, the student should certainly be aware of the limitations of the tables he uses.

In Example 12 above we calculated $^{19}/_{60}$ of 0.0008 and rounded off before adding on to 1.3490. We could, with equal reason, have found $^{19}/_{60}$ of 0.0008 to five decimal places and rounded off the tangent after addition. Usually it makes no difference. In the problems to follow it has been the policy to round off after addition.

In the absence of good reason to the contrary, all data in the following problems are assumed to have an accuracy consistent with the use of five-place tables with interpolation.

EXERCISE 3

Find the sine, cosine, tangent, cotangent, secant, and cosecant to five significant figures.

1. 2°28′15″	2. 6°42′29″	3. 14°17′13″	4. 23°19′52″
5. 40°12′48″	6. 49°36′27″	7. 52°47′35″	8. 71°28′18″
9. 80°59′40″	10. 85°43.4′	11. 27°15.3′	12. 42°27.6′
13. 72°19.8′	14. 85°26.2′	15. 17°15.7′	

EXERCISE 4

Find the acute angle to degrees, minutes, and seconds when the following functions are given:

1. $\sin\phi = 0.10572$	2. $\sin\phi = 0.32650$	3. $\sin\phi = 0.57461$
4. $\sin\phi = 0.81385$	5. $\sin\phi = 0.72645$	6. $\cos\phi = 0.49695$
7. $\cos\phi = 0.97808$	8. $\cos\phi = 0.99981$	9. $\cos\phi = 0.02391$

10. $\cos\phi = 0.54980$	11. $\tan\phi = 0.86901$	12. $\tan\phi = 1.1109$
13. $\tan\phi = 0.46430$	14. $\tan\phi = 12.271$	15. $\tan\phi = 1.0455$
16. $\cot\phi = 249.88$	17. $\cot\phi = 0.06315$	18. $\cot\phi = 2.7592$
19. $\cot\phi = 1.5476$	20. $\cot\phi = 1.3825$	21. $\sec\phi = 23.042$
22. $\sec\phi = 1.0670$	23. $\sec\phi = 1.6032$	24. $\sec\phi = 1.2130$
25. $\sec\phi = 2.3440$	26. $\csc\phi = 2.7290$	27. $\csc\phi = 9.3381$
28. $\csc\phi = 1.2880$	29. $\csc\phi = 1.3834$	30. $\csc\phi = 1.3119$

EXERCISE 5

Solve the following right triangles, using five-place functions.

The class may, of course, be instructed to round off both the data and the corresponding answers to whatever number of significant figures seems appropriate.

1. $A = 38°50'45''$	$c = 0.87500$ in	2. $A = 27°12'32''$	$c = 7.9143$ in
3. $A = 53°35.5'$	$c = 15.453$ in	4. $A = 37°50'10''$	$c = 98.268$ ft
5. $B = 22°32.1'$	$c = 2726.0$ ft	6. $A = 10°42'47''$	$c = 5.3805$ in
7. $B = 53°24'34''$	$c = 10.625$ in	8. $A = 38°14.9'$	$c = 8.1250$ ft
9. $B = 60°34'43''$	$c = 14.000$ ft	10. $A = 32°50'47''$	$c = 15.000$ ft
11. $A = 5°50'31''$	$a = 1250.0$ ft	12. $A = 11°16'44''$	$a = 457.31$ ft
13. $A = 45°15.8'$	$a = 986.91$ ft	14. $B = 36°44'2''$	$a = 12.500$ in
15. $A = 17°48.3'$	$a = 713.85$ ft	16. $B = 38°56'46''$	$b = 63.275$ ft
17. $B = 86°11.4'$	$b = 756.23$ ft	18. $B = 89°30.6'$	$b = 1.8750$ in
19. $A = 21°42'58''$	$b = 51.387$ ft	20. $A = 10°38'13''$	$b = 46.500$ ft
21. $a = 20.000$ in	$b = 37.998$ in	22. $a = 12.000$ in	$b = 23.828$ in
23. $a = 4.6397$ ft	$b = 17.927$ ft	24. $a = 389.72$ in	$b = 1303.1$ in
25. $a = 83.695$ ft	$b = 177.70$ ft	26. $a = 1.1250$ in	$b = 1.4462$ in
27. $a = 437.92$ ft	$b = 1284.9$ ft	28. $a = 76.392$ ft	$b = 191.67$ ft
29. $a = 31.250$ in	$b = 44.679$ in	30. $a = 2.1875$ ft	$b = 3.3878$ ft
31. $a = 147.00$ in	$c = 418.58$ in	32. $a = 23.458$ in	$c = 236.64$ in
33. $a = 39.738$ ft	$c = 42.973$ ft	34. $a = 358.03$ ft	$c = 369.16$ ft
35. $a = 939.52$ in	$c = 1{,}136.6$ in	36. $b = 0.34297$ ft	$c = 0.40083$ ft
37. $b = 125.00$ in	$c = 299.80$ in	38. $b = 1.6250$ in	$c = 2.5898$ in
39. $b = 13.794$ ft	$c = 18.667$ ft	40. $b = 53.187$ in	$c = 65.142$ in

The following problems are simplifications of various machine- and tool-design problems. Find the value of x to five significant figures or to the nearest second.

41. Solve for x in Fig. 14.5.
42. Solve for x in Fig. 14.6.
43. Solve for x in Fig. 14.7.
44. Solve for x in Fig. 14.8.

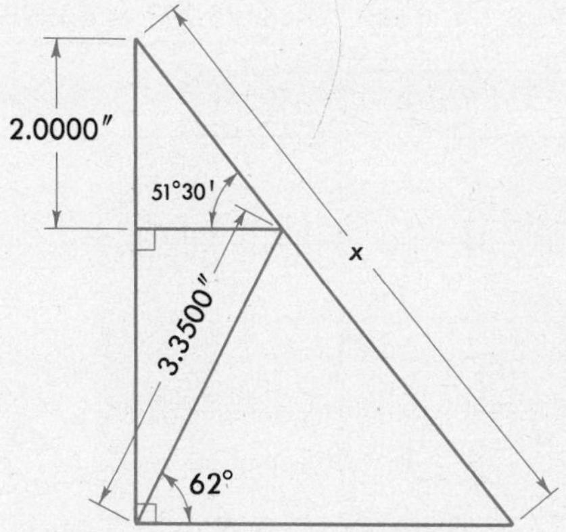

FIGURE 14.5

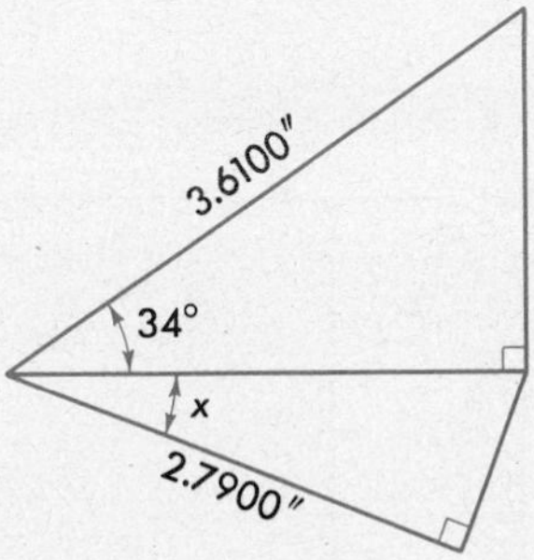

FIGURE 14.6

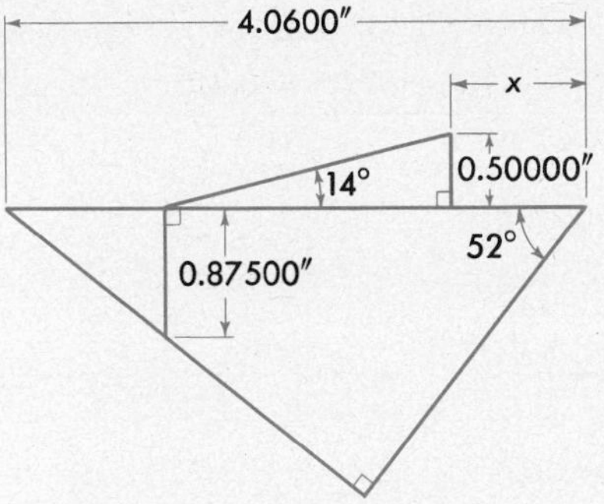

FIGURE 14.7

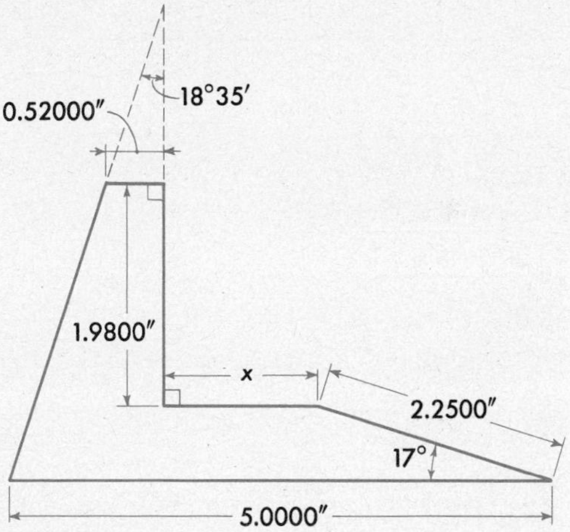

FIGURE 14.8

14.6 The Slide-rule Solution of Right Triangles

Within its inherent limit of accuracy, the slide rule may be used to solve problems in numerical trigonometry.

On the slide rule, linear dimensions can be used and computed to about 1 part in 1,000. Angles can be used and computed to about the nearest 0.05°. This is not strictly true over the entire scale, but it is a good working average.

On the particular rule used here for illustration, the S and T scales (Fig. 14.9) are calibrated in degrees and decimal parts of a degree. The long markers are double-numbered in pairs of complementary angles, for example, 82°/8°, 70°/20°, 60°/30°.

When the *right-hand* numerals are used, the hairline simultaneously indicates an angle on the S and T scales and the *sine* and *tangent,* respectively, of that angle on the C scale.

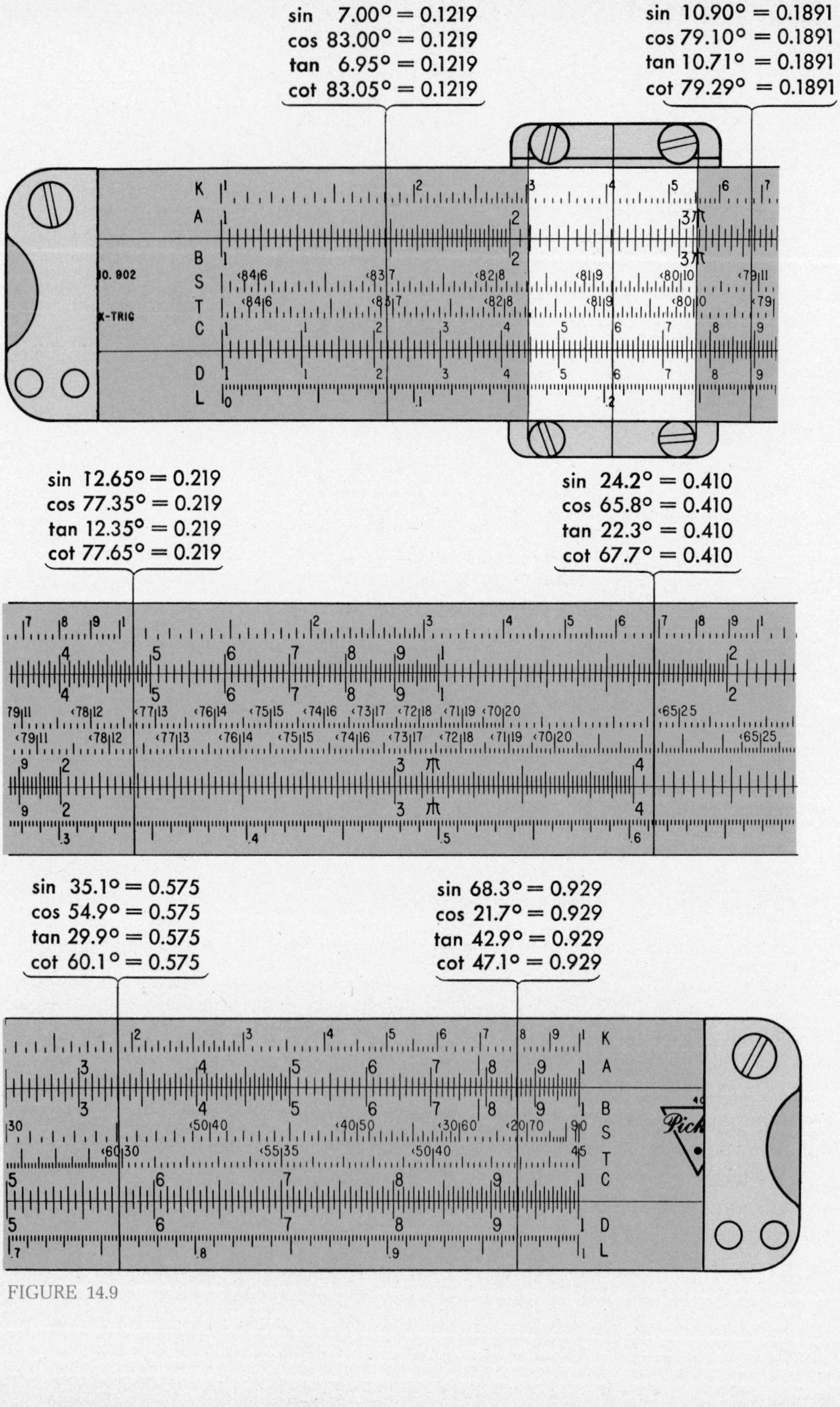
sin 7.00° = 0.1219
cos 83.00° = 0.1219
tan 6.95° = 0.1219
cot 83.05° = 0.1219
sin 10.90° = 0.1891
cos 79.10° = 0.1891
tan 10.71° = 0.1891
cot 79.29° = 0.1891
K
A
B
S
T
C
D
L
sin 12.65° = 0.219
cos 77.35° = 0.219
tan 12.35° = 0.219
cot 77.65° = 0.219
sin 24.2° = 0.410
cos 65.8° = 0.410
tan 22.3° = 0.410
cot 67.7° = 0.410
sin 35.1° = 0.575
cos 54.9° = 0.575
tan 29.9° = 0.575
cot 60.1° = 0.575
sin 68.3° = 0.929
cos 21.7° = 0.929
tan 42.9° = 0.929
cot 47.1° = 0.929

FIGURE 14.9

For example, with the indicator in the position shown in Fig. 14.9, the hairline indicates an angle of 9.21° on the S scale and the *sine* of that angle (0.1600) on the C scale. It also indicates an angle of 9.09° on the T scale and the *tangent* of that angle (0.1600) on the C scale.

By reading the *left-hand* numerals on the S and T scales with the same setting, we observe that the cosine of 80.79° is 0.1600 and the cotangent of 80.91° is of course also 0.1600.

Other positions of the hairline are also indicated in Fig. 14.9, showing certain angles and their sines, cosines, tangents, and cotangents.

The values of the sine, cosine, tangent, and cotangent are, as we have mentioned, found on the C scale. The left-hand index of the C scale is used as 0.1, and the right-hand index is used as 1.0. Therefore on this particular rule we are limited to angles whose sine is between 0.1 and 1.0, angles whose cosine is between 0.1 and 1.0, and angles whose tangent or cotangent is between 0.1 and 1.0. The smallest angle we can use directly is about 5.7°. When using sines, we can process angles up to 90°, although the scale is crowded near 90°. When using cosines, we can use angles up to about 84.3°. The upper limit of the tangent scale and the lower limit of the cotangent scale are 45°. However, as will be illustrated in subsequent examples, this does not put any additional limitations on the usefulness of the slide rule.

EXERCISE 6

1. Using a slide rule, find the sine and cosine of the following angles:

(*a*) 28°	(*b*) 8°	(*c*) 17°	(*d*) 13°	(*e*) 20°	(*f*) 30°
(*g*) 7.2°	(*h*) 12.2°	(*i*) 26.2°	(*j*) 7.63°	(*k*) 16.75°	(*l*) 41.4°

The slide-rule setting illustrated in Fig. 14.10 is adequate for solving Examples 16 and 17.

Example 16. The hypotenuse of a right triangle is 8 in, and one angle is 30°. Find the side opposite the 30° angle.

Here the slide rule is set to multiply 8 in by the sine of 30°, giving 4 in as the length of the opposite side (Fig. 14.10).

Example 17. The hypotenuse of a right triangle is 8 in, and one angle is 60°. Find the side adjacent to the 60° angle.

In Fig. 14.10 the slide rule is set to multiply 8 in by the cosine of 60°.

By reference to Examples 16 and 17 and Fig. 14.10 the student should justify for himself that when solving a right triangle where the hypotenuse appears as an unknown or a known side, (1) the 90° marker on the S scale matches the length of the hypotenuse on the D scale; (2) when using the right-hand numbers on the S scale, an acute angle on this scale matches the length of its opposite side on the D scale.

By using the above relations we can solve any right triangle (except those

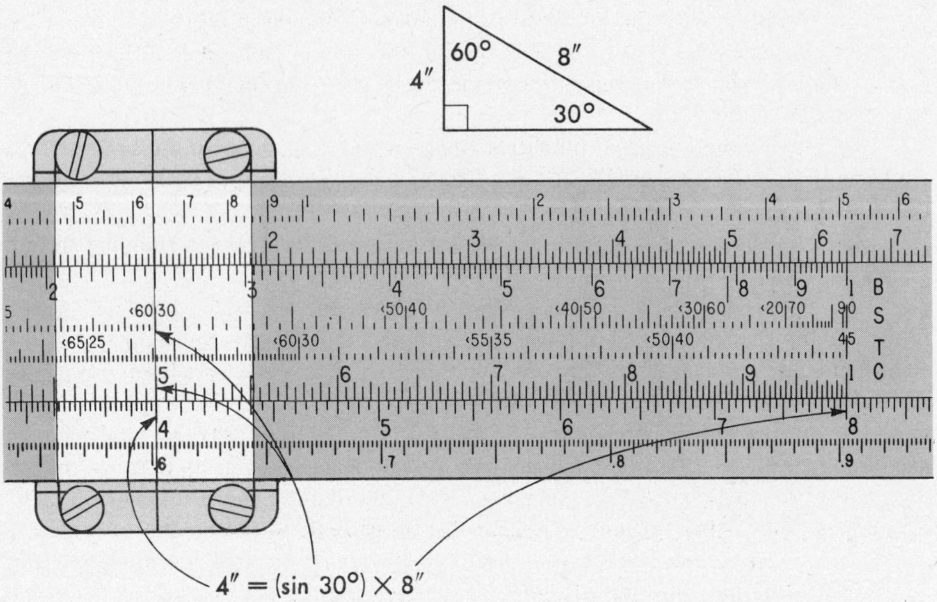

FIGURE 14.10

containing an angle less than 5.7°) if we know the hypotenuse and either acute angle or either leg. Similarly, we can solve right triangles if we know either leg and either acute angle.

EXERCISE 7

1. Verify the statement that the slide-rule setting shown in Fig. 1.5 is consistent with the following relations:

   (a) $\frac{2.53}{14.28} = \sin 10.21°$ (b) $\frac{2.53}{14.28} = \cos 79.79°$

   (c) $14.28 \cos 79.79° = 2.53$ (d) $14.28 \sin 10.21° = 2.53$

2. Verify the statement that the slide-rule setting in Fig. 1.7 is consistent with the following relations:

   (a) $\frac{8}{9.03} = \sin 62.4°$ (b) $\frac{8}{9.03} = \cos 27.6°$

   (c) $9.03 \sin 62.4° = 8$ (d) $9.03 \cos 27.6° = 8$

3. Write a series of four equations similar to those given in Probs. 1 and 2, but consistent with Figs. 1.4 and 1.11.

4. Using a slide rule, solve Probs. 1 to 20 and 26 to 34, Exercise 2.

The T scale is calibrated in degrees and decimal parts of a degree. The long markers are double-numbered in pairs of complementary angles in a way similar to the S scale.

When the *right-hand* numerals are used, the hairline simultaneously indicates an angle on the T scale and the *tangent* of that angle on the C scale. When the *left-hand* numerals are used, the hairline simultaneously indicates an angle on the T scale and the *cotangent* of that angle on the C scale.

EXERCISE 8

1. Using a slide rule, find

(*a*) tan 20°	(*b*) tan 35.76°	(*c*) tan 44.2°
(*d*) tan 7.9°	(*e*) tan 15.82°	(*f*) tan 29.62°
(*g*) cot 48.2°	(*h*) cot 82.1°	(*i*) cot 52.7°

The slide-rule setting illustrated in Fig. 14.11 is adequate for solving the following examples.

Example 18. One side of a right triangle is 6.93 in, and the adjacent angle is 30°. Find the side opposite the 30° angle.

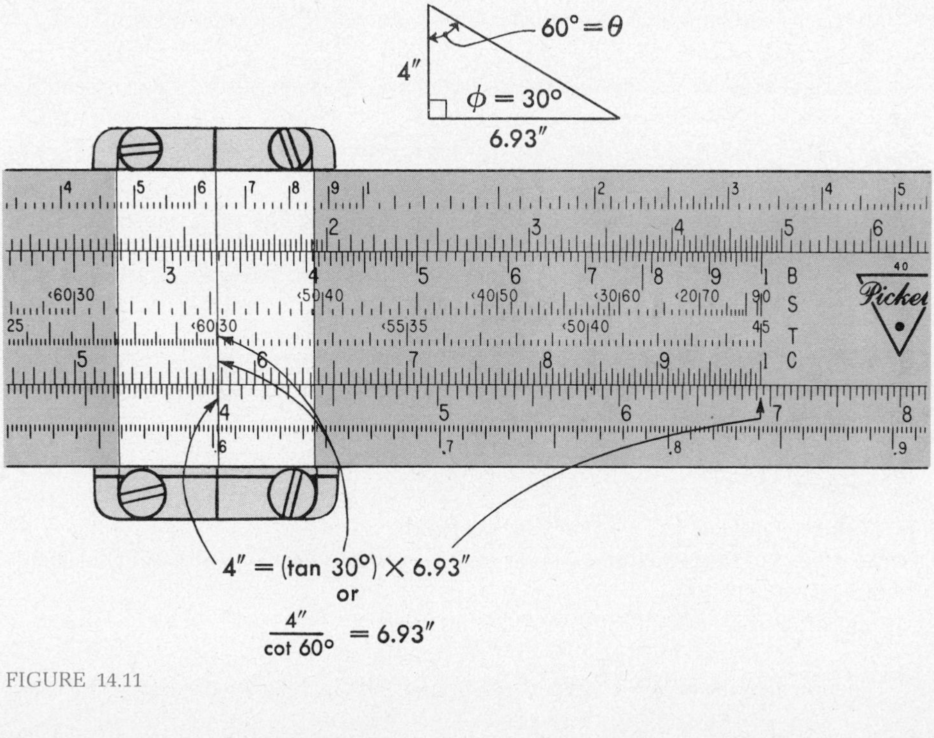

FIGURE 14.11

Use the equation

$$\text{Opposite side} = \text{adjacent side} \times \text{tangent } \phi$$

The slide-rule setting in Fig. 14.11 accomplishes this multiplication.

Example 19. One side of a right triangle is 4 in, and the adjacent angle is 60°. Find the side opposite the 60° angle.

Use the equation

$$\text{Opposite side} = \frac{\text{adjacent side}}{\cot \theta}$$

The slide-rule setting shown in Fig. 14.11 accomplishes this division. Thus we avoid using tangents of angles greater than 45°.

By reference to Examples 18 and 19 and Fig. 14.11 the student should justify for himself that (1) if the 45° marker on the T scale matches the longer leg on the D scale, (2) then, when using the right-hand numbers on the T scale, an acute angle on this scale matches the length of the shorter leg on the D scale.

It is assumed here, of course, that neither acute angle is smaller than about 5.7°.

By the rule above, if we are given two legs or a leg and an acute angle, we can solve the right triangle except for the hypotenuse. We have already discussed the situation in which the hypotenuse is involved.

EXERCISE 9

1. Verify the statement that the slide-rule setting shown in Fig. 1.5 is consistent with the following relations:

   (*a*) $\frac{2.53}{14.28} = \tan 10.05°$ (*b*) $\frac{2.53}{14.28} = \cot 79.95°$

   (*c*) $2.53 = 14.28 \tan 10.05°$ (*d*) $2.53 = 14.28 \cot 79.95°$
2. Verify the statement that the slide-rule setting shown in Fig. 1.7 is consistent with the following relations:

   (*a*) $\frac{8}{9.03} = \tan 41.55°$ (*b*) $\frac{8}{9.03} = \cot 48.45°$

   (*c*) $8 = 9.03 \tan 41.55°$ (*d*) $8 = 9.03 \cot 48.45°$
3. Write a series of four equations similar to those given in Probs. 1 and 2 but consistent with Figs. 1.9 and 1.11.
4. Using a slide rule, solve Probs. 21 to 25, Exercise 2.

Section 1.12 describes a method of solving Pythagorean theorem problems on the slide rule. The method illustrated in the following example is somewhat more convenient for those with a knowledge of trigonometry.

Example 20. The hypotenuse of a right triangle is 8 in, and one side is 4 in. Find the other side.

First find an acute angle, as in Fig. 14.10. Then, having found the smaller angle (in this case 30°), divide the opposite side by the tangent of the angle, as in Fig. 14.11.

Example 21. The two sides of a right triangle are 4 and 6.93 in. Find the hypotenuse.

First find an acute angle, as in Fig. 14.11. Then, having found the angle, divide the sine of this angle into the opposite side to find the hypotenuse, as in Fig. 14.10.

EXERCISE 10

Solve the following right triangles by slide rule.

1. $a = 141$ in	$b = 203$ in	2. $a = 17{,}960$ ft	$c = 43{,}650$ ft
3. $c = 455$ in	$b = 241$ in	4. $A = 19.35°$	$a = 47.40$ ft
5. $A = 48.67°$	$b = 8{,}125$ in	6. $A = 68.37°$	$c = 250$ in
7. $B = 47.58°$	$a = 312.5$ in	8. $B = 50.47°$	$b = 15.63$ in

EXERCISE 11

Solve the following right triangles by slide rule after converting angular measure to degrees and hundredths of a degree.

1. $A = 16°04'$	$a = 0.938$ ft
2. $A = 78°48'$	$b = 718.8$ ft
3. $A = 8°08'$	$c = 2.192$ in
4. $B = 47°35'$	$a = 312.5$ in
5. $B = 62°52'$	$c = 132.0$ ft
6. $B = 39°30'$	$c = 9.64$ in

14.7 Logarithmic Solution of Right Triangles

The multiplication and division necessary in solving triangles can, of course, be done by logarithms. For this purpose, tables have been published in which the logarithms of the functions are given directly. These tables are organized in exactly the same way as the corresponding tables of natural functions. See Table 14.3.

However, the number -10 must be appended to all logarithms given in Table 14.3 and Table 4 starting on page 885.

TABLE 14.3 LOGARITHMS OF THE TRIGONOMETRIC FUNCTIONS

17° (197°) (342°) **162°**

′	L Sin	d	L Tan	c d	L Ctn	L Cos	d	′
0	9.46 594	41	9.48 534	45	10.51 466	9.98 060	4	60
1	9.46 635	41	9.48 579	45	10.51 421	9.98 056	4	59
2	9.46 676	41	9.48 624	45	10.51 376	9.98 052	4	58
3	9.46 717	41	9.48 669	45	10.51 331	9.98 048	4	57
4	9.46 758	42	9.48 714	45	10.51 286	9.98 044	4	56
5	9.46 800	41	9.48 759	45	10.51 241	9.98 040	4	55
6	9.46 841	41	9.48 804	45	10.51 196	9.98 036	4	54
7	9.46 882	41	9.48 849	45	10.51 151	9.98 032	3	53
55	9.48 803	39	9.50 962	43	10.49 038	9.97 841	4	5
56	9.48 842	39	9.51 005	43	10.48 995	9.97 837	4	4
57	9.48 881	39	9.51 048	44	10.48 952	9.97 833	4	3
58	9.48 920	39	9.51 092	43	10.48 908	9.97 829	4	2
59	9.48 959	39	9.51 135	43	10.48 865	9.97 825	4	1
60	9.48 998		9.51 178		10.48 822	9.97 821		0
′	L Cos	d	L Ctn	c d	L Tan	L Sin	d	′

107° (287°) (252°) **72°**

For example (see Table 14.3),

$$\log \sin 17°55' = 9.48803 - 10$$

or

$$\log \sin 17°55' = 0.48803 - 1$$
$$\log \tan 17°55' = 10.50962 - 10$$

or

$$\log \tan 17°55' = 0.50962$$

Example 22. Find log sin 15°26′15″.

$$\log \sin 15°27' = 9.42553 - 10 = 0.42553 - 1$$
$$\log \sin 15°26' = \underline{9.42507 - 10 = 0.42507} - 1$$
$$0.00046 \qquad 0.00046$$

$$15/60 \times 0.00046 = 0.000115$$

$$\log \sin 15°26'15'' = 9.42507 - 10 + 0.000115$$
$$= 9.425185 - 10, \text{ or } 0.425185 - 1$$

In rounding off to five places, since the number ends in exactly 5, the last digit in the rounded-off number is left the nearest even digit, or

$$\log \sin 15°26'15'' = 9.42518 - 10 = 0.42518 - 1$$

Notice that the difference between adjacent tabular entries is published in the table under the *d* column. This avoids the need for an actual subtraction such as was done in the above example.

Example 23. Find ϕ if $\log \tan \phi = 0.42765$.

This number appears directly in the table and is the log tangent of 69°31′. Notice that $\log \tan 14°59' = 9.42755 - 10$, and the $\log \tan 1°32' = 8.42762 - 10$.

Therefore the student should be particularly careful to make sure to use the correct characteristic as well as the correct mantissa.

In the solution of right triangles, there is some question as to whether it is more efficient to use natural functions or log functions. With oblique triangles it is usually better to use log functions.

Example 24. In a certain right triangle, $a = 1.7320$ and $A = 26°30'$. Find b and c, using five-place log functions.

$$c = \frac{1.7320}{\sin 26°30'}$$

$$\log c = \log 1.7320 - \log \sin 26°30'$$

$$\log 1.7320 = 1.23855 - 1$$

$$\log \sin 26°30' = \underline{0.64953 - 1}$$

subtracting $\log c = 0.58902 + 0$

$$c = 3.8817$$

$$b = 1.7320 \cot 26°30'$$

$$\log b = \log 1.7320 + \log \cot 26°30'$$

$$\log 1.7320 = 0.23855$$

$$\log \cot 26°30' = \underline{0.30226}$$

adding $\log b = 0.54081$

$$b = 3.4738$$

EXERCISE 12

Solve the following right triangles, using five-place log functions:

1. $A = 37°42'16''$ $c = 146.32$ in
2. $A = 2°26'05''$ $c = 0.43792$ in
3. $B = 72°19'28''$ $c = 157.65$ in
4. $B = 36°28'45''$ $c = 29.463$ in
5. $A = 28°36'20''$ $c = 1.3752$ in
6. $A = 04°13'30''$ $b = 136.48$ in

7. $A = 88°25'14''$	$a = 15.358$ in	8. $B = 47°28'10''$	$a = 0.037940$ in
9. $A = 89°21'38''$	$b = 15,279$ in	10. $A = 45°13'05''$	$a = 28.365$ in
11. $a = 13.625$ in	$c = 142.98$ in	12. $a = 76.500$ ft	$c = 92.800$ ft
13. $a = 5.4360$ in	$c = 10.830$ in	14. $a = 26.9320$ in	$c = 41.8670$ in
15. $a = 0.36520$ in	$c = 0.58470$ in	16. $a = 10.932$ in	$b = 110.36$ in
17. $a = 95.632$ in	$b = 8.7305$ in	18. $a = 52.693$ in	$b = 27.956$ in
19. $a = 3.6571$ in	$b = 7.3058$ in	20. $a = 26.328$ in	$b = 21.497$ in

14.8 Isosceles Triangles

By definition, an isosceles triangle is a triangle in which two sides are equal. From this it follows that two angles must be equal. Thus in Fig. 14.12, if $a = b$, the triangle is isosceles and $A = B$. The altitude drawn to the base bisects the base and the angle C.

$$h^2 = b^2 - (\tfrac{1}{2}c)^2 \tag{13}$$

$$h = \sqrt{(b - \tfrac{1}{2}c)(b + \tfrac{1}{2}c)} \tag{14}$$

In general, for any triangle,

$$\text{Area} = \tfrac{1}{2} \times \text{base} \times \text{altitude}$$

In the case of the triangle in Fig. 14.12,

$$h = b \sin A$$

or

$$h = b \cos \tfrac{1}{2}C$$

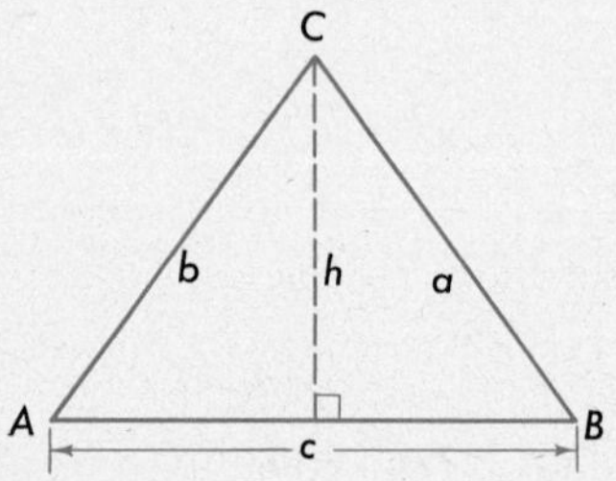

FIGURE 14.12

Therefore

$$\text{Area} = \tfrac{1}{2}cb \sin A \tag{15}$$

or

$$\text{Area} = \tfrac{1}{2}cb \cos \tfrac{1}{2}C \tag{16}$$

If angle C and either a or b are known, then

$$c = 2b \sin \tfrac{1}{2}C \tag{17}$$

or

$$c = 2a \sin \tfrac{1}{2}C \tag{18}$$

EXERCISE 13

1. The equal sides of an isosceles triangle are each 5.86 in long, and each base angle is 23°51′. Find the length of the base and the altitude of the triangle.
2. A sheet of metal 15 in wide is bent along its centerline to form a V-shaped gutter. Will the gutter have a greater capacity when it is 6 in wide at the top, or when 6 in deep? What angle of the V will result in maximum capacity?
3. Find the angle of bend for each case in Prob. 2.
4. A right prism has for its base an equilateral triangle 7.3 in on each side. It is cut by a plane which makes an angle of 25° with the base; one side of the section includes one side of the base. Find the sides, angles, and area of the section.
5. A sphere $5\tfrac{1}{2}$ in in diameter is dropped into a tin cone $8\tfrac{1}{2}$ in in diameter and $7\tfrac{1}{2}$ in deep. Is the top of the sphere above or below the rim of the cone, and how far?
6. The legs of a tripod are each 4 ft $2\tfrac{3}{4}$ in long, and their feet form an equilateral triangle 2 ft $1\tfrac{1}{2}$ in on a side. Find the angle between one leg and a plumb bob hung from its top.
7. Find the area of a segment cut off from a circle 16.82 in in diameter by a line 2.73 in from the center.
8. Each leaf of a swinging double door 3 ft 6 in wide has been opened through an angle of 64°. How far apart are their edges? How far is each edge from the line of closure? Each section of the door is opened inward.

14.9 The Functions of 30°, 45°, and 60°

The functions of these special angles appear frequently in the analysis of engineering problems. Consequently the student will be well advised to remember them or at least

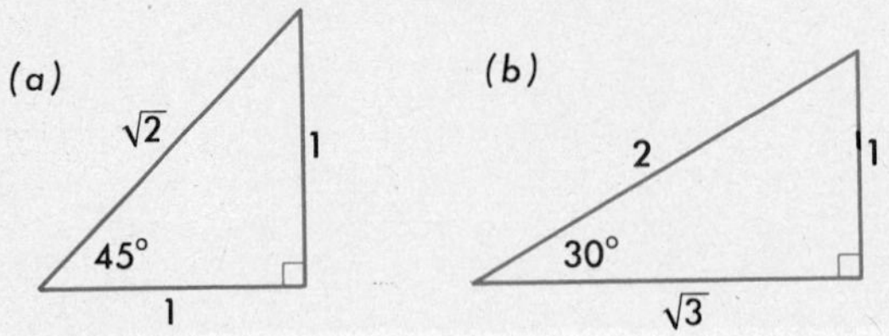

FIGURE 14.13

to be able to derive them at a moment's notice. (Also see geometric facts 79 and 81 on page 117.)

From Fig. 14.13*a* and consistent with Eqs. (1) to (6), it appears that

$$\sin 45° = \frac{1}{\sqrt{2}} = \frac{\sqrt{2}}{2} = 0.707 \tag{19}$$

$$\cos 45° = \frac{1}{\sqrt{2}} = \frac{\sqrt{2}}{2} = 0.707 \tag{20}$$

$$\tan 45° = \frac{1}{1} = 1 \tag{21}$$

$$\cot 45° = \frac{1}{1} = 1 \tag{22}$$

$$\sec 45° = \frac{\sqrt{2}}{1} = \sqrt{2} = 1.414 \tag{23}$$

$$\csc 45° = \frac{\sqrt{2}}{1} = \sqrt{2} = 1.414 \tag{24}$$

Referring to Fig. 14.13*b* and the same basic equations,

$$\sin 30° = \frac{1}{2} = 0.500 \tag{25}$$

$$\cos 30° = \frac{\sqrt{3}}{2} = 0.866 \tag{26}$$

$$\tan 30° = \frac{1}{\sqrt{3}} = \frac{\sqrt{3}}{3} = 0.577 \tag{27}$$

$$\cot 30° = \frac{\sqrt{3}}{1} = \sqrt{3} = 1.732 \tag{28}$$

$$\sec 30° = \frac{2}{\sqrt{3}} = \frac{2\sqrt{3}}{3} = 1.155 \tag{29}$$

$$\csc 30° = \frac{2}{1} = 2 \tag{30}$$

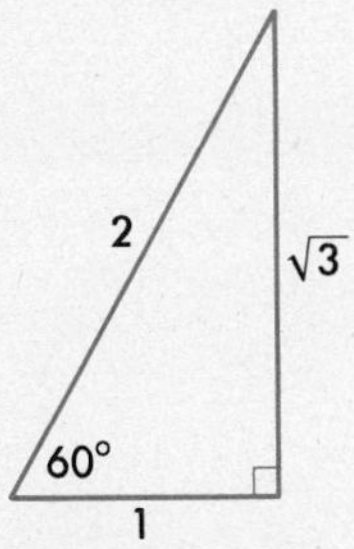

FIGURE 14.14

Referring to Fig. 14.14 and again using the same basic equations,

$$\sin 60^\circ = \frac{\sqrt{3}}{2} = 0.866 \tag{31}$$

$$\cos 60^\circ = \frac{1}{2} = 0.500 \tag{32}$$

$$\tan 60^\circ = \frac{\sqrt{3}}{1} = \sqrt{3} = 1.732 \tag{33}$$

$$\cot 60^\circ = \frac{1}{\sqrt{3}} = \frac{\sqrt{3}}{3} = 0.577 \tag{34}$$

$$\sec 60^\circ = \frac{2}{1} = 2 \tag{35}$$

$$\csc 60^\circ = \frac{2}{\sqrt{3}} = \frac{2\sqrt{3}}{3} = 1.155 \tag{36}$$

EXERCISE 14

It is intended that the following problems will be done on a slide rule without the use of trigonometric tables.

1. Find x in Fig. 14.15*a*.
2. Find x in Fig. 14.15*b*.
3. Find x in Fig. 14.15*c*.
4. Find x in Fig. 14.15*d*.
5. Find x in Fig. 14.15*e*.
6. Find x in Fig. 14.15*f*.
7. Find x in Fig. 14.15g.

14.10 Regular Polygons

A regular polygon (Fig. 14.16) is inscribed in a circle of radius R and circumscribed about a circle of radius r. Let

s = length of one side = $\overline{ab}$
n = number of sides

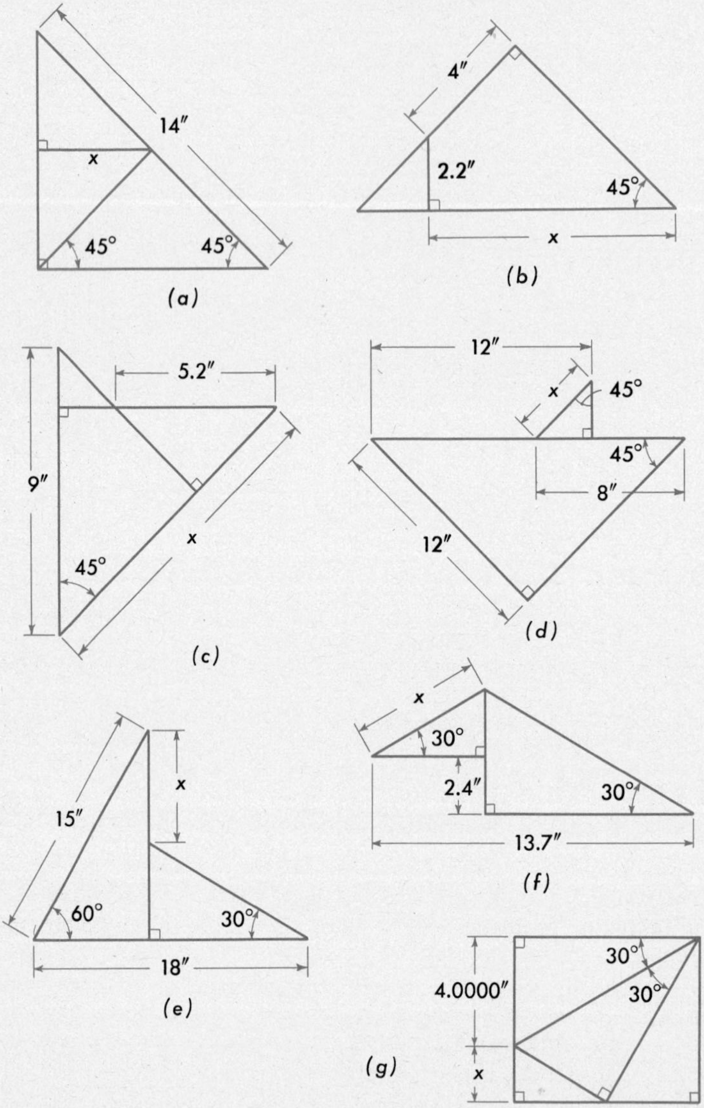

FIGURE 14.15

R = radius of circumscribed circle

r = radius of inscribed circle, sometimes called the *apothem*

p = perimeter of polygon = ns

A_t = area of a single triangle, as for example triangle abc

A_p = area of entire polygon

It can be proved that

$$A_t = \frac{s^2}{4} \cot \frac{180°}{n} \tag{37}$$

$$A_t = \frac{R^2}{2} \sin \frac{360°}{n} \tag{38}$$

$$A_t = r^2 \tan \frac{180°}{n} \tag{39}$$

$$r = \frac{s}{2} \cot \frac{180°}{n} \tag{40}$$

$$R = \frac{s}{2} \csc \frac{180°}{n} \tag{41}$$

$$p = 2nR \sin \frac{180°}{n} \tag{42}$$

$$p = 2nr \tan \frac{180°}{n} \tag{43a}$$

$$A_p = nA_t \tag{43b}$$

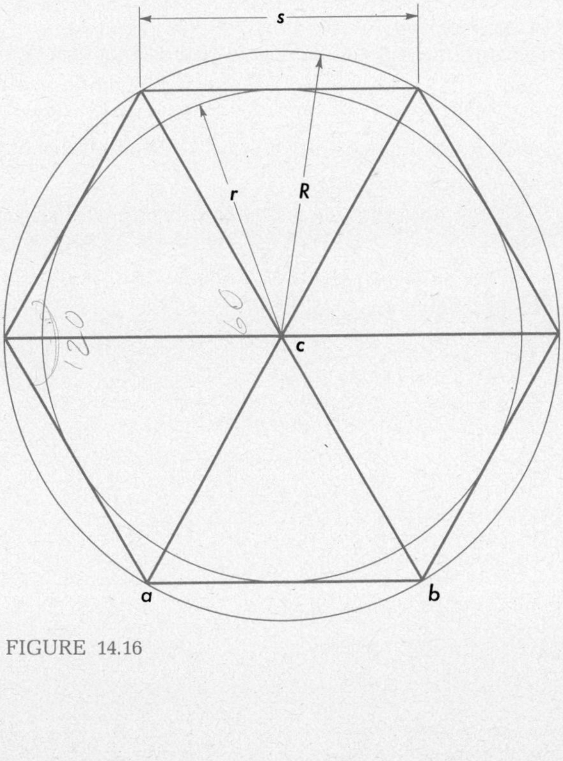

FIGURE 14.16

14.11 The Solution of Oblique Triangles

To solve any given triangle means to find the unknown sides and angles. Up to this point we have been dealing with right triangles only. Now we shall discuss methods of solving oblique triangles as well. An oblique triangle is one which has no 90° angle.

All triangles have six parts: three angles and three sides. We designate the angles by A, B, and C with side a opposite angle A, side b opposite angle B, and side c opposite angle C. See Fig. 14.17.

With one exception, if three parts of a triangle are given, of which at least one is a side, the other parts may be calculated. (We will mention this again presently.)

The exact method used in solving an oblique triangle will depend on which set of these three parts is given.

It is convenient to consider four ways in which the data may be given:

1. Three sides may be given.
2. Two sides and the angle between them may be given.
3. One side and two angles may be given.
4. Two sides and the angle opposite one of them may be given.

If, as in case 4, it is given that $A = 30°$, $b = 10$ in, and $a = 8$ in, then either Fig. 14.18*a* or Fig. 14.18*b* applies. Both triangles are consistent with the given data.

Obviously these two triangles are not congruent, even though they are both defined by the same data. Therefore we say that the data are ambiguous.

The question of ambiguity arises only with data given as in case 4. As a practical matter the question of ambiguity can usually be settled by a quickly made scale drawing.

There are several formulas useful in solving oblique triangles. We shall discuss two of them, the *sine law* and the *cosine law*.

The sine law is useful when the given data include a side and its opposite angle. This includes cases 3 and 4.

The cosine law is useful when three sides are given or when two sides and the angle included between them are given.

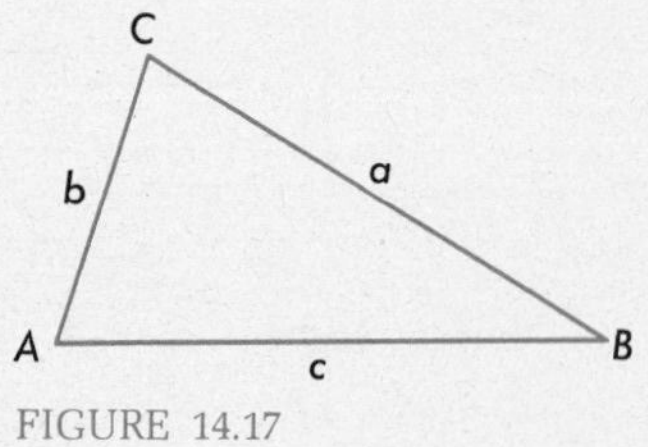

FIGURE 14.17

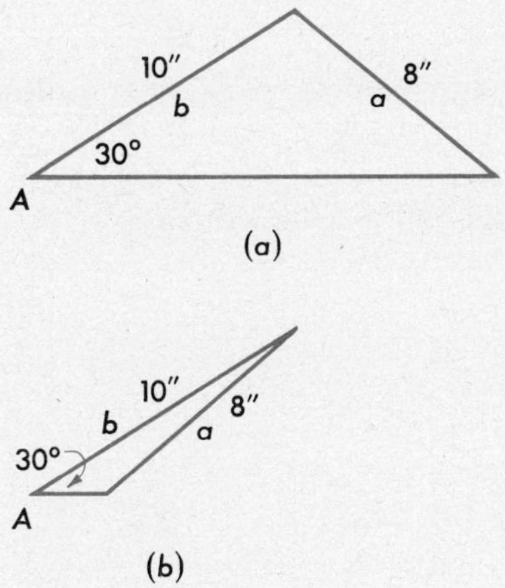

FIGURE 14.18

14.12 The Sine Law

This formula is useful when we know two angles and a side or when we know two sides and the angle opposite one of them. The formula is usually stated in the form

$$\frac{a}{\sin A} = \frac{b}{\sin B} = \frac{c}{\sin C} \qquad \textbf{(44)}$$

Equation (44) is equivalent to Eqs. (45) to (47):

$$\frac{a}{\sin A} = \frac{b}{\sin B} \qquad (45)$$

$$\frac{a}{\sin A} = \frac{c}{\sin C} \qquad (46)$$

$$\frac{b}{\sin B} = \frac{c}{\sin C} \qquad (47)$$

In general, when the angle A is an obtuse angle of a triangle,

$$\sin A = \sin (180° - A) \qquad (48)$$

14.13 Derivation of the Sine Law

Referring to Fig. 14.19,

$$y = b \sin A \qquad (49)$$

and

$$y = a \sin B' \tag{50}$$

But from the geometry of the figure the angles B and B' are supplementary angles; therefore, from Eq. (48), their sines are equal, and Eq. (50) may be written

$$y = a \sin B \tag{51}$$

Combining Eqs. (49) and (51),

$$a \sin B = b \sin A \tag{52}$$

Similarly, in Fig. 14.20,

$$y = a \sin B$$

and

$$y = b \sin A$$

Therefore

$$a \sin B = b \sin A \tag{53}$$

Equation (52) or (53) may be written

$$\frac{a}{\sin A} = \frac{b}{\sin B} \tag{54}$$

The same equation applies whether B is obtuse or acute. We may extend the above derivation to obtain

$$\frac{a}{\sin A} = \frac{b}{\sin B} = \frac{c}{\sin C} \tag{55}$$

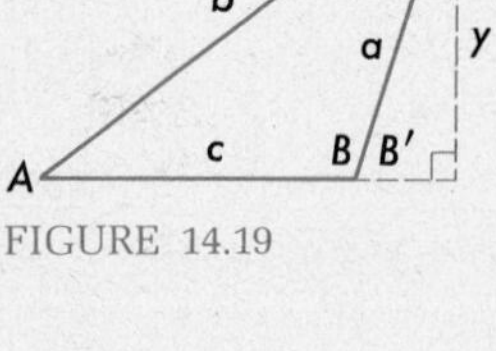

FIGURE 14.19

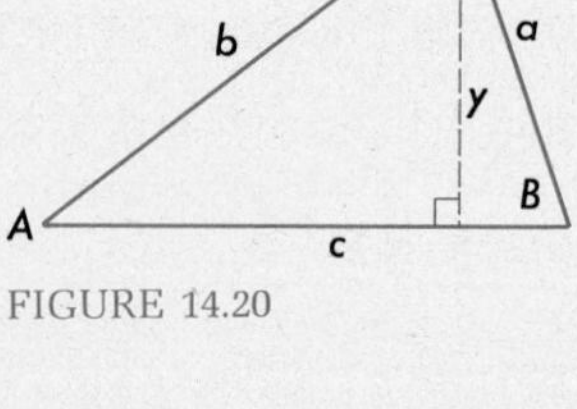

FIGURE 14.20

Example 25. In the oblique triangle ABC, $A = 31°30'$, $B = 28°04'$, and side b equals 94.1 in. Find side a. From Eq. (45)

$$\frac{a}{\sin A} = \frac{b}{\sin B}$$

$$\frac{a}{\sin 31°30'} = \frac{94.1}{\sin 28°04'}$$

$$\frac{a}{0.52250} = \frac{94.1}{0.47050}$$

$$a = \frac{94.1 \times \overset{0.1045}{\cancel{0.52250}}}{\underset{0.0941}{\cancel{0.47050}}} = \frac{94.1 \times 0.1045}{0.0941}$$

$$= 1{,}000 \times 0.1045 = 104.5 \text{ in}$$

Example 26. In the oblique triangle ABC, $A = 21°06'$, $C = 35°21'$, and side b equals 46.3 in. Find side a. See Eq. (45).

$$\frac{a}{\sin A} = \frac{b}{\sin B}$$

$$B = 180° - (21°06' + 35°21')$$

$$= 180° - 56°27' = 123°33'$$

$$\frac{a}{\sin 21°06'} = \frac{b}{\sin 123°33'}$$

$$\frac{a}{0.36000} = \frac{46.3}{0.83340}$$

$$a = \frac{46.3 \times \overset{0.04}{\cancel{0.36000}}}{\underset{0.0926}{\cancel{0.83340}}}$$

$$= \frac{46.3 \times \overset{0.02}{\cancel{0.04}}}{\underset{0.0463}{\cancel{0.0926}}} = 1{,}000 \times 0.02 = 20 \text{ in}$$

EXERCISE 15

The data for the problems given below refer to the general oblique triangle of which Fig. 14.17 is typical. These data have been chosen to minimize the arithmetical work. The student should reduce the fractions he encounters as far as he can.

Where ambiguous data are given, both answers should be calculated.

1. Find side a if $C = 99°20'$, $B = 41°29'$, and $b = 7.36$ in.
2. Find side c if $A = 119°42'$, $C = 48°50'$, and $b = 4.97$ in.
3. Find side b if $A = 95°02'$, $B = 37°09'$, and $c = 2.47$ in.
4. Find side a if $A = 114°13'$, $B = 10°18'$, and $b = 1.49$ in.
5. Find side c if $B = 138°42'$, $C = 24°01'$, and $b = 60$ in.
6. Find angle B if $A = 39°11'$, $a = 54$ in, and $b = 48$ in.
7. Find angle A if $B = 34°10'$, $a = 54$ in, and $b = 48$ in.

14.14 Sine-law Solution by the Slide Rule

The slide rule is a convenient device for solving a triangle by use of the sine law provided slide-rule accuracy is adequate.

For example, suppose we wish to find the side a by means of a slide rule when $A = 39.5°$, $B = 57°$, and $b = 6.00$ in. The angles are expressed in degrees and decimal parts of a degree to conform with the usual slide-rule calibration. See Fig. 14.21.

The general equation

$$\frac{a}{\sin A} = \frac{b}{\sin B}$$

may be applied to this problem by writing

$$\frac{a}{\sin 39.5°} = \frac{6.00}{\sin 57°} \tag{56}$$

Figure 14.22 shows the appropriate slide-rule setting for solving Eq. (56) for side a.

Observe that with the hairline in "position 1," it simultaneously indicates side b on the D scale and angle B on the S scale. With this setting the quotient of b divided

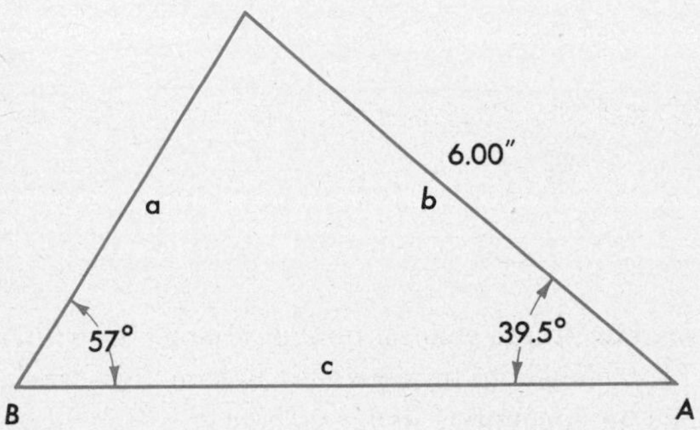

FIGURE 14.21

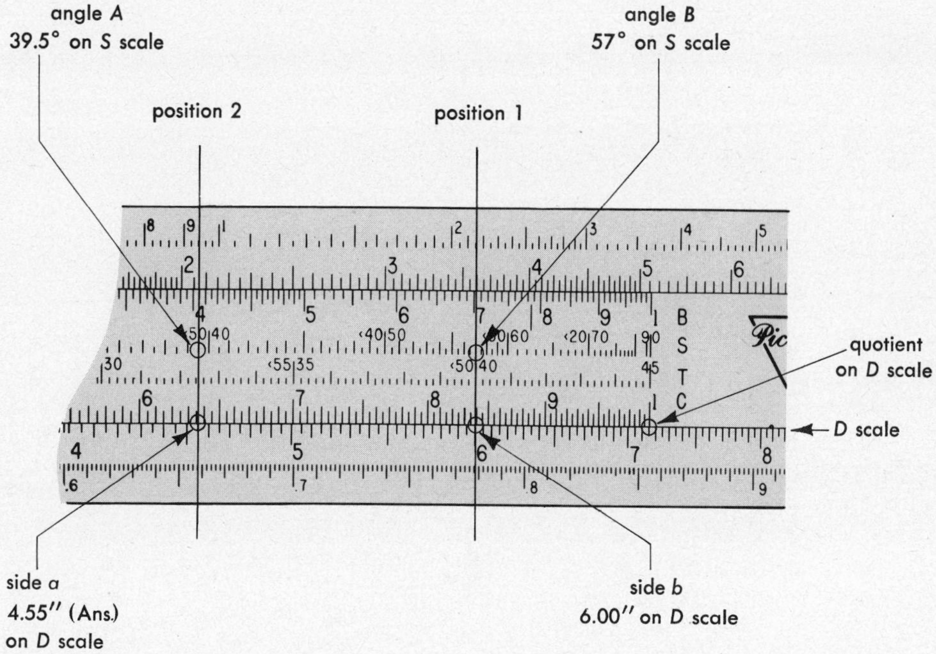

FIGURE 14.22

by sin B may be read on the D scale as shown in Fig. 14.22. (In this problem there is no occasion actually to read this number.)

Without moving the slide, if we move the hairline to "position 2," it will then simultaneously indicate angle A on the S scale and side a on the D scale. This setting indicates the quotient of a divided by sin A. From Eq. (56) it is quite evident that this quotient is equal to the one obtained before.

By direct reading of the slide rule (Fig. 14.22)

$$a = 4.55 \text{ in}$$

Now, the triangle shown in Fig. 14.23 has a different appearance from the one shown in Fig. 14.21. However, we observe that

$$\sin 123^\circ = \sin 57^\circ$$

since

$$123^\circ = 180^\circ - 57^\circ$$

(See Sec. 13.10.)

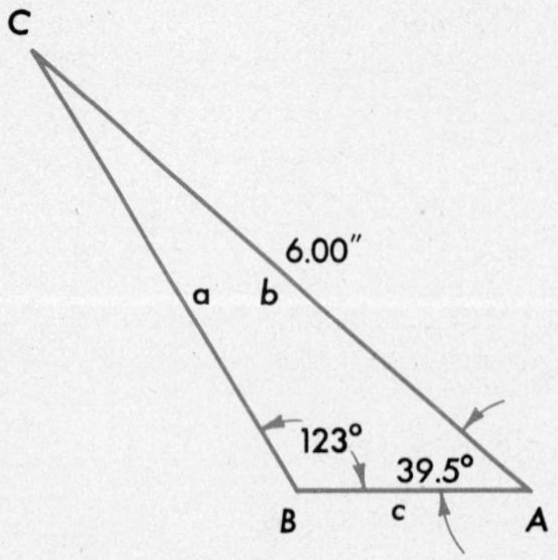

FIGURE 14.23

Thus the slide-rule setting shown in Fig. 14.22 applies to Fig. 14.23 as well as to Fig. 14.21.

To find the side c, we first find angle C, where

$$C = 180° - (57° + 39.5°) = 83.5° \qquad \text{(for Fig. 14.21)}$$
$$C = 180° - (123° + 39.5°) = 17.5° \qquad \text{(for Fig. 14.23)}$$

Then reset the indicator to find the side c in the corresponding drawing.

In Fig. 14.22, two sides and their opposite angles are involved. In general, if any three of these are known, the fourth can be found by using similar slide settings.

If we write Eq. (56) in the form

$$\frac{\sin 39.5°}{a} = \frac{\sin 57°}{6.00}$$

then we see that the relative position of these four quantities in the above equation is similar to their representation on the slide rule in Fig. 14.22.

14.15 Logarithmic Solutions Using the Sine Law

If slide-rule accuracy is unacceptable and a mechanical or electronic calculator is not available, then using logarithms may reduce the labor of the numerical calculations involved in the application of the sine law. See Sec. 14.12 and examples which follow.

Example 27. Solve the triangle $A = 42°10'00''$, $B = 78°40'00''$, $c = 150.00$ in.

$$C = 180° - (42°10' + 78°40') = 59°10'$$

$$\frac{a}{\sin A} = \frac{c}{\sin C} \qquad\qquad \frac{b}{\sin B} = \frac{c}{\sin C}$$

$$\frac{a}{\sin 42°10'} = \frac{150}{\sin 59°10'} \qquad\qquad \frac{b}{\sin 78°40'} = \frac{150}{\sin 59°10'}$$

$$a = \frac{150 \sin 42°10'}{\sin 59°10'} \qquad\qquad b = \frac{150 \sin 78°40'}{\sin 59°10'}$$

$$\begin{aligned} \log 150 \text{ in} &= 2.17609 \\ \log \sin 42°10' &= \underline{9.82691 - 10} \\ & 12.00300 - 10 \\ \log \sin 59°10' &= \underline{9.93382 - 10} \\ \log a &= 2.06918 \\ a &= 117.27 \text{ in} \end{aligned} \qquad\qquad \begin{aligned} \log 150 \text{ in} &= 2.17609 \\ \log \sin 78°40' &= \underline{9.99145 - 10} \\ & 12.16754 - 10 \\ \log \sin 59°10' &= \underline{9.93382 - 10} \\ \log b &= 2.23372 \\ b &= 171.28 \text{ in} \end{aligned}$$

The labor of calculation can be reduced somewhat by the use of cologarithms (see Sec. 8.21).

$$\begin{aligned} \log 150 \text{ in} &= 2.17609 \\ \log \sin 42°10' &= 9.82691 - 10 \\ \text{colog} \sin 59°10' &= \underline{0.06618} \\ \log a &= 12.06918 - 10 \\ a &= 117.27 \text{ in} \end{aligned} \qquad\qquad \begin{aligned} \log 150 \text{ in} &= 2.17609 \\ \log \sin 78°40' &= 9.99145 - 10 \\ \text{colog} \sin 59°10' &= \underline{0.06618} \\ \log b &= 12.23372 - 10 \\ b &= 171.28 \text{ in} \end{aligned}$$

If the basic equations are written in the form

$$\frac{\sin 42°10'}{a} = \frac{\sin 59°10'}{150}$$

and treated as a proportion, the problem may conveniently be checked on the slide rule.

Here if we match 59°10′ (59.2°) on the S scale to 150 on the D scale, we shall find 78°40′ (78.7°) opposite 171.3 and 42°10′ (42.2°) opposite 117.3.

Example 28. Solve the oblique triangle $B = 40°00'00''$, $C = 25°00'00''$, and $a = 23.529$ in.

$$A = 180° - (40° + 25°) = 180° - 65° = 115°$$

$$\frac{b}{\sin B} = \frac{a}{\sin A} \qquad \frac{c}{\sin C} = \frac{a}{\sin A}$$

$$\begin{aligned} \log \sin 115° &= \log \sin (180° - 115°) = \log \sin 65° \\ \log \sin 65° &= 9.95728 - 10 \end{aligned}$$

$$\log \sin 115° = 9.95728 - 10$$

$$\begin{aligned}\log 23.529 \text{ in} &= 1.37160 \\ \log \sin 40^\circ &= 9.80807 - 10 \\ \text{colog} \sin 115^\circ &= 0.04272 \\ \hline \log b &= 11.22239 - 10 \\ b &= 16.687 \text{ in}\end{aligned}$$

$$\begin{aligned}\log 23.529 \text{ in} &= 1.37160 \\ \log \sin 25^\circ &= 9.62595 - 10 \\ \text{colog} \sin 115^\circ &= 0.04272 \\ \hline \log c &= 11.04027 - 10 \\ c &= 10.972 \text{ in}\end{aligned}$$

Example 29. Solve the oblique triangle $A = 25°00'00''$, $b = 125.00$ in, and $a = 80.000$ in.

Here, two sides and the angle opposite one of them are given. In Sec. 14.11 it was indicated that under these conditions there is a possibility of two solutions being consistent with the given data.

Figure 14.24*a* and *b* is drawn approximately to scale. We shall solve both triangles.

$$\frac{b}{\sin B} = \frac{a}{\sin A} \quad \text{or} \quad \frac{\sin B}{b} = \frac{\sin A}{a} \quad \text{or} \quad \sin B = \frac{b \sin A}{a}$$

In Fig. 14.24*a*

$$\sin B = \frac{125 \sin 25^\circ}{80}$$

$$\begin{aligned}\log 125 &= 2.09691 \\ \log \sin 25^\circ &= 9.62595 - 10 \\ \text{colog } 80 &= 8.09691 - 10 \\ \hline \log \sin B &= 19.81977 - 20 \\ B &= 41^\circ 19'34''\end{aligned}$$

$$C = 180^\circ - (25^\circ + 41^\circ 19'34'') = 180^\circ - 66^\circ 19'34'' = 113^\circ 40'26''$$

$$\frac{c}{\sin C} = \frac{a}{\sin A}$$

$$\frac{c}{\sin 113^\circ 40'26''} = \frac{80}{\sin 25^\circ}$$

$$c = \frac{80 \sin 113^\circ 40'26''}{\sin 25^\circ}$$

$$\log \sin 113^\circ 40'26'' = \log \sin (180^\circ - 113^\circ 40'26'') = \log \sin 66^\circ 19'34''$$

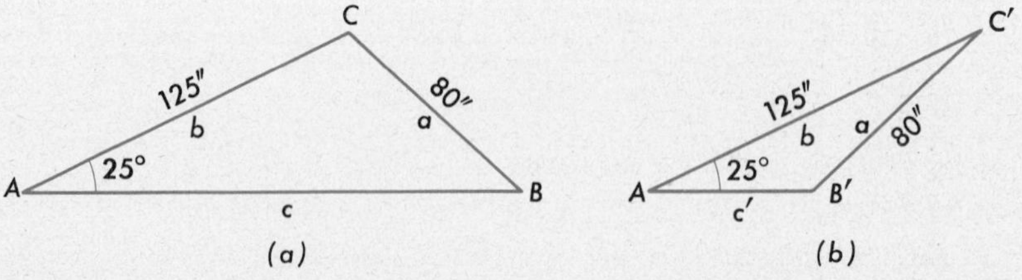

FIGURE 14.24

$$\begin{aligned}
\log \sin 66°19'34'' &= 9.96182 - 10 \\
\log \sin 113°40'26'' &= 9.96182 - 10
\end{aligned}$$

$$\begin{aligned}
\log 80 \text{ in} &= 1.90309 \\
\log \sin 113°40'26'' &= 9.96182 - 10 \\
\text{colog} \sin 25° &= 0.37405 \\
\hline
\log c &= 12.23896 - 10 \\
c &= 173.36 \text{ in}
\end{aligned}$$

In Fig. 14.24*b*

$$B' = 180° - B = 180° - 41°19'34'' = 138°40'26''$$
$$C' = 180° - (138°40'26'' + 25°) = 16°19'34''$$
$$c' = \frac{a \sin C'}{\sin A} = \frac{80 \sin 16°19'34''}{\sin 25°}$$

$$\begin{aligned}
\log 80 \text{ in} &= 1.90309 \\
\log \sin 16°19'34'' &= 9.44886 - 10 \\
\text{colog} \sin 25° &= 0.37405 \\
\hline
\log c' &= 11.72600 - 10 \\
c' &= 53.211 \text{ in}
\end{aligned}$$

EXERCISE 16

1. Redraw Figs. 14.19 and 14.20, and by the use of suitable construction lines prove that

$$\frac{b}{\sin B} = \frac{c}{\sin C}$$

2. In Fig. 14.25 prove that

$$2R = \frac{a}{\sin A} = \frac{b}{\sin B} = \frac{c}{\sin C}$$

3. Rewrite Eq. (45) for the case in which $B = 90°$.
4. In a certain triangle, the angles A, B, and C are, respectively, as 3:4:5. Side a is 10.000 in. Find sides b and c.
5. The sides of a triangle a, b, and c are, respectively, 25, 38, and 51 in. The angles (not listed in the same order as the sides) are approximately 28°05′, 106°15′, and 45°40′. Identify the angles A, B, and C.
6. Given $a = 10\sqrt{2}$, $A = 30°$, and $C = 105°$, find b and c.
7. If $A = 45°$ and $B = 30°$, find the sides a and b when $c = 10$ in.

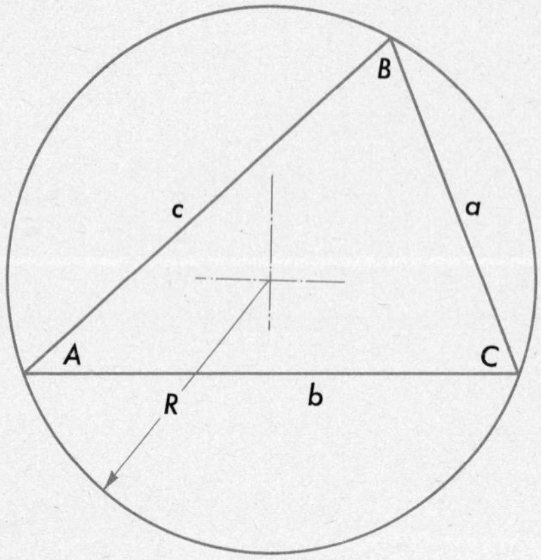

FIGURE 14.25

8. In Fig. 14.26 prove by the law of sines that

$$\frac{ab}{bc} = \frac{oa}{oc}$$

9. If $A = 30°$, $B = 120°$, and $c = 1{,}000$, find a, b, and the altitude drawn to c.
10. Referring to Fig. 14.27.
    (a) Find h, x, and $\angle ACO$.
    (b) Knowing h, find a, y, and $\angle BCO$.
    (c) Knowing x, y, $\angle ACO$, and $\angle BCO$, find C and side c.
11. (a) Angle A of a certain triangle is $17°27.7'$, side a is 30 in, and angle B is $42°$. Draw the triangle to scale and calculate side b.
    (b) If angle A is $162°32.3'$, $a = 30$ in, and $B = 10°$, draw the triangle to scale and solve for side b.
12. The base of a triangle is 4,500 ft, and the angles at the base are $10°20.4'$ and $15°34'$. Find the unknown sides.

In the problems below solve for unknown sides to five figures and unknown angles to the nearest minute.

13. $b = 1.5570$ ft	$A = 38°19'$	$C = 88°10'$
14. $b = 3.3492$ ft	$B = 144°10'$	$C = 13°02'$

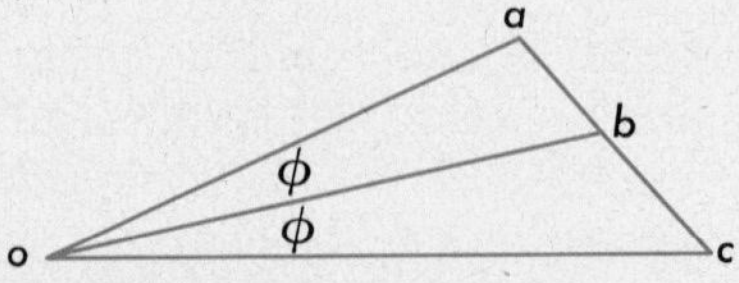

FIGURE 14.26

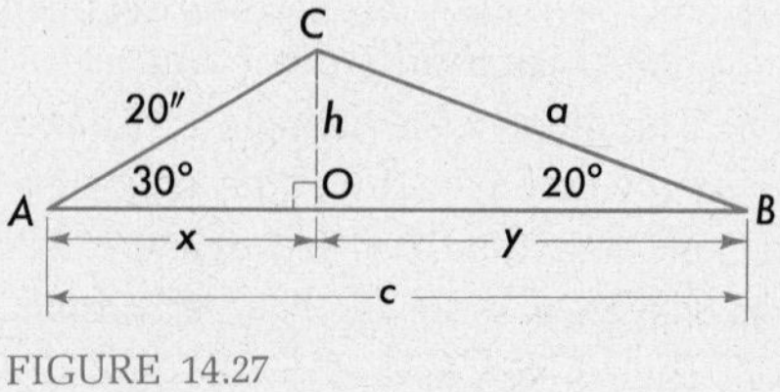

FIGURE 14.27

15. $b = 4.1759$ in	$A = 31°20'$	$C = 18°27'$
16. $b = 4.2997$ in	$A = 7°36'$	$C = 10°29'$
17. $b = 6.8926$ ft	$A = 9°36'$	$C = 47°38'$
18. $a = 1.1831$ in	$B = 8°41'$	$C = 29°54'$
19. $c = 11.863$ in	$A = 5°24'$	$B = 83°50'$
20. $b = 3.8372$ in	$A = 25°26'$	$B = 124°36'$
21. $a = 6.3397$ in	$C = 26°23'$	$B = 49°07'$
22. $c = 10.165$ in	$B = 20°12'$	$C = 75°50'$
23. $c = 39.862$ in	$B = 39°11'$	$A = 12°37'$
24. $a = 2.7570$ ft	$B = 43°7'$	$C = 35°14'$
25. $b = 1.7089$ in	$c = 1.2788$ in	$C = 48°21'$
26. $b = 4.8600$ ft	$a = 3.5683$ ft	$B = 68°01'$
27. $b = 7.2199$ ft	$A = 57°37'$	$a = 6.5867$ ft
28. $a = 1.1690$ in	$c = .63966$ in	$C = 28°04'$
29. $b = 4.4682$ ft	$A = 61°22'$	$a = 4.1244$ ft
30. $b = 1.0226$ ft	$c = 1.3378$ ft	$C = 70°14'$
31. $c = 3.7198$ in	$A = 62°31'$	$a = 3.3145$ in
32. $b = 5.2979$ ft	$A = 74°3'$	$C = 11°17'$
33. $a = 3.7956$ ft	$B = 38°7'$	$C = 82°41'$
34. $b = 0.43972$ in	$A = 51°8'$	$C = 36°28'$

Find the unknown sides to five figures and the unknown angles to the nearest second, using the sine law, in the following problems.

35. $a = 17.230$ in	$A = 56°22'13''$	$C = 35°53'16''$
36. $c = 11.855$ in	$A = 7°30'47''$	$C = 47°36'12''$
37. $c = 133.70$ in	$A = 4°17'22''$	$B = 165°29'23''$
38. $b = 105.46$ in	$B = 85°10'31''$	$c = 105.09$ in
39. $b = 145.70$ in	$a = 145.10$ in	$B = 85°09'55''$
40. $b = 16.683$ in	$A = 79°50'30''$	$a = 17.938$ in
41. $c = 16.481$ in	$b = 32.675$ in	$B = 109°13'16''$
42. $c = 12.781$ in	$a = 12.412$ in	$C = 46°28'50''$
43. $a = 17.219$ in	$c = 19.751$ in	$C = 88°56'3''$
44. $a = 6.6435$ in	$B = 53°21'9''$	$C = 48°48'37''$
45. $a = 10.959$ in	$A = 80°43'53''$	$B = 33°24'58''$
46. $c = 30.361$ in	$A = 21°14'28''$	$B = 146°40'26''$
47. $a = 23.293$ in	$A = 24°15'35''$	$C = 25°25'25''$
48. $b = 10.878$ in	$A = 44°40'38''$	$B = 49°41'43''$
49. $b = 36.234$ in	$A = 20°6'20''$	$C = 48°16'42''$
50. $a = 11.306$ in	$A = 25°24'44''$	$B = 92°24'3''$
51. $a = 6527.6$ in	$B = 70°55'29''$	$C = 52°9'43''$
52. $c = 1004.0$ in	$A = 79°19'25''$	$B = 53°27'10''$
53. $b = 14.752$ in	$B = 13°19.7'$	$C = 59°13.6'$

54. $b = 999.90$ in	$A = 37°58.7'$	$C = 65°2.9'$
55. $a = 497.32$ in	$A = 10°36.4'$	$B = 46°37.9'$
56. $a = 832.76$ in	$A = 82°36'42''$	$B = 45°32'10''$
57. $a = 796.38$ in	$A = 99°36'24''$	$C = 49°37'45''$
58. $a = 827.56$ in	$C = 12°48.3'$	$B = 140°59.7'$
59. $a = 143.62$ in	$B = 37°42.7'$	$C = 28°26.5'$

14.16 The Cosine Law

This law is useful when two sides and the included angle are known or when three sides are known.

Referring to Fig. 14.17,

$$a^2 = b^2 + c^2 - 2 \times b \times c \times \cos A \quad \textbf{(57)}$$
$$b^2 = a^2 + c^2 - 2 \times a \times c \times \cos B \quad \textbf{(58)}$$
$$c^2 = a^2 + b^2 - 2 \times a \times b \times \cos C \quad \textbf{(59)}$$

If one of the angles in the triangle is obtuse, its cosine may be found by the rule below:

To find the cosine of an obtuse angle, subtract the obtuse angle from 180° and use the negative of the cosine of the acute angle so found. (See Sec. 13.10.)

In general, when the angle A is obtuse,

$$\cos A = -\cos (180° - A) \quad (60)$$

Example 30. Find the cosine of 126°.

$$\cos 126° = -\cos (180° - 126°) = -\cos 54°$$

From the five-place tables,

$$\cos 54° = 0.58779$$

Therefore

$$\cos 126° = -0.58779$$

If the angle A, B, or C is obtuse, then Eqs. (57), (58), and (59) may be written

$$a^2 = b^2 + c^2 + 2 \times b \times c \times \cos (180° - A) \quad (61)$$

$$b^2 = a^2 + c^2 + 2 \times a \times c \times \cos(180° - B) \tag{62}$$
$$c^2 = a^2 + b^2 + 2 \times a \times b \times \cos(180° - C) \tag{63}$$

14.17 Derivation of the Cosine Law

Given the oblique triangle ABC in Fig. 14.28, where A, b, and c are known and where A is an acute angle, find a formula for a in terms of A, b, and c.

Drop the perpendicular h from B to side b.

$$x = c \times \cos A \tag{64}$$
$$h = c \times \sin A \tag{65}$$
$$a^2 = h^2 + (b - x)^2 \tag{66}$$

But

$$h^2 = c^2 - x^2 \tag{67}$$

Substituting the above value of h^2 in Eq. (66), we obtain

$$a^2 = c^2 - x^2 + (b - x)^2 \tag{68}$$

or

$$a^2 = c^2 - x^2 + b^2 - 2bx + x^2 \tag{69}$$

or

$$a^2 = c^2 + b^2 - 2bx \tag{70}$$

But

$$x = c \cos A \tag{71}$$

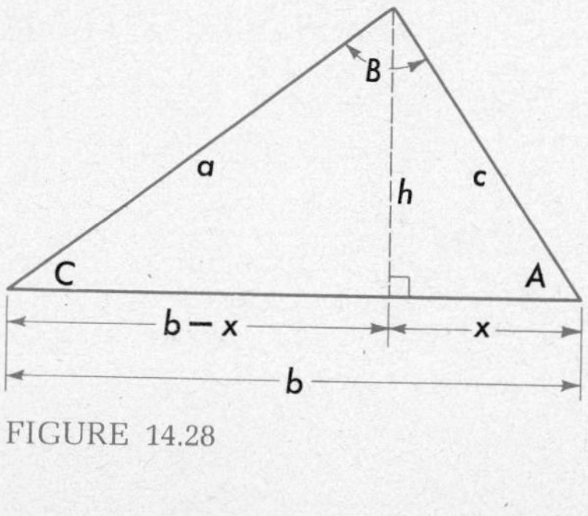

FIGURE 14.28

Substituting the above value of x in Eq. (70),

$$a^2 = c^2 + b^2 - 2bc \cos A \qquad (72)$$

Equations (58) and (59) can be derived in a similar way.

If the known angle is obtuse, the cosine law can be derived from Fig. 14.29. Here the angle A and the sides b and c are given. Angle A is obtuse.

Drop the perpendicular h from B to the side b extended.

$$h = c \sin A'$$
$$x = c \cos A'$$
$$a^2 = h^2 + (b + x)^2 \qquad (73)$$

But

$$h^2 = c^2 - x^2 \qquad (74)$$

Substituting the above value of h^2 in Eq. (73),

$$a^2 = c^2 - x^2 + (b + x)^2$$
$$a^2 = c^2 - x^2 + b^2 + 2bx + x^2$$
$$a^2 = c^2 + b^2 + 2bx$$

But

$$x = c \cos A'$$

Therefore

$$a^2 = b^2 + c^2 + 2bc \cos A'$$
$$A' = 180^\circ - A \qquad (75)$$

and

$$a^2 = b^2 + c^2 - 2bc \cos A \qquad (76)$$

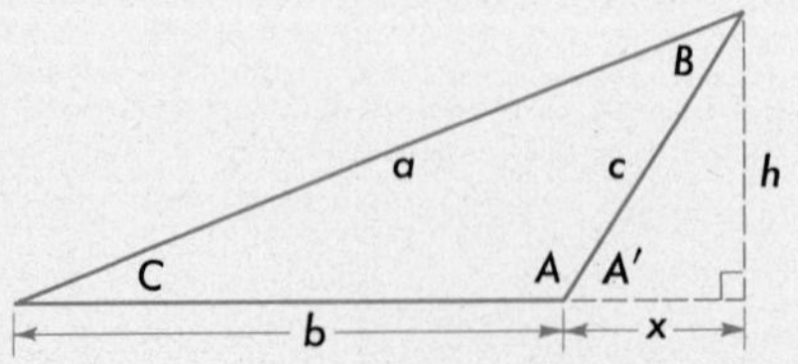

FIGURE 14.29

Therefore the cosine law as stated in Eqs. (57) to (59) is valid for both acute and obtuse angles.

It is not at all unusual to encounter situations in which it is more convenient to use the acute exterior angle A' than to use the obtuse interior angle A (Fig. 14.29). Such cases frequently occur in alternating-current and in concurrent-force problems. In these problems the side b, the side c, and the angle A' would naturally appear in the data.

If the angles A', B', and C' are exterior angles corresponding to the interior angles A, B, and C,

$$a^2 = b^2 + c^2 + 2bc \cos A' \tag{77}$$
$$b^2 = a^2 + c^2 + 2ac \cos B' \tag{78}$$
$$c^2 = a^2 + b^2 + 2ab \cos C' \tag{79}$$

As a special case, if $A' = 90°$, Eq. (77) becomes

$$\begin{aligned} a^2 &= b^2 + c^2 + 2bc \cos 90° \\ &= b^2 + c^2 + 2bc(0) \\ &= b^2 + c^2 \end{aligned}$$

which is the Pythagorean theorem. The cosine law is sometimes called the *generalized Pythagorean theorem* because, with the $\pm 2bc \cos A$ term included, the traditional Pythagorean theorem applies to all triangles.

Example 31. Solve the triangle $a = 25$ in, $b = 56$ in, $C = 36°52'12''$.

$$\begin{aligned} c^2 &= a^2 + b^2 - 2ab \cos 36°52'12'' \\ &= 25^2 + 56^2 - 2 \times 25 \times 56 \times 0.8 \\ &= 625 + 3{,}136 - 2{,}240 \\ &= 1{,}521 \\ c &= \sqrt{1{,}521} = 39 \end{aligned}$$

One of the unknown angles can now be computed by use of the sine law.

$$\frac{c}{\sin C} = \frac{b}{\sin B} \qquad \frac{39}{\sin 36°52'12''} = \frac{56}{\sin B}$$

$$\sin B = \frac{56 \sin 36°52'12''}{39}$$

$$\begin{aligned} \log 56 &= 1.74819 \\ \log \sin 36°52'12'' &= 0.77815 - 1 \\ \text{colog } 39 &= \underline{0.40894 - 2} \\ \log \sin B &= 0.93528 - 1 \end{aligned}$$

B would equal $59°29'26''$ *if B were acute*. However, from the scale drawing of the problem, B is obviously obtuse. Therefore

$$B = 180° - 59°29'26'' = 120°30'34''$$

Example 32. Solve the triangle $a = 25.000$ in, $b = 16.000$ in, $C = 143°7'48''$.

Here the known angle is obtuse, and there are two ways of thinking when attacking the problem. Equation (79) can be used, and

$$\begin{aligned} c^2 &= a^2 + b^2 + 2ab \cos (180° - 143°7'48'') \\ &= a^2 + b^2 + 2ab \cos 36°52'12'' \\ &= 25^2 + 16^2 + 2 \times 25 \times 16 \times 0.8 = 1{,}521 \\ c &= \sqrt{1{,}521} = 39.000 \text{ in} \end{aligned}$$

Or the fact stated in Eq. (60) may be used, and therefore

$$\cos 143°7'48'' = -\cos (180° - 143°7'48'') = -\cos 36°52'12'' = -0.8$$

$$\begin{aligned} c^2 &= a^2 + b^2 - 2ab \cos C \\ &= 25^2 + 16^2 - 2 \times 25 \times 16(-0.8) \\ &= 25^2 + 16^2 + 2 \times 25 \times 16 \times 0.8 = 1{,}521 \\ c &= \sqrt{1{,}521} = 39 \end{aligned}$$

Angle B can be calculated by the sine law, which is here illustrated by the use of natural functions rather than log functions.

$$\frac{\sin B}{b} = \frac{\sin C}{c}$$

$$\frac{\sin B}{16} = \frac{\sin 143°7'48''}{39}$$

Referring to Eq. (48),

$$\sin 143°7'48'' = \sin (180° - 143°7'48'') = \sin 36°52'12'' = 0.60000$$

$$\sin B = \frac{16 \times 0.6}{39} = 0.24615$$

$$B = 14°15'$$

$$A = 180° - (14°15' + 143°7'48'') = 22°37'12''$$

The cosine law is also useful when three sides are known.

Example 33. Solve for all the angles in the triangle $a = 13$ in, $b = 21$ in, $c = 20$ in. (Data are known to five significant digits.)

Use Eqs. (57) to (59):

$$a^2 = b^2 + c^2 - 2bc \cos A$$
$$13^2 = 21^2 + 20^2 - 2 \times 21 \times 20 \cos A$$
$$169 = 441 + 400 - 840 \cos A$$
$$= 841 - 840 \cos A$$
$$\cos A = {}^{672}\!/_{840} = 0.80000 \qquad \text{ANS.: } A = 36°52'11''$$
$$b^2 = a^2 + c^2 - 2ac \cos B$$
$$21^2 = 13^2 + 20^2 - 2 \times 13 \times 20 \cos B$$
$$441 = 169 + 400 - 520 \cos B$$
$$= 569 - 520 \cos B$$
$$\cos B = {}^{128}\!/_{520} = 0.24615 \qquad \text{ANS.: } B = 75°45'00''$$
$$c^2 = a^2 + b^2 - 2ab \cos C$$
$$20^2 = 13^2 + 21^2 - 2 \times 13 \times 21 \cos C$$
$$400 = 169 + 441 - 546 \cos C$$
$$= 610 - 546 \cos C$$
$$\cos C = {}^{210}\!/_{546} = 0.38462 \qquad \text{ANS.: } C = 67°22'47''$$
$$\text{CHECK: } = 179°59'58''$$

Example 34. Find the angle C in the triangle $a = 78$ in, $b = 35$ in, $c = 97$ in. (Data are known to five significant digits.)

$$c^2 = a^2 + b^2 - 2ab \cos C$$
$$97^2 = 78^2 + 35^2 - 2 \times 78 \times 35 \cos C$$
$$9{,}409 = 6{,}084 + 1{,}225 - 5{,}460 \cos C$$
$$= 7{,}309 - 5{,}460 \cos C$$

Here C is obviously obtuse, since c^2 actually is larger than $a^2 + b^2$; in other words, c^2 actually is larger than it would be if C were 90°. A scale drawing would indicate the same fact. Also,

$$-\cos C = \frac{2{,}100}{5{,}460}$$

Therefore, from Eq. (60),

$$\cos C = -2{,}100/5{,}460 = -0.38462$$
$$C = 180° - 67°22'47'' = 112°37'13''$$

EXERCISE 17

1. Verify the following:
   (a) $\cos 42° = 0.74314$ (b) $\cos 138° = -0.74314$
   (c) $\cos 130° = -0.64279$ (d) $\cos 179° = -0.99985$

2. Given the cosine of the angle, verify the following:
   (*a*) −0.89101 is the cosine of 153°. (*b*) 0.89101 is the cosine of 27°.
   (*c*) −0.96126 is the cosine of 164°. (*d*) 0.96126 is the cosine of 16°.
3. Show that with proper regard to signs

$$a = b \cos C + c \cos B$$

   whether B is acute or obtuse.
4. Prove that in a triangle with sides a, b, and c,

$$a^2 + b^2 + c^2 = 2(ab \cos C + bc \cos A + ca \cos B)$$

5. Show that if

$$\frac{\cos A}{b} = \frac{\cos B}{a}$$

   the triangle is either an isosceles triangle or a right triangle.
6. Prove that

$$\frac{\cos A}{a} + \frac{\cos B}{b} + \frac{\cos C}{c} = \frac{a^2 + b^2 + c^2}{2abc}$$

7. Prove that

$$\frac{c^2}{b} \cos B + \frac{b^2}{a} \cos A + \frac{a^2}{c} \cos C = \frac{a^4 + b^4 + c^4}{2abc}$$

   Also show that the equation is dimensionally correct.

Find the side opposite the given angle, using the cosine law.

8. $a = 4.0000$ in　$b = 5.0000$ in　$C = 66°25'18''$
9. $b = 7.0000$ in　$c = 10.000$ in　$A = 45°34'23''$
10. $a = 20.000$ in　$b = 35.000$ in　$C = 60°$
11. $a = 7.0000$ in　$b = 12.000$ in　$C = 123°22'02''$
12. $c = 11.000$ in　$b = 9.0000$ in　$A = 31°47'19''$
13. $a = 13.000$ in　$b = 18.000$ in　$C = 36°52'11''$
14. $a = 5.0000$ in　$b = 10.000$ in　$C = 126°52'13''$
15. $a = 15.000$ in　$b = 22.000$ in　$C = 130°32'30''$
16. $a = 17.000$ in　$b = 15.000$ in　$C = 154°9'28''$
17. $b = 10.000$ in　$c = 20.000$ in　$A = 36°52.2'$

Find all the angles. Make three separate calculations, one for each angle. Find angles to seconds.

18. $a = 61.000$ in	$b = 87.000$ in	$c = 74.000$ in
19. $a = 65.000$ in	$b = 87.000$ in	$c = 44.000$ in
20. $a = 78.000$ in	$b = 95.000$ in	$c = 97.000$ in
21. $a = 25.000$ in	$b = 28.000$ in	$c = 17.000$ in
22. $a = 3.0000$ in	$b = 4.0000$ in	$c = 6.0000$ in
23. $a = 4.0000$ in	$b = 5.0000$ in	$c = 7.0000$ in
24. $a = 5.0000$ in	$b = 7.0000$ in	$c = 9.0000$ in
25. $a = 5.0000$ in	$b = 6.0000$ in	$c = 7.0000$ in
26. $a = 6.0000$ in	$b = 9.0000$ in	$c = 11.000$ in
27. $a = 13.000$ in	$b = 16.000$ in	$c = 19.000$ in
28. $a = 5.0000$ in	$b = 8.0000$ in	$c = 12.000$ in
29. $a = 5.8750$ in	$b = 3.2500$ in	$c = 8.5000$ in

15 vectors

Quantities with which we deal in engineering and technology can be divided into two broad groups. These are *scalar* quantities and *vector* quantities.

Quantities like *time, temperature, money,* etc., whose measure can fully be described by numbers are called *scalar* quantities. Quantities like *displacement, force, velocity,* etc., which involve magnitude, direction, and sense† are called *vector* quantities.

15.1 Vectors

A vector is a line segment whose essential properties are *length, direction,* and *sense.*† Figure 15.1 shows a vector designated by the symbol $\overrightarrow{AB}$ whose length $|\overrightarrow{AB}|$ is 7 units and whose direction is given by the angle 30° measured counterclockwise from the positive side of the X axis. The sense is indicated by the arrowhead pointing away from A, here considered to be the *initial* point of $\overrightarrow{AB}$, and toward B considered to be the terminal point of $\overrightarrow{AB}$.

† The property of sense will be discussed in the following section.

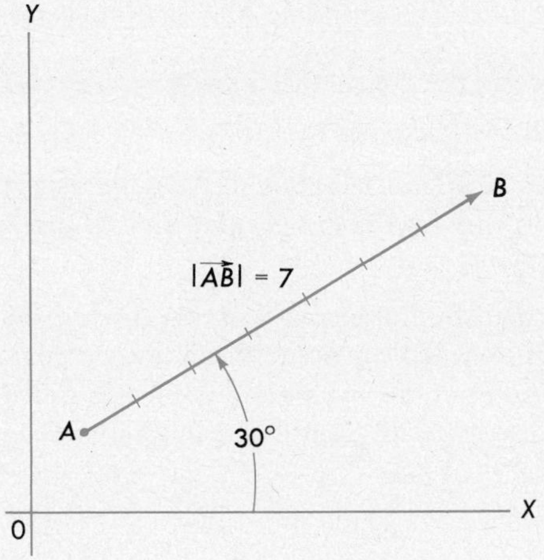

FIGURE 15.1

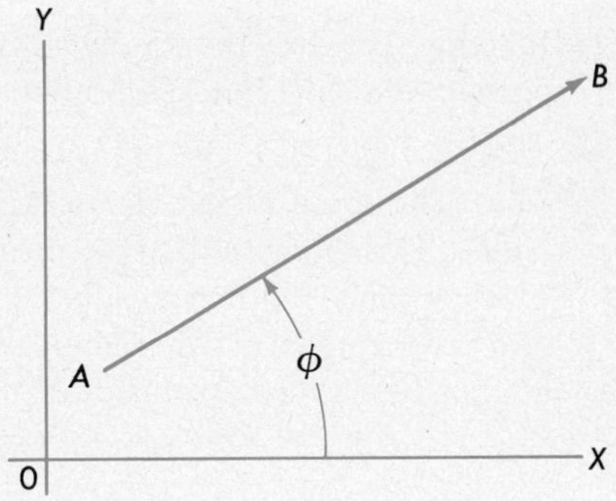

FIGURE 15.2

15.2 Displacement Vectors

In this and the following sections we shall illustrate some of the elementary properties of vectors by reference to a particular kind of a vector known as a *displacement* vector.

Suppose for example that a particle is moved in a plane of Cartesian coordinates from one point A to another point B. Its change in position, called its *displacement*, is represented by the vector $\overrightarrow{AB}$ in Fig. 15.2.

The actual path through which the particle may have been moved is not included in the concept of displacement.

For example, the displacement would have been exactly the same if the particle had been moved over the dashed line in Fig. 15.3.

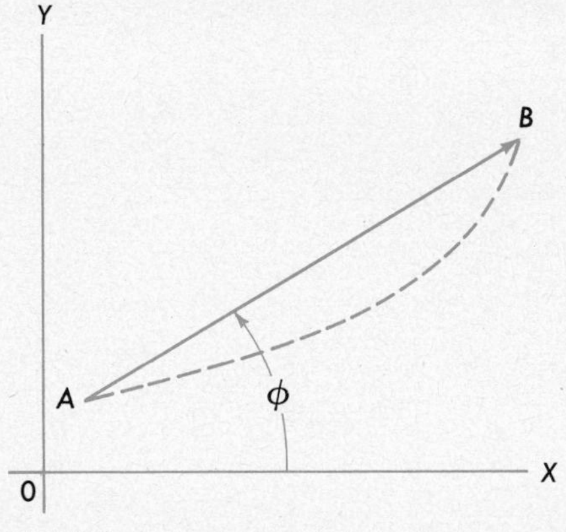

FIGURE 15.3

The vector $\overrightarrow{AB}$ shown in Fig. 15.2 has the three essential properties of a vector. These are:

1. *Length*. This is the length of the vector and is designated by $|\overrightarrow{AB}|$.
2. *Direction*. The direction of $\overrightarrow{AB}$ is given by the angular orientation of $\overrightarrow{AB}$ with respect to some reference line. The reference line in this case is the positive side of the X axis. See Fig. 15.2. The angle is designated by ϕ.
3. *Sense*. The sense of the vector $\overrightarrow{AB}$ is indicated by the arrow pointing toward the point B. This indicates that the displacement is away from point A and toward point B. Accordingly, point A is called the initial point of the vector, and point B is called the terminal point. In cases where sense is not specifically mentioned, it is understood to be included in the concept of *direction*.

15.3 Equality among Vectors

We shall consider two vectors in the same coordinate plane to be equal if they have the same length, direction, and sense even though they may occupy different positions in the plane. See Fig. 15.4 in which vectors $\overrightarrow{AB}$ and $\overrightarrow{CD}$ are equal. This property enables us to replace a given vector with an equal one drawn at a more convenient place in the coordinate plane.

Observe that in Fig. 15.4 the length of each of the three vectors is the same. That is,

$$|\overrightarrow{AB}| = |\overrightarrow{CD}| = |\overrightarrow{EF}| \tag{1}$$

It is also true that the direction of all three vectors is the same, since they are parallel.

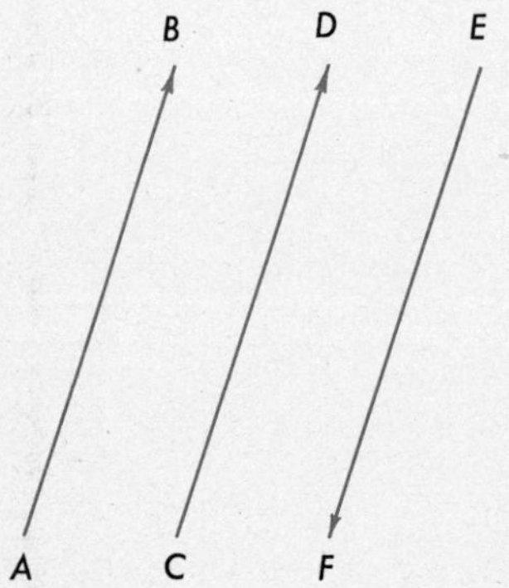

FIGURE 15.4

However, the sense of $\overrightarrow{EF}$ is not the same as the sense of $\overrightarrow{AB}$ and $\overrightarrow{CD}$. Therefore

$$\overrightarrow{EF} \neq \overrightarrow{AB} \tag{2}$$

$$\overrightarrow{EF} \neq \overrightarrow{CD} \tag{3}$$

The sense of $\overrightarrow{EF}$ is exactly opposite to the sense of $\overrightarrow{AB}$ and $\overrightarrow{CD}$. By definition, one vector is said to be the negative of another if their senses are exactly opposite while their magnitudes and directions are equal. Therefore

$$\overrightarrow{EF} = -\overrightarrow{AB} \tag{4}$$

$$\overrightarrow{EF} = -\overrightarrow{CD} \tag{5}$$

The vector having a length of 20 in and a direction given by 130° is shown in Fig. 15.5. These data can be written in a more compact form as

$$20 \text{ in} \underline{/130^\circ}$$

or in general as

$$|\overrightarrow{OP}| \underline{/\phi} \tag{6}$$

Equation (6) is said to express the vector in *polar form* where

$|\overrightarrow{OP}|$ = the length of the vector $\overrightarrow{OP}$

ϕ = the reference angle of the vector $\overrightarrow{OP}$ (usually measured counterclockwise from the positive side of the X axis)

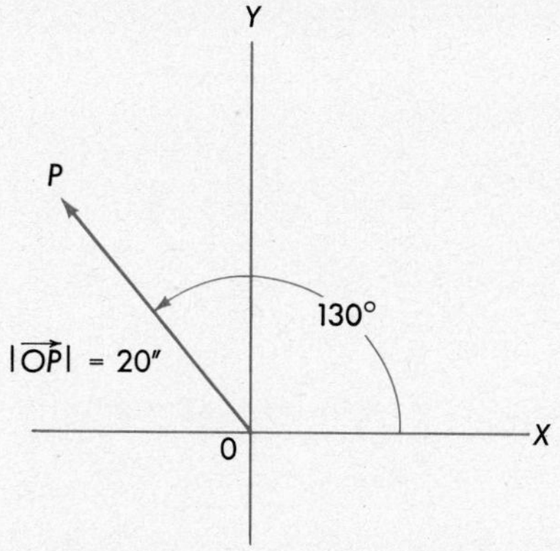

FIGURE 15.5

Without further specification, the vector 20 in$\underline{/130^\circ}$ could be drawn anywhere in the coordinate plane. However, in the absence of any requirements to the contrary we shall plot such vectors at the origin of a Cartesian coordinate system with their initial point at the origin and their reference angle measured counterclockwise from the positive side of the X axis. Vectors drawn in this way are sometimes called *position vectors.*

Figure 15.6 shows $|\overrightarrow{OP}|\underline{/\phi}$ rotated 180° (clockwise or counterclockwise) to become the vector $|\overrightarrow{OP}|\underline{/\phi \pm 180^\circ}$. Since these two vectors have the same length and direction but are opposite in sense, one is said to be the negative of the other. For example, we can write

$$-|\overrightarrow{OP}|\underline{/\phi} = |\overrightarrow{OP}|\underline{/\phi \pm 180^\circ} \tag{7}$$

If $\overrightarrow{OP} = 5\underline{/26^\circ}$, then we may write

$$-\overrightarrow{OP} = 5\underline{/26^\circ + 180^\circ} = 5\underline{/206^\circ}$$

To draw the negative of a given vector, we simply rotate the given vector 180° either clockwise or counterclockwise.

EXERCISE 1

1. Which of the vectors in Fig. 15.7 are equal?
2. Which of these vectors are the negative of $\overrightarrow{AB}$?
3. Which of these vectors have equal magnitudes?

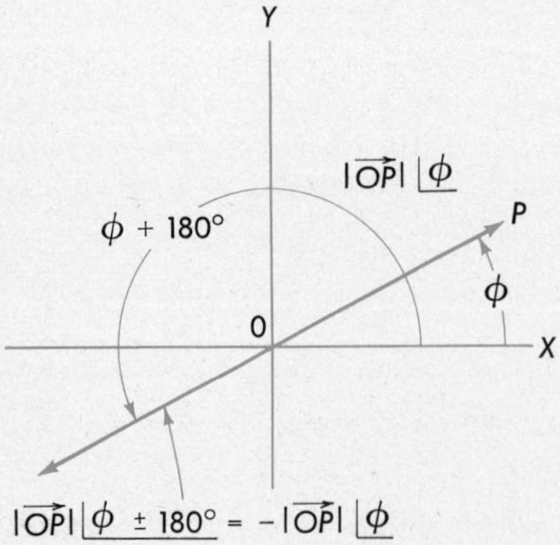

FIGURE 15.6

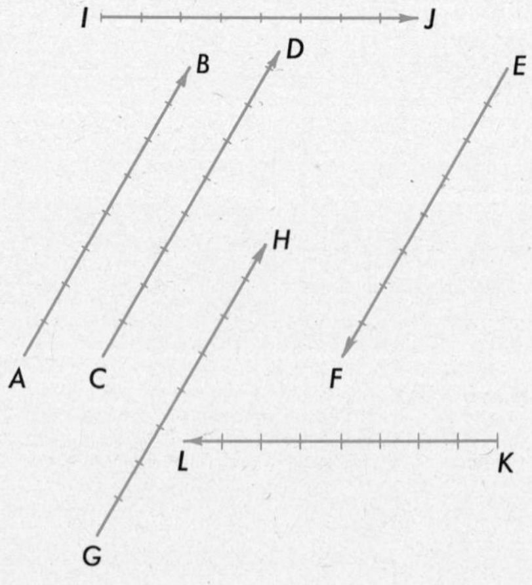

FIGURE 15.7

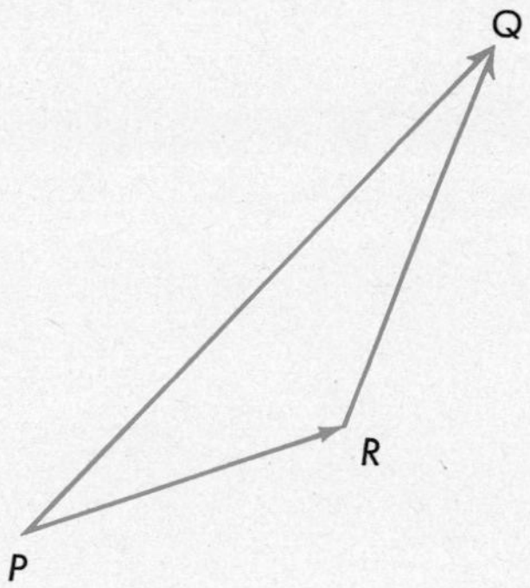

FIGURE 15.8

4. Plot the following vectors, full scale on a rectangular coordinate system.
   (a) 3 in $\underline{/90^\circ}$ (b) -2 in $\underline{/120^\circ}$ (c) 4 in $\underline{/-60^\circ}$
   (d) -2 in $\underline{/200^\circ}$ (e) 4.5 in $\underline{/-90^\circ}$ (f) 3 in $\underline{/270^\circ}$
5. Plot the negatives of the vectors in Prob. 4.

15.4 Graphical Methods of Vector Addition

These methods are quite simple in concept and highly useful, provided the drawings are made carefully using a ruler and protractor and are drawn to a convenient scale.

The Triangle Method

Suppose that a particle is moved from point P to a point R in Fig. 15.8, effecting a displacement given by the vector $\overrightarrow{PR}$. Then in addition it is moved from point R to point Q, effecting a displacement given by the vector $\overrightarrow{RQ}$. Now the resulting displacement is given by the single vector $\overrightarrow{PQ}$, which is called the *resultant*. We now consider the vector $\overrightarrow{PQ}$ to be the sum of the vectors $\overrightarrow{PR}$ and $\overrightarrow{RQ}$, and we may write

$$\overrightarrow{PQ} = \overrightarrow{PR} + \overrightarrow{RQ}$$

Expressed more formally, the vector sum or resultant of $\overrightarrow{PR}$ and $\overrightarrow{RQ}$ is found as follows: Place the initial point of $\overrightarrow{RQ}$ at the terminal point of $\overrightarrow{PR}$. The resultant of $\overrightarrow{PR}$ and $\overrightarrow{RQ}$ is the vector $\overrightarrow{PQ}$, drawn from the initial point of $\overrightarrow{PR}$ to the terminal point of $\overrightarrow{RQ}$.

More than two vectors can be added graphically by following the same general procedure.

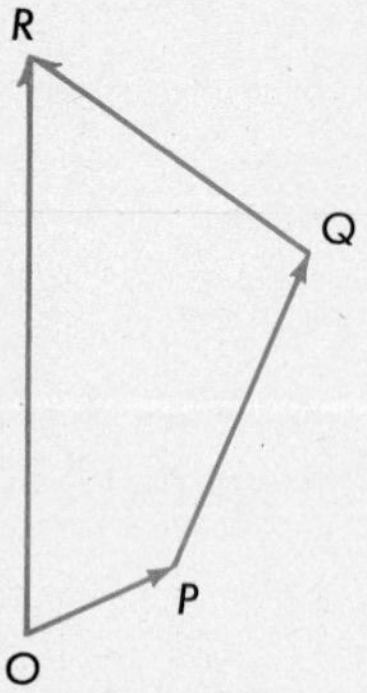

FIGURE 15.9

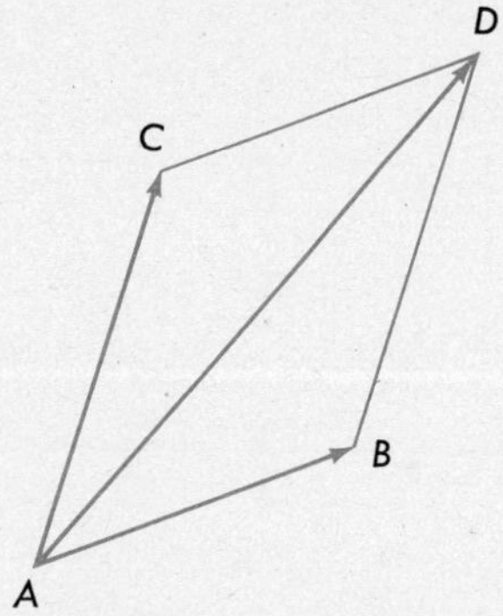

FIGURE 15.10

Having been given a set of vectors to be added such as $\overrightarrow{OP}$, $\overrightarrow{PQ}$, and $\overrightarrow{QR}$ in Fig. 15.9, one is arbitrarily chosen to be drawn first. Then, each of the others is drawn "head to tail" in any order. The resultant is the vector $\overrightarrow{OR}$, drawn from the initial point of the first vector plotted to the terminal point of the last.

The Parallelogram Method

The sum of two vectors drawn from a common point may be found as follows. (See Fig. 15.10.)

Here, the vectors $\overrightarrow{AB}$ and $\overrightarrow{AC}$ are given and are shown to be drawn from a common initial point A. The resultant is the vector $\overrightarrow{AD}$ which is the diagonal of the parallelogram drawn through the common initial point of the given vectors and included by them.

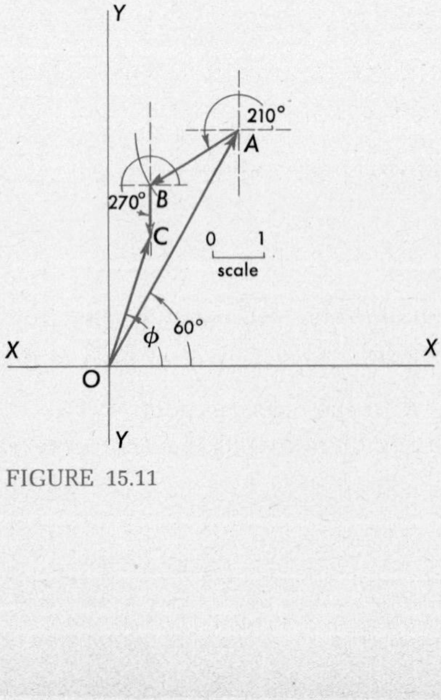

FIGURE 15.11

Example 1. Find the sum of the following vectors graphically:

$5\,\underline{/60^\circ} + 2\,\underline{/210^\circ} + 1\,\underline{/270^\circ}$

The three given vectors are plotted as $\overrightarrow{OA}$, $\overrightarrow{AB}$, and $\overrightarrow{BC}$ in Fig. 15.11. The vector $\overrightarrow{OC}$ is the sum of the given vectors. By scaling with a ruler, $|\overrightarrow{OC}| = 2.45$. By scaling with a protractor, $\phi = 72^\circ$. Therefore,

$\overrightarrow{OC} = 2.45\,\underline{/72^\circ}$

15.5 Vector Subtraction

To subtract one vector $\overrightarrow{OQ}$ from another vector $\overrightarrow{OP}$, we find the sum of $\overrightarrow{OP}$ and the negative of $\overrightarrow{OQ}$.

Figure 15.12 shows the graphical subtraction of the vector $1.08\underline{/248.2^\circ}$ from the vector $2.66\underline{/19.8^\circ}$. To find the negative of $1.08\underline{/248.2^\circ}$, we rotate it 180° to give $\overrightarrow{OQ'}$. See Eq. (7). Now we find the vector difference by adding $\overrightarrow{OP}$ to $\overrightarrow{OQ'}$. Then

$\overrightarrow{OP} - \overrightarrow{OQ} = \overrightarrow{OP} + \overrightarrow{OQ'} = \overrightarrow{OR}$

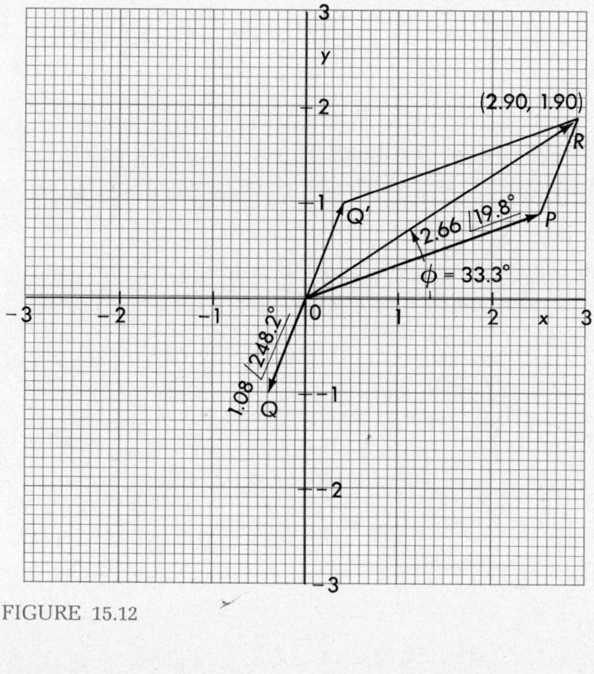

FIGURE 15.12

By measuring the length of $\overrightarrow{OR}$ with a ruler and the reference angle (ϕ) with a protractor, we find that

$\overrightarrow{OR} = 3.47 \underline{/33.3^\circ}$

EXERCISE 2

Plot the following vectors with the initial point of the first given vector at the origin. Find the resultant by using a ruler and protractor. Express the resultant in polar form. Also read the coordinates of the terminal point of the resultant by direct reading of the graph.

1. $30\underline{/45^\circ} - 20\underline{/90^\circ}$
2. $20\underline{/36^\circ} - 5\underline{/80^\circ}$
3. $15\underline{/160^\circ} - 20\underline{/330^\circ}$
4. $90\underline{/220^\circ} - 45\underline{/20^\circ}$
5. $25\underline{/110^\circ} - 60\underline{/220^\circ}$
6. $20\underline{/45^\circ} - 30\underline{/30^\circ} + 10\underline{/225^\circ}$
7. $100\underline{/90^\circ} + 200\underline{/180^\circ} - 100\underline{/0^\circ}$
8. $-25\underline{/330^\circ} + 40\underline{/160^\circ} - 20\underline{/260^\circ}$
9. $15\underline{/60^\circ} - 30\underline{/120^\circ} + 50\underline{/330^\circ}$
10. $20\underline{/115^\circ} - 15\underline{/250^\circ} - 30\underline{/25^\circ}$

15.6 Vector Components

Each of any set of vectors whose sum is a given vector is called a *vector component* of the given vector. For example, in Fig. 15.9 the vector sum of $\overrightarrow{OP}$, $\overrightarrow{PQ}$, and $\overrightarrow{QR}$ is the vector $\overrightarrow{OR}$. Therefore $\overrightarrow{OP}$, $\overrightarrow{PQ}$, and $\overrightarrow{QR}$ are each called *vector components* of $\overrightarrow{OR}$.

Of particular importance is the special case shown in Fig. 15.13. Here the vector $\overrightarrow{OP}$ is the sum of $\overrightarrow{OA}$ and $\overrightarrow{OB}$. These vectors are therefore vector components of $\overrightarrow{OP}$. They are each drawn on a coordinate axis with their initial points at the origin.

In Fig. 15.13, $\overrightarrow{OP} = 2.69\underline{/21.6^\circ}$. By making a scale drawing we find that within graphical accuracy for the scale used $\overrightarrow{OA} = 2.5\underline{/0^\circ}$ and $\overrightarrow{OB} = 1.0\underline{/90^\circ}$. These are, respectively, the vector components along the X and Y axes.

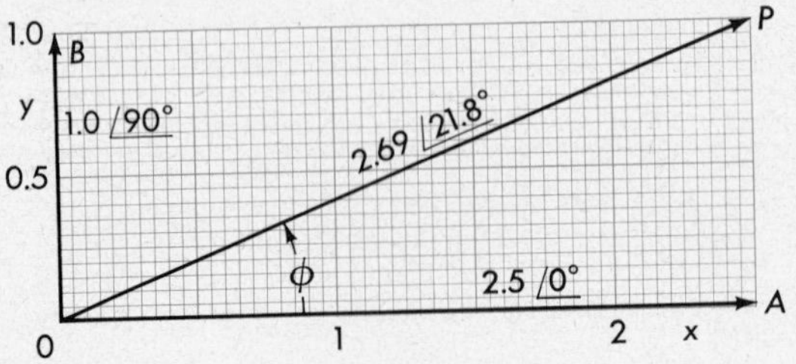

FIGURE 15.13

EXERCISE 3

Draw the following vectors to an appropriate scale. By reading your drawing, find the vector components along the X and Y axes.

1. $3\underline{/27^\circ}$	2. $4\underline{/320^\circ}$	3. $-10\underline{/-30^\circ}$
4. $3\underline{/-270^\circ}$	5. $7\underline{/90^\circ}$	6. $5\underline{/160^\circ}$
7. $15\underline{/29^\circ}$	8. $15\underline{/-250^\circ}$	9. $20\underline{/-135^\circ}$
10. $-7\underline{/-90^\circ}$	11. $2\underline{/220^\circ}$	12. $10\underline{/-140^\circ}$
13. $3\underline{/270^\circ}$	14. $4\underline{/225^\circ}$	15. $5\underline{/1{,}470^\circ}$

15.7 Other Vector Symbols

Thus far we have used symbols such as $\overrightarrow{OP}$ to denote a vector and $|\overrightarrow{OP}|$ to denote its length. There is another commonly used symbolism in which a boldface letter such as **v** denotes a vector and the italic letter v denotes its length.

We shall use the latter symbolism in the following section, partly for convenience and partly to acquaint the student with another common and useful symbolism.

15.8 Components and Projections

We shall introduce a most useful application of components and projections by reference to Fig. 15.14. Here, the vector **v** is drawn with its initial point at the origin of a set of rectangular coordinates. Its length is given by v, and its reference angle is ϕ. The X and Y coordinates of its terminal point P are $v \cos\phi$ and $v \sin\phi$. These are denoted by v_x and v_y, respectively.

The line segments Ob and Oa are measured by v_x and v_y. They are called X and Y projections of **v**. From right-triangle trigonometry the qualities we are discussing are related by

$$v_x = v\cos\phi \qquad v_y = v\sin\phi$$

$$v = \sqrt{{v_x}^2 + {v_y}^2} \qquad \tan\phi = \frac{v_y}{v_x} \tag{8}$$

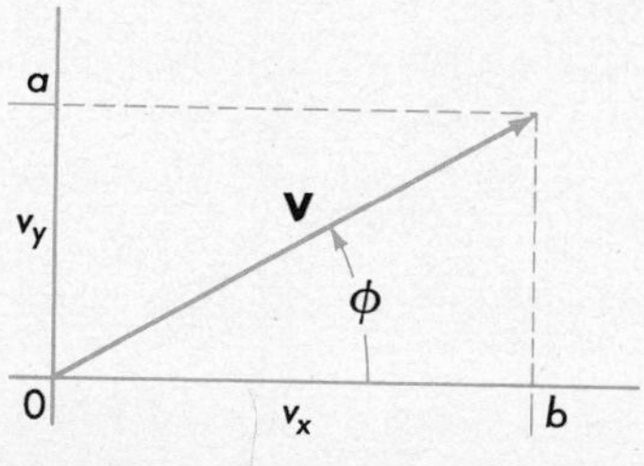

FIGURE 15.14

We recall from Chap. 6 that the coordinates of a point are algebraic numbers. Consequently the projections v_x and v_y are measured by algebraic numbers. Thus v_x and v_y can be either positive or negative numbers, indicating that the projection is either along the positive side of the X or Y axis or along the negative side of the X or Y axis, respectively.

Example 2. Find the X and Y projections of the vector $6\underline{/40^\circ}$.

$$\text{X projection} = 6 \cos 40^\circ = 6 \times 0.7660 = +4.596$$
$$\text{Y projection} = 6 \sin 40^\circ = 6 \times 0.6428 = +3.857$$

Example 3. Find the X and Y projections of the vector $5\underline{/120^\circ}$.

$$\text{X projection} = 5 \cos 120^\circ = 5 \times (-0.5) = -2.5$$
$$\text{Y projection} = 5 \sin 120^\circ = 5 \times (+0.8660) = +4.330$$

Example 4. Find the X and Y projections of the vector $3\underline{/260^\circ}$.

$$\text{X projection} = 3 \cos 260^\circ = 3 \times (-0.1737) = -0.5211$$
$$\text{Y projection} = 3 \sin 260^\circ = 3 \times (-0.9848) = -2.9544$$

Example 5. Find the X and Y projections of the vector $2\underline{/-30^\circ}$.

$$\text{X projection} = 2 \cos(-30^\circ) = 2 \times 0.8660 = +1.732$$
$$\text{Y projection} = 2 \sin(-30^\circ) = 2 \times -0.5000 = -1.000$$

The projections of a vector are often called *scalar* components. These are closely related to but distinct from the corresponding *vector* components.

Once we have been given the projections of a vector along the X and Y axes, the corresponding *vector* components are immediately evident.

In Example 2 the vector component along the X axis is $4.596\underline{/0^\circ}$, and the vector component along the Y axis is $3.857\underline{/90^\circ}$.

In Example 3 the vector component along the X axis is $2.5\underline{/180^\circ}$, and the vector component along the Y axis is $4.330\underline{/90^\circ}$.

In Example 4 the vector component along the X axis is $0.5211\underline{/180^\circ}$, and the vector component along the Y axis is $2.9544\underline{/270^\circ}$.

In Example 5 the vector component along the X axis is $1.732\underline{/0^\circ}$, and the vector component along the Y axis is $1\underline{/270^\circ}$.

15.9 Numerical Methods in Vector Addition and Subtraction

A general definition of vector addition is: The sum of several vectors is a vector, each of whose projections is the algebraic sum of the corresponding projections of the several vectors. The term *composition of vectors* is sometimes used synonymously with vector addition, particularly if the vectors represent forces.

If, for example, we wish to find the sum of several vectors such as $\overrightarrow{OM}$, $\overrightarrow{ON}$, $\overrightarrow{OP}$, and $\overrightarrow{OQ}$, we first find the X projection of each vector. We then add these X projections algebraically to find the X projection of the vector sum. Next we find the Y projection of each vector. Then we add these Y projections algebraically to find the Y projection of the vector sum.

If the vectors to be added are defined in rectangular notation, the process of finding the projections of the vector sum is one of simple algebraic addition.

If the vectors to be added are defined in polar notation, we must first calculate the respective X and Y projections and then proceed as above.

Example 6. Find the X and Y projections of the sum of the following vectors:

Vector	X projection	Y projection
$\overrightarrow{OA}$	+320	+200
$\overrightarrow{AB}$	−250	+100
$\overrightarrow{BC}$	−50	−500

The X projection of the vector sum is

$$+320 - 250 - 50 = +20$$

The Y projection of the vector sum is

$$+200 + 100 - 500 = -200$$

The vector sum is indicated as the vector $\overrightarrow{OC}$ in Fig. 15.15.

Example 7. Perform the following vector addition:

$$2\,\underline{/20^\circ} + 3\,\underline{/120^\circ} + 4\,\underline{/250^\circ} + 5\,\underline{/310^\circ}$$

A topographic diagram illustrating this problem is shown in Fig. 15.16.

The work will be easier and the correct answer more certain if the solution is organized according to some orderly scheme, such as the arrangement in Table 15.1.

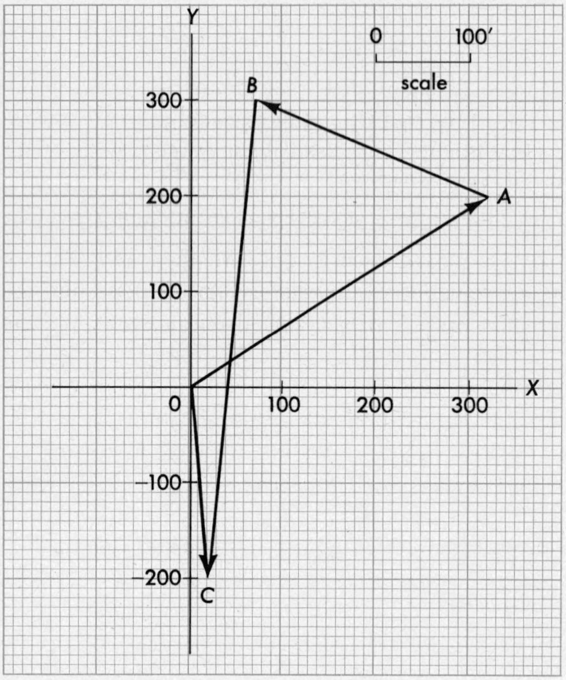

FIGURE 15.15

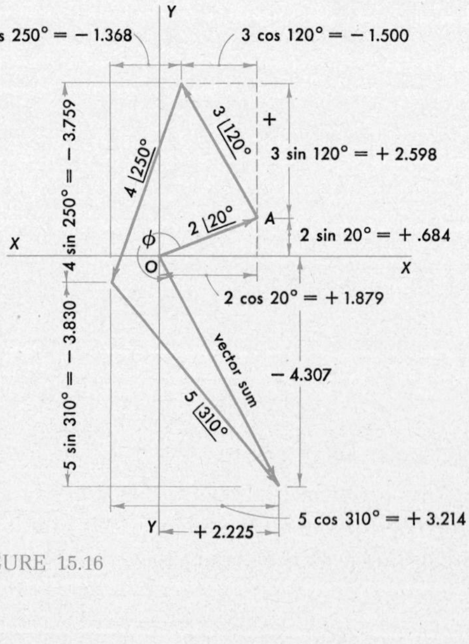

FIGURE 15.16

TABLE 15.1

Vector	cosine	X projection +	X projection −	sine	Y projection +	Y projection −
$2\angle 20^\circ$	+0.9397	1.879		+0.3420	0.684	
$3\angle 120^\circ$	−0.5000		1.500	+0.8660	2.598	
$4\angle 250^\circ$	−0.3420		1.368	−0.9397		3.759
$5\angle 310^\circ$	+0.6428	3.214		−0.7660		3.830
+X projection		5.093				
−X projection			2.868			
+Y projection					3.282	
−Y projection						7.589

Total X projection = 5.093 − 2.868 = 2.225
Total Y projection = 3.282 − 7.589 = −4.307

The magnitude of the vector sum is

$$r = \sqrt{2.225^2 + (-4.307)^2} = \sqrt{23.50} = 4.85$$

If ϕ is the reference angle of the vector sum,

$$\tan\phi = \frac{-4.307}{+2.225} = -1.936$$

$$\phi = 297^\circ 19'$$

In polar notation, the vector sum is $4.85\angle 297^\circ 19'$.

Example 8. If $\overrightarrow{OR} = 5\angle 20^\circ - 8\angle 50^\circ$, express $\overrightarrow{OR}$ in polar notation.

If $\overrightarrow{OR} = 5\angle 20^\circ - 8\angle 50^\circ$, then $\overrightarrow{OR}$ equals $5\angle 20^\circ$ plus the negative of $8\angle 50^\circ$. From Eq. (7) the negative of $8\angle 50^\circ$ is $8\angle 50^\circ + 180^\circ = 8\angle 230^\circ$

then

$$\overrightarrow{OR} = 5\angle 20^\circ + 8\angle 230^\circ$$

Note that we have reversed the sense of the vector $-8\angle 50^\circ$ and have changed the problem from a vector subtraction to a vector addition. The numerical solution is tabulated in Table 15.2.

$$|\overrightarrow{OR}| = \sqrt{(-0.444)^2 + (-4.418)^2} = 4.44$$

TABLE 15.2

Vector	cosine	X projection +	X projection −	sine	Y projection +	Y projection −
$5\underline{/20^\circ}$	+0.940	4.70		0.342	1.71	
$8\underline{/230^\circ}$	−0.643		5.144	−0.766		6.128
+X projection		4.70				
−X projection			5.144			
+Y projection					1.71	
−Y projection						6.128

Total X projection = +4.70 − 5.144 = −0.444
Total Y projection = +1.71 − 6.128 = −4.418

$$\tan \phi_{OR} = \frac{-4.418}{-0.444} = +9.95$$

$$\phi_{OR} = 264.3^\circ$$

$$\overrightarrow{OR} = 4.44\,\underline{/264.3^\circ}$$

When the magnitudes of two vectors are given with the angle between them, it may be convenient to find the resultant by use of the cosine law. See page 426.

EXERCISE 4

Add the vectors given in Exercise 2 and express the resultant in polar form. Use a four-place table of trigonometric tables or a slide rule for calculations.

15.10 Velocity As a Vector

The linear speed of a moving point is the straight-line distance over which the point moves per unit time, without regard to the sense of motion along that straight line. Velocity, on the other hand, is completely described only when speed, direction, and sense of motion are known. Velocity is a vector quantity; speed is a scalar quantity.

Suppose the propeller of an airplane is imparting a 200-mi/h northerly velocity to the plane while the plane is encountering a 50-mi/h cross wind blowing directly toward the east. Assuming that these velocities remain constant for 1 h, at the end of 1 h the plane will be 200 mi north and 50 mi east of the starting point.

A vector diagram of the distances will appear as in Fig. 15.17. The vector $\overrightarrow{OP}$ represents the course of the plane. The magnitude of $\overrightarrow{OP}$ represents the actual distance traveled in this hour.

The vectors $\overrightarrow{OV}$, $\overrightarrow{VP}$, and $\overrightarrow{OP}$ in Fig. 15.17 are distances. However, each of these vectors may be divided by the scalar quantity, time (in this case, 1 h), so that a similar

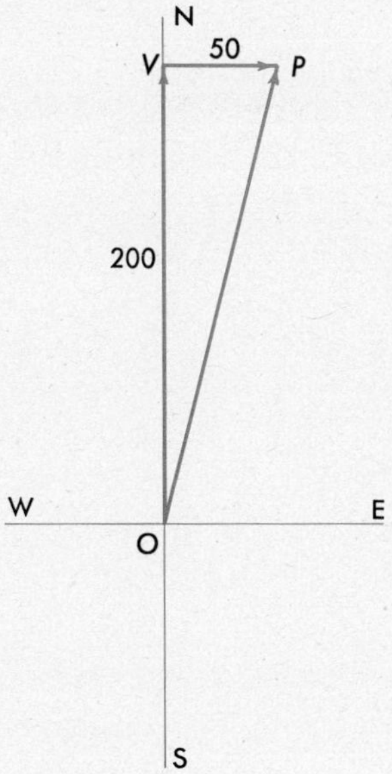

FIGURE 15.17

diagram in which the vectors represent velocities may be constructed. With this interpretation, Fig. 15.17 is identical in appearance with a corresponding velocity diagram.

15.11 Forces As Vector Quantities

Some vector quantities—for example, force—cannot be *completely* measured in terms of length, direction, and sense. The reasons for this are more appropriately left to a text in physics. We shall avoid difficulty arising from this restriction by dealing only with *concurrent* and *coplanar* forces. *Concurrent forces* are those which act at a common point. *Coplanar forces* are those which act along lines lying in the same plane.

It can be shown experimentally that a set of *concurrent, coplanar* forces can be replaced by a single force called their resultant. This is done by the vector operations already discussed.

15.12 Resolution of Forces

In Fig. 15.18 it is given that the magnitude of $\mathbf{F}_3$ is 10 lb and its line of action makes an angle of 30° with the line of action of $\mathbf{F}_1$. Also, it is given that $\mathbf{F}_1$ and $\mathbf{F}_2$ are at right angles and that $\mathbf{F}_3$ is the resultant of $\mathbf{F}_1$ and $\mathbf{F}_2$. The problem is to find the magnitudes of $\mathbf{F}_1$ and $\mathbf{F}_2$.

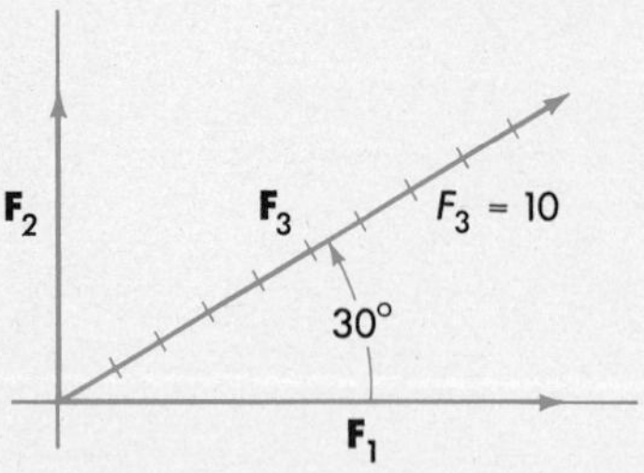

FIGURE 15.18

Graphically, this can be done by drawing the figure to scale, as in Fig. 15.18. Now F_1 and F_2 can be measured. By calculation,

$$F_2 = 10 \sin 30° = 10 \times 0.5 = 5$$
$$\mathbf{F}_2 = 5 \underline{/90°}$$
$$F_1 = 10 \cos 30° = 10 \times 0.866 = 8.66$$
$$\mathbf{F}_1 = 8.66 \underline{/0°}$$

This process is called the resolution of the force $\mathbf{F}_3$ into two rectangular components $\mathbf{F}_1$ and $\mathbf{F}_2$.

If it is assumed that $\mathbf{F}_2$ is vertical and $\mathbf{F}_1$ is horizontal, then $\mathbf{F}_2$ is called the vertical component of $\mathbf{F}_3$, and $\mathbf{F}_1$ is called the horizontal component of $\mathbf{F}_3$.

Example 9. Find the resultant $\mathbf{F}$ and the equilibrant of two concurrent forces $\mathbf{F}_1$ and $\mathbf{F}_2$ acting at right angles when $F_1 = 3$ kg and $F_2 = 4$ kg. See Fig. 15.19.

The equilibrant of a force is a force whose magnitude and direction are the same as the resultant but whose sense is opposite to that of the resultant.

Draw $\mathbf{F}_1$ and $\mathbf{F}_2$ to scale. The magnitude F of the resultant appears to be 5 kg as determined by measurement.

By calculation, since the angle $aob = 90°$,

$$F = \sqrt{3^2 + 4^2} = 5 \text{ kg}$$

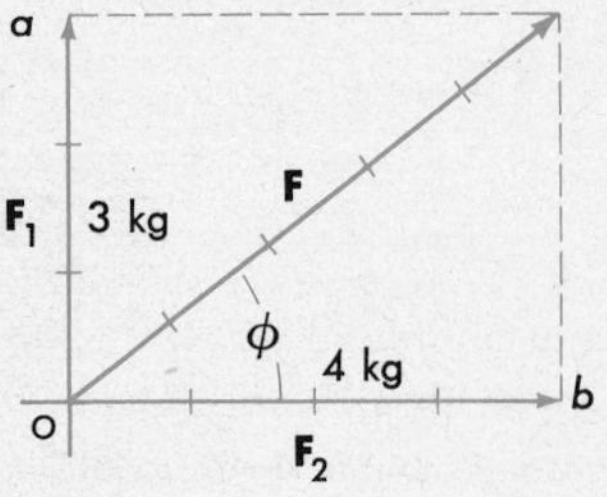

FIGURE 15.19

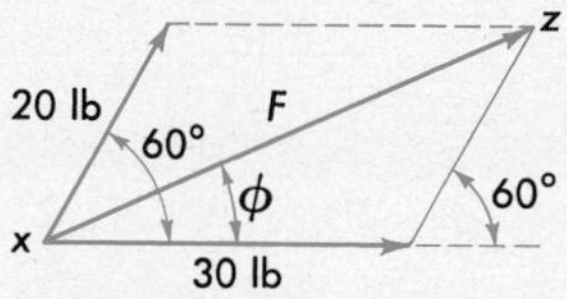

FIGURE 15.20

and

$$\tan\phi = \tfrac{3}{4} = 0.75000$$
$$\phi = 36°52'$$

Then

the resultant = 5 kg$\underline{/36°52'}$

and

the equilibrant = −5 kg$\underline{/36°52'}$

Example 10. Two forces act at a single point. The angle between them is 60°. The magnitudes of the forces are 20 and 30 lb, respectively. Find the magnitude F of the resultant and the equilibrant. Also find the angle which the resultant makes with the 30-lb force. See Fig. 15.20.

Following Sec. 14.16, we find

$$F = \sqrt{30^2 + 20^2 + 2 \times 20 \times 30 \cos 60°} = 43.6 \text{ lb}$$

$$\sin\phi = \frac{20 \times \sin 60°}{43.6} = \frac{20 \times 0.866}{43.6} = 0.397$$

$$\phi = 23.4°$$

The resultant is a force whose magnitude is 43.6 lb in the direction xz. The equilibrant is a force whose magnitude is also 43.6 lb, but which acts in the direction zx.

EXERCISE 5

1. Find the resultant of two concurrent forces, one of 253 and the other of 578 lb, acting at an angle of 18°27′20″ with each other.
2. Two forces acting at right angles with each other have a resultant of 350 lb, and one of the forces is 270 lb. Find the other force and the angle it makes with the resultant.

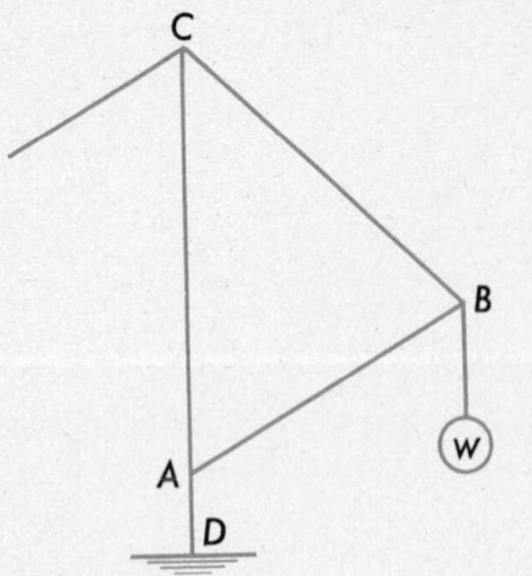

FIGURE 15.21

3. Two forces, of 70 and 85 lb, have a resultant of 125 lb. Find the angle which each of the forces makes with the resultant.
4. Find the horizontal and vertical components of a force of 5,680 lb acting at an angle of 23°46′25″ with the horizontal.
5. A horse pulls a canalboat with a force of 425 lb on the end of a towline which makes an angle of 6° with the side of the canal. Find the force tending to urge the boat toward shore and the effective force which pulls the boat forward.
6. Two forces, of 3,600 and 5,300 lb, have a resultant of 7,500 lb. Find the angle which the resultant makes with each force.
7. A man pushes a floating plank with a force of 25 lb on the end of a pole which makes an angle of 53° with the surface of the water. What force tends to submerge the plank, and what to move it horizontally?
8. Three forces, of 125, 150, and 175 lb, are concurrent and in equilibrium. The first pulls toward the north, and the second in a general direction south of east. Find the direction of the third force.
9. In the derrick shown in Fig. 15.21 the mast DC is 45 ft high, the boom AB is 42 ft long, and pin A is 2 ft above D. W is a weight of 1,000 lb, and angle CAB is 44°. Find the length of the line BC and the force in BC and in AB.

16 graphs of the trigonometric functions

In this chapter we shall graph each of the six trigonometric functions. By observing the nature of the graphs, we can deduce many of the properties of the functions themselves.

In addition to such theoretical uses, the graphs of the functions, particularly those of the sine and cosine, are very convenient devices to use in the analysis and solution of certain engineering problems.

Figure 16.1 shows the graphs of the six trigonometric equations

$$y = \sin \phi \tag{1}$$
$$y = \cos \phi \tag{2}$$
$$y = \tan \phi \tag{3}$$
$$y = \cot \phi \tag{4}$$
$$y = \sec \phi \tag{5}$$
$$y = \csc \phi \tag{6}$$

While it is true that the choice of scale is to a certain extent arbitrary, we do obtain a somewhat more characteristic shape of the graphs if we use the same scale on both axes and plot the angles in radians rather than in degrees. Figure 16.1 is plotted in this way.

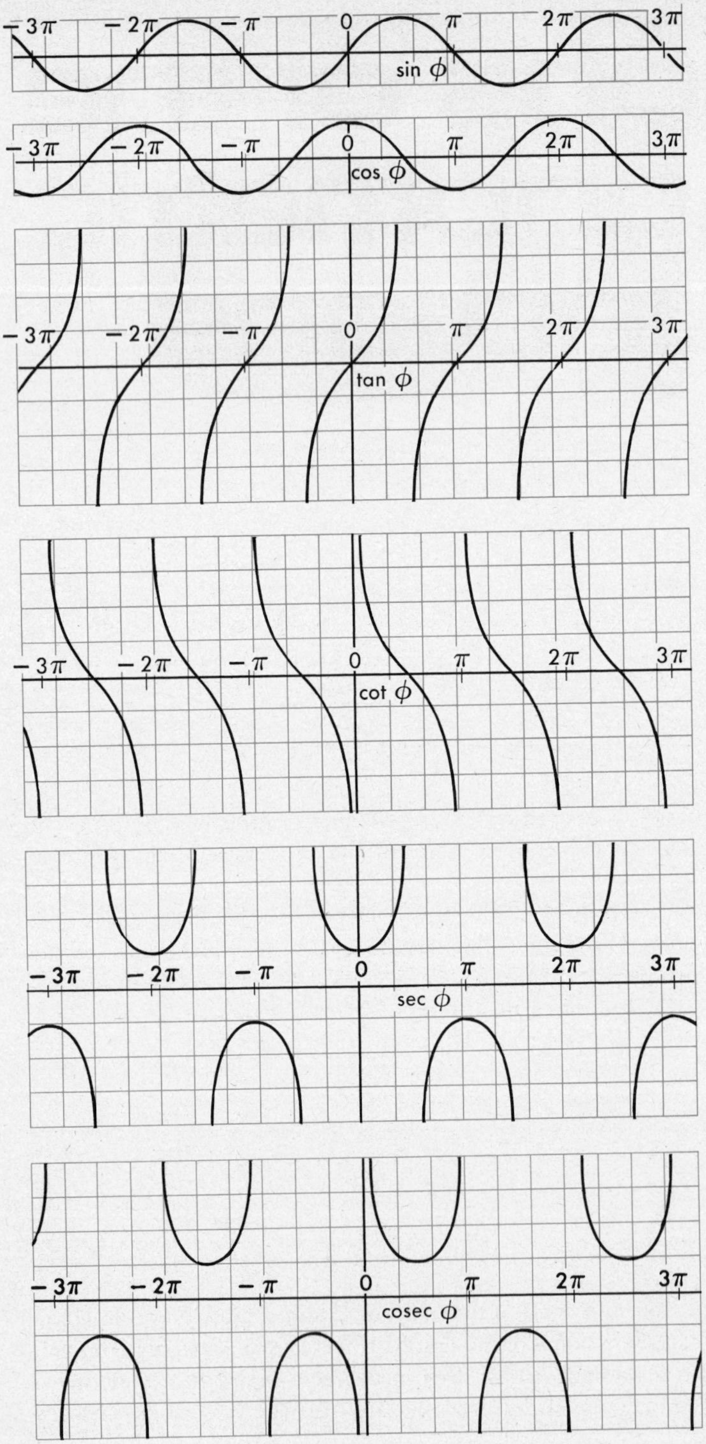

sin ϕ
cos ϕ
tan ϕ
cot ϕ
sec ϕ
cosec ϕ
-3π
-2π
$-\pi$
0
π
2π
3π

FIGURE 16.1

However, in technology the theoretical advantage gained by using radian measure rather than degree measure does not ordinarily outweigh the disadvantage of using the irrational number π.

16.1 Some Periodic Functions

One of the most important characteristics of the trigonometric functions is their repetitive nature.

A study of Fig. 16.1 will show that as the angle increases or decreases, the six functions undergo certain characteristic changes. As the angle indefinitely increases or decreases, these changes repeat periodically. The trigonometric functions are therefore called *periodic functions*. One *cycle* has elapsed when a function has traversed once all the variations of which that particular function is capable.

The *angular period* of any of the trigonometric functions is the angular interval required for the completion of one cycle.

Beginning at $\phi = 0$, let us trace the characteristic changes of the sine function. From $\phi = 0$ to $\phi = \pi/2$ rad, the sine increases from 0 to 1; from $\pi/2$ to π rad, the sine decreases from 1 to 0; from π to $3\pi/2$ rad, the sine decreases from 0 to -1; from $3\pi/2$ to 2π rad, the sine increases from -1 to 0. As ϕ begins to increase beyond 2π rad, the cycle begins to repeat. Thus the angular period of the sine function is 2π rad, or 360°.

The period of the tangent function is π rad. Over the interval $\phi = -\pi/2$ to $\phi = 0$, the tangent increases from $-\infty$ to 0. As the angle increases from 0 to $+\pi/2$ rad, the tangent increases from 0 to $+\infty$. If ϕ increases beyond $\pi/2$ rad, the tangent again traverses the complete array of values from $-\infty$ to $+\infty$, repeating the variation which took place in the previous angular period of π rad.

EXERCISE 1

1. In the equation $y = 5 \sin \beta$, find y from the tables when β is 10°, 50°, 160°, 250°, and 300°.
2. Using the same scale, plot the six trigonometric functions between $-360°$ and $+360°$.
3. On the same axes plot the curves of $y = \sin \beta$ and $y = \tan \beta$. Use radian measure rather than degree measure, and plot over the interval $\beta = 0$ to $\beta = 0.02$ rad. What is the approximate slope of the graphs in this region? What would you expect the slope to be when $\beta = 0$? For any given angle in this region, which is greater, the sine or the tangent?

16.2 Sine and Cosine Graphs

For our immediate purpose, the graphs of the sine and cosine are by far the most important.

Since the period of a sine or cosine curve is 2π rad, or 360°, we usually plot

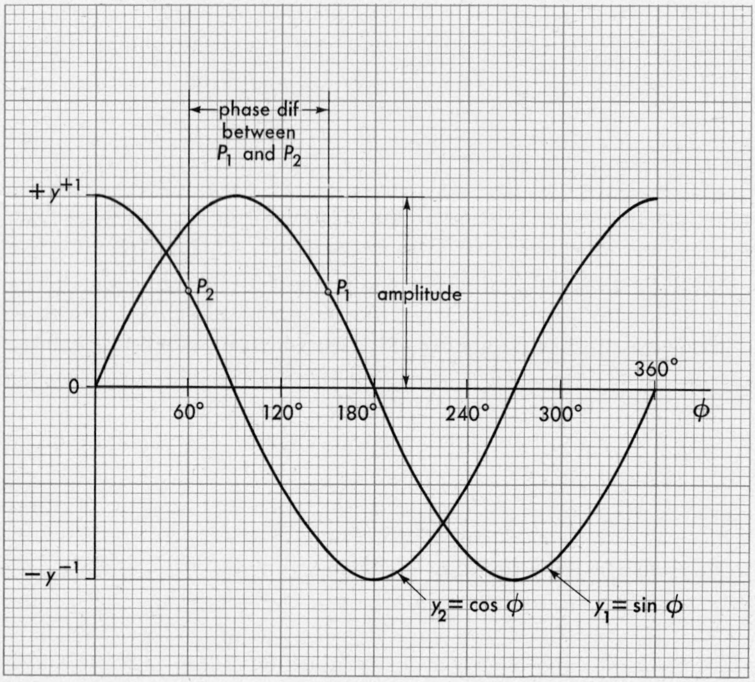

FIGURE 16.2

only in the interval between $\phi = 0$ and $\phi = 2\pi$ rad. All the characteristic changes of these functions appear in this region.

Figure 16.2 shows a plot of the equations

$$y_1 = \sin\phi \tag{7}$$
$$y_2 = \cos\phi \tag{8}$$

The horizontal axis is calibrated in degrees rather than in radians. A comparison between the shapes of the graphs of these functions in Figs. 16.1 and 16.2 will show the practical equivalence of the two plots even when ϕ is plotted in units of degrees rather than in radians.

Notice that the sine and cosine curves in Fig. 16.2 have exactly the same shape, but the cosine curve is displaced 90° to the left with respect to the sine curve.

The *amplitude* of a sine or cosine curve is the absolute value of the maximum and minimum ordinates. In Fig. 16.2 the amplitude of both curves is 1.

Observe that all the characteristic changes in the cosine functions of ϕ occur at angles differing by 90° from the corresponding changes in the sine functions of ϕ. Therefore a cosine function of ϕ is said to have a 90° phase shift when compared with a sine function of ϕ. Since, in scanning the curve from left to right in the direction of increasing angles, we observe points on the cosine curve before we observe the corresponding points on the sine curve, we say that the cosine function *leads* the sine function.

The student should verify that by plotting the equation

$$y = \sin(\phi + 90°) \tag{9}$$

he will obtain the graph of y_2 in Fig. 16.2. Thus he may conclude that

$$\cos\phi = \sin(\phi + 90°) \tag{10}$$

The equations for the sine and cosine functions may be generalized somewhat by writing

$$y = k\sin(\phi + \psi) \tag{11}$$

and

$$y = k\cos(\phi + \psi) \tag{12}$$

where k and ψ are constants.

When $\phi + \psi = 90°$ in Eq. (11), the ordinate of the sine curve is a maximum and equal to k. When $\phi + \psi = 0°$ in Eq. (12), the ordinate of the cosine curve is a maximum and also equal to k. The factor k is called the *amplitude* of the curve and is numerically equal to the maximum value of the function.

The constant angle ψ as used in Eqs. (11) and (12) is known as the *phase shift* and has the effect of shifting the graphs of the equations

$$y = k\sin\phi$$

or

$$y = k\cos\phi$$

to the right or left along the ϕ axis. The curve is shifted to the left when ψ is positive and to the right when ψ is negative. The effect of k and ψ is illustrated in Fig. 16.3.

EXERCISE 2

1. The amplitude of a sine curve is 25. What is the ordinate of the curve at the following positions in its cycle?
   (*a*) 20° (*b*) 90° (*c*) 130° (*d*) 180°
   (*e*) 210° (*f*) 270° (*g*) 300° (*h*) 360°

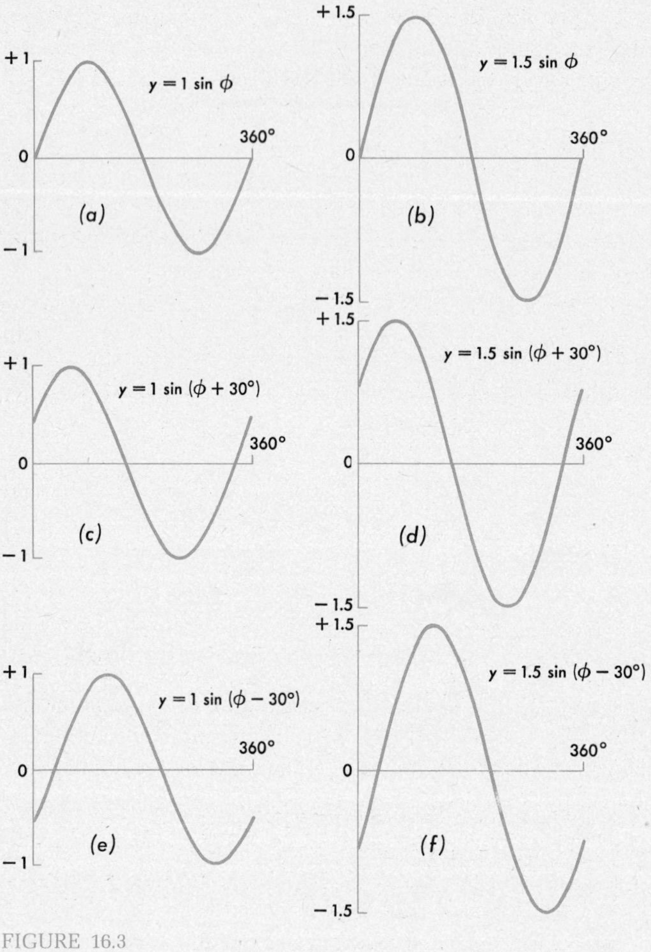

FIGURE 16.3

2. Write an equation for a sine function in which the amplitude is 23 and the phase constant is $+56°$.
3. Plot the following curves:
   (a) $y = \sin \phi$ (b) $y = \sin (\phi - 90°)$
   (c) $y = \sin (\phi - 60°)$ (d) $y = \sin (\phi - 30°)$
   (e) $y = \sin (\phi + 30°)$ (f) $y = \sin (\phi + 60°)$
   (g) $y = \sin (\phi + 90°)$
4. Plot the following curves:
   (a) $y = \cos \phi$ (b) $y = \cos (\phi - 90°)$
   (c) $y = \cos (\phi - 60°)$ (d) $y = \cos (\phi - 30°)$
   (e) $y = \cos (\phi + 30°)$ (f) $y = \cos (\phi + 60°)$
   (g) $y = \cos (\phi + 90°)$

Note: Be sure to compare the graphs obtained in Probs. 3g and 4a. Repeat for Probs. 3a and 4g.

5. The ordinate of a sine curve is +25 when 100° of its cycle has been completed. Find the amplitude.
6. The ordinate of a sine curve is 15 when 80° of its cycle has been completed. What is the ordinate when 300° has been completed?
7. At what positive angles less than 360° will the absolute value of the ordinate of a cosine curve be 70 percent of its amplitude?
8. The amplitude of a sine curve is 15. Find the ordinate at a phase 20° after its minimum.
9. What is the phase difference between the curves of the functions $y = 3 \sin \phi$ and $y' = 7 \sin (\phi + 40°)$?

16.3 Plotting the Sine and Cosine Functions by Geometric Methods

Thus far we have plotted the sine and cosine curves by the use of tables. There is a geometric method which is extremely useful in the analysis of certain problems. This method is illustrated in Fig. 16.4*a*. First a base line *ox* of arbitrary length is established. Then a circle is drawn with its center (*C*) on an extension of *ox*. The radius of this circle is the amplitude of the sine curve to be plotted. The length *ox* is to scale numerically equal to the angular measure of one period.

The circle is divided into a convenient number of equal arcs, and the line *ox* is calibrated with the same number of equally spaced angle markers.

The points *a*, *b*, *c*, *d*, etc., are projected from the circle parallel to *ox*. The points *a′*, *b′*, *c′*, *d′*, etc., are projected vertically from the *ox* axis. Points on the sine curve are found at the intersection of corresponding projections.

Figure 16.4*b* is a similar construction of a cosine curve. Note that the reference point *o* on the circle has been advanced 90° counterclockwise.

16.4 Phasors

The geometric method of plotting sine functions discussed in Sec. 16.3 is highly important in explaining the procedure used in solving many important engineering problems.

For these applications we shall consider that the radii in Fig. 16.5 represent successive, momentary positions of a rotating position vector.

We impose four critical conditions on such a rotating position vector:

1. *It rotates with a constant angular velocity.*
2. *It is of constant length.*

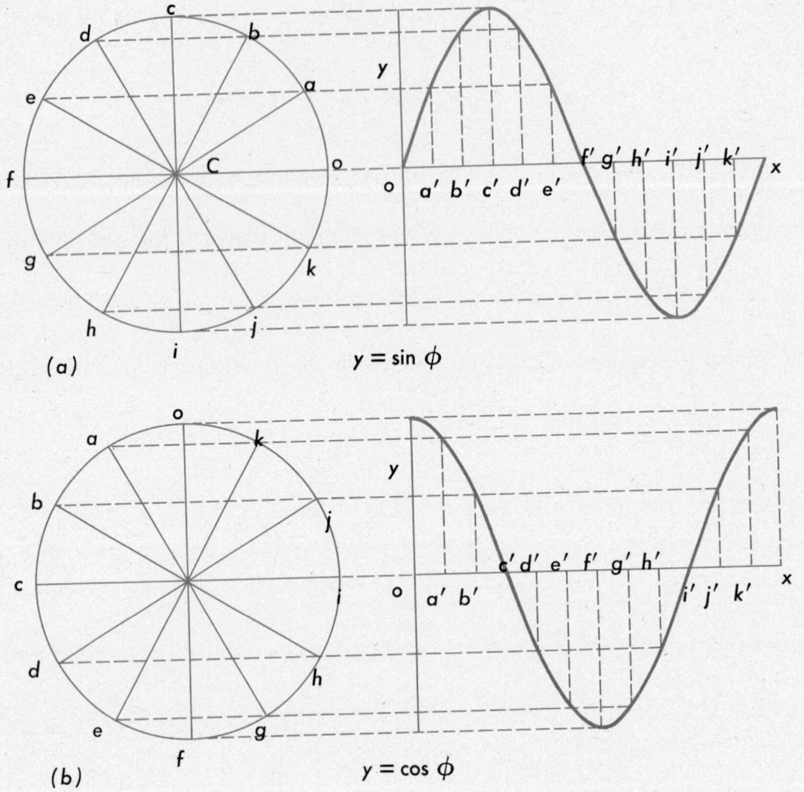

FIGURE 16.4

3. *It rotates in a coordinate plane about the origin of the coordinate system.*
4. *It rotates in a counterclockwise direction.*

A rotating position vector is sometimes called a *phasor*.

Referring to Fig. 16.5*a*, we note that this figure is similar to Fig. 16.4*a*. However, certain very important differences do exist. The phasors, $\overrightarrow{OR}_0$, $\overrightarrow{OR}_1$, $\overrightarrow{OR}_2$, etc., represent successive positions of the rotating phasor $\overrightarrow{OR}$ at times t_0, t_1, t_2, etc. The horizontal axis of the sine curve is calibrated with equally spaced *time* markers rather than with equally spaced angle markers. The ordinate of the sine curve at t_0, t_1, t_2, t_3, etc., is the momentary vertical projection of the position vector $\overrightarrow{OR}$ at that time.

During each revolution the position vector $\overrightarrow{OR}$ rotates through 360°, or 2π rad. The sequence of events which takes place during one revolution of the position vector is called a *cycle*.

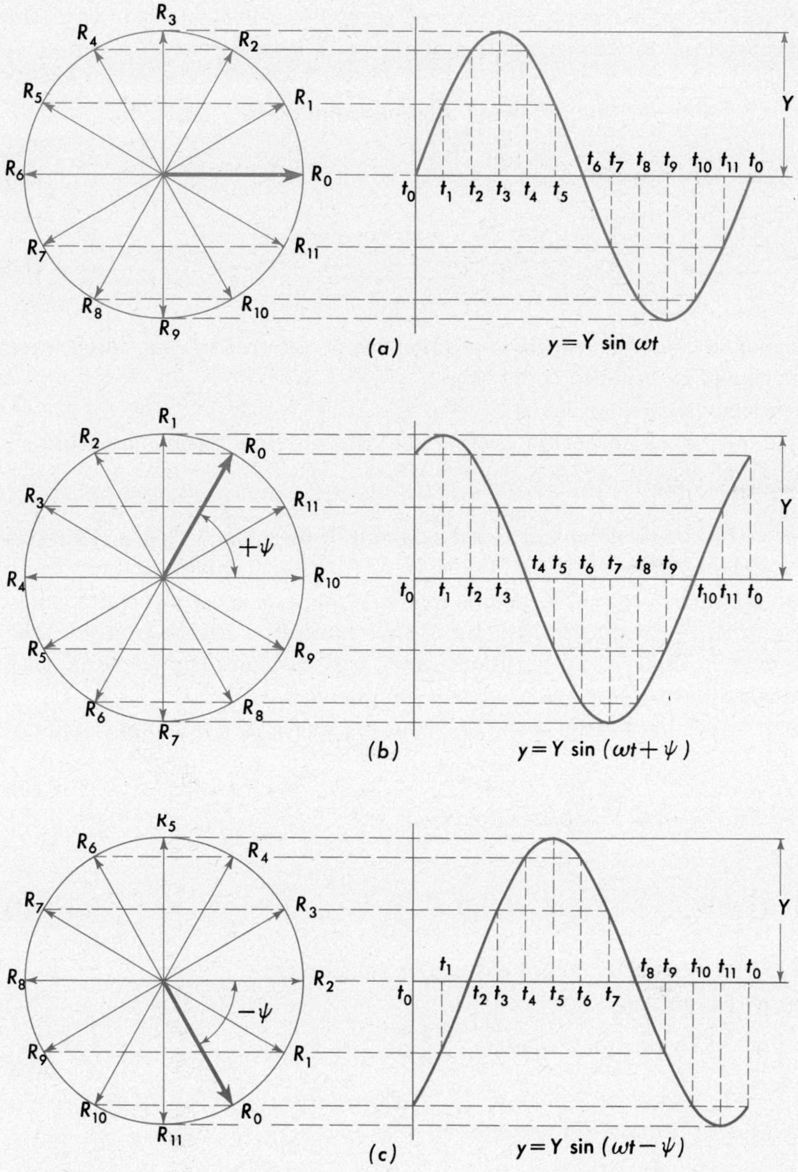
R3
R4
R2
R5
R1
R6
R0
R7
R11
R8
R10
R9
Y
t0 t1 t2 t3 t4 t5 t6 t7 t8 t9 t10 t11 t0
(a)
y = Y sin ωt
R1
R2
R0
R3
R11
+ψ
R4
R10
R5
R9
R6
R8
R7
Y
t0 t1 t2 t3 t4 t5 t6 t7 t8 t9 t10 t11 t0
(b)
y = Y sin (ωt + ψ)
R5
R6
R4
R7
R3
R8
R2
−ψ
R9
R1
R10
R0
R11
Y
t0 t1 t2 t3 t4 t5 t6 t7 t8 t9 t10 t11 t0
(c)
y = Y sin (ωt − ψ)

FIGURE 16.5

The number of cycles taking place in one second is called the *frequency*. The time in seconds required for the completion of one cycle is called the *time period*, or simply the *period*.

From these definitions the following relations appear:

$$\phi = 360° \times f \times t \qquad \text{(in degrees)} \tag{13}$$

$$\phi = 2\pi \times f \times t \qquad \text{(in radians)} \tag{14}$$

$$T = \frac{1}{f} \tag{15}$$

where ϕ = momentary reference angle of position vector, referred to its position when we choose to begin to count time

f = frequency, Hz (or cycles/s)

t = time during which position vector has been rotating from some arbitrary zero time-reference position, s

T = period, s

The *hertz* (Hz) is now commonly used as a unit of frequency. Thus 1 Hz means 1 cycle/s, 60 Hz means 60 cycles/s, etc.

The zero reference position R_0 can be rotated either clockwise or counterclockwise, as shown in Fig. 16.5*b* and *c*. In such cases we introduce the phase shift ψ. The momentary reference angle of the position vector now becomes $(\phi - \psi)$ or $(\phi + \psi)$, according as R_0 has been rotated clockwise or counterclockwise.

The general equation for the ordinate of the sine curve as a function of time is

$$y = Y \sin (2\pi f t \pm \psi) \tag{16}$$

or

$$y = Y \sin (360° f t \pm \psi) \tag{17}$$

The term $2\pi f$ or $360° f$ is in the nature of angular velocity.

Ordinarily, we let

$$\omega = 2\pi f \tag{18}$$

(when measuring ω in radians per second), or

$$\omega = 360° f \tag{19}$$

(when measuring ω in degrees per second). Equation (16) then becomes

$$y = Y \sin (\omega t \pm \psi) \tag{20}$$

where Y = constant amplitude
ω = angular velocity, rad (or deg)/s
t = time, s
ψ = phase shift measured in same angular units as ωt
$\omega t \pm \psi$ = momentary reference angle of position vector referred to conventional reference position of system of rectangular coordinates

As a matter of expediency, we usually plot y against the angle ωt rather than against t itself. However, if after plotting y against ωt, it seems worthwhile to show the plot of y against t, the horizontal scale can be altered to read directly in time units. Then the phase shift can be interpreted in terms of the appropriate time units.

The terms *amplitude, frequency, angular velocity, period,* and *phase shift* have been defined. Now let us interpret these terms in relation to specific quantities appearing in the general equation for a sine function.

With reference to Eq. (20), the constant Y is the amplitude. A change in Y alters each ordinate of the sine curve, but does not destroy the characteristic shape of the sine curve. A comparison of Fig. 16.3*a*, *c*, and *e* with Fig. 16.3*b*, *d*, and *f*, respectively, should illustrate this.

The phase shift ψ has no effect on the amplitude or the shape of the curve, but does have the effect of shifting the whole curve to the right or left along the time axis. A comparison among Fig. 16.3*a*, *c*, and *e* should illustrate this fact.

The constant ω or $2\pi f$ has no effect on either the amplitude or the relative position of the curve along the time axis. The constant ω or $2\pi f$ determines the number of cycles occurring in a given time interval. Figure 16.6 shows four curves all having the same amplitude and phase shift. In this case the phase shift is zero. The ω in curve *a* has been replaced by 2ω, 3ω, and 4ω in curves *b*, *c*, and *d*, respectively. This means that, referred to curve *a*, curve *b* has twice the frequency, curve *c* has 3 times the frequency, and curve *d* has 4 times the frequency.

When the frequency of one sine function occurs as an integral multiple of the frequency of another sine function, these two functions are said to be *harmonically* related.

Referred to Fig. 16.6, the function $y = \sin \omega t$ is called the *fundamental* frequency. The function $y = \sin 2\omega t$ is called the *second harmonic* of the fundamental frequency.

The third and fourth harmonics of the function $y = \sin \omega t$ are illustrated in Fig. 16.6*c* and *d*.

EXERCISE 3

1. To the same scale plot the following equations. Use y as the ordinate and ωt measured in degrees as the abscissa. Plot over an interval of 1 cycle.
   (*a*) $y = \sin \omega t$ (*b*) $y = 2 \sin \omega t$
   (*c*) $y = 3 \sin \omega t$ (*d*) $y = 4 \sin \omega t$

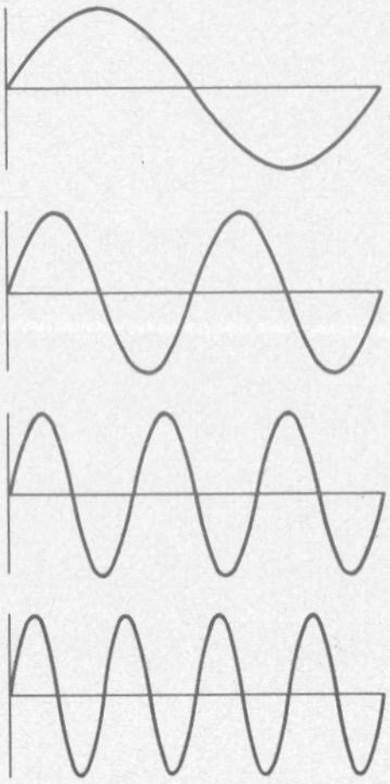

FIGURE 16.6

2. Plot the following equations as instructed in Prob. 1.
   (a) $y = \cos \omega t$ (b) $y = 2 \cos \omega t$
   (c) $y = 3 \cos \omega t$ (d) $y = 4 \cos \omega t$
3. Plot the following equations as instructed in Prob. 1.
   (a) $y = \sin \omega t$ (b) $y = \sin 2\omega t$
   (c) $y = \sin 3\omega t$ (d) $y = \sin 4\omega t$
4. Plot the following curves as instructed in Prob. 1.
   (a) $y = \cos \omega t$ (b) $y = \cos 2\omega t$
   (c) $y = \cos 3\omega t$ (d) $y = \cos 4\omega t$
5. Plot as instructed in Prob. 1:
   (a) $y = \sin(\omega t + 30°)$ (b) $y = 3 \sin(\omega t + 60°)$
   (c) $y = 3 \sin \omega t$ (d) $y = \sin(\omega t - 30°)$
   (e) $y = \sin(\omega t - 60°)$
6. In the following equations find the amplitude, frequency, period, angular velocity, and phase shift. Express angular velocity in both radians per second and degrees per second; also express the phase shift in both radians and degrees. Note carefully when the data are given in radians and when in degrees.
   (a) $y = 23 \sin(314.16t + \pi/6)$
   (b) $y = 144 \sin(157.08t - \pi)$
   (c) $y = 77 \sin(251.327t + 2\pi/7)$
   (d) $y = 100 \sin(9 \times 10^5 t + 45°)$
   (e) $y = 15 \sin(3.76992 \times 10^8 t - 3\pi/5)$
   (f) $y = 147 \sin(21{,}600t + 60°)$
   (g) $y = 200 \sin(6.2832t - 2\pi/5)$
   (h) $y = 300 \sin(1.6588 \times 10^{12} t + \pi/2)$

7. Using radian measure, write the equation for each of the sine curves described below:

	Amplitude	*Frequency*	*Phase shift*
(*a*)	200	30	$-50°$
(*b*)	150	3.0×10^8	$0°$
(*c*)	5	10^{12}	$\pi/2$
(*d*)	9	60	$0°$
(*e*)	10	1,000	$-45°$
(*f*)	20	500	$30°$
(*g*)	20	25	$0°$
(*h*)	115	40	-2π
(*i*)	100	50	$90°$

16.5 The Sum of Two Sine Functions of the Same Frequency

One of the typically characteristic problems in alternating-current electricity, vibrating mechanical bodies, certain types of wave motion, etc., involves the addition of two sine functions of the same frequency. If, for example,

$$y_1 = Y_1 \sin \omega t \tag{21}$$

and

$$y_2 = Y_2 \sin (\omega t + \psi) \tag{22}$$

let us investigate the properties of y_3, where

$$y_3 = y_1 + y_2 \tag{23}$$

That is to say, let us investigate some of the properties of the function

$$y_3 = Y_1 \sin \omega t + Y_2 \sin (\omega t + \psi) \tag{24}$$

where Y_1, Y_2, ω, and ψ are constants.

Figure 16.7 is a plot of Eqs. (21) and (22). In that figure we have arbitrarily let

$$Y_1 = 2$$
$$Y_2 = 3$$
$$\psi = 60°$$

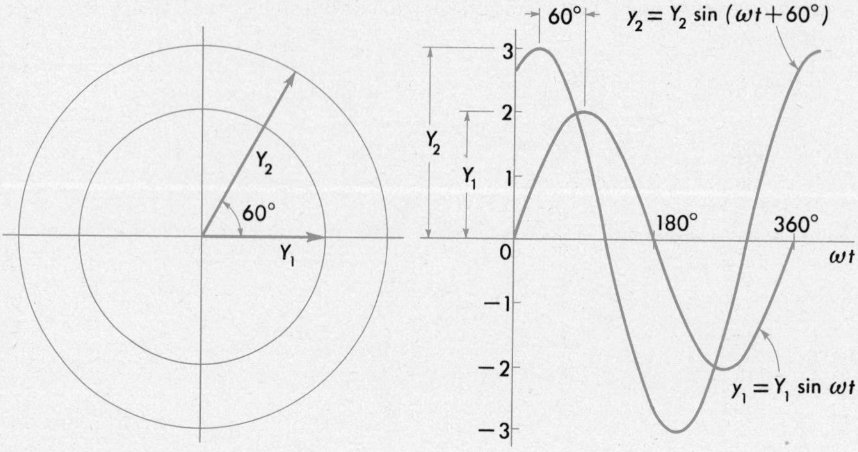

FIGURE 16.7

The points on y_1 and y_2 were located by the geometric method discussed in Sec. 16.3. In Fig. 16.7 the phasors Y_1 and Y_2 are shown in their zero-reference position.

For any given value of ωt, the ordinate of the graph of y_3 will be equal to the sum of the ordinates of y_1 and y_2. This is illustrated in Fig. 16.8. In this figure a succession of ordinates of y_1 and y_2 have been added to obtain a succession of points on the graph of y_3.

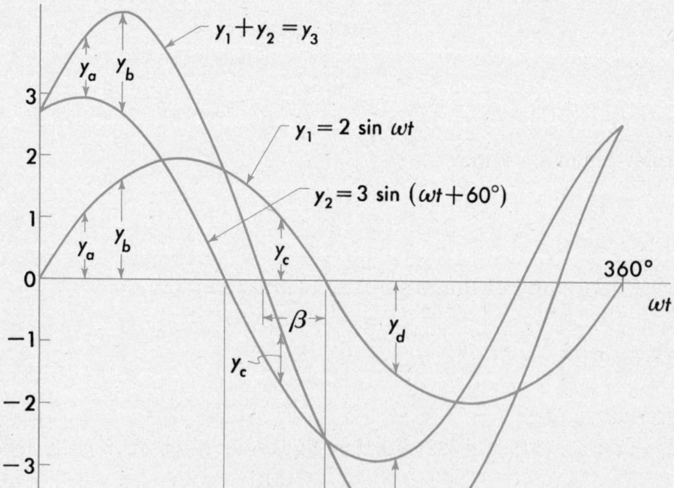

FIGURE 16.8

The shape of the graph of y_3 suggests that it may itself be a sine function. This fact will be demonstrated later.

Within the limits to which we can plot the graph, it would appear that the amplitude of y_3 is in the vicinity of 4.4 and that the phase of y_3 referred to y_1 is about 36°.

While this method of analysis has certain merits in describing the nature of y_3, it is quite cumbersome and its accuracy is limited by the strictly geometrical treatment.

A much more practical geometry is illustrated in Fig. 16.9. Here we have shown the three graphs plotted in Fig. 16.8, but we have also shown the phasors Y_1 and Y_2 which generated these curves, oriented in accordance with a randomly chosen value of ωt.

Now let us draw the line $\overline{P_1P_3}$ parallel to Y_2. Also let us draw the line $\overline{P_2P_3}$ parallel to Y_1, thus forming the parallelogram $OP_1P_3P_2$.

By the conditions of the problem, the lengths of Y_1 and Y_2 remain constant. Therefore the parallelogram $OP_1P_3P_2$ remains constant regardless of ωt.

Now let us draw the line $\overline{OP_3}$ and designate it as Y_3. From the geometry of the figure it is quite evident that

$$\overline{P_3a} = Y_2 \sin(\omega t + \psi) \tag{25}$$

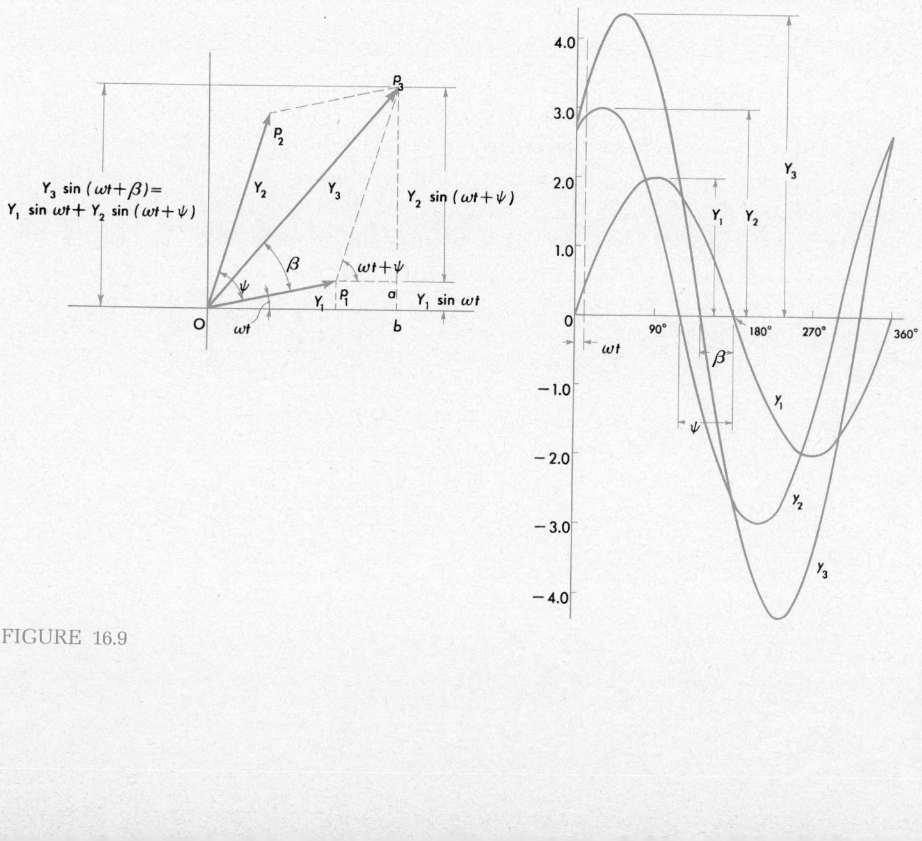

FIGURE 16.9

and

$$\overline{ab} = Y_1 \sin \omega t \tag{26}$$

Accordingly,

$$\overline{P_3b} = Y_1 \sin \omega t + Y_2 \sin (\omega t + \psi) \tag{27}$$

However,

$$\overline{P_3b} = Y_3 \sin (\omega t + \beta) \tag{28}$$

where β is indicated on the diagram. The evaluation of β will be discussed presently.

Therefore

$$Y_3 \sin (\omega t + \beta) = Y_1 \sin \omega t + Y_2 \sin (\omega t + \psi) \tag{29}$$

The form of Eq. (29) shows that the sum of two sine functions of the same frequency is itself a sine function of that frequency.

A particularly important problem involving this area of mathematics is illustrated in the following example.

Example 1. If $y_1 = 2 \sin \omega t$ and $y_2 = 3 \sin (\omega t + \psi)$ and if $y_3 = y_2 + y_1$, find the amplitude of y_3 and the phase of y_3 referred to y_1, where $\psi = 60°$.

If we let Y_3 be the amplitude of y_3, and if we let β be the phase angle of y_3 referred to the phase of y_1, we can solve for Y_3 and β by reference to Fig. 16.10. We do this rather than go through the somewhat unsatisfactory procedure of plotting all three graphs.

The student will observe that we can solve the triangle OP_3P_1 in Fig. 16.10 by the cosine law discussed in Secs. 14.16 and 14.17. That is,

$$\begin{aligned} Y_3^2 &= Y_1^2 + Y_2^2 + 2Y_1Y_2 \cos \psi \\ &= 2^2 + 3^2 + 2 \times 2 \times 3 \cos 60° \\ &= 4 + 9 + 6 = 19 \end{aligned} \tag{30}$$

$$Y_3 = \sqrt{19} = 4.359 \qquad \text{(ANS.)}$$

$$\frac{\sin \beta}{3} = \frac{\sin 120°}{4.359}$$

$$\sin \beta = 3 \times \frac{0.86603}{4.359} = 0.5960$$

$$\beta = 36°35' \qquad \text{(ANS.)}$$

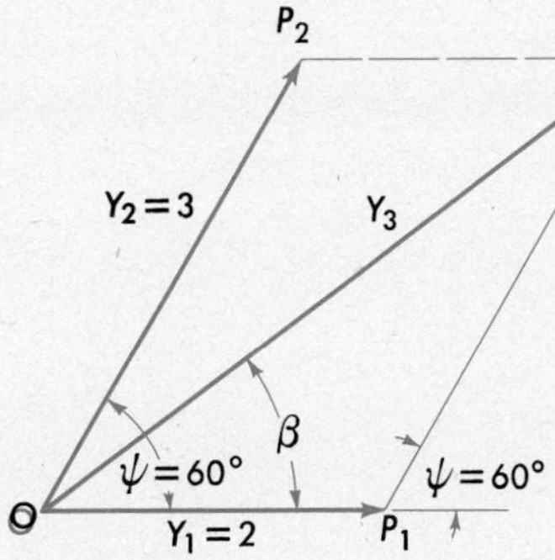

FIGURE 16.10

EXERCISE 4

Find the amplitude of the sum of the two sine functions given in Probs. 1 to 5. Also find the phase shift of the sum referred to y_1. It is suggested that the computations be done on a slide rule.

1. $y_1 = 65 \sin \omega t \qquad y_2 = 44 \sin (\omega t + 75.75°)$
2. $y_1 = 3 \sin \omega t \qquad y_2 = 4 \sin (\omega t + 62.7°)$
3. $y_1 = 5 \sin \omega t \qquad y_2 = 4 \sin (\omega t + 78.5°)$
4. $y_1 = 7 \sin \omega t \qquad y_2 = 5 \sin (\omega t - 84.2°)$
5. $y_1 = 5 \sin \omega t \qquad y_2 = 8 \sin (\omega t - 46.56°)$

16.6 Other Graphs Involving Sine and Cosine Functions

Figure 16.11 shows the graph of the equation

$$y = \sin \omega t + \sin 4\omega t$$

It is important to observe that while this equation does not represent a sine or cosine function, it does represent a periodic function. Such functions are useful when dealing with various aspects of electricity, electronics, servomechanisms, and other topics involving periodic motion.

A periodic motion is one that repeats itself in successive, equal intervals of time. Examples of periodic motion are the swing of a pendulum, the rotation of the moon about the earth, the motion of the ends of a vibrating tuning fork, the reciprocating motion of a piston, a point on a vibrating violin string, etc. A knowledge of periodic motions is necessary for an understanding of mechanical vibration, alternating-current electricity, electromagnetic waves, etc.

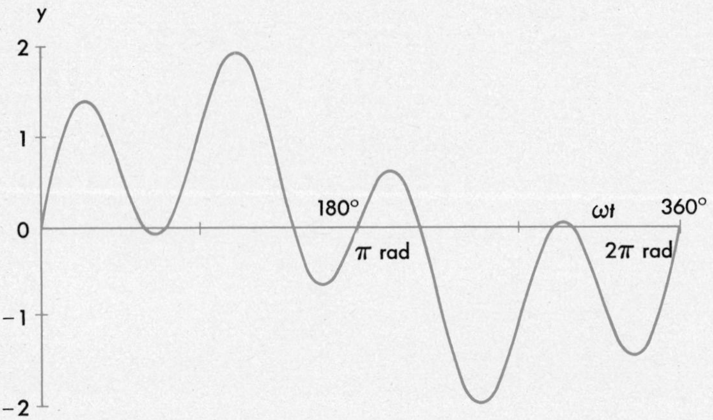

FIGURE 16.11

A few examples of periodic functions involving sines and cosines are given in Exercise 5. These are representative of some of the periodic functions encountered in the study of electricity, electronics, servomechanisms, and the like.

EXERCISE 5

Plot the graphs of the following equations. See Table 16.1.

1. $y = \sin \omega t + \cos 3\omega t$
2. $y = \sin \omega t + \sin 2\omega t$
3. $y = (\sin \omega t)(\sin 4\omega t)$
4. $y = \sin \omega t + \sin 3\omega t$
5. $y = e^{-0.1x} \sin 2x$
6. $y = \cos 4\omega t - \sin \omega t$

Note: Plot x in radians.

16.7 Simple Harmonic Motion

One of the simplest and most important types of periodic motion is *simple harmonic* motion. When a point P moves in a circular path at a constant angular velocity, the projection of P on any diameter will oscillate with a type of motion called *simple harmonic motion.*

16.8 Equations for Coordinates of P

Simple harmonic motion can be illustrated in terms of Fig. 16.12.

Here the vector $\overrightarrow{OP}$ is revolving about O with the constant angular velocity ω. The projections of P (that is Q and Q') will oscillate back and forth along their respec-

TABLE 16.1

ϕ	sin ϕ	sin 2ϕ	sin 3ϕ	sin 4ϕ	cos ϕ	cos 2ϕ	cos 3ϕ	cos 4ϕ
0	0	0	0	0	1.000	1.000	1.000	1.000
5	0.087	0.174	0.259	0.342	0.996	0.985	0.966	0.940
10	0.174	0.342	0.500	0.643	0.985	0.940	0.866	0.766
15	0.259	0.500	0.707	0.866	0.966	0.866	0.707	0.500
20	0.342	0.643	0.866	0.985	0.940	0.766	0.500	0.174
25	0.423	0.766	0.966	0.985	0.906	0.643	0.259	−0.174
30	0.500	0.866	1.000	0.866	0.866	0.500	0	−0.500
35	0.574	0.940	0.966	0.643	0.819	0.342	−0.259	−0.766
40	0.643	0.985	0.866	0.342	0.766	0.174	−0.500	−0.940
45	0.707	1.000	0.707	0	0.707	0	−0.707	−1.000
50	0.766	0.985	0.500	−0.342	0.643	−0.174	−0.866	−0.940
55	0.819	0.940	0.259	−0.643	0.574	−0.342	−0.966	−0.766
60	0.866	0.866	0	−0.866	0.500	−0.500	−1.000	−0.500
65	0.906	0.766	−0.259	−0.985	0.423	−0.643	−0.966	−0.174
70	0.940	0.643	−0.500	−0.985	0.342	−0.766	−0.866	+0.174
75	0.966	0.500	−0.707	−0.866	0.259	−0.866	−0.707	+0.500
80	0.985	0.342	−0.866	−0.643	0.174	−0.940	−0.500	+0.766
85	0.996	0.174	−0.966	−0.342	0.087	−0.985	−0.259	+0.940
90	1.000	0	−1.000	0	0	−1.000	0	+1.000

tive axes. When $\overrightarrow{OP}$ has rotated through 360° or 2π rad, then both Q and Q' will have traversed one complete cycle of motion.

The coordinates of P are given by the following equations:

$$x = |\overrightarrow{OP}| \times \cos \omega t = r \cos \omega t \tag{31}$$

$$y = |\overrightarrow{OP}| \times \sin \omega t = r \sin \omega t \tag{32}$$

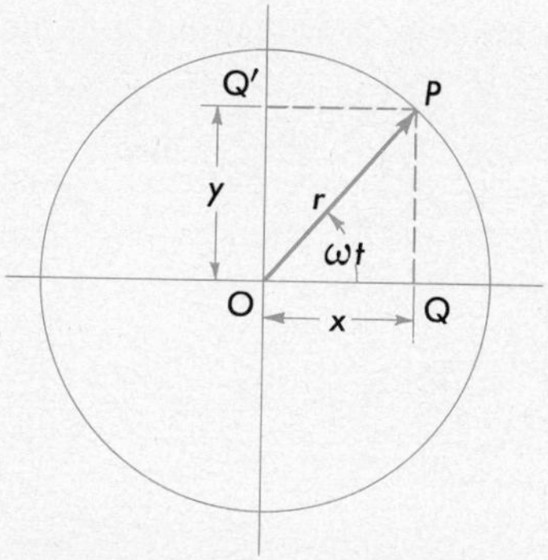

FIGURE 16.12

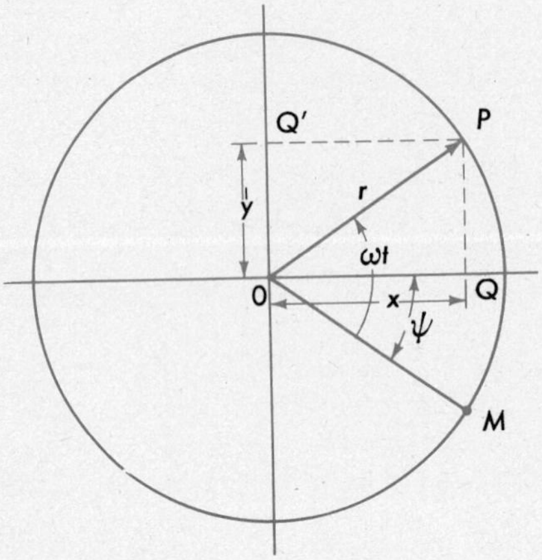

FIGURE 16.13

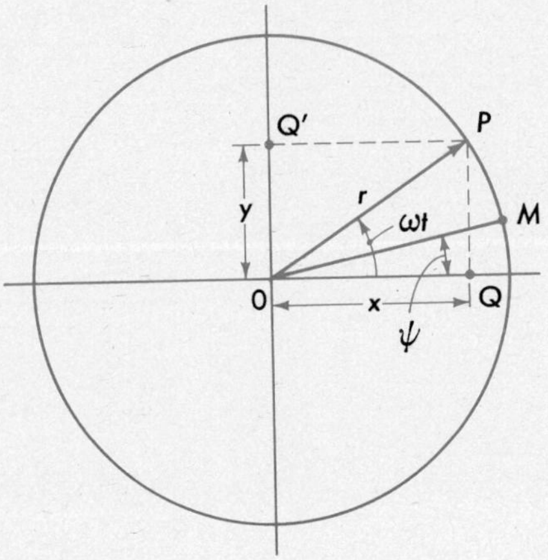

FIGURE 16.14

where $r = |\overrightarrow{OP}|$ = amplitude of the oscillatory motion
ω = constant angular velocity of r, often measured in radians per second, but sometimes measured in degrees per second
t = time in seconds

Note that r is the maximum displacement of Q and Q′. The displacements of Q and Q′ will be positive or negative in accordance with the convention of rectangular coordinates.

16.9 Phase

The angle of rotation can be referred to any stationary radius, such as *OM* in Fig. 16.13, then

$$x = r\cos(\omega t - \psi) \tag{33}$$
$$y = r\sin(\omega t - \psi) \tag{34}$$

Referring to Fig. 16.14,

$$x = r\cos(\omega t + \psi) \tag{35}$$
$$y = r\sin(\omega t + \psi) \tag{36}$$

The angle ψ is called the *phase constant.*

16.10 Parametric Equation

When the variable coordinates of a point are each expressed as a function of a third variable, the equations defining these coordinates are called *parametric equations*. The third variable is called the *parameter*. For example, in Figs. 16.13 and 16.14

$$x = r \cos(\omega t \pm \psi) \tag{37}$$

expresses the x coordinate of *P*. The equation

$$y = r \sin(\omega t \pm \psi) \tag{38}$$

expresses the *y* coordinate of *P*. Therefore, Eqs. (37) and (38) are parametric equations, and *t* is the parameter. Both Eqs. (37) and (38) are equations for simple harmonic motion. Equation (37) is the equation of motion for the point Q, and Eq. (38) is the equation of motion for the point *Q′*.

16.11 Parametric Equations for a Sine Curve

It is perfectly possible for a point to have a motion in one direction which is simple harmonic motion and simultaneously have a motion in another direction which is another kind of motion.

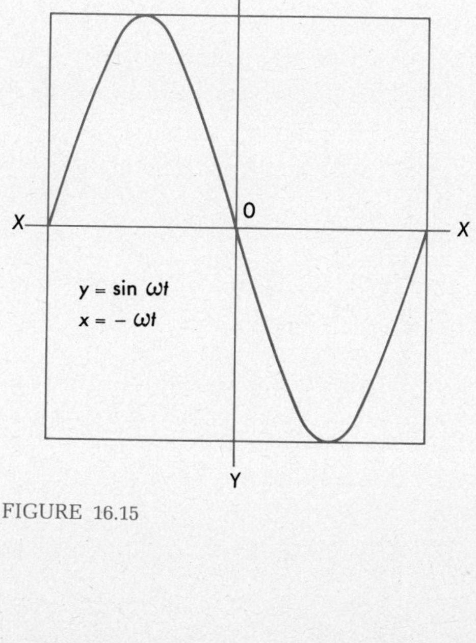

FIGURE 16.15

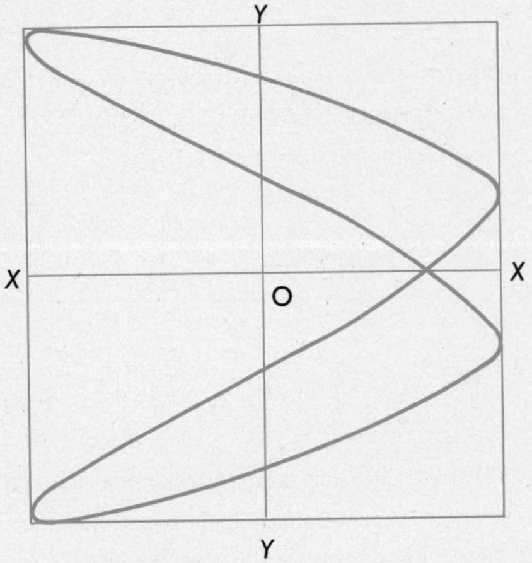

$y = \sin \omega t$

$x = \cos (2\omega t + 45°)$

FIGURE 16.16

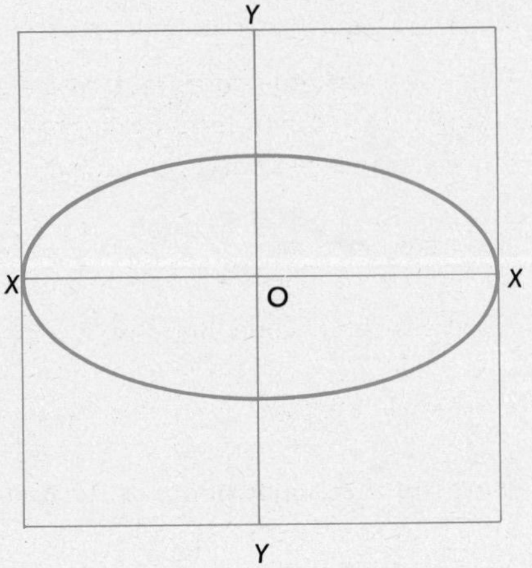

$y = \frac{1}{2} \sin \omega t$

$x = \cos \omega t$

FIGURE 16.17

For example, a point can move parallel to the Y axis in simple harmonic motion and parallel to the X axis in uniform linear motion. See Fig. 16.15 in which

$y = \sin \omega t$ (simple harmonic motion)

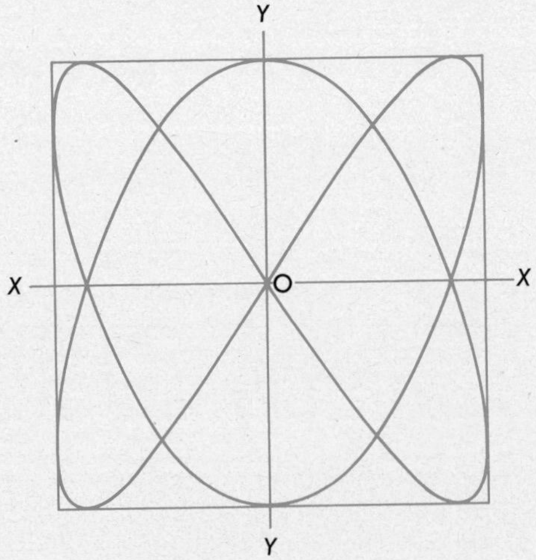

$y = \cos 3\omega t$

$x = \sin 2\omega t$

FIGURE 16.18

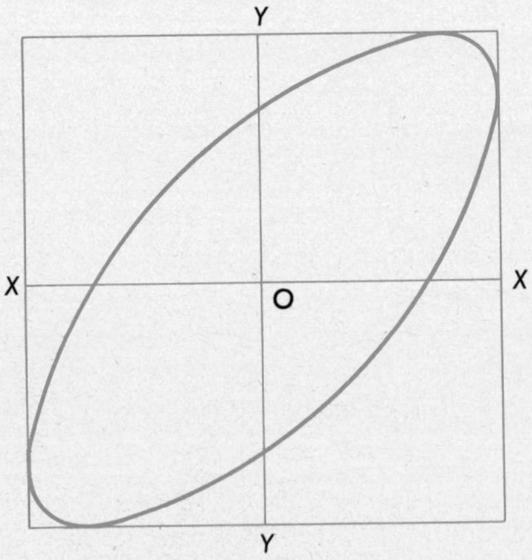

$y = \sin (\omega t + 45°)$

$x = \cos \omega t$

FIGURE 16.19

and

$$x = -\omega t \qquad \text{(uniform linear motion)}$$

16.12 Lissajou Figures

If a point moves in accordance to two simple harmonic motions at right angles to each other, its path is called a *Lissajou figure*. A knowledge of Lissajou figures is essential when making frequency comparisons with a cathode-ray oscilloscope.

A few Lissajou figures are shown in Figs. 16.16, 16.17, 16.18, and 16.19. Others are suggested by the problems in Exercise 6. Table 16.1 is given as a convenience to the student working these problems.

EXERCISE 6

Plot Lissajou figures for the following.

1. $y = \cos \omega t$
   $x = \cos 2\omega t$
2. $y = \sin \omega t$
   $x = \sin 3\omega t$
3. $y = \cos \omega t$
   $x = \cos 4\omega t$
4. $y = \cos (2\omega t + 30°)$
   $x = \sin \omega t$
5. $y = \sin \omega t$
   $x = \cos \omega t$
6. $y = \sin 3\omega t$
   $x = \sin 4\omega t$
7. $y = \sin \omega t$
   $x = \sin \omega t$
8. $y = \sin 2\omega t$
   $x = \sin 3\omega t$
9. $y = \cos \omega t$
   $x = \sin 3\omega t$
10. $y = \cos 2\omega t$
    $x = \sin (\omega t + 30°)$

17 complex numbers and position vectors

It has been discovered that complex numbers (see Sec. 2.26), the base of natural logarithms (see Sec. 9.6), the trigonometric functions, and position vectors (see Sec. 15.3) have certain related properties.

By taking advantage of these related properties we can develop some tremendously powerful mathematical tools with which to attack many important engineering problems.

In this chapter we shall relate some of the mathematical properties of exponential functions, complex numbers, trigonometric functions, and position vectors.

Unless otherwise stated or implied, the data in the examples and problems of this chapter are assumed to have an accuracy appropriate to a slide-rule solution.

In Chap. 15 we discussed ways in which vectors may be used to represent forces, velocities, displacements, and the like. In this chapter we shall see how vectors can be used to represent complex numbers. This is of the highest importance in electricity.

17.1 Graphical Representation of Complex Numbers

In Sec. 2.26 we discussed complex numbers in the binomial form $a + jb$ where a and b are real numbers and $j^2 = -1$.

We may represent the complex number $a + jb$ by the vector $\overrightarrow{OP}$. See Fig. 17.1. This is the vector drawn from the origin to the point P whose coordinates are (a,b).

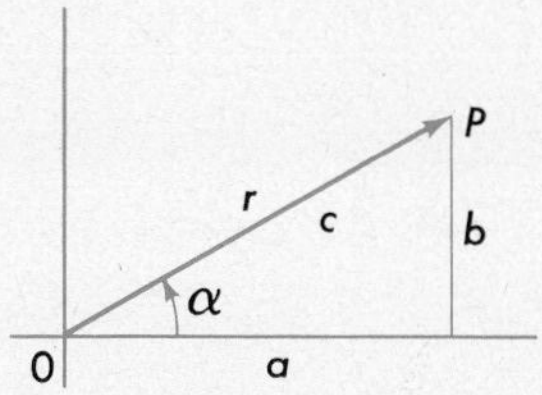

FIGURE 17.1

Therefore in this context we may write

$$\overrightarrow{OP} = a + jb \tag{1}$$

Observe that in the complex number $a + jb$ the number a is a real number and is plotted along the horizontal axis. The number jb is an imaginary number and is plotted along the vertical axis.

Evidently, if two complex numbers are equal, they both can be represented by the same position vector. Consequently, if two complex numbers are equal, their real and imaginary parts must be respectively equal.

The quantities involved in Fig. 17.1 are related by

$$a = r\cos\alpha \tag{2}$$
$$b = r\sin\alpha \tag{3}$$
$$r = \sqrt{a^2 + b^2} \tag{4}$$
$$\tan\alpha = \frac{b}{a} \tag{5}$$

The nonnegative, real number r is called the *modulus* or the absolute value of the complex number $a + jb$.

The argument of a complex number is an angle giving the direction of the vector representing this complex number.

From Fig. 17.1 we see that α is the argument of $a + jb$.

From Eqs. (2) and (3) we may express the complex number $a + jb$ and the vector $\overrightarrow{OP}$ in the form

$$\begin{aligned}\overrightarrow{OP} &= a + jb = r\cos\alpha + rj\sin\alpha \\ &= r(\cos\alpha + j\sin\alpha)\end{aligned} \tag{6}$$

Usually we express the direction of a vector in terms of an angle less than 360°. However, we can express the same direction as $(\alpha + 360°k)$ in degrees, where k is any integer including zero (see Fig. 17.2).

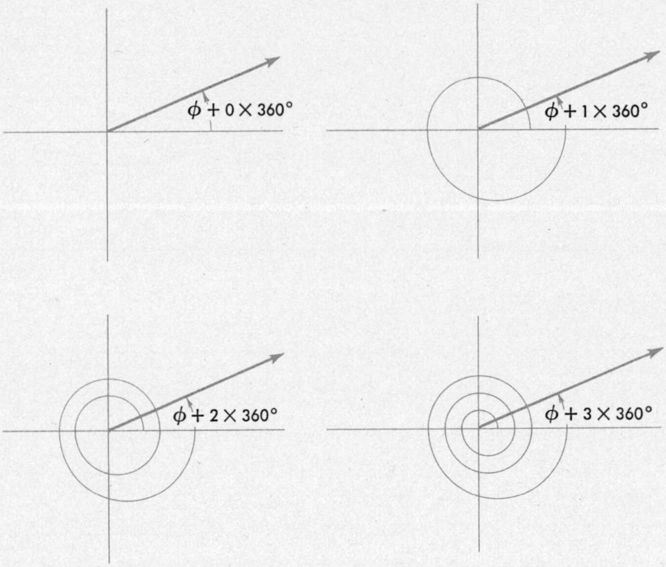

FIGURE 17.2

If the argument of any given complex number is α, then this same argument can be expressed as $\alpha + 360°k$.

The argument in radians can be expressed as $\alpha + 2\pi k$.

Figure 17.3 shows several complex numbers represented by the corresponding position vectors.

Example 1. Find the complex number corresponding to the vector $5\underline{/120°}$.

$a = 5 \cos 120° = 5 \times (-0.5) = -2.5$
$b = 5 \sin 120° = 5 \times (+0.8660) = +4.330$

ANS.: $-2.5 + j4.330$

Example 2. Find the complex number corresponding to the vector $2\underline{/-30°}$.

$a = 2 \cos(-30°) = 2 \times 0.8660 = +1.732$
$b = 2 \sin(-30°) = 2 \times (-0.5000) = -1.000$

ANS.: $1.732 - j1.000$

Example 3. Plot the vector corresponding to the complex number $2 + j9$. Calculate its modulus and its argument. Also express the vector in polar form. See Eq. (6), Chap. 15.

The vector $2 + j9$ is plotted in Fig. 17.4.

$$|\overrightarrow{OP}| = \sqrt{2^2 + 9^2} = \sqrt{4 + 81} = \sqrt{85} = 9.22$$
$$\tan \phi = 9/2 = 4.5$$
$$\phi = 77.5°$$
$$\overrightarrow{OP} = 9.22\,\underline{/77.5°}$$

EXERCISE 1

1. Certain vectors are defined below in polar notation. Calculate the corresponding complex number. Use a slide rule or a table of four-place natural functions.

(a) $3\,\underline{/27°}$	(b) $4\,\underline{/320°}$	(c) $-10\,\underline{/-30°}$
(d) $3\,\underline{/-270°}$	(e) $7\,\underline{/90°}$	(f) $5\,\underline{/160°}$
(g) $15\,\underline{/29°}$	(h) $15\,\underline{/-250°}$	(i) $20\,\underline{/-135°}$
(j) $-7\,\underline{/-90°}$	(k) $2\,\underline{/220°}$	(l) $10\,\underline{/-140°}$
(m) $3\,\underline{/270°}$	(n) $4\,\underline{/225°}$	(o) $5\,\underline{/1{,}470°}$

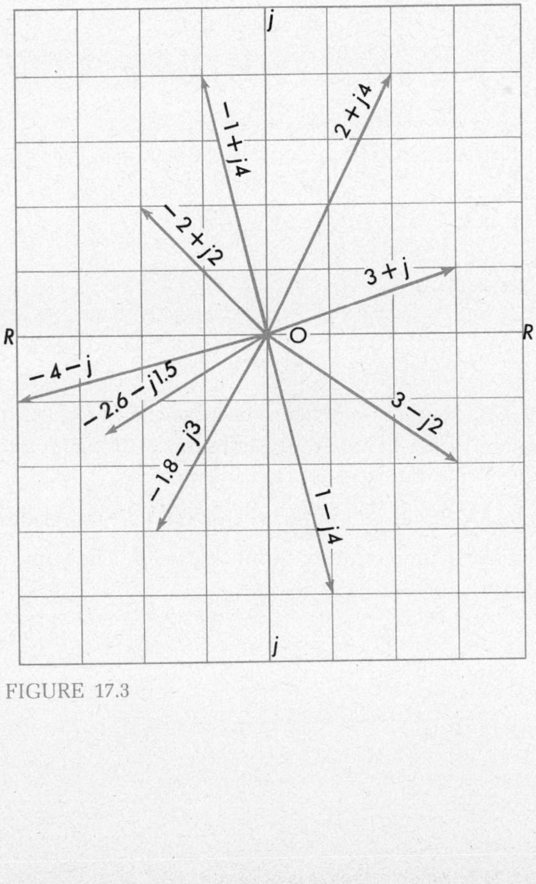

FIGURE 17.3

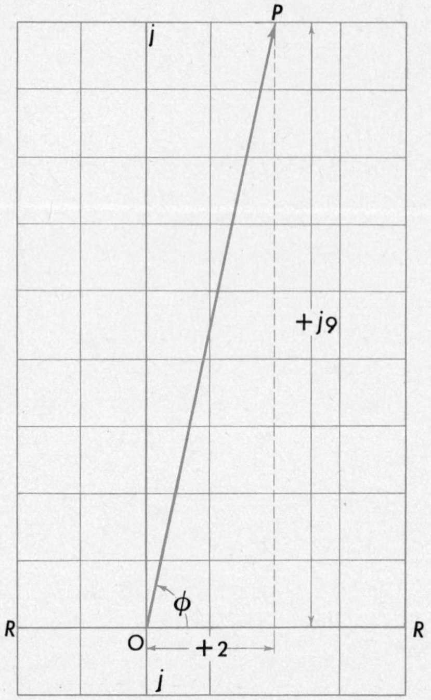

FIGURE 17.4

2. Plot the following vectors and calculate the modulus and argument of each. Also express the vector in polar form.
   (a) $3 + j4$ (b) $6 - j2$ (c) $-3 + j7$ (d) $-2 - j6$
   (e) $3 - j4$ (f) $4 + j2$ (g) $-5 - j3$ (h) $6 + j7$
   (i) $-2 + j2$ (j) $3 - j2$ (k) $-2 - j2$ (l) $7 - j6$

17.2 Addition and Subtraction of Complex Numbers

The addition and subtraction of complex numbers has been discussed in Sec. 2.26. In this section we shall limit the discussion to the vector representation of the sum and difference of complex numbers.

In Fig. 17.5 the sum of the vectors $\overrightarrow{OP}$ and $\overrightarrow{OQ}$ is the vector $\overrightarrow{OS}$. $\overrightarrow{OP}$ represents the complex number $a + jb$. $\overrightarrow{OQ}$ represents the complex number $c + jd$. The sum of these complex numbers is given by

$$\begin{array}{l} a + jb \\ \underline{c + jd} \\ (a + c) + j(b + d) \end{array}$$

This is the complex number represented by $\overrightarrow{OS}$. Its real part is shown in the figure to be $(a + c)$ and its imaginary part is shown to be $j(b + d)$.

This corresponds to the process of vector addition discussed in Sec. 15.9.

Example 4. Add the vectors $3 + j4$ and $2 + j5$ and express the sum in polar form. Let

$$\overrightarrow{OS} = (3 + j4) + (2 + j5)$$
$$\overrightarrow{OS} = 5 + j9$$

Then

$$|\overrightarrow{OS}| = \sqrt{5^2 + 9^2} = \sqrt{106} = 10.30$$
$$\tan \psi = 9/5 = 1.8$$

where ψ = reference angle of $\overrightarrow{OS}$

$= 60.9°$

$$\overrightarrow{OS} = 10.30 \underline{/60.9°}$$

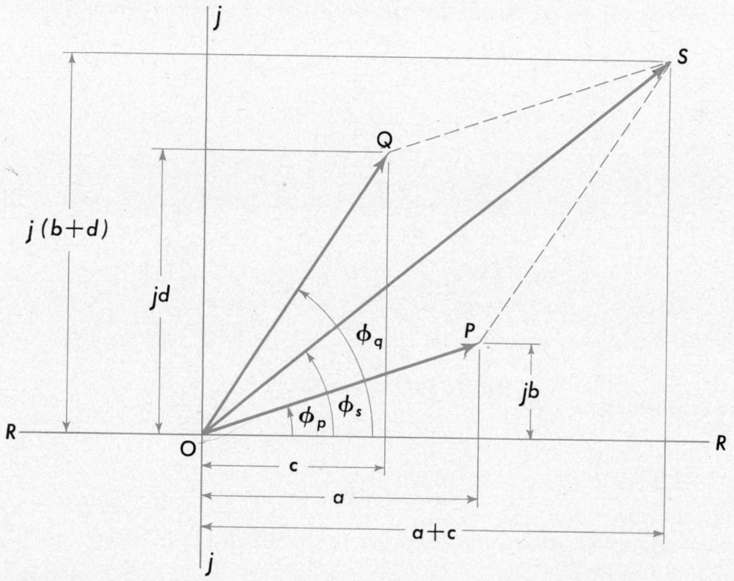

FIGURE 17.5

Example 5. Subtract the vector $5 + 3j$ from the vector $2 - 6j$. Let

$$\overrightarrow{OS} = (2 - 6j) - (5 + 3j)$$
$$= -3 - 9j$$
$$|\overrightarrow{OS}| = \sqrt{3^2 + 9^2} = \sqrt{9 + 81} = \sqrt{90} = 9.49$$
$$\tan \psi = \frac{-9}{-3} = +3$$

where ψ = reference angle of $\overrightarrow{OS}$
$= 251.6°$

$$\overrightarrow{OS} = 9.49\,\underline{/251.6°}$$

Example 6. Add the vectors $5\underline{/150°}$ and $10\underline{/45°}$. Express the sum as a complex number.
Let

$$\overrightarrow{OS} = 5\,\underline{/150°} + 10\,\underline{/45°}$$
$$\overrightarrow{OS} = (5 \cos 150° + j5 \sin 150°) + (10 \cos 45° + j10 \sin 45°)$$
$$= 5(-0.866) + (j5 \times 0.5) + (10 \times 0.707) + (j10 \times 0.707)$$
$$= -4.33 + j2.5 + 7.07 + j7.07$$
$$= 2.74 + j9.57$$

Example 7. Subtract the vector $30\underline{/60°}$ from the vector $10\underline{/30°}$. Express the answer as a complex number.
Let

$$\overrightarrow{OS} = 10\,\underline{/30°} - 30\,\underline{/60°}$$
$$30\,\underline{/60°} = 30 \cos 60° + j30 \sin 60°$$
$$= (30 \times 0.5) + (j30 \times 0.866)$$
$$= 15 + j26.0$$
$$10\,\underline{/30°} = 10 \cos 30° + j10 \sin 30°$$
$$= 10 \times 0.866 + j10 \times 0.5$$
$$= 8.66 + j5$$
$$\overrightarrow{OS} = (8.66 + j5) - (15 + j26.0)$$
$$= -6.34 - j21.0$$

EXERCISE 2

Perform the following vector additions, and express the sums in polar form:

1. $(2 + j3) + (4 + j5)$
2. $(5 + j7) + (-6 + j5)$
3. $(9 + j2) + (-3 + j2)$
4. $(8 + j7) + (-2 - j3)$

5. $(6 + j10) + (-9 - j5)$
6. $(4 + j3) + (-8 - j6)$
7. $(7 + j9) + (4 - j5)$
8. $(2 + j3) + (5 - j8)$
9. $(-5 + j2) + (-2 + j6)$
10. $(-2 + j5) + (-4 - j1)$
11. $(-3 + j8) + (-4 - j12)$
12. $(-5 + j12) + (3 - j4)$
13. $(-2 + j10) + (1 - j15)$
14. $(-2 + j2) + (6 - j5)$
15. $(-5 - j9) + (-2 - j6)$
16. $(-2 - j8) + (1 - j2)$
17. $(-5 - j10) + (10 - j5)$
18. $(3 - j2) + (7 - j5)$

Perform the following vector additions, and express the sums in complex form:

19. $6\underline{/40^\circ} + 10\underline{/70^\circ}$
20. $3\underline{/30^\circ} + 10\underline{/160^\circ}$
21. $15\underline{/20^\circ} + 20\underline{/100^\circ}$
22. $20\underline{/50^\circ} + 2\underline{/200^\circ}$
23. $20\underline{/20^\circ} + 10\underline{/150^\circ}$
24. $5\underline{/80^\circ} + 2\underline{/200^\circ}$
25. $5\underline{/40^\circ} + 2\underline{/205^\circ}$
26. $13\underline{/15^\circ} + 2\underline{/340^\circ}$
27. $25\underline{/10^\circ} + 25\underline{/300^\circ}$
28. $15\underline{/140^\circ} + 20\underline{/120^\circ}$
29. $10\underline{/170^\circ} + 5\underline{/260^\circ}$
30. $8\underline{/160^\circ} + 2\underline{/240^\circ}$

EXERCISE 3

Perform the following vector subtractions, and record the vector difference in both complex and polar forms:

1. $(3 + j5) - (2 - j3)$
2. $(4 + j6) - (10 - j9)$
3. $(-2 + j5) - (3 + j4)$
4. $(10 - j3) - (6 + j8)$
5. $(-1 + j2) - (-4 + j2)$
6. $10\underline{/42^\circ} - 30\underline{/160^\circ}$
7. $3\underline{/100^\circ} - 4\underline{/340^\circ}$
8. $2\underline{/250^\circ} - 3\underline{/40^\circ}$
9. $6\underline{/300^\circ} - 8\underline{/125^\circ}$
10. $3\underline{/270^\circ} - 2\underline{/180^\circ}$

17.3 Sines and Cosines Expressed As Infinite Series

In Sec. 9.5 we developed the series expansion of e^x, where e is the base of natural logarithms and x is a real number. Now we shall study some of the properties of the series obtained when x is replaced by an imaginary number.

Equation (5) of Sec. 9.5 is repeated below for reference.

$$e^x = 1 + x + \frac{x^2}{2!} + \frac{x^3}{3!} + \frac{x^4}{4!} + \frac{x^5}{5!} + \cdots \tag{7}$$

Let us replace the real number x by an imaginary number. In this chapter it will be convenient to let the imaginary exponent be $j\alpha$, where α is a real number and $j^2 = -1$. Then we may write

$$e^{j\alpha} = 1 + j\alpha + \frac{j^2\alpha^2}{2!} + \frac{j^3\alpha^3}{3!} + \frac{j^4\alpha^4}{4!} + \frac{j^5\alpha^5}{5!} + \frac{j^6\alpha^6}{6!} + \cdots \tag{8}$$

$$e^{j\alpha} = 1 + j\alpha - \frac{\alpha^2}{2!} - \frac{j\alpha^3}{3!} + \frac{\alpha^4}{4!} + \frac{j\alpha^5}{5!} - \frac{\alpha^6}{6!} \cdots$$

It can be proved that the terms in this particular series can be rearranged to yield

$$e^{j\alpha} = \left(1 - \frac{\alpha^2}{2!} + \frac{\alpha^4}{4!} - \frac{\alpha^6}{6!} \cdots\right) + j\left(\alpha - \frac{\alpha^3}{3!} + \frac{\alpha^5}{5!} - \frac{\alpha^7}{7!} \cdots\right) \tag{9}$$

Now we shall let

$$A = 1 - \frac{\alpha^2}{2!} + \frac{\alpha^4}{4!} - \frac{\alpha^6}{6!} \cdots \tag{10}$$

and let

$$B = \alpha - \frac{\alpha^3}{3!} + \frac{\alpha^5}{5!} - \frac{\alpha^7}{7!} \cdots \tag{11}$$

Then we may write

$$e^{j\alpha} = A + jB \tag{12}$$

Observe that both A and B are real numbers and are expressed as limits of infinite series. See Eqs. (10) and (11). In a more advanced treatment of infinite series, it can be shown that by multiplying as is done below we may obtain the series for A^2 and B^2. Thus

$$\begin{array}{rl}
& 1 - \frac{\alpha^2}{2} + \frac{\alpha^4}{24} - \frac{\alpha^6}{720} \cdots \\
& 1 - \frac{\alpha^2}{2} + \frac{\alpha^4}{24} - \frac{\alpha^6}{720} \cdots \\
\hline
& 1 - \frac{\alpha^2}{2} + \frac{\alpha^4}{24} - \frac{\alpha^6}{720} \cdots \\
& \quad - \frac{\alpha^2}{2} + \frac{\alpha^4}{4} - \frac{\alpha^6}{48} \cdots \\
& \qquad \frac{\alpha^4}{24} - \frac{\alpha^6}{48} \cdots \\
& \qquad\quad - \frac{\alpha^6}{720} \cdots \\
\hline
& A^2 = 1 - \alpha^2 + \frac{\alpha^4}{3} - \frac{2\alpha^6}{45} \cdots
\end{array}$$

$$\begin{array}{rl}
& \alpha - \frac{\alpha^3}{6} + \frac{\alpha^5}{120} \cdots \\
& \alpha - \frac{\alpha^3}{6} + \frac{\alpha^5}{120} \cdots \\
\hline
& \alpha^2 - \frac{\alpha^4}{6} + \frac{\alpha^6}{120} \cdots \\
& \quad - \frac{\alpha^4}{6} + \frac{\alpha^6}{36} \cdots \\
& \qquad \frac{\alpha^6}{120} \cdots \\
\hline
& B^2 = \alpha^2 - \frac{\alpha^4}{3} + \frac{2\alpha^6}{45} \cdots
\end{array}$$

This multiplication suggests that the sum of A^2 and B^2 may be indicated as

$$A^2 + B^2 = \left(1 - \alpha^2 + \frac{\alpha^4}{3} - \frac{2\alpha^6}{45} \cdots\right) + \left(\alpha^2 - \frac{\alpha^4}{3} + \frac{2\alpha^6}{45} \cdots\right) \tag{13}$$

Then

$$A^2 + B^2 = 1 \tag{14}$$

which the student will recognize as the equation for a circle of unit radius drawn with its center at the origin of the coordinate axes.

Thus any point on the circumference of the unit circle see (Fig. 17.6) will have coordinates (A,B) and the modulus of the complex number $A + jB$ is 1. Also

$$|\overrightarrow{OP}| = 1 \tag{15}$$

Referring to Fig. 17.6 and according to our earlier geometric definitions of the trigonometric functions,

$$\sin \alpha = \frac{B}{r} \tag{16}$$

$$\cos \alpha = \frac{A}{r} \tag{17}$$

In Fig. 17.6, $r = 1$; therefore we may write

$$\sin \alpha = B \tag{18}$$

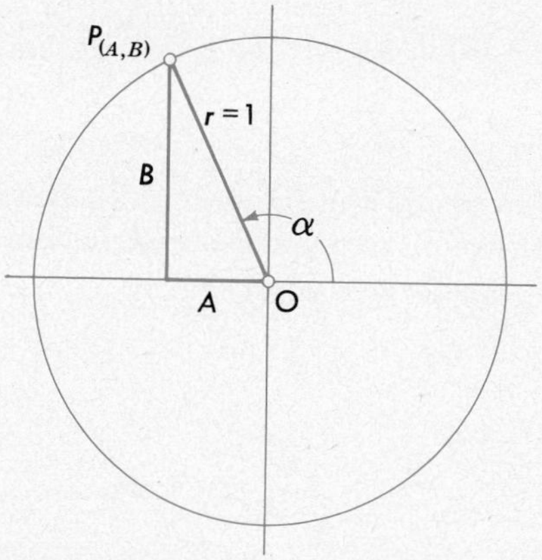

FIGURE 17.6

and

$$\cos \alpha = A \tag{19}$$

where α is measured in *radians*. (The student will have an opportunity to confirm this choice of angular units by arithmetical substitution in Exercise 4 below.)

From Eqs. (18), (19), and (12) we may write

$$e^{j\alpha} = \cos \alpha + j \sin \alpha \tag{20}$$

This is known as Euler's equation. It is sometimes abbreviated to

$$e^{j\alpha} = \text{Cis}\, \alpha \tag{21}$$

where the letters C, i, and s stand for the first letters in the words "cosine," "imaginary," and "sine."

By substituting (10) into (19) and (11) into (18), we find

$$\cos \alpha = 1 - \frac{\alpha^2}{2!} + \frac{\alpha^4}{4!} - \frac{\alpha^6}{6!} + \frac{\alpha^8}{8!} \cdots \tag{22}$$

and

$$\sin \alpha = \alpha - \frac{\alpha^3}{3!} + \frac{\alpha^5}{5!} - \frac{\alpha^7}{7!} + \frac{\alpha^9}{9!} \cdots \tag{23}$$

where α is measured in radians.

EXERCISE 4

Evaluate as indicated in the following problems. Unless otherwise indicated, the angles are in radians. Check your answers in a table of five-place trigonometric functions.

By using Table 17.1 much of the arithmetical labor can be eliminated.

Evaluate to six decimal places:

1. $\sin \pi/3$	2. $\cos \pi/3$	3. $\sin \pi/4$
4. $\cos \pi/4$	5. $\sin 2\pi/3$	6. $\cos 2\pi/3$
7. $\sin 300°$	8. $\cos 300°$	9. $\sin 270°$

Hint: $300° = -\pi/3$ rad; also $270° = -\pi/2$ rad.

TABLE 17.1

$\dfrac{\pi^1}{1!} = 3.1415927$	$\dfrac{\pi^{10}}{10!} = 0.0258069$
$\dfrac{\pi^2}{2!} = 4.9348022$	$\dfrac{\pi^{11}}{11!} = 0.0073704$
$\dfrac{\pi^3}{3!} = 5.1677128$	$\dfrac{\pi^{12}}{12!} = 0.0019296$
$\dfrac{\pi^4}{4!} = 4.0587121$	$\dfrac{\pi^{13}}{13!} = 0.0004663$
$\dfrac{\pi^5}{5!} = 2.5501640$	$\dfrac{\pi^{14}}{14!} = 0.0001046$
$\dfrac{\pi^6}{6!} = 1.3352628$	$\dfrac{\pi^{15}}{15!} = 0.0000219$
$\dfrac{\pi^7}{7!} = 0.5992645$	$\dfrac{\pi^{16}}{16!} = 0.0000043$
$\dfrac{\pi^8}{8!} = 0.2353306$	$\dfrac{\pi^{17}}{17!} = 0.0000008$
$\dfrac{\pi^9}{9!} = 0.0821459$	

17.4 Exponential Form of Complex Numbers

In our discussion so far we have been dealing with the relation

$$e^{j\alpha} = A + jB \tag{24}$$

where

$$A = \cos\alpha$$
$$B = \sin\alpha$$

Thus the magnitudes of A and B are restricted to the range -1 to $+1$.

We can generalize Eq. (24) somewhat while still preserving an equivalence between the exponential and complex forms.

Let us multiply both members of Eq. (24) by the nonnegative number r whose magnitude is unrestricted. We obtain

$$re^{j\alpha} = rA + jrB = r\cos\alpha + jr\sin\alpha \tag{25}$$

or

$$re^{j\alpha} = r(\cos\alpha + j\sin\alpha) = r\,\text{Cis}\,\alpha \tag{26}$$

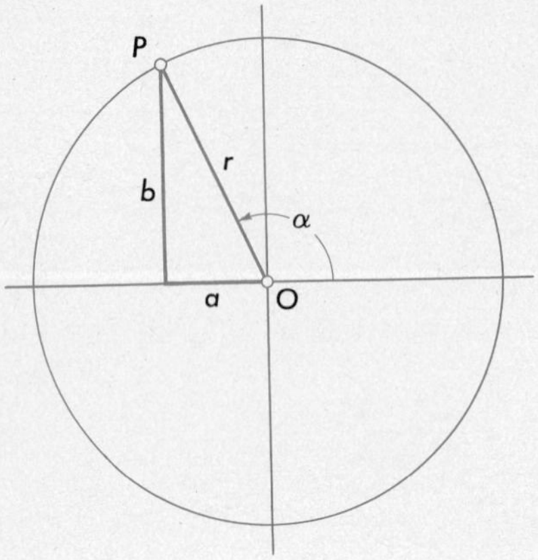

FIGURE 17.7

Just as Eq. (24) has a geometric application to the unit circle (see Fig. 17.6), so, as we shall see presently, Eqs. (25) and (26) have an application to a circle of any radius (see Fig. 17.7).

Following Sec. 17.1, Eqs. (2) and (3) as applied to Fig. 17.7,

$$a = r \cos \alpha \tag{27}$$

and

$$b = r \sin \alpha \tag{28}$$

Also we may write

$$re^{j\alpha} = r(a + jb) \tag{29}$$

or

$$re^{j\alpha} = r(\cos \alpha + j \sin \alpha) \tag{29a}$$

The nonnegative, real number r is called the *modulus* or the *absolute value* of the complex number $a + jb$. Thus we may write

$$r = |a + jb| = \sqrt{a^2 + b^2}$$

The angle α in Eq. (29a) above is called the *argument* of the complex number $a + jb$.

Thus we are no longer limited to the consideration of position vectors of unit length. We can define any position vector $\overrightarrow{OP}$ in the coordinate plane by a function expressed in the form

$$\overrightarrow{OP} = re^{j\alpha} \tag{30}$$

or

$$\overrightarrow{OP} = r(\cos\alpha + j\sin\alpha) \tag{30a}$$

17.5 Products and Quotients

In Sec. 2.26 we discussed products and quotients of complex numbers expressed in binomial form such as $a + jb$. We shall now emphasize these operations as applied to complex numbers expressed in exponential form.

Having been given two complex numbers, as for example $(a + jb)$ and $(c + jd)$, we may from Eq. (29) express them as

$$(a + jb) = r_1e^{j\alpha} \tag{31}$$

and

$$(c + jd) = r_2e^{j\phi} \tag{32}$$

where

r_1 = the modulus of $(a + jb) = \sqrt{a^2 + b^2}$
r_2 = the modulus of $(c + jd) = \sqrt{c^2 + d^2}$
α = the argument of $(a + jb)$
ϕ = the argument of $(c + jd)$

From Eqs. (31) and (32) we may write

$$(a + jb)(c + jd) = r_1r_2e^{j(\alpha+\phi)} \tag{33}$$

From Eq. (33) we may by inspection frame the following rule for multiplying complex numbers:

The modulus of the product of two complex numbers is the product of the moduli of the factors. The argument of the product is the sum of the arguments of the factors.

If two complex numbers are represented by $r_1\underline{/\alpha}$ and $r_2\underline{/\phi}$, their product is represented by the vector $r_1r_2\underline{/\alpha + \phi}$ (see Fig. 17.8). **(33*a*)**

The quotient of these same complex numbers can be expressed as

$$\frac{a + jb}{c + jd} = \frac{r_1e^{j\alpha}}{r_2e^{j\phi}} = \frac{r_1}{r_2}e^{j(\alpha-\phi)} \tag{34}$$

From an inspection of Eq. (34) we may frame the following rule for the division of complex numbers:

The modulus of the quotient of two complex numbers (denominator $\neq 0$) is the quotient of the modulus of the numerator divided by the modulus of the denominator. The argument of the quotient is the argument of the numerator minus the argument of the denominator.

If two complex numbers are represented by $r_1\underline{/\alpha}$ and $r_2\underline{/\phi}$, respectively, the quotient of the first divided by the second is represented by

$$\frac{r_1}{r_2}\underline{/\alpha - \phi} \qquad \textbf{(34}\boldsymbol{a}\textbf{)}$$

See Fig. 17.9.

Example 8. Find the product of $2(\cos 17° + j \sin 17°)$ and $5(\cos 180° + j \sin 180°)$.

Here the moduli are 2 and 5. The arguments are 17° and 180°. Thus the product is given by

The modulus of the product $= 2 \times 5 = 10$

The argument of the product $= 17° + 180° = 197°$

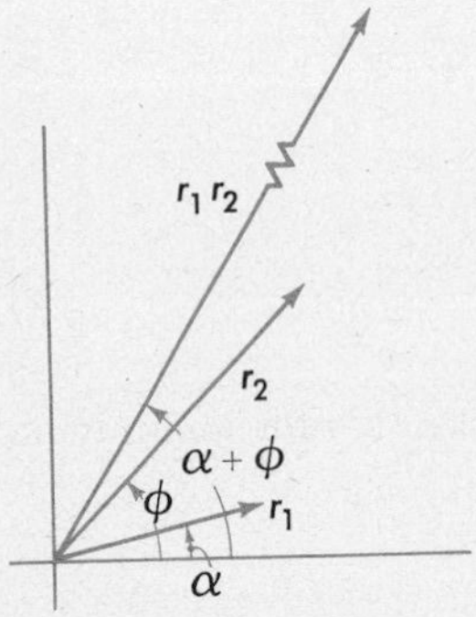

FIGURE 17.8

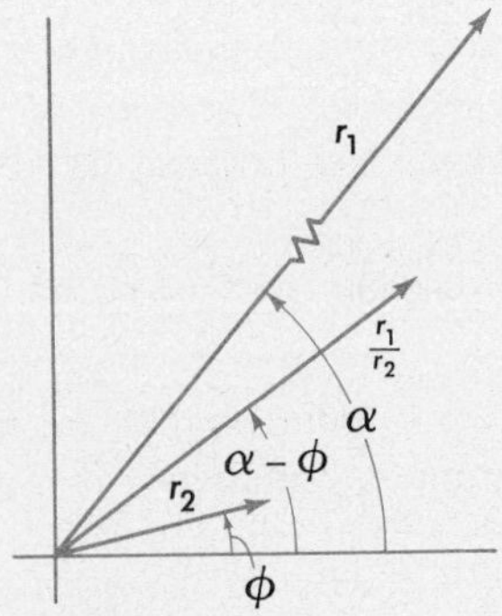

FIGURE 17.9

The product is

$$10(\cos 197^\circ + j \sin 197^\circ)$$

Example 9. Find the quotient of $16(\cos 40^\circ + j \sin 40^\circ)$ divided by $2(\cos [-20^\circ] + j \sin [-20^\circ])$.

Here again the moduli and arguments are given directly.

The modulus of the quotient is $16/2 = 8$
The argument of the quotient $= 40^\circ - (-20^\circ) = 60^\circ$

The quotient is

$$8(\cos 60^\circ + j \sin 60^\circ)$$

EXERCISE 5

Find the products or quotients of the following complex numbers expressed in the form $r(\cos \alpha + j \sin \alpha)$.

1. $2(\cos 20^\circ + j \sin 20^\circ) \times 3(\cos [-30^\circ] + j \sin [-30^\circ])$
2. $6(\cos 159^\circ + j \sin 159^\circ) \times 4(\cos 340^\circ + j \sin 340^\circ)$
3. $25(\cos [-120^\circ] + j \sin [-120^\circ]) \times 50(\cos 120^\circ + j \sin 120^\circ)$
4. $\dfrac{6(\cos 75^\circ + j \sin 75^\circ)}{2(\cos 15^\circ + j \sin 15^\circ)}$
5. $\dfrac{90(\cos [-27^\circ] + j \sin [-27^\circ])}{10(\cos [-50^\circ] + j \sin [-50^\circ])}$

In each of the following problems, two vectors representing complex numbers are given. Find the vector in the form $r\underline{/\alpha}$ which expresses the product or quotient of these complex numbers.

6. $6\underline{/75^\circ} \div 2\underline{/15^\circ}$
7. $15\underline{/150^\circ} \div 3\underline{/50^\circ}$
8. $25\underline{/300^\circ} \div 10\underline{/-20^\circ}$
9. $4\underline{/300^\circ} \times 5\underline{/60^\circ}$
10. $3\underline{/255^\circ} \times 2\underline{/40^\circ}$
11. $25\underline{/-120^\circ} \times 50\underline{/120^\circ}$

17.6 Demoivre's Theorem

From Eq. (26)

$$re^{j\alpha} = r(\cos \alpha + j \sin \alpha) \tag{35}$$

Now let us raise the expression $re^{j\alpha}$ to the nth power, obtaining

$$r^n e^{jn\alpha} \tag{36}$$

From Eq. (35) it is evident that

$$r^n e^{jn\alpha} = r^n(\cos n\alpha + j \sin n\alpha) \tag{37}$$

However, by raising both members of Eq. (35) to the nth power, we obtain

$$r^n e^{jn\alpha} = r^n(\cos \alpha + j \sin \alpha)^n \tag{38}$$

Now by equating the right-hand members of Eqs. (37) and (38), we obtain

$$[r(\cos \alpha + j \sin \alpha)]^n = r^n(\cos n\alpha + j \sin n\alpha) \tag{39}$$

Equation (39) is known as Demoivre's theorem.

17.7 Powers of Complex Numbers

Suppose we wish to find the cube of the complex number $2(\cos 20^\circ + j \sin 20^\circ)$. From Eq. (39) we may write

$$[2(\cos 20^\circ + j \sin 20^\circ)]^3 = 8(\cos 60^\circ + j \sin 60^\circ)$$

In Fig. 17.10, $\overrightarrow{OP}$ represents the complex number $2(\cos 20^\circ + j \sin 20^\circ)$, then $\overrightarrow{OQ}$ represents the cube of that complex number.

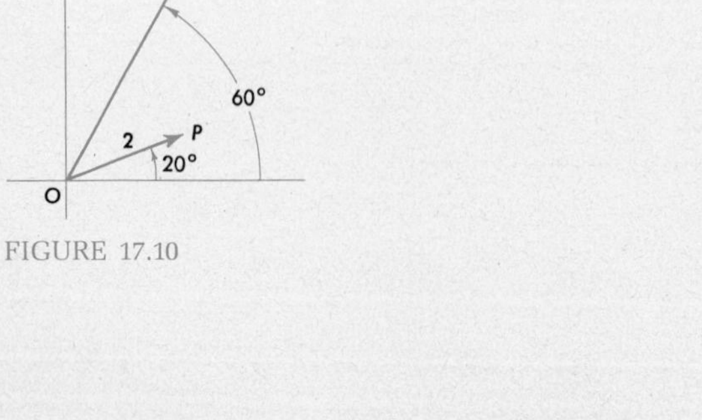

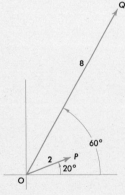

FIGURE 17.10

The vector representing the complex number $2(\cos 20^\circ + j \sin 20^\circ)$ could of course be expressed as $2\underline{/20^\circ}$. Then we could write

$$(2\underline{/20^\circ})^3 = 2^3\underline{/20^\circ \times 3} = 8\underline{/60^\circ}$$

See Fig. 17.10.

EXERCISE 6

In the following problems $\overrightarrow{OP}$ is a position vector representing a complex number. Find the indicated powers of $\overrightarrow{OP}$ expressed in the form $r\underline{/\alpha}$.

1. If $\overrightarrow{OP} = 5\underline{/20^\circ}$, find $\overrightarrow{OP}^3$.
2. If $\overrightarrow{OP} = 3\underline{/120^\circ}$, find $\overrightarrow{OP}^2$.
3. If $\overrightarrow{OP} = 2\underline{/150^\circ}$, find $\overrightarrow{OP}^4$.
4. If $\overrightarrow{OP} = 22\underline{/360^\circ}$, find $\overrightarrow{OP}^2$.
5. If $\overrightarrow{OP} = 5\underline{/90^\circ}$, find $\overrightarrow{OP}^4$.

17.8 Roots of Complex Numbers

It can be proved, although we shall not do so, that every complex number has exactly n nth roots. However, in order to solve for all of them, we shall have to recall Sec. 17.1 in which we pointed out that the argument of a complex number can be expressed by many different angles. If α expresses the argument of a given complex number, then $\alpha + 360^\circ k$, where k may be any integer including 0, also expresses the same argument.

Now we replace n by $1/n$ in Eq. (39) and obtain

$$[r(\cos\alpha + j\sin\alpha)]^{1/n} = r^{1/n}\left(\cos\frac{1}{n}\alpha + j\sin\frac{1}{n}\alpha\right) \tag{40}$$

We recall from the above that if the argument of a complex number is given by α, the same argument can be given by $\alpha + 360^\circ k$ where k is any integer. Therefore, we may in the right-hand member of Eq. (40) replace α with $\alpha + 360^\circ k$ to obtain

$$[r(\cos\alpha + j\sin\alpha)]^{1/n} = r^{1/n}\left(\cos\frac{\alpha + 360^\circ k}{n} + \sin\frac{\alpha + 360^\circ k}{n}\right) \tag{41}$$

where $r^{1/n}$ is the principal nth root of r and where we let $k = 0, 1, 2, \ldots, (n - 1)$.

Equation (41) is, in effect, a formula for finding the roots of a complex number when it is expressed in trigonometric form.

Example 10. Find the five fifth roots of 32(cos 30° + j sin 30°). By substituting in Eq. (41) we obtain

$$[32(\cos 30° + j \sin 30°)]^{1/5} = 2\left(\cos \frac{30° + 360°k}{5} + j \sin \frac{30° + 360°k}{5}\right)$$

Let us tabulate the angles $(30° + 360°k)/5$ for a succession of values of k:

k	$\frac{30° + 360°k}{5}$	
0	$\frac{30°}{5} = 6°$	(this is the reference angle of the principal fifth root)
1	$\frac{30° + 360°}{5} = 78°$	
2	$\frac{30° + 720°}{5} = 150°$	
3	$\frac{30° + 1{,}080°}{5} = 222°$	
4	$\frac{30° + 1{,}440°}{5} = 294°$	
5	$\frac{30° + 1{,}800°}{5} = 366°$, or a reference angle of 6°	
6	$\frac{30° + 2{,}160°}{5} = 438°$, or a reference angle of 78°	
7	$\frac{30° + 2{,}520°}{5} = 510°$, or a reference angle of 150°	
8	$\frac{30° + 2{,}880°}{5} = 582°$, or a reference angle of 222°	

From this series of arguments we can distinguish five and only five fifth roots of 32(cos 30° + j sin 30°). They are

2(cos 6° + j sin 6°)
2(cos 78° + j sin 78°)
2(cos 150° + j sin 150°)
2(cos 222° + j sin 222°)
2(cos 294° + j sin 294°)

The above complex numbers constitute the entire set of the required fifth roots. Subsequent roots found by making $k > n - 1$ (in this case, making $k > 4$) merely duplicate those already found.

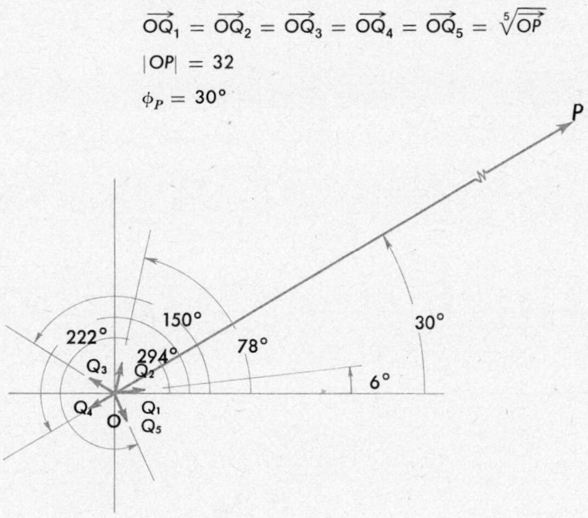

FIGURE 17.11

We could express these five roots by the position vectors $2\angle 6^\circ$, $2\angle 78^\circ$, $2\angle 150^\circ$, $2\angle 222^\circ$, and $2\angle 294^\circ$. See Fig. 17.11. The modulus of all the roots is the principal fifth root of 32. All these position vectors are equally spaced with the initial one having an argument of $\alpha\angle n$. In this case $\alpha\angle n = {}^{30}\!/_5 = 6^\circ$.

In general, the n nth roots of a complex number of modulus r and argument α can be represented by n position vectors each having the principal nth root of r for its modulus. Beginning with the vector whose argument is $\alpha\angle n$, the vector roots are equally spaced throughout a 360° arc.

EXERCISE 7

Find all the indicated roots of the complex numbers represented by the following vectors. Express your answer in polar form.

1. $\sqrt[3]{8\angle 30^\circ}$
2. $\sqrt[3]{27\angle 180^\circ}$
3. $\sqrt[2]{4\angle 0^\circ}$
4. $\sqrt[2]{9\angle 210^\circ}$
5. $\sqrt[4]{81\angle 280^\circ}$
6. $\sqrt[10]{1{,}024\angle 330^\circ}$

17.9 The nth Roots of Real Numbers

From the conventions which apply to position vectors in a complex plane it is evident that any positive real number N can be expressed as $|N|\angle 0^\circ$ and any negative real number N can be expressed as $|N|\angle 180^\circ$.

When $N > 0$, we may write

$$\sqrt[n]{N} = \sqrt[n]{|N|\angle 0^\circ} = \sqrt[n]{|N|}\left(\cos\frac{0^\circ + 360^\circ k}{n} + j\sin\frac{0^\circ + 360^\circ k}{n}\right)$$

When $N < 0$,

$$\sqrt[n]{N} = \sqrt[n]{|N|\angle 180^\circ} = \sqrt[n]{|N|}\left(\cos\frac{180^\circ + 360^\circ k}{n} + j\sin\frac{180^\circ + 360^\circ k}{n}\right)$$

Example 11. Find the three cube roots of 1.

When $k = 0$,

$$\sqrt[3]{1} = \sqrt[3]{|1|}\left(\cos\frac{360^\circ \times 0}{3} + j\sin\frac{360^\circ \times 0}{3}\right)$$
$$= 1(\cos 0^\circ + j\sin 0^\circ) = 1 + 0 = +1$$

When $k = 1$,

$$\sqrt[3]{1} = \sqrt[3]{|1|}\left(\cos\frac{360^\circ}{3} + j\sin\frac{360^\circ}{3}\right)$$
$$= 1(\cos 120^\circ + j\sin 120^\circ)$$
$$= 1\left(-\frac{1}{2} + j\frac{\sqrt{3}}{2}\right) = -\frac{1}{2} + j\frac{\sqrt{3}}{2}$$

When $k = 2$,

$$\sqrt[3]{1} = \sqrt[3]{|1|}\left(\cos\frac{360^\circ \times 2}{3} + j\sin\frac{360^\circ \times 2}{3}\right)$$
$$= 1(\cos 240^\circ + j\sin 240^\circ)$$
$$= 1\left(-\frac{1}{2} - j\frac{\sqrt{3}}{2}\right) = -\frac{1}{2} - j\frac{\sqrt{3}}{2}$$

These roots can also be found by the algebraic solution of the equation

$$x^3 - 1 = 0$$

Factoring,

$$(x - 1)(x^2 + x + 1) = 0$$

When

$$x - 1 = 0$$
$$x = 1$$

When

$$x^2 + x + 1 = 0$$

$$x = \frac{-1 \pm \sqrt{1-4}}{2}$$

$$= -\frac{1}{2} \pm \frac{j\sqrt{3}}{2}$$

That these roots are in fact cube roots of 1 can be verified by multiplication. By elementary algebra,

$$(1)^3 = \sqrt[3]{1} \times \sqrt[3]{1} \times \sqrt[3]{1} = 1$$

Also

$$\left(-\frac{1}{2} + j\frac{\sqrt{3}}{2}\right)^3$$

equals

$$\begin{array}{l} -\frac{1}{2} + j\frac{\sqrt{3}}{2} \\ -\frac{1}{2} + j\frac{\sqrt{3}}{2} \\ \hline +\frac{1}{4} - j\frac{\sqrt{3}}{4} - j\frac{\sqrt{3}}{4} + j^2\frac{3}{4} = -\frac{1}{2} - j\frac{\sqrt{3}}{2} \\ \qquad\qquad\qquad\qquad\qquad\qquad -\frac{1}{2} + j\frac{\sqrt{3}}{2} \\ \hline \qquad\qquad\qquad\qquad\qquad\qquad \frac{1}{4} + j\frac{\sqrt{3}}{4} - j\frac{\sqrt{3}}{4} - j^2\frac{3}{4} = 1 \end{array}$$

and

$$\left(-\frac{1}{2} - j\frac{\sqrt{3}}{2}\right)^3$$

equals

$$
\begin{array}{r}
-\frac{1}{2} - j\frac{\sqrt{3}}{2} \\
-\frac{1}{2} - j\frac{\sqrt{3}}{2} \\
\hline
+\frac{1}{4} + j\frac{\sqrt{3}}{4} + j\frac{\sqrt{3}}{4} + j^2\frac{3}{4} = -\frac{1}{2} + j\frac{\sqrt{3}}{2} \\
-\frac{1}{2} - j\frac{\sqrt{3}}{2} \\
\hline
+\frac{1}{4} - j\frac{\sqrt{3}}{4} + j\frac{\sqrt{3}}{4} - j^2\frac{3}{4} = 1
\end{array}
$$

EXERCISE 8

1. Find the two square roots of 1.
2. Find the four fourth roots of 1.
3. Find the five fifth roots of 1.
4. Show that the sum of the five fifth roots of 1 is zero.
5. Prove that, in general, the sum of the n nth roots of 1 is zero.
6. Draw a scale vector diagram to illustrate Probs. 1 to 4.

Example 12. Find the five fifth roots of 32.000.

$$\sqrt[5]{32\angle 0^\circ} = \sqrt[5]{|32|}\left(\cos\frac{360^\circ k}{5} + j\sin\frac{360^\circ k}{5}\right)$$

When $k = 0$,

$$
\begin{aligned}
\sqrt[5]{32\angle 0^\circ} &= 2(\cos 0/5 + j\sin 0/5) \\
&= 2(1 + 0) = 2
\end{aligned}
$$

When $k = 1$,

$$
\begin{aligned}
\sqrt[5]{32\angle 0^\circ} &= 2\left(\cos\frac{360^\circ}{5} + j\sin\frac{360^\circ}{5}\right) \\
&= 2(\cos 72^\circ + j\sin 72^\circ) = 2(0.30902 + j0.95106) \\
&= 0.61804 + j1.90212
\end{aligned}
$$

When $k = 2$,

$$
\begin{aligned}
\sqrt[5]{32\angle 0^\circ} &= 2\left(\cos\frac{720^\circ}{5} + j\sin\frac{720^\circ}{5}\right) \\
&= 2(-0.80902 + j0.58779) = -1.61804 + j1.17558
\end{aligned}
$$

When $k = 3$,

$$\sqrt[5]{32\angle 0^\circ} = 2\left(\cos\frac{1{,}080^\circ}{5} + j\sin\frac{1{,}080^\circ}{5}\right)$$
$$= 2(\cos 216^\circ + j\sin 216^\circ)$$
$$= 2(-0.80902 - j0.58779) = -1.61804 - j1.17558$$

When $k = 4$,

$$\sqrt[5]{32\angle 0^\circ} = 2\left(\cos\frac{1{,}440^\circ}{5} + j\sin\frac{1{,}440^\circ}{5}\right)$$
$$= 2(\cos 288^\circ + j\sin 288^\circ)$$
$$= 2(+0.30902 - j0.95106) = +0.61804 - j1.90212$$

EXERCISE 9

1. Find the three cube roots of 27.
2. Find the four fourth roots of -81.
3. Find the six sixth roots of 729.
4. Show that the square of one of the complex sixth roots of 729 is a cube root of 729.

17.10 Rotating Position Vectors

In Sec. 16.4 we discussed rotating position vectors and showed how a rotating position vector could be described, in terms of one of its projections, by an equation in the form

$$y = E\sin(\omega t + \psi) \tag{42}$$

In Eq. (6) we showed another nomenclature which can be used to describe a vector; for example,

$$\overrightarrow{OA} = E(\cos\alpha + j\sin\alpha) \tag{43}$$

The angle α may be a variable and a function of time. Therefore, we may let

$$\alpha = \omega t \tag{44}$$

To make the situation general, we shall introduce the phase constant ψ, and

$$\overrightarrow{OA} = E[\cos(\omega t + \psi) + j\sin(\omega t + \psi)] \tag{45}$$

Also in Eq. (30) we showed an equivalent expression with which we may describe the same rotating vector as

$$\overrightarrow{OA} = Ee^{j\alpha} \tag{46}$$

If α is a function of time, we may let $\alpha = \omega t$ and write

$$\overrightarrow{OA} = Ee^{j(\omega t+\psi)} \tag{47}$$

where ψ is a phase constant.

In Eqs. (42), (45), and (47), E is the amplitude of the function, ω is the angular velocity of the rotating vector, t is time, and ψ is a constant phase angle.

Any of these three forms may be used to describe a rotating vector. However, it may very well be that in some specific application one of these three forms is more convenient to use than the others. All three are in common use.

Equation (42) is more convenient to use when we are plotting a projection of the rotating vector. Equation (45) is more convenient when we wish to combine rotating vectors by addition, subtraction, multiplication, or division. Equation (47) is more convenient when transient terms are present.

EXERCISE 10

Find the amplitude, frequency, period, and phase constant for the following functions:

1. $v = 10 \sin (120\pi t + 60°)$
2. $v = 10[\cos (120\pi t + 60°) + j \sin (120\pi t + 60°)]$
3. $v = 10e^{j(120\pi t+60°)}$
4. $i = 15[\cos (628.32t + \pi/2) + j \sin (628.32t + \pi/2)]$
5. $i = 25e^{j(2,513.27t)}$
6. $i = 25 \sin (2,513.27t)$

18 trigonometric formulas, identities, and equations

In this chapter we shall derive some of the more fundamental relations between the trigonometric functions.

18.1 Some Simple Trigonometric Relations

As a first step, let us review the definitions of the trigonometric functions already familiar to the student.

These were discussed in Secs. 13.7 and 13.8 and are repeated below.

$$\sin \phi = \frac{y}{r} \tag{1}$$

$$\cos \phi = \frac{x}{r} \tag{2}$$

$$\tan \phi = \frac{y}{x} \tag{3}$$

$$\cot \phi = \frac{x}{y} \tag{4}$$

$$\sec \phi = \frac{r}{x} \qquad (5)$$

$$\operatorname{cosec} \phi = \frac{r}{y} \qquad (6)$$

A comparison between Eqs. (1) and (6) will show that

$$\sin \phi = \frac{1}{\operatorname{cosec} \phi} \qquad \operatorname{cosec} \phi = \frac{1}{\sin \phi} \qquad \textbf{(7)}$$

A similar comparison between Eqs. (2) and (5) will show that

$$\cos \phi = \frac{1}{\sec \phi} \qquad \sec \phi = \frac{1}{\cos \phi} \qquad \textbf{(8)}$$

Also, a comparison between Eqs. (3) and (4) will show that

$$\tan \phi = \frac{1}{\cot \phi} \qquad \cot \phi = \frac{1}{\tan \phi} \qquad \textbf{(9)}$$

Since $\sin \phi = y/r$ and $\cos \phi = x/r$, it follows that

$$\frac{\sin \phi}{\cos \phi} = \frac{y/r}{x/r} = \frac{y}{x} = \tan \phi \qquad \cos \phi \neq 0 \qquad \textbf{(10)}$$

Applying Eq. (9) to Eq. (10),

$$\frac{\cos \phi}{\sin \phi} = \cot \phi \qquad \sin \phi \neq 0 \qquad \textbf{(11)}$$

Referring to Fig. 13.6 and remembering the Pythagorean theorem,

$$r^2 = x^2 + y^2 \qquad (12)$$

Dividing both sides of Eq. (12) by r^2, x^2, and y^2 in turn gives

$$\frac{r^2}{r^2} = \frac{x^2}{r^2} + \frac{y^2}{r^2} \qquad (13)$$

$$1 = \cos^2 \phi + \sin^2 \phi \qquad \textbf{(14)}$$

$$\frac{r^2}{x^2} = \frac{x^2}{x^2} + \frac{y^2}{x^2} \qquad (15)$$

$$\sec^2 \phi = 1 + \tan^2 \phi \tag{16}$$

$$\frac{r^2}{y^2} = \frac{x^2}{y^2} + \frac{y^2}{y^2} \tag{17}$$

$$\text{cosec}^2 \phi = \cot^2 \phi + 1 \tag{18}$$

Observe carefully that the symbol $\sin^2 \phi$ means "the square of the sine of the angle ϕ." It does not mean "the sine of the square of the angle ϕ." For example, $\sin 30° = 0.5$ and $\sin^2 30° = 0.25$. On the other hand, $\sin (30°)^2 = \sin 900° = \sin 180° = 0$. The expressions $(\sin \phi)^2$ and $\sin^2 \phi$ are identical.

Among other values of the above relations is their use in simplifying otherwise complicated expressions. Broadly speaking, simplification is the process of transforming a given expression so that the arithmetical work involved in evaluating the expression is as simple as possible.

Example 1. By reference to appropriate trigonometric relationships given above, simplify the expression

$$\frac{1 - \text{cosec}\, \phi + \cot^2 \phi}{1 - \sin \phi} \qquad \sin \phi \neq +1$$

Note that when $\phi = 90°$, the denominator becomes zero and the expression has no meaning. Values of ϕ which make the expression meaningless are specifically excluded.

Following Eq. (18), we may write

$$\frac{1 - \text{cosec}\, \phi + \cot^2 \phi}{1 - \sin \phi} = \frac{\cot^2 \phi + 1 - \text{cosec}\, \phi}{1 - \sin \phi} = \frac{\text{cosec}^2 \phi - \text{cosec}\, \phi}{1 - \sin \phi}$$

By factoring,

$$\frac{\text{cosec}\, \phi\, (\text{cosec}\, \phi - 1)}{1 - \sin \phi}$$

Following Eq. (7), we may write

$$\frac{\text{cosec}\, \phi \left(\dfrac{1}{\sin \phi} - 1\right)}{1 - \sin \phi} = \frac{\text{cosec}\, \phi \left(\dfrac{1 - \sin \phi}{\sin \phi}\right)}{1 - \sin \phi}$$

or

$$\frac{(\text{cosec}\,\phi/\sin\phi)(1-\sin\phi)}{1-\sin\phi} = \frac{\text{cosec}\,\phi}{\sin\phi} = \text{cosec}^2\,\phi$$

where $\sin\phi \neq +1$.

One of the best ways to check a simplification is to substitute the numerical value of any convenient angle, both in the original expression as it is written and in the simplification. We may then compare the numerical equivalence of the original expression with the numerical value of the simplification.

Let us check the simplification in Example 1 by substituting some convenient numerical value for ϕ in the original expression. For convenience let us choose a value of 30° for ϕ. Any other angle would do as well.

Remember that

$$\begin{aligned} \text{cosec}\,30^\circ &= 2 \\ \cot 30^\circ &= \sqrt{3}/1 \\ \sin 30^\circ &= \tfrac{1}{2} \end{aligned}$$

Substituting in the original expression, we obtain

$$\frac{1-2+3}{1-\frac{1}{2}} = \frac{2}{\frac{1}{2}} = 4$$

Since cosec 30° = 2, it follows that $\text{cosec}^2\,30^\circ = 4$, and the simplification checks. The student should realize that it is possible that such a simplification may check and still be in error. However it is not likely.

EXERCISE 1

The work the student does in this exercise should, as in all other mathematical work, be arranged in a logical sequence of steps. Each step should clearly show that it may be justified in terms of the preceding steps. The student must provide a reason for each step.

By reference to appropriate trigonometric relations given in Eqs. (1) through (18), simplify the expressions below. If it is necessary to exclude certain values of the angle concerned in order to make the expression meaningful, tell what values of the angle must be excluded.

1. $\sin x\,(\sin x - 1) + \cos^2 x - 1$
2. $(1 - \sin A)(1 + \sin A) - \cos^2 A$
3. $3\sin^2 B + 3\cos^2 B - 2$
4. $\sin^2 A - 2 + \cos^2 A$
5. $\sin x + \cos^2 x - \sin x\,(1 - \sin x)$

6. $\cos x(\cos x - 1) + \sin^2 x + \cos x - 1$

7. $\dfrac{1 - \sin^2 A}{\cos A}$

8. $\dfrac{\cos\theta - \cos^3\theta}{\sin^2\theta}$

9. $\dfrac{\sin^2 A}{1 + \cos A}$

10. $\dfrac{1 - \cos^2 A}{\sin A}$

11. $\dfrac{\cos^2 A}{1 - \sin^2 A}$

12. $2\sin x\cos x + (\sin x - \cos x)^2$

13. $\cos^2 x + 1 - \sin^2 x$

14. $\sin^2\phi + (\cos\phi + 1)^2 - 2$

15. $\sin^3 x + \cos^2 x\sin x$

16. $1 - \sin^2 x + (1 - \sin x)^2 + 2\sin x$

17. $\dfrac{(\cos M + \sin M)^2 - 2\sin M\cos M}{\sin M}$

18. $\dfrac{\cos x\tan^2 x}{\sin^2 x}$

19. $\dfrac{\sin x\cos x\tan x}{1 + \cos x} - 1$

20. $\dfrac{1}{\sin^2\theta} - \dfrac{\cos\theta}{\sin\theta\tan\theta}$

21. $\cos^3 x(\tan^2 x + 1)$

22. $\tan P\sin P\cos P + \cos^2 P$

23. $\dfrac{\sin x\cos x}{(1 - \sin x)\tan x}$

24. $\dfrac{1}{\cot^2 x(\sec x - 1)}$

25. $\dfrac{\sec\theta}{\sin\theta\cot\theta}$

26. $\dfrac{\sec M - \cos M}{\sin M}$

27. $\left(\dfrac{\sec\phi}{\tan\phi} - \sin\phi\right)\sec\phi$

28. $\dfrac{(1 - \cos x)(1 + \cos x)\sec x}{\tan x}$

29. $\dfrac{\cot x - (\csc^2 x - 1)\sin x + \cos x\cot x}{\cot x}$

30. $\dfrac{\csc^2 x - \cot^2 x\csc^2 x}{\cot^2 x} + \csc^2 x$

31. $\left[\dfrac{\csc x(1 + \tan^2 x)}{\sec x}\csc x - \sec x\right]\sin x$

18.2 Trigonometric Identities

A trigonometric equation which is true for all values of the angles involved for which both members of the equation are defined is called a trigonometric identity. Any value of an angle involved which leads to an indicated division by zero is not a permissible value of that angle.

In the course of analyzing practical problems mathematically, we sometimes encounter a trigonometric equation that we suspect—without being certain—may be an identity. In such cases it is important to verify the equation and determine whether or not it is an identity.

For example, suppose that in the process of developing a certain formula we arrive at the mathematical statement

$$\sin^2 \phi = 1 - \cot^2 \phi \sin^2 \phi \tag{19}$$

and we feel that while this equation is probably true, it would be advisable to prove it.

Two somewhat different methods of attack are illustrated in the examples below. Example 3 is, perhaps, somewhat more rigorous, but the authors have no objection to the method illustrated in Example 2. In any case, however, the identity must be proved in the precise form in which it appears. No terms may be shifted across the equal sign.

Example 2. Prove that

$$\sin^2 \phi = 1 - \cot^2 \phi \sin^2 \phi \tag{20}$$

$$\cot \phi = \frac{x}{y} \tag{21}$$

$$\sin \phi = \frac{y}{r} \tag{22}$$

Substituting Eq. (21) in Eq. (20),

$$\sin^2 \phi = 1 - \frac{x^2}{y^2} \sin^2 \phi \tag{23}$$

Substituting Eq. (22) in Eq. (23),

$$\sin^2 \phi = 1 - \frac{x^2}{y^2}\frac{y^2}{r^2} = 1 - \frac{x^2}{r^2} = 1 - \cos^2 \phi \tag{24}$$

The expression $1 - \cos^2 \phi$ is recognized from Eq. (14) to be equal to $\sin^2 \phi$. Therefore

$$\sin^2 \phi = \sin^2 \phi \tag{25}$$

and the identity has been proved.

Example 3. Prove the identity

$$\sin^2 \phi = 1 - \cot^2 \phi \sin^2 \phi \tag{26}$$

From Eq. (11) it appears that

$$\cot^2 \phi = \frac{\cos^2 \phi}{\sin^2 \phi} \tag{27}$$

Substituting Eq. (27) in Eq. (26),

$$\sin^2 \phi = 1 - \frac{\cos^2 \phi}{\sin^2 \phi} \sin^2 \phi = 1 - \cos^2 \phi \tag{28}$$

But from Eq. (14),

$$1 - \cos^2 \phi = \sin^2 \phi \tag{29}$$

Therefore,

$$\sin^2 \phi = \sin^2 \phi \tag{30}$$

and the identity has been proved.

EXERCISE 2

Verify the following assumed identities. It is left to the student to decide which of the assumed identities are true and which are false.

1. $1 - \sin^2 A - \cos^2 A = 0$
2. $2 \cos^2 x + 2 (\sin^2 x - 2) = -2$
3. $\sin^2 B + 2 \cos^2 B - 1 = \cos^2 B$
4. $\cos^2 x - (1 - \sin x)(1 + \sin x) = \sin x$
5. $\sin \theta (1 - \sin \theta) - \cos^2 \theta + 1 = \sin \theta$
6. $\sin^2 y + (\cos y + 1)(\sin y + \cos y) - 1 - \sin y - \cos y = (\sin y)(\cos y - 1)$
7. $\sin^2 M - 2 (\cos M - 1)(\cos M + 1) - 3 \sin^2 M = -4 \sin^2 M$
8. $\dfrac{\sin^3 A}{1 - \cos^2 A} = \sin A$
9. $\dfrac{\sin^2 A}{1 - \cos A} = 1 + \cos A$
10. $\dfrac{\cos^2 M - 1}{\sin M} = \cos M$
11. $\dfrac{\cos^2 A}{1 - \sin A} = 1 + \sin A$
12. $\dfrac{\cos^2 x}{\sin x - \sin^2 x} = \csc x + 1$

13. $(\sin B + \cos B)^2 - 2 \sin B \cos B = 1$
14. $1 - (\cos y - \sin y)^2 = \cos y \sin y$
15. $(\sin x + 1)^2 + \cos^2 x - 2 = 2 \sin x$
16. $\dfrac{\tan x\,(1 - \cos x)}{\sin x} + 1 = \cos x$
17. $\dfrac{\cos B}{\tan B} + \sin B = \csc B$
18. $\dfrac{\cos^2 x \tan x}{\sin x} = \cos x$
19. $\sin x \left(\dfrac{1}{\tan x} + \tan x\right) = \sec x$
20. $\dfrac{1 - \cos^2 x}{\cos x \sin x} = \tan x$
21. $\left(\dfrac{1}{\sin^2 x} - \dfrac{1}{\sin x \tan x}\right)(1 + \cos x) = 1$
22. $\dfrac{\cos^3 x}{\sin^3 x + \sin^4 x} \div \dfrac{1 - \sin x}{\sin^3 x} = \csc x$
23. $\dfrac{\cos^2 x}{\sin^2 x}\,\dfrac{(1 - \cos^2 x)}{(\sin^2 x - \sin x)} = 1 - \csc x$
24. $\cot A \sin A = \cos A$
25. $\cot x \dfrac{1}{\tan x} = 2 \cot x$

18.3 The Sine and Cosine of the Sum and Difference of Two Angles

Before proceeding to the verification of more complicated trigonometric identities and to the solution of trigonometric equations, the student should become familiar with certain standard trigonometric identities, two of which we shall prove. Others we shall present as reference material without proof.

A common mistake made by students is to assume (quite erroneously) that the sine of the sum of two angles is equal to the sum of their sines. Let us put this erroneous notion to a numerical test.

We know that

$$\sin 45^\circ = \frac{\sqrt{2}}{2}$$

and that

$$\sin 30^\circ = \tfrac{1}{2}$$

Then

$$\sin 45^\circ + \sin 30^\circ = \frac{\sqrt{2} + 1}{2} = \frac{2.414}{2} = 1.207$$

However, the sine of $(45° + 30°) = \sin 75°$.

From a five-place table of trigonometric functions we find that

$$\sin 75° = 0.96593$$

Therefore we conclude that

$$\sin 45° + \sin 30° \neq \sin(45° + 30°)$$

In general,

$$\sin\phi + \sin\theta \neq \sin(\phi + \theta)$$

In the same way we can show that none of the trigonometric functions is additive in this way. That is,

$$\cos\phi + \cos\theta \neq \cos(\phi + \theta)$$
$$\cos\phi - \cos\theta \neq \cos(\phi - \theta)$$

and so on. Thus we need special formulas if we wish to find $\sin(\phi \pm \theta)$, $\cos(\phi \pm \theta)$, $\tan(\phi \pm \theta)$, etc.

We will find it convenient to first develop formulas for $\sin(\phi + \theta)$ and for $\cos(\phi + \theta)$.

From Eq. (20) in Chap. 17 we may write

$$e^{j\phi} = \cos\phi + j\sin\phi \tag{31}$$

and

$$e^{j\theta} = \cos\theta + j\sin\theta \tag{32}$$

By multiplying the left and right members, respectively, of Eqs. (31) and (32), we obtain

$$e^{j\phi}e^{j\theta} = e^{j(\phi+\theta)} = \cos\phi\cos\theta - \sin\phi\sin\theta + j(\sin\phi\cos\theta + \cos\phi\sin\theta) \tag{33}$$

But from Eq. (20) in Chap. 17 we may write

$$e^{j(\phi+\theta)} = \cos(\phi + \theta) + j\sin(\phi + \theta) \tag{34}$$

Now recall from Sec. 2.26 that if two complex numbers are equal, then their real and imaginary parts are respectively equal. Therefore we may equate the real parts and the imaginary parts of Eqs. (33) and (34), obtaining

$$\cos(\phi + \theta) = \cos\phi\cos\theta - \sin\phi\sin\theta \tag{35}$$

and

$$\sin(\phi + \theta) = \sin\phi\cos\theta + \cos\phi\sin\theta \tag{36}$$

Other standard forms of trigonometric identities will be presented without derivation in the following sections as reference material.

18.4 Functions of the Sum of Two Angles

$$\sin(\phi + \theta) = \sin\phi\cos\theta + \cos\phi\sin\theta \tag{37}$$

$$\cos(\phi + \theta) = \cos\phi\cos\theta - \sin\phi\sin\theta \tag{38}$$

$$\tan(\phi + \theta) = \frac{\tan\phi + \tan\theta}{1 - \tan\phi\tan\theta} \tag{39}$$

$$\cot(\phi + \theta) = \frac{\cot\phi\cot\theta - 1}{\cot\phi + \cot\theta} \tag{40}$$

18.5 Function of the Difference between Two Angles

$$\sin(\phi - \theta) = \sin\phi\cos\theta - \cos\phi\sin\theta \tag{41}$$

$$\cos(\phi - \theta) = \cos\phi\cos\theta + \sin\phi\sin\theta \tag{42}$$

$$\tan(\phi - \theta) = \frac{\tan\phi - \tan\theta}{1 + \tan\phi\tan\theta} \tag{43}$$

$$\cot(\phi - \theta) = \frac{\cot\phi\cot\theta + 1}{\cot\theta - \cot\phi} \tag{44}$$

18.6 Functions of Twice an Angle

$$\sin 2\phi = 2\sin\phi\cos\phi \tag{45}$$

$$\cos 2\phi = \cos^2\phi - \sin^2\phi \tag{46}$$

$$\tan 2\phi = \frac{2\tan\phi}{1 - \tan^2\phi} \tag{47}$$

$$\cot 2\phi = \frac{\cot^2\phi - 1}{2\cot\phi} \tag{48}$$

18.7 Functions of Half an Angle

$$\sin \frac{\phi}{2} = \pm\sqrt{\frac{1 - \cos \phi}{2}} \tag{49}$$

where the choice of sign before the radical depends on the magnitude of $\phi/2$.

$$\cos \frac{\phi}{2} = \pm\sqrt{\frac{1 + \cos \phi}{2}} \tag{50}$$

where the choice of sign before the radical again depends on the magnitude of $\phi/2$.

$$\tan \frac{\phi}{2} = \frac{1 - \cos \phi}{\sin \phi} \tag{51}$$

$$\cot \frac{\phi}{2} = \frac{\sin \phi}{1 - \cos \phi} \tag{52}$$

18.8 More Complicated Trigonometric Identities

Before attempting the formal verification of a suspected trigonometric identity, it is often more efficient to see if it is true for a special angle. If it is not true for a particular angle, it is certainly not true generally, and there would be no point in carrying the investigation any further.

For example, suppose we suspect that the equation

$$\frac{1 + \cos \phi}{1 - \cos \phi} = \frac{1 - \cos (\phi/2)}{\sin (\phi/2)}$$

is an identity. Let us substitute $\phi = 60°$. Then

$$\frac{1 + \frac{1}{2}}{1 - \frac{1}{2}} \stackrel{?}{=} \frac{1 - \sqrt{3}/2}{\frac{1}{2}}$$

$$\frac{\frac{3}{2}}{\frac{1}{2}} \stackrel{?}{=} 2 - \sqrt{3}$$

$$3 \stackrel{?}{=} 2 - \sqrt{3}$$

Obviously the given equation is not true when $\phi = 60°$; therefore it is not an identity. There may, however, be other values which, if substituted for ϕ, would check.

There are three formal methods by which we may prove an identity. We can substitute the proper ratios for the functions themselves, as was done in Example 2.

Sometimes we can prove a suspected identity by referring to an identity of which we are already sure. Again, we may resort to a geometrical proof.

When we use algebraic methods in proving an identity, the identity should be verified in the precise form in which it appears. We can alter either or both sides by appropriate substitution, but usually we do not transpose any quantities across the equality sign.

Example 4. Verify the identity

$$\tan \phi = \frac{2 \tan (\phi/2)}{1 - \tan^2 (\phi/2)}$$

First let us see if the identity is true when $\phi = 60°$:

$$\sqrt{3} \stackrel{?}{=} \frac{2 \times 1/\sqrt{3}}{1 - 1/3}$$

$$\sqrt{3} \stackrel{?}{=} \frac{2/\sqrt{3}}{2/3} = \frac{2}{\sqrt{3}} \times \frac{3}{2} = \sqrt{3}$$

We are now sure that the equation is true for at least one angle. Let us proceed with a more general check. A recommended arrangement of work is shown below:

$\tan \phi$	$\dfrac{2 \tan (\frac{1}{2}\phi)}{1 - \tan^2 (\frac{1}{2}\phi)}$
	From Eq. (10),
$\dfrac{\sin \phi}{\cos \phi}$	$\dfrac{2 \dfrac{\sin (\phi/2)}{\cos (\phi/2)}}{1 - \dfrac{\sin^2 (\phi/2)}{\cos^2 (\phi/2)}}$
	or
	$\dfrac{2 \cos (\phi/2) \sin (\phi/2)}{\cos^2 (\phi/2) - \sin^2 (\phi/2)}$
	From Eqs. (45) and (46) we obtain
	$\dfrac{\sin \phi}{\cos \phi}$

Example 5. Verify the identity

$$\pm\sqrt{\frac{1-\sin\beta}{1+\sin\beta}} = \frac{1-\sin\beta}{\cos\beta}$$

$\pm\sqrt{\dfrac{1-\sin\beta}{1+\sin\beta}}$	$\dfrac{1-\sin\beta}{\cos\beta}$
Rationalize by multiplying numerator and denominator by $1-\sin\beta$:	
$\pm\sqrt{\dfrac{(1-\sin\beta)(1-\sin\beta)}{(1+\sin\beta)(1-\sin\beta)}}$	
$\pm\sqrt{\dfrac{(1-\sin\beta)^2}{1-\sin^2\beta}}$	
$\dfrac{1-\sin\beta}{\cos\beta}$ ←	↑

Example 6. Verify the identity

$$\pm\sqrt{\frac{1-\sin\omega}{1+\sin\omega}} = \frac{\cos\omega}{1+\sin\omega}$$

$\pm\sqrt{\dfrac{1-\sin\omega}{1+\sin\omega}}$	$\dfrac{\cos\omega}{1+\sin\omega}$
Rationalize by multiplying numerator and denominator by $1+\sin\omega$:	
$\pm\sqrt{\dfrac{(1-\sin\omega)(1+\sin\omega)}{(1+\sin\omega)^2}}$	
$\pm\sqrt{\dfrac{1-\sin^2\omega}{(1+\sin\omega)^2}}$	
$\dfrac{\cos\omega}{1+\sin\omega}$ ←	↑

EXERCISE 3

Verify the following suspected identities. It is left to the student to determine which are identities and which are not.

1. $\sin^2\phi + \csc^2\phi = \dfrac{1+\sin^2\phi}{\sin^2\phi}$

2. $1-\sin\phi = \dfrac{\cos^2\phi}{1+\sin\phi}$

3. $\cos^2 \phi = 1 - 2\sin^2 \phi$

4. $\sin 2\phi = \dfrac{2\tan\phi}{1 + \tan^2\phi}$

5. $\sin 2\phi = \dfrac{1}{\tan\phi + \cot\phi}$

6. $\tan\phi = \dfrac{\sin\phi + \tan\phi}{\sin\phi\cos\phi + 1}$

7. $\sec\phi\csc\phi = \dfrac{\tan\phi - \cot\phi}{\sin^2\phi - \cos^2\phi}$

8. $\dfrac{\tan^2\phi - \sin^2\phi}{\tan^2\phi} = \dfrac{\sec^2\phi - 1}{1 + \tan^2\phi}$

9. $\dfrac{1 + \tan\phi}{1 - \tan\phi} = \tan(45° + \phi)$

10. $\dfrac{\cot\phi + \sin\phi}{\cot\phi\cos\phi} = \tan\phi + \sec\phi$

11. $\dfrac{\sin\phi}{1 - \cos\phi} + \dfrac{\sin\phi}{1 + \cos\phi} = 2\cot\phi$

12. $\sec\phi = \tan\phi\sin\phi + \sin\phi$

13. $\sin\phi = \dfrac{2\tan\frac{1}{2}\phi}{1 + \tan^2\frac{1}{2}\phi}$

14. $\sin\phi = \dfrac{\cos\phi - \sin\phi\tan\phi}{2\cot 2\phi}$

15. $\pm\sqrt{\dfrac{1 - \cos\phi}{1 + \cos\phi}} = \dfrac{\sin\phi}{1 + \cos\phi}$

16. $\cot\frac{1}{2}\phi = \dfrac{\sin\phi}{1 - \cos\phi}$

*17. $4\sin^3\phi + \sin 3\phi = 3\sin\phi$

18. $(\sin x + \cos x)^2 = 1 + \sin 2x$

19. $\cos^4 x - \sin^4 x = \cos 2x$

20. $\dfrac{\sin^3 x - \cos^3 x}{\sin x - \cos x} = 1 + \dfrac{1}{2}\sin 2x$

*21. $\operatorname{cosec} x \sin 3x = 2 + \sec x \cos 3x$

22. $\tan x = \dfrac{1 - \cos 2x}{\sin 2x}$

23. $-\cos 2x = \dfrac{1 - \cot^2 x}{\operatorname{cosec}^2 x}$

*24. $\cos 2x \cos 3x = \cos x - \sin 2x \sin 3x$

25. $\cot 2x = \dfrac{\cot x - \tan x}{2}$

26. $\dfrac{2\tan A}{\sin 2A} = 1 + \tan^2 A$

27. Let two wattmeter readings for a particular electric circuit be w_1 and w_2. Then the so-called "power factor" for the problem can be determined from these wattmeter readings by aid of the equation

$$\tan\theta = \frac{\sqrt{3}(w_2 - w_1)}{w_2 + w_1} = \frac{\sqrt{3}d}{s}$$

Show that $\cos\theta = 1/[1 + 3(d/s)^2]^{1/2}$.

28. The follower on a cam at a time t s has for its abscissa $x = 5\sin 2\pi\omega t$ in and for its ordinate $y = 4\cos 2\pi\omega t$ in. The quantity ω is a constant. Show that $x^2/25 + y^2/16$ always has the value $+1$, irrespective of the time.

*Hint: $\sin 3\phi = \sin(\phi + 2\phi)$
$\cos 3\phi = \cos(\phi + 2\phi)$

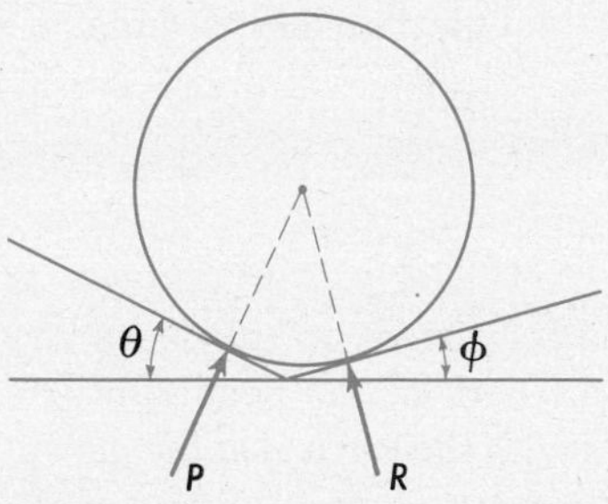

FIGURE 18.1

29. It is necessary to make a table of values of the function

$$\frac{x}{(16 - 9x^2)^{1/2}}$$

for $x = 0, 0.1, 0.2, \ldots, 1.3$. Show that this computation may be accomplished readily by replacing $3x$ by $4 \sin \theta$ and then simplifying the given expression to $\frac{1}{3} \tan \theta$. Make up the table of required values correct to four decimals.

30. A sphere weighing W lb rests between two smooth planes, as shown in Fig. 18.1. Figure 18.2 shows the weight of the sphere and the forces that the two planes exert upon the sphere. Since the algebraic sum of the horizontal components of the forces must be zero and the algebraic sum of the vertical forces must likewise be zero, we obtain

$$R \sin \phi - P \sin \theta = 0$$
$$R \cos \phi + P \cos \theta = W$$

Solve these two equations simultaneously for R and P in terms of W, θ, and ϕ, and show that your results can be put in the form

$$P = \frac{W \sin \phi}{\sin (\theta + \phi)} \qquad R = \frac{W \sin \theta}{\sin (\theta + \phi)}$$

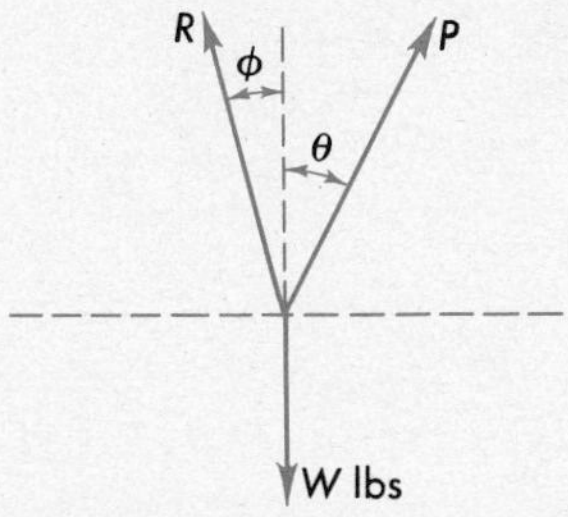

FIGURE 18.2

31. The period of vibration of a pendulum is given by the approximate formula

$$T = 2\pi\left(\frac{L}{g}\right)^{1/2}\left(1 + \frac{1}{4}\sin^2\frac{\theta}{2} - \frac{9}{64}\sin^4\frac{\theta}{2}\right)$$

which is much more accurate than the one customarily given in an elementary course in physics, namely, $T = 2\pi(L/g)^{1/2}$. L is the length of the pendulum and $g = 32.2$ ft/s^2. θ is the angle that the pendulum makes with the vertical at the instant it is released.
(a) Evaluate the part in parentheses for $\theta = 2$, 30, and 60°.
(b) Show that the quantity in parentheses can be written in the following form: $1 + {}^{91}\!/_{512} - {}^{25}\!/_{128}\cos\theta + {}^{9}\!/_{512}\cos 2\theta$.

32. The voltage in an electric circuit is

$$e = 40 \sin 120\pi t + 5 \sin 360\pi t \qquad \text{V}$$

The current is

$$i = 4 \sin 120\pi t + 2 \sin 360\pi t \qquad \text{A}$$

Determine an expression for the power $p = ei$ W and leave your final result in a form free of powers and products of trigonometric functions.

33. Two voltages

$$e_1 = 40 \sin(120\pi t + \pi/3) \qquad \text{V}$$
$$e_2 = 60 \sin(120\pi t - \pi/4) \qquad \text{V}$$

are simultaneously impressed in series on an electric circuit. Combine these into a single voltage by performing the operation $e = e_1 + e_2$. Give your final result in the form $E \sin(120\pi t + \theta)$.

34. If the voltage in an electric circuit is

$$e = E_m \sin\alpha$$

and the current is

$$i = I_m \sin(\alpha + \theta)$$

show that the power, $p = ei$ W, can be expressed in the form

$$p = \frac{E_m I_m}{2} [\cos \theta - \cos (2\alpha + \theta)]$$

This derivation is to be found in every text on ac circuits.

35. The value of the voltage e in volts due to "amplitude modulation" is given by

$$e = 100(1 + 0.7 \cos 4{,}000t - 0.3 \cos 8{,}000t) \sin 4{,}000{,}000t$$

where t is in seconds. Show that this can be rewritten in a form free of products of trigonometric functions, i.e., as the sum of simple sine functions. Then determine the amplitude, period, and frequency for each of the resulting terms.

36. Figure 18.3 shows a connecting-rod, crank-arm mechanism from an engine.
(a) Show that

$$\begin{aligned} x &= r \cos \theta + (L^2 - r^2 \sin^2 \theta)^{1/2} \\ &= r \cos \theta + L\left(1 - \frac{r^2}{L^2} \sin^2 \theta\right)^{1/2} \end{aligned}$$

(b) Expand the binomial to four terms by aid of the binomial theorem and obtain

$$x = r \cos \theta + L - \frac{r^2 \sin^2 \theta}{2L} - \frac{r^4 \sin^4 \theta}{8L^3} - \frac{r^6 \sin^6 \theta}{16L^5} - \cdots$$

(c) Transform this expression so that there are no powers of trigonometric functions present and show that the result is

$$\begin{aligned} x = {} & \left(L - \frac{r^2}{4L} - \frac{3r^4}{64L^3} - \frac{5r^6}{256L^5} - \cdots\right) + r \cos \theta \\ & + \cos 2\theta \left(\frac{r^2}{4L} + \frac{r^4}{16L^3} + \frac{13r^6}{512L^5} + \cdots\right) \\ & - \cos 4\theta \left(\frac{r^4}{64L^3} + \frac{3r^6}{256L^5} + \cdots\right) + \cdots \end{aligned}$$

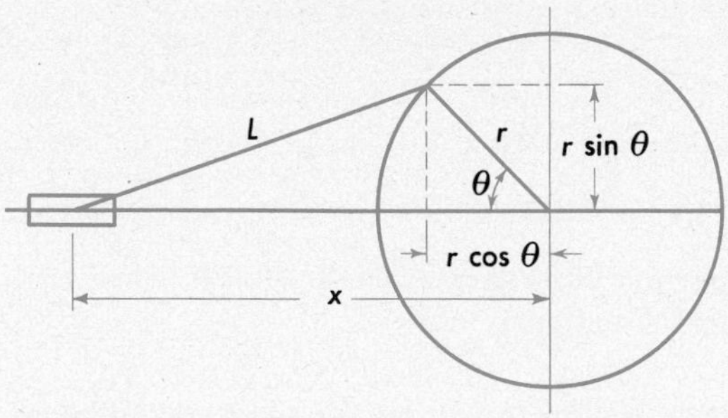

FIGURE 18.3

(*d*) Simplify the preceding expression if $L/r = 5$.

(*e*) What would this last result be if you used only the first two terms of the binomial expansion in part *b*?

The result in (*e*) is commonly used in engineering problems, since the coefficients of the higher harmonics are small ($L/r \geqq 5$). However, there are times when it is necessary to know something about the higher harmonics, and you obtained some of them in this problem.

37. Find $\sin^{-1} 0.999985$ using $\cos\theta = \sqrt{1 - \sin^2\theta}$.
38. Referring to Eq. (39), Sec. 17.6, and writing

$$(\cos\alpha + j\sin\alpha)^3 = \cos 3\alpha + j\sin 3\alpha$$

equate the real and imaginary parts and show that

$$\sin 3\alpha = 3\sin\alpha - 4\sin^3\alpha$$

also that

$$\cos 3\alpha = 4\cos^3\alpha - 3\cos\alpha$$

18.9 Trigonometric Equations

A conditional trigonometric equation or simply a trigonometric equation is an equation which is valid for some of but not all the possible values of the angles involved.

A solution of a trigonometric equation is a value of the angle, in degrees or radians, which satisfies the equation.

The three suggestions given below will take care of most cases but not all. Unfortunately no rules exist which will apply universally.

1. If only one function is involved, the equation can usually be solved algebraically (see Example 7).
2. If several functions of the same angle are involved, it is best to use some of the fundamental identities to express the entire equation in terms of a single function (see Example 8).

Very often it will be found that the equation will be easier to solve if the several functions are converted to sine and cosine functions.

3. If several angles are involved, it is usually best to express the entire equation in terms of functions of a single angle (see Example 9).

Example 7. Solve the equation

$$15 \cos^2 \phi - 7 \cos \phi - 2 = 0$$

This equation can be factored into

$$(3 \cos \phi - 2)(5 \cos \phi + 1) = 0$$

Therefore,

$$3 \cos \phi = 2$$
$$\cos \phi = 2/3$$

and

$$5 \cos \phi = -1$$
$$\cos \phi = -1/5$$

The quadratic formula could also have been used, and

$$\cos \phi = \frac{7 \pm \sqrt{49 + 120}}{30} = \frac{7 \pm \sqrt{169}}{30} = \frac{7 \pm 13}{30}$$

$$\cos \phi = 2/3 \text{ and } -1/5$$

When

$$\cos \phi = 2/3$$
$$\phi = 48°11' \text{ (to the nearest minute)}$$

or

$$\phi = 311°49' \text{ (to the nearest minute)}$$

When

$$\cos \phi = -1/5$$
$$\phi = 101°32'$$

or

$$\phi = 258°28'$$

To complete the problem, the results should be substituted in the original equation to eliminate any extraneous roots which may have been introduced in the process of solving.

Substituting $\cos\phi = 2/3$,

$$15 \times 4/9 - 7 \times 2/3 - 2 \stackrel{?}{=} 0$$
$$60/9 - 14/3 - 2$$
$$60/9 - 42/9 - 2$$
$$18/9 - 2$$
$$2 - 2 = 0 \qquad \text{(CHECK)}$$

Substituting $\cos\phi = -1/5$,

$$15 \times 1/25 - 7(-1/5) - 2 \stackrel{?}{=} 0$$
$$3/5 + 7/5 - 2 = 0$$
$$10/5 - 2 = 0 \qquad \text{(CHECK)}$$

Example 8. Solve the equation

$$2 \sin\phi = \cos\phi$$

or

$$2 = \frac{\cos\phi}{\sin\phi} = \cot\phi$$

By consulting the tables of trigonometric functions, we find that

$$\phi = 26°34' \text{ and } 206°34'$$

Example 9. Solve the equation

$$\sin 2\phi = \tan\phi$$

or

$$2 \sin\phi \cos\phi = \frac{\sin\phi}{\cos\phi}$$

Multiply both sides by $\cos\phi$:

$$
\begin{aligned}
2 \sin \phi \cos^2 \phi &= \sin \phi \qquad \cos \phi \neq 0 \\
2 \sin \phi \cos^2 \phi - \sin \phi &= 0 \\
\sin \phi (2 \cos^2 \phi - 1) &= 0 \\
\sin \phi &= 0 \\
2 \cos^2 \phi &= 1 \\
\cos^2 \phi &= 1/2 \\
\cos \phi &= \pm \frac{1}{\sqrt{2}} = \pm \frac{\sqrt{2}}{2}
\end{aligned}
$$

When $\sin \phi = 0$,

$\phi = 0°$ and $180°$

When $\cos \phi = +\sqrt{2}/2$,

$\phi = 45°$ and $315°$

When $\cos \phi = -\sqrt{2}/2$,

$\phi = 135°$ and $225°$

Check in the original problem:

When $\phi = 0°$,

$$
\begin{aligned}
\sin (2 \times 0)° &\stackrel{?}{=} \tan 0° \\
0 &= 0 \qquad \text{(CHECK)}
\end{aligned}
$$

When $\phi = 180°$,

$$
\begin{aligned}
\sin (2 \times 180)° &\stackrel{?}{=} \tan 180° \\
0 &= 0 \qquad \text{(CHECK)}
\end{aligned}
$$

When $\phi = 45°$,

$$
\begin{aligned}
\sin (2 \times 45)° &\stackrel{?}{=} \tan 45° \\
\sin 90° &\stackrel{?}{=} \tan 45° \\
1 &= 1 \qquad \text{(CHECK)}
\end{aligned}
$$

When $\phi = 315°$,

$$\sin(2 \times 315)° \stackrel{?}{=} \tan 315°$$
$$\sin 630° \stackrel{?}{=} \tan 315°$$
$$\sin 270° \stackrel{?}{=} \tan 315°$$
$$-1 = -1 \qquad \text{(CHECK)}$$

When $\phi = 135°$,

$$\sin(2 \times 135)° \stackrel{?}{=} \tan 135°$$
$$\sin 270° \stackrel{?}{=} \tan 135°$$
$$-1 = -1 \qquad \text{(CHECK)}$$

When $\phi = 225°$,

$$\sin(2 \times 225)° \stackrel{?}{=} \tan 225°$$
$$\sin 450° \stackrel{?}{=} \tan 225°$$
$$\sin 90° \stackrel{?}{=} \tan 225°$$
$$+1 = +1 \qquad \text{(CHECK)}$$

EXERCISE 4

Find all positive angles less than 360° which satisfy each of the following equations.

1. $\sqrt{2}\sin x = 1$
2. $\cos x - 1 = 0$
3. $\sec x - 2 = 0$
4. $5 \sin x - 2 = 0$
5. $\sqrt{3}\tan x + 1 = 0$
6. $3 \operatorname{cosec} x - 7 = 0$
7. $\tan^2 x = \tan x$
8. $5 \cot x = 2(-\cot x)$
9. $2 \cos x \sin x + \cos x = 0$
10. $\sqrt{3}\cos x + 2\cos^2 x = 0$
11. $2 \cos x + \cot x = 0$
12. $2 \sin^2 x = \cos x \tan x$
13. $\sqrt{3}\sec x \sin x = \tan^2 x$
14. $2 \cot x = \operatorname{cosec}^2 x - 1$
15. $\cos x + \sin^2 x = 1$
16. $\operatorname{cosec}^2 x = 1 + 3 \cos x \operatorname{cosec} x$
17. $\sqrt{3}\operatorname{cosec}^2 x = 2 \sin x + \sqrt{3}\cot^2 x$
18. $\sin^2 x \cos x - \sin x \cos x = 0$
19. $2 \sin^3 x \sec x + 3 \tan x = 0$
20. $2 \tan^2 x \cos x - \sin x = 0$
21. $\sin\phi = \cos 2\phi$
22. $\sin\phi = (\tan\phi)/2$
23. $\sin\phi = (\sec\phi)/2$
24. $\sin\phi - \cos 2\phi = 1$
25. $\tan\phi + \cot\phi = 1$
26. $\cos^2\phi + \cos 2\phi = 1$
27. $(\tan\phi)/(\sin\phi) = 5$
28. $\cos^2(\phi - 30°) = 1$
29. $3 \operatorname{cosec}^2\phi = 9$
30. $\sin 3\phi + 2 \sin\phi = 1$

31. The relation between the size of feed b, the space between the rolls $2a$, the radius of the rolls r, and the angle of "nip" $N°$ is

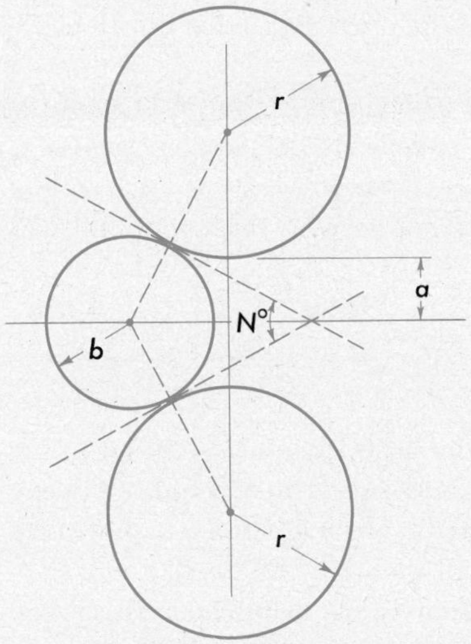

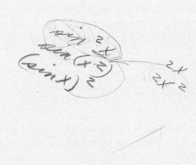

FIGURE 18.4

$$\cos\frac{N}{2} = \frac{r + a}{r + b}$$

(*a*) Derive this equation from Fig. 18.4.

(*b*) What is the relation for N in terms of r, a, and b? For r in terms of N, a, and b?

32. Figure 18.5 shows four circles that possess the indicated tangency properties. The radii of three circles are known: $\overline{OC} = 5$ in, $\overline{AB} = 3$ in, and $\overline{ED} = 2$ in. Determine

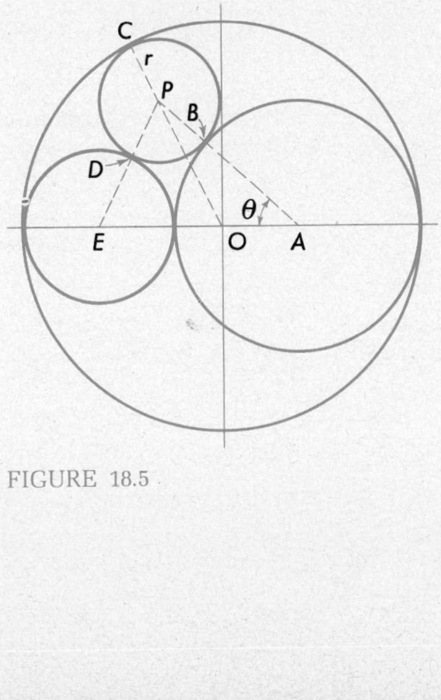

FIGURE 18.5

the coordinates of the center P and the radius r of the circle BCD, this fourth circle being tangent to each of the three given circles.

Suggestion: Angle θ is common to the two triangles OAP and EAP, and the dimensions of the sides of both these triangles can be expressed in terms of r.

33. When a block of weight W lb is pulled up an inclined plane by a horizontally directed force (P lb), the angle θ which the plane makes with the horizontal will make the efficiency a maximum if

$$\sin 2(\theta + \phi) = \sin 2\theta$$

Mechanical efficiency is defined as the ratio of the useful work performed to the total energy expended (see Fig. 18.7). Tan ϕ is a measure of the friction between the block and the plane. Solve for the smallest acute angle θ if $\tan \phi = 0.347$ (the proper value if the block is made of cast iron and the plane of steel).

34. A ski jumper starts down a hill from the point marked A (Fig. 18.6). The cross section of the hill is a circle of radius R. It can be shown, by methods of physics and mechanics, that the radius to the point at which he will leave the surface of the hill (neglecting friction, which is small) will make an angle θ with the horizontal, where

$$\sin \theta = 2(1 - \sin \theta)$$

Determine this angle.

35. A body weighing W lb rests on a rough plane inclined at an angle θ with the horizontal (Fig. 18.7). To determine the force P lb that will just cause the body to begin to slide up the hill, one applies methods of mechanics to obtain the following equations:

$$P \cos \theta - W \sin \theta = F \qquad N - W \cos \theta = P \sin \theta \qquad F = N \tan \phi$$

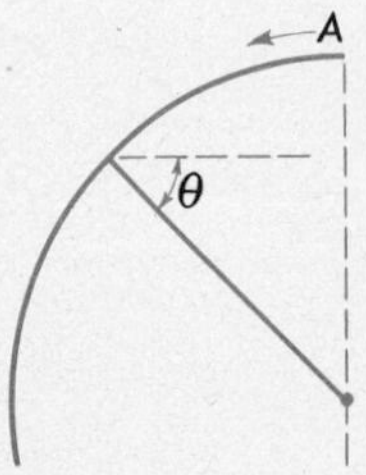

FIGURE 18.6

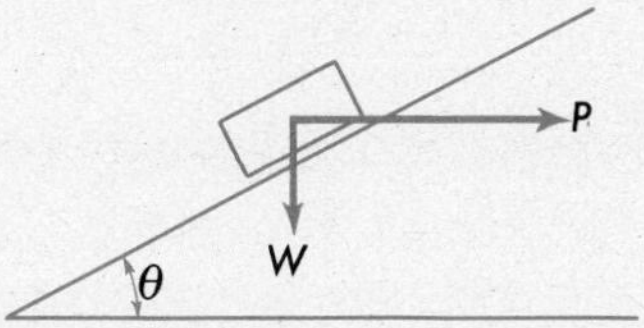

FIGURE 18.7

where $\tan \phi$ is a measure of the friction between the body and the plane and F is the frictional force. Solve these three equations simultaneously for P and obtain $P = W \tan(\theta + \phi)$.

36. The equation

$$\frac{\tan \alpha_2}{\tan \alpha_1} = \frac{u_1}{u_2}$$

is used in electrical engineering to determine the change in direction when magnetic lines pass from one medium to another. A special case yields

$$\tan \alpha_{\text{air}} = 1{,}000 \tan \alpha_{\text{iron}}$$

Compute α_{air} in degrees correct to the nearest minute when $\alpha_{\text{iron}} = 0, 0.1, 1, 15, 30,$ and $60°$.

37. Snell's law from physics is (see Fig. 18.8)

$$\frac{\sin \phi_1}{\sin \phi_2} = \frac{n_2}{n_1}$$

where n_1 *and* n_2 are the indices of refraction for two mediums through which light is passing, and ϕ_1 and ϕ_2 are the corresponding angles.

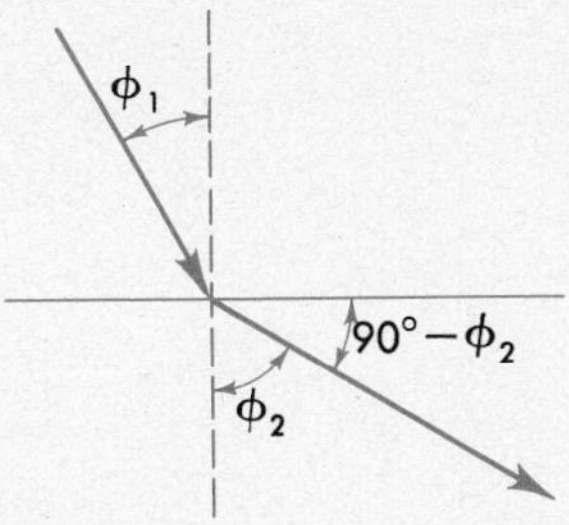

FIGURE 18.8

Let

n_1 = index of refraction of water = 1.33
n_2 = index of refraction of air = 1.000,292

Then we may write

$$\frac{\sin \phi_{\text{water}}}{\sin \phi_{\text{air}}} = \frac{1.000{,}292}{1.33}$$

If ϕ_{air} takes on successive values of 0, 1, 10, 30, 45, 60, and 90°, tabulate corresponding values of ϕ_{water}.

19 Graphical methods of calculus

In this chapter our approach will be highly intuitive and based on graphical analysis. In Chaps. 20 and 21 the treatment will be far more rigorous.

Before proceeding, the student should review Chap. 6, particularly Secs. 6.6 and 6.7.

19.1 The Slope of a Linear Graph

In Chap. 6 we learned that if we are given the graph of a linear function f, the slope of the graph between any two distinct points P_1 and P_2 on the graph (see Fig. 19.1) is

$$\text{Slope} = \frac{f(x_1 + \Delta x) - f(x_1)}{\Delta x} \tag{1}$$

where the meaning of x_1, Δx, $f(x_1)$, and $f(x_1 + \Delta x)$ is illustrated in Fig. 19.1.

The slope of the graph of a function is also the *rate of change in the value of the function* with respect to the independent variable.

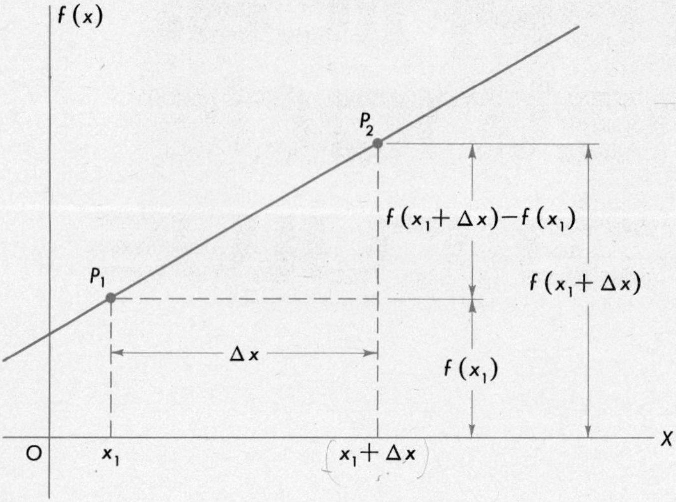

FIGURE 19.1

19.2 Slopes of Nonlinear Graphs

Figure 19.2*a* is the graph of a certain nonlinear function.

Intuitively, we can see that as x increases, the "slope" of the graph increases. That is, the curve rises "faster" as we scan it from left to right. Of course, the graph also rises higher as we progress to the right, but that is beside the point at the moment. The essential point is that the slope of the curve is not, in general, the same between different pairs of points on the graph.

What, then, shall we consider to be the slope of a nonlinear graph?

In Fig. 19.2*a* the tangent line AB is drawn to the curve at point P_1. It seems quite proper to let the slope of this tangent be a measure of what we intuitively think of as "the slope of the graph at point P_1."

However, we shall have to describe in more detail just what we mean by a "tangent."

In Fig. 19.2*a* the line DE is called a secant. A secant is a line of unlimited length cutting a curve. The line segment P_1P_2 is a part of the secant DE and is called a chord. One extremity of this chord will be fixed at P_1.

Now if the secant DE is rotated clockwise while always passing through P_1, the other end of the chord will pass through P_2, P_3, P_4, P_5, etc., as well as intermediate points. The chord will then progressively decrease in length.

At one particular position when the secant coincides with the line AB, the chord will disappear altogether. If the secant were rotated beyond this position, a chord would appear to the left of P_1. There is then a unique position of the secant DE where the length of the chord is zero.

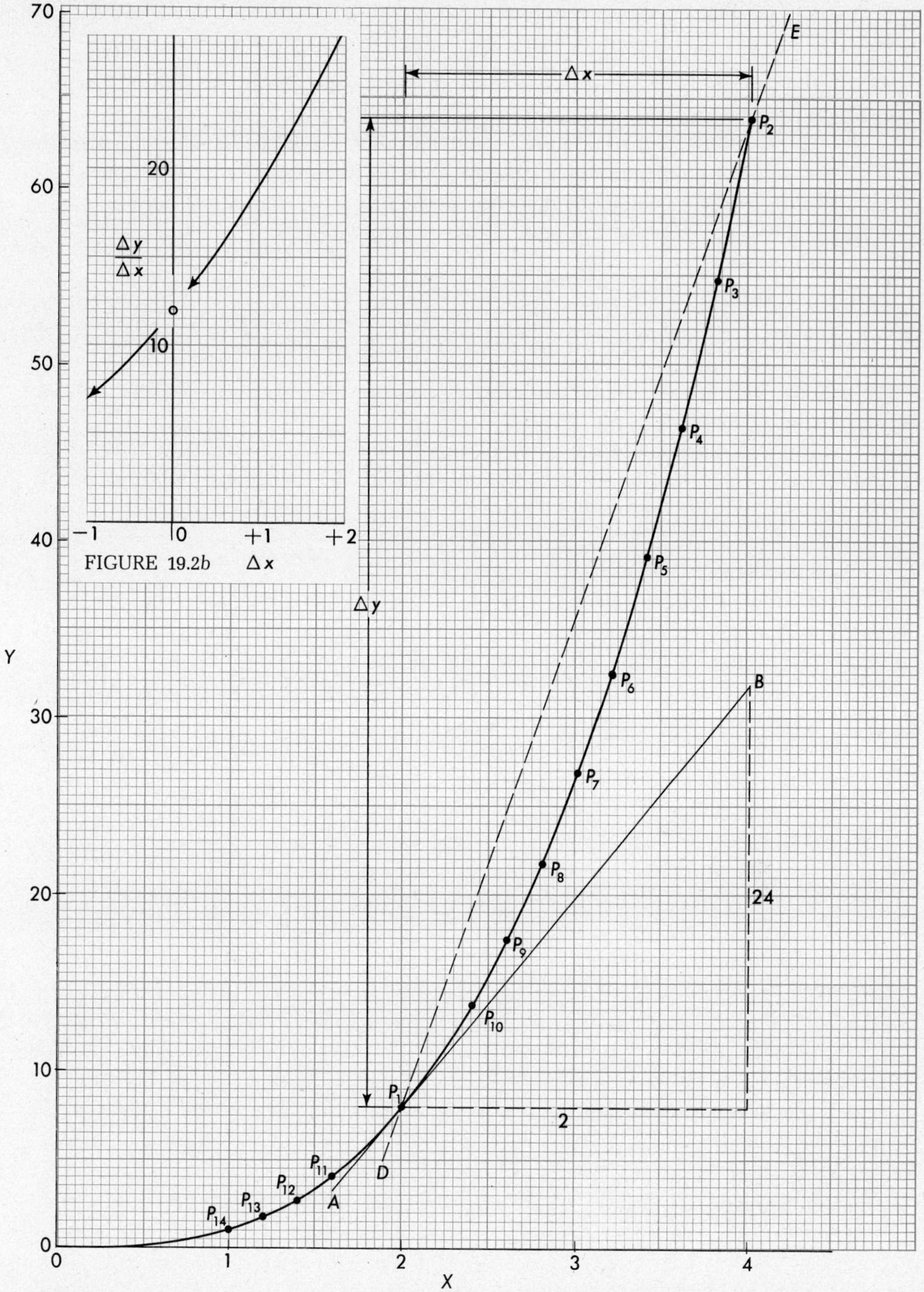

FIGURE 19.2b

FIGURE 19.2a

The tangent to the curve at a given point is therefore "the unique limiting position of the secant passing through that point as the length of the chord approaches zero."

To draw a tangent to a curve at a given point, we keep the edge of a straight edge through the point and adjust the direction of the straight edge until the chord appears to vanish. The slope of this straight edge is now a graphical approximation to the slope of the curve at the point under consideration.

19.3 Average and Instantaneous Slopes and Rates

In dealing with the graphs of nonlinear functions we distinguish between *average* and *instantaneous* slopes.

The average slope of the nonlinear graph illustrated in Fig. 19.2*a* between the point P_1 (whose x coordinate is x_1) and another point P_2 on the graph (whose x coordinate is $x_1 + \Delta x$) is given by

$$\begin{pmatrix}\text{Average slope}\\ \text{between } P_1 \text{ and } P_2\end{pmatrix} = \frac{f(x_1 + \Delta x) - f(x_1)}{\Delta x} \tag{2}$$

By reading the graph we find that in this case

$$\begin{aligned} x_1 &= 2 \\ f(x_1) &= 8 \\ \Delta x &= 2 \\ x_1 + \Delta x &= 4 \\ f(x_1 + \Delta x) &= 64 \end{aligned}$$

Then

$$\begin{pmatrix}\text{Average slope}\\ \text{between } P_1 \text{ and } P_2\end{pmatrix} = \frac{64 - 8}{2} = 28$$

We may also say that the average rate of change in the value of this function with respect to x between x_1 and $x_1 + \Delta x$ is 28 when $x_1 = 2$ and $x_1 + \Delta x = 4$.

The *instantaneous* slope of the graph at P_1 is the slope of the tangent to the graph at P_1, and

$$\begin{pmatrix}\text{Instantaneous}\\ \text{slope at } P_1\end{pmatrix} = \frac{24}{2} = 12$$

Also, the instantaneous rate of change in the value of the function with respect to x is 12 when x = 2. If we let

$$y = f(x)$$

it is quite common to let

$$\Delta y = f(x_1 + \Delta x) - f(x_1)$$

Then we may write

$$\frac{\Delta y}{\Delta x} = \begin{pmatrix} \text{average slope } \textit{between} \text{ two points} \\ P_1 \text{ and } P_2 \text{ on the graph} \end{pmatrix}$$

It is very important that the student observe that we speak of the *average* slope *between two points* and the *instantaneous* slope *at one single point*. Let us investigate the matter still further. We shall calculate the slopes of lines connecting P_1 and P_2, P_3, P_4, P_5, etc., in Fig. 19.2*a* and tabulate them in Table 19.1. The values $\Delta y = f(x_1 + \Delta x) - f(x_1)$ were read from a much larger graph than the one presented here. However, the student can verify them approximately.

The values of Δx and $\Delta y/\Delta x$ are plotted in Fig. 19.2*b*. As we scan this graph from right to left, we note that the trend of the graph is directly toward the point (0,12).

TABLE 19.1

Between points	$f(x_1)$	Δx†	$f(x_1 + \Delta x)$	$f(x_1 + \Delta x) - f(x_1) = \Delta y$	$\frac{f(x_1 + \Delta x) - f(x_1)}{\Delta x} = \frac{\Delta y}{\Delta x}$
P_1 and P_2	8.000	2.0	64.000	56.000	+28.00
P_1 and P_3	8.000	1.8	54.872	46.872	+26.04
P_1 and P_4	8.000	1.6	46.656	38.656	+24.16
P_1 and P_5	8.000	1.4	39.304	31.304	+22.36
P_1 and P_6	8.000	1.2	32.768	24.768	+20.64
P_1 and P_7	8.000	1.0	27.000	19.000	+19.00
P_1 and P_8	8.000	0.8	21.952	13.952	+17.44
P_1 and P_9	8.000	0.6	17.576	9.576	+15.96
P_1 and P_{10}	8.000	0.4	13.824	5.824	+14.56
			At P_1, $\Delta y/\Delta x$ is indeterminate		
P_1 and P_{11}	8.000	−0.4	4.096	−3.904	+ 9.76
P_1 and P_{12}	8.000	−0.6	2.744	−5.256	+ 8.76
P_1 and P_{13}	8.000	−0.8	1.728	−6.272	+ 7.84
P_1 and P_{14}	8.000	−1.0	1.000	−7.000	+ 7.00

†According to the conventions of rectangular coordinates, when measured from left to right, Δx is a positive number. When measured from right to left, it is a negative number.

As we pass the vertical axis in Fig. 19.2*b* and continue on to the left, we note that it appears that the graph has passed through the point (0,12).

However, $\Delta y/\Delta x$ is indeterminate when Δx is precisely zero since division by zero is indeterminate. This is indicated on the graph by the small circle whose center is at the point (0,12).

Let us be satisfied to see what $\Delta y/\Delta x$ *approaches* as Δx *approaches* zero. We have observed from this graphical work that $\Delta y/\Delta x$ (the average slope) approaches 12 (the instantaneous slope) as Δx approaches zero. The symbol $\Delta y/\Delta x$ indicates the *actual* change in y divided by the *corresponding* actual change in x. This is an *average* slope.

For the present we shall let the instantaneous slope be designated by the symbol dy/dx. In Chap. 20 we shall consider a more fundamental concept of this symbol.

The symbol dy/dx is called the "derivative of y with respect to x" and will be discussed somewhat further in the following section.

19.4 The Derivative

The relation between $\Delta y/\Delta x$ and Δx is exhibited in Fig. 19.2*b* and Table 19.1 with reference to point P_1 in Fig. 19.2*a*.

The derivative is "the limit which $\Delta y/\Delta x$ approaches as Δx approaches zero." This symbol is written

$$\frac{dy}{dx} = \lim_{\Delta x \to 0} \frac{\Delta y}{\Delta x}$$

In the function represented in Fig. 19.2*a*, therefore, the derivative of y with respect to x is 12 when x = 2, or

$$\lim_{\Delta x \to 0} \frac{\Delta y}{\Delta x} = 12$$

Thus

$$\frac{dy}{dx} = 12$$

Example 1. What is the slope of the graph shown in Fig. 19.3 at point Q?

First, we draw the tangent to the curve through point Q. Then we find the slope of this tangent. We see that the tangent passes through points *F* and *H* whose coordinates are (0.1,7.5) and (0.3,12.5), respectively. The slope of the tangent is given by

$$\text{Slope} = \frac{12.5 - 7.5}{0.3 - 0.1} = \frac{5}{0.2} = 25$$

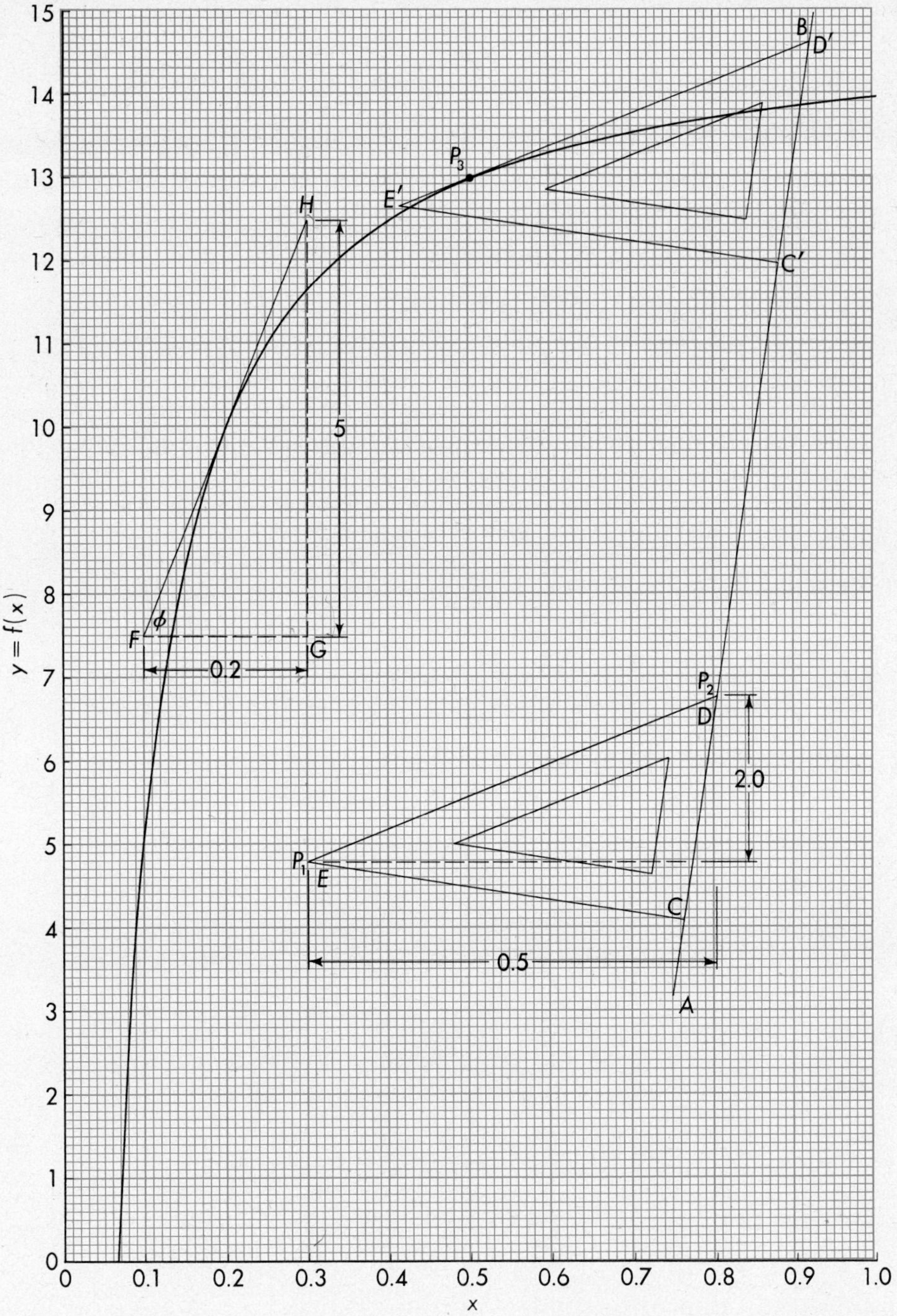

15
14
13
12
11
10
9
8
7
6
5
4
3
2
1
0
y = f(x)
0
0.1
0.2
0.3
0.4
0.5
0.6
0.7
0.8
0.9
1.0
x
B
D′
P3
E′
H
C′
5
F
ϕ
G
0.2
P2
D
2.0
P1
E
C
0.5
A

FIGURE 19.3

Consequently, the instantaneous slope of the graph itself is said to be 25 at the point Q.

Example 2. In Fig. 19.4 (curve *A*) find the average rate of change in y with respect to x between x = −1.73 and +1.73.

$$\frac{\Delta y}{\Delta x} = \frac{2.89 - (-2.89)}{-1.73 - (+1.73)} = \frac{+5.78}{-3.46} = -1.67$$

Thus the average rate of change in y with respect to x between x = −1.73 and x = +1.73 is −1.67. Observe also that these two points P_1 and P_2 are at the intersections of curves *A* and *C*. Therefore the *average* rate of change in y with respect to x is the same for both curves between these two points.

Thus, over a relatively large Δx the *average* slope is not necessarily very descriptive of the actual path of the curve throughout that interval.

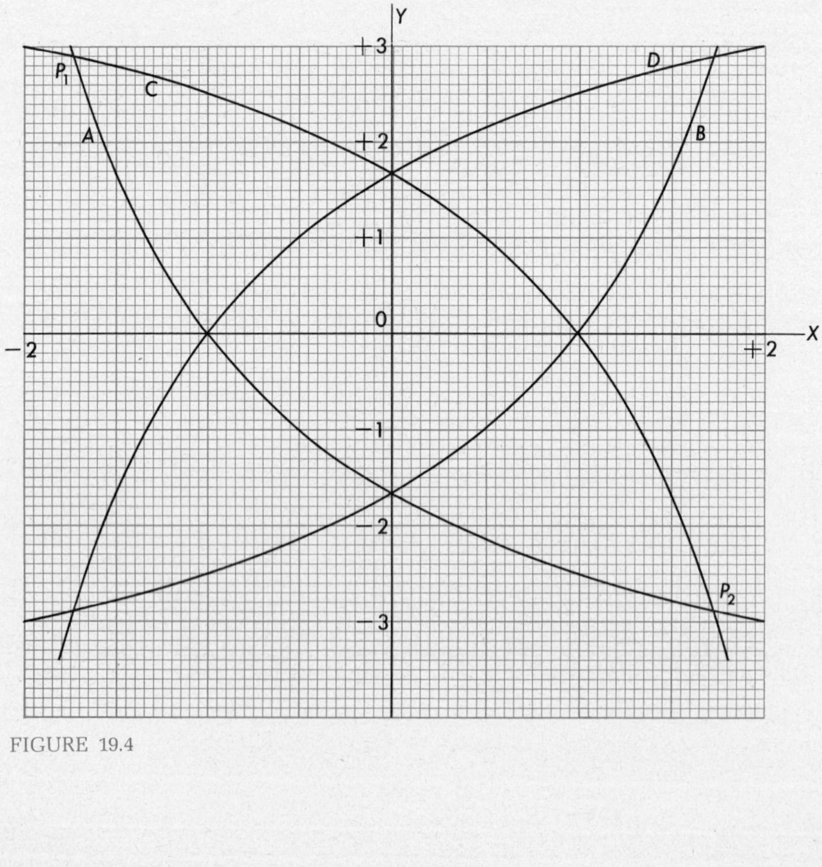

FIGURE 19.4

Example 3. In Fig. 19.3 find the coordinates of the point at which the instantaneous slope is +4.

A pair of convenient points such as P_1 and P_2 are located on the same coordinate system as the graph, such that the slope of the straight line between them is +4. Then one edge of a triangle, *ED*, is placed so that the edge of the triangle passes through P_1 and P_2.

A straight edge, *AB*, is pressed against another side of the triangle, *CD*.

The triangle is then moved along the straight edge until the side *ED* becomes tangent to the curve as shown by the position (*E'D'*).

The point of tangency P_3 has the coordinates (0.5,13.00).

Thus the coordinates of the point at which the instantaneous slope is +4 are (0.5,13.00).

Example 4. What is the angle ϕ in Fig. 19.3?

The angle ϕ is called the *inclination* of the tangent line *FH*. The inclination of a line is defined as "the smallest angle measured from the positive part of the X axis to the line." Angles measured in a counterclockwise direction from the X axis are positive angles. Angles measured in a clockwise direction from the X axis are negative angles.

This angle is one angle of the triangle *FGH*. If we take the distance between boldface lines on the grid to be one unit of length, then the side opposite this angle is 5 units long and the side adjacent is 2 units long. Therefore the tangent of the angle is

$$\tan \phi = 5/2 = 2.5$$

and

$$\phi = 68° \qquad \text{(approximately)}$$

Observe that in finding the tangent of the angle, the *same* scale is used for the opposite and adjacent sides, not the scales used on the axes. Therefore the tangent of the angle and the slope of the curve are identical *only* when the same scale is used on the vertical and horizontal axes.

19.5 Approximate Increments

Suppose we wished to find how much y increased when x increased from 0.2 to 0.2001 in Fig. 19.3. Of course it would be impossible to read this small increment directly from the graph. But from Example 1 above, we find that when x = 0.2 the rate of change of y with respect to x is 25. Now it is true that the rate of change of y with respect to x will be a little different at $x = 0.2001$ from what it was at exactly $x = 0.2000$, but not much different. Over this small interval we shall be approximately correct to assume that the rate is constant.

Therefore, we can say that if Δx is *small*, the *instantaneous* rate of change of y with respect to x is *approximately* the same as the average rate of change of y with respect to x at all points within the interval.

In mathematical symbols

$$\frac{dy}{dx} \approx \frac{\Delta y}{\Delta x} \qquad \text{(when } \Delta x \text{ is small)} \tag{3}$$

In the present example

$$\frac{dy}{dx} = 25$$

and $\Delta x = 0.0001$. Therefore,

$$\frac{\Delta y}{0.0001} \approx 25$$

$$\Delta y \approx 0.0025$$

and y increases approximately 0.0025 unit when x increases 0.0001 unit from $x = 0.2000$ to $x = 0.2001$.

EXERCISE 1

The following problems all refer to Fig. 19.4.

1. For curve *B*, find the average rate of change of y with respect to x between $x = -1.5$ and $x = 0$.
2. Find the instantaneous rate of change of y with respect to x for curve *B* when $x = -1.5$.
3. Find the average slope of curve *B* between $x = +1$ and $x = +1.5$.
4. Find the instantaneous slope of curve *B* when $x = +1$.
5. Find $\Delta y/\Delta x$ between $x = -0.5$ and $x = +0.5$ for curve *C*.
6. Find dy/dx at $x = 0$ for curve *A*.
7. For curve *D* find the coordinates of the point where the instantaneous slope is $+\frac{5}{8}$.
8. Find the angle which the tangent drawn to the curve *C* makes with the horizontal when $x = 0$.
9. Find the approximate change in y when x changes from -1.5 to -1.499 for curve *B* (see Prob. 2 above). Does y increase or decrease?

10. Find the approximate change in y when x changes from 1 to 1.03 for curve B (see Prob. 4 above). Does y increase or decrease?
11. Find the approximate change in y when x changes from 0 to 0.02 for curve A (see Prob. 6 above). Does y increase or decrease?

19.6 Maxima and Minima

Suppose we have a function f for which $y = f(x)$. This function is said to have a *relative maximum* at $x = a$ if $f(a)$ is equal to or greater than any other $f(x)$ in the immediate vicinity (see Fig. 19.5).

Similarly, this function is said to have a *relative minimum* at $x = b$ if $f(b)$ is equal to or less than any other $f(x)$ in the immediate vicinity (see Fig. 19.5).

A point whose ordinate is a maximum value of a function is called a maximum point. Similarly, a point whose ordinate is the minimum value of a function is called a minimum point.

We distinguish between relative maxima and minima as described above and *absolute* maxima and minima which are illustrated in Fig. 19.6. If a function is defined for the domain $a \leq x \leq b$ (see Fig. 19.6) and if $f(a)$ is greater than any other $f(x)$ for this domain, then the function is said to have an *absolute* maximum at $x = a$. This function is shown to have an *absolute* minimum at $x = b$ (see Fig. 19.6).

A function may have relative maxima and minima of the type illustrated in Fig. 19.7, although we shall have little to do with such situations.

Hereafter, when we use the words "maximum" and "minimum" without further qualification, we shall mean the sort of relative maximum or minimum illustrated in Fig. 19.5.

There are four important characteristics of relative maximum and minimum points.

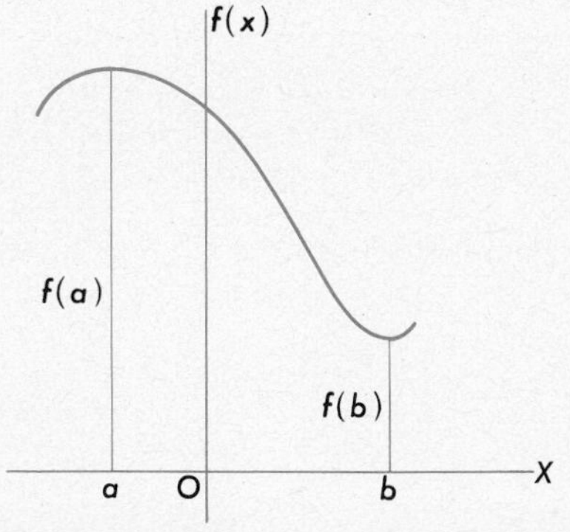

FIGURE 19.5

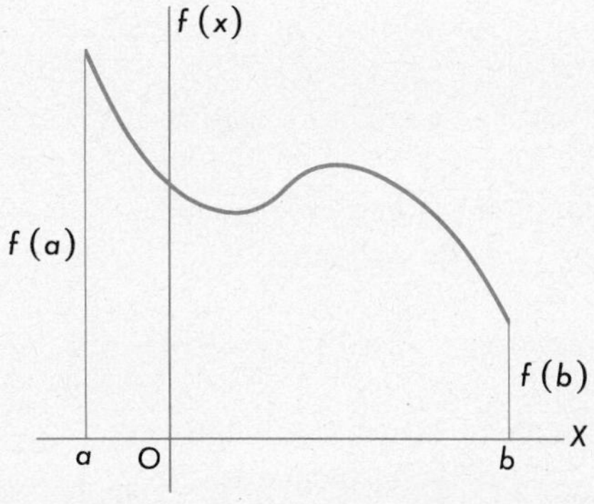

FIGURE 19.6

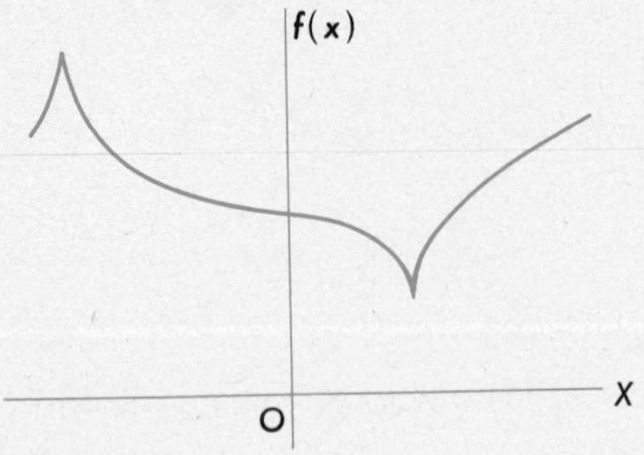

FIGURE 19.7

1. If a graph has a relative maximum or minimum point in a certain vicinity, and if a tangent whose slope is a finite real number can be drawn at this point, then the slope of this tangent must be zero.
2. A maximum point is higher than any other point in the immediate vicinity, and a minimum point is lower than any other point in the immediate vicinity.
3. In passing through a maximum point, if we scan the graph in the direction of increasing abscissa (that is, as we scan the graph from left to right), we find a positive slope, a zero slope, and a negative slope, *in that order*.
4. In passing through a minimum point, if we scan the graph in the direction of increasing abscissa, we find a negative slope, a zero slope, and a positive slope, *in that order*.

Consider the maximum point P_1 (Fig. 19.8*a*). At the point P_1 the slope is zero. The point P_1 is higher than any other point in the immediate vicinity. Immediately to the left the slope is positive, and immediately to the right the slope is negative.

A similar situation exists about the minimum point P_2. At the point P_2 the slope is zero. This point is lower than any other point in the immediate vicinity, and the slope is negative to the left of P_2 and positive to the right of P_2.

As we scan the graph from left to right, if the sign of the slope is in the sequence

Positive → zero → negative

the point is at a *maximum*.

If the sequence is

Negative → zero → positive

the point is at a *minimum*.

If the sequence is

Negative → zero → negative

or

Positive → zero → positive

the point is at neither a maximum nor a minimum.

Thus we cannot assume that just because the slope of a graph is zero at a given point either a maximum or a minimum must exist at that point.

19.7 Points of Inflection

Refer to Fig. 19.9. Consider the reverse curve *ABC* to be a map of a road. As we drive an automobile along the road from *A* toward *B*, we are steering to the right. When we reach point *B*, we must steer to the left. At point *B* the curvature *reverses*.

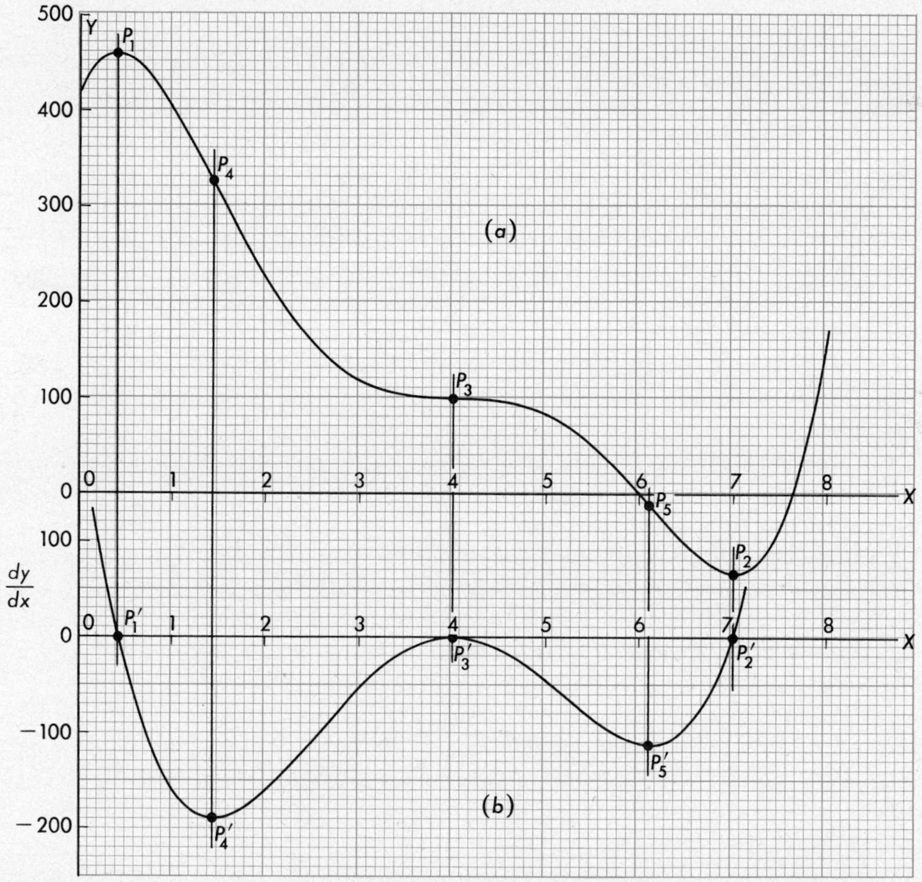

FIGURE 19.8

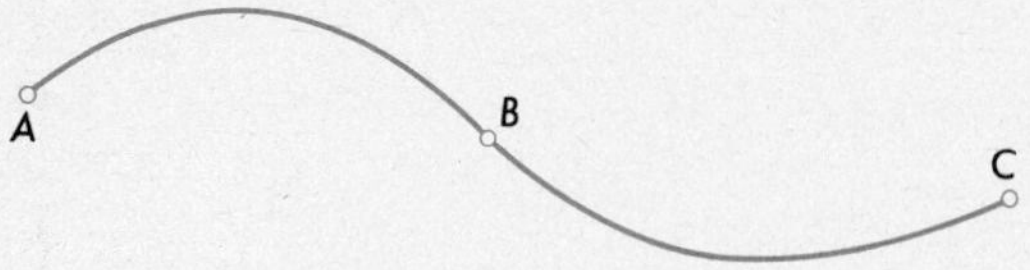

FIGURE 19.9

Any point on a graph where the curvature reverses is called a *point of inflection*.

Applying this notion to Fig. 19.8*a*, we note that points of inflection occur at P_3, P_4, and P_5. True, the slope at P_3 is zero, but this is not a necessary condition for a point of inflection. The slopes at the other two points of inflection, P_4 and P_5, are not zero.

It is a characteristic of a point of inflection having a horizontal tangent (such as P_3) that as we scan the graph in either direction the slope passes through zero but *does not change sign*.

Thus a point of horizontal tangency may be a maximum, a minimum, or simply a point of inflection.

19.8 Derived Curves

Figure 19.8*b* is a plot of dy/dx versus x, that is, for a given value of x, the numerical value of the slope in Fig. 19.8*a* is the ordinate of Fig. 19.8*b*.

For example, we can see that the slope in Fig. 19.8*a* is zero at P_1 because the tangent to the curve at that point is horizontal. The corresponding point P_1' in Fig. 19.8*b* shows that at this point $dy/dx = 0$. Precisely the same information in this respect is obtained from either graph.

Observe points P_2 and P_3 together with their corresponding points in Fig. 19.8*b* (P_2' and P_3'). In each case the slope of Fig. 19.8*a* and its synonym dy/dx are shown to be zero.

If we scan Fig. 19.8*a* from P_1 toward the right, we note that the slope decreases (increases numerically but in a negative direction). The slope continues to decrease until we reach P_4, a point of inflection.

Subsequently, the graph flattens out and the slope becomes zero again at P_3, which is another point of inflection. Considering signs, then, the slope at P_4 is a minimum. Now notice that a minimum dy/dx occurs at P_4' in Fig. 19.8*b*.

Observe that the slope is again a minimum at the point of inflection P_5 and is so indicated at P_5'.

The slope is at a maximum at P_3 and is also so indicated at P_3'. However, the student should be careful to notice that the point P_3 corresponds to a maximum slope in Fig. 19.8*a*. It does not correspond to a maximum ordinate on Fig. 19.8*a*.

EXERCISE 2

1. By laying a straight edge against curve *a* in Fig. 19.8 find the slope of this curve at the following values of x: 0.4, 1.0, 2.5, 4.0, 4.5, 5.0, 6.0, 6.1.

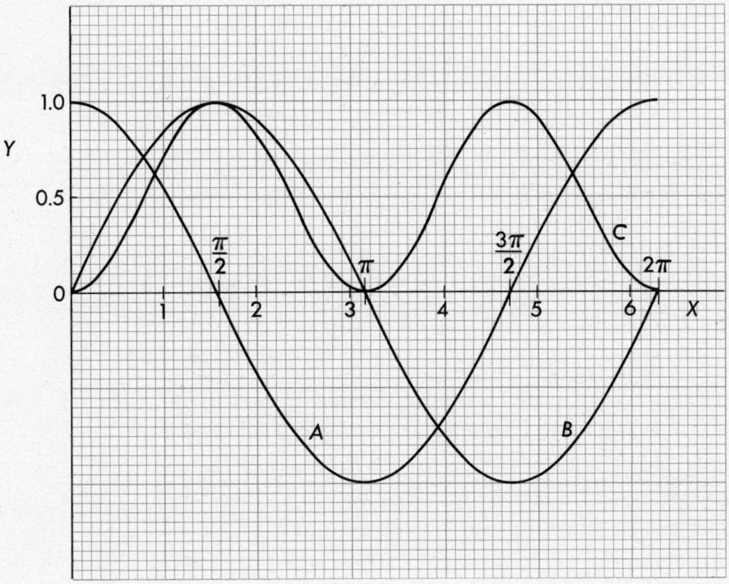

FIGURE 19.10

2. (*a*) Compare the slopes found in Prob. 1 with the corresponding ordinates of curve *b* in Fig. 19.8.
   (*b*) Find where the slope of curve *a* is a maximum; a minimum.
   (*c*) Find where the slope of curve *b* is a maximum; a minimum.
3. Curve *B* in Fig. 19.10 is the graph of $y = \sin x$, where x is in *radians*.
   (*a*) Find dy/dx for x equal to 0, 1.2, 1.57, 2.0, 3.14, 3.8, 4.71, 5.2, and 6.0 in curve *B*.
   (*b*) Compare the values of dy/dx found in (*a*) for each given value of x with the ordinate of curve *A* for the same value of x.
   (*c*) Curve *A* is the graph of $\cos x$ versus x. If $y = \sin x$, what is the equation for dy/dx?

19.9 Area under the Graphs of Nonlinear Functions

In Sec. 6.18 we discussed the areas under graphs of linear functions. There, we found that such areas are triangles, rectangles, and trapezoids. These areas may be calculated by simple formulas.

There are, in general, no such simple formulas for finding the areas under nonlinear graphs such as the one shown in Fig. 19.11. However, we can *approximate* these areas by the "narrow-strip method."

Suppose that we wish to find the area under the curve shown in Fig. 19.12 between ordinates erected at $x = a$ and $x = b$. This is the area aP_0P_1b.

To approximate this area, we divide it into narrow strips by lines perpendicular

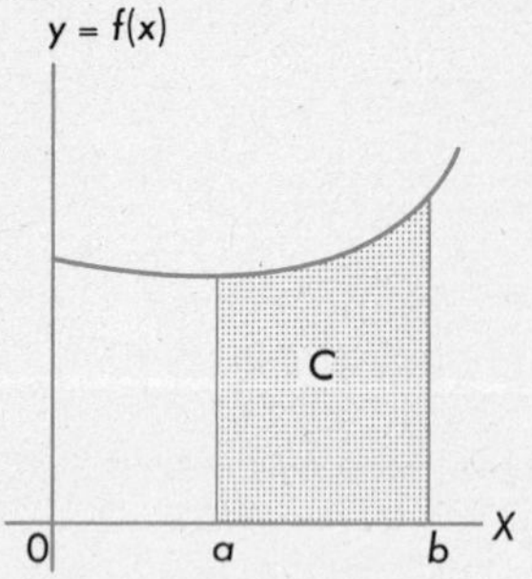

FIGURE 19.11

to the X axis. In this case we show ten strips numbered from 1 to 10. Although it is not entirely necessary, we have for simplicity used strips of equal width.

We have constructed a series of rectangles whose width is the width of the strip and whose altitude y^* is an ordinate of the curve drawn within the strip. The area of each rectangle approximates the area of its corresponding strip. We can approximate the area of each strip more closely by using good judgment in locating y^*. It should be intuitively evident that we can obtain a better approximation by placing y^* about midway of the strips than if we located it near either boundary. No generally applicable rule can be given, but the student's judgment in this matter will probably be much better than he may think.

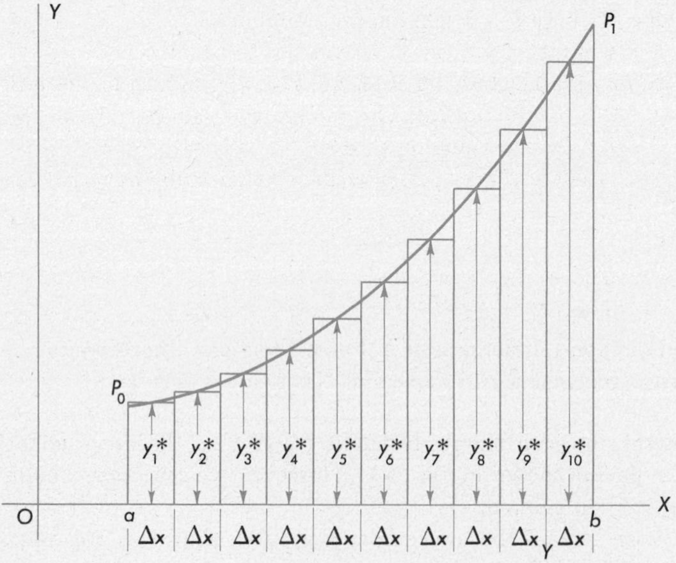

FIGURE 19.12

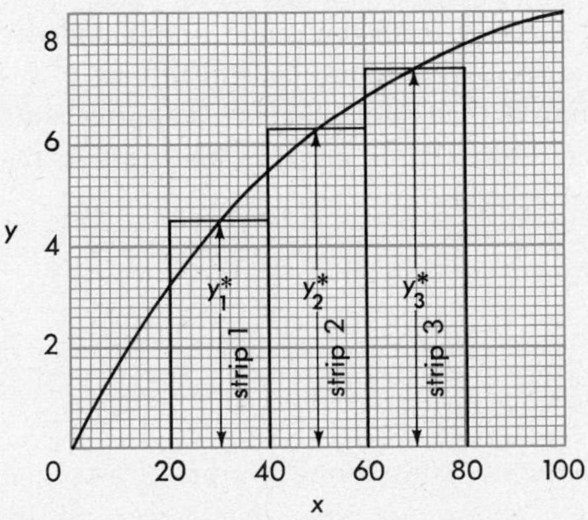

FIGURE 19.13

The area under the graph between $x = a$ and $x = b$ can now be approximated by the sum of the areas of the individual rectangles. This can be expressed symbolically as

$$A_a{}^b \approx y_1^*(\Delta x) + y_2^*(\Delta x) + y_3^*(\Delta x) + \cdots + y_n^*(\Delta x) \tag{4}$$

where

$A_a{}^b$ = area aP_0P_1b
$\Delta x = (b - a)/n$
y_1^* = an ordinate erected within first interval
y_2^* = an ordinate erected within second interval
y_3^* = an ordinate erected within third interval
y_n^* = an ordinate erected within nth interval

Example 5. Find the area under the graph in Fig. 19.13 between $x = 20$ and $x = 80$.

We arbitrarily divide this area into three strips, each 20 units wide. Therefore Δx in Eq. (4) is 20. Since there are three strips, n in Eq. (4) is 3.

The calculations involved are tabulated in Table 19.2.

TABLE 19.2

Strip	y^*	Width Δx	ΔA	$\Sigma y^*(\Delta x)$
1	4.5	20	90	90
2	6.3	20	126	216
3	7.5	20	150	366
		Total area =	366	

The ordinate y^* for each strip is read directly from the graph about midway of each strip. The approximate area of each strip (ΔA) is found by multiplying y^* for that strip by 20. Each entry in the $\Sigma y^*(\Delta x)$ column of the table includes the approximate area of the corresponding strip as well as the approximate areas of all strips to the left. (This is called cumulative area.) The total area is

$A_{20}^{80} \approx 366$ square units

19.10 Mean Ordinates of Curves

Figure 19.14 shows the graph of a function which is continuous and positive-valued on the closed interval with endpoints at $x = a$ and $x = b$. Now, leaning heavily on geometric intuition, it seems plausible that there is a point e between a and b on the X axis at which an ordinate $\bar{y}$ can be erected such that

$$\bar{y} = \frac{A_a{}^b}{b - a} \tag{5}$$

where

$A_a{}^b$ = area bounded above by the curve, below by the X axis, on the left by the ordinate erected at $x = a$, and on the right by the ordinate erected by $x = b$.

$\bar{y}$ = mean ordinate of the graph between a and b. Note that $\bar{y}$ is defined by Eq. (5) above. It is not necessarily the arithmetic average of the ordinates erected at a and b, as was the case with linear graphs.

Example 6. Find the mean ordinate of the graph shown in Fig. 19.13 between $x = 20$ and $x = 80$.

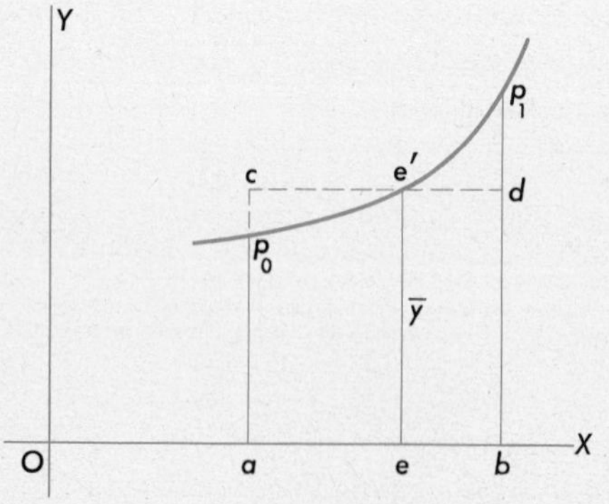

FIGURE 19.14

In this case, referred to Eq. (5), $a = 20$ and $b = 80$. From Table 19.2, $A_{20}^{80} = 366$. Therefore from Eq. (5) the mean ordinate between $x = 20$ and $x = 80$ is

$$\bar{y} = \frac{366}{80 - 20} = 6.1$$

EXERCISE 3

1. Find the mean ordinate of the curve in Fig. 19.2*A* between $x = 2$ and $x = 4$. In doing this problem, divide the area under the curve into strips such that $\Delta x = 0.2$. First find the area under the graph over the given interval.
2. The curve *C* in Fig. 19.10 is the graph of the equation $y = \sin^2 x$. Find $\bar{y}$ between $x = 0$ and $x = 3.14$. Also find $\bar{y}$ between $x = 3.14$ and 6.28. If the maximum value of y is k, write the equation for $\bar{y}$ in terms of k and x.

19.11 Dimensionality

It is important to observe that the dimension of the slope of a graph is the dimension of the vertical axis divided by that of the horizontal axis. Also, the dimension of the area under a graph is the product of the dimensions of the vertical and horizontal axes.

For example, if the vertical axis is calibrated in *speed* and the horizontal axis is calibrated in *time*, then the slope has the dimension of speed/time or *acceleration*. The area under this graph will have the dimension of speed times time, or *distance*.

EXERCISE 4

Refer to Fig. 19.15.

1. Acceleration is the rate of change in speed with respect to time. Find the average acceleration between 6 and 16 s.
2. Find the acceleration at 50 s.
3. Find the maximum speed in kilometers per hour. When did it occur?
4. Find and tabulate the distance in meters covered during each 5-s interval between $t = 0$ and $t = 70$ s. Plot a cumulative distance curve against time over the first 70 s. Find the mean speed in kilometers per hour for the first 70 s.
5. When was one-fourth of the total distance covered?
6. What was the acceleration at $t = 10$ s?
7. When was the acceleration -0.5 m/s^2?
8. What was the gain in speed between $t = 4$ and $t = 8$?
9. Find the instantaneous acceleration at 10-s intervals between $t = 0$ and $t = 70$. Plot acceleration versus time.

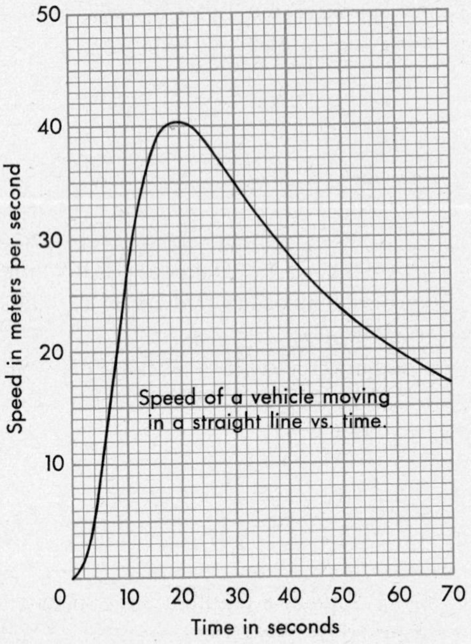

FIGURE 19.15

EXERCISE 5

Refer to Fig. 19.16.

1. Find dT/dt when $t = 10$.
2. Find dt/dT when $t = 10$.
3. Find dT/dt when $T = 10$.
4. Find dt/dT when $T = 10$.
5. Find t when $dT/dt = -5.0°$ per minute.
6. Find T when $dT/dt = -2.5°$ per minute.
7. Find the average rate of change of T with respect to t between $t = 2$ and $t = 8$.
8. Find the average slope between $t = 6$ and $t = 10$.
9. Find the average slope between $T = 30$ and $T = 10$.
10. Find the instantaneous slope at $t = 6$.
11. Find the instantaneous slope at $T = 30$.
12. How fast is T changing with t at $t = 10$?
13. How much does T change when t changes from 4 to 8?
14. How much does t change when T changes from 40 to 10?
15. About how much does T decrease when t increases from 3.99 to 4.00?
16. Find the area under the curve between $t = 4$ and $t = 8$.

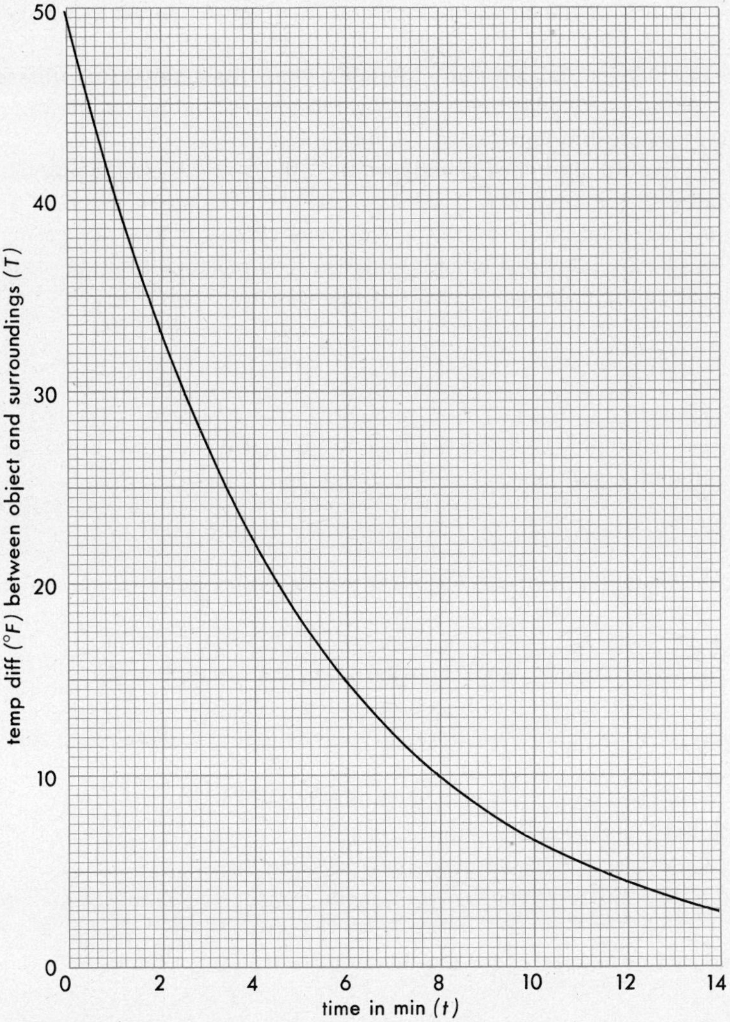

FIGURE 19.16

17. Find the average height of the curve between $t = 4$ and $t = 8$.
18. Find the average ordinate of the curve between $t = 4$ and $t = 8$.
19. Find the average T from 3 to 6 min.
20. Find the average rate of change of T between 3 to 6 min.
21. Find the instantaneous rate of temperature change at 4.5 min.
22. When is the rate of change of temperature difference equal to $-4°$ per min?
23. Approximately how long will it take for the temperature difference to go from 10° to 9.98°?

24. Approximately what will be the change in temperature difference between 2.0 and 2.06 min?
25. What is the rate of change of temperature difference when the temperature difference is 50°, 40°, 30°, 20°, 10°? Plot these rates against corresponding temperature differences. What relationship is revealed by this plot?
26. When will the temperature difference be reduced to $\frac{1}{2}$, $\frac{1}{4}$, $\frac{1}{8}$, and $\frac{1}{16}$ of the original value? What relationship is revealed?
27. If the temperature difference T decreased at the same rate as it was decreasing at $t = 0$, 2, 4, 6, and 8 min, how long would it take for T to reach its limiting value of 0°? This value is called the *time constant* of the system.
28. The curve shown in Fig. 19.16 was plotted from an equation in the form

$$T = ke^{mt}$$

where k and m are constants and e is the base of natural logarithms. From the graph find the value of k and m.

EXERCISE 6

The force on a piston versus the distance from one end of the cylinder is illustrated in Fig. 19.17.

1. How fast does the force decrease with distance when the distance is 4 ft?
2. What is the rate of change in force with respect to distance when the force is 6 lb?
3. Find dF/dD when $D = 5$ ft, where $F =$ force in pounds and $D =$ distance in feet.
4. Find dD/dF when $D = 5$ ft.
5. Find $\Delta F/\Delta D$ between $D = 2$ and $D = 3$. Also find $\Delta D/\Delta F$.
6. Find the average force between $D = 2$ and $D = 4$.
7. Plot a curve of work versus distance between $D = 1$ and $D = 6$.
8. For what force is the rate of change of force with respect to distance equal to -2 lb/ft?
9. Find the average rate of change in force with respect to distance between 1 and 4 ft.
10. Find the instantaneous rate of change in force with respect to distance when the distance is $3\frac{1}{3}$ ft.
11. Find the approximate change in force when the distance changes from $2\frac{1}{2}$ to 2.507 ft.

EXERCISE 7

The tangential speed of a point on the tread of an automobile tire during one revolution versus time is shown in Fig. 19.18.

1. Find the average acceleration of the point between $t = 0.02$ and $t = 0.03$. (Acceleration is the rate of change in velocity.)
2. Find the instantaneous acceleration at $t = 0.03$.

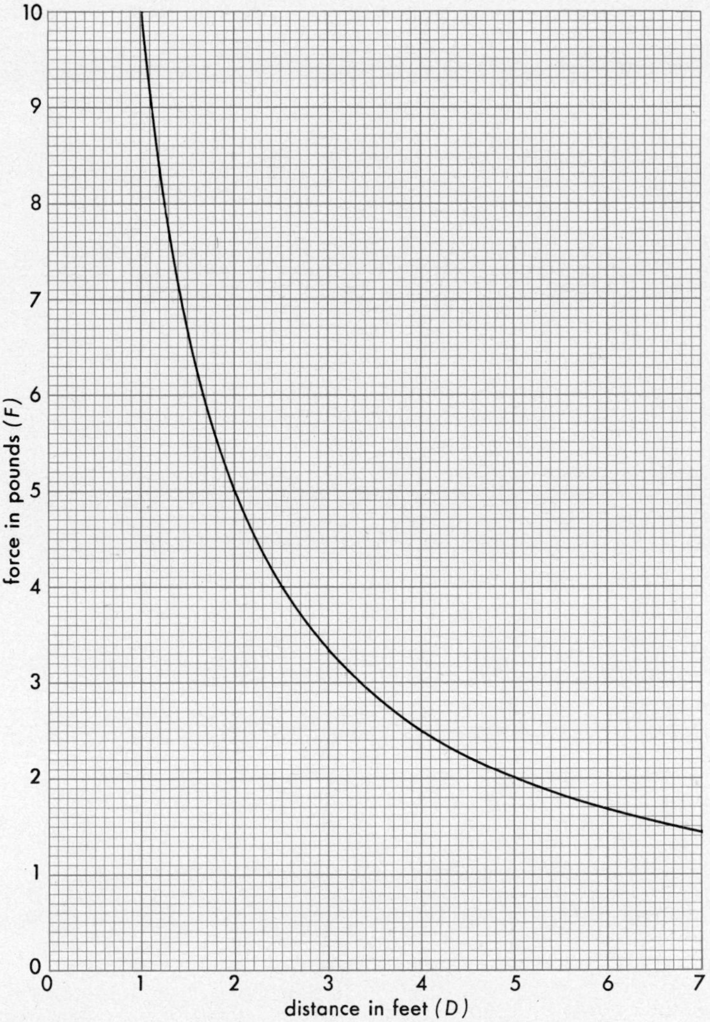

FIGURE 19.17

3. Find the time and value of the maximum speed.
4. Find the speed of the car.
5. Find the outside diameter of the tire.
6. Find the distance the point moves through space between $t = 0$ and $t = \frac{1}{8}$ s.

EXERCISE 8

The graph in Fig. 19.19 shows the relation between current and time in a certain series circuit containing inductance and resistance. The inductance, L, is 0.75 henry, the re-

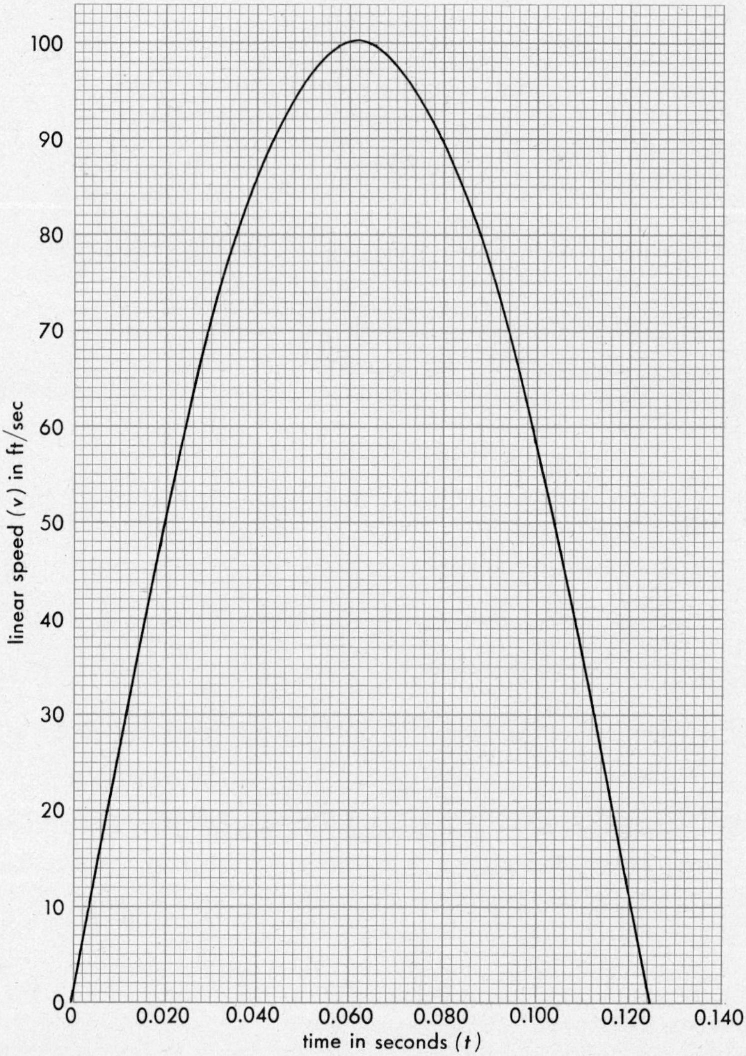

FIGURE 19.18

sistance is 15 Ω. A battery of 150 V is connected across this series combination when $t = 0$. Thereafter the current rises as shown in the curve.

1. Find di/dt, where t is in seconds, for 0, 0.02, 0.04, 0.06, 0.08, 0.10, and 0.12 s.
2. From Fig. 19.19 we read $i = 8.0$ A at $t = 0.08$ s. Confirm these data and those given above by substituting in the equation

$$i = \frac{E}{R}(1 - e^{-Rt/L})$$

3. If the current increased at the constant rates found in Prob. 1, how long would it take for the current to reach its limiting value of 10 A? This is called the *time constant* for the circuit.
4. Compare the values found in Prob. 3 with the ratio L/R.
5. Plot di/dt versus i between 0 and 120 ms.

EXERCISE 9

1. Complete the computations which have been started on Table 19.3. This table is an idealized set of trajectory data for a sounding rocket fired in an upward direction when $t = 0$.
2. Plot these data as indicated in the sketch (see Fig. 19.20).
3. Explain the physical significance of the shape of the acceleration curve.
4. (*a*) Find the change in altitude between $t = 120$ and $t = 140$ s from the velocity curve and also from the altitude curve.
   (*b*) Find the change in altitude between $t = 180$ and $t = 230$ s from the velocity curve and also from the altitude curve.
5. Find the vertical distance covered between 180 and 230 s (*a*) from the velocity curve and (*b*) from the height curve. (*c*) What would be the significance of a zero answer?
6. Find the average velocity from 260 to 270 s (*a*) using the velocity curve and (*b*) using the height curve.
7. Repeat Prob. 6 for the interval 300 to 360 s.
8. Use the height curve to find velocity at 250 s. Check by reading from velocity curve.

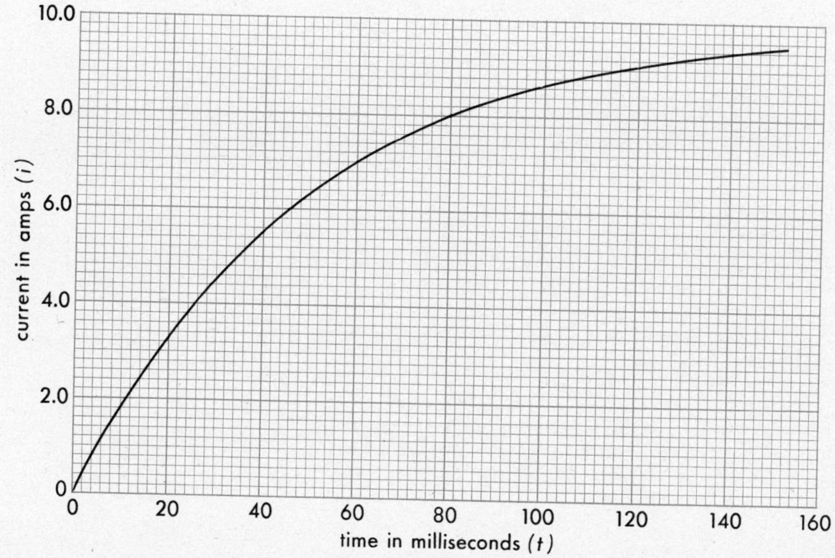

FIGURE 19.19

TABLE 19.3

Time, s	Velocity,† ft/s	Average†‡ velocity, ft/s	Average†§ acceleration ft/s²	Change‡ in altitude Δh, ft	Cumulative altitude, ft
0	0				0
		200	40	2,000	
10	400				2,000
		725	65	7,250	
20	1,050				9,250
		1,410	72	14,100	
30	1,770				23,350
		2,145	75	21,450	
40	2,520				44,800
50	3,270				
60	4,020				
		4,094	74	8,188	
62	4,168				
		4,238	70	8,476	
64	4,308				
66	4,348				135,520
68	4,292				
		4,256	−36	8,512	
70	4,220				
		4,045	−35	40,450	
80	3,870				
90	3,530				
100	3,200				263,772
		2,890	−31	57,800	
120	2,580				
		2,280	−30	45,600	
140	1,980				
160	1,380				
180	780				422,372
		480	−30	9,600	
200	180				431,972
220	−420				
		−730	−31	−14,600	
240	−1,040				
260	−1,660				387,972
		−1,970	−31	−39,400	
280	−2,280				
300	−2,760				298,172
320	−2,960				
340	−2,860				
		−2,690	17	−53,300	
360	−2,520				
380	−2,080				
400	−1,640				
420	−1,200				17,372

†All references to acceleration and velocity are in terms of their vertical components.
‡Do not plot. Used only to calculate cumulative altitude.
§Plot against midpoint of time interval.

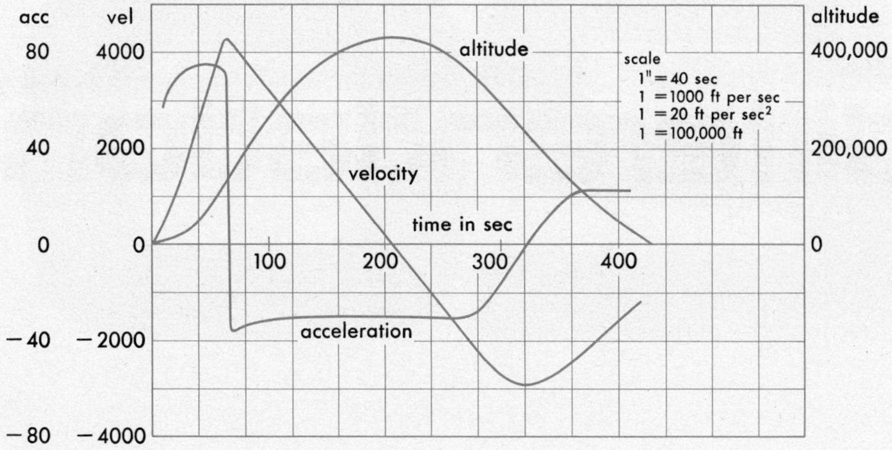

FIGURE 19.20

9. What was the probable time of impact?
10. What was the probable velocity of impact?
11. Find the acceleration at 42 s (*a*) from the velocity curve and (*b*) from the acceleration curve.
12. Find the average acceleration from 260 to 290 s (*a*) from the acceleration curve and (*b*) from the velocity curve.
13. Find time of maximum velocity, (*a*) using the velocity curve, (*b*) using the height curve, and (*c*) using the acceleration curve. (*d*) Find the value of maximum upward velocity.
14. Answer the same questions as in Prob. 13 for the minimum velocity.
15. Find the time of maximum height (*a*) from the height curve and (*b*) from velocity curve.
16. Find the probable value of the maximum height.
17. Calculate each of the following by the best method; also indicate (without calculating) an alternative method of doing the same thing: (*a*) velocity at 50 s, (*b*) average velocity from 54 to 96 s, (*c*) acceleration at 290 s, (*d*) average acceleration from 42 to 58 s, (*e*) actual distance covered from 160 to 250 s.

20 differentiation

In Chap. 19 we discussed methods of finding the average and the instantaneous rates of change in the value of certain functions when these functions are represented by graphs.

In this chapter we shall discuss methods of expressing the average and the instantaneous rates of change in the value of certain functions when these functions are represented by equations.

20.1 Average Rates of Change: Nonlinear Functions

In Chap. 19 we learned that if we are given a certain function f, and if we wish to find an average rate of change in $f(x)$, we start with a definite value of x which we designate as x_1 and let x change by a certain amount Δx. Then the *average* rate of change in $f(x)$ with respect to x is

$$\begin{pmatrix}\text{Average rate of}\\ \text{change of } f(x)\\ \text{with respect to } x\end{pmatrix} = \frac{f(x_1 + \Delta x) - f(x_1)}{\Delta x} \tag{1}$$

If we let

$$y = f(x) \tag{2}$$

then we may let

$$\Delta y = f(x_1 + \Delta x) - f(x_1) \tag{3}$$

and

$$\begin{pmatrix}\text{Average rate of}\\ \text{change of } f(x)\\ \text{with respect to } x\end{pmatrix} = \begin{pmatrix}\text{average rate of}\\ \text{change of } y \text{ with}\\ \textit{respect to } x\end{pmatrix} = \frac{\Delta y}{\Delta x}$$

$$= \frac{f(x_1 + \Delta x) - f(x_1)}{\Delta x} \tag{4}$$

Example 1. Find an expression for the average rate of change in the value of the function defined by

$$y = f(x) = x^3 \tag{5}$$

This is the equation of the graph plotted in Fig. 19.2*a* over the domain $0 \leq x \leq +4$. Following Eq. (3),

$$\Delta y = (x_1 + \Delta x)^3 - (x_1)^3 \tag{6}$$

$$\Delta y = x_1^3 + 3x_1^2(\Delta x) + 3x_1(\Delta x)^2 + (\Delta x)^3 - x_1^3$$

$$\Delta y = 3x_1^2(\Delta x) + 3x_1(\Delta x)^2 + (\Delta x)^3 \tag{7}$$

and

$$\frac{\Delta y}{\Delta x} = 3x_1^2 + 3x_1(\Delta x) + (\Delta x)^2 \tag{8}$$

Example 2. Find the average slope of the graph of $y = x^3$ between $x_1 = 2$ and $x_1 + \Delta x = 2.5$.

In this case $\Delta x = 2.5 - 2 = 0.5$ and $x_1 = 2$. Substituting these values in Eq. (8),

$$\frac{\Delta y}{\Delta x} = 3(2)^2 + 3 \cdot 2 \cdot 0.5 + 0.5^2$$

$$\frac{\Delta y}{\Delta x} = 12 + 3 + 0.25 = 15.25 \tag{9}$$

Check this value of average slope directly from Fig. 19.2*a*.

Example 3. Find an expression for the average rate of change of y with respect to x if

$$y = f(x) = 5x^2 + 3$$

Following Eq. (3),

$$\Delta y = 5(x_1 + \Delta x)^2 + 3 - (5x_1^2 + 3)$$
$$\Delta y = 5x_1^2 + 10x_1(\Delta x) + 5(\Delta x)^2 + 3 - 5x_1^2 - 3$$
$$\Delta y = 10x_1(\Delta x) + 5(\Delta x)^2$$
$$\frac{\Delta y}{\Delta x} = 10x_1 + 5(\Delta x)$$

Observe that the added constant 3 subtracts out in the course of doing the problem.

Example 4. Find the equation for the average rate of change in y with respect to x if $y = 1/x^2$.

$$\Delta y = \frac{1}{(x_1 + \Delta x)^2} - \frac{1}{x_1^2}$$
$$\Delta y = \frac{1}{x_1^2 + 2x_1(\Delta x) + (\Delta x)^2} - \frac{1}{x_1^2}$$
$$= \frac{x_1^2 - x_1^2 - 2x_1(\Delta x) - (\Delta x)^2}{x_1^2[x_1^2 + 2x_1(\Delta x) + (\Delta x)^2]}$$
$$\frac{\Delta y}{\Delta x} = \frac{-2x_1 - \Delta x}{x_1^2[x_1^2 + 2x_1(\Delta x) + (\Delta x)^2]}$$

EXERCISE 1

Find the equation for the average rate of change in the dependent variable with respect to the independent variable in the following problems.

1. $y = 5x^3$
2. $y = 5x^3 + 8$
3. $y = 7x^2 + 3$
4. $y = x^3 - 2x$
5. $w = u^2 - 3u - 18$
6. $w = 3/u$
7. $w = 1 + 2z - 1/z$
8. $g = t/(t + 3)$

*9. $w = \sqrt{x}$

10. $A = \pi R^2$
11. $V = \frac{4}{3}\pi R^3$

*The solution involves a fraction whose *numerator* must be rationalized.

12. Find ΔA in Prob. 10 if R increases from 5 to 5.2 in.
13. Confirm your answers to Probs. 10 and 11 by geometry.

20.2 Limits and Continuity

The concepts of limits and continuity are two of the most fundamental concepts in calculus. However, a rigorous treatment of them is somewhat beyond the scope of this book.

The more intuitive approach which we shall discuss below is entirely adequate for the needs of the student at present.

The statement that $f(x)$ approaches the number L as a limit when x approaches the number a is symbolized as

$$\lim_{x \to a} f(x) = L \tag{10}$$

This means that

1. if $|f(x) - L|$ can be made arbitrarily small
2. by making $|x - a|$ smaller and smaller (but still greater than zero)
3. we may say that $f(x)$ approaches L as x approaches a
4. and L is the limit which $f(x)$ approaches as x approaches a.

The above assumes, of course, that x remains within the domain of definition of the function.

For example, if $f(x) = x + 3$, let us see what limit if any $f(x)$ approaches as x approaches 3. Here the number 3 corresponds to a in Eq. (10). It seems intuitively evident that as x approaches 3, then $f(x)$ approaches 6. However, let us illustrate some of our ideas of limits by Table 20.1. Here we have calculated $|x - 3|$ and $|f(x) - 6|$ for a sequence of values of x. Note that 6 in this example corresponds to L in Eq. (10).

TABLE 20.1

x	$\|x - 3\|$	$f(x)$	$\|f(x) - 6\|$
3.05	0.05	6.05	0.05
3.04	0.04	6.04	0.04
3.03	0.03	6.03	0.03
3.02	0.02	6.02	0.02
3.01	0.01	6.01	0.01
3.00	0.00	6.00	0.00
2.99	0.01	5.99	0.01
2.98	0.02	5.98	0.02
2.97	0.03	5.97	0.03
2.96	0.04	5.96	0.04
2.95	0.05	5.95	0.05

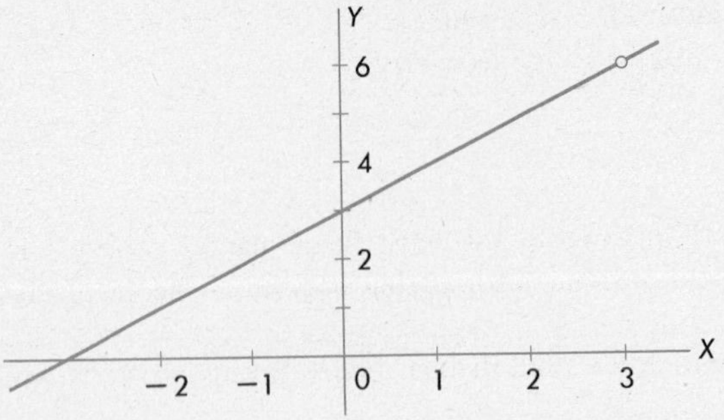

FIGURE 20.1

Thus we see that (1) as we make the absolute value $|x - 3|$ smaller and smaller, (2) the absolute value $|f(x) - 6|$ becomes smaller and smaller, (3) and we say that $f(x)$ approaches 6 as x approaches 3; (4) thus 6 is the limit that $f(x)$ approaches as x approaches 3.

Example 5. What limit if any does

$$y = f(x) = \frac{x^2 - 9}{x - 3}$$

approach as x approaches 3?

First let us form a table of values from which we can plot the graph of $f(x)$ versus x.

The graph of $f(x)$ versus x is plotted in Fig. 20.1. Note that $f(x)$ is *not defined* for $x = 3$. This is indicated on the graph by the circle with its center at the point (3,6).

Even so, we see from Table 20.2 that (1) as we make the absolute value $|x - 3|$ smaller and smaller, (2) the absolute value $|f(x) - 6|$ becomes smaller and smaller, (3) and we may say that $f(x)$ approaches 6 as x approaches 3; (4) thus 6 is the limit that $f(x)$ approaches as x approaches 3, even though $f(x)$ is undefined *at* $x = 3$.

TABLE 20.2

x	$\|x - 3\|$	$f(x)$	$\|f(x) - 6\|$
5	2	8	2
4	1	7	1
3	0	Undefined	Undefined
2	1	5	1
1	2	4	2
0	3	3	3

A somewhat more direct approach would be to factor the numerator of $(x^2 - 9)/(x - 3)$, obtaining

$$\frac{(x - 3)(x + 3)}{x - 3} = x + 3 \qquad x \neq 3$$

Though this equality does not hold for $x = 3$, it does hold for all other values of x, including those as close to 3 as we choose. Thus we may write

$$\lim_{x \to 3} \frac{x^2 - 9}{x - 3} = \lim_{x \to 3} (x + 3) = 6 \qquad x \neq 3$$

Observe that the function is undefined for $x = 3$, even though $f(x)$ approaches 6 as x approaches 3.

Example 6. If $y = f(x) = 1/x$, what limit, if any, does $f(x)$ approach when x approaches zero?

We can see intuitively that as the difference between x and 0 becomes less and less in absolute value, then $f(x)$ becomes larger and larger in absolute value without bound.

In symbols we may write

$$1/x \to \infty \qquad \text{as} \qquad x \to 0$$

The student should not be misled into thinking of the symbol ∞ as some enormous number called "infinity." It is not. It is simply used in this context to indicate that, as x approaches a fixed value (in this case 0), then $1/x$ increases (or decreases) without bound.

On account of the notation used in Eq. (10), we sometimes write

$$\lim_{x \to 0} \frac{1}{x} = \infty$$

However, since ∞ is not a real number, it is not, strictly speaking, a limit in the real-number system with which we are concerned at present.

Sometimes it is desirable to distinguish whether x approaches 0 while always remaining positive or approaches 0 while always remaining negative. In such cases we may write

$$\lim_{x \to 0} \frac{1}{x} = \infty + \qquad (\text{for } 0 < x) \tag{11}$$

or

$$\lim_{x \to 0} \frac{1}{x} = \infty - \qquad \text{(for } 0 > x\text{)} \tag{12}$$

Equation (11) means that as x approaches zero while always remaining a positive number, 1/x increases without bound. Equation (12) means that as x approaches zero while always remaining a negative number, 1/x decreases without bound.

Example 7. If $y = f(x) = 1/x$, what limit, if any, does y approach as x approaches infinity (that is, as x becomes larger and larger without bound)?

The student should have no difficulty in discovering for himself that we can bring the absolute value of y as near to 0 as we please by taking the absolute value of x large enough. Thus for this function we may write

$$\lim_{x \to \infty} \frac{1}{x} = 0$$

just as in Example 6 we can distinguish between the effect of positive and negative values of x by the following symbolism:

$$\lim_{x \to \infty} \frac{1}{x} = 0+ \qquad \text{(for } 0 < x\text{)}$$

and

$$\lim_{x \to \infty} \frac{1}{x} = 0- \qquad \text{(for } 0 > x\text{)}$$

Example 8. If $y = f(x) = x^2 + x - 2$, what limit, if any, does $f(x)$ approach as x approaches 5?

The student should have no difficulty in discovering for himself that $f(x)$ approaches 28 as x approaches 5.

Example 9. What limit if any does $y = f(x) = (8x^2 - 1)/(x^2 + 2)$ approach as x approaches infinity?

In this case, a direct substitution leads to the indeterminate form ∞/∞, and we would not know whether this function approaches any finite limit, and if so, what that limit is.

However, we can divide both numerator and denominator by x^2, obtaining

$$\frac{8 - 1/x^2}{1 + 2/x^2} \qquad x^2 \neq 0$$

Now it appears that

$$\lim_{x\to\infty} \frac{8x^2 - 1}{x^2 + 2} = \lim_{x\to\infty} \frac{8 - 1/x^2}{1 + 2/x^2} = 8$$

Now we shall briefly consider the matter of *continuity*.

A fairly satisfactory intuitive idea of continuity is expressed by the following statement.

If we can draw the graph of a function over a given interval without lifting the pencil from the paper, we say that the function is continuous over that interval.

Although the engineering technician will usually find this notion of continuity quite adequate for ordinary situations, there are occasions when he will need more precise ideas. Therefore, without attempting a high order of mathematical rigor, let us investigate the matter in more detail.

A function f for which $y = f(x)$ is said to be *continuous* for $x = a$ if all three of the following conditions are satisfied:

1. The value of the function is defined for $x = a$. That is,

   $f(a)$ is defined

2. The value of the function approaches a definite limit as x approaches a. That is,

   $\lim_{x\to a} f(x)$ exists

3. This limit is the value of the function when $x = a$. That is,

   $\lim_{x\to a} f(x) = f(a)$

A function f for which $y = f(x)$ is said to be *discontinuous* for $x = a$ if any of these conditions are not satisfied.

A function is said to be continuous over an interval if it is continuous for all points within that interval.

For example, the function for which $f(x) = x + 3$ is continuous at $x = 3$ because (1) $f(x)$ is defined for $x = 3$, since $f(3) = 6$, and (2) as x approaches 3, $f(x)$ approaches a definite limit (in this case the limit is 6), and (3) $\lim_{x\to 3} f(x) = f(3)$.

In Example 5 the function for which $f(x) = (x^2 - 9)/(x - 3)$ is *not* continuous for $x = 3$ because (1) $f(x)$ is not defined for $x = 3$.

We could, if we wished, extend the original definition of $f(x)$ to read

$$f_1(x) = \begin{cases} \dfrac{x^2 - 9}{x - 3} & x \neq 3 \\ 6 & x = 3 \end{cases}$$

Now $f_1(3)$ is defined, and $f_1(x)$ is continuous for $x = 3$. On the other hand, we could extend the original definition of $f(x)$ to read

$$f_2(x) = \begin{cases} \dfrac{x^2 - 9}{x - 3} & x \neq 3 \\ 10 & x = 3 \end{cases}$$

Then, $f_2(x)$ is not continuous at $x = 3$ because while (1) $f_2(x)$ is defined at $x = 3$, and (2) when x approaches 3, $f_2(x)$ does approach a definite limit (which in this case is 6), (3) this limit is *not* the value of the function when $x = 3$.

EXERCISE 2

Evaluate the limits indicated below when such limits exist. Discuss the continuity of each function, and sketch its graph near any points of discontinuity that you may discover.

1. If $f(x) = x^3 + 6x^2 - 16$, find $\lim\limits_{x \to -2} f(x)$.
2. If $f(x) = \dfrac{2x^2 - x - 10}{x + 2}$, find $\lim\limits_{x \to -2} f(x)$.
3. If $f(x) = \begin{cases} \dfrac{2x^2 - x - 10}{x + 2} & x \neq -2 \\ 5 & x = -2 \end{cases}$ find $\lim\limits_{x \to -2} f(x)$.
4. If $f(x) = \dfrac{x^2 - x - 20}{x - 5}$, find $\lim\limits_{x \to 5} f(x)$.
5. If $f(x) = \dfrac{3(x^2 - 1)}{x + 1}$, find $\lim\limits_{x \to -1} f(x)$.
6. If $f(x) = \dfrac{3x + 8}{x + 3}$, find $\lim\limits_{x \to -3} f(x)$.
7. If $f(x) = \dfrac{x - 9}{3(\sqrt{x} - 3)}$, find $\lim\limits_{x \to 9} f(x)$.
8. If $f(x) = x\sqrt{x - 3}$, find $\lim\limits_{x \to 0} f(x)$.
9. If $f(x) = \dfrac{5^{1/x} - 1}{5^{1/x} + 1}$, find $\lim\limits_{x \to 0} f(x)$.
10. If $f(x) = \dfrac{x^2 - 5x}{2x^2 - 4}$, find $\lim\limits_{x \to \infty} f(x)$.

20.3 The Derivative

By finding the limit (if one exists) that

$$\frac{f(x_1 + \Delta x) - f(x_1)}{\Delta x}$$

approaches as Δx approaches zero, we may find the *instantaneous* rate of change in y with respect to x at $x = x_1$ [see Eq. (4)].

This limit is called the *derivative* of y with respect to x or the derivative of $f(x)$ with respect to x.

The derivative can be designated as $f'(x)$, dy/dx, and sometimes in other ways. From Eq. (4) and the above we may write

$$\begin{pmatrix}\text{Derivative of } y \\ \text{with respect to } x\end{pmatrix} = f'(x) = \frac{dy}{dx} = \lim_{\Delta x \to 0} \frac{\Delta y}{\Delta x} = \lim_{\Delta x \to 0} \frac{f(x_1 + \Delta x) - f(x_1)}{\Delta x} \qquad \textbf{(13)}$$

provided this limit exists.

Thus far we have used the subscript 1 to emphasize the fact that x is held constant at the value x_1 while Δx varies and approaches zero. If we remember the above and also that most of the functions found in this book do have derivatives for all but perhaps a few values of the independent variable, we may omit the subscript 1 and write

$$\begin{pmatrix}\text{Derivative of } y \\ \text{with respect to } x\end{pmatrix} = f'(x) = \frac{dy}{dx} = \lim_{\Delta x \to 0} \frac{\Delta y}{\Delta x} = \lim_{\Delta x \to 0} \frac{f(x + \Delta x) - f(x)}{\Delta x} \qquad (14)$$

and understand that the symbol (x) so used represents any of the nonexceptional values of x.

The symbol dy/dx as it is used here *does not mean that some number dy is to be divided by some number dx*. It simply means

$$\lim_{\Delta x \to 0} \frac{\Delta y}{\Delta x} = \frac{dy}{dx}$$

A somewhat different interpretation will be made in Sec. 20.25.

Now let us return to Example 1. In this example we found an expression for the average rate of change in $f(x)$ with respect to x when $f(x) = y = x^3$ [See Eq. (8)]. This function was plotted in Fig. 19.2*a*. The student should refer to this graph frequently in order to gain a graphical concept of the algebraic operations below.

Equation (8) is repeated below for reference, with the subscript 1 omitted:

$$\frac{\Delta y}{\Delta x} = 3x^2 + 3x(\Delta x) + (\Delta x)^2 \qquad (15)$$

In Example 2 we calculated the average rate of change in the value of this function between $x = 2$ and $x + \Delta x = 2.5$. Now as a specific example, let us compute

Δy when x changes from 2 to a few other values in the vicinity of 2. When $x = 2$, Eq. (7) can be written as

$$\Delta y = 12\,\Delta x + 6(\Delta x)^2 + (\Delta x)^3$$

When $\Delta x = +0.1$,

$$\Delta y = 1.2 + 0.06 + 0.001 = 1.261$$

When $\Delta x = +0.01$,

$$\Delta y = 0.12 + 0.0006 + 0.000001 = 0.120601$$

When $\Delta x = -0.1$,

$$\Delta y = -1.2 + 0.06 - 0.001 = -1.141$$

Column 2 of Table 20.3 was calculated in this way.

The ratio $\Delta y/\Delta x$ can be calculated by dividing each value of Δy above by the corresponding value of Δx. The ratio $\Delta y/\Delta x$ can also be calculated by direct substitution in Eq. (15). Let us adopt the first method.

When $\Delta x = +0.1$,

$$\frac{\Delta y}{\Delta x} = \frac{1.261}{0.1} = 12.61$$

TABLE 20.3

(1) Δx	(2) Δy	(3) $\Delta y/\Delta x$
+0.1	+1.261	+12.61
+0.01	+0.120601	+12.0601
+0.001	+0.012006001	+12.006001
+0.0001	+0.001200060001	+12.00060001
+0.00001	+0.000120000600001	+12.0000600001
+0.000001	+0.000012000006000001	+12.000006000001
+0.0000001	+0.000001200000060000001	+12.00000060000001
0.00000000	0.000000000000000000000	Indeterminate
−0.0000001	−0.000001199999940000001	+11.99999940000001
−0.000001	−0.000011999994000001	+11.999994000001
−0.00001	−0.000119999400001	+11.9999400001
−0.0001	−0.001199940001	+11.99940001
−0.001	−0.011994001	+11.994001
−0.01	−0.119401	+11.9401
−0.1	−1.1414	+11.41

When $\Delta x = +0.01$,

$$\frac{\Delta y}{\Delta x} = \frac{0.120601}{0.01} = 12.0601$$

When $\Delta x = -0.1$,

$$\frac{\Delta y}{\Delta x} = \frac{-1.141}{-0.1} = 11.41$$

Column 3 of Table 20.3 was calculated in this way.

As we scan Table 20.3 from either the top or bottom, toward the center of the table, we observe that as Δx *approaches* zero, Δy also *approaches* zero. However, their ratio $\Delta y/\Delta x$ approaches the finite constant 12. But if we let $\Delta x = 0$, then the quotient $\Delta y/\Delta x$ becomes meaningless.

This is also indicated in Fig. 20.2. In this figure we show a graph of the equation

$$\frac{\Delta y}{\Delta x} = 3x^2 + 3x(\Delta x) + (\Delta x)^2$$

where $x = 2$, Δx is the independent variable, and $\Delta y/\Delta x$ is the dependent variable.

We note that $\Delta y/\Delta x$ is not defined when $\Delta x = 0$ and have indicated this fact by the small circle with its center at the point (0,12). Therefore we rest with the statement

$$\lim_{x \to 0} \frac{\Delta y}{\Delta x} = 12 \tag{16}$$

which we read: "The limit which $\Delta y/\Delta x$ approaches as Δx approaches zero is 12."

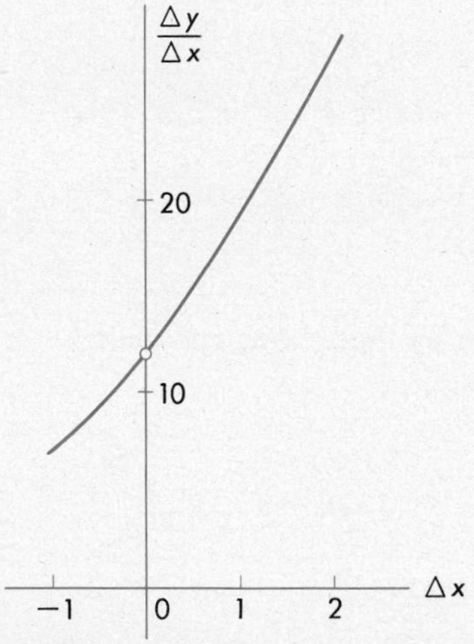

FIGURE 20.2

As we stated in Eq. (13), this limit is denoted by dy/dx and

$$\frac{dy}{dx} = \lim_{\Delta x \to 0} \frac{\Delta y}{\Delta x} \tag{17}$$

where dy/dx is called "the derivative of y with respect to x."

If y is the ordinate of a curve and x is the abscissa of the same curve, then dy/dx is the instantaneous slope of the curve.

The process of finding the derivative of a function is called *differentiation.*

Example 10. Find the derivative of y with respect to x if $y = x^2$.

$$\Delta y = (x + \Delta x)^2 - x^2$$
$$\Delta y = x^2 + 2x(\Delta x) + (\Delta x)^2 - x^2$$
$$\Delta y = 2x(\Delta x) + (\Delta x)^2$$
$$\frac{\Delta y}{\Delta x} = 2x + \Delta x$$
$$\lim_{\Delta x \to 0} \frac{\Delta y}{\Delta x} = \frac{dy}{dx} = 2x$$

The same answer would have been required if the problem had been stated in any of the following ways:

1. Differentiate $y = x^2$ with respect to x.
2. Find $\dfrac{d(x^2)}{dx}$ if $y = x^2$.
3. Find y' if $y = x^2$.
4. Find dy/dx if $y = x^2$.
5. Find the equation for the rate of change in y with respect to x if $y = x^2$.
6. Find the equation for the instantaneous slope of the graph of $y = x^2$.
7. Find the equation for the slope of any tangent to the graph of $y = x^2$.

EXERCISE 3

1. The cost of publishing a certain pamphlet is given by the following equation:

$$C = \$10.00 + 0.05n$$

where

C = total cost, dollars
n = number of pamphlets published

(*a*) Calculate the total cost of publishing 10, 100, 1,000, 10,000, 100,000, 1,000,000, and ∞ pamphlets.
(*b*) Divide the total cost as determined in (*a*) by the corresponding number of pamphlets to determine the cost per pamphlet.
(*c*) What limit does the cost per pamphlet approach as the number of pamphlets approaches ∞?
(*d*) Point out the fallacy in the following statement: "The cost per pamphlet when an infinite number are published is \$0.05 per pamphlet."

Differentiate the following (also see Exercise 1):

2. $y = 5x^3$
3. $y = 5x^3 + 8$
4. $y = 7x^2 + 3$
5. $y = x^3 - 2x$
6. $w = u^2 - 3u - 18$
7. $w = 3/u$
8. $w = 1 + 2z - 1/z$
9. $g = \dfrac{t}{t+3}$
10. $w = \sqrt{x}$

20.4 General Rule for Differentiating $y = kx^n$

In this section we shall develop a formula by which we can find dy/dx if $y = kx^n$ without using the rather laborious Δ method. In the development of this rule we shall restrict n to positive integers. However, it can be shown in a somewhat more advanced textbook on calculus that this rule applies also when n is any rational number. In an advanced calculus textbook based on an extensive consideration of the real-number system, it can be proved that the rule below applies when n is any real number.

Let us begin by finding dy/dx if

$$y = x^n \tag{18}$$

Following Eq. (3),

$$\Delta y = (x + \Delta x)^n - x^n \tag{19}$$

We can expand the right-hand member of Eq. (19) by the binomial theorem [see Eq. (1), Sec. 9.2].

$$\Delta y = x^n + nx^{n-1}\,\Delta x + \frac{n(n-1)x^{n-2}(\Delta x)^2}{2!} + \frac{n(n-1)(n-2)x^{n-3}\,(\Delta x)^3}{3!} + \cdots + (\Delta x)^n - x^n \tag{20}$$

By simplifying Eq. (20) we obtain

$$\Delta y = nx^{n-1}\,\Delta x + \frac{n(n-1)x^{n-2}(\Delta x)^2}{2!} + \frac{n(n-1)(n-2)x^{n-3}(\Delta x)^3}{3!} + \cdots + (\Delta x)^n \qquad (21)$$

Dividing Eq. (21) by Δx,

$$\frac{\Delta y}{\Delta x} = nx^{n-1} + \frac{n(n-1)x^{n-2}\,\Delta x}{2!} + \frac{n(n-1)(n-2)x^{n-3}(\Delta x)^2}{3!} + \cdots + (\Delta x)^{n-1} \qquad (22)$$

Now observe that all terms on the right-hand side of Eq. (22) except the first contain the factor Δx. Therefore, as Δx approaches zero, all terms on the right-hand side of (22) except the first also approach zero and

$$\lim_{\Delta x \to 0} \frac{\Delta y}{\Delta x} = nx^{n-1}$$

or

$$\frac{dy}{dx} = nx^{n-1}$$

Therefore, if

$$y = x^n \qquad (23)$$

where n is a positive integer, then

$$\frac{dy}{dx} = nx^{n-1} \qquad (24)$$

As we mentioned before, Eq. (24) is actually valid when n is any real number. Equations (23) and (24) can be summarized as

$$\frac{d(x^n)}{dx} = nx^{n-1} \qquad \textbf{(25)}$$

Rule 1. *To find the derivative of x with a constant exponent, multiply this constant exponent by a new power of x whose exponent is one less than the original exponent.*

Now let us find dy/dx if $y = kx^n$. Following Eq. (3), we may write

$$\Delta y = k(x + \Delta x)^n - kx^n$$

We can expand the right member of the above equation by the binomial theorem, obtaining

$$\Delta y = k\left[x^n + nx^{n-1}\,\Delta x + \frac{n(n-1)x^{n-2}(\Delta x)^2}{2!} + \frac{n(n-1)(n-2)x^{n-3}\,(\Delta x)^3}{3!} + \cdots + (\Delta x)^n\right] - kx^n$$

By simplifying the above equation we obtain

$$\Delta y = nkx^{n-1}\,\Delta x + \frac{kn(n-1)x^{n-2}(\Delta x)^2}{2!} + \frac{kn(n-1)(n-2)x^{n-3}(\Delta x)^3}{3!} + \cdots + k(\Delta x)^n$$

Dividing the above equation by Δx gives

$$\frac{\Delta y}{\Delta x} = nkx^{n-1} + \frac{kn(n-1)x^{n-2}\,\Delta x}{2!} + \frac{kn(n-1)(n-2)x^{n-3}(\Delta x)^2}{3!} + \cdots + k(\Delta x)^{n-1} \quad (26)$$

Now observe that all terms on the right-hand side of Eq. (26) except the first contain the factor Δx. Therefore, as Δx approaches zero, all terms on the right-hand side of (26) except the first also approach zero and

$$\lim_{\Delta x \to 0} \frac{\Delta y}{\Delta x} = nkx^{n-1}$$

or

$$\frac{dy}{dx} = nkx^{n-1}$$

or

$$\frac{d(kx^n)}{dx} = nkx^{n-1} \quad \textbf{(27)}$$

Rule 2. *To find the derivative of the product of a constant factor and a variable with a constant exponent, multiply the derivative of the variable with the constant exponent by the constant factor.*

For example, if

$$y = x^3$$

then

$$\frac{dy}{dx} = 3x^2$$

but if

$$y = 5x^3$$

then

$$\frac{dy}{dx} = 5 \cdot 3x^2 = 15x^2$$

It is important to note that in Eq. (27) it is the *independent variable itself* that is raised to the nth power. A very different situation exists for a function such as

$$y = (x^2 + 7)^n + C \tag{28}$$

Here it is not the independent variable itself that is raised to the nth power. Differentiating Eq. (28) requires a somewhat different approach, which will be discussed in Sec. 20.6.

In Examples 11 through 19 be sure to notice the different forms in which the result may be written.

Example 11. Differentiate $y = 3x^5$.

$$\frac{dy}{dx} = 15x^4$$

$$y' = 15x^4$$

$$\frac{d(3x^5)}{dx} = 15x^4$$

Example 12. Differentiate $y = 3x^{-5}$.

$$\frac{dy}{dx} = -15x^{-6}$$

$$y' = -15x^{-6}$$

$$\frac{d(3x^{-5})}{dx} = -15x^{-6}$$

Example 13. Differentiate $y = -3x^{-5}$.

$$\frac{dy}{dx} = +15x^{-6}$$

$$y' = +15x^{-6}$$

$$\frac{d(-3x^{-5})}{dx} = +15x^{-6}$$

Example 14. Differentiate $y = 5x^{7/4}$.

$$\frac{dy}{dx} = \frac{35}{4}x^{3/4}$$

$$y' = \frac{35}{4}x^{3/4}$$

$$\frac{d(5x^{7/4})}{dx} = \frac{35}{4}x^{3/4}$$

Example 15. Differentiate $y = x$.

$$\frac{dy}{dx} = 1$$

$$y' = 1$$

$$\frac{d(x)}{dx} = 1$$

Example 16. Differentiate $y = 5x^{1/3}$.

$$\frac{dy}{dx} = \frac{5}{3}x^{-2/3}$$

$$y' = \frac{5}{3}x^{-2/3}$$

$$\frac{d(5x^{1/3})}{dx} = \frac{5}{3}x^{-2/3}$$

Example 17. Differentiate $y = 7x^{-1/2}$.

$$\frac{dy}{dx} = -\frac{7}{2}x^{-3/2}$$

$$y' = -\frac{7}{2}x^{-3/2}$$

$$\frac{d(7x^{-1/2})}{dx} = -\frac{7}{2}x^{-3/2}$$

Example 18. Differentiate $y = 6x^{\pi}$.

$$\frac{dy}{dx} = 6\pi x^{\pi-1}$$

$$y' = 6\pi x^{\pi-1}$$

$$\frac{d(6x^{\pi})}{dx} = 6\pi x^{\pi-1}$$

Example 19. Differentiate $a = (\pi/16)h^2$.

$$\frac{da}{dh} = \frac{\pi}{8}h$$

$$a' = \frac{\pi}{8}h$$

$$\frac{d\left(\frac{\pi}{16}h^2\right)}{dh} = \frac{\pi}{8}h$$

Example 20. Differentiate $y = 5\sqrt{x}$.

Before we can apply Eq. (27) to this problem, we must convert the given equation to the form

$$y = 5x^{1/2}$$

Then

$$\frac{dy}{dx} = \frac{1}{2}(5)x^{-1/2} = \frac{5}{2\sqrt{x}}$$

Example 21. Differentiate $y = 5(3x)^2$.

Referring to Eq. (27), we note that there it is the *independent variable itself* that is raised to a power. In the present example we have the product of the independent variable and a constant raised to a power. Therefore, before we can apply Eq. (27) we must alter the given equation to

$$y = 5 \cdot 3^2 \cdot x^2 = 45x^2$$

Then

$$\frac{dy}{dx} = 90x$$

Example 22. Differentiate $F = 10/D$.

Again, before we can apply Eq. (27) directly, we alter the given equation to

$$F = 10D^{-1}$$

Then

$$\frac{dF}{dD} = -10D^{-2} = -\frac{10}{D^2}$$

Example 23. Express the derivative in Example 22 in terms of F.

From the original equation

$$D = \frac{10}{F}$$

Therefore

$$\frac{dF}{dD} = -\frac{10}{(10/F)^2} = -\frac{F^2}{10}$$

Example 24. If $F = 10/D$, find dD/dF.

From the given equation we note that

$$D = \frac{10}{F} = 10F^{-1}$$

Then

$$\frac{dD}{dF} = -10F^{-2} = -\frac{10}{F^2}$$

Compare with Example 23.

Example 25. Find the slope of the tangent to the graph of $F = 10/D$ drawn through the point on the graph where $D = 2$. This is the equation for the graph shown in Fig. 19.17.

From Example 22 we find that the slope of any tangent to the graph is, in general,

$$\frac{dF}{dD} = -\frac{10}{D^2}$$

At $D = 2$,

$$\frac{dF}{dD} = -\frac{10}{2^2} = -\frac{10}{4} = -2.5$$

The student should verify the above slope graphically from Fig. 19.17.

Example 26. Find the equation of the tangent to the graph of $F = 10/D$ through the point whose abscissa is 2.

In Example 25 we find that the slope of the tangent is -2.5.

The equation for this tangent is (see Sec. 6.10)

$$F = mD + b$$

where

m = slope
b = the F intercept

In this example $F = {}^{10}\!/_{2} = 5$ when $D = 2$. Thus we may write

$$5 = -2.5 \times 2 + b$$

and

$$b = 10$$

Then the equation for this tangent is

$$F = -2.5D + 10$$

EXERCISE 4

Differentiate the following:

1. $y = 3x^2$
2. $y = cx^3$
3. $y = 10x^9$
4. $y = 3x^{-2}$
5. $y = 3/x^2$
6. $y = {}^4\!/_3\pi x^3$
7. $y = 12x^{2/3}$
8. $y = 14x^{-1}$
9. $y = 14/x$
10. $y = 6x^{1/2}$
11. $y = 6\sqrt{x}$
12. $y = \sqrt{6x}$
13. $y = -8x^{-1/2}$
14. $y = -8/\sqrt{x}$

15. $y = 10x^{1/4}$
16. $y = 10\sqrt[4]{x}$
17. $y = (a/b)x^4$
18. $y = a/(bx)$
19. $y = 2x^{-3/4}$
20. $y = 2/\sqrt[4]{x^3}$
21. $y = 2/\sqrt[4]{7x^3}$
22. $y = 5x$
23. $y = 5$
24. $y = x^5$
25. $y = 4/\sqrt{x}$

The graph shown in Fig. 19.17 was plotted from the equation $F = 10/D$, where F is the force on a piston and D is the distance between the piston and one end of the cylinder. Using the above equation rather than the graph, solve Probs. 26 through 32.

26. Derive the equation for dF/dD in terms of F and then in terms of D. Also derive the equation for dD/dF in terms of F and in terms of D.
27. What is the rate of change in force with respect to distance when F is 6 lb?
28. Find dF/dD when $D = 5$ ft.
29. Find dD/dF when $D = 5$ ft.
30. Find $\Delta F/\Delta D$ between $D = 2$ and $D = 3$. Also find $\Delta D/\Delta F$ between $D = 2$ and $D = 3$.
31. For what force is the rate of change of force with respect to distance equal to -2 lb/ft?
32. Find the instantaneous rate of change in force with respect to distance when distance is $3\frac{1}{3}$ ft.

20.5 Some Further Rules for Differentiation

If $y = c$ where c is some constant, then y does not change at all, and its derivative with respect to any varying quantity is zero.

Rule 3. *The derivative of a constant is zero.*

That is, if $y = c$ where c is a constant, then

$$\frac{dy}{dx} = 0$$

Now let us differentiate $y = x^2 + x^3$ by the Δ method:

$$y = x^2 + x^3$$
$$\Delta y = x^2 + 2x\,\Delta x + (\Delta x)^2 + x^3 + 3x^2(\Delta x) + 3x(\Delta x)^2 + (\Delta x)^3 - x^2 - x^3$$
$$\Delta y = 2x\,\Delta x + (\Delta x)^2 + 3x^2(\Delta x) + 3x(\Delta x)^2 + (\Delta x)^3$$
$$\frac{\Delta y}{\Delta x} = 2x + \Delta x + 3x^2 + 3x\,\Delta x + (\Delta x)^2$$
$$\frac{dy}{dx} = 2x + 3x^2$$

Following Eqs. (23) and (24), we note that the derivative of x^2 is $2x$. Also, the derivative of x^3 is $3x^2$. Thus it seems plausible that rule 4 below is valid.

Rule 4. *The derivative of the sum of any finite number of differentiable functions is the sum of their derivatives.*

Example 27. Differentiate $y = 5/(3x) + x^2 + C$.

$$y = \tfrac{5}{3}x^{-1} + x^2 + C$$

$$\frac{dy}{dx} = -\frac{5}{3}x^{-2} + 2x = -\frac{5}{3x^2} + 2x$$

Example 28. Differentiate $y = 2x^{-6} + 5^e$ (note that 5^e is a constant).

$$\frac{dy}{dx} = -12x^{-7} = -\frac{12}{x^7}$$

Example 29. Differentiate $y = a/(bx) + bx^{-2} - 3\pi x$.

By convention the first letters of the alphabet are usually used to represent constants. Therefore we shall consider a and b to be constants.

$$y = \frac{a}{b}x^{-1} + bx^{-2} - 3\pi x$$

$$\frac{dy}{dx} = -\frac{a}{b}x^{-2} - 2bx^{-3} - 3\pi = -\frac{a}{bx^2} - \frac{2b}{x^3} - 3\pi$$

Example 30. Differentiate $y = 3/(4x) + 2x^3$.

$$y = \tfrac{3}{4}x^{-1} + 2x^3$$

$$\frac{dy}{dx} = -\frac{3}{4}x^{-2} + 6x^2 = -\frac{3}{4x^2} + 6x^2$$

Example 31. Figure 20.3 shows two parabolas. The equation for one is

$$y = \tfrac{1}{2}x^2$$

The equation for the other is

$$y = -(x - 6)^2 + 9$$

Find the coordinates of points on these curves through which a straight line may be drawn tangent to both curves.

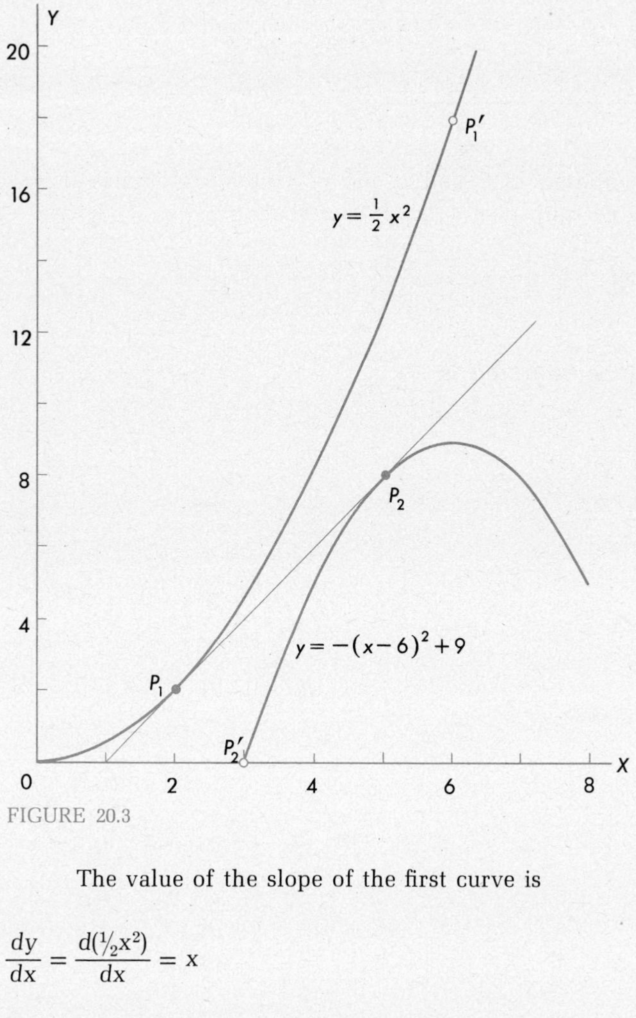

FIGURE 20.3

The value of the slope of the first curve is

$$\frac{dy}{dx} = \frac{d(\frac{1}{2}x^2)}{dx} = x$$

The value of the slope of the second curve is

$$\frac{dy}{dx} = \frac{d[-(x-6)^2 + 9]}{dx} = \frac{d(-x^2 + 12x - 27)}{dx} = -2x + 12$$

Let a tangent common to both curves be drawn through points P_1 and P_2 (see Fig. 20.3). Let the x coordinate of P_1 be x_1 and the x coordinate of P_2 be x_2.

Since the slope of both curves must be the same at these points of tangency, we may write

$$x_1 = -2x_2 + 12$$

From Eq. (2), Sec. 6.6, the slope of the tangent through P_1 and P_2 is

$$\frac{y_2 - y_1}{x_2 - x_1} = \frac{-(x_2 - 6)^2 + 9 - \frac{1}{2}x_1^2}{x_2 - x_1} = \frac{-x_2^2 + 12x_2 - 27 - \frac{1}{2}x_1^2}{x_2 - x_1}$$

where x_1 and y_1 are the coordinates of P_1 and x_2 and y_2 are the coordinates of P_2.

After replacing x_1 by its equivalent $-2x_2 + 12$, and simplifying, we obtain

$$\frac{y_2 - y_1}{x_2 - x_1} = \frac{-x_2^2 + 12x_2 - 33}{x_2 - 4}$$

But since the slope can also be expressed as

$$-2x_2 + 12$$

we may write

$$\frac{-x_2^2 + 12x_2 - 33}{x_2 - 4} = -2x_2 + 12$$

or

$$-x_2^2 + 12x_2 - 33 = -2x_2^2 + 20x_2 - 48$$

or

$$x_2^2 - 8x_2 + 15 = 0$$

and

$$(x_2 - 3)(x_2 - 5) = 0$$

Therefore

$$x_2 = +5 \text{ or } +3$$

When $x_2 = 5$,

$$y_2 = -(5 - 6)^2 + 9 = +8$$

and

$$x_1 = -2(5) + 12 = +2$$

Also

$$y_1 = \tfrac{1}{2}(2)^2 = +2$$

Thus one tangent passes through points $P_1(2,2)$ and $P_2(5,8)$. When

$$x_2 = 3$$

then

$$y_2 = -(3 - 6)^2 + 9 = 0$$

and

$$x_1 = -2(3) + 12 = +6$$

Also

$$y_1 = \tfrac{1}{2}(6)^2 = +18$$

Thus another tangent passes through the points $P_1'(6,18)$ and $P_2'(3,0)$.

Example 32. Figure 20.4 shows the graph of the equation

$$y = \tfrac{1}{4}(x - 3)^2 + 2 = 0.25x^2 - 1.5x + 4.25$$

A tangent is drawn through the point P whose x coordinate is $+5.4$. The line segment y_0P is drawn perpendicular to this tangent through the point P. The y coordinate of point Q is 5. Find the length of the line segment PQ.

The y coordinate of point P is

$$y_P = 0.25(5.4)^2 - 1.5(5.4) + 4.25 = 3.44$$

Thus the coordinates of P are (5.4,3.44).

The slope of a tangent drawn to the curve is, in general,

$$\text{Slope of tangent} = \frac{d(0.25x^2 - 1.5x + 4.25)}{dx} = 0.5x - 1.5$$

In particular, the slope of the tangent at P where $x = 5.4$ is

$$\text{Slope at } P = (0.5)(5.4) - 1.5 = 1.2 = \tfrac{6}{5}$$

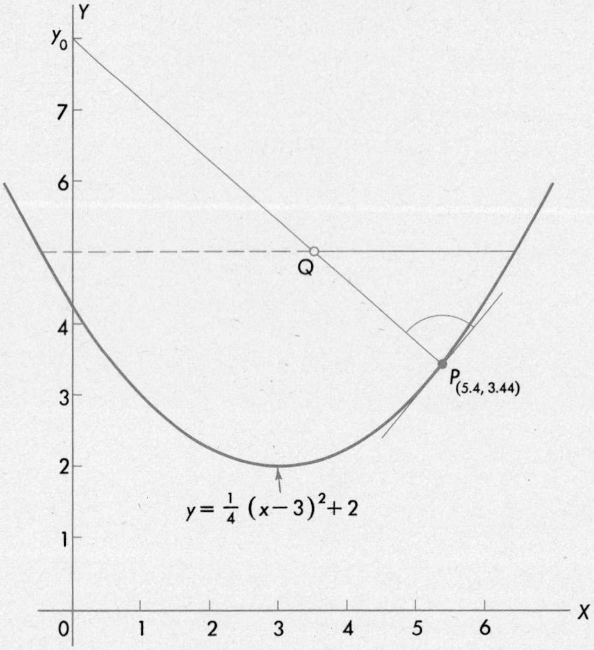

FIGURE 20.4

From Eq. (11), Sec. 6.14,

$$\text{Slope of } y_0P = -\frac{1}{6/5} = -\frac{5}{6}$$

The equation for the line y_0P is then in the form

$$y = -\tfrac{5}{6}x + y_0$$

But since the coordinates of P are (5.4,3.44), we may write

$$3.44 = -\tfrac{5}{6}(5.4) + y_0$$

and

$$y_0 = 7.94$$

Therefore the equation of the line y_0P is

$$y = -\tfrac{5}{6}x + 7.94$$

The y coordinate of point Q is given as 5; therefore

$$5 = -\tfrac{5}{6}x_Q + 7.94$$

and

$$x_Q = 3.53$$

From Eq. (14), Sec. 6.16,

$$PQ = \sqrt{(5.4 - 3.53)^2 + (3.44 - 5)^2} = 2.44$$

EXERCISE 5

Differentiate the following:

1. $y = ax^2 + bx + c$
2. $y = (4x^3 - 7x + 8)/x$
3. $y = (2x - 5)(3x + 1)$
4. $y = 4/\sqrt{x} - 4\sqrt{x}$
5. $y = \dfrac{1}{3x^2} - \dfrac{5}{2x}$
6. $y = \dfrac{ab}{x} - \dfrac{x}{b} + \dfrac{b}{ax}$
7. $y = \sqrt[n]{x^{n-1}}$
8. $y = \tfrac{1}{9}x^6$
9. $y = 3x^{-4} + \pi$
10. $y = -2x^{-4}/3 - 10^2$
11. $y = 26/x^4 - 3$
12. $y = -3/(5x^{20}) + \pi^2$
13. $y = kx^{-3} + 15$
14. $y = \pi/(2x^3) - 26$
15. $y = e^2 + 3x^5 + k$
16. $y = 3x^5 - 10/x^2$
17. $y = \pi x^2 + 30$
18. $y = 26/10^4$
19. $y = \pi/x^2 - e/x^3$

20. Power is defined as the rate of doing work with respect to time. If W denotes work, t time, and P power, give the mathematically equivalent definition of power.
21. Using the conclusion in Prob. 20, find the power at $t = 2$ s if the work being done by a force is $W = 3t^2 + 4t + 6$, where W is in foot-pounds.
22. If specific heat is defined to be dQ/dt, where Q is the quantity of heat necessary to raise the temperature of 1 g of a substance from 0 to t°C and if for ethyl alcohol

$$Q = 0.5068t + 0.00143t^2 + 0.0000018t^3$$

(valid for the range from 0 to 60°C), determine the specific heats of ethyl alcohol at $t = 10$, 20, 30, 40, and 50°C.

23. A parabolic arch is 10 ft high and 20 ft wide, as shown in Fig. 20.5. A brace AB is inserted as shown in the figure. Find its length.
24. Euler's column formula from studies of strength of materials is

$$\frac{P}{A} = \frac{\pi^2 E}{(L/r)^2}$$

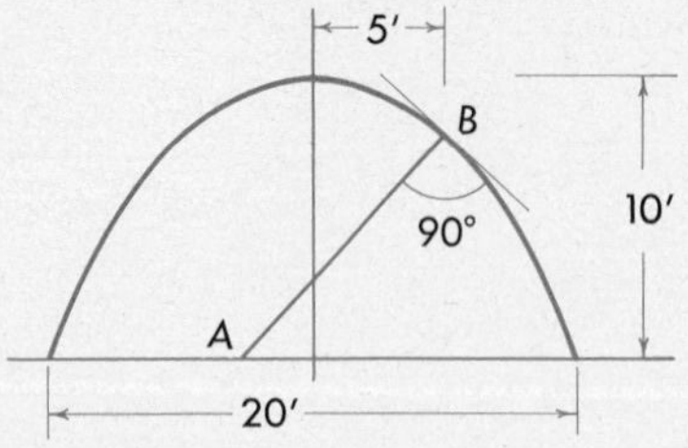

FIGURE 20.5

where P is the total load, A is the cross-sectional area of the column, E is a property of the material from which the column is made (the modulus of elasticity), L is the length of the column, and r depends on the shape of the cross section.

(a) Sketch a graph of P/A as a function of L/r. E is a positive quantity.

(b) Determine the equation of the tangent to this curve at the point where $L/r = (3\pi^2 E/p)^{1/2}$, $P/A = p/3$.

Remark: p is the load required to crush the column. Your resulting straight-line equation is known as the *straight-line column formula.*

25. In constructing a certain type of cam for accelerating a lift, it is necessary to find two parabolas that have a common tangent at points on two given abscissas. Find a and b so that the tangent to $x^2 = ay$ at $x = 2$ shall coincide with the tangent to $(x - 10)^2 = b(y - 8.5)$ at $x = 9$.
26. Devise a graphical solution for the common tangent line in Prob. 25 based on the following theorem for parabolas. Also prove the theorem:

Theorem. *The tangent at the vertex of a parabola bisects the segment of any other tangent which is included by the principal axes and the point of tangency.*

27. If $V = dM/dx$ and if

$$M = \frac{2Px}{7} \qquad \text{for } 0 < x < 10 \qquad (P \text{ is a positive constant})$$

$$M = 10P - \frac{5Px}{7} \qquad \text{for } 10 < x < 14$$

(a) Sketch a graph of M/P as a function of x for x from 0 to 14.

(b) Determine V for $0 < x < 10$ and for $10 < x < 14$. Then sketch the graph for V/P as a function of x for x from 0 to 14.

(c) Does the graph of V as a function of x have a discontinuity in the range $0 < x < 14$?

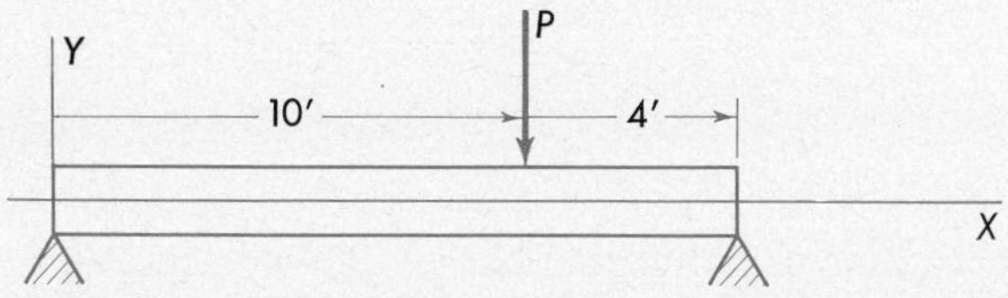

FIGURE 20.6

Remark: The beam and loading for this problem are shown in Fig. 20.6. The mathematical analysis of such beams gives a shear graph (V as a function of x) with discontinuities at each point where there was a concentrated load. The mathematical analysis of such problems assumes that the concentrated load is applied *at a point* (which is physically impossible). However, the results from this analysis are accurate enough for most purposes.

28. A cantilever beam of length L ft bears a uniform load of w lb/ft for the length $L/2$ ft next to the wall as shown in Fig. 20.7. The equation for this part of the curve of the beam is

$$EIy = -\frac{wx^4}{24} + \frac{wLx^3}{12} - \frac{wL^2x^2}{16} + \frac{wL^3x}{24} - \frac{wL^4}{48}$$

that is, this equation is valid for x between $L/2$ and L. If the weight of the beam itself is neglected, the part of the beam to the left of this load will be straight and will be along the tangent to the preceding curve at the point whose abscissa is $x = L/2$.

Determine the maximum deflection; that is, find the largest numerical value of y in the entire range (which is clearly the ordinate at $x = 0$).

20.6 Composite Functions

Thus far we have discussed methods of finding the derivative with respect to x of the sum of various powers of x. For example, we can find the derivative of y with respect

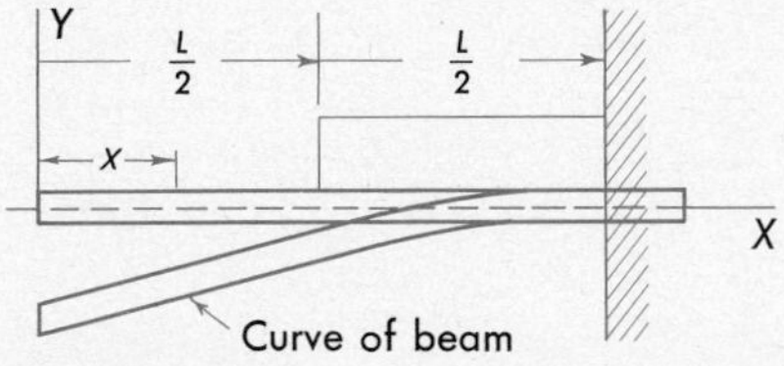

FIGURE 20.7

to x if

$$y = x^2 + 3x + 5 \tag{29}$$

However, without multiplying out we cannot find the derivative of y with respect to x if

$$y = (x^2 + 3x + 5)^3 \tag{30}$$

because as the equation stands it is not expressed as the sum of powers of x [also see Eq. (28)].

Fortunately, a method does exist for differentiating Eq. (30) as it stands. This method depends upon the theorem:

Theorem. *If y is the value of a differentiable function of u, and u is the value of a differentiable function of x, then y is the value of a differentiable function of x, and*

$$\frac{dy}{dx} = \frac{dy}{du}\frac{du}{dx} \tag{31}$$

Since y depends on u, and u depends on x, we sometimes call y the value of a *composite* function.

A rigorous proof of the above theorem is quite involved and will not be presented here. However, the interested student can easily find such a proof in almost any textbook devoted entirely to calculus.

Let us proceed to differentiate Eq. (30) directly by use of Eq. (31). If

$$y = (x^2 + 3x + 5)^3 \tag{32}$$

and if we let

$$u = x^2 + 3x + 5 \tag{33}$$

then

$$y = u^3 \tag{34}$$

and

$$\frac{dy}{du} = 3u^2 \tag{35}$$

Substituting (33) in (35) gives

$$\frac{dy}{du} = 3(x^2 + 3x + 5)^2 \tag{36}$$

Now from (33) we may write

$$\frac{du}{dx} = 2x + 3 \tag{37}$$

By substituting (37) and (36) in (31) we obtain

$$\frac{dy}{dx} = 3(x^2 + 3x + 5)^2(2x + 3) \tag{38}$$

Thus we obtain the derivative of y with respect to x.
In general, if

$$y = u^n \tag{39}$$

where u is the value of a differentiable function of x, then

$$\frac{dy}{dx} = nu^{n-1}\frac{du}{dx} \tag{40}$$

or

$$\frac{d(u^n)}{dx} = nu^{n-1}\frac{du}{dx} \tag{41}$$

and

$$\frac{d(ku^n)}{dx} = nku^{n-1}\frac{du}{dx} \tag{41a}$$

EXERCISE 6

Differentiate the following functions with respect to the independent variable.

1. $y = (3x^2 + 2x + 5)^4$
2. $y = (7x^3 - 5x^2 + 2x)^{-3/4}$
3. $z = \sqrt[3]{(-5x^2 + 3x)}$
4. $w = \sqrt{3t + 7}$
5. $v = \sqrt[4]{6 - 7t^2}$
6. $w = 37/\sqrt{6 - t^2}$

7. $y = -2/\sqrt[4]{(1 - t^2)^3}$
8. $y = (4 - x^2)^3$
9. $y = \sqrt{2t} + 2\sqrt[3]{t}$
10. $R = 5/\sqrt[3]{3t^2 - 6t}$
11. $S = 2\sqrt[3]{(1 + y^2)^2}$
12. $y = 1/8(3 - 2t)^2$
13. $y = \dfrac{4}{1 - x^3}$
14. $y = \dfrac{4}{(1 - x)^3}$
15. $x = 4\sqrt[5]{5t^3 - t^5}$

16. Sketch the graph of $y = 10/(3 - x) - 5$ between $x = -2$ and $x = +2$. Compare with Fig. 19.4, curve *B*. Find the equation for dy/dx. Find dy/dx when $x = -1.5$. Check graphically from Fig. 19.4.
17. Sketch the graph of $y = 10/(3 + x) - 5$ between $x = -2$ and $x = +2$. Compare with Fig. 19.4, curve *A*. Find the equation for dy/dx. Find dy/dx when $x = 0$. Check graphically from Fig. 19.4.
18. Sketch the graph of $y = 5 - 10/(x + 3)$ between $x = -2$ and $x = +2$. Compare with Fig. 19.4, curve *D*. Find the equation for dy/dx. Find x and y when $dy/dx = 5/8$. Check graphically from Fig. 19.4 as far as possible. Explain the two answers.

Note. *Some of the work in Sec. 20.22 will be based on the problems below which can be done by direct application of Eq. (31).*

19. Show that $\dfrac{d(y^2)}{dx} = 2y\dfrac{dy}{dx}$.
20. Show that $\dfrac{d(x^2)}{dx} = 2x$.
21. Show that $\dfrac{d(x^5)}{dx} = 5x^4$.
22. Show that $\dfrac{d(7y^5)}{dx} = 35y^4\dfrac{dy}{dx}$.

20.7 The Derivative of a Product and a Quotient

If *u* and *v* are the values of differentiable functions of x, we shall now develop a formula for $d(u \cdot v)/dx$.

We shall let

$$y = u \cdot v \tag{42}$$

Now if x changes by some amount Δx, then *u* will change by some amount Δu, and *v* will change by some amount Δv. Also *y* will change by another amount Δy; then

$$y + \Delta y = (u + \Delta u)(v + \Delta v)$$

or, multiplying the factors on the right together,

$$y + \Delta y = uv + v\,\Delta u + u\,\Delta v + \Delta u\,\Delta v \tag{43}$$

Subtracting (42) from (43)

$$\Delta y = v\,\Delta u + u\,\Delta v + \Delta u\,\Delta v$$

Dividing both sides by Δx and reversing the positions of the first two terms on the right,

$$\frac{\Delta y}{\Delta x} = u\frac{\Delta v}{\Delta x} + v\frac{\Delta u}{\Delta x} + \frac{\Delta u}{\Delta x}\Delta v \tag{44}$$

As Δx approaches zero, the quantity $\Delta u/\Delta x$ may very well approach some finite value. But as Δx approaches zero, Δv also approaches zero; therefore the product of $\Delta u/\Delta x$ and Δv will approach zero. Consequently, when we approach the limits

$$\frac{dy}{dx} = u\frac{dv}{dx} + v\frac{du}{dx}$$

or

$$\frac{d(u \cdot v)}{dx} = u\frac{dv}{dx} + v\frac{du}{dx} \tag{45}$$

Rule 5. *The derivative of a product is the first factor multiplied by the derivative of the second factor plus the second factor multiplied by the derivative of the first factor.*

In Example 33 below we have chosen, for illustration, to use the product of two rather simple algebraic functions. However, Eq. (45) applies generally, and we shall have occasion to use it in connection with more complicated algebraic functions as well as for logarithmic and trigonometric functions.

Example 33. Find dy/dx if $y = (3x + 5)^2(2x^2 - 7)$.

Following Eq. (45),

$$\begin{aligned}\frac{d[(3x + 5)^2(2x^2 - 7)]}{dx} &= (3x + 5)^2\frac{d(2x^2 - 7)}{dx} + (2x^2 - 7)\frac{d(3x + 5)^2}{dx} \\ &= (3x + 5)^2(4x) + (2x^2 - 7) \cdot 2(3x + 5) \cdot 3 \\ &= (9x^2 + 30x + 25)(4x) + 6(2x^2 - 7)(3x + 5) \\ &= 36x^3 + 120x^2 + 100x + 6(6x^3 - 21x + 10x^2 - 35) \\ &= 72x^3 + 180x^2 - 26x - 210\end{aligned}$$

The student should verify the above answer by multiplying the given factors and differentiating term by term.

In a similar way we can develop a formula for $d(u/v)/dx$. Let

$$y = \frac{u}{v} \tag{46}$$

Now let x increase by the amount Δx, and as a consequence u will change by the amount Δu, v will change by the amount Δv, and y will change by the amount Δy.

Accordingly

$$y + \Delta y = \frac{u + \Delta u}{v + \Delta v} \tag{47}$$

Subtracting (46) from (47) gives

$$\Delta y = \frac{u + \Delta u}{v + \Delta v} - \frac{u}{v} \tag{48}$$

or, by combining the right-hand side of (48)

$$\Delta y = \frac{uv + v\,\Delta u - uv - u\,\Delta v}{v(v + \Delta v)}$$

or

$$\Delta y = \frac{v\,\Delta u - u\,\Delta v}{v(v + \Delta v)} \tag{49}$$

Dividing both sides of (49) by Δx,

$$\frac{\Delta y}{\Delta x} = \frac{v(\Delta u/\Delta x) - u(\Delta v/\Delta x)}{v(v + \Delta v)} \tag{50}$$

Now as Δx approaches zero, the denominator of (50) approaches v^2, and in the limit

$$\frac{dy}{dx} = \frac{v(du/dx) - u(dv/dx)}{v^2}$$

or

$$\frac{d(u/v)}{dx} = \frac{v(du/dx) - u(dv/dx)}{v^2} \tag{51}$$

Rule 6. *The derivative of a quotient is the denominator times the derivative of the numerator minus the numerator times the derivative of the denominator divided by the denominator squared.*

Example 34. If $y = (5x^2 - 3)/(x + 1)$, find dy/dx.

By rule 6 above,

$$\frac{dy}{dx} = \frac{(x + 1)(10x) - (5x^2 - 3)(1)}{(x + 1)^2}$$
$$= \frac{10x^2 + 10x - 5x^2 + 3}{(x + 1)^2}$$
$$= \frac{5x^2 + 10x + 3}{(x + 1)^2}$$

We may also use Rule 5 by first writing

$$y = (5x^2 - 3)(x + 1)^{-1}$$

Then

$$\frac{dy}{dx} = (5x^2 - 3)(-1)(x + 1)^{-2}(1) + (x + 1)^{-1}(10x)$$

or

$$\frac{dy}{dx} = \frac{-(5x^2 - 3)}{(x + 1)^2} + \frac{10x}{x + 1}$$
$$= \frac{-5x^2 + 3 + 10x^2 + 10x}{(x + 1)^2}$$
$$= \frac{5x^2 + 10x + 3}{(x + 1)^2}$$

In this case we can avoid the use of either rule 5 or rule 6 by dividing as indicated:

$$y = \frac{5x^2 - 3}{x + 1} = 5x - 5 + \frac{2}{x + 1}$$
$$= 5x - 5 + 2(x + 1)^{-1}$$

The actual division is shown below.

$$\begin{array}{r l}
 & 5x \quad - 5 \\
x + 1 \,\big) & 5x^2 \qquad\quad - 3 \\
 & 5x^2 + 5x \\
\hline
 & \quad - 5x - 3 \\
 & \quad - 5x - 5 \\
\hline
 & \qquad\quad + 2
\end{array}$$

Then

$$\frac{dy}{dx} = 5 - 2(x + 1)^{-2}(1) = 5 - \frac{2}{(x + 1)^2}$$

$$= \frac{5x^2 + 10x + 5 - 2}{(x + 1)^2}$$

$$= \frac{5x^2 + 10x + 3}{(x + 1)^2}$$

Example 35. If $y = \sqrt{(3t^2 + 2)/(t^2 - t)}$, find dy/dt.

If we first write

$$y = \frac{(3t^2 + 2)^{1/2}}{(t^2 - t)^{1/2}}$$

and apply Eq. (51), we obtain

$$\frac{dy}{dt} = \frac{(t^2 - t)^{1/2}(\frac{1}{2})(3t^2 + 2)^{-1/2}(6t) - (3t^2 + 2)^{1/2}(\frac{1}{2})(t^2 - t)^{-1/2}(2t - 1)}{t^2 - t}$$

$$= \frac{3t}{(t^2 - t)^{1/2}(3t^2 + 2)^{1/2}} - \frac{(2t - 1)(3t^2 + 2)^{1/2}}{2(t^2 - t)^{3/2}} = \frac{-3t^2 - 4t + 2}{2(t^2 - t)^{3/2}(3t^2 + 2)^{1/2}}$$

EXERCISE 7

By use of Eq. (45) or Eq. (51), find the derivative of the following functions with respect to the independent variable.

1. $y = x\sqrt{3 + x^2}$
2. $y = x^2\sqrt{6 - x^2}$
3. $y = (x + 5)^2(3x^3 - 7)^3$
4. $y = (2x + 5)/(x^2 - 2)$
5. $y = \left(\frac{x + 5}{x - 2}\right)^2$
6. $y = \frac{x}{x^3 - 5}$
7. $y = \frac{x + 1/x}{2x^2 + 5}$
8. $y = x^3(3x^2 + 5)^{-2}$
9. $y = \frac{2x}{\sqrt{4x^2 - 9}}$
10. $y = \frac{(x^2 - 1)^{3/2}}{x^2}$

Problems 11 through 14 involve the verification of the rules for relative error of products, quotients, powers, and roots. (The factor 100 is used to convert to percent.)

The relative, or percentage, error of the product of two rounded numbers is approximately the algebraic sum of the relative errors of the multiplier and the multiplicand.

11. Show that if $p = uv$, then

$$100\frac{\Delta p}{p} \approx 100\frac{\Delta u}{u} + 100\frac{\Delta v}{v}$$

The relative error of the quotient of two rounded numbers is approximately the algebraic difference obtained by subtracting the relative error in the divisor from the relative error in the dividend.

12. Show that if $q = u/v$, then

$$100\frac{\Delta q}{q} \approx 100\frac{\Delta u}{u} - 100\frac{\Delta v}{v}$$

The relative error of a power of a rounded number is approximately the relative error of the number multiplied by the degree of the power.

13. Show that if $y = x^n$, then

$$100\frac{\Delta y}{y} \approx n(100)\frac{\Delta x}{x}$$

The relative error of a root of a rounded number is approximately the relative error of the rounded number divided by the index of the root.

14. Show that if $y = \sqrt[k]{x} = x^{1/k}$, then

$$100\frac{\Delta y}{y} \approx \frac{1}{k}(100)\frac{\Delta x}{x}$$

20.8 Maxima and Minima

The subject of maxima and minima was introduced in Sec. 19.6. The student should review that section before proceeding with the discussion below.

In Sec. 19.6 and in Exercise 2 of Chap. 19 we considered relative maxima and minima in connection with certain graphs. We noted that these maximum and minimum points are transition points between rising and falling portions of a graph.

We also noted in Sec. 19.6 that there may be exceptional cases as illustrated by the "cusp" type of relative maximum and minimum shown in Fig. 19.7.

In general, if $y = f(x)$ is defined over a certain interval and if y has a relative maximum or minimum within that interval at, for example, $x = c$ and if dy/dx exists at $x = c$, then

$$\frac{dy}{dx} = 0$$

at $x = c$.

The statement above specifically avoids mention of situations

1. Involving the endpoints of the interval of definition of the function
2. Involving points for which the derivative does not exist

Furthermore, the fact that the derivative is zero for a certain value of the function does not guarantee the occurrence of either a maximum or minimum. Note, for example, the point P_3 in Fig. 19.8.

If $y = f(x)$, we shall call the value of x_1 for which

$$\frac{dy}{dx} = 0$$

a *critical* value.

As we learned in Sec. 19.7, the derivative may be zero for a point of inflection.

The procedure for identifying maxima and minima will be illustrated in the following examples.

Example 36. Find what values of x will make y maximum or minimum if

$$y = x^3 - 3x^2 - 9x + 10$$

Differentiating, we obtain

$$\frac{dy}{dx} = 3x^2 - 6x - 9 = 3(x - 3)(x + 1) \tag{52}$$

Any maximum or minimum values must occur when $dy/dx = 0$. Accordingly, setting $dy/dx = 0$, we obtain

$$0 = 3(x - 3)(x + 1)$$

whereby

$$x = 3, -1$$

In order to explore the properties of the curve at $x = 3$ and $x = -1$, we shall compute the values of the slope at various points:

x	-2	-1	0	$+3$	$+4$
$\frac{dy}{dx}$	$+15$	0	-9	0	$+15$

In this example let us draw possible tangents whose slopes are in the order positive, zero, negative, zero, and positive. We shall then roughly sketch a reasonable curve to fit these tangents. This is done in Fig. 20.8. Thus we have indicated a maximum at $x = -1$ and a minimum at $x = 3$.

We might confirm this conclusion by substituting values of x in the original equation, noting how y varies in the vicinity of $x = 3$ and $x = -1$. This is done as follows:

x	-3	-2	-1	0	1	2	3	4	5
y	-17	$+8$	$+15$	$+10$	-1	-12	-17	-10	$+15$

At $x = 3$, where $y = -17$, we have a minimum, this point being the lowest point in the immediate vicinity. Likewise at $x = -1$, $y = 15$, we have a maximum point, this point being the highest point in the immediate vicinity.

The labor involved in identifying a critical point as a maximum, a minimum, or a point of inflection can be reduced considerably by simply investigating the signs

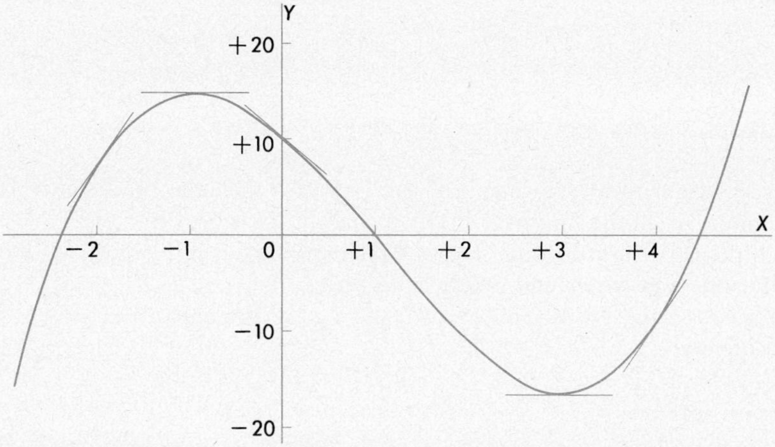

FIGURE 20.8

of the derivative in the vicinity of the critical points without actually calculating the numerical value of the derivative.

If the sign of the derivative is in the sequence

$$\underset{\text{for } x < +3}{\text{Positive}} \longrightarrow \underset{\text{for } x = +3}{\text{zero}} \longrightarrow \underset{\text{for } x > +3}{\text{negative}}$$

the value of the function has a maximum at $x = +3$.

If the sign of the derivative is in the sequence

$$\underset{\text{for } x < +3}{\text{Negative}} \longrightarrow \underset{\text{for } x = +3}{\text{zero}} \longrightarrow \underset{\text{for } x > +3}{\text{positive}}$$

the value of the function has a minimum at $x = +3$.

When x is near $+3$

The first and third factors of Eq. (52), that is, 3 and $x + 1$, are obviously positive if x is near $+3$. However, if x is a little less than $+3$, say $+2.999$, then the second factor is negative, the product of all factors is negative, and dy/dx is *negative*.

If x is a little *more* than $+3$, say, $+3.0001$, then the second factor is positive, the product of all factors is positive, and dy/dx is *positive*.

As x increases, then, in the vicinity of $x = +3$, the sign of the derivative traverses the following sequence:

Negative → zero → positive

and we have a *minimum*.

When x is near -1

The first factor, 3, is obviously positive, and the second factor, $x - 3$, is obviously negative.

However, if x is a little less than -1, say, -1.0001, then the third factor is negative, the product of all the factors is positive, and dy/dx is *positive*.

If x is a little *more* than -1, say, -0.9999, then the third factor is positive, the product of all factors is negative, and dy/dx is *negative*.

As x increases in the vicinity of $x = -1$, the sign of the derivative traverses the following sequence:

Positive → zero → negative

and we have a *maximum*.

Example 37. Find the critical values of x, and identify them, if

$$y = 3x^2 - 2x + 7$$

Differentiating the above equation,

$$\frac{dy}{dx} = 6x - 2 = 2(3x - 1)$$

Setting this equation equal to zero,

$$0 = 2(3x - 1)$$

and the critical value of x is

$$x = +\tfrac{1}{3}$$

When x is a little less than $\frac{1}{3}$, the derivative is negative; when x is just $\frac{1}{3}$, the derivative is 0; when x is a little more than $\frac{1}{3}$, the derivative is positive. Therefore we can identify the point at which $x = \frac{1}{3}$ as a *minimum* point.

Example 38. A uniform bar weighing $1\frac{1}{2}$ lb/ft is to be used to lift a 100-lb load as shown in Fig. 20.9. What length of bar will require the minimum force, and what is the force?

We have two clockwise-force moments 100(0.5) due to the load and $(1.5L)(L/2)$ due to the weight of the bar itself. These are balanced by the moment FL. Accordingly we may write

$$FL = 100(0.5) + 1.5L\frac{L}{2}$$

or

$$F = \frac{50}{L} + 0.75L$$

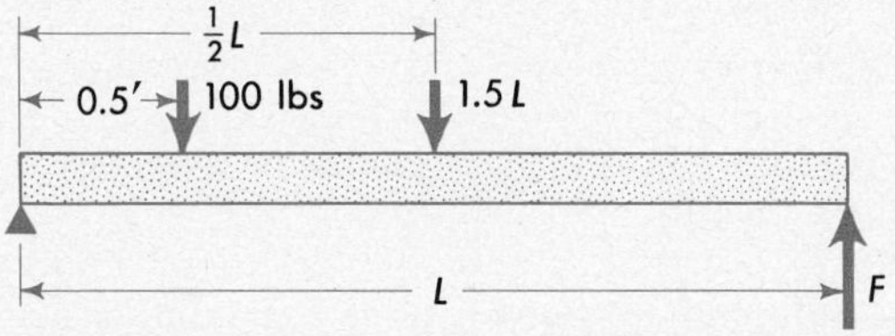

FIGURE 20.9

Differentiating,

$$\frac{dF}{dL} = -\frac{50}{L^2} + 0.75$$

Equating the derivative to zero,

$$0 = -\frac{50}{L^2} + 0.75$$

or

$$L = 8.16 \text{ ft}$$

and

$$F = \frac{50}{8.16} + 0.75(8.16) = 12.25 \text{ lb}$$

The student should convince himself that when $L = 8.16$ ft, the force is actually a minimum and not a maximum.

Example 39. We are given $y = x^3 - 6x^2 + 12x - 20$.

Let us investigate any horizontal slopes as we did in the preceding examples. In this example we obtain

$$\frac{dy}{dx} = 3x^2 - 12x + 12$$

Equating to zero and solving, we obtain

$x = 2, 2$ (thus the two roots are identical)

If we calculate values of the slope and tabulate, we have

x	+4	+3	+2	+1	0
$\frac{dy}{dx} = 3x^2 - 12x + 12$	+12	+3	0	+3	+12

Graphically, this is shown in Fig. 20.10 and we have neither a maximum nor a minimum but a point of inflection or reversal of curvature (see Sec. 19.7).

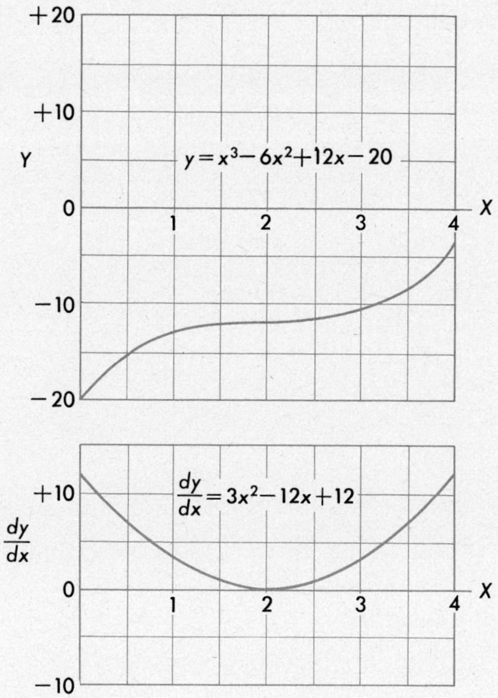

FIGURE 20.10

Example 40. Locate and identify the critical points on the graph of

$y = 2\sqrt{3x^3 - 16x + 20}$ (see Fig. 20.11)

Change to the form

$$y = 2(3x^3 - 16x + 20)^{1/2} \tag{53}$$

Then

$$\frac{dy}{dx} = (3x^3 - 16x + 20)^{-1/2}(9x^2 - 16)$$

or

$$\frac{dy}{dx} = \frac{9x^2 - 16}{\sqrt{3x^3 - 16x + 20}} \tag{54}$$

Values of x for which $\sqrt{3x^3 - 16x + 20}$ is either imaginary or zero are excluded.

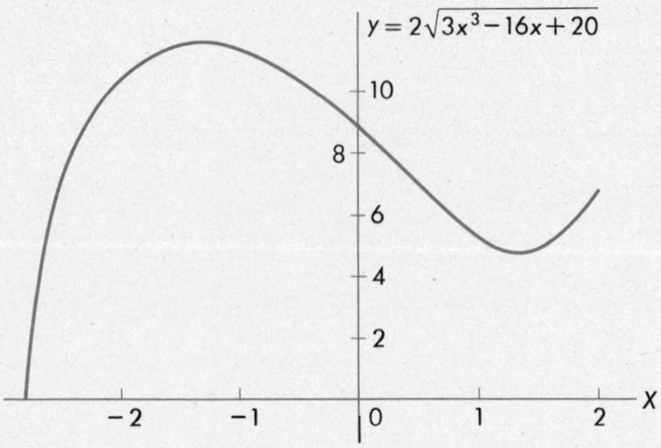

FIGURE 20.11

It can be found by solving

$$3x^3 - 16x + 20 = 0$$

that when $x = -2.785$ (approximately), the quantity

$$\sqrt{3x^3 - 16x + 20} = 0$$

Also for values of x less than -2.785 the quantity $\sqrt{3x^3 - 16x + 20}$ is imaginary. Therefore values of x equal to or less than -2.785 are excluded, and the derivative is undefined for these values.

Now let us find values of x for which $dy/dx = 0$. From Eq. (54) $dy/dx = 0$ when

$$9x^2 - 16 = 0 \qquad (55)$$

Solving (55), we obtain

$$x^2 = 16/9$$
$$x = \pm 4/3$$

Since the above values of x are not excluded, we shall investigate the sign of the derivative in Eq. (54) in the vicinity of $x = +4/3$ and $x = -4/3$ in order to identify the corresponding critical points.

The sign of the derivative in Eq. (54) is determined entirely by the sign of the numerator. The denominator is positive anyway. The numerator can be written

$$(3x + 4)(3x - 4) \qquad (56)$$

When x is in the vicinity of $+\frac{4}{3}$, the left-hand factor of expression (56) is positive, and the sign of the numerator of Eq. (54) will be governed by the sign of the quantity $3x - 4$.

When x is a little less than $+\frac{4}{3}$, the expression $3x - 4$ is negative. When x is a little more than $\frac{4}{3}$, the expression $3x - 4$ is positive.

Thus, as x traverses through this critical point in an increasing direction, the signs of the derivative are in the sequence

Negative → zero → positive

and this critical point is a *minimum*.

The student should justify for himself that when $x = -\frac{4}{3}$, the given function is a maximum.

Example 41. Locate and identify the critical points if

$$y = x^{2/3}(x - 4)^2 \tag{57}$$

Equation (57) may be written

$$y = x^{8/3} - 8x^{5/3} + 16x^{2/3}$$

and

$$\frac{dy}{dx} = \frac{8}{3}x^{5/3} - \frac{40}{3}x^{2/3} + \frac{32}{3}x^{-1/3}$$

or

$$\frac{dy}{dx} = \frac{8}{3}x^{-1/3}(x^2 - 5x + 4)$$

or

$$\frac{dy}{dx} = \frac{8}{3\sqrt[3]{x}}(x - 4)(x - 1) \qquad x \neq 0$$

Therefore, $dy/dx = 0$ when $x = +4$ and when $x = +1$. By testing for the sign of the derivative in the vicinity of these critical values as we have done in the previous examples, we find that $x = 1$ corresponds to a relative maximum, and $x = 4$ corresponds to a relative minimum.

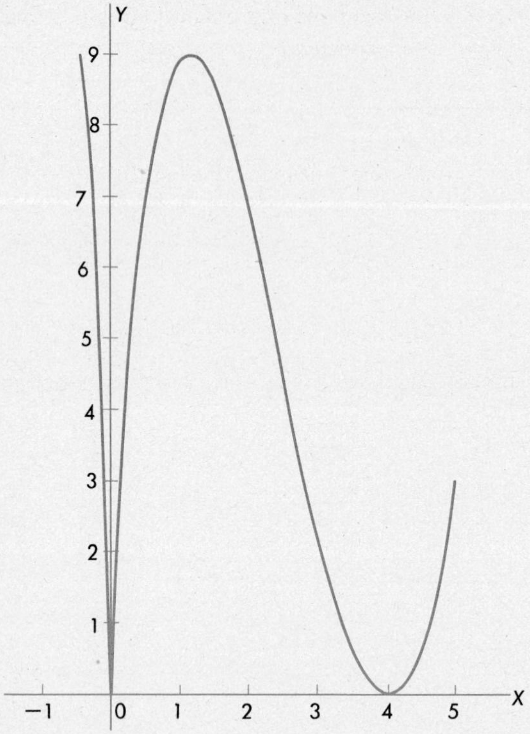

FIGURE 20.12

However, it is important to investigate the behavior of the function in the vicinity of $x = 0$ since for this value of x the derivative is not defined.

The plot of Eq. (57) is shown in Fig. 20.12. From this figure it is evident that when $x = 0$, we have a cusp minimum which we would have overlooked had we failed to investigate.

Thus we have a relative maximum at $x = 1$ and *two* relative minima, one at $x = 4$ and another at $x = 0$.

EXERCISE 8

Locate and identify any points where the tangent is horizontal.

1. $y = 2x^3 + 9x^2 - 24x + 12$
2. $y = -x^4 + 24x^2 + 2$
3. $y = x + 9/x$
*4. $y = (x^2 + 4)/x$
*5. $y = (x^3 - 16)/x$
6. $y = \sqrt{3x^3 - 4x + 11}$
7. $y = 5/(2x^4 - 9x^2)$

* *Hint:* Divide out before differentiating.

8. The sum of two numbers is 12, and their product is to be a maximum. Find the numbers.
9. One of the factors considered in choosing the size of wire for a transmission circuit is cost. The larger the cross-sectional area, the greater will be the first cost and hence also the annual charges for interest, taxes, and depreciation. At the same time the larger the cross-sectional area, the lower will be the cost of lost power since the heating losses will be lower. For bare wire the investment is directly proportional to the area, and the lost power is inversely proportional to the area; hence the total part of the line cost depending on wire size can be written as $C = k_1a + k_2/a$, where a is the area and k_1 and k_2 are positive constants.

   Show that the area of the wire which makes C a minimum is that for which the two terms are equal, that is, that for which $k_1a = k_2/a$. Illustrate by sketching the two components and their sum, all on the same axes.

   Remark: The basic law as stated in this problem is known as Kelvin's law.

10. A rectangle has a perimeter of 40 ft. Find the dimensions of the rectangle to give the greatest area.
11. A sheet-iron trough is to be made by bending up two edges so as to give a rectangular cross-sectional area. The width of the sheet is 20 in. Therefore $20 = x + 2y$. Find y to give the maximum cross-sectional area (see Fig. 20.13).
12. A utility company wishes to determine the size wire to be used on a power transmission line for maximum economy. Initial cost and investment charges may be expressed by the equation $s_1 = ka + b$, where s_1 is the cost, a is the cross-sectional area of the wire, and k and b are constants. The energy loss may be written $s_2 = c/a$, where s_2 is the cost of lost power and c is a constant. If $k = 0.18$, $b = 15{,}000$, and $c = 40$, find the optimum cross-sectional area. (This is total area and may be distributed among n wires.)
13. The total cost of operating a pipeline may be expressed as $C = Ad^2 + B/d^5$, where d is the diameter of the pipe, and A and B are positive and are substantially constants for a given range of diameter values. Determine the diameter for minimum cost.

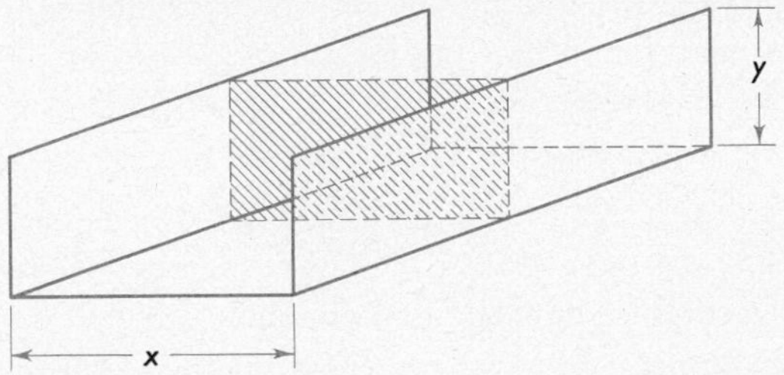

FIGURE 20.13

14. An electric battery whose internal electromotive force is E_g V and whose internal resistance is $r\,\Omega$ has the terminal voltage $E = E_g - Ir$ V, the output power $P = E_gI - I^2r$, and the efficiency $\eta = P/(E_gI)$ as functions of the current I A. Sketch the graphs of E, P, and η, each in terms of I in the range from open circuit ($I = 0$) to short circuit ($E = 0$). Determine by inspection the largest and smallest values of E, P, and η that occur at the endpoints of this range and whether any occur at intermediate points. Then differentiate to determine the latter. Tabulate all such values together with the values of I at which they occur. (Notice that the "maxima" for E and P actually occur, while the "maximum" for η does not, since it arises as an indeterminate form.)
15. The total cost of manufacturing a certain article is fixed by:
    (a) The fixed organization cost which is \$90 per day.
    (b) The unit production cost of each article which is \$0.09.
    (c) The cost of repairs, maintenance, etc., which is $x^2/10{,}000$ per day (in dollars) as estimated by past records. x is the number of articles produced per day.
    (1) Show that the total unit cost for each article in dollars is

$$U = \frac{90}{x} + 0.09 + \frac{x}{10{,}000}$$

    (2) Determine the number of articles to be produced each day to make the unit cost least.
16. A rectangular package has square ends. If the sum of the girth and length may not exceed 80 in, what dimensions will correspond to the maximum volume?
17. A rectangular open-top box is to be made from a sheet of copper 8 by 15 in by cutting a square from each corner and turning up the sides. What size squares must be cut out to make the capacity of the box a maximum?
18. Find the dimensions of the largest rectangle that can be contained in a right triangle whose sides are 3, 4, and 5 in. One angle of the rectangle coincides with the right angle of the triangle.
19. It is desired to determine the optimum number of checks on the quality of a finished product. It is assumed that the cost of checking one unit is proportional to the number of checks; that is, $y_1 = kn$. It is further assumed that the cost of errors and defective units becomes progressively less with more frequent checks but can never be eliminated entirely. It has been found that the formula $y_2 = b/(n + a)$ applies, where a and b are constants. To summarize,

$$E = kn + \frac{b}{n + a}$$

where E = total cost of checks and errors—to be made a minimum
k = constant = \$0.13
n = number of checks

b = constant = \$1.36

a = constant = 0.32

Find the number of checks for a minimum total cost E. What is the minimum E?

20. A man is able to hire one dump truck at \$8/h for truck and driver. The truck takes half an hour to deliver a load of sand and return. It takes 4 man-hours to load the truck. Laborers get \$2/h whether they are loading the truck or standing around idle while waiting for the truck to return. How many laborers should be hired to realize the minimum cost per load? What is the minimum cost?
21. Two lights whose intensities are as 1:4 are 100 ft apart. How far from the weaker light is the point of minimum total illumination? (Intensity of illumination at any point varies as i/l^2, where i is the intensity of the light source, and l is the distance from the point to the light source.)
22. Three towns are to be served by a high-voltage line which takes the form of a letter Y 16 mi high and 12 mi across the top. Find the length of the stem of the Y for a minimum length of wire.
23. What are the dimensions of a covered gallon cylindrical container which will make its total surface a minimum?
24. A cylindrical cup is to be made of sheet metal. Find the ratio of height to diameter that will require the least material.
25. A totally enclosed cylindrical can is to be made of sheet metal. Find the ratio of height to diameter that will give a maximum volume for a given amount of material.
26. The hourly cost of operating a ship, in dollars per hour, is $c = 120 + 0.02v^3$, where v equals speed in miles per hour. Find the speed corresponding to a minimum cost per mile.
27. The tops of two vertical poles ax and cy are connected by a rope abc. Plot the length of the rope against the distance xb and find the length of xb for a minimum length of the rope (see Fig. 20.14).
28. Let c = cost of one Mazda lamp plus installation charge in cents

    b = cost of power for lamp in cents per kilowatthour

    V = actual operating voltage

    V_0 = rated voltage for lamp

    P_0 = watts input at voltage V_0

    F_0 = luminous output in lumens at voltage V_0

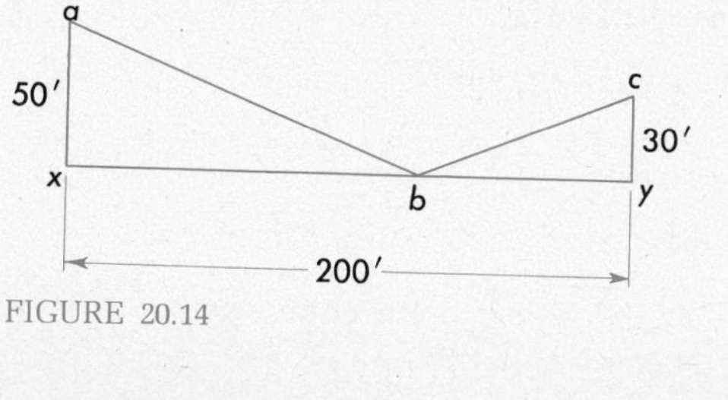

FIGURE 20.14

The cost per lumen for 1,000 h (assuming 1,000 h of life on the rated voltage of the lamp) is

$$y = \frac{c}{F_0}\left(\frac{V}{V_0}\right)^{B_5-B_2} + \frac{bP_0}{F_0}\left(\frac{V}{V_0}\right)^{B_3-B_2}$$

where the B's are constants that are determined experimentally.

(a) Determine the value of $x = V/V_0$ that makes y a minimum.

(b) For Mazda-C lamps from 60 to 150 W: $B_2 = 3.613$; $B_3 = 1.523$; $B_5 = 13.50$. If $b = 6$ cents per kilowatthour, $P_0 = 100$ W, and $c = 20$ cents, determine x_{min}, and hence determine the best value for the rated voltage V_0 if the operating voltage V is 120 V.

29. Determine the value of $x = p_2/p_1$ that will make the expression $y = (p_2/p_1)^{2/k} - (p_2/p_1)^{(k+1)/k}$, for $k > 1$, a maximum and thus determine p_2 in terms of p_1 when y is a maximum. What is the value of the coefficient of p_1 in your result if $k = 1.4$?

Remark: This problem occurs in thermodynamics in the study of flow in a nozzle.

30. The study of the formation of producer gas in chemical engineering leads to the equation

$$(b - a)v = x - x^{b/a}$$

where b and a are constants that depend on the process. x is the proportion of residual water remaining undecomposed, and v is the corresponding value for the amount of carbon dioxide.

(a) Determine a relation for the maximum value for v (amount of carbon dioxide), assuming that b is larger than a.

(b) If $a = 3.17$ and $b = 4.18$, determine the maximum value for v correct to slide-rule accuracy.

31. The fuel tank of an experimental rocket is a cylinder 40 ft long, and it flies with the axis of the tank vertical. The tank has a uniform cross-sectional area of 5 ft^2. It is filled with liquid fuel weighing 50 lb/ft^3. As the fuel is consumed, the joint center of gravity of the vertical tank and the remaining fuel will move along the axis of the tank. What depth of fuel will correspond to the minimum distance between the center of gravity and the bottom of the tank? The empty tank weighs 500 lb.

20.9 The Derivative of Sin x and Cos x

In this section we shall develop formulas for dy/dx when $y = \sin x$ and when $y = \cos x$.

First, we shall recall from Sec. 17.3 that

$$\sin x = x - \frac{x^3}{3!} + \frac{x^5}{5!} - \frac{x^7}{7!} + \frac{x^9}{9!} \cdots \tag{58}$$

and

$$\cos x = 1 - \frac{x^2}{2!} + \frac{x^4}{4!} - \frac{x^6}{6!} + \frac{x^8}{8!} \cdots \tag{59}$$

If $y = \sin x$ and if we differentiate Eq. (58) term by term, we obtain

$$\frac{dy}{dx} = \frac{d(\sin x)}{dx} = 1 - \frac{3x^2}{3!} + \frac{5x^4}{5!} - \frac{7x^6}{7!} + \frac{9x^8}{9!} \cdots$$

or

$$\frac{dy}{dx} = 1 - \frac{x^2}{2!} + \frac{x^4}{4!} - \frac{x^6}{6!} + \frac{x^8}{8!} \cdots \tag{60}$$

By inspection we see that the infinite series found in Eq. (60) is actually the infinite series for $\cos x$ shown in (59). Therefore we conclude that if

$$y = \sin x \tag{61}$$

then

$$\frac{dy}{dx} = \frac{d(\sin x)}{dx} = \cos x \tag{62}$$

where x is measured in *radians*.

If $y = \cos x$ and if we differentiate Eq. (59) term by term, we obtain

$$\frac{dy}{dx} = \frac{d(\cos x)}{dx} = -\frac{2x}{2!} + \frac{4x^3}{4!} - \frac{6x^5}{6!} + \frac{8x^7}{8!} \cdots$$

or

$$\frac{dy}{dx} = -x + \frac{x^3}{3!} - \frac{x^5}{5!} + \frac{x^7}{7!} \cdots \tag{63}$$

By inspection we see that the infinite series found in Eq. (63) is actually the negative of the infinite series for $\sin x$ shown in Eq. (59). Therefore we conclude that if

$$y = \cos x \tag{64}$$

then

$$\frac{dy}{dx} = \frac{d(\cos x)}{dx} = -\sin x \tag{65}$$

20.10 The Derivative of Sin u and Cos u

If

$$y = \sin u$$

and u is the value of a differentiable function of x, we may from Eqs. (65) and (31) write

$$\frac{dy}{dx} = \cos u \frac{du}{dx}$$

or

$$\frac{d(\sin u)}{dx} = \cos u \frac{du}{dx} \tag{66}$$

and

$$\frac{d(k \sin u + C)}{dx} = k \cos u \frac{du}{dx} \tag{67}$$

Example 42. If $y = \sin (4\pi\theta - \pi/2)$, find $dy/d\theta$.
Following Eq. (66),

$$\frac{dy}{d\theta} = \left[\cos\left(4\pi\theta - \frac{\pi}{2}\right)\right] 4\pi = 4\pi \sin 4\pi\theta \tag{68}$$

Example 43. If $y = \sin \theta^{(t-1)/t}$, find $dy/d\theta$ where t is a constant.
The problem can be simplified somewhat by restating.

$$y = \sin \theta^{1-1/t}$$

Following Eqs. (66) and (27),

$$\frac{dy}{d\theta} = (\cos \theta^{1-1/t})\left(1 - \frac{1}{t}\right)\theta^{-1/t} \tag{69}$$

Example 44. If $y = \sin^2 4\theta$, find $dy/d\theta$.

$$y = (\sin 4\theta)^2$$

Following Eqs. (66) and (27),

$$\frac{dy}{d\theta} = 2[(\sin 4\theta)(\cos 4\theta)]4$$

From Eq. (45), Chap. 18, we may write

$$\frac{dy}{d\theta} = 8 \sin 4\theta \cos 4\theta = 4 \sin 8\theta$$

Example 45. If $y = \sin (4\theta)^2$, find $dy/d\theta$.

Restate the problem to make the expression for the angle match Eq. (27).

$$y = \sin 16\theta^2$$

$$\frac{dy}{d\theta} = (\cos 16\theta^2)32\theta$$

Example 46. If $y = -\sin (4\pi\theta^2 - \pi/2)$, find $dy/d\theta$.

Following Eq. (66),

$$\frac{dy}{d\theta} = -\left[\cos\left(4\pi\theta^2 - \frac{\pi}{2}\right)\right] 8\pi\theta = -8\pi\theta \sin 4\pi\theta^2$$

If

$$y = \cos u$$

and u is the value of a differentiable function of x, we may, from Eqs. (65) and (31), write

$$\frac{dy}{dx} = -\sin u \frac{du}{dx} \tag{70}$$

or

$$\frac{d(\cos u)}{dx} = -\sin u \frac{du}{dx} \tag{71}$$

and

$$\frac{d(k \cos u + C)}{dx} = -k \sin u \frac{du}{dx} \tag{72}$$

Example 47. If $y = \cos(4\pi\theta - \pi/2)$, find $dy/d\theta$.

Following Eq. (71),

$$\frac{dy}{d\theta} = \left[-\sin\left(4\pi\theta - \frac{\pi}{2}\right)\right] 4\pi = 4\pi \cos 4\pi\theta$$

Example 48. If $y = \cos \theta^{(t-1)/t}$, find $dy/d\theta$, where t is a constant.

The problem can be simplified somewhat by restating, as

$$y = \cos \theta^{1-1/t}$$

Following Eqs. (72) and (27),

$$\frac{dy}{d\theta} = (-\sin \theta^{1-1/t})\left(1 - \frac{1}{t}\right)\theta^{-1/t}$$

Example 49. If $y = \cos^2 4\theta$, find $dy/d\theta$.

$$y = (\cos 4\theta)^2$$

Following Eqs. (27) and (72),

$$\frac{dy}{d\theta} = (2 \cos 4\theta)(-\sin 4\theta)4 = -8 \cos 4\theta \sin 4\theta = -4 \sin 8\theta \qquad \text{[Eq. (45), Chap. 18]}$$

Example 50. If $y = \cos (4\theta)^2$, find $dy/d\theta$.

To make the expression for the angle match Eq. (27), we can restate the problem as

$$y = \cos 16\theta^2$$

Then

$$\frac{dy}{d\theta} = (-\sin 16\theta^2)32\theta$$

20.11 The Derivative of Sec u and Cosec u

Since

$$\sec u = \frac{1}{\cos u} = (\cos u)^{-1}$$

$$\frac{d(\sec u)}{dx} = \frac{d(1/\cos u)}{dx} = \frac{d(\cos u)^{-1}}{dx}$$

$$= -(\cos u)^{-2}(-\sin u)\frac{du}{dx}$$

or

$$\frac{d(\sec u)}{dx} = \frac{\sin u}{(\cos u)^2}\frac{du}{dx} = \tan u \sec u \frac{du}{dx} \tag{73}$$

Also since

$$\operatorname{cosec} u = \frac{1}{\sin u} = (\sin u)^{-1}$$

$$\frac{d(\operatorname{cosec} u)}{dx} = \frac{d(1/\sin u)}{dx} = \frac{d(\sin u)^{-1}}{dx}$$

$$= -(\sin u)^{-2}\cos u \frac{du}{dx}$$

or

$$\frac{d(\operatorname{cosec} u)}{dx} = \frac{-\cos u}{(\sin u)^2}\frac{du}{dx} = -\cot u \operatorname{cosec} u \frac{du}{dx} \tag{74}$$

Example 51. If $y = \sqrt{3}\sec 2\pi\phi^2$, find $dy/d\phi$.

From Eq. (73),

$$\frac{dy}{d\phi} = \sqrt{3}\tan 2\pi\phi^2(\sec 2\pi\phi^2)4\pi\phi$$

$$= 4\pi\sqrt{3}\,\phi\tan 2\pi\phi^2 \sec 2\pi\phi^2$$

Example 52. If $y = \operatorname{cosec}^2 4\phi$, find $dy/d\phi$.

From Eq. (74),

$$\frac{dy}{d\phi} = (2\operatorname{cosec} 4\phi)(-\cot 4\phi \operatorname{cosec} 4\phi)4$$

$$= -8\operatorname{cosec}^2 4\phi \cot 4\phi$$

20.12 The Derivative of Tan u and Cot u

Since

$$\tan u = \frac{\sin u}{\cos u}$$

by following Eq. (51) we may write

$$\frac{d(\tan u)}{dx} = \frac{\cos u \cos u \, du/dx - \sin u(-\sin u)\, du/dx}{\cos^2 u}$$

or

$$\frac{d(\tan u)}{dx} = \frac{\cos^2 u + \sin^2 u}{\cos^2 u} \frac{du}{dx}$$

$$= \frac{1}{\cos^2 u} \frac{du}{dx} = \sec^2 u \frac{du}{dx} \quad \textbf{(75)}$$

Similarly, since

$$\cot u = \frac{\cos u}{\sin u}$$

by following Eq. (51) we may write

$$\frac{d(\cot u)}{dx} = \frac{\sin u(-\sin u)\, du/dx - \cos u \cos u \, du/dx}{\sin^2 u}$$

$$\frac{d(\cot u)}{dx} = -\frac{\sin^2 u + \cos^2 u}{\sin^2 u} \frac{du}{dx}$$

$$= -\frac{1}{\sin^2 u} \frac{du}{dx} = -\operatorname{cosec}^2 u \frac{du}{dx} \quad \textbf{(76)}$$

Example 53. If $y = 4 \tan (\theta/2 - \pi/3)$, find $dy/d\theta$.
By Eq. (75),

$$\frac{dy}{d\theta} = \left[4 \sec^2 \left(\frac{\theta}{2} - \frac{\pi}{3}\right)\right] \frac{1}{2} = 2 \sec^2 \left(\frac{\theta}{2} - \frac{\pi}{3}\right)$$

Example 54. If $y = 3 \cot (1 - \phi^2)$, find $dy/d\phi$.
From Eq. (76),

$$\frac{dy}{d\phi} = [-3 \operatorname{cosec}^2 (1 - \phi^2)](-2\phi) = 6\phi \operatorname{cosec}^2 (1 - \phi^2)$$

Example 55. If $y = \cos 2\theta \tan \theta$, find $dy/d\theta$.

$$\frac{dy}{d\theta} = \cos 2\theta \sec^2 \theta - 2 \sin 2\theta \tan \theta$$

$$= (2 \cos^2 \theta - 1)\left(\frac{1}{\cos^2 \theta}\right) - 4 \sin \theta \cos \theta \frac{\sin \theta}{\cos \theta}$$

$$= 2 - \frac{1}{\cos^2 \theta} - 4 \sin^2 \theta$$

EXERCISE 9

Differentiate the following:

1. $y = \sin x^4$
2. $y = (\sin x)^4$
3. $y = \sin^4 x$
4. $u = \sin (2/\phi)$
5. $y = -6 \sin \phi^{3/4}$
6. $w = \sin \sqrt{\theta}$
7. $z = 25\sqrt{\sin x}$
8. $y = \sin^2 (\phi - 1)$
9. $y = \sqrt{3} \cos \sqrt[3]{\phi}$
10. $E = 10 \sin (\omega t + \pi/2)$
11. $y = 3 \cos (2/\phi)$
12. $y = 3 \cos \sqrt{x}$
13. $y = \cos (x - 1/x)$
14. $u = \cos^2(x - 1)$
15. $y = \tan^4 x$
16. $z = 3 \tan^{2/3} x$
17. $y = \tan (x + 1/x)$
18. $y = \cot^2 (\phi - 1)$
19. $w = \cot \sqrt{\theta}$
20. $u = \cot^4 x$
21. $s = 25\sqrt{\sec x}$
22. $y = \cos^4 x - \sin^4 x$
23. $y = 3 \sec \sqrt{x}$
24. $y = \operatorname{cosec} (1 - 1/x)$
25. $w = 4 \operatorname{cosec} (3\phi + 2)$
26. $u = 4 \operatorname{cosec}^2 (x + 1/x)$

27. A block that weighs 100 lb rests on a horizontal surface for which the coefficient of friction is μ. A force of P lb acts on the block as shown in Fig. 20.15, the action line of the force making an *acute* angle θ with the horizontal. The force just necessary to start this block in motion can be shown, by methods of physics and mechanics, to be

$$P = \frac{100\mu}{\cos \theta + \mu \sin \theta}$$

If $\mu = 0.2$, determine the smallest value for P. Can you give a physical interpretation for your result?

28. Given $y = 6 \sin (\pi t/2)$, where the angle is in radians, find the smallest positive value of t for which $dy/dt = 0$.

29. The linear speed of a point on the tread of an automobile tire is given by the equation $v = 32\pi \sin 8\pi t$, where v is in feet per second and t is in seconds (see Fig. 19.18 and Exercise 7, Chap. 19).

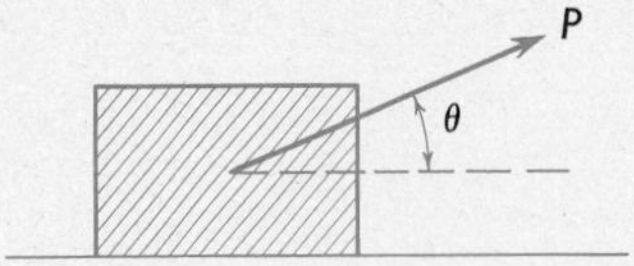

FIGURE 20.15

(a) What significance if any can be attached to the above equation when $\frac{1}{4} > t > \frac{1}{8}$?
(b) What time is required for one revolution?

30. From the equation in Prob. 29 find the following:
(a) The average acceleration from $t = 0.02$ to $t = 0.03$. (Acceleration is the rate of change in velocity.)
(b) The instantaneous acceleration at $t = 0.03$.
(c) The maximum speed of the point.
(d) The speed of the car.
(e) The outside diameter of the tire.
(f) When the acceleration is zero.

31. The equation

$$e = \tan\lambda \frac{\cos\phi - f\tan\lambda}{\cos\phi\tan\lambda + f}$$

gives the efficiency e for a worm drive which has a lead angle λ, a pressure angle ϕ, and friction f.
(a) Show that the given equation can be rewritten in the form

$$\frac{2f}{1-e} = \cos\phi \sin 2\lambda + f + f\cos 2\lambda$$

(b) Show that the value of λ that makes the efficiency e a maximum is given by $\tan 2\lambda = (\cos\phi)/f$.

Note: The result in (a) will facilitate the solution to (b).

20.13 The Derivative of Arcsin u, Arccos u, and Arctan u

Consider the functions defined by

$$x = \sin\phi$$
$$x = \cos\phi$$
$$x = \tan\phi$$

In these equations ϕ is regarded as the independent variable, and x is regarded as the dependent variable.

With certain restrictions to be discussed below, we may reverse the roles of x and ϕ. We may regard ϕ as the dependent variable and x as the independent variable. Accordingly, we shall introduce the notation.

$$\phi = \arcsin x$$
$$\phi = \arccos x$$
$$\phi = \arctan x$$

In this chapter the symbol "arcsin x" means *the radian measure of the angle whose sine is* x. Similarly, we interpret the symbol "arccos x" to mean *the radian measure of the angle whose cosine is* x, and the symbol "arctan x" to mean *the radian measure of the angle whose tangent is* x. In Fig. 20.16 we display the graphs of $\phi = \arcsin x$, $\phi = \arccos x$, and $\phi = \arctan x$ without indicating any restrictions on the range of ϕ. Without such restrictions, it is evident that there are infinitely many values of ϕ corresponding to any of the permissible values of x.

To avoid this multiplicity of values of ϕ, we ordinarily do restrict the range of ϕ and define:

1. Arcsin x as the number ϕ for which $-\pi/2 \leq \phi \leq \pi/2$ and $\sin\phi = x$, where $|x| \leq 1$
2. Arccos x as the number ϕ for which $0 \leq \phi \leq \pi$ and $\cos\phi = x$, where $|x| \leq 1$
3. Arctan x as the number ϕ for which $-\pi/2 < \phi < \pi/2$ and $\tan\phi = x$

In accordance with the restrictions above, the heavy lines in Fig. 20.16 indicate the graphs of arcsin x, arccos x, and arctan x.

The arccot x, arcsec x, and arccosec x are so seldom encountered in practice that we shall omit further discussion of them here. Now let

$$\phi = \arcsin x$$

Then, from the above definitions,

$$x = \sin\phi \qquad -\frac{\pi}{2} \leq \phi \leq +\frac{\pi}{2} \tag{77}$$

By differentiating with respect to x we obtain

$$\frac{dx}{dx} = 1 = \cos\phi\,\frac{d\phi}{dx} \tag{78}$$

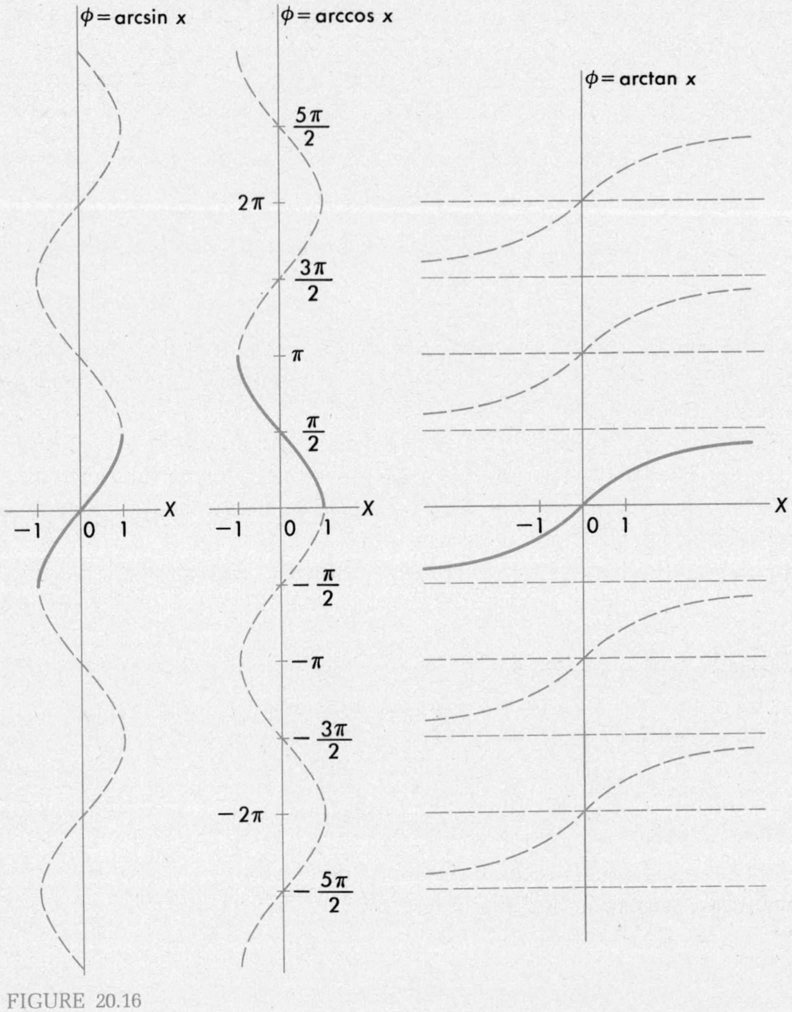

FIGURE 20.16

or

$$\frac{d\phi}{dx} = \frac{1}{\cos \phi} \qquad -\frac{\pi}{2} < \phi < +\frac{\pi}{2} \tag{79}$$

Observe that in Eq. (79) the derivative $d\phi/dx$ is undefined for $\phi = \pm\pi/2$. Now from the relation

$$\sin^2 \phi + \cos^2 \phi = 1$$

we may write

$$\cos\phi = \pm\sqrt{1 - \sin^2\phi} \qquad -\frac{\pi}{2} \leq \phi \leq +\frac{\pi}{2} \tag{80}$$

However, for the range

$$-\frac{\pi}{2} \leq \phi \leq +\frac{\pi}{2}$$

$\cos\phi$ is always nonnegative, and we may write

$$\cos\phi = \sqrt{1 - \sin^2\phi} \qquad -\frac{\pi}{2} \leq \phi \leq +\frac{\pi}{2} \tag{81}$$

but since

$$\sin\phi = x$$

we may write

$$\cos\phi = \sqrt{1 - x^2} \tag{82}$$

By substituting Eq. (82) in Eq. (79) we obtain

$$\frac{d\phi}{dx} = \frac{1}{\sqrt{1 - x^2}} \tag{83}$$

or since $\phi = \arcsin x$,

$$\frac{d(\arcsin x)}{dx} = \frac{1}{\sqrt{1 - x^2}} \qquad |x| < 1 \tag{84}$$

By a similar argument we could show that

$$\frac{d(\arccos x)}{dx} = -\frac{1}{\sqrt{1 - x^2}} \qquad |x| < 1 \tag{85}$$

and

$$\frac{d(\arctan x)}{dx} = \frac{1}{1 + x^2} \tag{86}$$

From Sec. 20.6, if u is the value of a differentiable function of x, we may write

$$\frac{d(\arcsin u)}{dx} = \frac{1}{\sqrt{1-u^2}}\frac{du}{dx} \qquad |u| < 1 \tag{87}$$

$$\frac{d(\arccos u)}{dx} = \frac{-1}{\sqrt{1-u^2}}\frac{du}{dx} \qquad |u| < 1 \tag{88}$$

$$\frac{d(\arctan u)}{dx} = \frac{1}{1+u^2}\frac{du}{dx} \tag{89}$$

Example 56. Find $d\phi/dx$ if $\phi = \arcsin x^2$.
From Eq. (87),

$$\frac{d\phi}{dx} = \frac{2x}{\sqrt{1-x^4}}$$

Example 57. Find dx/dy if $x = \arccos \sqrt{y}$.
From Eq. (88),

$$\frac{dx}{dy} = \frac{-1}{\sqrt{1-y}}\frac{1}{2}y^{-1/2} = -\frac{1}{2\sqrt{y-y^2}}$$

Example 58. Find $d\phi/dx$ if $\phi = \arctan (1/x)$.
From Eq. (89),

$$\frac{d\phi}{dx} = \frac{1}{1+(1/x^2)}\left(-\frac{1}{x^2}\right) = \frac{-1}{x^2+1}$$

EXERCISE 10

Differentiate the following:

1. $y = 3 \arcsin (x/3)$
2. $\phi = \arcsin 4x$
3. $\phi = \arccos x^5$
4. $y = \arctan (2x + 5)$
5. $\phi = \arccos (4 - 2y)$
6. $y = \arctan 25x$

20.14 The Derivative of $\log_b x$

Consider the function $y = \log_b x$. Recall from Sec. 8.1 that $b > 0$ and $b \neq 1$. Also, following Sec. 8.1, we shall for the present consider that $x > 0$.

Now if $y = \log_b x$ and if we let x change by some amount Δx, then, in general, y will change by some amount Δy, and

$$\frac{\Delta y}{\Delta x} = \frac{\log_b (x + \Delta x) - \log_b x}{\Delta x} \tag{90}$$

From Sec. 8.2 we may rewrite the numerator of Eq. (90) as

$$\frac{\Delta y}{\Delta x} = \frac{\log_b \dfrac{x + \Delta x}{x}}{\Delta x} \tag{91}$$

As Eq. (91) is written, it is by no means evident what if any limit is approached as Δx approaches zero. However, by a certain amount of algebraic manipulation as indicated below, we can make the situation clearer.

$$\frac{\Delta y}{\Delta x} = \frac{x}{x}\frac{1}{\Delta x}\log_b\left(1 + \frac{\Delta x}{x}\right) = \frac{1}{x}\frac{x}{\Delta x}\log_b\left(1 + \frac{\Delta x}{x}\right)$$

From Sec. 8.2 we may write

$$\frac{\Delta y}{\Delta x} = \frac{1}{x}\log_b\left(1 + \frac{\Delta x}{x}\right)^{x/\Delta x}$$

If we let

$$m = \frac{x}{\Delta x}$$

we may write

$$\frac{\Delta y}{\Delta x} = \frac{1}{x}\log_b\left(1 + \frac{1}{m}\right)^{m}$$

Now as Δx approaches zero, m becomes larger and larger without limit. We have had occasion (see Sec. 9.5) to present an argument showing that

$$\lim_{m\to\infty}\left(1 + \frac{1}{m}\right)^{m} = 2.7183\ldots = e$$

Thus we may write

$$\lim_{\Delta x\to 0}\frac{\Delta y}{\Delta x} = \frac{dy}{dx} = \frac{1}{x}\log_b e$$

In Sec. 8.9 we showed that

$$\log_e e = 1$$

Therefore, if we choose to use the natural logarithm system, we find that if

$$y = \ln x$$

then

$$\frac{dy}{dx} = \frac{1}{x}$$

or

$$\frac{d(\ln x)}{dx} = \frac{1}{x} \tag{92}$$

and

$$\frac{d(k \ln x + C)}{dx} = \frac{k}{x} \qquad x \neq 0 \tag{93}$$

Example 59. Differentiate the function $y = \ln x^6$.

From Sec. 8.2 we recall that $\ln x^6 = 6 \ln x$. Then we may write

$$y = 6 \ln x$$

and

$$\frac{dy}{dx} = \frac{6}{x}$$

Exercise 11

Differentiate the following:

1. $y = \ln x$
2. $y = 3 \ln x$
3. $y = \ln x^5$
4. $y = \ln \theta^6 - 3 \sin \theta + e$
5. $y = \ln 6x - \ln (5/x^2)$
6. $y = 2 \ln x - 3 \ln x + \ln x - \frac{1}{5} \sin x + 10e^5$
7. $y = 15 \ln x^{10}$

20.15 The Derivative of the Natural and Common Logarithm of u

If

$$y = \ln u \tag{94}$$

and u is the value of a differentiable function of x, we may from Eqs. (92) and (31) write

$$\frac{dy}{dx} = \frac{1}{u}\frac{du}{dx} \tag{95}$$

or

$$\frac{d(\ln u)}{dx} = \frac{1}{u}\frac{du}{dx} \tag{96}$$

and we may write

$$\frac{d(k \ln u + C)}{dx} = \frac{k}{u}\frac{du}{dx} \qquad 0 < u \tag{97}$$

From Eq. (8), Sec. 9.8, we observe that

$$\log u = 0.4343 \ln u$$

Therefore

$$\frac{d(k \log u + C)}{dx} = \frac{0.4343k}{u}\frac{du}{dx} \tag{98}$$

Example 60. Differentiate the function $y = \log x^6$.
Following Eq. (98),

$$y = 0.4343 \ln x^6$$

or

$$y = 0.4343(6) \ln x = 2.6058 \ln x$$

Therefore

$$\frac{dy}{dx} = \frac{2.6058}{x}$$

Example 61. If $y = 5 \ln (x^2 - 7)$, following Eq. (97),

$$\frac{dy}{dx} = \frac{5}{x^2 - 7} 2x = \frac{10x}{x^2 - 7}$$

Example 62. If $y = \ln [1/(1 - x^2)]$, find dy/dx.

First we may rearrange the expression $\ln [1/(1 - x^2)]$, obtaining

$$\ln 1 - \ln (1 - x^2) = 0 - \ln (1 - x^2) = -\ln (1 - x^2)$$

Then, if $y = -\ln (1 - x^2)$,

$$\frac{dy}{dx} = -\frac{1}{1 - x^2}(-2x) = \frac{2x}{1 - x^2}$$

Example 63. If $y = \log_{10} [(4 - x^2)/(6 - 2x)]$, find dy/dx.

We may convert to the base e as follows:

$$y = 0.4343[\ln (4 - x^2) - \ln (6 - 2x)]$$

Then

$$\frac{dy}{dx} = 0.4343\left[\frac{1}{4 - x^2}(-2x) - \frac{1}{6 - 2x}(-2)\right] = 0.4343\left(\frac{2x}{x^2 - 4} + \frac{2}{6 - 2x}\right)$$

Example 64. If $y = \ln^2 (25 - x^2)$, find dy/dx.

$$y = [\ln (25 - x^2)]^2$$

$$\frac{dy}{dx} = 2[\ln (25 - x^2)]\frac{1}{25 - x^2}(-2x) = \frac{4x \ln (25 - x^2)}{x^2 - 25}$$

EXERCISE 12

Differentiate the following:

1. $y = \ln (x^2 + 2)$
2. $y = \ln \sqrt{x^2 - 1}$
3. $y = \ln (x^2 + 3)^4$
4. $y = \ln (1/x)$

5. $z = \ln\sqrt[3]{4 - 3x}$

6. $z = \ln\dfrac{1}{4 - y}$

7. $y = \log(4 - x^2)$

8. $y = \log(4 - x)^2$

9. $y = \log\dfrac{1}{\sqrt{9 - x^2}}$

10. $z = \log\dfrac{2x + 5}{x - 3}$

11. $y = \log\dfrac{4x^2 - 9}{2x + 3}$

12. $y = \ln\left(x - \dfrac{1}{x}\right)$

13. $z = \ln^2(x^3 - 8)$

14. $y = \ln^4\sqrt{9 - x^2}$

15. $y = \log\sin(\theta + \pi)$

16. $y = \log\cos(2\theta - \pi/2)$

20.16 The Derivative of e^x

If

$$y = e^x \tag{99}$$

where e is the base of natural logarithms, then from Eq. (2), Sec. 8.1,

$$x = \ln y$$

Since both members of this equation are equal for all permissible values of the variables involved, the derivatives of both members with respect to x must be equal.

Differentiating both members with respect to x, we obtain on the left

$$\frac{dx}{dx} = 1 \qquad \text{(see Example 15)}$$

and on the right

$$\frac{d(\ln y)}{dx} = \frac{1}{y}\frac{dy}{dx} \qquad \text{[see Eq. (96)]}$$

Consequently we may write

$$1 = \frac{1}{y}\frac{dy}{dx} \tag{100}$$

or

$$\frac{dy}{dx} = y \tag{101}$$

By substituting Eq. (99) in Eq. (101) we obtain

$$\frac{dy}{dx} = e^x$$

or

$$\frac{d(e^x)}{dx} = e^x \tag{102}$$

20.17 The Derivative of e^u

If

$$y = e^u$$

and u is the value of a differentiable function of x, we may from Eqs. (31) and (102) write

$$\frac{dy}{dx} = e^u \frac{du}{dx} \tag{103}$$

or

$$\frac{d(e^u)}{dx} = e^u \frac{du}{dx} \tag{104}$$

and we may write

$$\frac{d(ke^u + C)}{dx} = ke^u \frac{du}{dx} \tag{105}$$

Example 65. If $y = 3e^{1/x}$, find dy/dx.

According to Eq. (105),

$$\frac{dy}{dx} = 3e^{1/x}\left(-\frac{1}{x^2}\right) = -\frac{3e^{1/x}}{x^2}$$

Example 66. If $y = (3e^{\sqrt{x}})^2$, find dy/dx.

Squaring, as indicated, we obtain

$$y = 9e^{2\sqrt{x}}$$

Hence

$$\frac{dy}{dx} = 9e^{2\sqrt{x}}(2)\left(\frac{1}{2}\right)\left(\frac{1}{\sqrt{x}}\right) = \frac{9e^{2\sqrt{x}}}{\sqrt{x}}$$

Example 67. Find the derivative of $y = A_1e^{k_1x} + A_2e^{k_2x}$.
Following Eq. (105),

$$\frac{dy}{dx} = A_1k_1e^{k_1x} + A_2k_2e^{k_2x}$$

Example 68. Find the derivative of $z = A_1k_1e^{k_1x} + A_2k_2e^{k_2x}$.
Following Eq. (105),

$$\frac{dz}{dx} = A_1k_1{}^2e^{k_1x} + A_2k_2{}^2e^{k_2x}$$

EXERCISE 13

Differentiate:

1. $y = e^{5x2}$	2. $y = e^{\sqrt{x}}$	3. $y = e^{x+8}$
4. $y = e^{(2-x)/x}$	5. $y = e^{\sqrt{1-x}}$	6. $y = \sin e^t$

7. The graph shown in Fig. 19.16 was plotted from the equation $T = 50e^{-0.2t}$ where T is the temperature difference between a warm body and its surroundings and t is time in minutes. Using the above equation rather than the graph:
   (*a*) Find dT/dt when $t = 10$.
   (*b*) Find dt/dT when $t = 10$.
   (*c*) Find dT/dt when $T = 10$.
   (*d*) Find dt/dT when $T = 10$.
   (*e*) Find t when $dT/dt = -5.0°$ per min.
   (*f*) Find T when $dT/dt = -2.5°$ per min.
   (*g*) Find the average rate of change of T with respect to t between $t = 2$ and $t = 8$.
   (*h*) Find the average slope between $t = 6$ and $t = 10$.
   (*i*) Find the average slope between $T = 30$ and $T = 10$.
   (*j*) Find the instantaneous slope at $t = 6$.
   (*k*) Find the instantaneous slope at $T = 30$.
   (*l*) How fast is T changing with t at $t = 10$?
8. From Prob. 7 write the equation for dT/dt in terms of T. If dT/dt were plotted against T, what would the shape of the plot be?
9. Sketch the graph of $i = (E/R)(1 - e^{-Rt/L})$

where $E = 150$ V
$R = 15\ \Omega$
$L = 0.75$ henry
$i = $ A
$t = $ s

This is an equation giving the relation between current and time in a certain series circuit containing inductance and resistance. The inductance is 0.75 henry, the resistance is 15 Ω. A battery of 150 V is connected across this series combination when $t = 0$. Thereafter the current rises in accordance with the above equation. Compare your sketch with Fig. 19.19.

(a) Find di/dt when $t = 0$.
(b) Find the "maximum" value of current. When will it be reached?
(c) If the current increased at the rate it was increasing when $t = 0$, how long would it take for the current to reach its "maximum" value?
(d) Compare the value found in part (c) with the ratio L/R where L is inductance and R is resistance. This ratio is called the "time constant of the circuit."
(e) Find the rate of change of current with respect to time at frequent points between $t = 0$ and $t = 150$ ms. Plot a graph of di/dt versus i between $t = 0$ and $t = 150$ ms.

Problems 10 and 11 use the symbol ϵ to designate the base of natural logarithms to avoid confusion with the symbol e used here to designate a voltage.

10. In a resistance of r Ω the current i A is given in terms of the voltage (e V) by the equation (Ohm's law) $i = e/r$. In a capacitor (C F) the relation (on discharge) is $i = -C(de/dt)$.

    If $e = E_0\epsilon^{-t/Cr}$, determine equations for i in terms of t for the case of a resistance and for the case of a capacitor (C, r, and E are constants).

    Sketch graphs of e as a function of $t/(Cr)$, i as a function of $t/(Cr)$ for both the resistance and capacitor cases.

11. If the current in an electric circuit is given by $i = I\epsilon^{-at}$, where I and a are positive constants, determine the length of the subtangent to this curve at the time $t = 0$. (The subtangent is the difference between the x intercept of the tangent and the abscissa of its point of tangency.)

Remark: This result is of importance in electrical engineering. It is called the *time constant* T of the electric circuit and has the following properties:

1. It is the length of the subtangent at $t = 0$.
2. It is the time required for the ordinate (current) to change from an arbitrary value A to the value A/ϵ (a decrease of about 60 percent). In an interval equal to $3T$ the ordinate decreases from A to A/ϵ^3, that is, to about 5 percent of the value at A. Five time constants of time would reduce the current to about 0.67

percent of the value at the beginning of that time interval. Since this last result is often negligible as compared with the starting value by ordinary standards of engineering accuracy, the following statement is apparent: "The duration of the current, if of exponential form, is five time constants."

3. The time constant is the time it would take i to reduce to zero if i decreased at a constant rate equal to the rate at which i is decreasing when $t = 0$.
4. The area of the rectangle whose base is the time constant and whose altitude is along the i axis from $i = 0$ to $i = I$ is equal to the area under the curve $i = I\epsilon^{-at}$ in the first quadrant.

Prove that properties 2 and 3 are true. Property 4 can be established after you have studied integral calculus.

12. A catenary is the curve that a cable assumes when hanging between two supports. If the two supports are of equal height and are at $x = -a$ and $x = +a$, the equation for the curve is

$$y = c + k \cosh \frac{x}{a} = c + \frac{k}{2}(e^{x/a} + e^{-x/a})$$

Determine an expression for the angle that the cable makes with the vertical support at $x = +a$.

20.18 The Derivative of a^x

If

$$y = a^x \tag{106}$$

where a is any positive real number other than 1, then from Eq. (5), Sec. 8.2,

$$x \ln a = \ln y$$

Now, remembering that $\ln a$ is a constant, we may as in Sec. 20.16 differentiate both members of the above equation with respect to x, obtaining on the left

$$\frac{d[x(\ln a)]}{dx} = \ln a$$

and on the right

$$\frac{d(\ln y)}{dx} = \frac{1}{y}\frac{dy}{dx}$$

or

$$\ln a = \frac{1}{y}\frac{dy}{dx}$$

Thus

$$\frac{dy}{dx} = y \ln a \tag{107}$$

By substituting Eq. (106) in Eq. (107) we obtain

$$\frac{dy}{dx} = a^x \ln a$$

or

$$\frac{d(a^x)}{dx} = a^x \ln a \qquad 0 < a,\ a \neq 1 \tag{108}$$

The process we have just used is called *logarithmic differentiation.*

20.19 The Derivative of a^u

If

$$y = a^u \tag{109}$$

and u is the value of a differentiable function of x, we may from Eq. (108) write

$$\frac{dy}{dx} = a^u(\ln a)\frac{du}{dx} \tag{110}$$

or

$$\frac{d(a^u)}{dx} = a^u(\ln a)\frac{du}{dx} \tag{111}$$

and

$$\frac{d(ka^u + C)}{dx} = ka^u(\ln a)\frac{du}{dx} \tag{112}$$

Example 69. If $y = (3^{x^2+2x})/4$, find dy/dx.

According to Eq. (112),

$$\frac{dy}{dx} = \frac{1}{4} 3^{x^2+2x}(2x + 2) \ln 3$$

$$= \frac{x + 1}{2} (3)^{x^2+2x} \ln 3$$

Example 70. If $y = 3 \ln^x 4$, this equation can be rewritten as

$$y = 3 (\ln 4)^x$$

Now following Eq. (112),

$$\frac{dy}{dx} = (3 \ln^x 4)(1)[\ln (\ln 4)]$$

By using some of the principles illustrated in this and the preceding three sections we can differentiate many nonlogarithmic functions which would be rather awkward or even impossible to differentiate otherwise.

Example 71. Differentiate $y = x^x$ where $x > 0$.

Observe that in this case both the base and the exponent are variables. None of the differentiation formulas previously given cover this case. However, by writing the given equation in an equivalent logarithmic form we obtain

$$\ln y = x \ln x \qquad x > 0$$

Then

$$\frac{1}{y}\frac{dy}{dx} = x\frac{1}{x} + (\ln x)(1) = 1 + \ln x$$

or

$$\frac{dy}{dx} = y(1 + \ln x) = x^x(1 + \ln x)$$

Example 72. Differentiate

$$y = x^{x^2} \qquad x > 0$$

Again, none of the differentiation formulas previously given will apply since both the base and the exponent are variables. However,

$$\ln y = x^2 \ln x \qquad x > 0$$

and

$$\frac{1}{y}\frac{dy}{dx} = x^2 \frac{1}{x} + (\ln x)(2x) = x + 2x \ln x$$

and

$$\frac{dy}{dx} = y(x + 2x \ln x) = x^{x^2}(x + 2x \ln x)$$

Example 73. Differentiate

$$y = \sqrt{\frac{x^4 - 1}{x^4 + 1}}$$

Although this function can be differentiated by rules already discussed, it can probably be more easily differentiated by the use of logarithms. We may write

$$\ln y = \frac{1}{2} \ln \frac{x^4 - 1}{x^4 + 1} = \frac{1}{2}[\ln (x^4 - 1) - \ln (x^4 + 1)]$$

$$= \frac{1}{2} \ln (x^4 - 1) - \frac{1}{2} \ln (x^4 + 1)$$

$$\frac{1}{y}\frac{dy}{dx} = \frac{1}{2(x^4 - 1)}(4x^3) - \frac{1}{2(x^4 + 1)}(4x^3)$$

$$= \frac{2x^3}{x^4 - 1} - \frac{2x^3}{x^4 + 1}$$

$$\frac{dy}{dx} = y\left(\frac{2x^3}{x^4 - 1} - \frac{2x^3}{x^4 + 1}\right)$$

$$= y \frac{4x^3}{(x^4 - 1)(x^4 + 1)}$$

$$= \frac{(x^4 - 1)^{1/2}}{(x^4 + 1)^{1/2}} \frac{4x^3}{(x^4 - 1)(x^4 + 1)}$$

$$\frac{dy}{dx} = \frac{4x^3}{\sqrt{x^4 - 1}\,(x^4 + 1)^{3/2}}$$

EXERCISE 14

Differentiate the following by use of Eq. (112):

1. $y = a^x$ where a is constant
2. $y = a^{1/2}$ where a is constant
3. $z = 2^{\sqrt{x}}$
4. $y = 5^{e(x+1)}$ where e is constant

Differentiate the following by rewriting the given equation in an equivalent logarithmic form.

5. $y = kx^n$
6. $y = kuv$ where u and v are functions of x
7. $y = k\dfrac{u}{v}$ where u and v are functions of x
8. $y = ke^u$ where u is a function of x
9. $y = ka^u$ where u is a function of x
10. $y = a^{3x^2}$
11. $y = x^2 \cdot 3^x$
12. $y = ae^{-b^2x^2}$
13. $y = \sqrt{(3t^2 + 2)/(t^2 - t)}$ (Compare with Example 35, Sec. 20.7.)
14. $y = \dfrac{3e^{(3x^2-1)}}{x^{\sqrt{x}}}$
15. $y = \dfrac{x}{x^3 - 2}$
16. $y = 3x^2(x^3 - 1)^4$
17. $y = x^3/(x^5 + 3)$
18. $y = e^{2x}\sqrt{1 - x^3}$
19. $y = e^x/(4 + x)$
20. $y = x^{2\sqrt{x}}$
21. $y = \sqrt{x} \cdot e^{2x}$
22. $y = (x + 2)^x$
23. $y = x^{\sin x}$

EXERCISE 15

Differentiate the following:

1. $y = e^x \cos 2x$
2. $y = 3e^{-t} \sin t$
3. $y = \sin 3\theta \cos 3\theta$
4. $y = (x^2 + 3x) \ln x^2$
5. $y = x \ln x - x^2$
6. $y = (2x^3 + 5)^{2/3} x^{-1/5}$
7. $z = 3 \sin 2\phi \tan 4\phi$
8. $w = 5 \cos^2 2\phi \cos(-2\phi)$
9. $s = 5 \tan^2 x \cdot e^{3x^2}$
10. $y = (x^2 - 3)^{1/2} \ln 3x^5$
11. $y = \sqrt{2x^3 + 3x} \sin^2(7x^3 + 5)$
12. $y = \ln x^2 \tan x^2$
13. $y = 3e^{2x} \ln(1/x)$
14. $w = (x^2 + 3)^{1/2} \tan 4x$
15. $y = x^{-1/2} \cos \sqrt{x}$
16. $y = 3 \cos 3\phi \ln(3\phi + 5)$
17. $y = \dfrac{\sin x}{e^{2x}}$
18. $y = \dfrac{e^x + e^{-x}}{e^x - e^{-x}} + x$
19. $y = -\dfrac{x}{9\sqrt{x^2 - 9}}$
20. $y = \dfrac{\sin 3\phi}{\cos(\phi/2)}$

21. $y = \dfrac{x^2 + 3x}{\ln x^2}$

22. $y = \dfrac{5 \tan^2 x}{e^{3x^2}}$

23. $w = \dfrac{(x^2 + 3)^{1/2}}{\tan 4x}$

24. $y = \dfrac{3e^{2x}}{\ln (1/x)}$

25. $y = \dfrac{3 \cos 3x}{\ln (3x - 6)}$

26. $y = \dfrac{(x^2 + 5x)^{1/2}}{\ln 3x^5}$

Differentiate the following in preparation for Exercise 19:

27. $y = \dfrac{100x}{(x + 0.2)^2}$

28. $y = 5x(x^2 + 100)^{-3/2}$

29. $y = \dfrac{Ax}{Ax + C + Bx^2}$ where A, B, and C are constants

30. $y = \dfrac{A}{B} \cos \phi \sin^2 \phi$

31. $y = \dfrac{100x - 5x^2}{x + 0.8}$

32. $y = 3 \sin 3t + \dfrac{3 \sin 6t}{\sqrt{A - \sin^2 3t}}$ where A is a constant

The following problems are inserted here as a general review of differentiation formulas.

EXERCISE 16

Differentiate and simplify the following:

1. $y = \ln \sin x$
2. $y = \ln \cos x$
3. $q = \sin^3 5x$
4. $y = \sqrt{\sin 4x^2}$
5. $y = -\dfrac{1}{ax} + \dfrac{b}{a^2} \ln \dfrac{a + bx}{x}$
6. $y = \ln (x + \sqrt{x^2 - a^2})$
7. $y = \sqrt{x^2 + a^2} + \dfrac{a^2}{\sqrt{x^2 + a^2}}$
8. $y = \sin 3\theta \cos 3\theta$
9. $y = x/(x^3 - 4)$
10. $y = (x^2 + 3x) \ln x^2$
11. $y = \dfrac{\sin x}{e^{2x}} + e^{2x}$
12. $y = 5 \ln e^{2x} - e^2$
13. $y = \dfrac{e^x + e^{-x}}{e^x - e^{-x}}$
14. $y = \log (x^2 - 4x + 4)$
15. $y = \dfrac{5x}{(x - 1)^2} - \dfrac{5}{x - 1}$
16. $y = \dfrac{\sqrt{1 - x^2}}{1 - x}$
17. $y = \sqrt{x^2 - 1/x}$
18. $y = x \ln x - x$
19. $y = \frac{1}{2}[x\sqrt{x^2 + a^2} + a^2 \ln (x + \sqrt{x^2 + a^2})]$

20. $y = -\dfrac{x^2}{9\sqrt{x^2 - 9}}$

21. $y = \dfrac{x}{16\sqrt{16 - x^2}}$

22. $y = \dfrac{\sqrt{x^2 - a^2}}{a^2 x}$

23. $y = -\dfrac{\sqrt{8x - 2x^2}}{4x}$

24. $y = -\tfrac{1}{5}(x^2 + 6)(9 - x^2)^{3/2}$

25. $y = \tfrac{1}{2}x + \tfrac{1}{4}\sin 2x$

26. $y = \ln\tan\left(\dfrac{\pi}{4} + \dfrac{x}{2}\right)$

27. $y = \dfrac{x^2}{4} - \dfrac{x\sin 2x}{4} - \dfrac{\cos 2x}{8}$

28. $y = \tan(x/2)$

29. $y = \tan x - x$

30. $y = \tfrac{1}{2}\tan^2\theta + \ln\cos\theta$

31. $y = \cos x + x\sin x$

20.20 Repeated Differentiation

If we are given

$$y = x^5 - 19.25x^4 + 130x^3 - 352x^2 + 224x + 420 \qquad (113)$$

which we shall call the *primary* equation, we may differentiate to obtain dy/dx or y'. Thus

$$y' = \frac{dy}{dx} = 5x^4 - 77x^3 + 390x^2 - 704x + 224 \qquad (114)$$

This is called the *first* derivative. We can differentiate again to obtain the *second* derivative which we shall designate as y'' or d^2y/dx^2. Thus

$$y'' = \frac{d^2y}{dx^2} = 20x^3 - 231x^2 + 780x - 704 \qquad (115)$$

We can differentiate a third time to obtain the *third* derivative designated as y''' or d^3y/dx^3. Thus

$$y''' = \frac{d^3y}{dx^3} = 60x^2 - 462x + 780 \qquad (116)$$

The *fourth* derivative is

$$\frac{d^4y}{dx^4} = 120x - 462 \qquad (117)$$

the *fifth* derivative is

$$\frac{d^5y}{dx^5} = 120 \tag{118}$$

and the *sixth* derivative is

$$\frac{d^6y}{dx^6} = 0 \tag{119}$$

In Fig. 20.17 graph *A* is plotted from Eq. (113), graph *B* from Eq. (114), graph *C* from Eq. (115), graph *D* from Eq. (116), and graph *E* from Eq. (117).

EXERCISE 17

Solve the following problems by direct reading of the graphs shown in Fig. 20.17 rather than by algebraic methods. Observe the vertical "tielines" connecting corresponding points on successive curves.

1. Read the value of x on curve *B* for which curve *A* has a maximum. What is the sign of the second derivative for this value of x? Is the first derivative in this region increasing or decreasing?
2. Read the value of x on curve *B* for which curve *A* has a minimum. What is the sign of the second derivative for this value of x? Is the first derivative increasing or decreasing in this region?
3. Read the value of x on curve *C* for which curve *B* has a maximum. What is the sign of the third derivative for this value of x? Is the second derivative in this region increasing or decreasing?
4. Read the values of x on curve *C* for which curve *B* has a minimum. What are the signs of the third derivative for these values of x? Is the second derivative in this region increasing or decreasing?
5. Read the value of x on curve *D* for which curve *C* has a maximum. What is the sign of the fourth derivative for this value of x? Is the third derivative increasing or decreasing in this region?
6. Read the value of x on curve *D* for which curve *C* has a minimum. What is the sign of the fourth derivative for this value of x? Is the third derivative increasing or decreasing in this region?
7. For what values of x does graph *A* have a maximum slope? A minimum slope?
8. For what values of x does graph *B* have a maximum slope? A minimum slope?
9. For what values of x does graph *C* have a maximum slope? A minimum slope?
10. For what values of x does graph *D* have a maximum slope? A minimum slope?

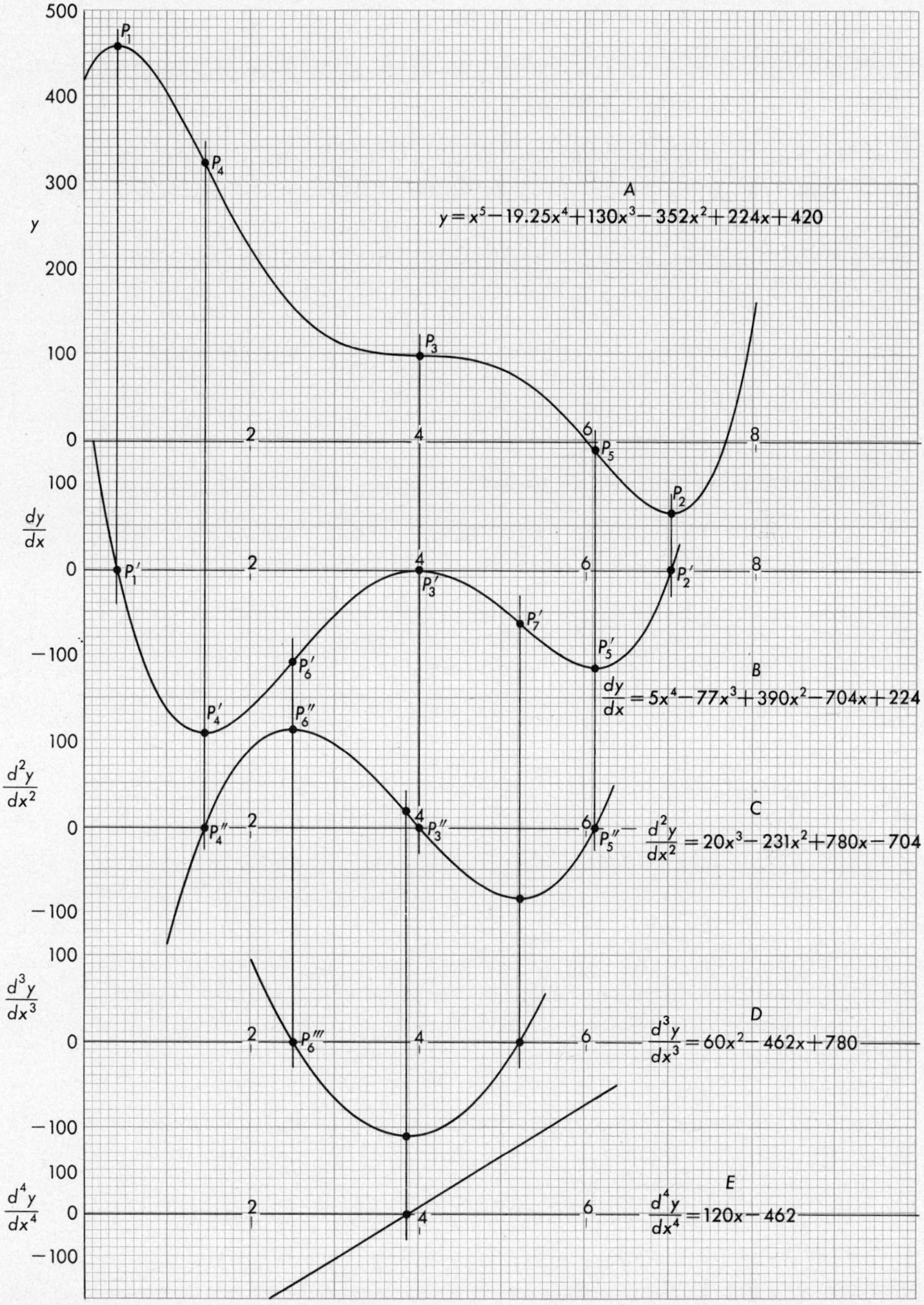

A
$y = x^5 - 19.25x^4 + 130x^3 - 352x^2 + 224x + 420$
B
$\frac{dy}{dx} = 5x^4 - 77x^3 + 390x^2 - 704x + 224$
C
$\frac{d^2y}{dx^2} = 20x^3 - 231x^2 + 780x - 704$
D
$\frac{d^3y}{dx^3} = 60x^2 - 462x + 780$
E
$\frac{d^4y}{dx^4} = 120x - 462$
y
$\frac{dy}{dx}$
$\frac{d^2y}{dx^2}$
$\frac{d^3y}{dx^3}$
$\frac{d^4y}{dx^4}$
P_1
P_2
P_3
P_4
P_5
P_1'
P_2'
P_3'
P_4'
P_5'
P_6'
P_7'
P_3''
P_4''
P_5''
P_6''
P_6'''

FIGURE 20.17

20.21 Tests for Maxima and Minima by Use of the Second Derivative

From Exercise 17 we note that at least for the functions involved, if a maximum occurs at x_m, then the sign of the second derivative at x_m is *negative*. If a minimum occurs at x_m, then the sign of the second derivative at x_m is positive.

This is actually a general principle. Without formal proof we shall assume that $y = f(x)$ has a relative maximum at $x = x_m$, provided that $dy/dx = 0$ at $x = x_m$ and that $d^2y/dx^2 < 0$ when $x = x_m$. Also, $f(x)$ will have a relative minimum at $x = x_m$, provided that $dy/dx = 0$ at $x = x_m$ and $d^2y/dx^2 > 0$ at $x = x_m$.

Sometimes it is more convenient to test critical values for maxima and minima by use of the second derivative rather than by the methods illustrated in Sec. 20.8.

Example 74. Find the value of x at P_1, P_2, and P_3 in curve *A* of Fig. 20.17. At these points the curve has a zero slope.

The ordinate of curve *A* is given by

$$y = x^5 - 19.25x^4 + 130x^3 - 342x^2 + 224x + 420 \tag{120}$$

Then

$$\frac{dy}{dx} = 5x^4 - 77x^3 + 390x^2 - 704x + 224 \tag{121}$$

Zero slopes occur for values of x such that

$$0 = 5x^4 - 77x^3 + 390x^2 - 704x + 224 \tag{122}$$

The algebra involved in solving Eq. (122) is quite laborious, even though elementary. However, from curve *B* the roots of this equation appear to be 4, 4, 7, and 0.4. That these roots are precise can be verified by direct substitution in Eq. (122).

In Example 75 below we shall identify these roots as the abscissas of maximum points or minimum points, or as points of inflection.

Example 75. By means of the second derivative, identify the roots found in Example 74 as values of x for which y is either a maximum or a minimum or for which x is the abscissa of a point of inflection.

The second derivative of the primary equation is [see Eq. (115)]

$$y'' = 20x^3 - 231x^2 + 780x - 704 \tag{123}$$

When $x = 4$,

$$y'' = 20(4)^3 - 231(4)^2 + 780(4) - 704 \quad (124)$$
$$y'' = 1{,}280 - 3{,}696 + 3{,}120 - 704 = 4{,}400 - 4{,}400 = 0 \quad (125)$$

Since the second derivative is zero, its sign is neither positive nor negative, and $x = 4$ corresponds to neither a maximum nor a minimum. In this case it corresponds to a point of inflection.

When $x = 0.4$,

$$y'' = 20(0.4)^3 - 231(0.4)^2 + 780(0.4) - 704 \quad (126)$$
$$y'' = 1.280 - 36.96 + 312.00 - 704.00 \quad (127)$$
$$y'' = -427.68 \quad (128)$$

Since the sign of the second derivative is negative, $x = 0.4$ is the abscissa of a maximum point.

When $x = 7$,

$$y'' = 20(7)^3 - 231(7)^2 + 780(7) - 704 \quad (129)$$
$$y'' = 6{,}860 - 11{,}319 + 5{,}460 - 704 = +297 \quad (130)$$

Since the sign of the second derivative is positive, $x = 7$ is the abscissa of a minimum point.

Example 76. Find the values of x for which the slope of curve *A* of Fig. 20.17 is a maximum or minimum. Remember that the ordinate of curve *B* is numerically equal to the slope of curve *A*.

The ordinate of curve *B* is given by

$$y' = \frac{dy}{dx} = 5x^4 - 77x^3 + 390x^2 - 704x + 224 \quad (131)$$

and

$$y'' = \frac{d^2y}{dx^2} = 20x^3 - 231x^2 + 780x - 704 \quad (132)$$

The slope of curve *A* may be a maximum or minimum when

$$0 = 20x^3 - 231x^2 + 780x - 704 \quad (133)$$

The algebra in solving Eq. (133) is quite arduous although elementary. However, it can be found that $x = 4$, $x = 1.440343$, and $x = 6.109657$ are all solutions of Eq. (133).

Example 77. By means of the second derivative, identify the roots found in Example 76 as values of x for which y is either a maximum or a minimum or for which x is the abscissa of a point of inflection.

Considering

$$y' = 5x^4 - 77x^3 + 390x^2 - 704x + 224 \tag{134}$$

as the primary equation for these two examples, the second derivative of this primary equation is

$$\frac{d^3y}{dx^3} = 60x^2 - 462x + 780 \tag{135}$$

When $x = 4$,

$$\frac{d^3y}{dx^3} = 60 \cdot 16 - 462 \cdot 4 + 780 = -108 \tag{136}$$

Since the sign of the second derivative of the primary equation is negative, $x = 4$ is the abscissa of a maximum point on the graph.

When $x = 1.440343$, the substitution would be quite involved. However, as a practical matter 1.4 or 1.5 would probably be a good enough approximation for our purpose.

Let us use $x = 1.5$. Then

$$\frac{d^3y}{dx^3} = 60 \cdot 2.25 - 462 \cdot 1.5 + 780 = +222$$

Since the second derivative of the primary equation is positive, $x = 1.440343$ is the abscissa of a minimum point on the graph.

Again, when $x = 6.109657$ the substitution would be quite laborious. However, as a practical matter in this case $x = 6.1$ is probably a satisfactory approximation for our purpose.

Let us use $x = 6.1$. Then

$$\frac{d^3y}{dx^3} = 60 \cdot 37.21 - 462 \cdot 6.1 + 780 = +194.4$$

Since the second derivative of the primary equation is positive, $x = 6.109657$ is the abscissa of a minimum point on the graph.

Example 78. If y is given by Eq. (120), find the value of x for which d^2y/dx^2 is a maximum or a minimum.

In this case

$$\frac{d^2y}{dx^2} = 20x^3 - 231x^2 + 780x - 704 \qquad \text{(see graph } C \text{ in Fig. 20.17)}$$

The above equation will be a maximum or minimum when $d^3y/dx^3 = 0$.

$$\frac{d^3y}{dx^3} = 60x^2 - 462x + 780 \tag{137}$$

Set the above equation to zero, and solve for x.

$$0 = 60x^2 - 462x + 780$$

or

$$0 = x^2 - 7.7x + 13$$

and

$$x = \frac{7.7 \pm \sqrt{(7.7)^2 - 4 \times 13}}{2} \tag{138}$$

$$= \frac{7.7 \pm \sqrt{59.29 - 52}}{2} \tag{139}$$

$$= \frac{7.7 \pm \sqrt{7.29}}{2} = \frac{7.7 \pm 2.7}{2} = \frac{5}{2}, \frac{10.4}{2}$$

$$x = 2.5 \text{ (max)}, 5.2 \text{ (min)}$$

The student will observe that the second derivative of the primary curve in this problem is $120x - 462$. When $x = 2.5$, the sign of this quantity is negative. When $x = 5.2$, the sign of the same quantity is positive. Consequently, $x = 5.2$ corresponds to a minimum, and $x = 2.5$ corresponds to a maximum.

EXERCISE 18

In Probs. 1 through 18, sketch the graph of the given equation. Then

(*a*) Sketch the graph of the first and second derivatives if they exist.

(*b*) Find the value of the independent variable for which the primary curve has a maximum, a minimum, or a point of inflection if such exists.

(*c*) Identify the critical values found in (*b*) above by means of the second derivative where practical.

(*d*) Find the slope of the primary curve for each point of inflection.

1. $y = \frac{4}{3}\pi x^3$	$0 \le x \le +10$
2. $y = x^3 - x + 1$	$-1 \le x \le +1$
3. $y = x^3 - 6x^2 + 8$	$-1 \le x \le +5$
4. $y = x^4 - 4x^2 - 21$	$-3 \le x \le +3$
5. $z = 7x^2 - 8\sqrt{x}$	$0 \le x \le +2$
6. $y = 3x^2 - 5x + 7 - \dfrac{4}{x}$	$-2 \le x \le +2$
7. $y = x^2 - \dfrac{1}{x^2}$	$-3 \le x \le +3$
8. $y = \dfrac{4x}{x^2 + 1}$	$-3 \le x \le +3$
9. $y = \cos 2x$	$0 \le x \le +\pi$
10. $y = \sin x + \cos 2x$	$0 \le x \le 2\pi$
11. $y = \frac{1}{4}\cos^2\theta + \sin^2\theta$	$0 \le \theta \le 2\pi$
12. $y = \sin^2\theta$	$0 \le \theta \le 2\pi$
13. $y = \ln(2/x)$	$0 < x \le +3$
*14. $y = (1/\sqrt{2\pi})e^{-x^2/2}$	$-2 \le x \le 2$
15. $y = x \ln x - x$	$0 \le x \le +4$
16. $y = 3e^{2t}$	$-0.5 \le t \le +1$
17. $y = e^{-0.1x}\sin x$	$0 \le x \le 2\pi$
18. $y = \sin 2x + 2\sin x$	$0 \le x \le 2\pi$

EXERCISE 19

1. If the height of a ball at any time t is given by the equation $h = 72t - 16t^2$, find the velocity and acceleration at any time.
2. Repeat Prob. 1, if $h = 120 + 72t^2 + t^3$. How fast is the acceleration changing at $t = 2$?
3. The distance traveled by a moving object is $d = 20t^4 - t^5$. Find when the acceleration is changing most rapidly.
4. The distance traveled by a moving object is given by the equation $d = 10t^3 - t^4$. Find when the speed is a maximum. Also find when the acceleration is a maximum.
5. A solenoid has a fixed internal diameter D and has a laminated core of the form shown in Fig. 20.18. Determine the dimension s and t of the core so that the cross-sectional area of the core will be a maximum.
6. The electric field intensity on the axis of a uniformly charged ring is found to be $E = Qx/(x^2 + a^2)^{3/2}$, where Q is the total charge on the ring. Also, a and Q are constants (see Fig. 20.19).
   (*a*) Sketch E as a function of x with the origin of the coordinate axes at the center of the ring using $Q = 3$ and $a = 2$. Plot between $x = -4$ and $x = +4$.

*The curve of normal distribution.

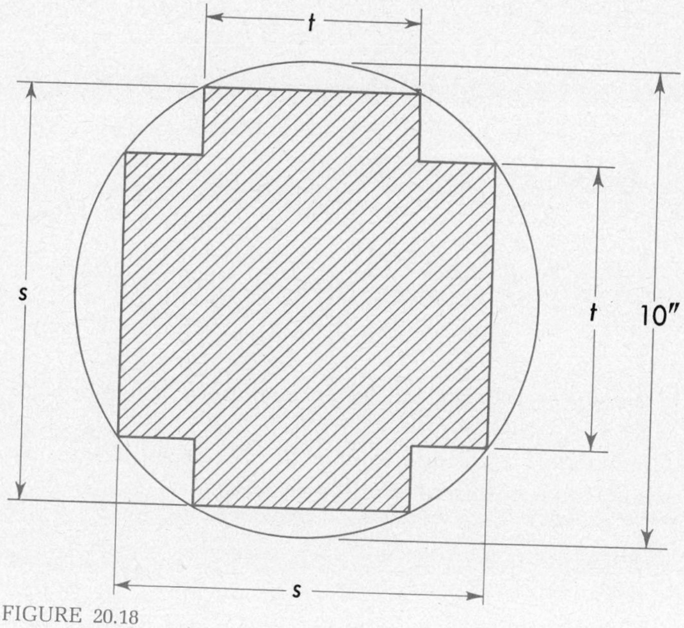

FIGURE 20.18

(b) At what value of x is E a maximum?

(c) What is the value of x which makes d^2E/dx^2 zero?

7. Find the dimensions of the largest rectangle that can be inscribed in a semicircle of diameter 24 ft.

Referring to Fig. 20.20, the area of this rectangle can be expressed as

(a) $$A = 2h\sqrt{144 - h^2}$$

or

(b) $$A = (12 \sin \theta)(12 \cos \theta) \cdot 2$$

Find the required dimensions by use of (a) and again by use of (b).

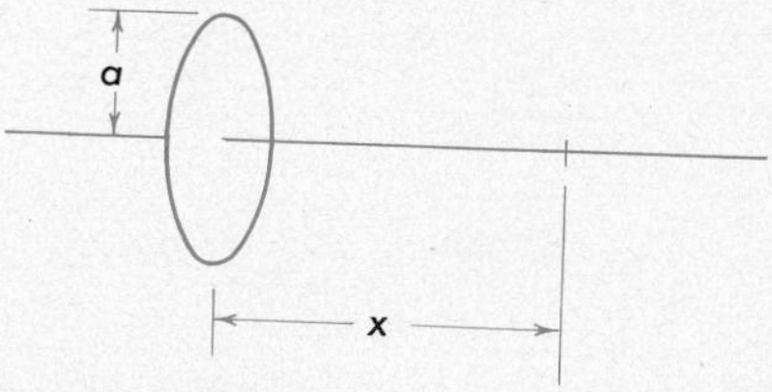

FIGURE 20.19

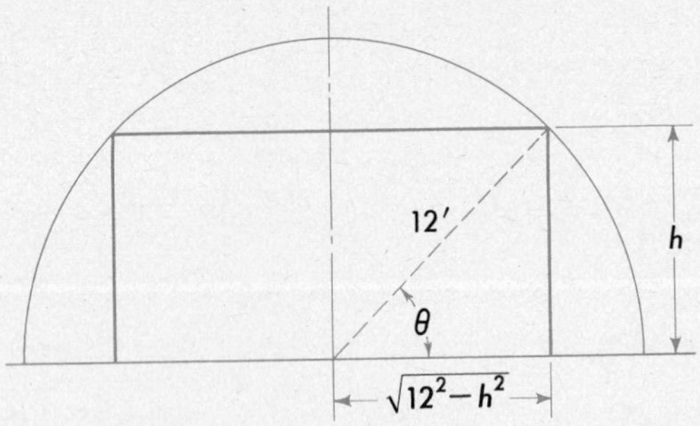

FIGURE 20.20

8. Find the dimensions of the largest rectangle which can be inscribed in a circle 20 in in diameter.
9. The beam in Fig. 20.21 supports a uniform load of w lb/ft of beam. If axes are chosen as indicated, the equation of the curve of the beam is

$$EIy = \frac{wLx^3}{12} - \frac{wx^4}{24} - \frac{wL^3x}{24}$$

where E, I, w, and L = positive constants.

Studies of the strength of materials show that the bending moment is given by $M = EI(d^2y/dx^2)$, the shear by $V = dM/dx$, and the load by $EI(d^4y/dx^4)$. Determine M, V, and $EI(d^4y/dx^4)$ for this beam, and sketch these three curves (these variables as functions of x) on the same graph.
10. The power lost in resistor R (see Fig. 20.22) is given by the equation

$$P = \frac{(10 - 0.2i)^2}{R}$$

where $i = \dfrac{10}{R + 0.2}$

Find the value of R such that the power dissipated in R is a maximum.

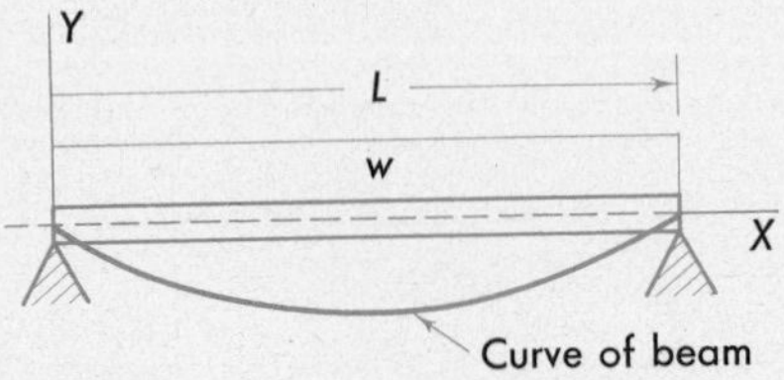

FIGURE 20.21

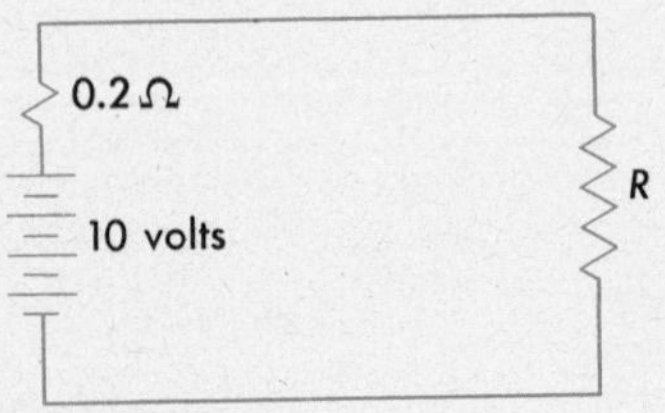

FIGURE 20.22

11. A source of light is to be placed directly over the center of a circular table of diameter 20 ft. The intensity of illumination at any point on the circumference of the table varies directly as the cosine of the angle between the vertical and the light ray, and inversely as the square of the distance of the point from the light. How high should the light be placed above the table to obtain the maximum intensity on a horizontal surface at the edge of the table?
    (a) Express the light intensity I in terms of the height h and a constant of proportionality k before differentiating.
    (b) Express I in terms of trigonometric functions of the angle ϕ between the vertical and the light ray and a proportionality constant k before differentiating.
12. The turning effect of a ship's rudder may be shown theoretically to be $k \sin^2 \theta \cos \theta$, where θ is the angle the rudder makes with the keel and k is a constant. At what value of θ is the rudder most effective?
13. The power output of an electric generator is EI, where E is the constant terminal voltage and I the current. The power loss in the generator is the sum of a constant component P_0 and a variable component (due to heating loss) I^2R, R being the internal resistance of the generator. The efficiency of the generator may be written

$$\eta = \frac{\text{output}}{\text{input}} = \frac{\text{output}}{\text{output} + \text{losses}} = \frac{EI}{EI + P_0 + I^2R}$$

Determine the maximum value for the efficiency as the current I varies and express the result in terms of E, R, and P_0. Also give the relation between the fixed and variable losses (P_0 and I^2R) when the efficiency is a maximum.
14. Given a sphere of radius 10 in, find:
    (a) The altitude of an inscribed right cylinder of maximum volume.
    (b) The altitude of an inscribed right cylinder of maximum total surface.
    (c) The altitude of an inscribed right cone of maximum volume.
15. Write the equation for the area of the trapezoid shown in Fig. 20.23 in terms of h, and find h to give a maximum area.

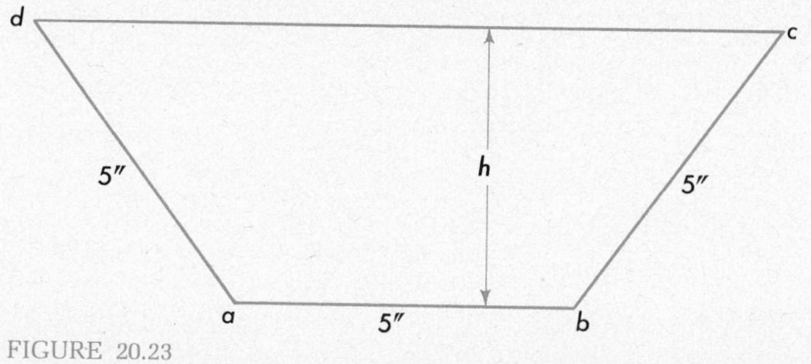

FIGURE 20.23

16. It has been determined that a painter will paint 100 ft^2/h of surface at the beginning of a day and that his rate decreases by 10 ft^2/h as the day progresses. Allowing 0.4 h for work preparations and another 0.4 h to clean up at the end of the day, what total time, including preparation and clean up, will result in a maximum overall square feet of coverage per hour?
17. A minor sector is removed from a disk of brass. The remaining major sector is formed into a cone. Find the central angle of the minor sector required to make the capacity of the cone a maximum.
18. It has been determined that the cutting rate of a tool will diminish linearly to 98 percent of its original value in 1 h of use. Loss of 0.2 h operating time occurs each time the tool is sharpened, and 100 h total time is available for the job. How often during this interval should the tool be sharpened for maximum output? (There will be one more cutting period than sharpening period.)
19. Figure 20.24 shows a crank arm OA, which revolves at the constant rate of ω rad/s and has a length of r ft. The connecting rod AB has a length of L ft. B is a piston which moves along the horizontal axis.
    (a) Show that $x = r(1 - \cos \omega t) + L - (L^2 - r^2 \sin^2 \omega t)^{1/2}$.
    (b) Expand the binomial to two terms by aid of the binomial theorem and obtain the approximate expression for x:

$$x = r(1 - \cos \omega t) + \left(\frac{r^2}{4L}\right)(1 - \cos 2\omega t)$$

    (c) Determine dx/dt and d^2x/dt^2, using both the original and the approximate expressions for x.
    (d) Tabulate the values for dx/dt and d^2x/dt^2 from both results in (c) when $\omega t = 0$, $\pi/4$, $\pi/2$, π, and $3\pi/2$. Assume that $r = 1$ ft, $L = 5$ ft, and $\omega = \frac{1}{2}$ rad/s.
    (e) When is the acceleration of the piston a maximum and hence what is the maximum inertia force which the piston can transmit? (The maximum inertia

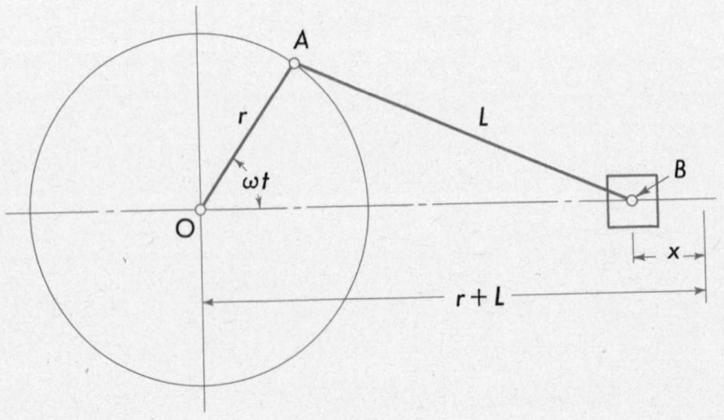

FIGURE 20.24

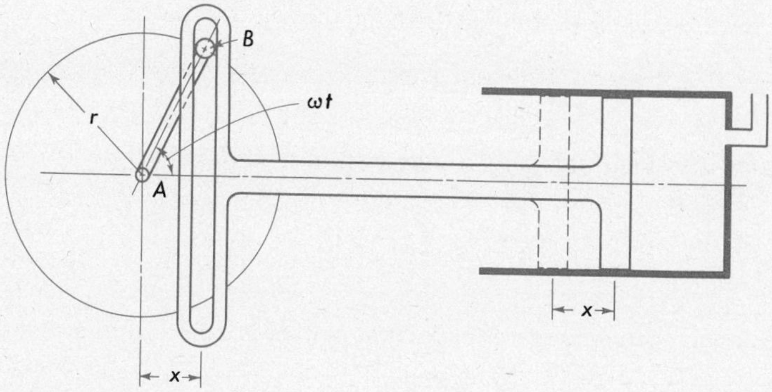

FIGURE 20.25

force is given by $F = ma$, where m is the mass of the piston, and a is the maximum acceleration.) Use the approximate expression for d^2x/dt^2 to answer this question.

20. The mechanism shown in Fig. 20.25 is an air compressor. The displacement of the piston from its position when the crank arm AB is vertical is given by $x = r \cos \omega t$, where r is the length of the crank arm, and the crank arm is rotating at ω rad/s.
    (a) If $r = 0.8$ ft and $\omega = 4\pi$ rad/s, sketch the space-time, velocity-time, and acceleration-time graphs, and label the amplitude and period of each.
    (b) If the weight of the piston and connecting rod is 100 lb, what is the force transmitted to the piston when $\omega t = \pi/6$? (Use force = mass × acceleration; the mass = $^{100}/_{32}$, approximately.)
    (c) What is the maximum inertia force which the piston can transmit to the crank arm and connecting rod?

20.22 Implicit Differentiation

Thus far we have differentiated functions in the form

$$y = f(x) \tag{140}$$

where x and y are related by an equation such as

$$y = 3x^2 + 2x + 5 \tag{141}$$

in which we regard the dependent variable y as being directly expressed in terms of the independent variable x. Such functions are commonly called *explicit* functions.

Quite often we have occasion to differentiate functions in the form

$$F(x,y) = 0 \tag{142}$$

in which two variables x and y are related by means of an equation such as

$$y^2 + x^2 - 36 = 0 \tag{143}$$
$$x^5 + 5xy^3 - 7y^5 = 0 \tag{144}$$

where both x and y are involved in the same equation but neither is explicitly expressed in terms of the other.

After studying equations such as (143) and (144) above, the student may surmise that by implication y must be a function of x in each of them.

Sometimes this surmise can be verified by solving the equation for y, although such a solution may yield just one, more than one, or possibly no explicit function of x.

A study into the matter of when and in what sense there is an explicit function in the form of $y = f(x)$ corresponding to a given implicit function in the form $F(x,y) = 0$ is beyond the scope of this book. In fact, it is ordinarily beyond the scope of an introductory textbook in calculus at any level. The interested student may consult one of the many excellent textbooks in advanced calculus when he is ready.

In any event, in this book the student will not be confronted with an implicit function expressed in the form $F(x,y) = 0$ which cannot be expressed as an explicit differentiable function of x (or perhaps one of several explicit functions of x) in the form $y = f(x)$.

The student may proceed on these assumptions for the rest of this book.

To calculate dy/dx when y is a differentiable function of x given implicitly by an equation in x and y, we differentiate with respect to x by rules already given. Then we solve for dy/dx in terms of x and y.

This process is called *implicit differentiation.*

Example 79. In Eq. (143) find dy/dx.

Differentiating with respect to x, we find

$$\frac{d(y^2)}{dx} + \frac{d(x^2)}{dx} - \frac{d(36)}{dx} = \frac{d(0)}{dx} \tag{145}$$

From Prob. 19, Exercise 6, we know that

$$\frac{d(y^2)}{dx} = 2y\frac{dy}{dx} \tag{146}$$

From Prob. 20, Exercise 6, we know that

$$\frac{d(x^2)}{dx} = 2x\frac{dx}{dx} \tag{147}$$

But from Example 15 we know that

$$\frac{dx}{dx} = 1 \tag{148}$$

By substituting Eqs. (146), (147), and (148) in Eq. (145) we obtain

$$2y\frac{dy}{dx} + 2x = 0$$

or

$$\frac{dy}{dx} = -\frac{x}{y} \tag{149}$$

By solving the equation

$$y^2 + x^2 - 36 = 0$$

for y, we find

$$y = \pm\sqrt{36 - x^2} \tag{150}$$

Thus Eq. (150) yields two explicit, single-valued functions of x. One function is represented by the equation

$$y_1 = +\sqrt{36 - x^2} \tag{151}$$

and the other by the equation

$$y_2 = -\sqrt{36 - x^2} \tag{152}$$

Since we are dealing with only real numbers, x is restricted such that

$$-6 \leq x \leq 6 \tag{153}$$

The plot of Eq. (151) is a semicircle entirely above the x axis with its center at the origin.

The plot of Eq. (152) is the lower half of the same circle.

In a specific practical problem we would have to have more information about the problem in order to determine whether Eq. (151) or Eq. (152) would apply.

If we substitute Eq. (151) in Eq. (149), we find

$$\frac{dy}{dx} = -\frac{x}{\sqrt{36 - x^2}} \tag{154}$$

If we substitute Eq. (152) in Eq. (149), we find

$$\frac{dy}{dx} = +\frac{x}{\sqrt{36 - x^2}} \tag{155}$$

From Eq. (154) and (155) we note a further precaution necessary when working with these equations. Since division by zero is undefined, $x \neq \pm 6$.

Example 80. In Eq. (144) find dy/dx.

By differentiating with respect to x we obtain

$$\frac{d(x^5)}{dx} + \frac{d(5xy^3)}{dx} - \frac{d(7y^5)}{dx} = \frac{d(0)}{dx} \tag{156}$$

From Prob. 21, Exercise 6,

$$\frac{d(x^5)}{dx} = 5x^4 \frac{dx}{dx} = 5x^4 \tag{157}$$

Following Eq. (45), we obtain

$$\frac{d(5xy^3)}{dx} = 5x(3y^2)\frac{dy}{dx} + 5y^3\frac{dx}{dx} = 15xy^2\frac{dy}{dx} + 5y^3 \tag{158}$$

In Prob. 22, Exercise 6,

$$\frac{d(7y^5)}{dx} = 35y^4\frac{dy}{dx} \tag{159}$$

Substituting Eqs. (157), (158), and (159) in Eq. (156), we obtain

$$5x^4 + 5y^3 + \frac{dy}{dx}(15xy^2 - 35y^4) = 0 \tag{160}$$

By rearranging Eq. (160) we obtain

$$\frac{dy}{dx}(15xy^2 - 35y^4) = -5x^4 - 5y^3 \tag{161}$$

or

$$\frac{dy}{dx} = \frac{5x^4 + 5y^3}{35y^4 - 15xy^2} = \frac{x^4 + y^3}{7y^4 - 3xy^2} \tag{162}$$

EXERCISE 20

In Probs. 1 to 9 find dy/dx by differentiating implicitly.

1. By differentiating implicitly show that if $x^2 + y^2 = -1$, $dy/dx = -(x/y)$. Also show why this derivative is meaningless.

2. $x^2 + y^2 = K^2$
3. $5x^2 + 3y^2 = 25$
4. $x^2 - y^2 = 10$
5. $y^2 = 15x$
6. $xy - y - 3x = 8$
7. $x^3 + 3y^2 = y$
8. $2x^3 + 3xy^2 + 5y^3 = 15$
9. $x^5y^5 = x^5 + y^5$

20.23 Related Rates

Let us consider a specific problem.

Example 81. A spherical balloon is being inflated at the rate of 15 ft³/min. How fast is the radius increasing when the radius is 6 ft?

In this problem, the volume and the radius are varying quantities but for all permissible values of time they are related by the equation

$$V = \tfrac{4}{3}\pi r^3 \tag{163}$$

Since V and r are both functions of time, we may differentiate Eq. (163) with respect to time, obtaining

$$\frac{d(V)}{dt} = \frac{4}{3}\pi\frac{d(r^3)}{dt} = 4\pi r^2\frac{dr}{dt}$$

Now by using the given data we may write

$$15 = 4\pi \cdot 36\frac{dr}{dt}$$

or

$$\frac{dr}{dt} = \frac{5}{48\pi} = 0.0332 \text{ ft/min}$$

EXERCISE 21

1. A ladder 10 ft long rests against a vertical wall. If the foot of the ladder is moved horizontally away from the wall at the rate of 5 ft/min, how fast is the top of the ladder moving downward when the foot of the ladder is 8 ft from the base of the building?
2. A spherical balloon is being inflated by pumping gas into it at the rate of 12 ft^3/min. How fast is the radius of the balloon increasing when it is 0.5 ft in radius?
3. A particle A moves along the x axis at a constant rate of 3 ft/s while a particle B moves along the y axis with a constant speed of -5 ft/s. How fast is the distance between them changing when A is at (1,0) and B is at (0,12)?
4. A conical tank has an altitude of 15 ft and a diameter at the top of 15 ft. Water is flowing out of the apex (at the bottom) at the rate of 5 ft^3/h. How fast is the water level dropping when it is 10 ft above the apex?
5. A particle moves in a circular path according to the equation $x^2 + y^2 = 4$. If the x component of velocity is y, find the y component of velocity.
6. A crankshaft (see Fig. 20.24) turns at the rate of 900 rpm. Find the speed of the piston dx/dt when $\omega t = \pi/2$ rad. Let $r = 1$ ft and $L = 5$ ft.
7. If the quantity of wood in a tree is approximately proportional to the cube of the diameter at its base and if the diameter increases approximately 0.8 in/year, what is the approximate rate of change in the volume? Give your result in terms of the constant of variation and the radius of the tree.
8. A given quantity of gas is expanding according to the adiabatic law $pV^{1.4} = k =$ constant. If the volume is 10 in^3 when the pressure is 20 lb/in^2 and if the pressure is increased at the constant rate of 0.5 (lb/in^2)/s, what is the rate of change of the volume when the volume is 5 in^3?
9. The relation between altitude above sea level (h ft) and the pressure (p lb/ft^2) at a certain place on the earth and at a certain time of year is given by

   $$p = 2{,}140e^{-0.000{,}035h}$$

   If an airplane is climbing at this particular spot on the earth and at the stated time at a vertical component of 200 mi/h, what is the rate of change of the pressure due to change in altitude when the airplane is 3 mi up?
10. A boat is pulled in by means of a rope wound around a windlass on the dock which is 20 ft above the deck of the boat. If the windlass is pulling the rope in at 10 ft/s,

determine, when there is 100 ft of rope out:

(a) The speed of the boat

(b) The acceleration of the boat

20.24 Approximate Increments

We have become accustomed to the type of thinking that is involved in the equation

$$\lim_{\Delta x \to 0} \frac{\Delta y}{\Delta x} = \frac{dy}{dx} \tag{164}$$

For small values of Δx it appears evident that $\Delta y/\Delta x$ and its limit dy/dx are nearly equal. That is,

$$\frac{\Delta y}{\Delta x} \approx \frac{dy}{dx} \tag{165}$$

For a discussion of the error involved in this approximation the student is referred to a more advanced textbook in calculus.

Example 82. The diameter of a sphere changes from 20 to 20.04 in. Approximately what is the change in volume?

The volume of a sphere is given by the formula

$$V = \tfrac{4}{3}\pi r^3$$

$$\frac{dV}{dr} = 4\pi r^2$$

When $r = 10$, $dV/dr = 400\pi$, and this quantity can be evaluated easily from the number tables.

$$\frac{dV}{dr} = 400\pi = 1{,}257 \qquad \text{(to four significant digits)} \tag{166}$$

From Eq. (165),

$$\frac{\Delta V}{\Delta r} \approx 1{,}257$$

and

$$\Delta V \approx 1{,}257 \cdot \Delta r$$

But

$\Delta r = 0.02$

Thus

$\Delta V \approx 1{,}257 \times 0.02 = 25.1$ (to three significant digits)

By the far more laborious operation of evaluating the equation

$\Delta V = \frac{4}{3}\pi(10.02^3 - 10^3)$

we obtain

$\Delta V = 25.2$ (to three significant digits)

If this accuracy is sufficient in a particular problem, the first method is to be preferred because it involves less work.

EXERCISE 22

1. If a circle has a radius of 7 in, approximately what changes in radius will result from a change in area of 3 in^2?
2. A cube expands so that its edge increases from 5 to 5.04 in. What is the approximate change in volume?
3. To three significant digits, what is the actual change in volume in Prob. 2 above?
4. A cylinder exactly 15 in high has a nominal radius of 8 in, but the radius is 0.05 in oversize. Find the approximate error this causes in (*a*) the volume and (*b*) the lateral surface.
5. If the radius of a sphere increases slightly, show that the increase in volume is approximately proportional to the surface area.
6. A sphere is to be fired (baked) out of a certain kind of clay that has a linear shrinkage of 4 percent. Determine the approximate radius of the sphere before firing (baking) if the final radius is to be 6 in. Determine the approximate change in volume.
7. The heat Q required to raise the temperature T of a certain liquid 1 K (one degree on the Kelvin or absolute Celsius scale) is given by $Q = a + bT + cT^2$. Determine an expression for the amount of heat necessary to heat the material from $T = 300.0$ to $T = 300.1$ K.
8. Determine the approximate change in $\tan\theta$ if θ increases from 45°10′ to 45°11′. Then check with your tables.
9. If $y = \sin x$, and x is to increase by 1 min, determine the value of x that makes the largest change in y. Then refer to your tables and check.

10. Bernoulli's equation from fluid mechanics may be written

$$p + \frac{\rho v^2}{2} = H$$

where p is pressure, ρ is the constant density of the fluid, v is velocity, and H is a constant. Obtain an approximate formula for the change in pressure Δp due to a small change in velocity Δv.

11. If two resistors R_1 and R_2 are connected in parallel, the equivalent resistance R of the combination is given by the equation

$$R = \frac{R_1 \times R_2}{R_1 + R_2}$$

If the nominal value of R_1 is 5 Ω, and the nominal value of R_2 is 10 Ω, what would be the change in R if R_2 were increased by 0.5 Ω?

12. In Example 31, Sec. 14.17, find the approximate error in the length of side c if 36°52″ is used for angle C instead of 36°52′12″. Find the equivalent percent error.

13. The equation of the LL-3 scale on a 10-in log-log slide rule is

$$y \text{ in} = 10 \log_{10} (\log_e x)$$

where the numbers that appear on the scale are values of x, and y is measured from the left-hand side of the rule. Use increments to determine the approximate distance in inches (Δy) between the numbers marked $x = 3$ and $x = 3.2$.

Note: The true length is 25 cm.

20.25 Differentials

We remember that the symbol dy/dx has been used to designate the derivative of y with respect to x. Where it is used in this sense we have given meaning to dy/dx only when this symbol is considered as a whole. We have not, thus far, given meaning to dy and dx when they are considered separately.

We can, however, interpret dy and dx in such a way that they do have meaning when considered separately. When we do so, we call them *differentials*. Thus dy is called the *differential* of y, and dx is called the *differential* of x.

Suppose that we are given a function f for which $y = f(x)$ and that this function has a derivative for each value of x with which we are concerned. Now let dx be any increment of x (of course, $dx \neq 0$). Then dy is defined by

$$dy = f'(x)\,dx \tag{167}$$

where $f'(x)$ = derivative of y with respect to x

We can divide both sides of Eq. (167) by the differential of x, that is, dx, obtaining

$$\frac{dy}{dx} = f'(x) \tag{168}$$

We note that Eq. (168) has a familiar appearance. However, there is this new concept involved in it. In Eq. (168) we have given *separate meanings to dy and dx so that now dy/dx is considered to be a quotient.*

From now on, in situations where it is convenient to do so, we may consider a derivative to be the quotient of two differentials.

It is sometimes convenient to give a geometric interpretation to differentials.

In Fig. 20.26 Δx is the increment of x between P_1 and P_2, and Δy is the corresponding increment in y. The quotient $\Delta y/\Delta x$ is the average slope of the graph between P_1 and P_2.

If we let $\Delta x = dx$, then dy is the corresponding increment in the tangent ab.

The quotient of the differentials dy and dx is then the slope of the tangent drawn to the graph through the point P_1.

Throughout this chapter we have, from time to time, introduced certain formulas for derivatives. We can now present corresponding formulas for differentials.

For example, from Eq. (27),

$$\frac{d(kx^n)}{dx} = nkx^{n-1}$$

Now we may write the differential of kx^n as

$$d(kx^n) = nkx^{n-1}\,dx$$

From Eq. (41) if

$$\frac{d(u^n)}{dx} = nu^{n-1}\frac{du}{dx}$$

then

$$d(u^n) = nu^{n-1}\,du \tag{169}$$

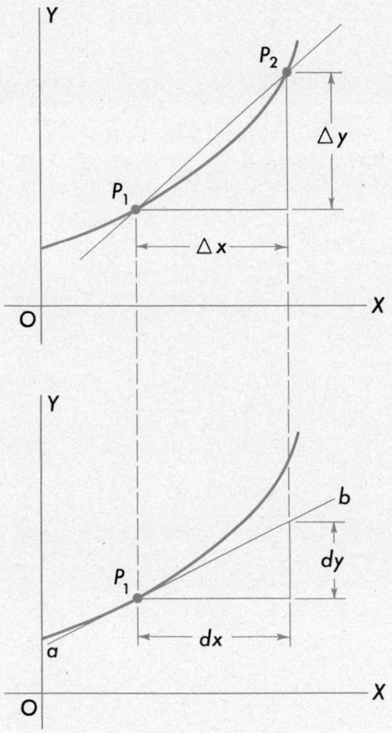

FIGURE 20.26

Also, if

$$\frac{d(ku^n)}{dx} = knu^{n-1}\frac{du}{dx}$$

then

$$d(ku^n) = knu^{n-1}\,du \tag{170}$$

In the special case where $n = 1$, we may write

$$d(ku) = k\,du \tag{171}$$

From rule 4, Sec. 20.5

$$\frac{d(u+v)}{dx} = \frac{du}{dx} + \frac{dv}{dx}$$

Then

$$d(u + v) = du + dv \tag{172}$$

From Eq. (45),

$$\frac{d(uv)}{dx} = u\frac{dv}{dx} + v\frac{du}{dx}$$

Then

$$d(uv) = u\,dv + v\,du \tag{173}$$

From Eq. (51),

$$\frac{d(u/v)}{dx} = \frac{v(du/dx) - u(dv/dx)}{v^2} \tag{174}$$

Then

$$d\left(\frac{u}{v}\right) = \frac{v\,du - u\,dv}{v^2} \tag{175}$$

From Eq. (66),

$$\frac{d(\sin u)}{dx} = \cos u\frac{du}{dx}$$

Then

$$d(\sin u) = \cos u\,du \tag{176}$$

From Eq. (71),

$$\frac{d(\cos u)}{dx} = -\sin u\frac{du}{dx}$$

Then

$$d(\cos u) = -\sin u\,du \tag{177}$$

From Eq. (96),

$$\frac{d(\ln u)}{dx} = \frac{1}{u}\frac{du}{dx}$$

Then

$$d(\ln u) = \frac{1}{u}\,du = u^{-1}\,du \tag{178}$$

From Eq. (104),

$$d(e^u) = e^u\,du \tag{179}$$

EXERCISE 23

Find the differential of y in the following problems. The letters a and b represent constants.

1. $y = \frac{1}{3}\arccos\frac{3}{x}$
2. $y = \frac{1}{a}\arctan\frac{x}{a}$
3. $y = \frac{2}{3b}\sqrt{(a + bx)^3}$
4. $y = \frac{1}{2b}\ln\left(x^2 + \frac{a}{b}\right)$
5. $y = \frac{1}{b^2}\left[-\frac{1}{a + bx} + \frac{a}{2(a + bx)^2}\right]$
6. $y = \frac{1}{5a}\ln\frac{x^5}{a + bx^5}$
7. $y = \frac{\sqrt{x^2 - a^2}}{2a^2x^2} + \frac{1}{2a^3}\arccos\frac{a}{x}$
8. $y = -\frac{1}{a}\ln\frac{a + \sqrt{a^2 + x^2}}{x}$
9. Van der Waals' equation for real gases is

$$\left(p + \frac{a}{v^2}\right)(v - b) = nRT$$

where a, b, n, R are constants; p is pressure; v is volume; and T is temperature.
(a) Determine an equation for dv if T is a constant.
(b) Determine an equation for dv if p is constant.

21 integration

In Chap. 20 we considered the problem of finding the derivative of a given function. The process involved is called differentiation.

We shall begin this chapter by considering the problem of reconstructing a function when its derivative is given. This process is called *antidifferentiation* or *indefinite integration*.

The appropriateness of the word "indefinite" when used in this context will be discussed in Sec. 21.2.

In Secs. 21.11 and 21.13 we shall discuss some further aspects of integration leading to the notion of the *definite integral*.

21.1 Introduction to Integration

Differentiation is an orderly, algebraic process based on the Δ method (see Sec. 20.3). Indefinite integration is largely a matter of trial and memory.

Suppose we are given the equation

$$\frac{dy}{dx} = 15x^4 \tag{1}$$

An equation such as Eq. (1) is called a *differential* equation. A differential equation is an equation that relates variables with their derivatives. The differential equations which we shall consider here are, of course, very special ones and very simple ones.

Now suppose we are asked to solve Eq. (1). To solve this differential equation means to find some y value such that

$$\frac{dy}{dx} = 15x^4$$

From our experience with differentiation (see Example 11, Sec. 20.4) we recall that *one* possible solution is

$$y = 3x^5$$

In general, if two functions F and f have the property that

$$\frac{d[F(x)]}{dx} = f(x) \tag{2}$$

then $F(x)$ is called a solution of this differential equation. $F(x)$ is also called an antiderivative of $f(x)$ or an indefinite integral of $f(x)$.

In the above example

$$f(x) = 15x^4 \tag{3}$$

and

$$F(x) = 3x^5 \tag{4}$$

This, of course, assumes that $F(x)$ is differentiable over the range of interest and that both $F(x)$ and $f(x)$ are continuous over this range. From Sec. 20.5, rules 3 and 4, we observe that if $F(x)$ is an integral of $f(x)$, then $F(x) + C$ is also an integral of $f(x)$. For example, $3x^5 + 8$, $3x^5 + \pi$, $3x^5 + e$, or $3x^5 +$ (any constant) will satisfy Eq. (1).

The elongated s written $\int$ is the symbol which designates the process of integration. It is customary to use differential notation (See Sec. 20.25) in connection with the symbol $\int$ to indicate this process. Thus

$$\int 15x^4\, dx = 3x^5 + C \tag{5}$$

is read "the indefinite integral of $15x^4$ with respect to x is $3x^5 + C$."

Similarly, if we wish to indicate that $F(x)$ is an antiderivative, or an indefinite integral of $f(x)$, we may write

$$\int f(x)\,dx = F(x) + C \tag{6}$$

In Eq. (5) the expression $15x^4\,dx$ is called the *integrand,* and C is called the *constant of integration.*

21.2 The Indefinite Integral

There is a certain "indefiniteness" about the above problem. If all we know about a function is its derivative, then we do not know what the added constant is. Consequently, an integral in the form of Eq. (6) is called an *indefinite* integral.

21.3 Some Important Integration Formulas

The formulas listed below are basic and will be used frequently in the work to follow. The symbols k, K, m, n, and C designate constants.

$$\int u^n\,du = \frac{u^{n+1}}{n+1} + C \qquad n \neq -1 \tag{7}$$

This can be verified by differentiating as follows:

$$\frac{d\left(\dfrac{u^{n+1}}{n+1} + C\right)}{du} = \frac{(n+1)u^{n+1-1}}{n+1} = u^n$$

For example,

$$\int u^4\,du = \frac{u^5}{5} + C$$

By differentiation we obtain

$$\frac{d(u^5/5 + C)}{du} = \frac{5u^4}{5} = u^4$$

$$\int ku^n\,du = \frac{ku^{n+1}}{n+1} + C \qquad n \neq -1 \tag{8}$$

This can be verified by differentiation. Thus

$$\frac{d\left(\frac{ku^{n+1}}{n+1}+C\right)}{du} = \frac{k(n+1)u^n}{n+1} = ku^n \tag{9}$$

By comparing Eqs. (7) and (8) it seems plausible that

$$\int ku^n\,du = k\int u^n\,du \tag{10}$$

or, somewhat more generally,

$$\int kf(u)\,du = k\int f(u)\,du \tag{11}$$

From rule 4, Sec. 20.5, we note that the derivative of the sum of any finite number of differentiable functions is the sum of their derivatives. Therefore, we are led to write

$$\int [f(u) + g(u)]\,du = \int f(u)\,du + \int g(u)\,du \tag{12}$$

For example,

$$\int\left(-\frac{5}{3u^2} + 2u\right)du = \int -\frac{5}{3u^2}\,du + \int 2u\,du \tag{13}$$

$$= -\tfrac{5}{3}\int u^{-2}\,du + 2\int u\,du$$

$$= -\frac{5}{3}\cdot\frac{u^{-1}}{-1} + C_1 + \frac{2u^2}{2} + C_2 \tag{14}$$

If we let

$$C_1 + C_2 = C$$

$$\int\left(-\frac{5}{3u^2} + 2u\right)du = \frac{5}{3}u^{-1} + u^2 + C = \frac{5}{3u} + u^2 + C \tag{15}$$

To verify the above by differentiation, see Example 27, Sec. 20.5. Thus we conclude that the integral of the sum of a finite number of terms is the sum of their integrals.

The question frequently arises, Is integration unique? That is, for example, if

$$\frac{dy}{du} = 10u$$

can y be expressed by an equation (perhaps a very complicated one), other than

$y = 5u^2 +$ an arbitrary constant

Without attempting a rigorous proof, suppose for a moment that z is the value of a function such that

$$\frac{dy}{du} = \frac{dz}{du} \tag{16}$$

Since the above derivatives are equal, it means that the rate of change of both y and z with respect to u is the same. Hence the difference between y and z does not change but remains constant. Thus y and z can differ only by an arbitrary constant.

Therefore functions defined by

$$y = 5u^2 + C \tag{17}$$

(where C is a constant) are the only functions which if differentiated will yield

$$\frac{dy}{du} = 10u \tag{18}$$

In a more advanced work, it can be proved rigorously that any two antiderivatives of the same function differ only by a constant.

Figure 21.1 illustrates the graphs of four equations. The only difference in these equations is in the added constant. The effect of the added constant is simply to raise or lower the graph. It has no effect whatever on the *shape* of the graph. It is the *shape* of the graph that determines the derivative. Therefore the added constant has no effect on the derivative.

EXERCISE 1

Verify the following indefinite integrals:

1. $\int 3x^5\,dx = \frac{3x^6}{6} + C = \frac{1}{2}x^6 + C$
2. $\int 2x^{5/3}\,dx = \frac{3}{4}x^{8/3} + C$
3. $\int 7x^{-5}\,dx = -\frac{7}{4}x^{-4} + C$
4. $\int 3x^{-1/2}\,dx = 6x^{1/2} + C$
5. $\int 8x^{-8/5}\,dx = -40/(3x^{3/5}) + C$
6. $\int -\frac{7}{8}x^{3/2}\,dx = -\frac{7x^{5/2}}{20} + C$
7. $\int 4\sqrt[3]{x^2}\,dx = \frac{12x^{5/3}}{5} + C$
8. $\int -32\,dx = -32x + C$

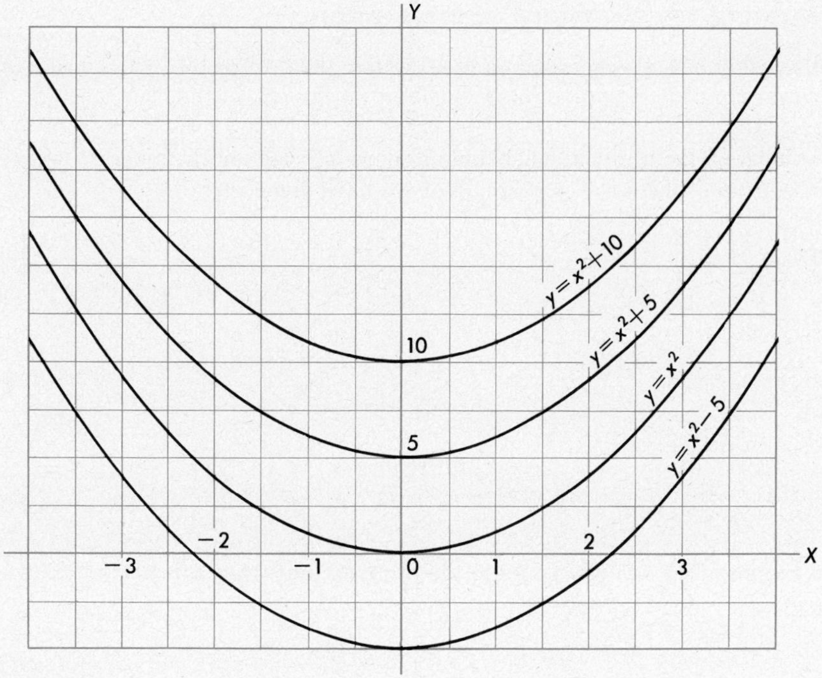

FIGURE 21.1

Find the indefinite integrals in Probs. 9 and 10 below.

9. $\int(x^3 - 6x^2 + 500x + 7)\,dx$
10. $\int(x^{3/4} - 2x^{-5/6} + 2\sqrt[3]{x^2} + \pi)\,dx$

In Probs. 11 through 18 find $F(x)$ as illustrated in Eq. (6).

11. $f(x) = \frac{5}{6}\sqrt{x}$
12. $f(x) = -\frac{3}{4}\sqrt[3]{x}$
13. $f(x) = 3x^2 + \sqrt{2}$
14. $f(x) = x^{-10}$
15. $f(x) = 1/x^5$
16. $f(x) = k/x^5$
17. $f(x) = \pi + 3x^{5/7}$
18. $f(x) = 3e + 5\sqrt{x^7}$

Solve the following differential equations.

19. $dy/dx = 2x$
20. $dy/dx = 3x^2$
21. $dy/dx = x$
22. $dy/dx = 10$
23. $dy/dx = -2$
24. $dy/dx = x^{5/2}$
25. $dy/dx = x^{1/3}$
26. $dy/dx = x^{-1/3}$
27. $dy/dx = 3x^{-1/2}$

21.4 Evaluating the Constant of Integration

As we mentioned in Sec. 21.2, the integral expressed in the form of Eq. (6) has a certain "indefiniteness" about it. Equation (6) is indefinite to the extent that the constant is not known. As a matter of fact, it could be anything, including zero. If the constant C is to be evaluated, the problem must contain more information than merely to give the derivative of the function. For example, if we have given that

$$dy = 10x\,dx \tag{19}$$

we could write

$$y = \int 10x\,dx \tag{20}$$

and according to Eq. (8)

$$y = 5x^2 + C \tag{21}$$

Now let us suppose that it is also given in the problem that when x is 2, y is 35; then we may write

$$35 = 5(2^2) + C \tag{22}$$

As a consequence,

$$35 = 20 + C \tag{23}$$

and

$$C = 15 \tag{24}$$

Therefore, with this bit of added information, commonly called a *boundary condition*, we can evaluate the constant of integration and find that

$$y = 5x^2 + 15$$

Example 1. We have given that

$$\frac{d^2y}{dx^2} = 6x + 2 \qquad \text{(also see Sec. 21.20)}$$

Also we have given the boundary conditions that $dy/dx = 20$ when $x = 2$ and that $y = 0$ when $x = -10$. Find the equation for y in terms of x.

By integrating once, we obtain

$$\frac{dy}{dx} = 3x^2 + 2x + C_1$$

From the first boundary condition we know that

$$20 = 3 \cdot (2)^2 + 2 \cdot 2 + C_1$$
$$20 = 12 + 4 + C_1 = 16 + C_1$$
$$C_1 = 4$$

Therefore

$$\frac{dy}{dx} = 3x^2 + 2x + 4$$

By integrating again we obtain

$$y = x^3 + x^2 + 4x + C_2$$

From the second boundary condition we may write

$$0 = (-10)^3 + (-10)^2 + 4(-10) + C_2$$

or

$$0 = -1{,}000 + 100 - 40 + C_2 = -940 + C_2$$

Therefore

$$C_2 = 940$$

and

$$y = x^3 + x^2 + 4x + 940$$

This equation can be verified by calculating the second derivative of y with respect to x.

Example 2. We have given that

$$\frac{d^4y}{dx^4} = 120x$$

Also we have given the following boundary conditions:

(a) When $x = 3$,

$$\frac{d^3y}{dx^3} = 552 \tag{25}$$

(b) When $x = 0$,

$$\frac{d^2y}{dx^2} = 6 \tag{26}$$

(c) When $x = 0$,

$$y = 0 \tag{27}$$

(d) When $x = 2$,

$$y = 0 \tag{28}$$

Find the equation for y in terms of x.

By integrating once we obtain

$$\frac{d^3y}{dx^3} = 60x^2 + C_1$$

From boundary condition (a)

$$552 = 60(3)^2 + C_1 = 540 + C_1$$
$$C_1 = 12$$

and

$$\frac{dy^3}{dx^3} = 60x^2 + 12$$

By integrating again we obtain

$$\frac{d^2y}{dx^2} = 20x^3 + 12x + C_2$$

From boundary condition (b)

$$6 = 0 + 0 + C_2$$

and

$$C_2 = 6$$

Therefore

$$\frac{d^2y}{dx^2} = 20x^3 + 12x + 6 \qquad (29)$$

By integrating again we obtain

$$\frac{dy}{dx} = 5x^4 + 6x^2 + 6x + C_3 \qquad (30)$$

Here we have no boundary condition explicitly involving dy/dx. However, in this case, as we shall see below, there are enough data so that C_3 can still be evaluated.

By integrating again we obtain

$$y = x^5 + 2x^3 + 3x^2 + C_3x + C_4$$

From boundary condition (c) it is quite evident that $C_4 = 0$. Therefore

$$y = x^5 + 2x^3 + 3x^2 + C_3x$$

From boundary condition (d) we may write

$$0 = (2)^5 + 2(2)^3 + 3(2)^2 + 2C_3 = 32 + 16 + 12 + 2C_3$$
$$C_3 = -30$$

and

$$y = x^5 + 2x^3 + 3x^2 - 30x$$

EXERCISE 2

In Probs. 1 through 9 below find the equation for y. The boundary conditions in each problem are that $y = 20$ when $x = 4$ (see Exercise 1, Probs. 19 through 27).

1. $y = \int 2x\, dx$
2. $y = \int 3x^2\, dx$
3. $y = \int x\, dx$
4. $y = \int 10dx$
5. $y = \int -2dx$
6. $y = \int x^{5/2}\, dx$
7. $y = \int x^{1/3}\, dx$
8. $y = \int x^{-1/3}\, dx$
9. $y = \int 3x^{-1/2}\, dx$

10. A simply supported beam is loaded with a load w in pounds per foot that varies directly as the distance from the left support, as indicated in Fig. 21.2. Given, from studies of strength of materials,

$$EI\frac{d^4y}{dx^4} = -w = -100x$$

where $E = 200{,}000{,}000\ \text{lb/ft}^2$, $I = 0.00800\ \text{ft}^4$, and y is the ordinate to the curve of the beam at abscissa x ft from the left support.

Given $EI(d^3y/dx^3) = {}^{5{,}000}\!/_3$ when $x = 0$, $d^2y/dx^2 = 0$ when $x = 0$, and $y = 0$ when $x = 0$ and when $x = 10$. Determine the equation for y as a function of x, that is, the curve of the beam.

11. Determine the maximum deflection of the beam from a horizontal position in Prob. 10.
12. A wooden beam is 12 ft long, 4 in wide, and 8 in deep and is loaded with a uniform load of 400 lb/ft, as shown in Fig. 21.3. From studies of strength of materials one can obtain the equation

$$\frac{d^2y}{dx^2} = 0.00204x - 0.000{,}170x^2$$

where x and y are in feet.

Determine the equation for y in terms of x and also determine the minimum value of y, that is, the largest deflection of the beam.

13. Given is the equation $mv(dv/dx) = -mkx$, where m is a constant mass and k is a constant of variation. Integrate this equation and transpose all variable terms

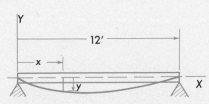

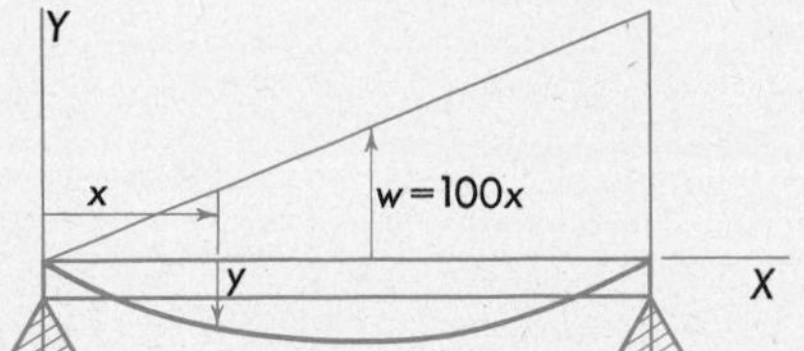

FIGURE 21.2

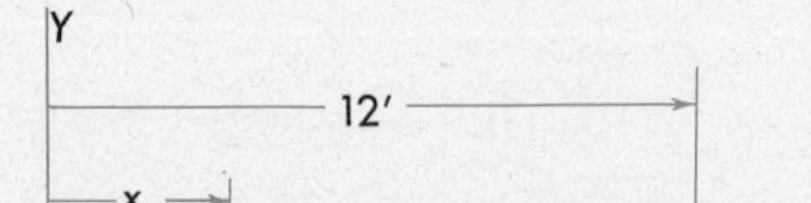

FIGURE 21.3

to the left-hand side. If kinetic energy (energy due to motion) is $mv^2/2$ and if potential energy (energy due to position) is $mkx^2/2$, what does your resulting equation state?

21.5 Integration by Substitution

As we mentioned in Sec. 21.1, indefinite integration is largely a matter of trial and memory. It involves reconstructing a function whose differential is the given integrand.

In the discussion immediately to follow we shall lean heavily on Eq. (8). However, it is very common to find that although a given integrand may not be in such a form that we can apply Eq. (8) directly, it may be possible, by making suitable substitutions, to reduce the integrand to a form such that Eq. (8) is directly applicable.

For example, let us find

$$\int 5(4x^2 + 3x + 8)^2(8x + 3)\, dx \tag{31}$$

Observe that, if we let

$$u = 4x^2 + 3x + 8 \tag{32}$$

then

$$du = (8x + 3)\, dx \tag{33}$$

and (31) may be written as

$$\int 5u^2\, du \tag{34}$$

Also

$$\int 5u^2\, du = \tfrac{5}{3}u^3 + C \tag{35}$$

We may now substitute Eqs. (32) and (33) in (35) to obtain

$$\int 5u^2\, du = \int 5(4x^2 + 3x + 8)^2(8x + 3)\, dx \tag{36}$$

$$= \tfrac{5}{3}(4x^2 + 3x + 8)^3 + C \tag{37}$$

Of course, after a certain amount of practice, the student will learn to do most of this work mentally. Having been given the integrand in (31), he will be able to write the integral in (37) by inspection.

Example 3. Find

$$\int(3x^2 + 5)^2 x\,dx \tag{38}$$

Here we let

$$u = (3x^2 + 5) \tag{39}$$

Then

$$du = 6x\,dx$$

and (38) does *not* contain *du exactly*. However, we may multiply and divide by 6 without changing the value of (38) and write the equivalent of (38) as

$$\int \tfrac{1}{6}(3x^2 + 5)^2\, 6x\,dx \tag{40}$$

Now Eq. (8) does apply directly and

$$\begin{aligned}\int(3x^2 + 5)^2\, x\,dx &= \int \tfrac{1}{6}(3x^2 + 5)^2(6x)\,dx \\ &= \tfrac{1}{18}(3x^2 + 5)^3 + C\end{aligned} \tag{41}$$

EXERCISE 3

Evaluate the following indefinite integrals.

1. $\int(3 - t)^4\,dt$
2. $\int(3 - 5x)^{-6}\,dx$
3. $\int\sqrt{4 - m}\,dm$
4. $\int\sqrt{4\phi - 1}\,d\phi$
5. $\int t^3(3 - t^4)^5\,dt$
6. $\displaystyle\int \frac{\phi^3}{(2 - \phi^4)^6}\,d\phi$
7. $\displaystyle\int \frac{t + 1}{\sqrt{t^2 + 2t}}\,dt$
8. $\int(r - 3)\sqrt{r^2 - 6r - 7}\,dr$
9. $\int 15x(4x^2 - 9)^{3/2}\,dx$

21.6 Accelerated Motion

In this section it is assumed that the student has had a course in general physics and is therefore familiar with the elementary notions of distance, velocity, and acceleration.

We shall limit ourselves to bodies moving in a straight line and to some of the more elementary aspects of rotary motion.

We learn from mechanics that velocity is the time rate of change in distance.

That is,

$$v = \frac{ds}{dt} \tag{42}$$

where v = velocity
s = distance
t = time

We also learn from mechanics that acceleration is the time rate of change in velocity. That is,

$$a = \frac{dv}{dt} \tag{43}$$

where a = acceleration.

In general, then, we may write

$$v = \int a\, dt \tag{44}$$

and

$$s = \int v\, dt \tag{45}$$

In accordance with engineering expediency, the data for any particular problem may be based on acceleration or velocity or distance in terms of time. Therefore, the student will be well advised to avoid relying entirely on memorized formulas which apply only to strictly limited situations.

Example 4. The velocity in feet per second of a certain body moving in a straight line and starting from rest at $t = 0$ is given by

$$v = 3t^2 + 4t$$

(a) Find the acceleration at $t = 3$. (b) Find the distance moved between $t = 0$ and $t = 3$.

$$\text{Acceleration} = a = \frac{dv}{dt} = 6t + 4$$

At $t = 3$,

$$a = 6 \cdot 3 + 4 = 22 \text{ ft/s}^2$$

Distance $= s = \int v\,dt = \int (3t^2 + 4t)\,dt = t^3 + 2t^2 + C$

When $t = 0$, $s = 0$ and $C = 0$; therefore

$s = t^3 + 2t^2$

When $t = 3$,

$s = 3^3 + 2 \cdot 9 = 27 + 18 = 45$ ft

Example 5. An automobile moves along a straight, level road with a speed of v_0 ft/s. The operator applies the brakes at $t = 0$ in such a way as to bring the automobile to a stop with a constant, negative acceleration in 6 s. The distance required to stop the automobile is 270 ft. Find the constant acceleration and v_0.

The velocity at any time is given by

$v = \int a\,dt = at + C_1$

When $t = 0$, $v = v_0$; therefore $C_1 = v_0$, and

$v = at + v_0$

When $t = 6$, $v = 0$ and $v_0 = -at = -6a$. Therefore $v = at - 6a$. Distance is given by

$$s = \int v\,dt = \frac{a}{2}t^2 - 6at + C_2$$

But when $t = 0$, $s = 0$ and $C_2 = 0$; therefore

$$s = \frac{a}{2}t^2 - 6at$$

When $t = 6$, $s = 270$ ft; therefore

$$270 = \frac{a}{2}6^2 - 6 \cdot a \cdot 6 = 18a - 36a = -18a$$

Then

$a = -{}^{270}\!/_{18} = -15$ ft/s^2

and

$v_0 = -6(-15) = 90$ ft/s

Example 6. A flywheel is turning at the rate of ω_0 rpm at the instant the power is turned off. Over the next 5 s the angular speed is given by

$$\omega = 100 - 15t + t^2$$

where ω is the angular speed in revolutions per minute. (a) Find ω_0. (b) Find the angular acceleration at $t = 2$ s. (c) Find the number of revolutions that the flywheel makes in the first 2 s.

From the given equation we see by inspection that $\omega_0 = 100$. The angular acceleration is given by

$$\alpha = \frac{d\omega}{dt} = -15 + 2t$$

At $t = 2$,

$$\alpha = -15 + 4 = -11 \text{ rev/s}^2$$

The number of revolutions is given by

$$\text{rev} = \int \omega\, dt = \int (100 - 15t + t^2)\, dt$$

$$= 100t - 7.5t^2 + \frac{t^3}{3} + C$$

By the conditions of the problem $C = 0$.

From $t = 0$ to $t = 2$,

$$\text{rev} = 100 \cdot 2 - 7.5 \cdot 4 + 8/3 = 172.7$$

EXERCISE 4

1. A ship, while being launched, started from rest at $t = 0$ and slipped down the ways with a constant acceleration. The ship slid the first foot in 10 s. That is, $s = 1$ ft when $t = 10$ s, where s is the distance moved from the rest position. How long did it take the ship to slip 400 ft along the ways from the rest position?
2. The ram of a pile driver hits a pile at $t = 0$ and travels with it. The pile is driven 4 in before coming to rest at $t = 0.05$ s. Assuming the deceleration of the driver to be constant, find the speed of the ram (v_0 in/s) at the instant of impact.
3. An automobile is moving along a straight road at a speed v_0 of 60 mi/h when the driver decides to stop the car. The brakes are applied at $t = 0$ and slow the car down with a constant deceleration. The car comes to rest at $d = 75$ ft, where d is measured from the position of the car when $t = 0$. What is the deceleration, and how long does it take to stop the car?

4. During the 4-s interval after the current is shut off at $t = 0$ the angular speed ω of a certain electric motor is given with sufficient accuracy for engineering purposes by the equation

$$\omega = 200 - 20t + 0.5t^2 \qquad \text{rad/s}$$

where t is the time in seconds since the current was turned off.
   (a) What was the angular speed at $t = 0$?
   (b) What was the angular acceleration α at $t = 3$ s?
   (c) How many revolutions did the motor make between $t = 0$ and $t = 4$ s?
   (d) Does the angular acceleration increase or decrease during the interval between $t = 0$ and $t = 4$? Why?
5. The driver of a truck increases the power output of the engine by depressing the accelerator. The tractive effort on the road increases at a uniform rate of 24 lb/s. The truck weighs 16,100 lb, and the frictional resistance to motion is always 400 lb. Determine the distance (s ft) that the truck moves in terms of time (t s) since the driver started to increase power at $t = 0$. The speed of the truck at $t = 0$ was 10 ft/s.

   Solution: By aid of Newton's second law of motion,

   Total horizontal force = (mass)(acceleration in horizontal direction)

   Hence

$$24t - 400 = \frac{16{,}100}{32.2}\frac{d^2s}{dt^2}$$

6. The braking resistance of a truck is 200 lb for each 1,000 lb of weight. If a truck weighs 15,000 lb and is traveling at a speed v_0 of 24 mi/h, determine the time t required to stop the truck and the distance s it will travel (in a horizontal direction) from its position at $t = 0$. *Hint:* From Newton's second law applied to this problem,

$$-200 \cdot 15 = \frac{15{,}000}{32.2}\frac{d^2s}{dt^2}$$

21.7 Freely Falling Bodies

It has been found that bodies falling freely near the earth's surface have, to a satisfactory approximation, a constant acceleration. This, of course, neglects air resistance.

It has been found that the acceleration of gravity is approximately

$$a = -32 \text{ ft/s}^2$$

The negative sign appears because, conventionally, distances measured toward the center of the earth are considered to be negative whereas distances measured away from the center of the earth are considered to be positive.

From Eq. (43) it follows that

$$\frac{dv}{dt} = -32 \text{ ft/s}^2 \tag{46}$$

or

$$v = \int -32\,dt \tag{47}$$

and

$$v = -32t + C_1 \tag{48}$$

Evidently C_1 is the velocity when $t = 0$. This is called the *initial velocity* and may also be designated as v_0. Thus Eq. (48) may be written

$$v = -32t + v_0 \tag{49}$$

Since

$$\frac{ds}{dt} = v$$

where $s =$ the distance measured from some arbitrary zero reference point, we may write

$$s = \int v\,dt = \int(-32t + v_0)\,dt$$
$$s = -16t^2 + v_0 t + C_2 \tag{50}$$

Example 7. A stone is dropped from a height of 288 ft. Write the equation for acceleration, velocity, and distance fallen.

This is a freely falling body; therefore acceleration is

$$a = -32 \text{ ft/s}^2$$

Following Eq. (49),

$$v = -32t + v_0 \tag{51}$$

Since the stone was dropped and not thrown, its initial velocity v_0 is zero, and

$$v = -32t$$

From Eq. (50) where $v_0 = 0$,

$$s = 16t^2 + C_2$$

The constant C_2 is the distance when $t = 0$. In this case when $t = 0$, s is also zero, and therefore $C_2 = 0$. Consequently,

$$s = -16t^2$$

When dealing with freely falling bodies, it is perhaps more natural to write Eq. (50) with the following symbols:

$$h = -16t^2 + v_0 t + h_0 \tag{52}$$

where h = altitude of freely falling body measured from surface of earth at time t
t = time measured from zero reference time t_0
v_0 = velocity at $t = 0$ (initial velocity)
h_0 = altitude when $t = 0$ (initial altitude)

Incidentally, the term "free fall" applies to upward motion as well as to downward motion.

Since in this example the initial velocity $v_0 = 0$ and the initial altitude $h_0 = 288$, the equation for altitude may be written

$$h = -16t^2 + 288$$

Example 8. In Example 7 find the velocity with which the stone hit the ground.

The stone hit the ground when $h = 0$. Therefore

$$0 = -16t^2 + 288$$

or

$$16t^2 = 288$$

and

$$t = \pm\sqrt{288/16} = \pm\tfrac{1}{4}\sqrt{288} = \pm\tfrac{1}{4} \times 16.97 = \pm 4.24 \text{ s}$$

We shall reject the negative root as physically meaningless in this particular problem.

The stone hit the ground when $t = 4.24$ s. The equation for velocity is

$$v = -32t$$

Therefore, when the stone hit the ground,

$$v = -32 \times 4.24 = -135.7 \text{ ft/s}$$

Example 9. A stone is thrown straight up from a roof 288 ft high with an initial speed of 48 ft/s. Find the equations for acceleration, velocity, and altitude.

As is always the case with a freely falling body,

$$a = -32$$

From Eq. (49) applied to this problem

$$v = -32t + 48$$

Note that since the initial velocity is in a positive direction, the sign of the initial velocity (in this case 48 ft/s) is positive.

From Eq. (52) applied to this problem

$$h = -16t^2 + 48t + 288$$

Example 10. Find the velocity of the stone in Example 9 when $t = 1$ and when $t = 2$.

When $t = 1$,

$$v = -32(1) + 48 = +16 \text{ ft/s}$$

When $t = 2$,

$$v = -32(2) + 48 = -16 \text{ ft/s}$$

Since the sign of the velocity when $t = 1$ is positive, we know that the direction of motion at that time is upward. Since the sign of the velocity is negative when $t = 2$, we know that the direction of motion at that time is downward.

Example 11. Find the altitude in Example 9 when $t = 1$ and when $t = 2$.
When $t = 1$,

$$h = -16(1)^2 + 48(1) + 288 = 320 \text{ ft}$$

When $t = 2$,

$$h = -16(2)^2 + 48(2) + 288 = 320 \text{ ft}$$

In other words, the stone passes the 320-ft line, going up when $t = 1$. It passes the same level going down when $t = 2$.

Example 12. Find the maximum altitude attained by the stone in Example 9.
The maximum altitude occurs when the velocity is zero, that is, when

$$0 = -32t + 48$$

or

$$t = {}^{48}\!/_{32} = 1.5$$

When $t = 1.5$, the altitude is

$$h = -16(1.5)^2 + 48(1.5) + 288 = -16(2.25) + 48(1.5) + 288 = 324 \text{ ft (max)}$$

Example 13. With what velocity did the stone hit the ground in Example 9?
The stone hit the ground when $h = 0$. Therefore we shall find what value of t makes the altitude zero.

$$0 = -16t^2 + 48t + 288$$
$$0 = -t^2 + 3t + 18$$
$$0 = (-t + 6)(t + 3)$$

or

$$t = 6, -3$$

Discarding the root $t = -3$ as physically meaningless for this particular problem, we substitute $t = 6$ in the equation for velocity, obtaining

$$v = -32(6) + 48 = -192 + 48 = -144 \text{ ft/s}$$

Example 14. If a stone is thrown upward from ground level with an initial speed of 144 ft/s, when will it reach a velocity of +48 ft/s?

$$48 = -32t + 144$$
$$32t = 96$$
$$t = 3 \text{ s}$$

Compare with the rejected root in Example 13.

Example 15. What maximum altitude will the stone in Example 14 reach?

Maximum altitude occurs when $v = 0$.

$$0 = -32t + 144$$
$$t = 4.5 \text{ s}$$
$$h_{max} = -16(4.5)^2 + 144(4.5) = (-16 \times 20.25) + (144 \times 4.5)$$
$$= -324 + 648 = +324$$

(Compare with Example 12.)

Example 16. If the stone had been thrown straight down with a speed of 48 ft/s from a height of 288 ft, find the equation for acceleration, velocity, and altitude.

As is always the case with a freely falling body

$$a = -32 \text{ ft/s}^2$$

From Eq. (49) applied to this problem

$$v = -32t - 48$$

Note that, since the initial velocity is in a negative direction, the sign of the initial velocity (in this case 48 ft/s) is negative.

From Eq. (52) applied to this problem

$$h = -16t^2 - 48t + 288$$

Example 17. With what velocity will the stone hit the ground in Example 16?

$$0 = -16t^2 - 48t + 288$$
$$0 = -t^2 - 3t + 18$$
$$0 = (-t + 3)(t + 6)$$
$$t = 3, -6$$

We shall reject the root $t = -6$ as physically meaningless in this problem. The stone hit the ground when $t = 3$, and

$$v = -32(3) - 48 = -144$$

Compare with the velocity found in Example 13. Explain.

Figure 21.4 is a plot of the equation

$$h = -16t^2 + 48t + 288$$

Observe that the region of the graph between $t = 0$ and $t = 6$ applies to Examples 9, 10, and 11.

Note that from the symmetry of the graph, the slope at $t = 1$ and $t = 2$ must be equal in magnitude and opposite in sign (see Example 10).

The axis of symmetry of the graph is at $t = 1.5$, and at this time the altitude is 324 ft, which is the maximum altitude (see Example 12).

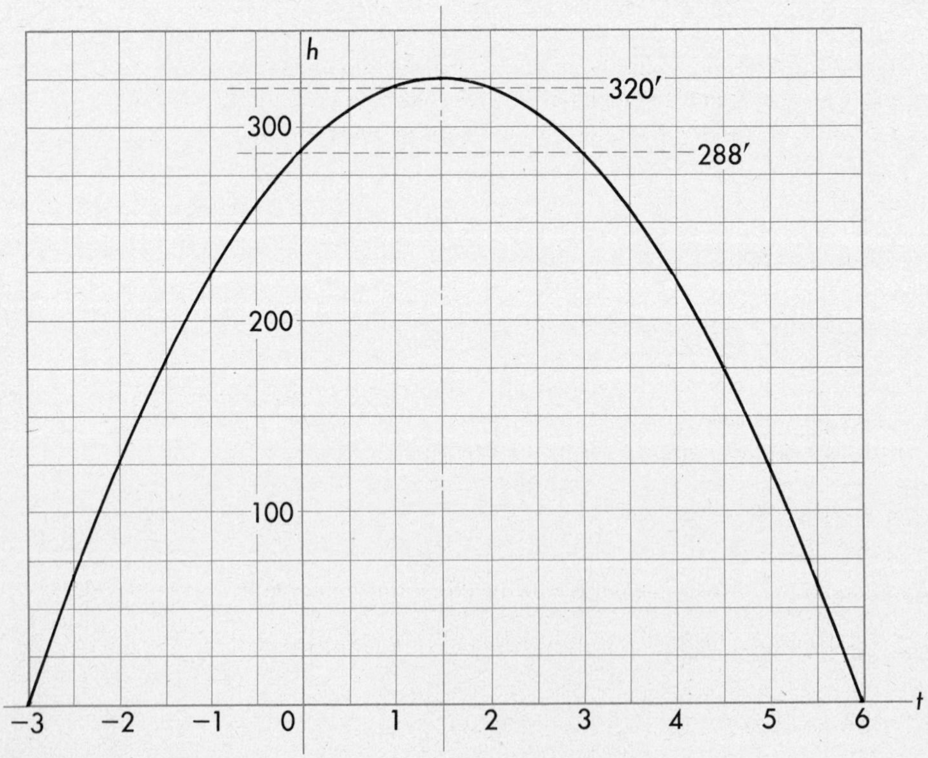

FIGURE 21.4

Considering only the mathematical relationship in the above equation, we find that $h = 0$ when $t = -3$ and when $t = +6$. Within the physical limitations imposed by the wording of Example 9, the root of $t = -3$ is meaningless (see Example 13).

However, if a stone had been thrown directly upward, 3 s before our arbitrarily chosen zero reference time, with sufficient velocity to pass the 288-ft level with a velocity of +48 ft/s, the subsequent trajectory would be identical with the one prescribed by the statement of Example 9 (see Examples 14 and 15).

Observe that at the 288-ft level there are two velocities, equal in magnitude and opposite in sign, one occurring at $t = 0$ and the other occurring at $t = 3$. Considering, for example, the negative velocity when $t = +3$, it makes no difference to the subsequent trajectory whether this velocity is caused by a momentary thrust as is indicated in Example 16 or whether it is the cumulative effect of the force of gravity (see Examples 9, 10, 11, 12, and 13).

Example 18. A ball is thrown horizontally from the top of a building 288 ft high with a speed of 50 ft/s (see Examples 7 and 8).

(a) How long did it take for the ball to reach the ground?
(b) What was the vertical component of velocity v_v at impact with the ground?
(c) What was the horizontal component of velocity v_h at impact?
(d) What was the angle between the trajectory at impact and the vertical?
(e) What was the absolute value of the impact velocity $|v|$?

It is shown in mechanics that if a projectile is thrown in a horizontal direction from a height h above ground, the horizontal component of velocity is constant and equal to the initial horizontal velocity. This is, of course, an approximation based on certain simplifying assumptions, one of which is the neglect of air resistance.

The vertical component of velocity is the same at any time t as it would be had the projectile been dropped instead of having been thrown in a horizontal direction. Therefore the situation discussed in Examples 7 and 8 is descriptive of the vertical component of the trajectory of the ball in this example. From Example 8, the time of flight is 4.24 s.

The horizontal distance the ball travels in air is

$$d_h = v_h t = 50 \times 4.24 = 212 \text{ ft}$$

From Example 8 the vertical component of velocity v_v at impact is -135.7 ft/s.

If ϕ is the angle that the trajectory of the ball makes with the vertical at impact,

$$\cot \phi = \frac{135.7}{50} = 2.714$$

$$\phi = 20.2^\circ$$

The absolute value of the total velocity v_t at impact is

$$|v| = \sqrt{{v_h}^2 + {v_v}^2} = \sqrt{50^2 + (-135.7)^2} = 144.6 \text{ ft/s}$$

EXERCISE 5

1. A stone is dropped from a certain height h_0. Write the equation for its velocity and altitude in terms of time.
2. A stone is thrown downward with a velocity of 100 ft/s from a height of 192 ft. Write the equation for its velocity and altitude in terms of time.
3. A stone is thrown upward with a velocity of 100 ft/s from a height of 192 ft. Write the equation for its velocity and altitude as a function of time.
4. How long did it take the stone to reach the ground in Prob. 2? In Prob. 3?
5. With what velocity did the stone hit the ground in Prob. 2? In Prob. 3?
6. A ball is thrown upward from a roof 96 ft high with an initial speed of 80 ft/s. (*a*) When was the maximum altitude reached? (*b*) What was the maximum altitude? (*c*) When did the ball impact with the ground? (*d*) What was the speed at impact? (*e*) When was the ball 150 ft high (two answers)? (*f*) Find the arithmetic average of the altitudes in part e. On the same coordinate axes plot $y_1 = -16t^2$, $y_2 = 80t$, and $y_3 = 96$. By adding these ordinates, produce the graph of altitude versus time.
7. How long will it take for a stone to reach the ground if it is dropped from a height of 1,024 ft?
8. A bomber is traveling horizontally at a height of h ft with a speed of 300 mi/h = 440 ft/s. Neglecting air resistance, etc., determine how far ahead of a target the bomb should be released if (*a*) h = 10,000 ft; (*b*) h = 20,000 ft; (*c*) h = 30,000 ft. Also, compute for each case the angle that the bomb makes with the vertical on impact with a horizontal target. What is the theoretical speed of the bomb for each of these three cases just before impact?

   The following table gives the *observed* striking speeds and angles of impact:

Altitude, ft	*Striking speed, mi/h*	*Angle of impact with vertical, deg*
2,000	540	50
4,000	620	40
6,000	690	34
8,000	750	30
10,000	790	26
12,000	830	24
15,000	870	21
20,000	940	17

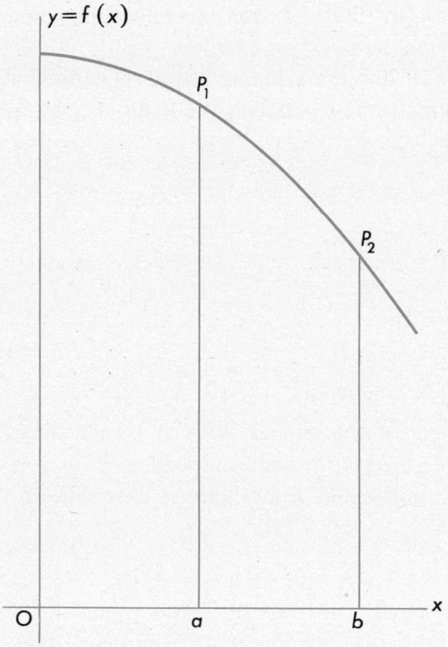

FIGURE 21.5

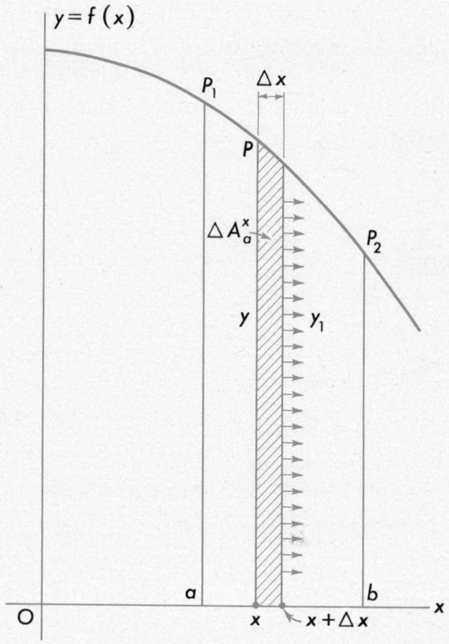

FIGURE 21.6

21.8 Area under Graphs

One of the most important uses for the integration process is in finding the area under curvilinear graphs (see also Sec. 19.9).

Suppose we have given a function f where $y = f(x)$ such as the one illustrated in Fig. 21.5, which is continuous and positive valued over the domain $a \leq x \leq b$. We wish to find the area aP_1P_2b.

To develop a technique for finding such areas, we shall make free use of geometric intuition. Therefore, the details of the argument which we shall present will depend on the appearance of the graphs we have chosen to use.

In Fig. 21.6 we think of the ordinate y as a movable ordinate sweeping over a portion of the area involved and now momentarily occupying the position shown in Fig. 21.6. The momentary value of the area passed over by the moving ordinate depends on the momentary value of x.

Let the area passed over by the moving ordinate y between $x = a$ and some value of x equal to or greater than a be designated as A_a^x. Then the area A_a^x is a variable area bounded by the arc P_1P_2, the fixed ordinate aP_1, that portion of the x axis between a and x, and the movable ordinate y.

Now let us move the ordinate y to the right, Δx units, so that it then occupies position y_1, thereby increasing A_a^x by the amount ΔA_a^x.

Note that the motion along the X axis is in the direction conventionally considered to be positive. Consequently, Δx is considered to be positive.

Now see Fig. 21.7. In this figure we shall assume what is intuitively obvious, that there is an ordinate y^* which can be constructed between the ordinates y and y_1 such that

$$\Delta A_a^x = y^* \, \Delta x \tag{53}$$

Then

$$\frac{\Delta A_a^x}{\Delta x} = y^* \tag{54}$$

Now from Sec. 20.3 the limit which $\Delta A_a^x/\Delta x$ approaches as Δx approaches zero is dA_a^x/dx. By observing Fig. 21.7 we see that as Δx approaches zero, the ordinate y_1 is moved to the left in such a way that y^* approaches the length y. It is therefore appropriate to write

$$\lim_{\Delta x \to 0} \frac{\Delta A_a^x}{\Delta x} = \frac{dA_a^x}{dx} = y \tag{55}$$

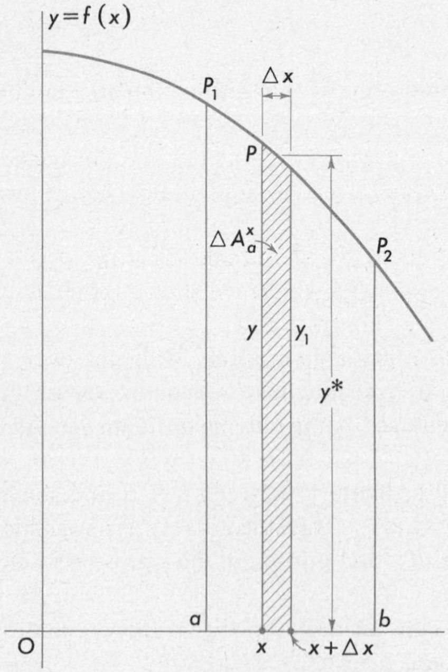

FIGURE 21.7

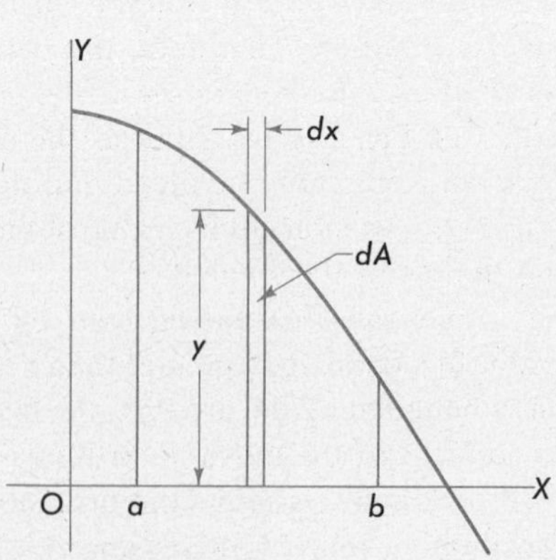

FIGURE 21.8

Thus while we have not yet found an explicit equation for A_a^x in terms of x, we have found a differential equation which A_a^x must satisfy.

This differential equation shows that the rate of change in A_a^x equals the ordinate of the *right-hand* boundary of the area A_a^x. This rate depends not at all on the choice of the *left-hand* boundary. However, the importance of the left-hand boundary will be made evident in Example 19 below.

From Eq. (55) we may write

$$dA_a^x = y\,dx \tag{56}$$

or

$$A_a^x = \int y\,dx$$

It is also common to designate the area involved simply as A, without explicitly indicating the boundaries. Therefore, we may write

$$A_a^x = A = \int y\,dx \tag{57}$$

When actually doing area problems where there is no need for considering the details of the theory involved, we frequently work from simplified drawings such as Fig. 21.8. Here we sometimes speak of the very narrow strip shown as having an area dA, an altitude y, and a width dx, where

$$dA = y\,dx$$

thus suggesting Eq. (57) above.

If $y = f(x)$ we may, following Eq. (57), write

$$A_a^x = \int f(x)\,dx \tag{58}$$

In Sec. 21.9 we shall find it convenient to use the symbolism shown in Eq. (6) and write Eq. (58) as

$$A_a^x = \int f(x)\,dx = F(x) + C \tag{59}$$

Example 19. Find the area under the graph of $y = 100 - x^2$ between $x = 3$ and $x = 6$ (see Fig. 21.9).

Following Eq. (57),

$$A_a^x = \int y\,dx = \int (100 - x^2)\,dx = 100x - \frac{x^3}{3} + C \tag{60a}$$

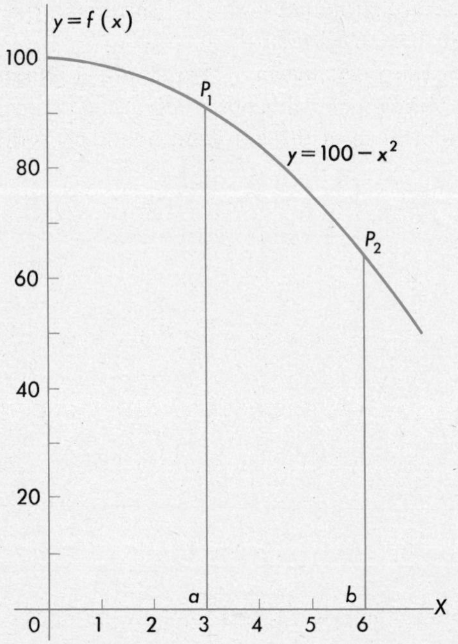

FIGURE 21.9

Now let A_3^x designate the area under the curve between the ordinate erected at x = 3 and any ordinate erected at some abscissa distance equal to or greater than 3. Then we may write

$$A_3^x = 100x - \frac{x^3}{3} + C$$

The problem now is to evaluate the constant of integration. As we indicated in Sec. 21.4, this is done in accordance with some known boundary condition. The appropriate boundary condition to use here is that at the left-hand boundary of the area under consideration (namely, x = 3) the area is zero. Therefore we may write

$$A_3^3 = 0 = 100 \cdot 3 - \frac{3^3}{3} + C \qquad (60b)$$

and

$$0 = 300 - 9 + C = 291 + C \qquad (60c)$$

and

$$C = -291 \tag{60d}$$

Substituting the value of the constant found above, we obtain

$$A_3^x = 100x - \frac{x^3}{3} - 291 \tag{60e}$$

Equation (60e) gives the area under the graph of $y = 100 - x^2$ between an ordinate erected at $x = 3$ and an ordinate erected at some arbitrary value of x equal to or greater than 3, say at $x = b$. Of course, over the interval $a \to b$ it is understood that the graph is everywhere continuous and nonnegative.

When $x = 6$, we have

$$A_3^6 = 100 \cdot 6 - \frac{6^3}{3} - 291 = 600 - 72 - 291 = 237 \tag{60f}$$

Observe that in the above argument we have restricted Δx to positive values. That is, we have considered the moving ordinate always to move from left to right. We could as well have adopted the opposite convention of motion. The same result is obtained in either case. The only difference would be in a reversal of certain signs in the course of the argument.

Let us now apply Eq. (57) to the equation given in Example 20 below.

Example 20. Find the area under the graph of $y = -100 + x^2$ between $x = 3$ and $x = 6$ (see Fig. 21.10).

Following Eq. (57),

$$A_a^x = \int y\,dx = \int (-100 + x^2)\,dx = -100x + \frac{x^3}{3} + C \tag{61a}$$

From the left-hand boundary condition,

$$0 = A_3^3 = -100 \cdot 3 + \frac{3^3}{3} + C = -300 + 9 + C \tag{61b}$$

$$0 = -291 + C \tag{61c}$$

and

$$C = +291 \tag{61d}$$

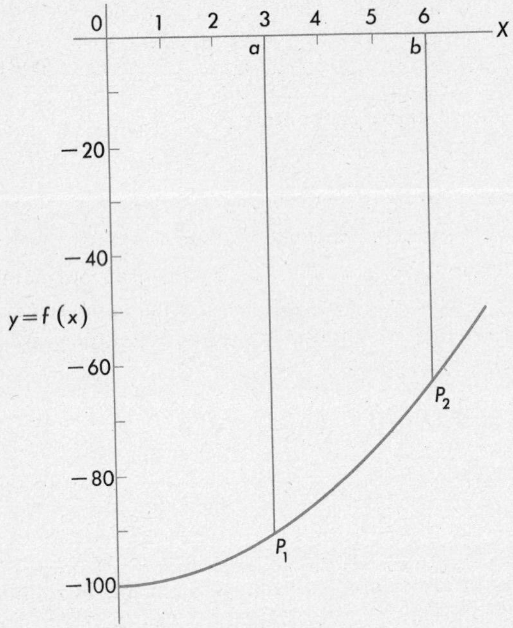

FIGURE 21.10

Consequently,

$$A_3^x = -100x + \frac{x^3}{3} + 291 \tag{61e}$$

When x = 6, we have

$$A_3^6 = -100 \cdot 6 + \frac{6^3}{3} + 291 = -600 + 72 + 291 = -237 \tag{61f}$$

If we compare Eq. (60*f*) and Fig. 21.9 with Eq. (61*f*) and Fig. 21.10, it would appear that in this context we may consider a region which lies below the x axis as having a "negative" area.

Example 21. Find the area under the graph of $y = 25 - x^2$ between $x = 3$ and $x = 5$ (see Fig. 21.11).

Following Eq. (57),

$$A_a^x = \int y\,dx = \int (25 - x^2)\,dx = 25x - \frac{x^3}{3} + C \tag{62a}$$

From the left-hand boundary condition,

$$0 = A_3^{\,3} = 25 \cdot 3 - \frac{3^3}{3} + C \tag{62b}$$

$$0 = 25 \cdot 3 - \frac{3^3}{3} + C = 75 - 9 + C \tag{62c}$$

and

$$C = -66 \tag{62d}$$

Consequently,

$$A_3^{\,x} = 25x - \frac{x^3}{3} - 66 \tag{62e}$$

When $x = 5$, we have

$$A_3^{\,5} = 25 \cdot 5 - \frac{5^3}{3} - 66 = 125 - 41\tfrac{2}{3} - 66 = 17\tfrac{1}{3} \tag{62f}$$

Example 22. Find the area under the graph of $y = 25 - x^2$ between $x = 5$ and $x = 7$ (see Fig. 21.11).

Following Eq. (57),

$$A_a^{\,x} = \int y\,dx = \int (25 - x^2)\,dx = 25x - \frac{x^3}{3} + C \tag{63a}$$

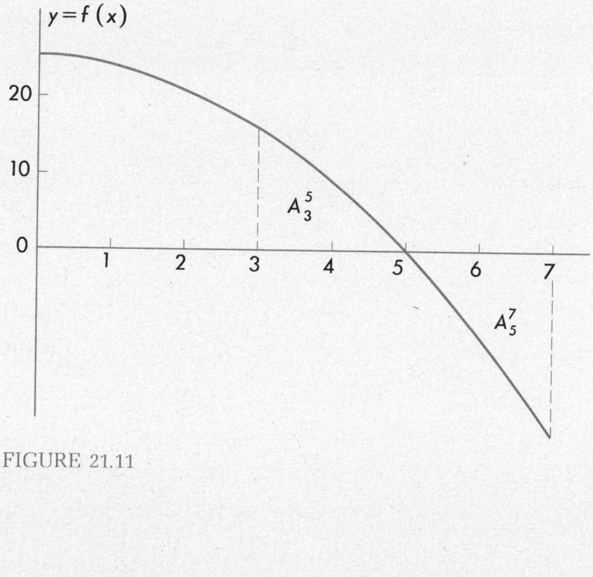

FIGURE 21.11

From the left-hand boundary condition,

$$0 = A_5^5 = 25 \cdot 5 - \frac{5^3}{3} + C = 125 - 41\tfrac{2}{3} + C \tag{63b}$$

and

$$0 = 83\tfrac{1}{3} + C \tag{63c}$$

and

$$C = -83\tfrac{1}{3} \tag{63d}$$

Consequently,

$$A_5^x = 25x - \frac{x^3}{3} - 83\tfrac{1}{3} \tag{63e}$$

When x = 7, we have

$$A_5^7 = 25 \cdot 7 - \frac{7^3}{3} - 83\tfrac{1}{3} = 175 - 114\tfrac{1}{3} - 83\tfrac{1}{3} = -22\tfrac{2}{3} \tag{63f}$$

Example 23. Find the area under the graph of $y = 25 - x^2$ between $x = 3$ and $x = 7$ (see Fig. 21.11).

Following Eq. (57),

$$A_a^x = \int y\,dx = \int (25 - x^2)\,dx = 25x - \frac{x^3}{3} + C \tag{64a}$$

From the left-hand boundary condition,

$$0 = A_3^3 = 25 \cdot 3 - \frac{3^3}{3} + C = 75 - 9 + C \tag{64b}$$

and

$$0 = 66 + C \tag{64c}$$

$$C = -66 \tag{64d}$$

Consequently,

$$A_3^x = 25x - \frac{x^3}{3} - 66 \tag{64e}$$

When x = 7,

$$A_3^{\,7} = 25 \cdot 7 - \frac{7^3}{3} - 66 = 175 - 114\tfrac{1}{3} - 66 = -5\tfrac{1}{3} \qquad (64f)$$

We note here that within the context of our present discussion the process of integration automatically counts the area of a region above the x axis as positive and the region below the x axis as negative. The result is the algebraic sum of these areas. That is, from Examples 21, 22, and 23 referred to Fig. 21.11:

$$A_3^{\,7} = A_3^{\,5} + A_5^{\,7} = 17\tfrac{1}{3} + (-22\tfrac{2}{3}) = -5\tfrac{1}{3}$$

If the graph crosses the x axis between $x = a$ and $x = b$, say, for example, at $x = c$, and if we want the absolute value of the area (sometimes called the geometric area) between ordinates erected at $x = a$ and $x = b$, we integrate between $x = a$ and $x = c$ to find $A_a^{\,c}$. We integrate again between $x = c$ and $x = b$ to find $A_c^{\,b}$. Then

$$|A_a^{\,b}| = |A_a^{\,c}| + |A_c^{\,b}| \qquad (65)$$

Example 24. Find the area under the graph of $y = \tfrac{1}{2}x - 6$ between $x = 0$ and $x = 12$ (see Fig. 21.12).

$$A = \int y\,dx = \int \left(\frac{1}{2}x - 6\right) dx = \frac{x^2}{4} - 6x + C \qquad (66)$$

When $x = 0$, $A = 0$, and $C = 0$; therefore

$$A_0^{\,x} = \frac{x^2}{4} - 6x \qquad (67)$$

When x = 12,

$$A_0^{\,12} = {}^{144}\!/_4 - 72 = 36 - 72 = -36$$

Example 25. Find the area under the graph $y = \tfrac{1}{2}x - 6$ between $x = 12$ and $x = 24$ (see Fig. 21.12).

$$A = \frac{x^2}{4} - 6x + C$$

When $x = 12$, $A = 0$, and

$$0 = \frac{12^2}{4} - 6(12) + C = 36 - 72 + C$$

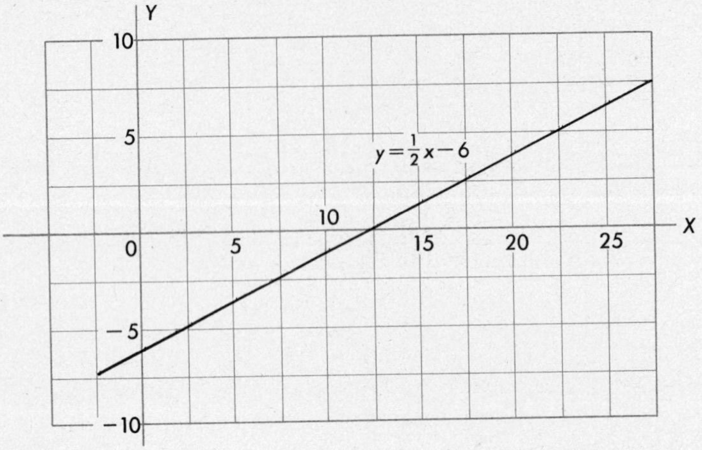

FIGURE 21.12

$C = +36$

$A_{12}^{24} = {}^{576}\!/_4 - 144 + 36 = 144 - 144 + 36 = 36$

Example 26. Find the area under the graph of $y = \frac{1}{2}x - 6$ between $x = 0$ and $x = 24$.

$$A_0^x = \frac{x^2}{4} - 6x \qquad \text{[see Eq. (67)]}$$

$$A_0^{24} = {}^{576}\!/_4 - 144 = 144 - 144 = 0$$

From an observation of Fig. 21.12 we can see the reason for the zero answer. The area between $x = 0$ and $x = 12$ is -36. The area between $x = 12$ and $x = 24$ is $+36$. The sum of these two areas is (algebraically) zero.

However, the absolute value of A_0^{24} is

$$|A_0^{24}| = |A_0^{12}| + |A_{12}^{24}| = |-36| + |+36| = 72$$

Example 27. Find the absolute value of the area under the graph of $y = 100 - x^2$ between $x = 5$ and $x = 15$.

Let us find what value of x makes y equal to zero.

$$0 = 100 - x^2$$
$$x^2 = 100$$
$$x = \pm 10$$

The root $x = +10$ occurs between the two boundary ordinates of the problem. (The boundary ordinates occur at $x = +5$ and $+15$.)

As a first step we shall find the area under the graph between $x = 5$ and $x = 10$. Then we shall find the area between $x = 10$ and $x = 15$.

$$A = \int y\,dx = \int (100 - x^2)\,dx = 100x - \frac{x^3}{3} + C$$

When $x = 5$, $A = 0$; therefore

$$0 = 500 - \frac{125}{3} + C = \frac{1{,}500 - 125}{3} + C$$

$$C = -\frac{1{,}375}{3}$$

$$A_5^x = 100x - \frac{x^3}{3} - \frac{1{,}375}{3} \tag{68}$$

$$A_5^{10} = 1{,}000 - {}^{1{,}000}/_3 - {}^{1{,}375}/_3 = {}^{625}/_3$$

Now let us find the area under the graph between $x = 10$ and $x = 15$. When $x = 10$, $A = 0$; therefore

$$0 = 1{,}000 - {}^{1{,}000}/_3 + C$$
$$C = -{}^{2{,}000}/_3$$

$$A_{10}^x = 100x - \frac{x^3}{3} - \frac{2{,}000}{3}$$

$$A_{10}^{15} = \frac{4{,}500 - 3{,}375 - 2{,}000}{3} = -\frac{875}{3}$$

The *absolute* value of the required area is

$$|A_5^{15}| = {}^{625}/_3 + {}^{875}/_3 = {}^{1{,}500}/_3 = 500$$

Had we integrated directly over the entire region between $x = 5$ and $x = 15$, we would have substituted $x = 15$ in Eq. (68), obtaining

$$A_5^{15} = 1{,}500 - \frac{3{,}375}{3} - \frac{1{,}375}{3} = \frac{4{,}500 - 3{,}375 - 1{,}375}{3} = -\frac{250}{3} \tag{69}$$

Observe that the *algebraic* sum of the area between $x = 5$ and $x = 10$ added to the area between $x = 10$ and $x = 15$ is

$${}^{625}/_3 - {}^{875}/_3 = -{}^{250}/_3$$

which agrees with Eq. (69).

Example 28. Find the area under the graph of $y = 3\sqrt{x}$ between $x = +9$ and $x = +36$.

$$A = \int y\,dx = \int 3\sqrt{x}\,dx = \int 3x^{1/2}\,dx = 2x^{3/2} + C$$

When $x = +9$, $A = 0$, and

$$0 = 2(9)^{3/2} + C$$
$$C = -54$$

Then

$$A_9^x = 2x^{3/2} - 54$$
$$A_9^{36} = 2(36)^{3/2} - 54 = 432 - 54 = 378$$

Example 29. Find the area under the graph of $y = 6/x^2$ between $x = 2$ and $x = \infty$.

$$A = \int y\,dx = \int \frac{6}{x^2}\,dx = \int 6x^{-2}\,dx = -6x^{-1} + C = -\frac{6}{x} + C$$

When $x = 2$, $A = 0$, and

$$0 = -6/2 + C$$
$$C = +3$$

$$A_2^x = -\frac{6}{x} + 3$$

$$A_2^\infty = -\frac{6}{\infty} + 3 = 0 + 3 = 3$$

EXERCISE 6

Find the areas under the following curves between the specified limits:

1. $y = x^2/4$ between $x = 4$ and $x = 10$
2. $y = 6\sqrt{x}$ between $x = 4$ and $x = 9$
3. $y = 9 - x^2$ between $x = -3$ and $x = +3$
4. $y = x^2 - 4$ between $x = -2$ and $x = +2$
5. $y = 16/x^3$ between $x = 1$ and $x = 4$
6. $y = 8/x^2$ between $x = 1$ and $x = \infty$
7. $y = \sqrt{x + 9}$ between $x = 0$ and $x = 16$

8. Find the area under the graph of $y = mx + b$ between $x = 0$ and $x = h$. Show that your answer confirms the formula for the area of a trapezoid.
9. If the area under the graph of $y = 6\sqrt{x}$ is 108 between $x = 4$ and $x = b$, find b.

21.9 The Definite Integral

Let us approach the problem of finding the area under a curve in a somewhat different way.

Example 30. Find the area under the graph of $y = f(x)$ between $x = a$ and $x = b$ (see Fig. 21.9).

The student will find it profitable to compare the following steps with those in Examples 19, 20, and 21.

Following Eq. (58),

$$A_a^x = \int f(x)\, dx \tag{70}$$

For the work to follow, it will be convenient to adopt the symbolism of Eq. (6) and let

$$\int f(x)\, dx = F(x) \tag{71}$$

[The constant of integration which the student might expect to see in the above equation will be incorporated in Eq. (72) below.] Then

$$A_a^x = F(x) + C \tag{72}$$

Compare with Eqs. (60*a*), (61*a*), and (62*a*) in Examples 19, 20, and 21.

However, from the left-hand boundary condition, $A = 0$ when $x = a$. We may now write

$$0 = F(a) + C \tag{73}$$

or

$$C = -F(a) \tag{74}$$

Then Eq. (72) becomes

$$A_a^x = F(x) - F(a) \tag{75}$$

which is a formula for the area A between the ordinate erected at $x = a$ and the ordinate erected at any x_1 such that $x_1 \geq x$. In particular, for this example,

$$A_a^b = F(b) - F(a) \tag{76}$$

Equation (76) above is particularly important. The value of $A_a{}^b$ is obtained by integrating $f(x)$ to obtain $F(x)$. Then x is replaced in $F(x)$ by b and a in turn. The final result is obtained by subtracting $F(a)$ from $F(b)$.

Where $F(x)$ is an indefinite integral of $f(x)$, we commonly express $F(b) - F(a)$ by the symbol $\int_a^b f(x)\,dx$. Thus

$$\int_a^b f(x)\,dx = F(b) - F(a) \tag{77}$$

where $\int_a^b f(x)\,dx$ is called the *definite integral* of $f(x)$ between the limits $x = a$ and $x = b$.

By reference to Eqs. (77) and (58) we see that we may write

$$A_a{}^b = \int_a^b f(x)\,dx \tag{78}$$

If we let

$$y = f(x)$$

then we may write Eq. (78) as

$$A_a{}^b = \int_a^b y\,dx \tag{79}$$

The problem layout for Example 19, using the definite-integral techniques, would be constructed as shown below.

$$A_3{}^6 = \int_3^6 y\,dx \tag{80}$$

In this case $y = 100 - x^2$. Therefore we may write

$$\begin{aligned} A_3{}^6 &= \int_3^6 (100 - x^2)\,dx = \left[100x - \frac{x^3}{3}\right]_3^6 \\ &= \left(100 \cdot 6 - \frac{6^3}{3}\right) - \left(100 \cdot 3 - \frac{3^3}{3}\right) \\ &= (600 - 72) - (300 - 9) = 528 - 291 = 237 \end{aligned}$$

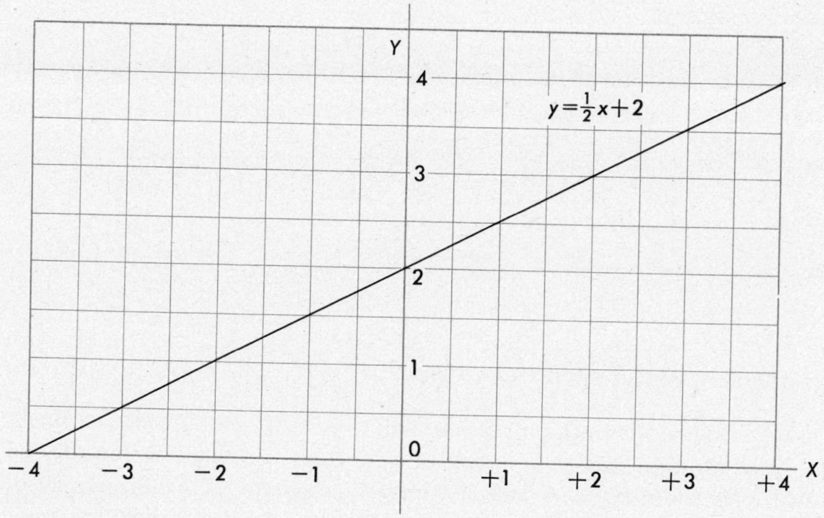

FIGURE 21.13

Example 31. Find the area under the graph of $y = \frac{1}{2}x + 2$ between $x = -4$ and $x = 0$ (see Fig. 21.13).

$$A_{-4}^{0} = \int_{-4}^{0} \left(\frac{1}{2}x + 2\right) dx = \left[\frac{x^2}{4} + 2x\right]_{-4}^{0} = 0 - \left(\frac{16}{4} - 8\right)$$

$$= -(4 - 8) = -(-4) = +4$$

Example 32. Find the area under the graph of $y = \frac{1}{2}x + 2$ between $x = -4$ and $x = +4$.

$$A_{-4}^{+4} = \int_{-4}^{+4} \left(\frac{1}{2}x + 2\right) dx$$

$$= \left[\frac{x^2}{4} + 2x\right]_{-4}^{+4} = \left(\frac{16}{4} + 8\right) - \left(\frac{16}{4} - 8\right) = (4 + 8) - (4 - 8)$$

$$= 12 - (-4) = 12 + 4 = 16$$

Example 33. Find the area under the graph of $y = 3\sqrt{x}$ between $x = +9$ and $x = +36$.

$$A_9^{36} = \int_9^{36} 3x^{1/2}\, dx$$

$$= [2x^{3/2}]_9^{36} = (2 \times 216) - (2 \times 27)$$

$$= 432 - 54 = 378$$

Compare with Example 28.

Example 34. Find the area under the graph of $y = 6/x^2$ between $x = 2$ and $x = \infty$.

$$A_2^\infty = \int_2^\infty 6x^{-2}\,dx$$

$$= [-6x^{-1}]_2^\infty = \left[-\frac{6}{x}\right]_2^\infty = 0 - (-3) = +3$$

21.10 The Mean Value of a Function

In Sec. 19.10 we discussed in an intuitive way what we mean by the *mean* ordinate of a graph. Figure 19.14 illustrates the graph of a function that is continuous on the closed interval with endpoints at a and b. We let $\bar{y}$ designate the average or mean ordinate of the graph between the limits a and b. We then defined $\bar{y}$ such that

$$\bar{y} = \frac{1}{b-a} \times \text{area under graph between } a \text{ and } b$$

Now that we have seen how to calculate the area under a graph, we may write

$$\bar{y} = \frac{1}{b-a}\int_a^b y\,dx \tag{81}$$

The above definition of a mean ordinate is suggestive of a useful definition unrestricted by any graphical context.

If we have a function f which is continuous for $a \le x \le b$, we define the mean value $\bar{y}$ of the function over this interval to be such that

$$\bar{y} = \frac{1}{b-a}\int_a^b f(x)\,dx \tag{82}$$

The practical applications of Eqs. (81) and (82) are many and varied. We shall point out some of them as we proceed through the rest of this chapter.

Example 35. Find the mean ordinate of the graph of the equation

$$y = 100 - x^2$$

between $x = 4$ and $x = 6$.

$$A_4{}^6 = \int_4^6 (100 - x^2)\,dx = \left[100x - \frac{x^3}{3}\right]_4^6 = (600 - 72) - (400 - 21.33)$$

$$= 528 - 378.67 = 149.33$$

$$\bar{y} = \frac{149.33}{6 - 4} = \frac{149.33}{2} = 74.67 \tag{83}$$

Example 36. Find the mean ordinate of the graph in Example 33.

The area under this graph within the prescribed limits is 378. The base interval is $36 - 9 = 27$. Therefore

$$\bar{y} = {}^{378}\!/_{27} = 14.00$$

EXERCISE 7

Find the mean value of the functions defined in Probs. 1 through 6 below between the specified limits. Use the definite-integral symbolism (also see Exercise 6).

1. $y = x^2/4$ between $x = 4$ and $x = 10$
2. $y = 6\sqrt{x}$ between $x = 4$ and $x = 9$
3. $y = 9 - x^2$ between $x = -3$ and $x = +3$
4. $y = x^2 - 4$ between $x = -2$ and $x = +2$
5. $y = 16/x^3$ between $x = 1$ and $x = 4$
6. $y = \sqrt{x + 9}$ between $x = 0$ and $x = 16$

7. Figure 21.14 shows a cantilever beam of length L ft loaded with a concentrated load of P lb at the free end. The equation of the curve of the beam with respect to the indicated axes is $EIy = (P/6)(3Lx^2 - x^3)$, where E and I are constants.

   Figure 21.15 shows a similar cantilever beam of the same length and cross section but loaded with a uniform load of w lb/ft. The equation of the curve of the beam in this case is $EIy = (w/24)(6L^2x^2 - 4Lx^3 + x^4)$, where E and I are the same constants as before.

   Suppose that the total load is the same in both cases so that $P = wL$ lb. Show that the *mean ordinate* to the first curve for the span L ft is equal to the largest ordinate (the ordinate at $x = L$) to the second curve. Hence show that for any cantilever beam the *mean* deflection produced by a vertical load applied at the free end is equal to the deflection at the free end caused by the same load distributed uniformly over the length of the beam.

21.11 An Area As the Limit of a Sum

In Sec. 19.9 and also in Secs. 21.8 and 21.9 we discussed, in some detail, methods of calculating the area of plane figures bounded by at least one curve.

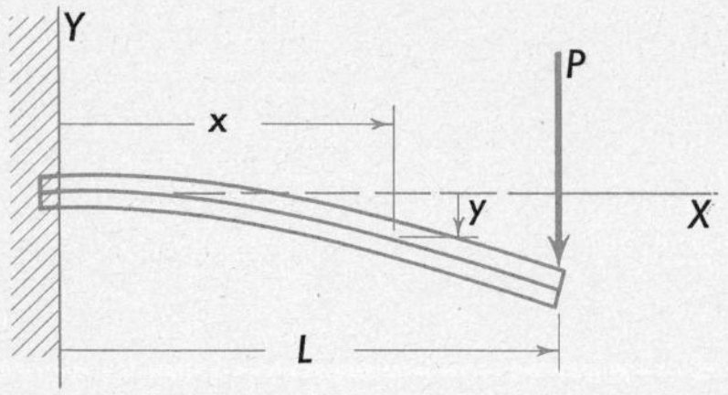

FIGURE 21.14

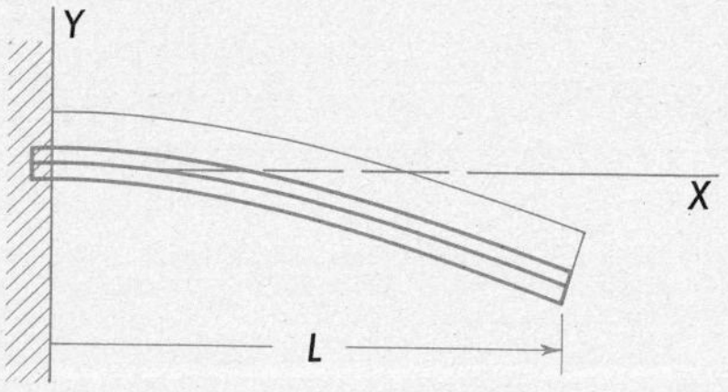

FIGURE 21.15

It might appear that it is hardly worthwhile to go into this matter any further. However, by doing so we can develop techniques for many highly important problems having nothing to do with areas.

At this time the student should review Sec. 19.9, with particular emphasis on Eq. (4).

To continue the present discussion, let the curve in Fig. 21.16 represent a function f such that $f(x) = y$, which is continuous and positive-valued over the domain $a \leq x \leq b$. We now divide this interval into n equal parts. Although it is not strictly necessary that they be equal, it is a convenience and does no harm. This division is accomplished by establishing partition points at

$$(a = x_0) < x_1 < x_2 < x_3 < x_{n-1} < (x_n = b)$$

Ordinates are erected at these points. The region under the graph between $x = a$ and $x = b$ is thus divided into strips of width $\Delta x = x_1 - x_0$, $\Delta x = x_2 - x_1$, $\Delta x = x_3 - x_2$, etc.

An approximation to the area of each strip can be obtained by multiplying Δx by some intermediate ordinate such as y_1^*, y_2^*, y_3^*, y_n^*, etc. This product, of course, gives the exact area of the corresponding rectangle (see Fig. 21.16).

Once again we remind the student that certain of the more sophisticated aspects of the present argument are omitted here. His geometric intuition should be quite sufficient, however.

The area under the graph between $x = a$ and $x = b$ can be approximated by

$$A_a{}^b \approx y_1^*(\Delta x) + y_2^*(\Delta x) + y_3^*(\Delta x) + \cdots + y_n^*(\Delta x) \tag{84}$$

[Also see Eq. (4), Chap. 19.]

The right member of Eq. (84) is exactly the sum of the areas of the rectangles, where

$$\Delta x = \frac{b - a}{n}$$

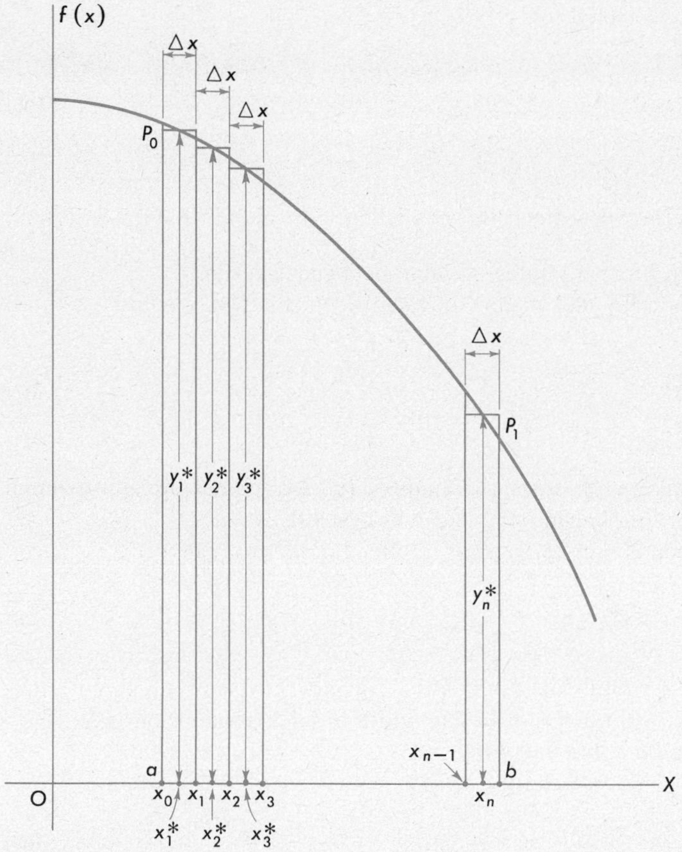

FIGURE 21.16

y_1^* = any ordinate erected within first interval

y_2^* = any ordinate erected within second interval

y_3^* = any ordinate erected within third interval

y_n^* = any ordinate erected within nth interval

It should be intuitively evident that the area aP_0P_1b is the limit that the sum of the areas of these rectangles approaches as the number of the rectangles increases. That is, we may write

$$A_a{}^b = \lim_{n\to\infty} [y_1^*(\Delta x) + y_2^*(\Delta x) + y_3^*(\Delta x) + \cdots + y_n^*(\Delta x)] \tag{85}$$

Equation (85) can be abbreviated to

$$A_a{}^b = \lim_{n\to\infty} \sum_{k=1}^{k=n} (y_k^*)\,\Delta x \tag{86}$$

The symbol $\sum_{k=1}^{k=n} (y_k^*)\,\Delta x$ designates the sum whose typical (or kth) term is $(y_k^*)\,\Delta x$, where k may take on, in turn, any integral value between 1 and n.

If we replace $A_a{}^b$ in Eq. (86) by its equivalent from Eq. (79), we find

$$\int_a^b y\,dx = \lim_{n\to\infty} \sum_{k=1}^{k=n} (y_k^*)\,\Delta x \tag{87}$$

When we are dealing with areas, the quantity $(y_k^*)\,\Delta x$ denotes the approximate area of a typical strip whose height is y_k^* and whose width is Δx.

If $y = f(x)$, it is sometimes convenient to alter Eq. (87) to read

$$A_a{}^b = \lim_{n\to\infty} [f(x_1^*) + f(x_2^*) + f(x_3^*) + \cdots + f(x_n^*)]\,\Delta x \tag{88}$$

where $x_1^*, x_2^*, x_3^*, \cdots, x_n^*$ are points within the first, second, third, and nth subdivisions of the interval between $x = a$ and $x = b$. The width of each subdivision is Δx.

Equation (88) can be abbreviated to

$$A_a{}^b = \lim_{n\to\infty} \sum_{k=1}^{k=n} f(x_k^*)\,\Delta x \tag{89}$$

The symbol $\sum_{k=1}^{k=n} f(x_k^*)\,\Delta x$ designates the sum whose typical (or kth) term is $f(x_k^*)\,\Delta x$, where k may take on, in turn, any integral value between 1 and n.

If we replace $A_a{}^b$ in Eq. (89) by its equivalent from Eq. (78), we obtain

$$\int_a^b f(x)\,dx = \lim_{n\to\infty} \sum_{k=1}^{k=n} f(x_k^*)\,\Delta x \tag{90}$$

To avoid the use of relatively complex working drawings such as Fig. 21.16, indicating a large number of elemental areas, we often simplify a drawing such as Fig. 21.16 to one such as Fig. 21.17. Here we show only one elementary area, but the implication is clear that the area under the curve between $x = a$ and $x = b$ is the limit that the sum of a series of these elemental areas approaches as their number increases without limit.

It is quite common to indicate the area of an elemental strip as

$$dA = y\,dx \tag{91}$$

Then, without giving much attention to the details of the reasoning involved, we write

$$A_a{}^b = \int_a^b y\,dx \tag{92}$$

21.12 The Area between Curves

In Sec. 21.11 we discussed methods of finding the area of a particular kind of region in a coordinate plane (see Fig. 21.18). This region is bounded *above* by the graph of $y_1 = f_1(x)$, *below* by the x axis, on the *left* by the straight line $x = a$, and on the *right* by the straight line $x = b$.

Now let us investigate methods of finding the area of a somewhat different kind of region (see Fig. 21.19). Here we wish to find the area bounded *above* by the graph of the function f_1 for which $y_1 = f_1(x)$, *below* by the graph of the function f_2 for which $y_2 = f_2(x)$, on the *left* by the straight line $x = a$, and on the *right* by the line $x = b$.

In this discussion we assume that both y_1 and y_2 are continuous over the interval $a \le x \le b$, and that over this interval, $y_1 \ge y_2$.

In Fig. 21.19 we shall divide the area between the curves in the interval from

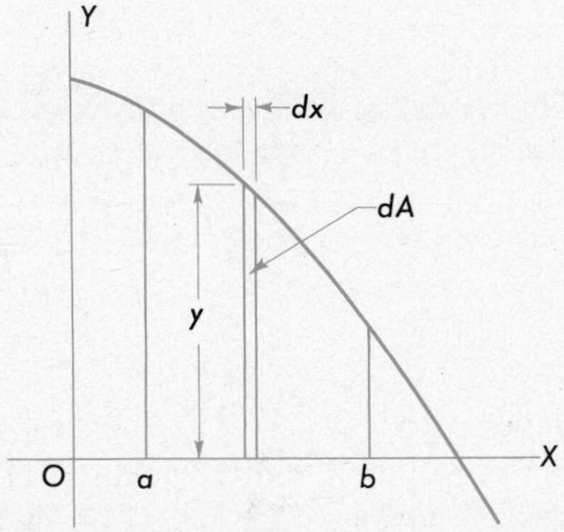

FIGURE 21.17

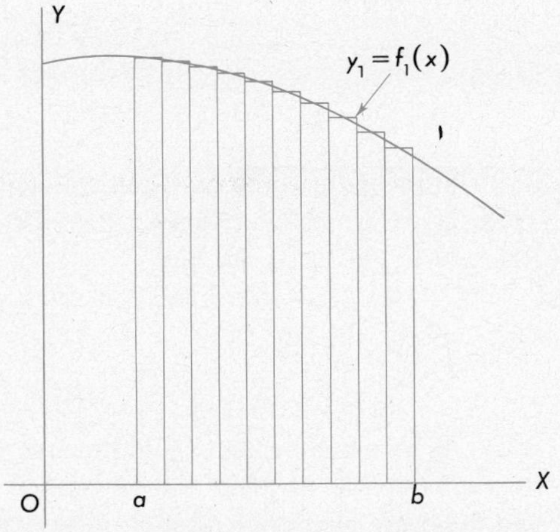

FIGURE 21.18

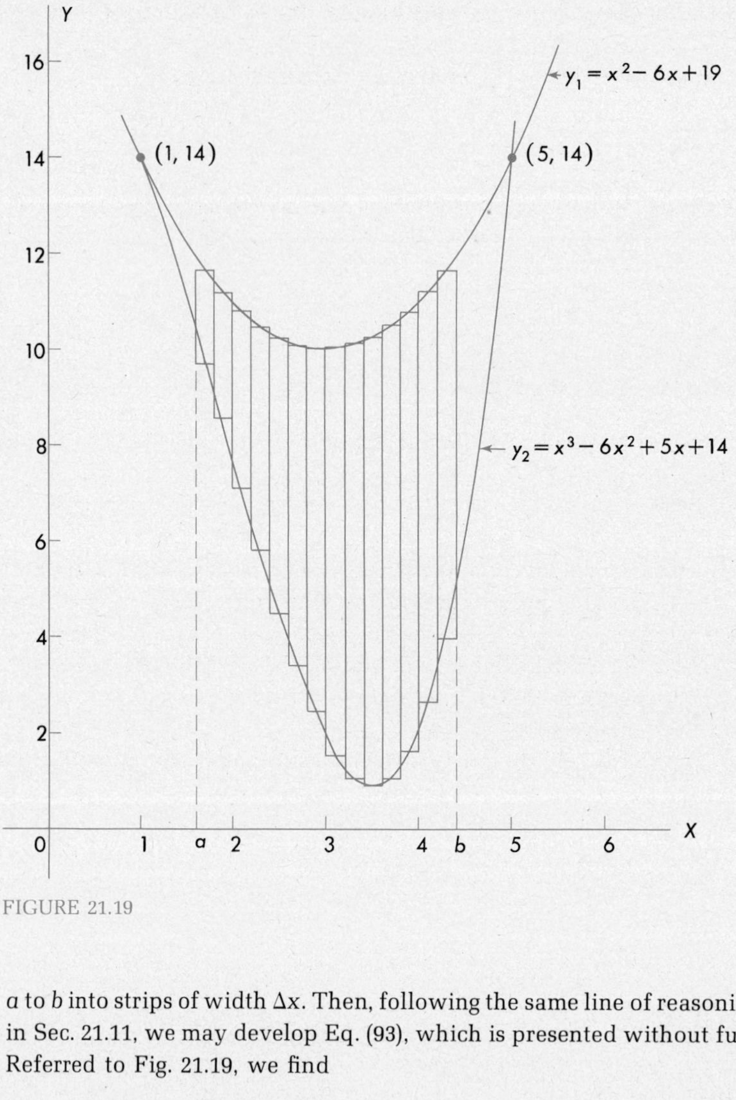

FIGURE 21.19

a to b into strips of width Δx. Then, following the same line of reasoning as was outlined in Sec. 21.11, we may develop Eq. (93), which is presented without further justification. Referred to Fig. 21.19, we find

$$A_a{}^b = \int_a^b (y_1 - y_2)\, dx \tag{93}$$

As an example, let us find the area between the curves of y_1 and y_2 from $x = 1$ to $x = 5$ (see Fig. 21.19). It can be verified by direct substitution that the points (1,14) and (5,14) are at the intersection of the two curves. Also observe for $1 \leq x \leq 5$ that $y_1 \geq y_2$.

In Fig. 21.19 we divide the interval from a to b into strips whose axes are parallel to the Y axis and whose width is Δx. Then, following Eq. (93), we may write

$$A_1^5 = \int_1^5 [(x^2 - 6x + 19) - (x^3 - 6x^2 + 5x + 14)]\,dx$$

$$A_1^5 = \int_1^5 (-x^3 + 7x^2 - 11x + 5)\,dx$$

$$A_1^5 = \left[-\frac{x^4}{4} + \frac{7x^3}{3} - \frac{11x^2}{2} + 5x\right]_1^5$$

$$A_1^5 = (-625/4 + 875/3 - 275/2 + 25) - (-1/4 + 7/3 - 11/2 + 5)$$

$$A_1^5 = 21\tfrac{1}{3}$$

Frequently we encounter a situation such as illustrated in Fig. 21.20. Here we wish to find the area bounded by the curve of the relation

$$y^2 - 8y + 16 = x$$

and the line $x = 4$. However, by writing this relation as

$$(y - 4)^2 = x$$

or

$$y - 4 = \pm\sqrt{x}$$

or

$$y = 4 \pm \sqrt{x}$$

we see that $y^2 - 8y + 16 = x$ expresses not *one* but *two functions* of x. Thus we may write

$$y_1 = f_1(x) = 4 + \sqrt{x}$$

for the portion of the curve from P to Q and

$$y_2 = f_2(x) = 4 - \sqrt{x}$$

for the portion of the curve from P to R.

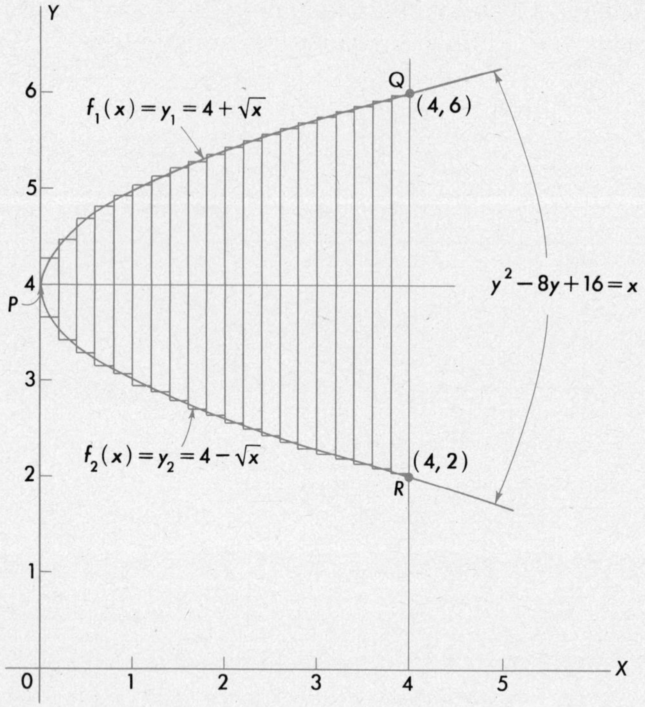

FIGURE 21.20

Now we can apply Eq. (93) which requires that y_1 and y_2 be *functions* of x and write

$$A_0^4 = \int_0^4 [(4 + \sqrt{x}) - (4 - \sqrt{x})]\, dx$$

$$A_0^4 = \int_0^4 (\sqrt{x} + \sqrt{x})\, dx = \int_0^4 2\sqrt{x}\, dx$$

$$A_0^4 = \int_0^4 2x^{1/2}\, dx = [\tfrac{4}{3}x^{3/2}]_0^4 = \tfrac{32}{3}$$

By changing our point of view somewhat, we can draw the elemental strips as shown in Fig. 21.21. Then we may consider y to be the independent variable and x to be the dependent variable. The width of each elemental strip is now Δy. The length of each elemental strip is $(4 - x)$. The area is given by

$$A_2^6 = \int_2^6 (4 - x)\, dy = \int_2^6 [4 - (y^2 - 8y + 16)]\, dy$$

$$A_2^6 = \int_2^6 (-y^2 + 8y - 12)\,dy = \left[-\frac{y^3}{3} + 4y^2 - 12y\right]_2^6$$

$$A_2^6 = (-72 + 144 - 72) - (-8/3 + 16 - 24)$$

$$A_2^6 = 0 - (-8/3 - 8) = 32/3$$

A somewhat more complicated situation is illustrated in Fig. 21.22. Here we wish to find the area between the graphs of

$$y^2 - 8y + 28 = 4x_2$$

and

$$y^2 - 8y + 16 = x_1$$

It can be verified by direct substitution that the points (4,6) and (4,2) are the intersections of the curves.

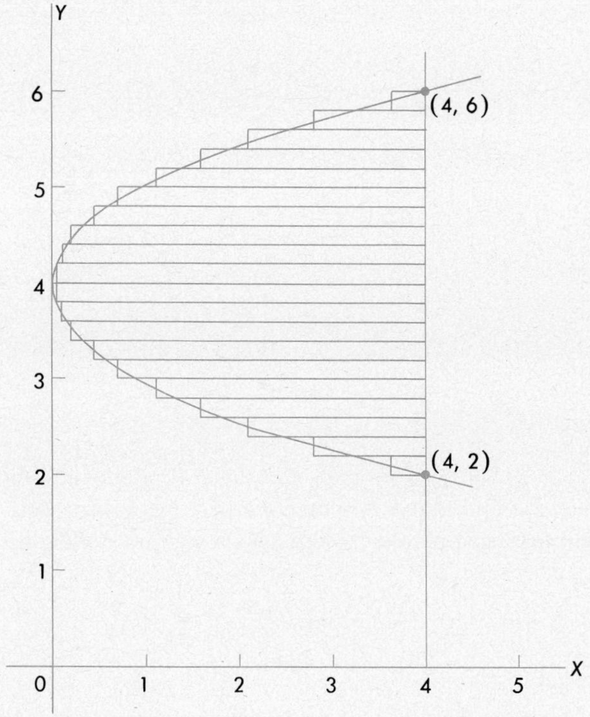

FIGURE 21.21

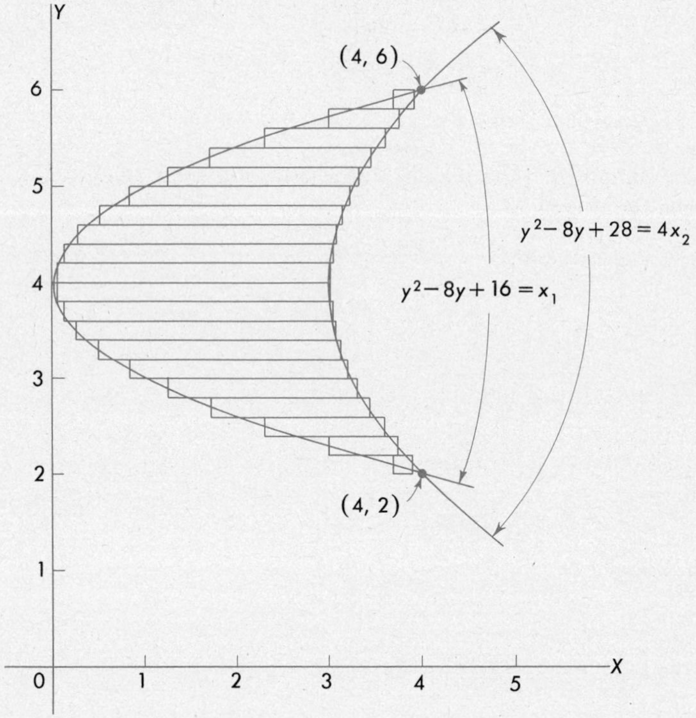

FIGURE 21.22

Observe that both

$$y^2 - 8y + 28 = 4x_2$$

and

$$y^2 - 8y + 16 = x_1$$

express two functions of x. However, as before, if we view x as the dependent variable and y as the independent variable, we find that x is a function of y for both curves. By drawing the axes of the elemental strips parallel to the X axis we find, following Eq. (93), that

$$A_2{}^6 = \int_2^6 (x_2 - x_1)\, dy$$

$$= \int_2^6 \left[\left(\frac{y^2}{4} - 2y + 7\right) - \left(y^2 - 8y + 16\right)\right] dy$$

$$A_2{}^6 = \int_2^6 \left(-\frac{3y^2}{4} + 6y - 9\right) dy = \left[-\frac{y^3}{4} + 3y^2 - 9y\right]_2^6$$

$$A_2{}^6 = (-54 + 108 - 54) - (-2 + 12 - 18)$$

$$A_2{}^6 = 0 - (-8) = 8$$

Other areas with more complicated shapes can often be calculated similarly by decomposing them into a number of areas with simple shapes.

Suppose we wish to find the area between the graph of

$$y_1 = 3x - 10$$

and

$$y_2 = x^2 + 10x \qquad \text{(see Fig. 21.23)}$$

Here the coordinates of the points of intersection of both curves are not given. However, we may find these coordinates by solving the two given equations simultaneously. For example, in this case for an intersection to occur,

$$x^2 + 10x = 3x - 10$$

$$x^2 + 7x + 10 = 0$$

$$(x + 5)(x + 2) = 0$$

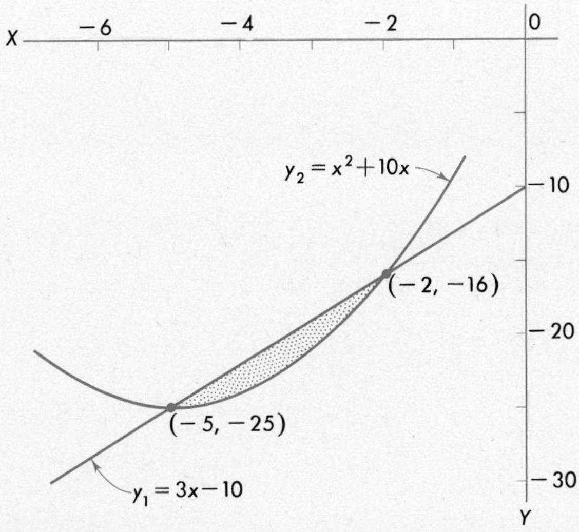

FIGURE 21.23

and

$x = -5 \quad \text{or} \quad x = -2$

By substituting in

$y = 3x - 10$

we find that when $x = -5$,

$y = -15 - 10 = -25$

and when $x = -2$,

$y = -6 - 10 = -16$

The coordinates of the points of intersection are, therefore, $(-5,-25)$ and $(-2,-16)$ (see Fig. 21.23). Then

$$A_{-5}^{-2} = \int_{-5}^{-2} [(3x - 10) - (x^2 + 10x)]\,dx = \int_{-5}^{-2} (-x^2 - 7x - 10)\,dx$$

$$A_{-5}^{-2} = \left[-\frac{x^3}{3} - \frac{7x^2}{2} - 10x\right]_{-5}^{-2}$$

$$A_{-5}^{-2} = \left(\frac{8}{3} - 14 + 20\right) - \left(\frac{125}{3} - \frac{7 \times 25}{2} + 50\right)$$

$$A_{-5}^{-2} = \left(\frac{26}{3}\right) - \left(\frac{250 - 525 + 300}{6}\right)$$

$$A_{-5}^{-2} = (26/3) - (25/6) = 52/6 - 25/6 = 27/6 = 4\tfrac{1}{2}$$

EXERCISE 8

Find the area between the following graphs.

1. $y = \frac{1}{4}x^2$ and $y = 1.5x - 2$
2. $y = x^2 + 4x + 2$ and $y = 2x + 5$
3. $y = x^3 - 1$, $x = 2$, $y = -3$, and $x = 0$
4. $y = 18 - x^2$ and $y = x^2$
5. $y^2 = x$ and $y = x - 6$
6. $y = 9 - x^2$ and $y = 3 - x$
7. $y = x^2$ and $y = 6 - x$
8. $y = x^2 - 3x$ and $y = -x^2 + 7x$
9. $x = y^2 - 3y$ and $x = -y^2 + 7y$

21.13 Broader Implications of the Definite Integral

Although it is quite true that we arrived at Eq. (88) by reasoning in terms of areas, this equation is not by any means limited to problems about areas.

If we are given a function f where $y = f(x)$ which is continuous for $a \leq x \leq b$, the definite integral

$$\int_a^b f(x)\,dx \tag{94}$$

is a number obtained as follows.

1. Divide the interval $a \leq x \leq b$ into n equal parts, each of width

   $$\Delta x = \frac{b-a}{n}$$

   As we mentioned before, these widths need not be equal, but it is convenient if they are.
2. Form the sum

   $$[f(x_1^*) + f(x_2^*) + f(x_3^*) + \cdots + f(x_n^*)]\,\Delta x \tag{95}$$

   where x_1^*, x_2^*, x_3^*, $\cdots$, x_n^* are points (or numbers) within their respective intervals.
3. Take the limit of the above sum as n approaches ∞ to obtain

   $$\int_a^b f(x)\,dx = \lim_{n\to\infty} \sum_{k=1}^{k=n} (y_k^*)\,\Delta x \tag{96}$$

It is important to note that regardless of the context out of which this number $\int_a^b f(x)\,dx$ arose, still it is always possible to plot $y = f(x)$ in the xy plane. Then there will be a region in this plane whose area is measured by the same number.

In the work to follow we shall relate the arguments presented in this section to a variety of applications.

21.14 Volumes by Integration

Figure 21.24a is a pictorial drawing of a solid such that the area A_s of every cross section perpendicular to the line X is the value of a continuous function of x. Then

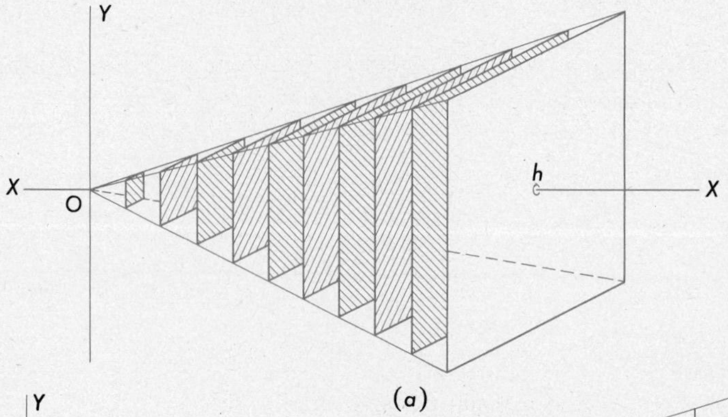

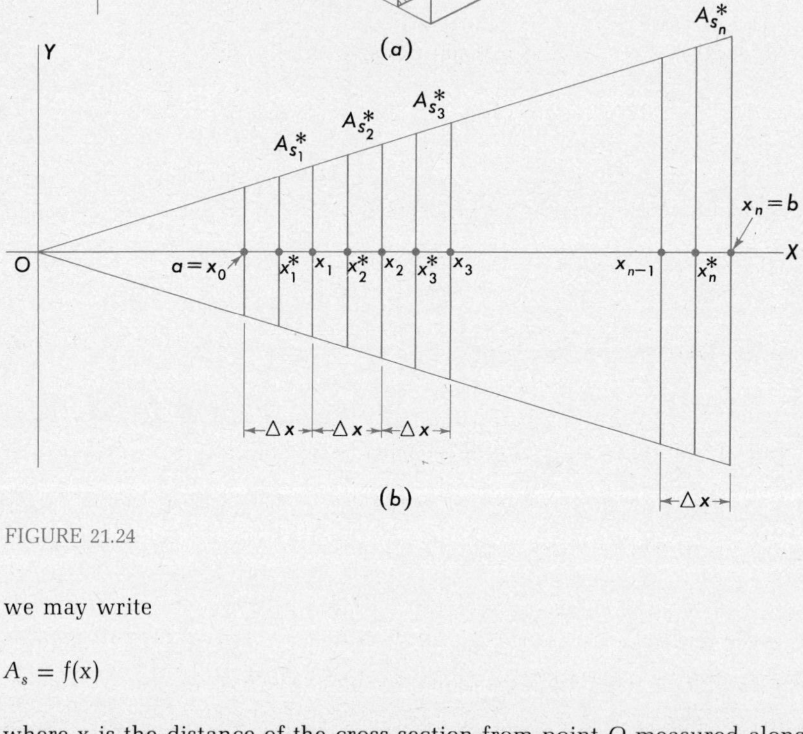

FIGURE 21.24

we may write

$$A_s = f(x) \tag{97}$$

where x is the distance of the cross section from point O measured along the line X. Figure 21.24*b* is a view in orthographic projection of the same solid.

We now divide the interval from a to b into n equal parts. Though it is not strictly necessary for our argument that they be equal, it is a convenience and does no harm. This division is accomplished by establishing partition points at

$$(a = x_0) < x_1 < x_2 < x_3 < \cdots < x_{n-1} < (x_n = b)$$

Planes are passed through each partition point perpendicular to the line X. The volume of the solid between $x = a$ and $x = b$ is thus divided into slices of width $\Delta x = x_1 - x_0$, $\Delta x = x_2 - x_1$, $\Delta x = x_3 - x_2$, etc.

The volume of the solid between $x = a$ and $x = b$ can be approximated by

$$V_a{}^b \approx A^*_{s_1}(\Delta x) + A^*_{s_2}(\Delta x) + A^*_{s_3}(\Delta x) + \cdots + A^*_{s_n}(\Delta x) \tag{98}$$

where $\Delta x = \dfrac{b - a}{n}$

$A^*_{s_1}$ = any cross-sectional area within first interval
$A^*_{s_2}$ = any cross-sectional area within second interval
$A^*_{s_3}$ = any cross-sectional area within third interval
$A^*_{s_n}$ = any cross-sectional area within nth interval

It should be intuitively evident that the volume of the solid between $x = a$ and $x = b$ is the limit that the sum of the volumes of these slices approaches as the number of slices increases.

Therefore we may write

$$V_a{}^b = \lim_{n\to\infty} \sum_{k=1}^{k=n} A^*_{s_k}\,\Delta x \tag{99}$$

The symbol $\sum_{k=1}^{k=n} A^*_{s_k}\,\Delta x$ designates the sum of a series of elemental volumes whose typical (or kth) elemental volume is $(A^*_{s_k})\,\Delta x$, where k may take on in turn any integral value between 1 and n.

As we shall see presently, these elemental volumes need not be bounded on two sides by parallel planes. They may have other shapes.

Since we require that A_s be the value of some known and continuous function of x, we may write

$$V_a{}^b = \int_a^b (A_s)\,dx \tag{100}$$

To avoid the use of relatively complex working drawings such as Fig. 21.24a and b, indicating a large number of elemental volumes, we often simplify and work from a drawing such as Fig. 21.25. Here we indicate only one elemental volume, but the implication is clear that the volume of the solid between $x = a$ and $x = b$ is the limit that the sum of a series of these elemental volumes approaches as their number increases without limit.

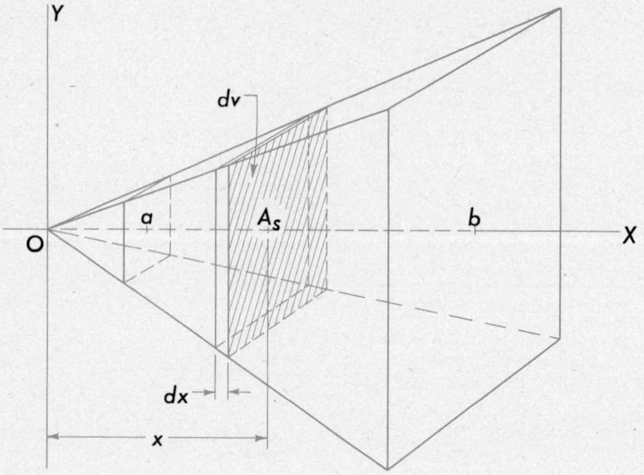

FIGURE 21.25

It is quite common to indicate the typical elemental volume in some such form as

$$dV = A_s\, dx \tag{101}$$

Then if there is no need for going into the details of the theory involved, we may write immediately

$$V_a{}^b = \int_a^b A_s\, dx \tag{102}$$

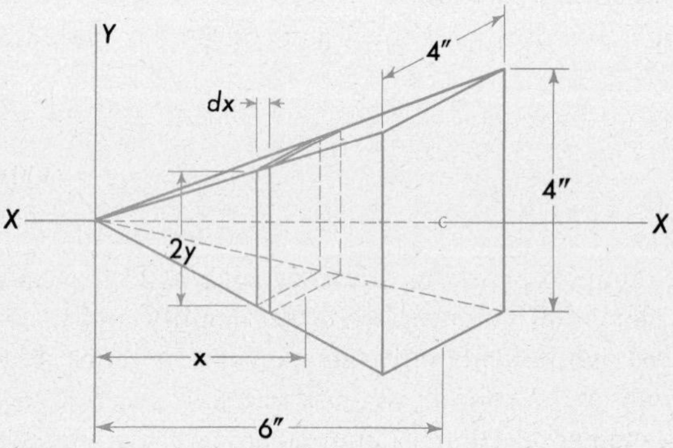

FIGURE 21.26

Example 37. Find the volume of the square pyramid shown in Fig. 21.26.

Following Eq. (100)

$$V_0^6 = \int_0^6 A_s \, dx$$

In this case

$$A_s = (2y)^2$$

But by similarity

$$\frac{2y}{x} = \frac{4}{6}$$

and

$$2y = \tfrac{4}{6}x = \tfrac{2}{3}x$$

Therefore

$$A_s = \tfrac{4}{9}x^2$$

and

$$V_0^6 = \int_0^6 \frac{4}{9}x^2 \, dx = \left[\frac{4x^3}{27}\right]_0^6 = \frac{(4)(6)^3}{27} = \frac{(4)(216)}{27} = 32$$

By elementary geometry

$$V = \tfrac{1}{3} \times \text{area of the base} \times \text{height} = \tfrac{1}{3}(4 \times 4) \times 6 = 32 \qquad \text{(CHECK)}$$

In the following examples we shall find the volume of a hemisphere 10 in in radius.

There are actually several different ways that this can be accomplished. All these ways involve dividing the hemisphere into certain elementary volumes and finding the limit which the total of these volumes approaches as the number of the volumes approaches infinity.

Example 38. Find the volume of the hemisphere shown in Fig. 21.27.

We shall divide the hemisphere into circular slabs of equal thickness. One of these circular slabs is shown in the figure.

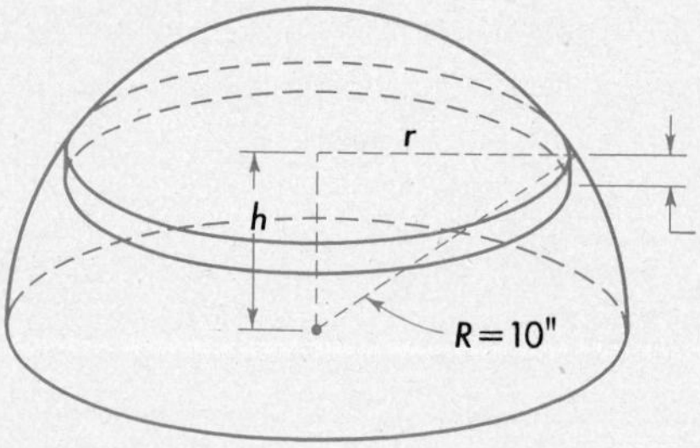

FIGURE 21.27

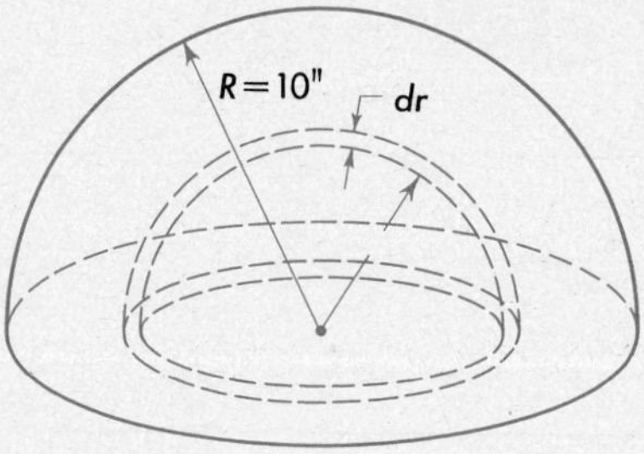

FIGURE 21.28

Following Eq. (100),

$$V_0^{10} = \int_0^{10} A_s\, dh$$

By inspection of the figure,

$$A_s = \pi r^2$$

Therefore,

$$V_0^{10} = \int_0^{10} \pi r^2\, dh$$

But in this figure

$$r^2 = 10^2 - h^2 \qquad (103)$$

Therefore, from Eq. (103),

$$V_0^{10} = \int_0^{10} \pi(10^2 - h^2)\, dh = \int_0^{10} (100\pi - \pi h^2)\, dh$$

$$= \left[100\pi h - \frac{\pi h^3}{3}\right]_0^{10} = 1{,}000\pi - \frac{1{,}000\pi}{3} = \frac{2{,}000\pi}{3}$$

Example 39. Find the volume of the hemisphere shown in Fig. 21.28.

We shall divide the hemisphere into hollow hemispherical shells. One of these shells is shown in the figure.

Following Eq. (100),

$$V_0^{10} = \int_0^{10} A_s\, dr$$

From the figure by inspection,

$$A_s = 2\pi r^2$$

Therefore,

$$V_0^{10} = \int_0^{10} 2\pi r^2\, dr = \left[\frac{2\pi r^3}{3}\right]_0^{10} = \frac{2\pi(1{,}000)}{3} = \frac{2{,}000\pi}{3}$$

Example 40. Find the volume of the hemisphere shown in Fig. 21.29.

We shall divide the hemisphere into hollow tubes. One of these hollow tubes is shown in the figure.

Following Eq. (100),

$$V_0^{10} = \int_0^{10} A_s\, dr$$

From the figure by inspection,

$$A_s = 2\pi rh$$

But

$$h = \sqrt{100 - r^2}$$

Therefore,

$$V_0^{10} = \int_0^{10} 2\pi r\sqrt{100 - r^2}\, dr = \int_0^{10} 2\pi r(100 - r^2)^{1/2}\, dr$$

$$= 2\pi \int_0^{10} r(100 - r^2)^{1/2}\, dr = 2\pi[-\tfrac{1}{3}(100 - r^2)^{3/2}]_0^{10}$$

$$= -\frac{2\pi}{3}[-(100)^{3/2}] = \frac{2{,}000\pi}{3}$$

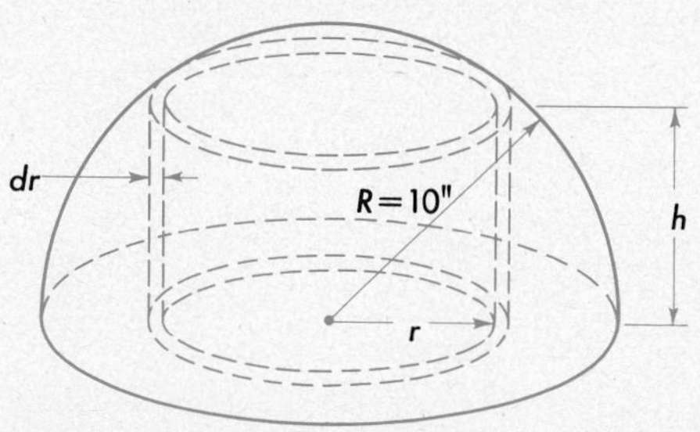

FIGURE 21.29

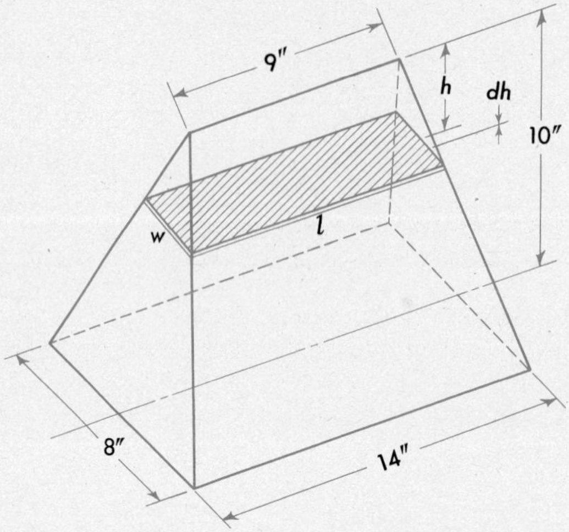

FIGURE 21.30

Example 41. Find the volume of the wedge illustrated in Fig. 21.30.

We shall consider the wedge to be made up of a stack of horizontal sections of width w, length l, and thickness dh. Accordingly,

$$V_0^{10} = \int_0^{10} wl\,dh$$

Since w is at all times proportional to h and is 8 when $h = 10$, we may replace w by $0.8h$. l is a linear function of h, and since l is 9 when $h = 0$ and l is 14 when $h = 10$, it can be readily shown that $l = 9 + 0.5h$.

Therefore we may write

$$V_0^{10} = \int_0^{10} 0.8h(9 + 0.5h)\,dh$$

or

$$V_0^{10} = \int_0^{10} (7.2h + 0.4h^2)\,dh$$

and

$$V_0^{10} = [3.6h^2 + \tfrac{2}{15}h^3]_0^{10} = 360 + 133.3 = 493.3$$

Checking by the prismoidal formula, we obtain

$$V = \tfrac{1}{6}(10)[0 + 4(4 \times 11.5) + (8 \times 14)] = \tfrac{10}{6}(0 + 184 + 112) = 493.3$$

(See Prob. 48, in Exercise 1, Chap. 5.)

Example 42. Find the volume of the wedge cut from the cylinder in Fig. 21.31.

If we divided the volume into many vertical right-triangular slabs of thickness dx, we obtain

$$V_{-5}^{5} = 2\int_0^5 \tfrac{1}{2}hy\,dx$$

(Note that we could just as logically have written

$$V_{-5}^{5} = \int_{-5}^{5} \tfrac{1}{2}hy\,dx$$

but the first method is shorter.)

In each triangular element $h = 3y$, or the area of the elemental section is

$$\tfrac{1}{2}hy = \tfrac{3}{2}y^2$$

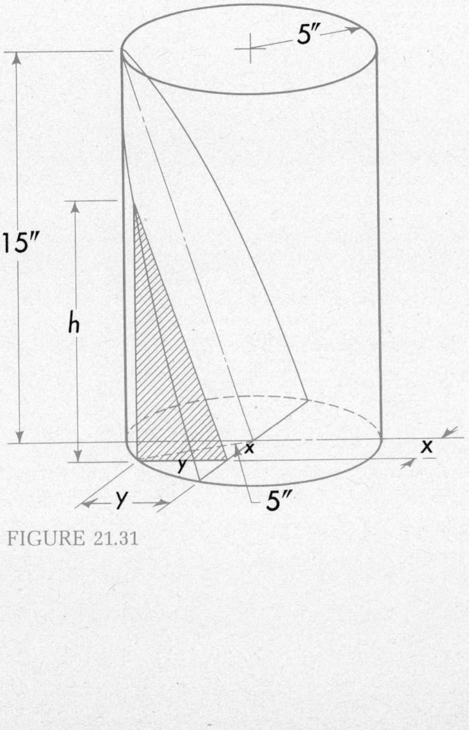

FIGURE 21.31

But

$$y^2 = 25 - x^2$$

Therefore the area of the elemental section is

$$\text{Area} = \tfrac{3}{2}(25 - x^2)$$

Hence we may write

$$V_{-5}{}^{5} = 2\int_0^5 \tfrac{3}{2}(25 - x^2)\,dx$$
$$= 3\int_0^5 (25 - x^2)\,dx$$
$$= 3\left[25x - \frac{x^3}{3}\right]_0^5$$

Therefore

$$V = 3(125 - {}^{125}\!/_3) = 250$$

Example 43. Find the volume common to two cylinders (see Fig. 21.32), each of radius 3 in, whose axes intersect at right angles.

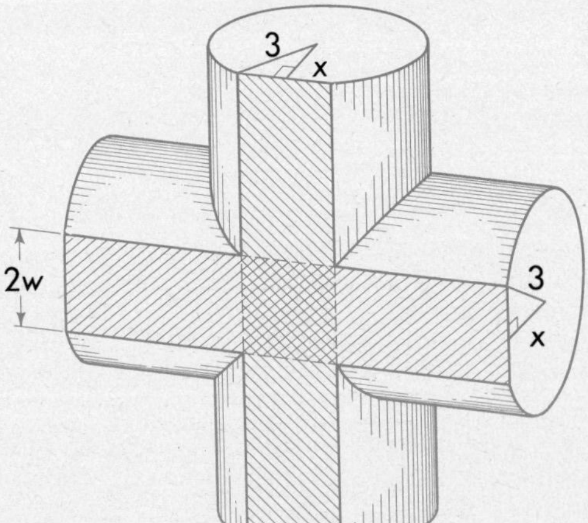

FIGURE 21.32

It will be seen that the volume of one of the elemental slabs making up the volume of intersection is

$$dv = (2w)^2\,dx$$

But

$$w = \sqrt{9 - x^2}$$

or

$$4w^2 = 36 - 4x^2$$

Hence

$$V = 2\int_0^3 (36 - 4x^2)\,dx = 2[36x - \tfrac{4}{3}x^3]_0^3 = 2\{[(36)(3) - \tfrac{4}{3}(3)^3] - 0\}$$

$$= 2(108 - 36) = 144 \text{ in}^3$$

EXERCISE 9

1. Find, by integration, the volume of a sphere 20 in in radius.
2. A plane is passed through the sphere in Prob. 1, 10 in from the center. Find the smaller and the larger volumes' cutoff.
3. Water is poured from a cylindrical cup 5 in in diameter and 5 in high. Find the volume of water remaining when the surface of the water coincides with a diameter of the bottom of the cup.
4. A hemispherical tank 20 ft in diameter is filled with water to a depth of 4 ft. How many cubic feet of water are there in the tank?
5. A cylindrical block of wood 10 in in radius has a 20-in-diameter hole bored in it such that the axis of the hole and the axis of the cylinder intersect at right angles. Find the volume of the material bored out.
6. Every cross section of the solid shown in Fig. 21.33 is a square whose sides are $0.2x^2$. Find the volume of the solid.
7. A metal sphere 10 in in radius has a 12-in-diameter hole bored in it. The axis of the hole passes through the center of the sphere. Find the volume of material removed.
8. Estimate the number of cubic yards of crushed rock necessary to make a roadbed of the dimensions shown in Fig. 21.34. The road is to be 1 mi long. Assume that any other material added merely fills up the voids. Also assume that the crown of the pavement is an arc of a parabola.

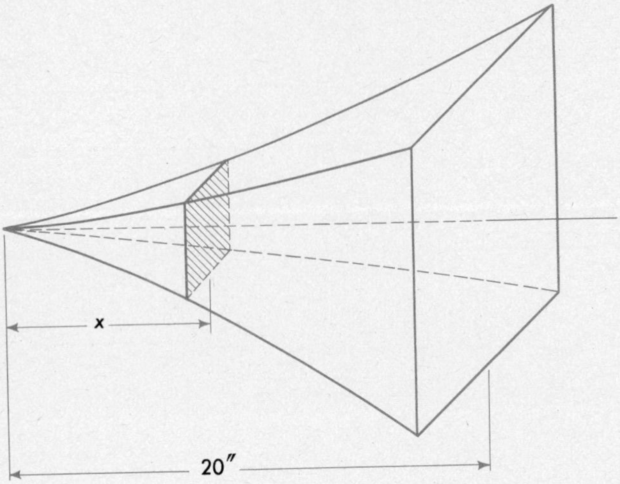

FIGURE 21.33

21.15 Volumes of Revolution

There is a class of solids called *solids of revolution*. A solid of revolution is a solid having an axis of symmetry such that every section of the solid perpendicular to the axis of symmetry is a circle. In all solids of revolution, then, the area of cross section A_s in Eq. (100) is a circle. Therefore, in this special case, Eq. (100) can be written

$$V_a{}^b = \int_a^b \pi r^2\, dx \tag{104}$$

where r = radius of circular cross section.

Figure 21.35 is a solid of revolution since each section perpendicular to the X axis is a circle.

By similarity

$$\frac{r}{x} = \frac{2.5}{8}$$

$$r = \frac{2.5}{8}x$$

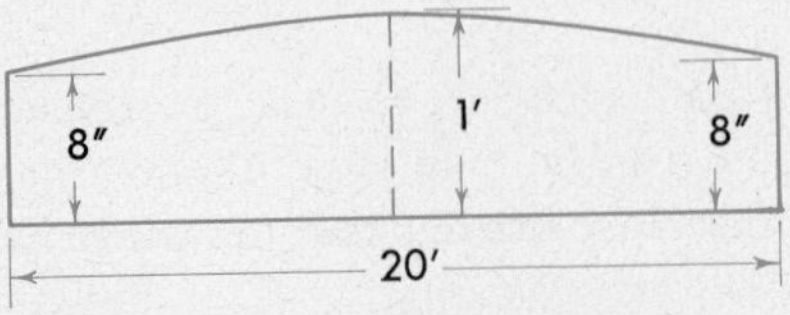

FIGURE 21.34

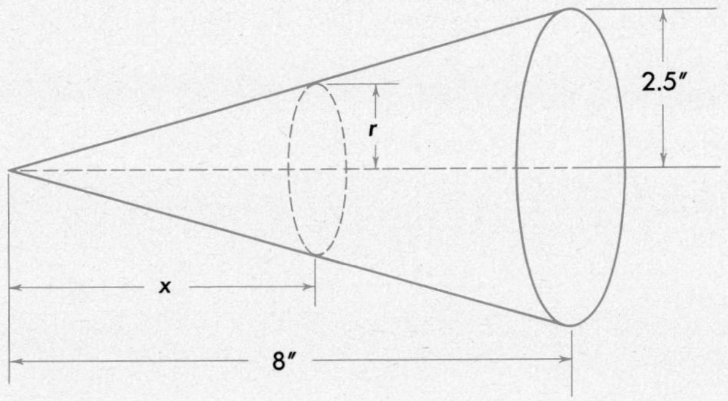

FIGURE 21.35

and

$$r^2 = \frac{6.25}{64} x^2$$

Equation (104) then becomes

$$V_0{}^8 = \int_0^8 \pi \frac{6.25}{64} x^2 \, dx$$

$$= \left[\frac{6.25\pi}{3 \times 64} x^3\right]_0^8 = \frac{6.25 \times 8^3\pi}{3 \times 64} = \frac{3{,}200\pi}{192} = 52.36 \text{ in}^3$$

Example 44. Find the volume of revolution generated when the section of the curve $y = x^2$ between $x = 2$ and $x = 5$ is revolved about the X axis.

The cross-sectional area is

$$A_s = \pi y^2$$

But

$$y = x^2$$

Therefore

$$A_s = \pi x^4$$

and

$$V_2{}^5 = \int_2^5 \pi x^4 \, dx = \left[\frac{\pi x^5}{5}\right]_2^5 = 625\pi - \frac{32x}{5} = 625\pi - 6.4\pi = 618.6\pi$$

$$= 1{,}943$$

Example 45. Find the volume generated by revolving about the X axis the area bounded by the lines $y = x^3$, $x = 2$, $x = 4$, and $y = 0$.

$$A_s = \pi y^2$$

But

$$y = x^3$$

Therefore

$$A_s = \pi x^6$$

and

$$V_2^4 = \int_2^4 \pi x^6\, dx = \left[\frac{\pi x^7}{7}\right]_2^4 = \frac{16{,}384\pi}{7} - \frac{128\pi}{7} = \frac{16{,}256\pi}{7} = 7{,}295.7$$

EXERCISE 10

Find the volume generated by revolving about the X axis the area bounded by the following sets of curves:

1. $y = x^2$, $y = 0$, $x = 5$
2. $y = \sqrt{9 - x^2}$, $y = 0$, $x = 3$
3. $y = \sqrt{10x}$, $y = 0$, $x = 10$
4. $y = x$, $x = 2$, $x = 5$, $y = 0$
5. $y = 12/x$, $x = 2$, $x = 6$, $y = 0$

21.16 Work

Before proceeding with this section, the student is advised to review the concept of work in any good general physics textbook.

Briefly, however, work is done only when a force is exerted on a body, causing it to move so that the force has a component along the line of motion.

When the body moves in a straight line and when the magnitude of the force component along this straight line remains constant, we have the elementary definition of work expressed as

$$W = Fx \qquad (105)$$

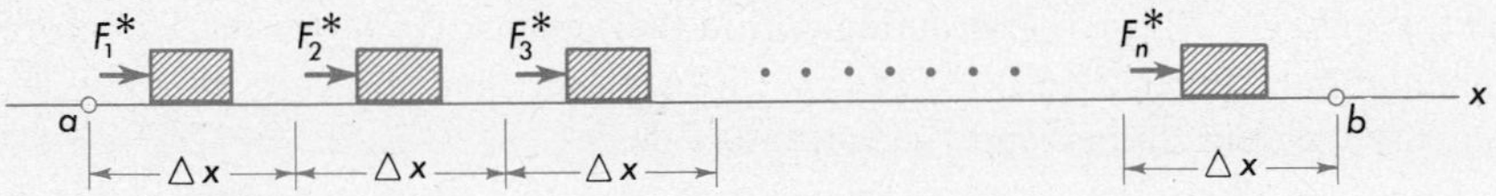

FIGURE 21.36

where F = component of force along line of motion
x = distance the body moves along line of motion (for the present at least we shall limit ourselves to positive distances)
W = work done on the body by applied force

If F is measured in pounds and x in feet, then work W is measured in foot-pounds. Work can also be measured in newton-meters, dyne-centimeters, etc., depending on the units in which F and x are measured.

If the force component along the line of motion is not constant, then the arithmetical definition of work given in Eq. (105) no longer applies.

For example, see Fig. 21.36 in which we illustrate a variable force component F along a straight line, which we take to be the X axis. If this variable force component displaces the body from $x = a$ to $x = b$, we define the work done to be

$$W_a{}^b = \int_a^b F\,dx \tag{106}$$

Here, of course, we assume the force F to be the value of a continuous function of x.

Although the above equation is a definition and hence not subject to proof, there is a plausible motivation for choosing this particular definition.

To develop this motivation we shall proceed as follows:

1. Divide the interval $a \leq x \leq b$ into n equal parts, each of width

$$\Delta x = \frac{b - a}{n}$$

2. Form the sum

$$F_1^*(\Delta x) + F_2^*(\Delta x) + F_3^*(\Delta x) + \cdots + F_n^*(\Delta x) \tag{107}$$

or

$$[F_1^* + F_2^* + F_3^* + \cdots + F_n^*]\,\Delta x \tag{108}$$

where $F_1^*, F_2^*, F_3^*, \ldots, F_n^*$ are forces acting within their respective intervals. Therefore we conclude that $F_1^*(\Delta x), F_2^*(\Delta x), F_3^*(\Delta x), \ldots, F_n^*(\Delta x)$ represent the work done by $F_1^*, F_2^*, F_3^*, \ldots, F_n^*$ within their respective subintervals.

It seems intuitively evident that the work done between $x = a$ and $x = b$ is approximated by the sum of the work done in each of the successive subintervals. That is,

$$W_a{}^b \approx \sum_{k=1}^{k=n} F_k^*(\Delta x) \tag{109}$$

The symbol $\sum_{k=1}^{k=n} F_k^*(\Delta x)$ designates the sum whose typical (or kth) term is $F_k^*(\Delta x)$, where k may take on in turn any integral value between 1 and n.

Now by applying Eqs. (89) and (90) to Eq. (109), we obtain

$$W_a{}^b = \int_a^b F\,dx = \lim_{n\to\infty} \sum_{k=1}^{k=n} F_k^*(\Delta x) \tag{110}$$

Example 46. Within certain limits, the force required to stretch a spring is proportional to the amount of stretch. The constant of proportionality is called the *modulus* of the spring.

A given spring having a normal length of 10 in requires a force of 25 lb to stretch it $\frac{1}{4}$ in. Calculate the amount of work done in stretching it from 11 to 12 in.

By the statement of the problem,

$$F = Kx$$

where x is the elongation in inches. We can evaluate the constant of proportionality from the conditions that $F = 25$ when $x = \frac{1}{4}$ in.

$$25 = \tfrac{1}{4}K$$

or

$$K = 100$$

and, in general,

$$F = 100x$$

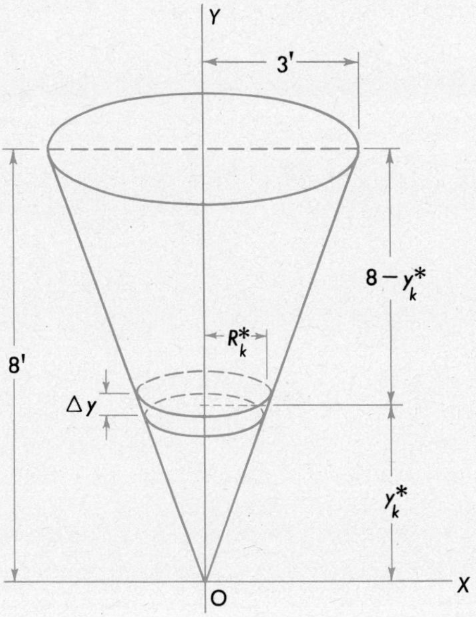

FIGURE 21.37

From Eq. (106),

$$W_1{}^2 = \int_1^2 F\,dx = \int_1^2 (100x)\,dx = [50x^2]_1^2 = 50 \cdot 4 - 50 \cdot 1 = 150 \text{ in-lb}$$

Example 47. A reservoir filled with water is in the form of a right circular cone whose top diameter is 6 ft and whose height is 8 ft. Find the amount of work done in pumping the water over the top of the reservoir.

We approximate the conical volume of water by a set of elementary circular disks, each Δy thick. The kth (or typical) disk is shown in Fig. 21.37.

The work required to lift the kth elementary volume over the top of the reservoir is approximately

$$W_k^* = (\text{weight of } k\text{th disk})(8 - y_k^*)$$

The weight of the kth disk of water is

Weight $= 62.5 \times$ volume of kth disk in ft^3
Volume of kth disk $= \pi R_k^{*2}\,\Delta y$

The weight of the kth disk is therefore

Weight of kth disk $= 62.5\pi R_k^{*2}\,\Delta y$
$W_k^* = 62.5\pi R_k^{*2}(8 - y_k^*)\,\Delta y$

By similar triangles

$R_k^* = \frac{3}{8}y_k^*$

Therefore

$$W_k^* = \frac{9 \cdot 62.5 \cdot \pi}{64}(8 - y_k^*)y_k^{*2}\,\Delta y = \frac{9 \times 62.5 \times \pi}{64}(8y_k^{*2} - y_k^{*3})\,\Delta y$$

By following the same general line of reasoning as outlined in Sec. 21.11 we may write

$$W_0^8 = \int_0^8 \frac{9 \times 62.5 \times \pi}{64}(8y^2 - y^3)\,dy$$
$$= \frac{9 \times 62.5 \times \pi}{64}\left[\frac{8y^3}{3} - \frac{y^4}{4}\right]_0^8$$
$$= \frac{9 \times 62.5 \times \pi}{64}\left(\frac{8^4}{3} - \frac{8^4}{4}\right) = 3{,}000\pi$$

EXERCISE 11

1. A certain coil spring requires a force of 12 lb to stretch it ½ in. Find the work done in stretching it 3 in beyond its free length.
2. The coil spring on a bumping post in a freight yard is compressed 1 in by a force of 36,000 lb. Find the work done in compressing it ½ in.
3. The natural length of a coil spring is 10 in. The modulus of this spring is 24 lb/in. How much work is done in stretching it from a length of 11 in to a length of 13 in?
4. If 84 in-lb of work is done on a spring whose initial elongation is 1 in and whose modulus is 32 lb/in, find the final elongation.
5. The force used in driving a piston varies as follows: $F = 10/x^{1.5}$. Find the work done between $x = 20$ and $x = 50$.
6. A downward force is applied to a horizontal beam at its midpoint. If the deflection is proportional to the force and is ¼ in when the force is 1,200 lb, find the work done as the force increases from 1,200 to 3,600 lb.
7. A cable 50 ft long and weighing 3 lb/ft supports a weight of 800 lb. Find the work done in winding this cable on a windlass until the weight has been lifted 50 ft.
8. A right circular cylindrical tank having a depth of 12 ft and a radius of 4 ft is

one-third full of water. Find the work done in pumping the water to the top of this tank. (Weight of water equals 62.5 lb/ft^3.)

9. A right circular cylindrical tank is 18 ft deep and 8 ft in diameter. Find the work done in filling this tank if water is pumped in through the bottom of it from a depth of 16 ft below the bottom.
10. Calculate the work done in pumping out the water from a hemispherical reservoir whose radius is 10 ft, assuming that the reservoir is full of water at the time the pump starts work.
11. The inner surface of a tank has the form of a paraboloid of revolution whose axis is vertical. The depth of this tank and the diameter of the circular top are each 12 ft. If the tank is initially full of water, find the work done in pumping the water to the top of the tank.
12. A derrick lifts a shovel of sand through a vertical distance of 30 ft. The sand in the shovel weighs originally 400 lb and leaks out at a rate directly proportional to the square root of the distance traversed. If 320 lb of sand reaches the top, find the work done.
13. A volume of gas (V_1 in^3) is enclosed in the tube shown in Fig. 21.38 under an absolute pressure of P_1 lb/in^2 when the movable piston is at position h_1. A continuously

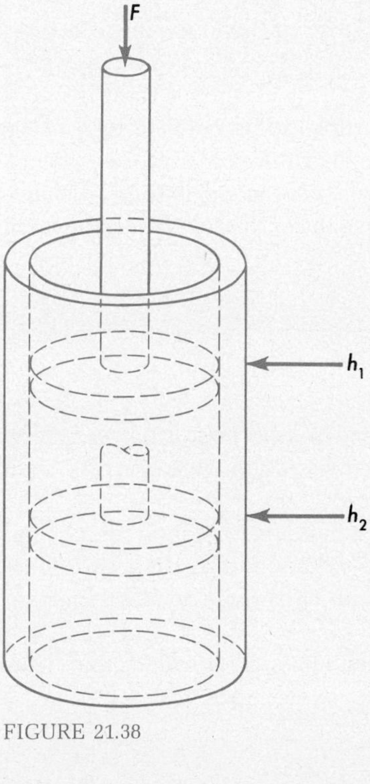

FIGURE 21.38

increasing force F is applied to the piston until it comes to rest at h_2. Then the unit pressure is P_2 and the volume is V_2. Show that the work done in compressing this gas is

$$W = \int_{V_1}^{V_2} P\,dV$$

14. If in Prob. 13 the unit pressure P is given by $P = C/V^{\gamma}$, show that when the gas is compressed from P_1, V_1 to P_2, V_2, the work done on the gas is given by

$$W = \frac{P_2V_2 - P_1V_1}{1 - \gamma}$$

where C and γ are constants.

15. In the adiabatic compression of air the formula

$$PV^{1.4} = C$$

applies where P = pressure, V = volume, and C = a constant. If $V = 32\ \text{ft}^3$ when P is 1 atm, find the work done in compressing 32 ft^3 of air at 1 atm to 5 ft^3 (1 atm = 14.7 lb/in^2).

16. The earth's gravitational force on a given mass varies as $1/x^2$ where x is the distance of the mass from the center of the earth. The earth's radius is taken to be 4,000 mi, and the formula applies for distances greater than the radius of the earth. A certain amount of work will be needed to lift a given mass to an "infinite" distance from the surface of the earth. To what altitude above the surface of the earth would one-half of this work lift an object?

21.17 Fluid Pressure

The student may find it advisable to review the matter of fluid pressure in a general physics textbook before proceeding with a study of this section. However, we shall present a brief review of the physical principles below.

We can confirm from experiment that for any incompressible fluid at constant temperature the fluid pressure at any point below the surface is directly proportional to the distance of the point below the surface of the fluid. The proportionality constant is the weight density of the fluid.

We may assume that variations in the acceleration of gravity are negligible. Thus

$$P = \rho h \tag{111}$$

where P = unit pressure

ρ = weight density of fluid

h = distance of point under consideration below surface of fluid

The quantities P, ρ, and h are, of course, measured in some compatible units. For example, P might be in pounds per square foot when ρ is measured in pounds per cubic foot and h is measured in feet.

Evidently from Eq. (111) the pressure varies with depth. Therefore the pressure on the vertical walls of a container enclosing a fluid is not constant but is greater near the bottom of the container and less near the surface of the fluid.

If the pressure were constant, the fluid force on a given area of sidewall would be given by Eq. (112) below. The student is reminded that F, as the symbol is used in Eq. (112), refers to the force caused by the weight of the fluid alone. The *total* force would include the effect of atmospheric pressure on the surface of the fluid.

$$F = P \times A \tag{112}$$

where F = force on area A due to fluid pressure

A = area on which force is exerted

P = unit pressure

However, this simple arithmetic formula is not adequate if we wish to calculate the total force that is exerted by a fluid on a given portion of a vertical wall which forms a part of the container.

Example 48. Find the total fluid force exerted on one end of the trough indicated in Fig. 21.39 when it is full of water. Only the end view of the trough is shown in the figure.

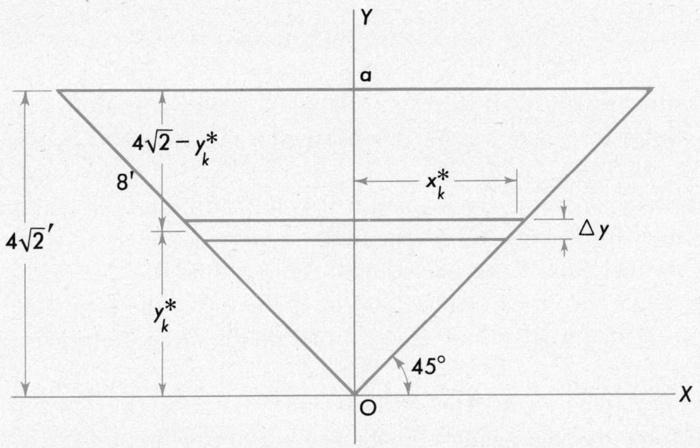

FIGURE 21.39

Following the same general line of approach as we have taken previously, we divide the interval $0 \le y \le 4\sqrt{2}$ into n equal parts, each Δy units in width, thus establishing n horizontal strips. A typical (or kth) strip is shown in the figure.

The total force exerted by the water on the kth strip is approximately

$$F_k^* \approx (4\sqrt{2} - y_k^*) \cdot 62.5 \cdot 2 \cdot x_k^* \, \Delta y$$

where 62.5 is the density of water in pounds per cubic foot.

By the geometry of the figure

$$y_k^* = x_k^*$$

Therefore

$$F_k^* \approx 125(4\sqrt{2}y_k^* - y_k^{*2}) \, \Delta y$$

or

$$F_0^{4\sqrt{2}} \approx \lim_{n\to\infty} \sum_{k=1}^{k=n} 125(4\sqrt{2}y_k^* - y_k^{*2}) \, \Delta y$$

Thus we are led to write

$$F_0^{4\sqrt{2}} = 125 \int_0^{4\sqrt{2}} (4\sqrt{2}y - y^2) \, dy = 125 \left[2\sqrt{2}y^2 - \frac{y^3}{3}\right]_0^{4\sqrt{2}}$$

$$= 125\left(64\sqrt{2} - \frac{2 \cdot 64 \cdot \sqrt{2}}{3}\right) = 3{,}771 \text{ lb}$$

EXERCISE 12

1. The vertical end of a water trough is an isosceles triangle 5 ft across the top and 5 ft deep. Calculate the total force exerted on the end when this trough is full of water. (Water weighs 62.5 lb/ft^3.)
2. A horizontal cylindrical tank having a diameter of 8 ft is half full of oil weighing 60 lb/ft^3. Calculate the total force exerted on one end.
3. A rectangular gate in a vertical dam is 10 ft wide and 6 ft deep. Find the total force exerted against this gate when the water level is 8 ft above the top of the gate. Also find how much higher the water must rise in order to double the force against this gate.
4. A vertical cylindrical tank having a diameter of 30 ft and a height of 50 ft is full of water. Find the total force exerted against the curved surface of this tank.

EXERCISE 13

The following problems are intended to illustrate a few of the many and varied applications of the definite integral.

1. The potential energy stored in a rod because of a torque (twist) which has been applied to one end (the other end of the rod being fixed) and which twisted the bar through an angle of 30° is given by

$$\mathrm{PE} = \int_0^{30\pi/180} \frac{200\phi}{\pi}\, d\phi$$

Evaluate.

2. Evaluate the following definite integral that appeared in a test on aeronautics:

$$\int_{r_0}^{r} \left(\frac{R}{r^2}\right)\left(\frac{G^2}{4\pi^2 r^2}\right) dr$$

where R, G, and r_0 are constants.

3. If a battery of E V and zero internal resistance is connected to a long uncharged submarine cable of capacitance C F and resistance R Ω (each per mile), the battery current t s later is given by

$$i = E\left(\frac{C}{\pi R t}\right)^{1/2} \qquad \text{A}$$

(a) Sketch a graph of i as a function of t. To show the general shape of this curve, let $C = 2\pi \times 10^{-8}$, $R = 18$, and $E = 30$.

(b) Are the current i and the power $P = Ei$ undefined (momentarily infinite) when the battery is first connected?

(c) Determine the charge

$$Q = \int_0^T i\, dt$$

and the energy

$$W = \int_0^T P\, dt$$

taken from the battery up to the time T s. Are these ever undefined (infinite)? Sketch each as a function of t.

Remark: A mathematically "infinite" current is not physically possible, since no circuit can actually have zero resistance. However, the resistance can be so small that the momentary current is enormous compared with the normal current in the circuit and may be called "physically" infinite.

4. A sled is being pulled along level ice by a rope, which is inclined at an angle of 11° with the horizontal. The force pulling the sled varies thus with the time: $F = 24t - 0.9t^2$ (F in pounds and t in seconds). The change in momentum of the sled is defined to be the product of the force component in the direction of motion multiplied by the time interval during which this constant force acts. Find the change in momentum of the sled during the interval from $t = 1$ to $t = 5$ s.

5. Integrate

$$A = 232 + \int_{176}^{t} (0.000{,}374t + 0.251)\, dt$$

6. The force ejecting a projectile from a gun changes with the time after firing according to the equation

$$F = \frac{4.35}{(0.05 + t)^4} \qquad \text{lb}$$

where t is in seconds. The total momentum given the projectile (momentum is defined as mass times velocity) during the 0.04 s required for the projectile to pass through the bore of the gun is obtained by evaluating the definite integral

$$\int_{t_1}^{t_2} F\, dt = \int_{0}^{0.04} \frac{4.35\, dt}{(0.05 + t)^4}$$

Evaluate this definite integral.

7. The two following empirical formulas were found for the *specific heat* at constant pressure for hydrogen:

$$c_p = 3.45 - 0.0000551T + 0.0000000736T^2$$

$$c_p = 2.86 + 0.0000287T + \frac{10}{\sqrt{T}}$$

Compute

$$\int_{1{,}000}^{1{,}500} c_p\, dT$$

for the two approximate formulas and thus determine the total heat required to raise the temperature of 1 lb of hydrogen from 540 to 1040°F (T = absolute temperature = degrees Fahrenheit plus 460).

21.18 The Integral of $ku^n \cdot du$ Where $n = -1$

We recall from Sec. 20.15, particularly Eq. (96), that

$$\frac{d(\ln u)}{dx} = \frac{1}{u}\frac{du}{dx} = u^{-1}\frac{du}{dx}$$

The above equation leads directly to the integration formula

$$\int \frac{1}{u}\,du = \int u^{-1}\,du = \ln u + C \qquad \textbf{(113)}$$

where u is positive. The restriction was stated directly after Eq. (97) in Sec. 20.15.

If, in Eq. (113) above, u is negative, then $-u$ is positive, and

$$\int \frac{d(-u)}{-u} = \ln(-u) + C \qquad (113a)$$

Equations (113) and (113a) can be combined into a single formula:

$$\int \frac{du}{u} = \ln|u| + C \qquad u \neq 0 \qquad \textbf{(114)}$$

Example 49. Find

$$\int \frac{9x^2\,dx}{1 - 2x^3} \qquad (115)$$

If we let

$$u = 1 - 2x^3$$

then

$$du = -6x^2\,dx$$

and expression (115) does *not* contain *du exactly*. Therefore Eq. (114) does not apply directly. However, we may multiply and divide expression (115) by $-\frac{2}{3}$ without changing the value of (115) and obtain an equivalent expression,

$$-\frac{3}{2}\int \frac{-\tfrac{2}{3}\cdot 9x^2\,dx}{1-2x^3} = -\frac{3}{2}\int \frac{-6x^2\,dx}{1-2x^3}$$

for which Eq. (114) does apply directly and

$$\int \frac{9x^2\,dx}{1-2x^3} = -\frac{3}{2}\int \frac{-6x^2\,dx}{1-2x^3} = -\frac{3}{2}\ln(1-2x^3) + C$$

The equation for the graph shown in Fig. 19.17 is

$$F = \frac{10}{D}$$

The area under this graph is proportional to work w done by the force F in forcing the piston through the distance D. Therefore

$$w = \int \frac{10}{D}\,dD$$

Work done is

$$w = 10 \ln D + C$$

Now we wish to find the work accomplished when the piston moves from $D = 1$ to $D = 6$. When $D = 1$ the work in which we are interested is 0; therefore

$$0 = 10 \ln 1 + C$$

but

$$\ln 1 = 0$$

Therefore

$$C = 0$$

and

$$w = 10 \ln D$$

When $D = 6$,

$$w = 10 \ln 6$$
$$= 10 \times 1.792 = 17.92$$

EXERCISE 14

Find the following definite integrals.

1. $\displaystyle\int_0^9 \frac{dx}{x+3}$

2. $\displaystyle\int_3^5 \frac{s\,ds}{s^2-4}$

3. $\displaystyle\int_{-3}^0 \frac{8h^2\,dh}{1-4h^3}$

4. $\displaystyle\int_{0.1}^{0.5} \frac{(2t^2-4)\,dt}{6t-t^3}$

5. $\displaystyle\int_2^5 \frac{(\theta-1)^2\,d\theta}{\theta^3-3\theta^2+3\theta}$

6. $\displaystyle\int_{2.5}^{3.2} \frac{(x-1)\,dx}{x^2-2x}$

7. $\displaystyle\int_2^4 \frac{(t+1)(t-1)\,dt}{t^3-3t}$

8. $\displaystyle\int_0^2 -\frac{h\,dh}{3(9-h^2)}$

9. The area under the curve of $y = s/(s^2 - 4)$ is 0.8 when the lower limit is 5. Find the upper limit.
10. Figure 19.17 was plotted from the equation $F = 10/D$. By integration, confirm the answer to Prob. 6, Exercise 6, Chap. 19.
11. Figure 21.40 shows the relation between pressure and volume in a cylinder, as the piston completes a full cycle. Determine the net work done by finding the shaded area.

Data:

A. $V = 1$ ft^3, $p = 14{,}400$ lb/ft^3, $C_1 = 14{,}400$
B. $V = 2$ ft^3, $p = 7{,}200$ lb/ft^3, $C_2 = 19{,}000$
C. $V = 6$ ft^3, $p = 1{,}545$ lb/ft^3, $C_3 = 9{,}270$
D. $V = 3$ ft^3, $p = 3{,}090$ lb/ft^3, $C_4 = 14{,}400$

12. Show that

$$\int_a^b V^{-1}\,dV = \int_c^d V^{-1}\,dV$$

if $b/a = d/c$.

13. During a certain process in an engine, the pressure p lb/ft^2 changes with the volume (V ft^3) according to the law

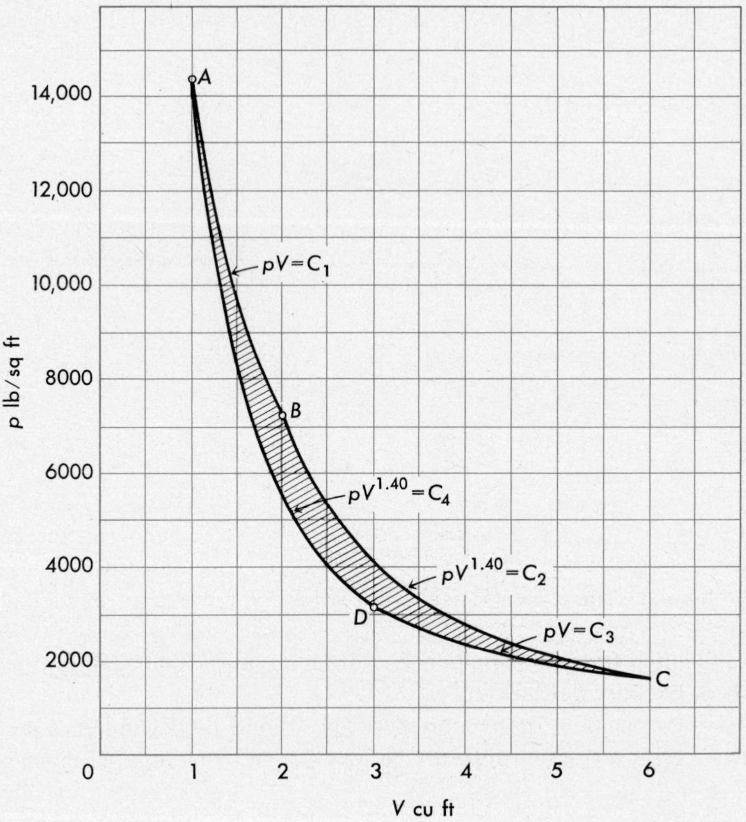

FIGURE 21.40

$$p = \left(\frac{3V^2}{5} + \frac{10}{V}\right)(144)$$

Determine the work done by evaluating

$$W = \int_{V_1}^{V_2} p\, dV$$

if the volume changes from $V_1 = 1$ ft^3 to $V_2 = 3$ ft^3.

14. If the pressure (p lb/ft^2) changes with the volume (V ft^3) during a certain process in an engine according to the law $pV^n = C$, where C and n are constants, show that the work

$$W = \int_{V_1}^{V_2} p\, dV$$

is given by the two following equations:

(a) $W = \dfrac{p_2V_2 - p_1V_1}{1 - n} \qquad n \neq 1$

(b) $W = p_1V_1 \ln \dfrac{V_2}{V_1} \qquad n = 1$

Remark: The proofs of these two results are to be found in texts on thermodynamics, and the resulting equations are fundamental in that study.

15. A ship whose weight is 100 tons is traveling at the speed of 40 ft/s when the power is cut off. The acceleration at any time t s later is given by

$$a = -\frac{1{,}600}{(t + 50)^2} \qquad \text{ft/s}^2$$

and this is valid for about 5 min. Determine the velocity and distance traveled (assuming that the ship moves along a straight path) as functions of the time t s. What are their values at the time $t = 4$ min?

21.19 The Integral of Sin $u\,du$ and Cos $u\,du$

From Sec. 20.10 we note that if

$$y = k \sin u$$

then

$$\frac{dy}{du} = k \cos u$$

or

$$dy = k \cos u\, du$$

Consequently,

$$\int k \cos u\, du = k \sin u + C \qquad \textbf{(116)}$$

Also from Sec. 20.10 we note that if

$$y = k \cos u$$

then

$$\frac{dy}{du} = -k \sin u$$

or

$$dy = -k \sin u \, du$$

Consequently,

$$\int -k \sin u \, du = k \cos u + C$$

Also

$$\int k \sin u \, du = -k \cos u + C \tag{117}$$

Example 50. Find

$$\int 6 \sin\left(2\theta + \frac{\pi}{2}\right) d\theta \tag{118}$$

If we let

$$u = 2\theta + \pi/2$$

then

$$du = 2\, d\theta$$

and expression (118) does *not* contain *du exactly*. Therefore Eq. (117) does not apply directly. However, we may multiply and divide expression (118) by ⅓ without changing the value of this expression and obtain an equivalent expression,

$$3 \int \frac{6}{3} \sin\left(2\theta + \frac{\pi}{2}\right) d\theta = 3 \int 2 \sin\left(2\theta + \frac{\pi}{2}\right) d\theta$$

for which Eq. (117) does apply directly and

$$\int 6 \sin\left(2\theta + \frac{\pi}{2}\right) d\theta = 3 \int 2 \sin\left(2\theta + \frac{\pi}{2}\right) d\theta = -3 \cos\left(2\theta + \frac{\pi}{2}\right) + C = 3 \sin 2\theta + C$$

Example 51. Find

$$\int -\tfrac{1}{2}\cos 2\phi\, d\phi \tag{119}$$

If we let

$$u = 2\phi$$

then

$$du = 2d\phi$$

and expression (119) does not contain du exactly. Therefore Eq. (116) does not apply directly. However, we may multiply and divide expression (119) by 4 without changing the value of this expression and obtain an equivalent expression

$$\tfrac{1}{4}\int -\tfrac{4}{2}\cos 2\phi\, d\phi = \tfrac{1}{4}\int -2\cos 2\phi\, d\phi$$

for which Eq. (116) does apply directly and

$$\int -\tfrac{1}{2}\cos 2\phi\, d\phi = \tfrac{1}{4}\int -2\cos 2\phi\, d\phi = -\tfrac{1}{4}\sin 2\phi + C$$

EXERCISE 15

Integrate the following:

1. $\int 4\cos 2\theta\, d\theta$
2. $\displaystyle\int -\frac{\sin(\phi/2)}{8}\, d\phi$
3. $\int x\cos x^2\, dx$
4. $\int 2\sin\theta\cos\theta\, d\theta$
5. $\int \cos(4 - x)\, dx$
6. $\int \sin(\pi - \phi/4)\, d\phi$

One important application of the integral of a sine function occurs in the problem of finding the mean ordinate of the sine wave over a half-cycle. It will be recalled that we find the mean ordinate of a curve by first finding the area under the curve and, second, by dividing that area by the abscissa distance between the limits chosen (see Sec. 21.10). We shall now proceed to find the mean ordinate of the curve defined in the equation

$$y = \sin\phi \qquad 0 \le \phi \le \pi$$

The area under this curve over one-half the cycle is

$$A_0{}^{\pi} = \int_0^{\pi} \sin\phi\, d\phi = [-\cos\phi]_0^{\pi} \tag{120}$$

Evaluating (120), we write

$$\begin{aligned} A_0{}^{\pi} &= (-\cos\pi) - (-\cos 0) \\ &= [-(-1)] - [-(+1)] \end{aligned} \tag{121}$$

Therefore

$$A_0{}^{\pi} = (+1) + 1 = 2$$

Thus the area under a sine curve over the interval between 0 and π rad is 2. The mean height will be, therefore,

$$\text{Mean height} = \frac{2}{\pi} = 0.6366 \tag{122}$$

The student should be careful to note that we are here finding the mean ordinate of a sine curve, not the so-called effective ordinate of a sine curve. It would also be instructive to find the mean ordinate of a sine curve over one entire cycle, that is, between the limits of 0 and 2π rad. Accordingly, let us alter Eq. (120) to find the area under a sine curve between the limits of 0 and 2π.

$$\begin{aligned} A_0{}^{2\pi} &= \int_0^{2\pi} \sin\phi\, d\phi = [-\cos\phi]_0^{2\pi} \\ &= (-\cos 2\pi) - (-\cos 0) \\ &= (-1) - (-1) = -1 + 1 = 0 \end{aligned} \tag{123}$$

Now let us find the *root-mean-square* value of a sine curve between $\phi = 0$ and $\phi = \pi$. The root-mean-square value of the sine curve is the square root of the mean value of

$$y = \sin^2\phi$$

between $\phi = 0$ and $\phi = \pi$.

The mean value of this function is (see Sec. 21.10)

$$\bar{y} = \frac{A_0{}^{\pi}}{\pi}$$

but

$$A_0^\pi = \int_0^\pi \sin^2 \phi \, d\phi \tag{124}$$

We have as yet no formula by which we can integrate Eq. (124), but by Sec. 18.6 we can write the equivalent of Eq. (124) as

$$A_0^\pi = \int_0^\pi \left(\frac{1}{2} - \frac{\cos 2\phi}{2}\right) d\phi$$

Then

$$A_0^\pi = \int_0^\pi \frac{1}{2}\, d\phi - \int_0^\pi \frac{\cos 2\phi}{2}\, d\phi$$

From Example 51 above and Sec. 21.3 we may write

$$A_0^\pi = [\tfrac{1}{2}\phi]_0^\pi - [\tfrac{1}{4}\sin 2\phi]_0^\pi$$

Then

$$A_0^\pi = (\pi/2 - 0) = \pi/2$$

The mean ordinate of $y = \sin^2 \phi$ is therefore

$$\frac{\pi/2}{\pi} = \frac{1}{2}$$

However, the *effective* ordinate of a curve of sin u is, by definition, "the square root of the mean ordinate of the curve of $\sin^2 \phi$"; that is, if $y = \sin \phi$,

$$y_{\text{eff}} = \sqrt{\frac{1}{2}} = \frac{\sqrt{2}}{2} = 0.707$$

The effective value of the function

$$y = k \sin \phi$$

is

$$y_{\text{eff}} = k\frac{\sqrt{2}}{2} = k \cdot 0.707 \tag{125}$$

EXERCISE 16

1. Find the area under the graph of each equation below between the specified limits. Also find the mean ordinate between these limits.

(a) $y = 4 \cos 2\theta$	between $\pi/6$ and $\pi/4$
(b) $y = -\frac{1}{8} \sin (\phi/2)$	between $\pi/2$ and $2\pi/3$
(c) $y = x \cos x^2$	between 0.2 and 0.5
(d) $y = 10 \sin 2\phi$	between $\pi/2$ and $3\pi/4$
(e) $y = \cos (4 - x)$	between 4 and 5
(f) $y = \sin \left(\pi - \frac{\theta}{4}\right)$	between 4π and 5π
(g) $y = \sin \theta / \cos^2 \theta$	between 0 and $\pi/3$
(h) $y = \dfrac{\cos x}{5 \sin^3 x}$	between $\dfrac{\pi}{3}$ and $\dfrac{2\pi}{3}$

2. The equation for the linear speed of a point on the tread of an automobile tire traveling at a constant speed is

$$v = 32\pi \sin 8\pi t$$

where t is in seconds, and v is in feet per second. This is the equation from which Fig. 19.18 was plotted.

(a) Find the acceleration of the point when $t = 0.03$ (compare with Prob. 2, Exercise 7, Chap. 19).

(b) Find the time and value of the maximum speed (compare with Prob. 3, Exercise 7, Chap. 19).

(c) Find the speed of the car (compare with Prob. 4, Exercise 7, Chap. 19).

(d) Find the outside diameter of the tire (compare with Prob. 5, Exercise 7, Chap. 19).

(e) Find the distance the point moves between $t = 0$ and $t = \frac{1}{8}$ s (compare with Prob. 6, Exercise 7, Chap. 19).

3. The voltage and current in an electric circuit are, respectively, given by

$$e = 25 \sin \omega t \quad \text{V} \qquad i = 20 \sin (\omega t - \pi/6) \quad \text{A}$$

(a) Determine the mean power, defined as

$$\frac{1}{T}\int_0^T ei\, dt$$

where T is the period of both the voltage and the current (T is to be determined).

(b) Sketch the voltage and current waves from $t = 0$ to $t = 2\pi/\omega$. Sketch on the same graph the curve for instantaneous power, defined by $p = ei$. Then show the graphical meaning of the preceding definite integral.

4. The voltage in an electric circuit is given by

$$e = E \sin \omega t \qquad \text{V}$$

where E and ω are constants. You may assume, if you wish, that $\omega = 60$ Hz $= 120\pi$ rad/s.

(a) Determine the mean voltage for the interval of time from $t = 0$ to $t = \pi/\omega$. Also determine the mean voltage from $t = 0$ to $t = 2\pi/\omega$.

(b) Find the root-mean-square value of the voltage; that is, find the square root of the mean value of the ordinate to the curve $y = E^2 \sin^2 \omega t$ from $t = 0$ to $t = 2\pi/\omega$.

(c) Use your result from (b) to determine to three significant figures the value of E so that the root-mean-square value will be 120 V.

(d) Sketch graphs of $e = E \sin \omega t$ and $y = E^2 \sin^2 \omega t$, each for a complete period, and indicate the mean ordinate for each curve for the complete period.

5. An alternating current is given by

$$i = I_1 \sin \omega t + I_3 \sin 3\omega t + \cdots + I_k \sin k\omega t \qquad \text{A}$$

where k is an odd number. Determine formulas for (a) the mean value of the current from $t = 0$ to $t = \pi/\omega$ s, (b) the root-mean-square value of the current from $t = 0$ to $t = 2\pi/\omega$ s.

6. An alternating voltage is given by

$$e = 100 \sin 100\pi t + 50 \sin 300\pi t + 10 \sin 500\pi t \qquad \text{V}$$

(a) Sketch a graph of the voltage wave for one complete period.

(b) Determine the mean value of the voltage from (1) $t = 0$ to $t = 0.01$ s, (2) $t = 0$ to $t = 0.02$ s.

(c) Determine the root-mean-square value of the voltage over a complete period.

7. The voltage in the circuit discussed in Prob. 5 is given by

$$e = E_1 \sin \omega t + E_3 \sin 3\omega t + \cdots + E_k \sin k\omega t \qquad \text{V}$$

Determine the mean power defined by

$$P = \frac{1}{T}\int_0^T ei\, dt$$

where $T = 2\pi/\omega$.

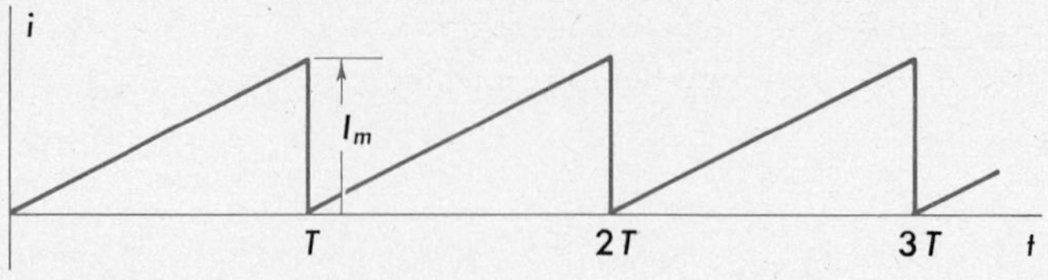

FIGURE 21.41

Remark: Textbooks on alternating currents derive comparable formulas, but use equations for the voltage and current that involve both sine and cosine terms.

8. The instantaneous rate of heat production of a current i A flowing in a constant resistance $r\ \Omega$ is i^2r W. Determine the mean rate of heat production over a cycle (one complete period) for the following periodic curves. Thus, determine the mean ordinate to the curve $y = i^2r$ for a complete period.
(a) $i = I \sin 2\pi ft$, I is a constant.
(b) $i = I_1 \sin 2\pi ft + I_3 \sin 6\pi ft$, I_1 and I_3 are constants.
(c) $i = I_1 \sin \omega t + I_3 \sin (3\omega t - \theta)$; I_1, I_3, and θ are constants.
(d) Find the mean ordinate to the curve $y = i^2r$ from Fig. 21.41.
(e) Do the same as in (d) for Fig. 21.42.
Portions of rectified sine waves (output of a controlled rectifier) are shown in Fig. 21.42.

Remark: This heat production is the basis of the definition of the effective (root-mean-square) value of a periodically varying current; that is, $(I_{\text{effective}})^2(r)$ is the mean rate of heat production over one cycle (one complete period).

9. The potential energy (PE) stored in a beam is given by

$$\text{PE} = \frac{EI}{2}\int_0^L \left(\frac{d^2y}{dx^2}\right)^2 dx$$

where E, I, and L are constants. Determine the potential energy stored in a cantilever

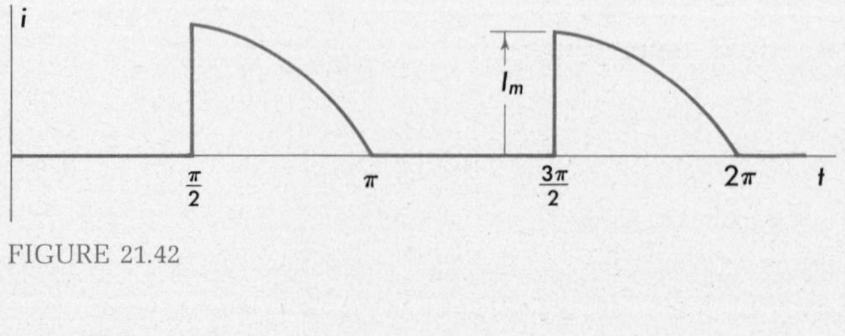

FIGURE 21.42

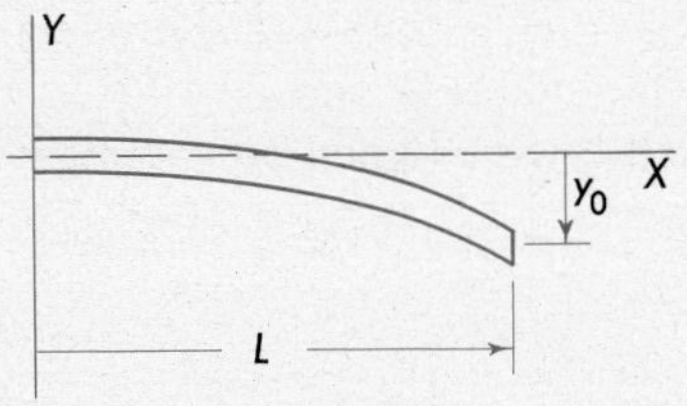

FIGURE 21.43

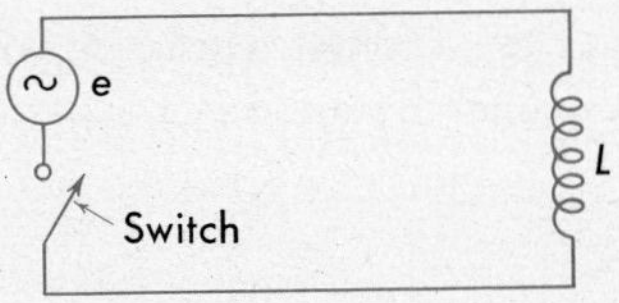

FIGURE 21.44

beam (see Fig. 21.43) which has for its equation

$$y = y_0\left(1 - \cos\frac{\pi x}{2L}\right)$$

10. A circuit (see Fig. 21.44) consists of an inductance $L = 0.2$ henry connected to a generator with an electromotive force $e = 100 \sin \omega t$ V ($\omega = 60$ Hz $= 120\pi$ rad/s). The switch is to be closed at the time $t = 0$; hence, when $t = 0$, the current $i = 0$ A.

    Given $L(di/dt) = e = 100 \sin \omega t$, determine a formula for i in terms of the time t s. Sketch the graph of i as a function of t for t from 0 to $\frac{1}{20}$ s. Also determine the current flowing in the circuit when $t = \frac{1}{180}$ s.
11. A bead of weight w lb slides without friction on the arc of a circle, which lies in a vertical plane. The radius of the arc is R ft. Starting with the expression for the work done by gravity as the bead moves from A to B (see Fig. 21.45)

$$W = \int_A^B w \cos\theta \, ds$$

where ds is an element of length of the circular wire, and θ is the angle which

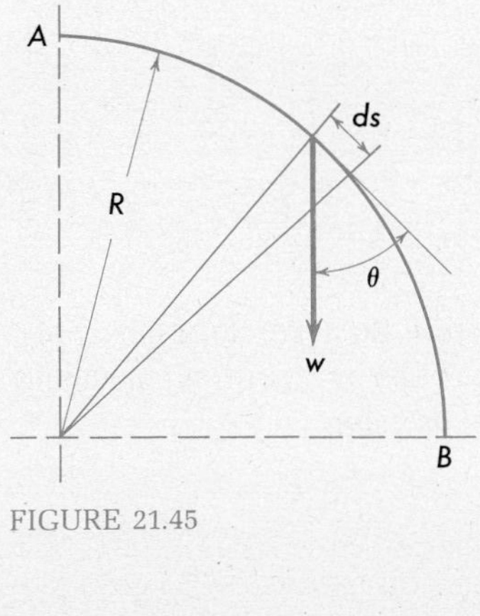

FIGURE 21.45

the tangent to this arc makes with the vertical, show that W is equal to the product of the weight w and the vertical distance between the points A and B.

What would be your result if the points A and B were joined by a straight line? By an arc of a parabola with vertex at A?

21.20 The Integral of $ke^u\,du$

From Sec. 20.17 we note that if

$$y = ke^u$$

then

$$\frac{dy}{du} = ke^u$$

or

$$dy = ke^u\,du$$

Consequently,

$$\int ke^u\,du = ke^u + C \qquad \textbf{(126)}$$

For example, let us find

$$\int 10xe^{x^2}\,dx \qquad (127)$$

If we let

$$u = x^2$$

then

$$du = 2x\,dx$$

and expression (127) does not contain du exactly. Therefore Eq. (126) does not apply directly. However, we may multiply and divide expression (127) by $\frac{1}{5}$ without changing the value of this expression and obtain an equivalent expression

$$5\int {}^{10}\!/_{5}\,xe^{x^2}\,dx = 5\int 2xe^{x^2}\,dx$$

for which Eq. (126) does apply directly and

$$\int 10xe^{x^2}\,dx = 5\int 2xe^{x^2}\,dx = 5e^{x^2} + C$$

EXERCISE 17

Integrate:

1. $\int e^{1-4x}\,dx$
2. $\int dx/e^{x}$
3. $\int e^{\pi x}\,dx$
4. $\int 6x^2e^{x^3}\,dx$
5. $\int \frac{e^{1/x}}{5x^2}\,dx$
6. $\int (e^{2x} + e^{-2x})^2\,dx$
7. $\int e^{3x+1}\,dx$
8. $\int xe^{x^2}\,dx$
9. $\int (e^{x} - e^{-2x})^2\,dx$
10. $\int (e^{2x} - e^{-2x})^2\,dx$
11. $\int \left(e^{3x} - \frac{1}{e}\right)^2 dx$
12. $\int \frac{e^{x} + 1}{e^{2x}}\,dx$
13. $\int (e^{2x} - e^{x/2})^2\,dx$
14. $\int \frac{x - 1}{e^{x^2-2x}}\,dx$

15. Evaluate the following definite integral that was found in textbooks in chemical engineering and in technical journals for chemical engineering:

$$\int_0^1 y_n\,dw \qquad \text{if } y_n = e^{ELw}(y_{n0} - Y_{n-1}) + Y_{n-1} \text{ and } E,\ L,\ y_{n0}, \text{ and } Y_{n-1} \text{ are constants}$$

16. In a circuit containing resistance and inductance in series, the power supplied to the magnetic field of the inductance is given by

$$P = \frac{E^2}{R}(e^{-Rt/L} - e^{-2Rt/L})$$

Show that the total energy stored in the magnetic field, a quantity defined by

$$W = \int_0^{\infty} P\,dt$$

has the value $W = LI^2/2$, where $I = E/R$.

17. If $h(x) = 2.995e^{-14.627x} + 2.18e^{-82.22x} + 1.006e^{-212x}$, obtain the equation for $\theta(x)$ if

$$1 - \theta(x) = 4\int_0^{x} h(x)\,dx$$

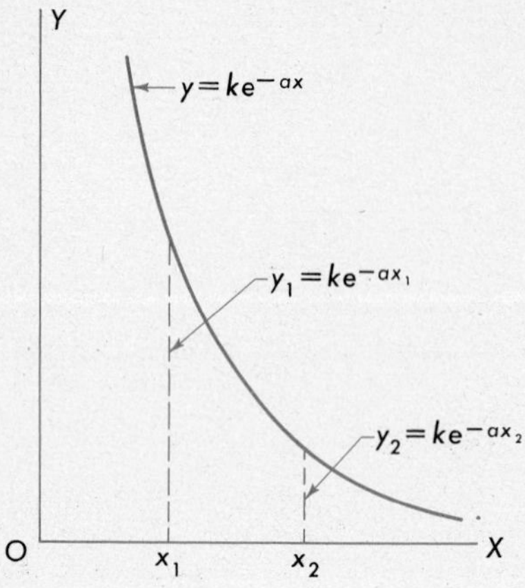

FIGURE 21.46

18. Figure 21.46 shows the graph of $y = ke^{-ax}$. Show that the mean ordinate $\bar{y}$ is

$$\bar{y} = \frac{y_1 - y_2}{\ln (y_1/y_2)}$$

This relation is used in heat-exchanger problems to determine the average temperature difference, knowing the temperature differences at the beginning and the end of the heat exchanger.

19. Figure 19.16 was plotted from the equation

$$T = 50e^{-0.2t}$$

where T is the temperature difference between a warm body and its cooler surroundings. Find the average temperature difference during the first 10 min (see Prob. 18 above).

21.21 Integral Tables

There are far too many types of integrals for the student to remember them all. Up to this point we have specifically discussed the following integration formulas, where u is assumed to be the value of a differentiable function of x.

$$\int u^n \, du = \frac{u^{n+1}}{n+1} + C \qquad n \neq -1$$

$$\int e^u \, du = e^u + C$$

$$\int \frac{1}{u}\,du = \ln|u| + C$$

$$\int \sin u\,du = -\cos u + C$$

$$\int \cos u\,du = \sin u + C$$

The student may sometimes encounter integrals which do not match any of the above formulas. In such cases he can search a more extensive list of formulas found in a table of standard integrals such as:

Burington, R. S.: "Handbook of Mathematical Tables and Formulas," 4th ed., McGraw-Hill Book Company, New York, 1964.

Hoag, Albert L., and Donald G. McNeese: "Engineering and Technical Handbook," Prentice-Hall, Inc., Englewood Cliffs, N.J., 1957.

"C.R.C. Standard Mathematical Tables," The Chemical Rubber Publishing Co., Cleveland, Ohio.

Peirce, B. O., and R. M. Foster: "A Short Table of Integrals," 4th ed., Ginn and Company, Boston, 1956.

For convenience, the expressions which are integrated are classified into types. In some cases, specific limitations are given. In addition, no formula is valid when zero occurs in the denominator or when an even root of a negative number is involved.

Many times the student will be unable to find in the table of integrals the precise form he wishes to integrate. Yet he may be able to alter the expression he wishes to integrate into an equivalent form which is in the integral table.

Some of the more common forms are illustrated in the following examples.

Example 52. Find

$$\int \frac{5x\,dx}{3x - 2}$$

From a table of integrals we find the equation

$$\int \frac{x\,dx}{a + bx} = \frac{1}{b^2}[bx - a\ln(a + bx)] \tag{128}$$

(Note that the constant is usually omitted in the table of integrals.) We may alter the given expression to read

$$5\int \frac{x\,dx}{-2 + 3x} \tag{129}$$

Note that expression (129) and the left-hand side of Eq. (128) are identical in form and that

$a = -2 \qquad b = 3$

Therefore we may write

$$5\int \frac{x\,dx}{-2+3x} = (5)(1/9)[3x - (-2)\ln(-2+3x)]$$
$$= 5/9[+3x + 2\ln(-2+3x)]$$

Example 53. Find

$$\int_0^{2/3} \frac{dx}{4+9x^2} \tag{130}$$

From a table of integrals we find the equation

$$\int \frac{dx}{a+bx^2} = \frac{1}{\sqrt{ab}} \tan^{-1} \frac{x\sqrt{ab}}{a} \tag{131}$$

Note that expression (130) and the left-hand side of Eq. (131) are identical in form and that

$a = 4 \qquad b = 9$

Therefore we may write

$$\int_0^{2/3} \frac{dx}{4+9x^2} = \frac{1}{6}\left[\tan^{-1}\frac{6}{4}x\right]_0^{2/3}$$
$$= 1/6[\tan^{-1}(3/2 \times 2/3) - \tan^{-1}(3/2)(0)]$$
$$= \frac{1}{6}\left(\frac{\pi}{4} - 0\right) = \frac{\pi}{24}$$

Example 54. Find

$$\int \frac{x\,dx}{2x^2 - 3x - 5} \tag{132}$$

From a table of integrals we find the equation

$$\int \frac{x\,dx}{X} = \frac{1}{2c}\ln X - \frac{b}{2c}\int \frac{dx}{X} \tag{133}$$

where

$$X = a + bx + cx^2$$

Also, from a table of integrals we find the equation

$$\int \frac{dx}{X} = \frac{1}{\sqrt{-q}} \ln \frac{2cx + b - \sqrt{-q}}{2cx + b + \sqrt{-q}} \tag{134}$$

$$\text{where } X = a + bx + cx^2 \tag{135}$$

$$q = 4ac - b^2 \qquad b^2 > 4ac \tag{136}$$

Substituting Eq. (134) in Eq. (133), we obtain

$$\int \frac{x\,dx}{X} = \frac{1}{2c} \ln X - \frac{b}{2c}\left(\frac{1}{\sqrt{-q}} \ln \frac{2cx + b - \sqrt{-q}}{2cx + b + \sqrt{-q}}\right) \tag{137}$$

Note that expression (132) and the left-hand side of Eq. (137) are identical in form and that

$$X = 2x^2 - 3x - 5$$
$$a = -5$$
$$b = -3$$
$$c = 2$$
$$q = 4ac - b^2 = -40 - 9 = -49$$

Substituting, we have

$$\int \frac{x\,dx}{2x^2 - 3x - 5} = \frac{1}{4} \ln (2x^2 - 3x - 5) + \frac{3}{4}\left(\frac{1}{7} \ln \frac{4x - 10}{4x + 4}\right)$$

Example 55. Find

$$\int \sqrt{4 + \frac{9}{x^2}}\,dx \tag{138}$$

From a table of integrals we find the equation

$$\int \frac{\sqrt{x^2 + a^2}}{x}\,dx = \sqrt{x^2 + a^2} - a \ln\left(\frac{a + \sqrt{x^2 + a^2}}{x}\right) \tag{139}$$

We may alter expression (138) to read

$$\sqrt{\frac{4}{x^2}\left(x^2+\frac{9}{4}\right)}=\frac{2\sqrt{x^2+9/4}}{x} \tag{140}$$

Note that the expression on the right-hand side of Eq. (140) and the expression on the left-hand side of Eq. (139) are identical in form and that $a^2 = 9/4$. Therefore

$$2\int\frac{\sqrt{x^2+9/4}}{x}\,dx = 2\left[\sqrt{x^2+\frac{9}{4}}-\frac{3}{2}\ln\left(\frac{3/2+\sqrt{x^2+9/4}}{x}\right)\right]$$

Example 56. Find

$$\int_0^{1/2}\sqrt{1-4x^2}\,dx \tag{141}$$

From a table of integrals we find the equation

$$\int\sqrt{a^2-x^2}\,dx=\frac{1}{2}\left(x\sqrt{a^2-x^2}+a^2\sin^{-1}\frac{x}{a}\right) \tag{142}$$

We can alter the form of expression (141) to read

$$2\int_0^{1/2}\sqrt{1/4-x^2}\,dx \tag{143}$$

Note that expression (143) and the left-hand side of Eq. (142) are identical in form and that $a^2 = 1/4$. Therefore we may write

$$\begin{aligned}\int_0^{1/2}\sqrt{1-4x^2}\,dx &= (2)(1/2)[x\sqrt{1/4-x^2}+1/4\sin^{-1}2x]\\ &= (1/2\sqrt{0}+1/4\sin^{-1}1)-(0\sqrt{1/4}+1/4\sin^{-1}0)\\ &= 1/4\sin^{-1}1=\pi/8\end{aligned}$$

Example 57. Find, by integration, the area of a circle 10 in in radius.

We shall first find the area of the quadrant shown in Fig. 21.47.

$$A=\int y\,dx$$

The limits between which we shall integrate are $x = 0$ and $x = 10$ in. Also, we see that

$$y=\sqrt{100-x^2}$$

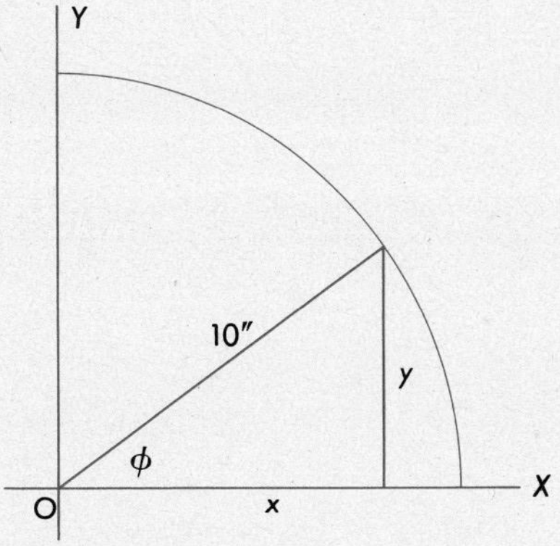

FIGURE 21.47

Therefore

$$A = \int_0^{10} \sqrt{100 - x^2}\, dx$$

Now by applying Eq. (142) we may write

$$A = \left[\frac{1}{2}\left(x\sqrt{100 - x^2} + 100 \sin^{-1}\frac{x}{10}\right)\right]_0^{10}$$
$$= \tfrac{1}{2}(10\sqrt{100 - 100} + 100 \sin^{-1} {}^{10}\!/_{10}) - \tfrac{1}{2}(0\sqrt{100 - 0} + 100 \sin^{-1} {}^{0}\!/_{10})$$

Note that

$$\sin^{-1} {}^{10}\!/_{10} = \sin^{-1} 1 = \frac{\pi}{2} \text{ rad}$$

$$A = \frac{1}{2}\left(100\,\frac{\pi}{2}\right) = 25\pi$$

The area of the entire circle is $4 \times 25\pi$, or 100π.

Example 58. Find

$$\int_{\pi/4}^{\pi/2} x \sin^2 x\, dx \tag{144}$$

From a table of integrals we find the equation

$$\int x \sin^2 x\, dx = \frac{x^2}{4} - \frac{x \sin 2x}{4} - \frac{\cos 2x}{8}$$

Therefore we may write

$$\int_{\pi/4}^{\pi/2} x \sin^2 x \, dx = \left[\frac{(\pi/2)^2}{4} - \frac{(\pi/2)\sin \pi}{4} - \frac{\cos \pi}{8}\right] - \left[\frac{(\pi/4)^2}{4} - \frac{(\pi/4)\sin(\pi/2)}{4} - \frac{\cos(\pi/2)}{8}\right]$$

$$= \left(\frac{\pi^2}{16} + \frac{1}{8}\right) - \left(\frac{\pi^2}{64} - \frac{\pi}{16}\right)$$

$$= \frac{3\pi^2}{64} + \frac{1}{8} + \frac{\pi}{16} = 0.784$$

Example 59. Find

$$\int x^3 \ln x \, dx \tag{145}$$

From a table of integrals we find the equation

$$\int x^p \ln(ax)\, dx = \frac{x^{p+1}}{p+1}\ln(ax) - \frac{x^{p+1}}{(p+1)^2} \qquad p \neq -1 \tag{146}$$

Note that expression (145) and the left-hand side of Eq. (146) are identical in form, and

$p = 3 \qquad a = 1$

Therefore we may write

$$\int x^3 \ln x \, dx = \frac{x^4}{4}\ln x - \frac{x^4}{16}$$

Example 60. Find

$$\int x^2 e^{3x}\, dx \tag{147}$$

From a table of integrals we find the equation

$$\int x^m e^{ax}\, dx = \frac{x^m e^{ax}}{a} - \frac{m}{a}\int x^{m-1} e^{ax}\, dx \tag{148}$$

Note that expression (147) and the left-hand side of Eq. (148) are identical in form and that

$m = 2 \qquad a = 3$

Also note that in this special case the quantity $m - 1$ in Eq. (148) is unity; therefore we may write

$$\int x^2e^{3x}\,dx = \frac{x^2e^{3x}}{3} - \frac{2}{3}\int xe^{3x}\,dx \tag{149}$$

Also from a table of integrals we find the equation

$$\int xe^{ax}\,dx = \frac{e^{ax}}{a^2}(ax - 1)$$

Therefore we may rewrite Eq. (148) as

$$\begin{aligned}\int x^2e^{3x}\,dx &= \frac{x^2e^{3x}}{3} - \frac{2}{3}\left[\frac{e^{3x}}{9}(3x - 1)\right]\\ &= \frac{e^{3x}}{27}(9x^2 - 6x + 2)\end{aligned}$$

21.22 Simpson's Rule

One of the primary uses of antidifferentiation in engineering and technology is to find a formula by which the numerical value of a definite integral may be calculated.

Unfortunately, the student will probably encounter functions for which he cannot find an antiderivative. However, if the given function is continuous over the interval from a to b, we know that its definite integral has a specific value.

In this section we shall discuss a method by which we can approximate

$$\int_a^b f(x)\,dx \qquad f(x) \geq 0$$

where $f(x)$ is continuous and $f(x) \geq 0$ for $a \leq x \leq b$.

As we have learned in the previous work, any definite integral $\int_a^b f(x)\,dx$ can be interpreted as an area. This sort of an integral can therefore be approximated by any method by which areas may be approximated. One such method is Simpson's rule, which we shall not derive.

Simpson's rule states that to find the approximate area under the graph of a function of the sort described above, we divide the area under the graph into an *even* number of strips of equal width by erecting an *odd number* of equally spaced ordinates. If we let h represent the distance between ordinates and designate the ordinates by $y_0, y_1, y_2, y_3, \ldots, y_n$, then the area under the graph is approximately

$$A \approx \frac{h}{3}(y_0 + 4y_1 + 2y_2 + 4y_3 + 2y_4 \cdots + 4y_{n-1} + y_n)$$

where y_0 is the ordinate erected at the lower limit of the area to be found and y_n is the ordinate erected at the upper limit of the area.

Thus we may write

$$\int_a^b y\,dx \approx \frac{h}{3}(y_0 + 4y_1 + 2y_2 + 4y_3 + 2y_4 + \cdots + 4y_{n-1} + y_n) \tag{150}$$

where a = lower limit of integration (left-hand limit)
b = upper limit of integration (right-hand limit)
y_0 = value of function when $x = a$
y_n = value of function when $x = b$
n is an even number

Example 61. Evaluate the definite integral

$$\int_2^{14} \frac{5x}{3x-2}\,dx$$

Following Eq. (150),

$$\int_2^{14} \frac{5x}{3x-2}\,dx \approx \frac{h}{3}(y_0 + 4y_1 + 2y_2 + 4y_3 + 2y_4 + \cdots + 4y_{n-1} + y_n)$$

where h = distance between successive ordinates y_0, y_1, y_2, y_3, etc.
y_0 = value of function

$$\frac{5x}{3x-2} \qquad \text{when } x = 2$$

and y_n is the value of the same function when $x = 14$.

It will be instructive to see how the answer varies depending on the number of strips used. While the student is cautioned against making too sweeping conclusions, the results should be highly suggestive.

We shall first use 2 strips; therefore $h = 6$.

x	$5x$	$3x - 2$	$\frac{5x}{3x-2}$	
2	10	4	2.5	$\times 1 = 2.50000 = y_0$
8	40	22	1.81818	$\times 4 = 7.27272 = 4y_1$
14	70	40	1.750000	$\times 1 = 1.75000 = y_2$
				11.52272

$$\int_2^{14} \frac{5x}{3x-2}\,dx \approx \frac{6}{3}(11.52272) = 23.045$$

Next we shall use 4 strips; therefore $h = 3$.

x	$5x$	$3x-2$	$\frac{5x}{3x-2}$	
2	10	4.0	2.50000	$\times 1 = 2.50000 = y_0$
5	25	13.0	1.92307	$\times 4 = 7.69228 = 4y_1$
8	40	22	1.81818	$\times 2 = 3.63636 = 2y_2$
11	55	31	1.77419	$\times 4 = 7.09676 = 4y_3$
14	70	40	1.75000	$\times 1 = 1.75000 = y_4$
				22.67540

$$\int_2^{14} \frac{5x}{3x-2}\,dx \approx \frac{3}{3}(22.67540) = 22.6754$$

Next we shall use 12 strips; therefore $h = 1$.

x	$5x$	$3x-2$	$\frac{5x}{3x-2}$	
2	10	4	2.50000	$\times 1 = 2.50000 = y_0$
3	15	7	2.14286	$\times 4 = 8.57144 = 4y_1$
4	20	10	2.00000	$\times 2 = 4.00000 = 2y_2$
5	25	13	1.92307	$\times 4 = 7.69228 = 4y_3$
6	30	16	1.87500	$\times 2 = 3.75000 = 2y_4$
7	35	19	1.84211	$\times 4 = 7.36844 = 4y_5$
8	40	22	1.81818	$\times 2 = 3.63636 = 2y_6$
9	45	25	1.80000	$\times 4 = 7.20000 = 4y_7$
10	50	28	1.78571	$\times 2 = 3.57142 = 2y_8$
11	55	31	1.77419	$\times 4 = 7.09676 = 4y_9$
12	60	34	1.76471	$\times 2 = 3.52942 = 2y_{10}$
13	65	37	1.75676	$\times 4 = 7.02704 = 4y_{11}$
14	70	40	1.75000	$\times 1 = 1.75000 = y_{12}$
				67.69316

$$\int_2^{14} \frac{5x}{3x-2}\,dx \approx \frac{1}{3}(67.69316) = 22.564$$

Next we shall use 24 strips; therefore $h = 0.5$.

x	$5x$	$3x - 2$	$\frac{5x}{3x - 2}$	
2.0	10.0	4.0	2.50000	$\times 1 = 2.50000 = y_0$
2.5	12.5	5.5	2.27272	$\times 4 = 9.09088 = 4y_1$
3.0	15.0	7.0	2.14286	$\times 2 = 4.28572 = 2y_2$
3.5	17.5	8.5	2.05882	$\times 4 = 8.23528 = 4y_3$
4.0	20.0	10.0	2.00000	$\times 2 = 4.00000 = 2y_4$
4.5	22.5	11.5	1.95652	$\times 4 = 7.82608 = 4y_5$
5.0	25.0	13.0	1.92307	$\times 2 = 3.84614 = 2y_6$
5.5	27.5	14.5	1.89655	$\times 4 = 7.58620 = 4y_7$
6.0	30.0	16.0	1.87500	$\times 2 = 3.75000 = 2y_8$
6.5	32.5	17.5	1.85714	$\times 4 = 7.42856 = 4y_9$
7.0	35.0	19.0	1.84211	$\times 2 = 3.68222 = 2y_{10}$
7.5	37.5	20.5	1.82927	$\times 4 = 7.31668 = 4y_{11}$
8.0	40.0	22.0	1.81818	$\times 2 = 3.63636 = 2y_{12}$
8.5	42.5	23.5	1.80851	$\times 4 = 7.23404 = 4y_{13}$
9.0	45.0	25.0	1.80000	$\times 2 = 3.60000 = 2y_{14}$
9.5	47.5	26.5	1.79245	$\times 4 = 7.16980 = 4y_{15}$
10.0	50.0	28.0	1.78571	$\times 2 = 3.57142 = 2y_{16}$
10.5	52.5	29.5	1.77966	$\times 4 = 7.11864 = 4y_{17}$
11.0	55.0	31.0	1.77419	$\times 2 = 3.54838 = 2y_{18}$
11.5	57.5	32.5	1.76923	$\times 4 = 7.07692 = 4y_{19}$
12.0	60.0	34.0	1.76471	$\times 2 = 3.52942 = 2y_{20}$
12.5	62.5	35.5	1.76056	$\times 4 = 7.04224 = 4y_{21}$
13.0	65.0	37.0	1.75676	$\times 2 = 3.51352 = 2y_{22}$
13.5	67.5	38.5	1.75325	$\times 4 = 7.01300 = 4y_{23}$
14.0	70.0	40.0	1.75000	$\times 1 = 1.75000 = y_{24}$
				135.34950

$$\int_2^{14} \frac{5x}{3x - 2}\,dx \approx \frac{0.5}{3}(135.3495) = 22.5583$$

By reference to Example 52 we note that

$$\begin{aligned}\int_2^{14} \frac{5x}{3x - 2}\,dx &= \frac{5}{9}[3x + 2\ln(3x - 2)]_2^{14}\\ &= \tfrac{5}{9}\{[42 + 2\ln(42 - 2)] - [6 + 2\ln(6 - 2)]\}\\ &= \tfrac{5}{9}(42 + 2\ln 40 - 6 - 2\ln 4)\\ &= \tfrac{5}{9}(36 + 2\ln 10) = \tfrac{5}{9}(36 + 2 \times 2.30259) = 22.5584\end{aligned}$$

Example 62. Evaluate the definite integral

$$\int_{1.817}^{14.328} \frac{5x}{3x-2}\,dx$$

We could, of course, divide the region between $x = 1.817$ and $x = 14.328$ into strips, using, for example, 10 strips. However, in so doing we would be committed to using five- or six-digit abscissa distances. It will be much easier to consider three regions separately, as, for example, the region between $x = 1.817$ and $x = 2$, the region between $x = 2$ and $x = 14$, and finally the region between $x = 14$ and $x = 14.328$. Then we shall apply Simpson's rule to each region. The region between $x = 2$ and $x = 14$ has been evaluated in Example 61. We shall now evaluate the other two intervals by Simpson's rule.

Interval between $x = 1.817$ and $x = 2$

x	$5x$	$3x - 2$	$\frac{5x}{3x-2}$	
1.817	9.085	3.451	2.6326	$\times 1 = 2.6326 = y_0$
1.9085	9.5425	3.7255	2.5614	$\times 4 = 10.2456 = 4y_1$
2.000	10.000	4.0000	2.500	$\times 1 = 2.5000 = y_2$
				15.3782

$$\text{Area} = \frac{0.0915}{3}(15.3782) = 0.4690$$

Interval between $x = 14$ and $x = 14.328$

x	$5x$	$3x - 2$	$\frac{5x}{3x-2}$	
14.000	70.000	40.000	1.7500	$\times 1 = 1.7500 = y_0$
14.164	70.820	40.492	1.7490	$\times 4 = 6.9960 = 4y_1$
14.328	71.640	40.984	1.7480	$\times 1 = 1.7480 = y_2$
				10.4940

$$\text{Area} = \frac{0.164}{3}(10.4940) = 0.574$$

The area between $x = 2$ and $x = 14$ was found in Example 61 to be 22.558.

$$\int_{1.817}^{14.328} \frac{5x}{3x-2}\,dx \approx 0.469 + 0.574 + 22.558 = 23.601$$

Example 63. Evaluate the definite integral

$$\int_0^{2/3} \left(1 + \frac{e^x}{4}\right)^{1/2} dx$$

Following Eq. (150),

$$\int_0^{2/3} \left(1 + \frac{e^x}{4}\right)^{1/2} dx \approx \frac{h}{3}(y_0 + 4y_1 + 2y_2 + \cdots + 4y_{n-1} + y_n)$$

where h = distance between successive ordinates. We shall use 8 strips. The calculations are tabulated below.

x	e^x	$1 + \frac{e^x}{4}$	$\sqrt{1 + \frac{e^x}{4}}$	
0	1.00000	1.25000	1.11803	$\times 1 = 1.11803 = y_0$
$\frac{1}{12}$	1.08690	1.27172	1.12771	$\times 4 = 4.51084 = 4y_1$
$\frac{2}{12}$	1.18136	1.29534	1.13813	$\times 2 = 2.27626 = 2y_2$
$\frac{3}{12}$	1.28402	1.32101	1.14935	$\times 4 = 4.59740 = 4y_3$
$\frac{4}{12}$	1.39561	1.34890	1.16142	$\times 2 = 2.32284 = 2y_4$
$\frac{5}{12}$	1.51690	1.37922	1.17440	$\times 4 = 4.69760 = 4y_5$
$\frac{6}{12}$	1.64872	1.41218	1.18835	$\times 2 = 2.37670 = 2y_6$
$\frac{7}{12}$	1.79200	1.44800	1.20333	$\times 4 = 4.81332 = 4y_7$
$\frac{8}{12}$	1.94773	1.48693	1.21940	$\times 1 = 1.21940 = y_8$
				27.93239

$$\int_0^{2/3} \left(1 + \frac{e^x}{4}\right)^{1/2} dx \approx \frac{1/12}{3}(27.93239) = 0.7759$$

EXERCISE 18

Evaluate the following definite integrals by such methods as the instructor directs.

1. $\displaystyle\int_5^8 x\sqrt{3x + 1}\, dx$

2. $\displaystyle\int_2^6 \frac{dx}{5x + 8x^3}$

3. $\displaystyle\int_{0.2}^{0.4} \frac{x\, dx}{3 - 4x}$

4. $\displaystyle\int_0^3 \frac{dx}{16 - x^2}$

5. $\displaystyle\int_2^5 \frac{x^2\, dx}{\sqrt{3x + 5}}$

6. $\displaystyle\int_{0.1}^{0.5} \frac{dx}{x^2(2 + 3x)}$

7. $\displaystyle\int_{-0.5}^{+0.5} \sqrt{\frac{1 + x}{1 - x}}\, dx$

8. $\displaystyle\int_0^5 \frac{dx}{\sqrt{x^2 + 3x + 1}}$

9. $\int_0^6 (100 - x^2)^{3/2}\,dx$

10. $\int_4^{10} \frac{x^3\,dx}{2x + 1}$

11. $\int_0^{1.6} \frac{(1 + x^2)\,dx}{\sqrt{4 - x^2}}$

12. $\int_0^{\pi/2} \sin^4 x\,dx$

13. $\int_0^7 3x(x + 1)^{-1/3}\,dx$

14. $\int_{\pi/6}^{\pi/3} \sin^2\theta \cos^2\theta\,d\theta$

15. $\int_0^2 x^2 e^{-x}\,dx$

16. $\int_0^8 e^{-x}\sqrt{3 - 2e^{-x}}\,dx$

17. $\int_1^3 \left(\frac{e^{2x}}{2x} + e^{2x}\ln x\right) dx$

18. $\int_{1.5}^{2.7} x^3 \ln x\,dx$

19. $\int_2^3 \frac{dx}{\ln x^2}$

20. $\int_1^8 (\ln x)^3\,dx$

21. Evaluate the integral in Prob. 1 by substituting

$$x = z - \tfrac{1}{3}$$

22. Evaluate the integral in Prob. 10(*a*) by dividing numerator by denominator obtaining four terms, (*b*) by substituting $(z - 1)/2$ for x.

23. In calculating the capacity of absorption towers in chemical engineering, it is necessary to evaluate certain definite integrals by approximate methods. Evaluate the following definite integrals by use of Simpson's rule using the given data (x_i is an empirical function of x; y_i is an empirical function of y):

$$\int_2^{12} \frac{dx}{x_i - x} \qquad \int_{0.010}^{0.026} \frac{dy}{y - y_i} \qquad \int_{0.010}^{0.026} \frac{(1 + y)(1 + y_i)}{y - y_i}\,dy$$

x	x_i	$\frac{1}{x_i - x}$	y	y_i	$\frac{1}{y - y_i}$
2	5.10	0.322	0.010	0.0008	108
3	5.55	0.392	0.012	0.0040	125
4	6.13	0.469	0.014	0.0082	172
5	6.70	0.587	0.016	0.0122	263
6	7.40	0.715	0.018	0.0156	416
7	8.15	0.869	0.020	0.0183	588
8	9.05	0.952	0.022	0.0203	588
9	10.10	0.909	0.024	0.0220	500
10	11.40	0.715	0.026	0.0233	370
11	13.25	0.444			
12	16.00	0.250			

24. The length of an indicator card is 3.6 in. The widths of the diagram at intervals 0.3 in apart are 0, 0.40, 0.52, 0.63, 0.72, 0.93, 0.99, 1.00, 1.00, 1.00, 1.00, 0.97, 0. Determine the area of the indicator card by Simpson's rule and divide by the length of the card to obtain the mean effective pressure. Work this problem using 6 subdivisions and 12 subdivisions and compare your results.
25. A cylindrical tank is mounted with its axis horizontal. The tank is 15 ft in diameter and 40 ft long. How many gallons of liquid are there in the tank if the surface of the liquid is 5 ft from the bottom of the tank?

appendix a
treatment of measured data

A.1 Measured Data

Many of the data with which the average technical man works are obtained experimentally. There is a definite limit to their reliability. The *reliability* of a number may be expressed in terms of either precision or accuracy. *Precision* is gauged by the position of the last reliable digit relative to the decimal point, whereas *accuracy* is measured by the number of significant figures. *Significant figures* are those known to be reliable and include any zeros not merely used to locate the decimal point.

For instance, if the diameters of several wires had been measured with a micrometer and found to be 0.118, 0.056, 0.008, and 0.207 in, one might say that these diameters had been measured to a precision of 0.001 in and to accuracies of three, two, one, and three figures, respectively.

The following statements apply to significant figures:

1. *All nonzero digits are significant.*
2. *Zero digits which lie between significant digits are significant.*
3. *Zero digits which lie to the right of both the decimal point and the last nonzero digit are significant.*
4. *Zeros at the beginning of a decimal fraction are not significant.*

5. *Zeros at the end of a whole number, if used only to locate the decimal point, are not significant. When one or more such zeros are known to be significant, the "tilde" (~) is written over the last significant zero to indicate this fact.*

Example 1.

Number	Significant figures	Number of significant figures
35.62	3,5,6,2	4
3,020	3,0,2	3
0.00046	4,6	2
0.000850	8,5,0	3
5.600	5,6,0,0	4
3.0080	3,0,0,8,0	5
$12{,}6\tilde{0}0$	1,2,6,0	4
$12{,}60\tilde{0}$	1,2,6,0,0	5
40,000	4	1

Should the definition of significant figures seem somewhat arbitrary, let us consider the computation of the volume of a rectangular sheet of metal. Suppose that the measured length, width, and thickness are 165.2, 5.07, and 0.0021 in, respectively, and that these measurements are correct to the last digit given. Let us now compare the effect on the volume of changing the last digit of each measurement by one. It will be seen that such a change introduces respective errors of about one-sixteenth of 1 percent, one-fifth of 1 percent, and 5 percent. The length, then, is the most accurate, and the thickness the least accurate.

A.2 Absolute and Relative Errors

Closely allied to the concepts of precision and accuracy discussed in Sec. A.1 are absolute and relative errors, respectively. The *absolute error* is the approximate value minus the true value of a number. It is positive or negative according to whether the approximate value is larger or smaller than the true value.

The *relative error* is the ratio of the absolute error to the exact value. Since the relative error is a ratio between two like quantities, it is an abstract number and is often expressed as a percentage.

Example 2. The actual length of a metal bar is 11.52 in. The length as measured with a scale with a worn end is 11.56 in. Find the absolute and relative errors.

The absolute error is $11.56 - 11.52 = 0.04$ in
The relative error is $(11.56 - 11.52)/11.52 = 0.00347 = 0.3$ percent

A.3 Rounding Off Numbers

Frequently a result will be rounded off because the last several digits either are in doubt or are not required in that particular computation. The operation of rounding off is governed by the following rule:

If the figures to be rejected represent less than half a unit in the last place to be retained, they are dropped. If they represent more than half a unit in the last place to be retained, the last retained digit is increased by one. If the rejected part is known to represent just half a unit in the last place to be retained, the last retained significant digit, if even, is left even or, if odd, is raised to the nearest even number.

Example 3.

	Rounded off to		
Number	**Four figures**	**three figures**	**Two figures**
3.1416	3.142	3.14	3.1
14.815	14.82	14.8	15.
321.35	321.4	321	320
6,274.5	6,274	6,270	6,300
20,018	20,020	$20,\tilde{0}00$	20,000
71,853	71,850	71,900†	72,000

†71,853 is nearer to 71,900 than to 71,800.

In addition and subtraction the precision of the answer corresponds to the least precise of the quantities involved. *Perform the addition or subtraction and round off by eliminating any digits resulting from operations on broken columns on the right.*

Example 4. Add:

175.6
2.126
13.04
0.0028
―――――
190.7688

Since the last unbroken column on the right is that immediately after the decimal point, we round off to 190.8.

In multiplication and division the accuracy of the answer corresponds to the least accurate of the quantities involved. *Perform the multiplication or division and round off the answer to a number of significant figures equal to that in the least accurate quantity in the computation.*

Example 5. Multiply:

$$3.14159 \times 47.82 = 150.2308338$$

Although the multiplicand has six significant figures, the multiplier has only four; therefore, we round off the product to four significant figures and get 150.2.

A.4 Scientific Notation

In scientific work a very large or very small number is expressed as a number between 1 and 10 times an integral power of 10. Thus 2,580,000 would be written 2.58×10^6, and 0.0000258 would be written 2.58×10^{-5}. This is called scientific notation. The magnitude of the number is revealed by a glance at the exponent (see Table 8.2).

Several other advantages in this notation will become apparent. Space is saved, a particularly important point in tabulating data. The labor of counting figures to the right or left of the decimal point—a labor attended by risk of error—is eliminated. The accuracy with which a quantity is known is indicated by the number of figures to the right of the decimal point. For example, when we consider the number 72,000, we cannot tell whether there are two, three, four, or five significant figures. No uncertainty exists when we write 7.2×10^4, 7.20×10^4, 7.200×10^4, or 7.2000×10^4.

The ease of dealing with large and small quantities in this manner is illustrated by the following problem:

Simplify the expression

$$\begin{aligned} \frac{40\tilde{0},000 \times 8,\tilde{0}00,000 \times 0.0045}{60,0\tilde{0}0 \times 0.025 \times 10\tilde{0}} &= \frac{4 \times 10^5 \times 8 \times 10^6 \times 4.5 \times 10^{-3}}{6 \times 10^4 \times 2.5 \times 10^{-2} \times 10^2} \\ &= \frac{4 \times 8 \times 4.5}{6 \times 2.5} \times 10^{(5+6-3)-(4-2+2)} \\ &= 9.6 \times 10^4 = 96,000 \end{aligned}$$

There are two instances in which we depart from the rule of expressing a quantity as a number between 1 and 10 times a suitable power of 10.

If we were to extract the square root of 2.5×10^{-7}, we should write this as 25×10^{-8} in order to make the exponent of 10 divisible by the index of the root. The square root is readily seen to be 5×10^{-4}. Also, when quantities are to be added and subtracted, they must have the same exponents. Thus $4 \times 10^{-7} + 7 \times 10^{-5} = 4 \times 10^{-7} + 700 \times 10^{-7} = 704 \times 10^{-7} = 7.04 \times 10^{-5}$.

appendix b computational aids

B.1 Aids to Computation

In Appendix B we shall outline a few of the more useful work-saving concepts in computation. (For more extended treatment see the Bibliography and Rice and Knight's "Technical Mathematics," 3d ed.)

Since most special methods are soon forgotten unless routinely used, the authors hope that the student will recall that such methods exist and will seek them out as the need arises.

B.2 Abbreviated Division

This is a relatively fast method of obtaining a quotient containing a certain number of significant figures.

1. *The dividend and divisor are each rounded off to one more significant figure than is to be contained in the quotient. It may be necessary to retain still another digit in the dividend in order to make it larger than the divisor. Decimal points are disregarded during the operation, the position of the decimal point in the quotient being determined by inspection.*

2. *The first division is made using the entire divisor. Thereafter each successive division is made after rounding off successive digits from the right-hand side of the divisor.*

Example 1. Divide 32,586.70143 by 481.60732, carrying out the division to five significant figures in the quotient. Division carried out in the usual manner gives an answer of 67.662388 to eight figures. In the abbreviated division the dividend and divisor are rounded off to seven and six figures, respectively.

```
               6
481607/3258670
       2889642
 48161/ 369028/7
        337127
  4816/  31901/6
         28896
   482/   3005/6
          2892
    48/    113/2
            96
```

ANS.: 67.662

B.3 Shortcut in the Use of the Pythagorean Theorem

When the sides of a right triangle are given in the common binary system of linear measurement (for example, $\frac{1}{2}$ in, $\frac{1}{4}$ in, $\frac{1}{8}$ in, etc.), the work involved in the application of the Pythagorean theorem may be reduced by taking as a unit of length $1/n$, where n is the least common denominator.

Example 2. Find the hypotenuse of a right triangle whose sides are $1\frac{5}{8}$ and $2\frac{3}{16}$ in.

Since 16 is the LCD, we shall take $\frac{1}{16}$ in as the unit of length. Then

$1\frac{5}{8} = 26$ units

and

$2\frac{3}{16} = 35$ units

and

$\sqrt{26^2 + 35^2} = 43.60$ units

$$\frac{43.60}{16} = 2.725 \text{ in}$$

If the nearest $\frac{1}{64}$ in is desired,

$$\frac{43.60}{16} = \frac{x}{64}$$

$$x = 174.4 \qquad \text{(call it 174)}$$

$$\tfrac{174}{64} = \tfrac{87}{32} = 2\tfrac{23}{32} \text{ in}$$

B.4 Iterative Process for Obtaining a Square Root

An iterative, or repetitive, process is based on assuming a value of the quantity to be found. The assumed value is tested against known information, which leads to a second and closer approximation. The second approximation is "fed back" into the process, giving us a third and still better approximation, and so on until the desired accuracy is obtained.

Specifically, in applying an iterative process to finding the square root of a number, we obtain from tables, slide rule, or mental estimate a reasonable first approximation for the square root. The number is divided by the first approximation, giving a quotient somewhat different from the divisor. Evidently the true square root must be between the values of the first trial divisor and the quotient; therefore the average of these quantities is taken for the second trial divisor. The process may be repeated (hence the term "iterative") until the desired accuracy is achieved. The process has the advantage of being self-correcting. An error, or a poor choice of the first trial divisor, will merely increase the number of iterations needed to obtain the desired answer. This method is very well adapted for use with a desk calculator.

In the next paragraph it will be shown that if the trial divisor and quotient agree to n significant figures, their average accurately represents the square root to at least $2n$ significant figures.

Assume $\sqrt{a^2}$ to be taken as equal to $a + b$ (our first trial divisor).

$$\frac{a^2}{a+b} = a - b + \frac{b^2}{a+b}$$

The average of the trial divisor and the quotient is

$$\frac{a + b + a - b + b^2/(a+b)}{2} = a + \frac{b^2}{2(a+b)}$$

If $b = a \times 10^{-n}$, the trial divisor will equal $a + a \times 10^{-n}$, and the quotient $\approx a - b \approx a - a \times 10^{-n}$. The relative difference between trial divisor and quotient (compared to a) is

$$\frac{(a + a \times 10^{-n}) - (a - a \times 10^{-n})}{a} = 2 \times 10^{-n} \qquad (1)$$

Substituting $a \times 10^{-n}$ for b in the second approximation,

$$a + \frac{b^2}{2(a+b)} \approx a + \frac{b^2}{2a} \approx a + \frac{a^2 \times 10^{-2n}}{2a} \approx a + \frac{a \times 10^{-2n}}{2}$$

The error in the average relative to a is

$$\frac{(a \times 10^{-2n})/2}{a} = \frac{10^{-2n}}{2} \qquad (2)$$

A comparison between Eqs. (1) and (2) shows conservatively twice as many digits in agreement in Eq. (2) as in Eq. (1).

Example 3. Find $\sqrt{10}$ to eight decimal places.

Assume

$$\sqrt{10} = 3 \text{ (first trial divisor)} \qquad \frac{10}{3} = 3.33$$

$$\frac{3.33 + 3}{2} = 3.16 \text{ (second trial divisor)} \qquad \frac{10}{3.16} = 3.16456$$

$$\frac{3.16456 + 3.16}{2} = 3.16228 \text{ (third trial divisor)} \qquad \frac{10}{3.16228} = 3.1622753203\dagger$$

$$\frac{3.16228 + 3.1622753203}{2} = 3.1622776602$$

which we round off to 3.16227766, since only eight decimal places were required.

†(3.1622753203 may be rounded off to 3.16228; hence there are six significant digits of agreement and we are justified in retaining all 11 digits of 3.1622776602.)

appendix C
interpolation

C.1 Limitations on Interpolation

A common type of table lists values of y corresponding to given values of x, y being a function of x. Reliability of an interpolated value of y may be limited by any of the following:

1. Number of significant figures in x. This is frequently unlimited, any limit present being imposed by an accuracy of measurement.
2. Precision of tabulated values of y.
3. Departure from linearity of the relationship between x and y.
4. Size of the interval within which interpolation is being calculated.

Examples of these factors are given below:

1. If values of y are *exact* and *linear*, the interpolated value may be calculated to as fine a degree as desired, subject only to the accuracy of x, if x is a measured quantity.

Example 1.

	x Miles	y Feet (= 5,280 × miles)	
1 [0.4 [	3	15,840	] Δy] 5,280
	3.4	?	
	4	21,120	

$$\Delta y = \left(\frac{0.4}{1}\right)(5{,}280) = 2{,}112$$

and our interpolated value of y is 15,840 + 2,112, or 17,952. However, this must be rounded off to 18,000 ft. The answer is limited to an accuracy of two significant figures solely because 3.4 mi, a measured quantity, is thus limited.

2. If values of y are *rounded* and *linear,* interpolation may be carried out either (a) to as many significant figures as there are in x, if x is a measured quantity, or (b) to the precision of the tabulated values of y, whichever is less reliable.

Example 2.

	x Diameter	y Circumference (= 3.1416 × diameter)	
1 [0.74 [	4	12.5664	] Δy] 3.1416
	4.74	?	
	5	15.7080	

$$\Delta y = \left(\frac{0.74}{1}\right)(3.1416) = 2.3248$$

Therefore, $y = 12.5664 + 2.3248 = 14.8912$, but we say that the circumference of a 4.74-in circle is 14.9 in. The accuracy is limited by the three-figure accuracy in the diameter.

Example 3.

Diameter	Circumference
9	28.27
9.0852	?.
10	31.42

The circumference of a 9.0852-in circle is 28.54 in. Limit is set by the precision of 0.01 in circumferences.

Note that interpolation does not improve the precision of a value; that is, $28.27 + (0.0852)(3.15)$ cannot be written $28.27 + 0.268$, or 28.538 (see Example 4, Appendix A).

3. If values of y are *exact* and *nonlinear*, the extent of interpolation is limited to the less reliable of either (a) the accuracy of a measured value of x or (b) the precision corresponding to the position of the first digit in Δy showing variation. (Attainable precision may occasionally be one place better than this.)

Example 4.

x	$y (= x^2)$	Δy
71	5,041	143
72	5,184	
72.2	?	145
73	5,329	

The interpolated value of $(72.2)^2$ is 5,210, a limit of three significant figures of accuracy being set by the measured value 72.2. Also Δy shows a variation in the units digit. Therefore the units digit in our answer must be rounded off.

Example 5.

x	$y (= x^3)$	Δy
11	1,331	
11.875	?	397
12	1,728	469
13	2,197	

The calculated value of $(11.875)^3$ is 1,674.56+, but as Δy shows a variation in the hundreds digits we are justified in expressing our answer only to the nearest 100, or 1,700.

4. If values of y are *rounded* and *nonlinear*, the controlling factor is the least reliable of the following: (a) accuracy of measurement of x; (b) precision of tabulated values of y; (c) precision depending upon the variation in Δy.

Example 6.

x	$y (= \sqrt{x})$	Δy	$\Delta^2 y$
37	6.0828		
37.6	?	0.0816	−0.0010
38	6.1644	0.0806	
39	6.2450		

$\Delta^2 y$ represents the second difference, or the "change in the change" in y.

The interpolated value of $\sqrt{37.6} = 6.13$. Note that if x had been given as 37.600, then, making the change in Δy the controlling factor, we might have written $\sqrt{37.600} = 6.132$. (It will be shown in Sec. C.2 that the maximum interpolation error $\leqq \frac{1}{8}\,\Delta^2 y$.)

Example 7.

x	$y(=\sqrt[3]{x})$	Δy	$\Delta^2 y$
55	3.803		
		0.023	
56	3,826		
56.314	?		0
		0.023	
57	3.849		

Since $\Delta^2 y = 0$, the controlling factor here is the precision of y (nearest thousandth); therefore we write $\sqrt[3]{56.314} = 3.833$.

Example 8.

x	$y\left(=\frac{1}{x}\right)$	Δy	$\Delta^2 y$
15	0.06667		
		0.00417	
16	0.06250		
16.375	?		−0.00049
		0.00368	
17	0.05882		

The interpolated value of $1/16.375 = 0.0611$ [precision is limited by the fact that $\frac{1}{8}(0.00049) = 0.00006$].

As an example of the effect of the width of the interval on the accuracy of interpolation, find the square of 5.283, the actual value of which is 27.910089.

Interpolation between 5 and 6 gives us $(5.283)^2 = 28$. Interpolation between 5.2 and 5.3 [looking up $(52)^2$ and $(53)^2$ and shifting the decimal point two places to the left] gives us 27.91.

Finally, by interpolation between 5.28 and 5.29 [looking up $(528)^2$ and $(529)^2$ and shifting the decimal point four places to the left], we obtain $(5.283)^2 = 27.9101$.

C.2 Second Difference as a Guide to Interpolation

If we are concerned only with the limitations imposed by a nonlinear relationship, a helpful guide makes use of the value of the second difference $\Delta^2 y$. (We are assuming evenly spaced values of x.) The rule is: *The interpolation error does not, in general, exceed one-eighth of the second difference, that is,* $\epsilon \leqq \frac{1}{8}\,\Delta^2 y$.

The derivation of the expression for maximum error ϵ assumes a parabolic function $y = ax^2 + bx + c$. With reference to Fig. C.1, it can be shown that in the interval between x_o and $x_o + k$, the greatest departure from a straight line occurs at $x_o + k/2$.

Any three points not in the same straight line may be represented by a parabola. We shall designate these points as x_o, y_o; $x_o + k, y_1$; $x_o + 2k, y_2$. It follows that

$$y_o = ax_o^2 + bx_o + c \tag{1}$$

and

$$y_1 = a(x_o + k)^2 + b(x_o + k) + c = ax_o^2 + 2akx_o + ak^2 + bx_o + bk + c \tag{2}$$

Subtracting Eq. (1) from Eq. (2), we obtain

$$y_1 - y_o = \Delta_1 y = 2akx_o + ak^2 + bk \tag{3}$$

Also

$$y_2 = a(x_o + 2k)^2 + b(x_o + 2k) + c = ax_o^2 + 4akx_o + 4ak^2 + bx_o + 2bk + c \tag{4}$$

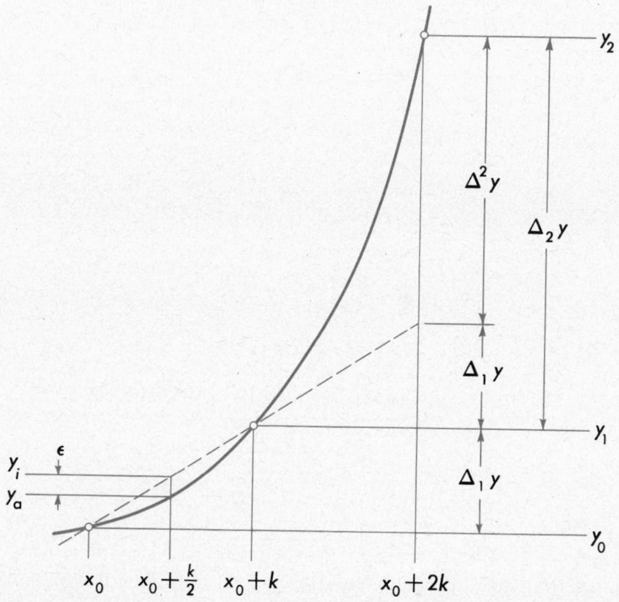

FIGURE C.1

Subtracting Eq. (2) from Ex. (4), we obtain

$$y_2 - y_1 = \Delta_2 y = 2akx_o + 3ak^2 + bk \tag{5}$$

Subtracting Eq. (3) from Eq. (5), we have

$$\Delta_2 y - \Delta_1 y = \Delta^2 y = 2ak^2 \tag{6}$$

At $x_o + k/2$, the interpolated value of y is

$$y_i = \frac{1}{2}(y_1 + y_o) = ax_o^2 + akx_o + \frac{ak^2}{2} + bx_o + \frac{bk}{2} + c \tag{7}$$

Also at $x_o + k/2$, the actual value of y is

$$y_a = a\left(x_o + \frac{k}{2}\right)^2 + b\left(x_o + \frac{k}{2}\right) + c$$

This reduces to

$$y_a = ax_o^2 + akx_o + \frac{ak^2}{4} + bx_o + \frac{bk}{2} + c \tag{8}$$

Subtracting Eq. (8) from Eq. (7), we have $y_i - y_a = \epsilon = ak^2/4$. Since from Eq. (6) $\Delta^2 y = 2ak^2$, $\frac{1}{8}\Delta^2 y = ak^2/4$ and

$$\epsilon = \tfrac{1}{8}\Delta^2 y \tag{9}$$

More accurate interpolation may be performed through the use of the Gregory-Newton or the Lagrange formula which may be found in any standard numerical analysis text and in many calculus texts.

Example 9. Find $(2.5)^2$.

x	y (= x^2)	Δy	$\Delta^2 y$
1	1		
		3	
2	4		2
		5	
3	9		2
		7	
4	16		

According to our rule, the maximum error is $\frac{1}{8}\Delta^2 y = \frac{1}{8}(2) = 0.25$. This is confirmed by comparing the interpolated value, 6.5, and the true value, 6.25. Note that we have chosen the most unfavorable condition—the middle of an interval. If we had chosen to find $(2.1)^2$, the interpolated and true values, 4.5 and 4.41, respectively, would have been in better agreement.

Example 10. Find $\sqrt[3]{1{,}085}$.

x	y (= $\sqrt[3]{x}$)	Δy	$\Delta^2 y$
1,070	10.228091		
		31765	
1,080	10.259856		−196
		31569	
1,090	10.291425		−193
		31376	
1,100	10.322801		

If we take −194 as representative of $\Delta^2 y$, the maximum error is $\frac{1}{8}(-194) = -24$; that is, $\epsilon = -0.000024$.

Checking, we find

$$\begin{aligned} \text{Interpolated value of } \sqrt[3]{1{,}085} &= 10.275641 \\ \text{Actual value of } \sqrt[3]{1{,}085} &= \underline{10.275664} \\ \text{Error} &= -0.000023 \end{aligned}$$

Example 11. Find the reciprocal of 0.003125.

x	y (= 1/x)	Δy	$\Delta^2 y$
0.00311	321.5434		
		−10306	
0.00312	320.5128		+66
		−10240	
0.00313	319.4888		+65
		−10175	
0.00314	318.4713		

$$\begin{aligned} \text{Interpolated value} &= 320.0008 \\ \text{Actual value} &= \underline{320.0000} \\ \text{Error} &= 0.0008 \end{aligned}$$

[By our rule, the maximum error is $\frac{1}{8}(0.0066) = 0.0008$.]

appendix d
solution of higher-degree equations

Occasionally it may be necessary to solve an equation of the type $Ax^n + Bx^{n-1} + \cdots + Px + Q = 0$, when n is 3 or some higher integer. This may be done by extending the principles set forth on pages 274 and 290. [Newton's method, which employs calculus, is more direct.]

There we had occasion to state in effect that if $(x - a)(x - b) = 0$, then $x - a = 0$, $x - b = 0$, and the roots are $x = a$ and $x = b$. It can be shown that a polynomial expression of the type $Ax^n + Bx^{n-1} + \cdots + Px + Q = 0$ may be written as follows:

$$(x - a)(x - b)(x - c) \cdots = 0$$

When the expression is written in the factored form, it can also be shown that there are as many factors involving x (and therefore as many roots) as the degree of the equation.

The greater portion of our solution depends upon plotting the function. Plotting requires a tabulation of coordinate values—a process which can be greatly simplified by *synthetic substitution*.

To illustrate synthetic substitution, let us refer to the equation in Example 3 below. If we substitute any value a for x in the polynomial expression, we obtain

$2a^3 - 17a^2 + 47a - 24$

Rearranging,

$a[a(2a - 17) + 47] - 24$

It is evident that in this process we have multiplied 2 by a three times, -17 by a twice, and 47 by a once; -24 has not been affected.

Example 1. Evaluate $2x^3 - 17x^2 + 47x - 24$ when $x = 3$.

The sequence of steps would be

$$\begin{aligned} (2)(3) &= 6 \\ 6 - 17 &= -11 \\ (-11)(3) &= -33 \\ -33 + 47 &= 14 \\ (14)(3) &= 42 \\ 42 - 24 &= 18 \end{aligned}$$

It can readily be shown that direct substitution of 3 for x in the usual way will lead to the same result.

When a is a less simple number, such as 2.087, synthetic substitution is easily performed on a calculating machine by setting the machine for a constant multiplier of 2.087 and performing the additions and subtractions mentally or on scratch paper.

We shall now illustrate how to evaluate to any desired degree of accuracy the real roots of a higher degree equation in a single variable.

Example 2. Find all the real roots of the equation

$$x^4 - 2x^3 - 14x^2 + 15x + 36 = 0$$

Since this is a fourth-degree equation, it may be expected to have four roots, of which some or all may be complex numbers. Using synthetic substitution, we obtain the following table.

x	6	5	4	3	2	1	0	−1	−2	−3	−4	−5
y	486	136	0	−18	10	36	36	10	−18	0	136	486

Since, at each end of the table, y is receding from zero at an increasing rate, it is apparent that no points of interest will be outside of this range.

These data are plotted as Fig. D.1, which confirms the table in indicating that

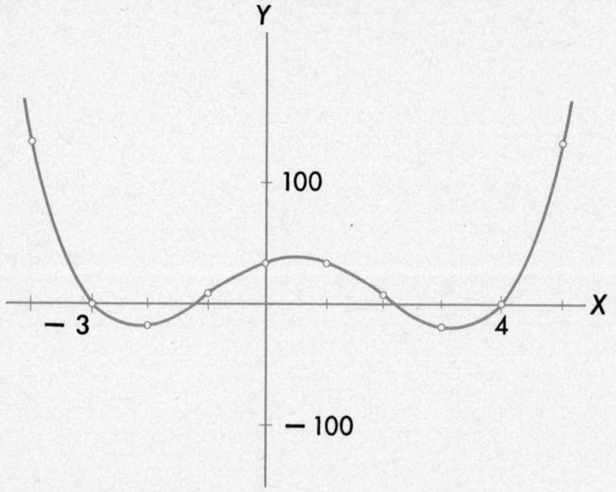

FIGURE D.1

two roots are $x_1 = 4$ and $x_2 = -3$. It follows that $x - (4)$ and $x - (-3)$, or $x - 4$ and $x + 3$, must be factors of the original expression.

If we divide the original equation through by $x - 4$ and by $x + 3$ (or by $x^2 - x - 12$), we shall obtain an equation of lower degree from which we can calculate the remaining factors. Accordingly, dividing the equation $x^4 - 2x^2 - 14x^2 + 15x + 36 = 0$ through by $x^2 - x - 12$, we obtain the equation

$$x^2 - x - 3 = 0$$

Solving by the quadratic formula,

$$x_3 = \frac{1 + \sqrt{13}}{2} = 2.303 \qquad \text{(to three decimal places)}$$

$$x_4 = \frac{1 - \sqrt{13}}{2} = -1.303 \qquad \text{(to three decimal places)}$$

Therefore all four roots are real; they are $+4$, -3, $+2.303$, and -1.303.

Example 3. Compute to three decimal places the values of any real roots of the equation $2x^3 - 17x^2 + 47x - 24 = 0$.

Since this is a third-degree equation, we may expect to find three roots—not all of which will necessarily be real. Using synthetic substitution, we obtain this table:

x	−1	0	1	2	3	4	5
y	−99	−24	8	18	18	20	36

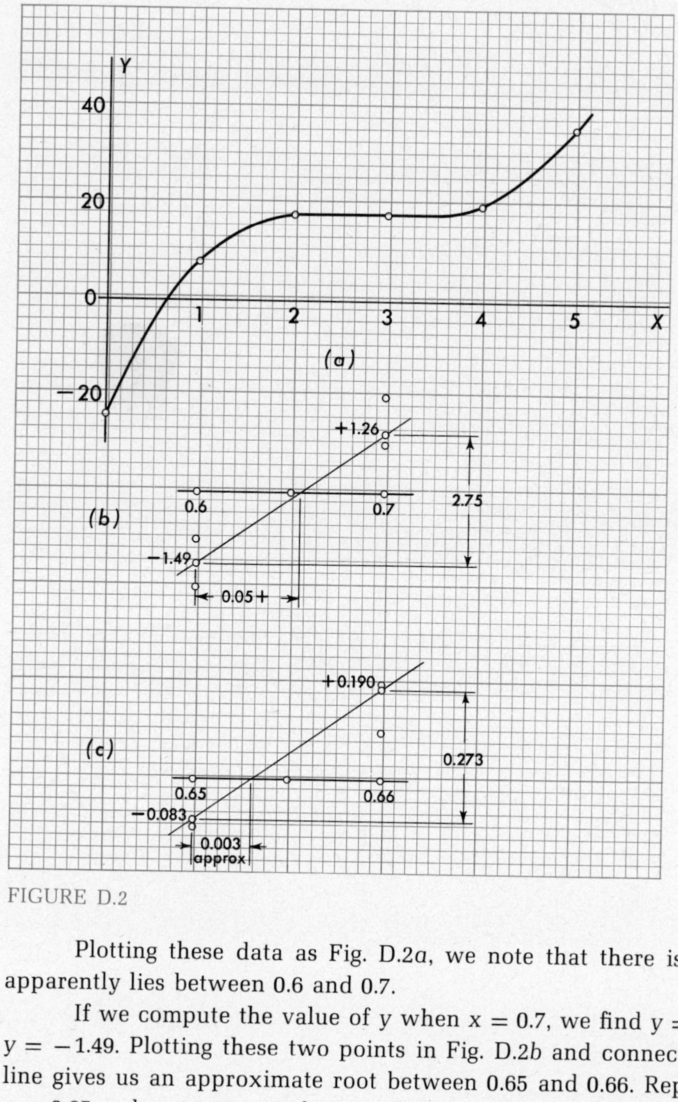

FIGURE D.2

Plotting these data as Fig. D.2*a*, we note that there is only one real root. It apparently lies between 0.6 and 0.7.

If we compute the value of y when $x = 0.7$, we find $y = +1.26$. When $x = 0.6$, $y = -1.49$. Plotting these two points in Fig. D.2*b* and connecting them by a straight line gives us an approximate root between 0.65 and 0.66. Repeating this process for $x = 0.65$ and $x = 0.66$, we obtain corresponding respective values for y of -0.083 and $+0.190$. These points and the connecting straight line are shown in Fig. D.2*c*. The indicated approximate root is 0.653, correct to the nearest thousandth.

The last two approximations might have been calculated by interpolating without graph paper. Figure D.2*b* corresponds to the computation

$$0.1\left(\frac{1.49}{1.49 + 1.26}\right) = 0.05$$

and Fig. D.2*c* corresponds to the computation

$$0.01\left(\frac{0.083}{0.083 + 0.190}\right) = 0.003$$

Since 0.653 is the only x intercept, we conclude that the other two roots are complex numbers. These might have been found by dividing the equation $2x^3 - 17x^2 + 47x - 24 = 0$ by $x - 0.653$ and solving the resulting equation by the quadratic formula.

appendix e
weights and measures

Dry Measure

1 bushel (bu) = 4 pk = 2,150.4 in^3 = 35.238 l
1 peck (*pk*) = 8 qt = 537.6 in^3 = 8.810 l
1 quart (qt) = 2 pt = 67.20 in^3 = 1.101 l
1 pint (pt) = 33.60 in^3 = 0.551 l

Miscellaneous Units

1 *nautical mile* = 1.151 statute mi = length one min. longitude at equator
1 knot = 1 nautical mi/h
Temperature: °C = $\frac{5}{9}$(°F − 32); °F = $\frac{9}{5}$°C + 32 (F = Fahrenheit, C = Celsius)
Pressure: 1 lb/in^2 = 70.37 g/cm^2
Density: 1 lb/in^3 = 27.7 g/cm^3; 1 lb/ft^3 = 0.01603 g/cm^3
Energy: 1 ft.lb = 0.1383 kg.m; 2,654 ft.lb = 1 watt hour (Wh) 1 British thermal unit (Btu) = 778 ft.lb = 252 calories (cal) = 0.2930 Wh
Power: 1 horsepower (hp) = 0.746 kilowatts (kW) = 550 ft.lb/s = 33,000 ft.lb/min
1 mil = 0.001 in
1 circular mil = area of circle of diameter one mil
Volts = Amps X Ohms ($V = A\Omega$)
Watts = (Amps)^2 X Ohms ($W = A^2\Omega$) = Volts X Amps ($W = VA$) = (Volts)^2/Ohms ($W = V^2/\Omega$)

LENGTH UNITS

	in	ft	yd	mi	mm	cm	m	km
1 inch (in) =	1	0.0833	0.0278		25.4	2.54	0.0254	
1 foot (ft) =	12	1	0.333	1.89×10^{-4}	304.8	30.48	0.3048	3.048×10^{-4}
1 yard (yd) =	36	3	1	5.68×10^{-4}	914.4	91.44	0.9144	9.144×10^{-4}
1 mile (mi) =	63,360	5,280	1,760	1			1,609.34	1.60934
1 millimeter (mm) =	3.937×10^{-2}	3.281×10^{-3}	1.094×10^{-3}		1	10^{-1}	10^{-3}	10^{-6}
1 centimeter (cm) =	0.3937	3.281×10^{-2}	1.094×10^{-2}		10	1	10^{-2}	10^{-5}
1 meter (m) =	39.37	3.281	1.094	6.21×10^{-4}	1,000	100	1	10^{-3}
1 kilometer (km) =	39,370	3,281	1,094	0.621	10^{6}	10^{5}	10^{3}	1

Spaces are left blank where related units are not of comparable magnitude.

AREA UNITS

	in^2	ft^2	yd^2	A	mi^2	cm^2	m^2	ha	km^2
1 square inch (in^2) =	1	6.944×10^{-3}				6.452	6.452×10^{-4}		
1 square foot (ft^2) =	144	1	0.1111			929.0	0.0929		
1 square yard (yd^2) =	1,296	9	1	2.066×10^{-4}		8361.3	0.83613		
1 acre (A) =		43,560	4,840	1	1.5625×10^{-3}		4,047	0.4047	4.047×10^{-3}
1 square mile (mi^2) =				640	1			259.0	2.590
1 square centimeter (cm^2) =	0.1550	1.076×10^{-3}				1	10^{-4}		
1 square meter (m^2) =	1,550	10.764	1.1960	2.471×10^{-4}		10^4	1	10^{-4}	10^{-6}
1 hectare (ha) =		107,640	11,960	2.471	3.861×10^{-3}	10^8	10^4	1	10^{-4}
1 square kilometer (km^2) =				247.1	0.3861		10^6	100	1

VOLUME UNITS

	in^3	ft^3	yd^3	cm^3	m^3
1 cubic inch (in^3) =	1	5.787×10^{-4}		16.387	
1 cubic foot (ft^3) =	1,728	1	0.03704	28,317	0.028317
1 cubic yard (yd^3) =	46,656	27	1		0.7646
1 cubic centimeter† (cm^3) =	0.06102	3.532×10^{-5}		1	10^{-6}
1 cubic meter (m^3) =	61,024	35.315	1.308	10^6	1

† 1 cm^3 and 1 ml are equivalent for all ordinary calculations.

CAPACITY UNITS (LIQUID MEASURE)

	fl oz	pt	qt	gal	in^3	ft^3	ml	l
1 fluid ounce (fl oz) =	1	0.0625	0.03125	7.812×10^{-3}	1.8047	1.044×10^{-3}	29.57	0.02957
1 pint (pt) =	16	1	0.5	0.125	28.875	0.01671	473.2	0.4732
1 quart (qt) =	32	2	1	0.25	57.75	0.03342	946.35	0.94635
1 gallon (gal) =	128	8	4	1	231	0.1337	3,785.4	3.7854
1 cubic inch (in^3) =	0.5541	0.03463	0.01732	4.329×10^{-3}	1	5.787×10^{-4}	16.387	0.016387
1 cubic foot (ft^3) =	957.5	59.844	29.922	7.481	1,728	1	28,317	28.317
1 milliliter (ml) =	0.033814	2.1134×10^{-3}	1.0567×10^{-3}	2.642×10^{-4}	0.061023	3.532×10^{-5}	1	10^{-3}
1 liter (l) =	33.814	2.1134	1.0567	0.2642	61.023	0.03532	10^3	1

WEIGHT UNITS

	oz	lb	ton	mg	g	kg	t
1 ounce (oz) =	1	0.0625		28,350	28.350	0.02835	
1 pound (lb) =	16	1	5×10^{-4}		453.6	0.4536	4.536×10^{-4}
1 ton =	32,000	2,000	1			907.2	0.9072
1 milligram (mg) =	3.527×10^{-5}			1	10^{-3}	10^{-6}	10^{-9}
1 gram (g) =	3.527×10^{-2}	2.205×10^{-3}		1,000	1	10^{-3}	10^{-6}
1 kilogram (kg) =	35.27	2.205	1.102×10^{-3}	10^6	10^3	1	10^{-3}
1 metric tonne (t) =		2,205	1.102	10^9	10^6	10^3	1

Prefixes Used in Metric System

Prefix	*Meaning*	*Example*
milli	$0.001 = 10^{-3}$	1 millimeter = 0.001 meter
centi	$0.01 = 10^{-2}$	1 centimeter = 0.01 meter
deci	$0.1 = 10^{-1}$	1 decimeter = 0.1 meter
deka	10	1 dekameter = 10 meters
hecto	$100 = 10^{2}$	1 hectometer = 100 meters
kilo	$1{,}000 = 10^{3}$	1 kilometer = 1,000 meters
mega	$1{,}000{,}000 = 10^{6}$	

Other Metric Units

1 micrometer (μm) = 0.000001 meter	$= 10^{-6}$ meter
1 millimicrometer (mμm)	$= 10^{-9}$ meter
1 micromicrometer ($\mu\mu$m)	$= 10^{-12}$ meter
1 angstrom (Å)	$= 10^{-10}$ meter

appendix F planetary data

Formulas Used in Satellite Problems (Circular Orbits Only)

Mass: $\frac{M_b}{M_e} = M$

where M_b = mass of attracting body
M_e = mass of earth
M = mass of attracting body relative to mass of earth (earth = 1)

Acceleration of gravity: $g = \frac{32.2M}{(r/3{,}960)^2}$ (1)

where g = gravitational acceleration, ft/s^2
r = distance from center of attracting body, mi

Orbital velocity: $v = 4.91\sqrt{M} \cdot \sqrt{\frac{3{,}960}{r}}$ where v is in mi/s (2)

Period of revolution: $T = 84.6\left(\frac{r}{3{,}960}\right)^{3/2} \cdot \sqrt{\frac{1}{M}}$ where T is in min (3)

$vT = 2\pi r$ (using consistent units)

PLANETARY DATA

(Some of these data represent a compromise among several sources).

	Average diameter, mi	Relative mass (Earth = 1)	Period of revolution	Surface gravity, ft/s^2	Average distance from sun, 10^6 mi	Surface† escape velocity, mi/s	Period of rotation on axis	Mean velocity in orbit, mi/s
Earth	7,920	1.000	365.3 days	32.2	93	6.97	23 h 56 min	18.5
Moon	2,160	0.0122	27.3 days	5.28	‡	1.49	27.3 days	0.63
Sun	864,000	330,000		900		387	25 days	
Mars	4,200	0.108	1.88 years	12.4	141.7	3.22	24 h 37 min	15
Venus	7,700	0.81	224.7 days	27.5	67.3	6.4	245 days	22
Mercury	3,100	0.041	88.0 days	8.60	36.0	2.2	88 days	30
Saturn	74,500	95	29.46 years	34.5	886	22	10 h 14 min	6
Jupiter	88,640	317	11.86 years	85.0	484	37	9 h 50 min	8
Uranus	32,000	14.7	84.0 years	29.3	1,783	13	10.8 h	4
Neptune	31,000	17.2	164.8 years	36.1	2,795	14	15.8 h	3
α Centauri					§			

† Assuming no atmosphere.

‡ 239,000 mi from earth center to center (mean value).

§ 4.31 light-years. 1 light-year = distance light can travel in 1 year at 186,000 mi/s = 5.86×10^{12} mi.

Velocity of escape: $v_e = 6.97\sqrt{M}\cdot\sqrt{\frac{3,960}{r}}$ where v_e is in mi/s (4)

For an artificial earth satellite (AES) in equatorial orbit (as opposed to a polar orbit) the rotation of the earth must be allowed for in observing the period.

For W-E revolution: $\frac{1}{T_a} = \frac{1}{T} - \frac{1}{24}$ (5)

where T is the true period of the AES in hours and T_a is the apparent period as observed from a given point on the equator.

For E-W revolution: $\frac{1}{T_a} = \frac{1}{T} + \frac{1}{24}$ (6)

bibliography

General

Bakst, A.: "Mathematics: Its Magic and Mastery," D. Van Nostrand Company, Inc., Princeton, N.J., 1945.

Bell, E. T.: "Men of Mathematics," Simon & Schuster, Inc., New York, 1965.

Berkeley, E.: "A Guide to Mathematics for the Intelligent Non-mathematician," Simon & Schuster, Inc., New York, 1966.

Boehm, G.: "The New World of Mathematics," The Dial Press, Inc., New York, 1959.

Cooley, H. R., D. Gans, M. Kline, and H. E. Wahlert: "Introduction to Mathematics," Houghton Mifflin Company, Boston, 1968.

Dadourian, H. M.: "How to Study—How to Solve," Addison-Wesley Publishing Company, Inc., Reading, Mass., 1951.

Griffin, F. L.: "Introduction to Mathematical Analysis," Houghton Mifflin Company, Boston, 1936.

Kline, M.: "Mathematics: A Cultural Approach," Addison-Wesley Publishing Company, Reading, Mass., 1962.

———: "Mathematics and the Physical World," Thomas Y. Crowell Company, New York, 1959.

———: "Mathematics in Western Culture," Oxford Book Company, Inc., New York, 1953.

Kramer, E. E.: "The Main Stream of Mathematics," Fawcett World Library, New York, 1951.

"Mathematics in the Modern World," readings from *Scientific American*, W. H. Freeman and Company, San Francisco, 1968.

"Mathematics Teacher," National Council of Teachers of Mathematics, Washington. Numerous articles of interest.

Mellor, J. W.: "Higher Mathematics for Students of Chemistry and Physics," Dover Publications, Inc., New York, 1946.

Newman, J. R.: "World of Mathematics," Simon & Schuster, Inc., New York, 1956.

Polya, G.: "How to Solve It," Doubleday & Company, Inc., Garden City, N.Y., 1957.

———: "Mathematics and Plausible Reasoning," Princeton University Press, Princeton, N.J., 1954.

Struik, D. J.: "A Concise History of Mathematics," Dover Publications, Inc., New York, 1948.

Vergara, W. C.: "Mathematics in Everyday Things," Harper & Row, Publishers, Incorporated, New York, 1959.

Applications

Cell, J. W.: "Engineering Problems Illustrating Mathematics," McGraw-Hill Book Company, New York, 1943.

Cooke, N. M., and H. Adams: "Basic Mathematics for Electronics," 3d ed., McGraw-Hill Book Company, New York, 1970.

Corrington, M. S.: "Applied Mathematics for Technical Students," Harper & Row, Publishers, Incorporated, New York, 1952.

Dull, R., and R. Dull: "Mathematics for Engineers," McGraw-Hill Book Company, New York, 1951.

Mira, J. A.: "Geometry through Practical Applications," Barnes & Noble, Inc., New York, 1961.

Palmer, C. I., S. F. Bibb, J. A. Jarvis, and L. A. Mrachek: "Practical Mathematics," 5th ed., McGraw-Hill Book Company, New York, 1970.

"Source Book of Mathematical Applications: 17th Yearbook," National Council of Teachers of Mathematics, Washington, 1944.

Waldron, R. A.: "Waves and Oscillations," D. Van Nostrand Company, Inc., Princeton, N.J., 1964.

Recreational and Enrichment

Beiler, A. H.: "Recreations in the Theory of Numbers," Dover Publications, Inc., New York, 1964.

Bergamini, D.: "The Mathematics of Beauty in Nature and Art," Time-Life's Life Science Library Series, 1963, pp. 88–102.

Bowers, H., and J. E. Bowers: "Arithmetical Excursions," Dover Publications, Inc., New York, 1961.

Bryant, S. J., K. G. Wiley, and G. E. Graham: "Non-routine Problems in Algebra, Geometry, and Trigonometry," McGraw-Hill Book Company, New York, 1965.

Charosh, M. (ed.): "Mathematical Challenges," selected problems from *Mathematics Student Journal,* National Council of Teachers of Mathematics, Washington, 1965.

Courant, R., and H. Robbins: "What is Mathematics?" Oxford Book Company, Inc., New York, 1953.

Cundy, H. M., and A. P. Rollett: "Mathematical Models," Oxford University Press, London, 1953.

Dantzig, T.: "Number, the Language of Science," Doubleday & Company, Inc., Garden City, N.Y., 1954.

Gamow, G.: "One, Two, Three—Infinity," The Viking Press, Inc., New York, 1961.

Gardiner, M.: "Mathematics, Magic and Mystery," Dover Publications, Inc., New York, 1956.

Glenn, W., and D. A. Johnson: "Exploring Mathematics on Your Own," Doubleday & Company, Inc., Garden City, N.Y., 1961.

Graham, L. A.: "The Surprise Attack in Mathematical Problems," Dover Publications, Inc., New York, 1968.

———: "Ingenious Mathematical Problems and Methods," Dover Publications, Inc., New York, 1959.

Hogben, L.: "Mathematics in the Making," Doubleday & Company, Inc., Garden City, N.Y., 1960.

———: "Mathematics for the Millions," 4th ed., W. W. Norton and Company, Inc., New York, 1968.

Huntley, H. E.: "The Divine Proportion," Dover Publications, Inc., New York, 1970.

Jacobs, H. R.: "Mathematics, a Human Endeavor," W. H. Freeman and Company, San Francisco, 1970.

Kasner, E.: "Mathematics and the Imagination," Simon & Schuster, Inc., New York, 1940.

Land, F.: "The Language of Mathematics," Doubleday & Company, Inc., Garden City, N.Y., 1963.

Menninger, K. W.: "Mathematics in Your World," The Viking Press, Inc., New York, 1962.

Meyer, J. S.: "Fun with Mathematics," Fawcett World Library, New York, 1958.

Radamacher, H., and O. Toeplitz: "The Equipment of Mathematics," Princeton University Press, Princeton, N.J., 1957.

Sawyer, W. W.: "The Search for Pattern," Penguin Books, Inc., Baltimore, 1970.

———: "Prelude to Mathematics," Penguin Books, Inc., Baltimore, 1955.

———: "Mathematician's Delight," Penguin Books, Inc., Baltimore, 1952.

Schuh, F.: "The Master Book of Mathematical Recreations," Dover Publications, Inc., New York, 1968.

Singh, J.: "Great Ideas of Modern Mathematics," Dover Publications, Inc., New York, 1959.

Steinhaus, H.: "Mathematical Snapshots," Oxford Book Company, Inc., New York, 1969.

answers to odd-numbered problems

Chapter 1

Exercise 1 (*page 4*): **1a.** 1,270 **1c.** 1,872 **1e.** 341 **1g.** 792 **1h.** 207 **1j.** 153 **1l.** 432 **1n.** 875 **1o.** 138 **1q.** 243 **1s.** 476 **1u.** 96

Exercise 2 (*page 6*): **1.** 68.0 **3.** 29.7 **5.** 110,000 **7.** 887,000 **9.** 907,000 **11.** 416,000 **13.** 2,240 **15.** 1.16 **17.** 0.252 **19.** 2,100,000 **21.** 7,500

Exercise 3 (*page 6*): **1.** 0.360 **3.** 136 **5.** 14.6 **7.** 0.0440 **9.** 0.0267 **11.** 0.000497 **13.** 2.40

Exercise 4 (*page 8*): **1.** 1.6×10^{2} **3.** 1.54×10^{-2} **5.** 1.216×10^{2} **7.** 6.12×10^{-2} **9.** 3.1×10^{-3} **11.** 6.56×10^{-5}

Exercise 5 (*page 9*): **1.** 9.41 **3.** 5.43 **5.** 8.34 **7.** 11.9

Exercise 6 (*page 14*): **1.** 324 **3.** 36.6 **5.** 28,200 **7.** 0.01111 **9.** 268,000 **11.** 720,000,000 **13.** 0.136 **15.** 6.27 **17.** 1.677 **19.** 4.66 **21.** 0.0838 **23.** 0.915 **25.** 0.233 **27.** 214 **29.** 2,660 **31.** 343 **33.** 1,685 **35.** 0.00387 **37.** 12,470 **39.** 109,200,000 **41.** 480,000,000 **43.** 8.48 **45.** 0.191 **47.** 2.38 **49.** 42.4 **51.** 211 **53.** 7.79 **55.** 34.55

Exercise 7 (*page 15*): **1.** $d = 12.6$ mi, $C = 39.6$ mi, $A = 124.7$ mi^2 **3.** $d = 156$ ft; $C = 490$ ft; $A = 19{,}100$ ft^2 **5.** $r = 5.6$ yd; $C = 35.2$ yd; $A = 98.5$ yd^2 **7.** $r = 7/16$ in; $C = 2.75$ in; $A = 0.602$ in^2 **9.** $r = 1.343$ in; $d = 2.685$ in; $A = 5.66$ in^2 **11.** $r = 1.785$ in; $d = 3.57$ in; $C = 11.22$ in

Exercise 8 (*page 18*): **1.** 60.6 **3.** 663 **5.** 27.4 **7.** 16.65 **9.** 4,150 **11.** 2.53 in

Exercise 9 (*page 19*): **1.** 52.0865 **3.** 15.0047 in **5.** 1.75183

Chapter 2

Exercise 1 (*page 25*): **1a.** 13 **1c.** 14 **1e.** -14 **1g.** 4 **2a.** 3 **2c.** -6 **2e.** 8 **2g.** -22 **3a.** 4 **3c.** 5 **4a.** 40 **4c.** 48 **4e.** -24 **4g.** -36 **5a.** 4 **5c.** -5 **5e.** $4/3$ **5g.** $-5/3$

Exercise 2 (*page 26*): **1.** $3a$ **3.** y^4 **5.** $4xy^2z^3$ **7.** w^4x^2 **9.** 7 **11.** 77 **13.** 20 **15.** 15 **17.** 49 **19.** 25 **21.** 9 **23.** 5 **25.** -8 **27.** 0 **29.** 900 **31.** $11x$ **33.** $13mn$ **35.** $6x + 9y$ **37.** $12m + 8p$ **39.** $4k^2 - 2km + 5m^2$ **41.** $9x - 2y - 3z$ **43.** $4x - y$ **45.** $12p$ **47.** $2k^2 - 2km - 3m^2$ **49.** $-x - 2y + 3z$

Exercise 3 (*page 28*): **1.** $5a + 3b$ **3.** $2x$ **5.** $4m - n$ **7.** $-6b - c$ **9.** $16ab - a^2b - 2ab^2$ **11a.** $5a + 2b - (4c - m + x)$ **11b.** $5a + 2b + (-4c + m - x)$ **13a.** $7mn + 3m^2 - 4n^2 - (8m - 5n - 2mn)$ **13b.** $7mn + 3m^2 - 4n^2 + (-8m + 5n + 2mn)$

Exercise 4 (*page 30*): **1.** x^6 **3.** -16 **5.** a^{2n} **7.** $0.008x^3$ **9.** b^{x+3} **11.** $-8x^3$ **13.** a^{n^2} **15.** $a^{3n}b^6$ **17.** a^2 **19.** $9/16$ **21.** $1/y^4$ **23.** y^{2n-2}/x^n

Exercise 5 (*page 30*): **1.** $32m^2nx$ **3.** $-36ab^2c^2d$ **5.** $a^3m^3x^3$ **7.** $-72a^5b^{11}c^9m^{11}$ **9.** $-18my + 15ty$ **11.** $30a^4b - 42a^3b^2 - 54a^2b^3$ **13.** $24a^3h^4k^4 - 66bh^2k^5$

Exercise 6 (*page 31*): **1.** $ac + bc + ad + bd$ **3.** $h^2 - k^2$ **5.** $6m^2 + mw - 35w^2$ **7.** $24x^2 - 78x - 39y - 6y^2$ **9.** $b^2 - x^2 - 2xy - y^2$

Exercise 7 (*page 31*): **1.** $17 - 120x$ **3.** $120x$

Exercise 8 (*page 32*): **1.** $3c$ **3.** $-5c^2$ **5.** $4x^9$ **7.** $8xy^3/(wz^2)$ **9.** $3b - 4c$ **11.** $-2m + 3k$ **13.** $r + 2$

Exercise 9 (*page 32*): **1.** $a + 8$ **3.** $4m - 5w$ **5.** $2k^4 + 4k^2 + 8$ **7.** $h^4 - h^3 - h + 1$ **9.** $1 - x + x^2 - x^3 + \cdots$

Exercise 10 (*page 34*): **1.** $3(5x - 6y)$ **3.** $6(5ab - 7km)$ **5.** $a(a - c)$ **7.** $c(ab + bm + mx)$ **9.** $6x^2y(7a - 4bxy + 3cx^2)$ **11.** $5(2a^2x^2 - 3abxy + 4b^2y^2)$ **13.** No common factors

Exercise 11 (*page 34*): **1.** $(x + 2)(x - 2)$ **3.** $(6 + y)(6 - y)$ **5.** $(7m + 1)(7m - 1)$ **7.** $(5d + 8m)(5d - 8m)$ **9.** $(10yz + 7cd)(10yz - 7cd)$ **11.** $(4n^4 + 1)(2n^2 + 1)(2n^2 - 1)$ **13.** 49 **15.** 17, 23

Exercise 12 (*page 34*): **1.** $10x$ **3.** $14z$ **5.** $4a$ **7.** $30n$ **9.** $80bh$ **11.** 25 **13.** $49q^2$ **15.** $25x^2$

Exercise 13 (*page 34*): **1.** $(x - 2)^2$ **3.** $(6 - m)^2$ **5.** $(3 + 7z)^2$ **7.** $(8a - 5n)^2$ **9.** $(9m^2 - 4p)^2$

Exercise 14 (*page 35*): **1.** $(y + 3)(y + 4)$ **3.** $(m - 5)(m - 7)$ **5.** $(x + 3)(x + 16)$ **7.** $(h - 5)(h + 6)$ **9.** $(k^2 + 9)(k^2 - 8)$ **11.** $(x + 3y)(x + 18y)$ **13.** $(a + 1)(2a + 1)$ **15.** $(4m - 3)(m - 2)$ **17.** $(4b + 3)(2b + 3)$ **19.** $(9h - 10)(6h + 5)$

Exercise 15 (*page 35*): **1.** $\frac{y}{w + z}$ **3.** $\frac{m + n}{b - c}$ **5.** $\frac{1}{a + b}$ **7.** $\frac{2}{a - 2b}$ **9.** $\frac{3}{2a - 3b}$ **11.** $-\frac{a + 3}{3a}$ **13.** Not reducible **15.** Not reducible **17.** Not reducible **19.** 1

Exercise 16 (*page 36*): **1.** $\frac{3(a + b)}{4}$ **3.** $\frac{d(x^2 - x + 12)}{a(x^2 + x - 6)}$ **5.** 1 **7.** $\frac{3m}{2(n - m)}$ **9.** $\frac{2a}{3(a - 2)}$ **11.** $-\frac{8y}{9a}$

Exercise 17 (*page 38*): **1.** $\frac{8x}{15}$ **3.** $\frac{x^2 + y^2 + z^2}{xyz}$ **5.** $\frac{109a - 39b}{72}$ **7.** $\frac{24bc - 6c^2 - 4a^2 - ab - 3b^2}{24abc}$ **9.** $\frac{m}{30}$ **11.** $\frac{a^2 - c^2}{a}$ **13.** $\frac{b^2 + 2b + 1}{b}$ **15.** $\frac{3a}{a^2 - b^2}$ **17.** $\frac{x - 3}{x - 6}$ **19.** $\frac{11}{c^2 - 9}$ **21.** $\frac{3c^2 - 2cd - 6d^2}{(c - d)^3}$

Exercise 18 (*page 40*): **1.** $\frac{y - x}{y + x}$ **3.** $\frac{c + d}{cd}$ **5.** -1 **7.** $q - 1$ **9.** $\frac{1}{r - 1}$ **11.** $2m^2 - 1$

Exercise 19 (*page 42*): **1.** $\sqrt[3]{-8} = -2$ **3.** $\sqrt[4]{81} = 3$ **5.** $\sqrt{1/25} = 1/5$ **7.** $\sqrt{49} = 7$ **9.** 5 **11.** 8 **13.** 3 **15.** 12 **17.** 2 **19.** -1 **21.** 0.2 **23.** 40 **25.** $-3/5$ **27.** $2ab^2c^3$

Exercise 20 (*page 45*): **1.** 2 **3.** $1/25$ **5.** $-1/27$ **7.** $27/8$ **9.** -2 **11.** 2.5 **13.** 81 **15.** $1/81$ **17.** 0.001 **19.** $1/2$ **21.** -32 **23.** $-1/2$ **25.** $x^{7/6}$ **27.** $4x^8$ **29.** $25x^3y^4$ **31.** $243a^2b^3$ **33.** $18y^2z^2/x^3$ **35.** w^4/x^2y **37.** $x - 2 + 1/x$ **39.** $a - 9/a$

Exercise 21 (*page 46*): **1.** $2\sqrt{2}$ **3.** $2\sqrt{10}$ **5.** $15\sqrt{2}$ **7.** $12\sqrt{2}$ **9.** $2\sqrt[3]{3}$ **11.** $15\sqrt[3]{2}$ **13.** $-5\sqrt[3]{2}$ **15.** $10\sqrt[4]{6}$ **17.** $x^3\sqrt{x}$ **19.** $xy\sqrt{xy}$ **21.** $2xy^2\sqrt{3xy}$ **23.** $x\sqrt{a+b}$ **25.** $2\sqrt{m^2 - 4n^2}$ **27.** $a\sqrt[n]{a}$ **29.** $a^n\sqrt[n+1]{a^2}$ **31.** $a^2\sqrt[n+1]{a}$ **33.** $x^2y^2\sqrt[3]{y^a}$ **35.** $x^2y^2\sqrt[3]{x^2}$

Exercise 22 (*page 47*): **1.** $\frac{1}{2}\sqrt{2} = 0.7071$ **3.** $\frac{3}{2}\sqrt{2} = 2.121$ **5.** $\frac{2}{5}\sqrt{15} = 1.549$ **7.** $\frac{1}{2}\sqrt[3]{4} = 0.7937$ **9.** $2\sqrt[3]{4} = 3.175$ **11.** $2\sqrt[4]{3}$ **13.** $\frac{1}{3}\sqrt{6} = 0.8165$ **15.** $\frac{3}{5}\sqrt{15} = 2.324$

17. $\frac{1}{15}\sqrt[3]{180} = 0.3764$ **19.** $\dfrac{1}{x^2}\sqrt{x}$ **21.** $\dfrac{1}{a}\sqrt[3]{a}$ **23.** $\dfrac{1}{x}\sqrt[3]{x}$ **25.** $\dfrac{2a}{9c^2}\sqrt{6abc}$

27. $\dfrac{\sqrt{a^2 - b^2}}{a + b}$ **29.** $\dfrac{\sqrt[n]{x^{n-1}}}{x}$ **31.** $\dfrac{1}{a^{n+1}}\sqrt{a}$

Exercise 23 (*page 48*): **1.** $\sqrt{5}$ **3.** $\sqrt[3]{4}$ **5.** $\sqrt{xy}$ **7.** $yz\sqrt[3]{5x^2z}$ **9.** $\sqrt{x}$ **11.** $\frac{1}{2}\sqrt[3]{4}$ **13.** $\dfrac{1}{c}\sqrt[3]{c^2}$

Exercise 24 (*page 49*): **1.** $7\sqrt{2}$ **3.** $13\sqrt{3}$ **5.** $\frac{17}{2}\sqrt{2}$ **7.** $\frac{74}{7}\sqrt{7}$ **9.** $\sqrt{6}$ **11.** $-6\sqrt{7}$ **13.** $(1 + x + x^2)\sqrt{x}$

Exercise 25 (*page 52*): **1.** $\sqrt{6} = 2.449$ **3.** $7\sqrt{2} = 9.899$ **5.** 66 **7.** $2a\sqrt{3b}$ **9.** $bc\sqrt{ad}$ **11.** $3\sqrt[3]{10} = 6.463$ **13.** $2\sqrt[6]{54}$ **15.** $2\sqrt[4]{2}$ **17.** 7 **19.** 7 **21.** $9 - 6\sqrt{2} = 0.515$ **23.** $5 + \sqrt{6} = 7.449$ **25.** $6\sqrt{10} + 20\sqrt{6} - 6 - 4\sqrt{15} = 46.47$ **27.** $\frac{1}{3}\sqrt{21} = 1.528$

29. $\frac{6}{5}\sqrt{5} = 2.683$ **31.** $\dfrac{1}{2z}\sqrt{6xz}$ **33.** $\sqrt[6]{24}$ **35.** $\sqrt[4]{3}$ **37.** $2(\sqrt{7} + 2) = 9.292$

39. $\dfrac{2(5 + \sqrt{7})}{3} = 5.097$ **41.** $\dfrac{3(2\sqrt{5} + \sqrt{6})}{2} = 10.38$ **43.** $\dfrac{15\sqrt{2} - 4\sqrt{5}}{37} = 0.3316$

45. $\dfrac{78 + 17\sqrt{15}}{33} = 4.359$ **47.** $\dfrac{x\sqrt{z} + z\sqrt{x}}{xz}$

Exercise 26 (*page 54*): **1.** -1 **3.** $-j$ **5.** $-j$

Exercise 27 (*page 57*): **1.** $2(-1 + j5)\sqrt{3}$ **3.** $(-4 + j9)\sqrt{2}$ **5.** $j7\sqrt{5}$ **7.** $j6 + (4 + j4)\sqrt{5}$ **9.** $-j2\sqrt{2}$ **11.** $-15xy^2$ **13.** $45ab$ **15.** $\sqrt{105}$ **17.** -40 **19.** -6 **21.** $-5 - 2\sqrt{6}$ **23.** $-j5\sqrt{6}$ **25.** $-\sqrt{30} + \sqrt{10} - 3\sqrt{2} + \sqrt{6}$ **27.** $\sqrt{2}/2$ **29.** $7/3$ **31.** $j2\sqrt{5}$ **33.** $\sqrt{14}/2$ **35.** $28\sqrt{2}$

Exercise 28 (*page 62*): **1.** $-1 + j31$ **3.** $-51 + j484$ **5.** -53 **7.** $4{,}282 - j1{,}475$ **9.** $11.0754 - j3.465$ **11.** 1 **13.** $-\frac{9}{20} + j\frac{3}{5}$ **15.** $\frac{1}{2} - \frac{j}{2}$ **17.** $\frac{2}{7} - \frac{j3\sqrt{5}}{7}$ **19.** $-\frac{1}{3} - j\frac{\sqrt{2}}{3}$ **21.** $-j\frac{\sqrt{10}}{2}$ **23.** $-\frac{3}{34} + j\frac{5}{34}$ **25.** $\frac{504}{157} + j\frac{332}{157}$ **27.** $0.931 + j0.361$

Chapter 3

Exercise 1 (*page 67*): **1.** 2 **3.** -2 **5.** $\frac{3}{5}$ **7.** 4 **9.** 3 **11.** 8 **13.** 4 **15.** 0.7 **17.** $\frac{1}{2}$ **19.** $\frac{2}{3}$ **21.** 28 **23.** $\frac{1}{3}$ **25.** $(c - b)/b$ **27.** $ab(a - b)$ **29.** $1/m$ **31.** $2/(3a - 5b)$

Exercise 2 (*page 70*): **1.** $\frac{WL}{Q}$ **3.** $E - IR$ **5.** $\frac{eR}{E - e}$ **7.** $\frac{Cb}{Kb + C}$ **9.** $\frac{\rho(d^2 - L^2)}{2L}$ **11.** $T = \frac{2{,}097Q}{EI}$ **13.** $\frac{9}{5}C + 32$ **15.** $\frac{HL}{0.4\pi N}$ **17.** $\frac{f(n + 1)}{n}$ **19.** $\frac{1.299}{T - S}$ **21.** $\frac{r_1 r_2}{r_1 + r_2}$ **23.** $\frac{T_1 h}{T_1 h - (T_1 - T)(h_0)}$ **25.** $\frac{6V - Bh - bh}{4h}$ **27.** $\frac{273(V_1 - V_0)}{V_0}$

Exercise 3 (*page 75*): **1.** 33×47 ft **3.** $57\frac{1}{7}$ lb solder; $22\frac{6}{7}$ lb type metal **5.** 2 h 40 min **7.** 14 **9.** 30 min **11.** 100 L **13.** $12\frac{1}{2}$ oz of 20 percent alloy; $27\frac{1}{2}$ oz of 12 percent alloy **15.** 1,300 lb **17.** $6\frac{1}{4}$ in; 7 in; $7\frac{3}{4}$ in; $8\frac{1}{2}$ in; $9\frac{1}{4}$ in **19.** \$1,115 **21.** 8.7 h **23.** \$3.30 **25.** 2.4 gal **27.** 60 mi **29.** $9\frac{1}{3}$ mi **31.** 20 mi/h **33.** 50.1 ft^3/min **35.** 30 percent **37.** 7.5 kg **39.** 1 in **41.** \$250 **43.** 142,857 **45.** 12,500 mi

Chapter 4

Exercise 1 (*page 82*): **1.** 6:1 **3.** 1:9 **5.** 10:3 **7.** 10:3 **9.** 3:8 **11.** $3x:4a$ **13.** 4:3

Exercise 2 (*page 83*): **1.** 6 **3.** 21 **5.** $\frac{ac}{b}$ **7.** $\frac{bc}{a + b}$ **9.** $\frac{ab - bc}{a - b + c - d}$ **11.** ± 12 **13.** $\pm\frac{5}{4}$ **15.** $\pm 4abx$ **17.** $\pm 2(x + y)$ **19.** $\pm 6ab$

Exercise 3 (*page 89*): **1.** $W = kxy$ **3.** $V = \frac{kx^3}{d}$ **5.** $R = \frac{kw\sqrt{x}}{h^3}$ **7.** $N = \frac{7}{y}$ **9.** $V = \frac{4.8m}{t^2}$

Exercise 4 (*page 90*): **1.** $k = 2{,}520$ in-lb; $V = 40$ in^3 **3.** $k = 1.8$ ft/s^2; $V = 108$ ft/s **5.** $k = 43{,}560$ ft^2/acre; $N = 1{,}440$ plants/acre **7.** $k = 1.63$ (no units); $V = 7.3$ ft/s **9.** 56 **11.** $V = 819.2$

Exercise 5 (*page 91*): **1.** 174.2 kg **3.** 2 h 59 min **5.** 505 **7.** 9.73 in **9.** Johnson, $185.08; Miller, $299.59; Spencer, $336.64; Weston, $412.36 **11.** 41.8 g **13.** 542 ft^3 **15.** $50.16 **17.** 14.8 hp **19.** 8.1 percent zinc oxide; 32.4 percent titanium dioxide; 13.5 percent lithopone **21.** 284 ft^2 **23.** Streets, 109°; police, etc., 79°; schools, 172° **25a.** $v = (20/3)\sqrt{h}$ **25b.** 25.8 g/min **25c.** 3.24 ft **27.** Approximately 5,000 **29.** $81 **31.** $8,750 **35.** 16.9 ft/s^2 **39.** Moon, 24.7 lb; Mars, 57.9 lb; Jupiter, 397 lb **41.** 23.9 mi **43.** 13.8 hp **45.** 27,800 lb **47.** 100 ml, 8.32 cm; 200 ml, 10.5 cm **49.** 17.1 lb **51.** 6 extra men **53.** 205 Hz

Chapter 5

Exercise 1 (*page 97*): **1.** $a = b = 132°32'$; $c = d = 47°28'$ **3.** $a = 29°10'$; $b = 150°50'$ **5a.** 25.2 in^2 **5b.** 6.76 in **7.** 1.28 in **9.** 9.08 in^2 **11.** 45° **13.** $a = 45°$; $b = 128°$ **15.** 34.8 in^2 **17.** Vol = 58.3 in^3; area = 99.3 in^2; edge = 7.85 in **19a.** 30 in^2 **19b.** 41.0 in^2 **19c.** 43.3 in^2 **19d.** 44.0 in^2 **19e.** $56\frac{1}{4}$ in^2 **19f.** 65.0 in^2 **19g.** 71.7 in^2 **21.** 2,850 kg approx **23.** 950 lb approx **25.** 7,880 mi **27.** Surface 935 in^2; vol 1,780 in^3 **29.** 3,410 A **31.** 20 mi **33.** $7/9$ **35.** $8\frac{5}{8}$ in **37.** 54.8 g/min **39.** $a = 11.196\ s^2$ **41.** 80.83 in^3 **43.** 6.08 in **45.** 37.3 in **49.** $\theta = 180d/S$ **51.** 2.98 in **53.** 3.89 in **55.** Speed, 49.5 ft/s; diam, 2.52 ft **57.** 1.09 in **59.** 3,960 mi **65.** 90° **67.** 73°15′ **69.** 3.62 in **73.** $w = (Ha - ha + hb)/H$ **75.** 4.13 ft **77.** 72 ft **81.** 0.38 mm **83.** 2,495 ft^2 **85.** 19 min **87.** 300 rev/min; 1,125 to 180 rev/min

Chapter 6

Exercise 1 (*page 124*): **1.** -5 **3.** -5 **5.** 24 **7.** $-20/3$ **9.** $4(3a - 4)/[a(8 - 3a)]$

Exercise 3 (*page 125*): **1.** Square **3.** Triangle **5.** Right triangle **7.** Right triangle

Exercise 5 (*page 130*): **1.** $1/3$ **3.** $-3/4$ **5.** $5/2$ **7a.** $\sqrt{3}/3$ **7c.** $\sqrt{3}$ **7e.** -1

Exercise 6 (*page 134*): **1a.** $f(x_1) = 94$; $f(x_1 + \Delta x) = 96$; $\Delta y/\Delta x = 1/3$ **1c.** $f(x_1) = 100$; $f(x_1 + \Delta x) = 105$; $\Delta y/\Delta x = 1/3$ **2a.** $f(x_1) = 7{,}400$; $f(x_1 + \Delta x) = 6{,}950$; $\Delta y/\Delta x = -150$ **2c.** $f(x_1) = 5{,}000$; $f(x_1 + \Delta x) = 3{,}800$; $\Delta y/\Delta x = -150$ **3.** 0.85

Exercise 7 (*page 136*): **1.** $y = \frac{5}{2}x + 20$ **3.** $y = \frac{4}{5}x$ **5.** $y = \frac{8}{3}x - \frac{92}{3}$ **7.** $y = -\frac{24}{5}x - 60$

Exercise 8 (*page 142*): **1.** $x - 2y = -8$ **3.** $2x - y = 11$ **5.** $x - y = -4$ **7.** $x\sqrt{3} - y = 5 + 2\sqrt{3}$ **9.** $y = 7$ **11.** $y = -x + 8$ **13.** $y = \frac{1}{3}x - 4$ **15.** $y = \frac{1}{4}x + \frac{5}{2}$ **17.** $y = \frac{7}{5}x + \frac{14}{5}$ **19.** $y = \frac{3}{2}$ **21.** $y = -\frac{2}{3}x$ **23.** $x - 3y = -3$

25. $3x + 4y = -10$ **27.** $x + 4y = 3$ **29.** $y = 5$ **31.** $x - 2y = -4$
33. $2x + 3y = -18$ **35.** $3x - 4y = -24$ **37.** $2x + 3y = -30$

Exercise 9 (*page 146*): **1a.** $C = 0$ **1b.** $B = 0$ **1c.** $A = 0$ **1d.** $A = 24$ **1e.** $B = 2$
3. 6 **5.** 9 **7.** 5 **9.** $\sqrt{85} = 9.23$ **13.** (1.2,1.2) and (−6,6) **15.** $2x + 3y = 14$
17. $y = 3x - 19$ **19.** B, $y = -3x - 20$; C, $y = 3x + 20$; D, $y = 3x - 20$;
E, $y = -\frac{1}{3}x + \frac{20}{3}$; F, $y = -\frac{1}{3}x - \frac{20}{3}$; G, $y = \frac{1}{3}x + \frac{20}{3}$; H, $y = \frac{1}{3}x - \frac{20}{3}$

Exercise 10 (*page 150*): **1.** 48 **3.** 56 **5.** $55\frac{1}{2}$ **9.** 56 **11.** $66\frac{1}{2}$

Exercise 11 (*page 155*): **1a.** 30 lb **1b.** 60 in-lb **3.** 1,840 ft · lb

Exercise 12 (*page 156*): **1.** 54, 62, 70, 78, 86, 94, 102, 110 ft

Chapter 7

Exercise 1 (*page 159*): **1.** $x = 5$; $y = 3$ **3.** $x = -\frac{1}{2}$; $y = -4$ **5.** $x = -1$; $y = 2$
7. $x = \frac{7}{2}$; $y = 1$ **9.** Dependent **11.** $x = \frac{7}{3}$; $y = -\frac{1}{3}$ **13.** $x = \frac{1}{4}$; $y = -\frac{3}{5}$

Exercise 2 (*page 162*): **1.** $x = 4$; $y = 4$ **3.** $x = 6$; $y = 6$ **5.** $x = 5$; $y = 4$ **7.** $x = 6$;
$y = -2$ **9.** $x = -3$; $y = 11$ **11.** $x = 9$; $y = 4$ **13.** $y = 5$; $z = \frac{7}{2}$ **15.** $x = 4$; $w = 3$
17. $x = 5$; $y = -2$ **19.** $x = -2$; $y = 4$ **21.** $x = 8$; $y = 3$ **23.** $x = \frac{1}{5}$; $w = \frac{2}{5}$
25. $x = \frac{16}{3}$; $y = \frac{20}{3}$ **27.** $w = 5$; $z = 1$ **29.** $x = 36.5$; $y = 7.06$

Exercise 3 (*page 167*): **1.** $x = c + d$; $y = c - 3d$ **3.** $x = 2a - b$; $y = a - 2b$
5. $x = \dfrac{3}{a}$; $y = \dfrac{1}{2b}$ **7.** $x = \dfrac{3c}{a}$; $y = \dfrac{4c}{b}$ **9.** $x = c$; $y = b$ **11.** $x = \dfrac{m+n}{2}$; $y = \dfrac{m-n}{2}$
13. $x = \frac{1}{5}$; $y = 1$ **15.** $x = 2$; $y = 3$ **17.** $x = \frac{1}{12}$; $y = \frac{1}{18}$

Exercise 4 (*page 169*): **1.** $x = 3$; $y = 4$; $z = 5$ **3.** $x = 7$; $y = 3$; $z = -2$ **5.** $x = -3$;
$y = 5$; $z = 8$ **7.** $x = 6$; $y = 5$; $z = 4$ **9.** $x = \frac{2}{3}$; $y = \frac{3}{4}$; $z = -1$

Exercise 5 (*page 171*): **1.** 34, 19 **3.** Current, $\frac{3}{4}$ mi/h, boat, $6\frac{3}{4}$ mi/h
5. 30 by 48 ft **7.** Man, 9 days; boy, 36 days **9.** $A = 4\frac{1}{2}$ in; $B = 9$ in; $C = 8$ in
11. Father, \$250, son, \$350 **13.** 14 quarters **15.** 3.2 qt **17.** 114 adults
19. $x = 5\frac{1}{8}$ in; $y = 8\frac{1}{8}$ in **21.** $\dfrac{\pi}{4}\overline{AB}^2$ **23.** $a = \$1.00$; $b = \$0.45/M\ ft^3$ **25.** $\frac{1}{2}$, $\frac{1}{3}$
27. A, 9.8 s; B, 10.0 s **29a.** 22 min **29b.** 132 s
31. Rate of bus = 6 times rate of hiker. They passed 30 min after starting.
33. $a = 3$; $b = 4$; $c = 2$

Exercise 6 (*page 178*): **1.** -1 **3.** 32 **5.** $9a^2 - 20b^2$

Exercise 7 (*page 181*): **1.** Inconsistent **3.** Dependent **5.** $x = a/2$; $y = a/3$ **7.** $x = a - b$; $y = b - a$ **9.** $x = 4$; $y = -5$

Exercise 8 (*page 189*): **1.** -47 **3.** -48 **5.** -9 **7.** $15a$ **9.** $8a + 36b + 6c$ **11.** -812 **13.** -445

Exercise 9 (*page 192*): **1.** $x = 7$; $y = 5$; $z = 3$ **3.** $x = -4$; $y = 3/2$; $z = 5$ **5.** $x = 3a + 2b + c$; $y = a + 2b + 3c$; $z = a + 3b + c$ **7.** $x = 5$; $y = 4$; $z = 3$; $w = 2$

Exercise 10 (*page 193*): **1a.** $I_1 = -0.638$; $I_2 = 6.68$ **1c.** $I_1 = -13.50$; $I_2 = 14.97$ **2a.** $I_1 = \dfrac{E_1 - I_2R_3}{R_1 + R_3}$; for negative I_1, $I_2R_3 > E_1$ **3.** $R_2 = 2$

Exercise 11 (*page 194*): **1a.** $I_1 = 1.474$; $I_2 = 1.068$; $I_3 = 0.0642$ **1c.** $I_1 = 0.165$; $I_2 = 0.101$; $I_3 = 0.0306$ **1e.** $I_1 = 2.252$; $I_2 = 1.492$; $I_3 = -0.0446$

Exercise 12 (*page 195*): **1.** 8 oz *A*, 8 oz *B*, 12 oz *C* **3.** 12.5 kg *A*, 28.6 kg *B*, 8.9 kg *C* **5.** $W_2 = -2.191.5$; $W_3 = -3{,}331$; $W_4 = -2{,}606$; $W_5 = -1{,}548$ **7.** 1st group walks 4.91 mi; 2d group walks 3.57 mi; time for entire transfer = 1.87 h

Exercise 13 (*page 200*): **1a.** $y = -1.5x + 80$ **1b.** $y = -70$ **1c.** $x = 62$ **1d.** $x = y = 32$ **3.** $y = 0.628x + 13.3$; $y = 47.8$ **5.** $y = 0.696x + 4.09$ **7.** $h = -926P + 27{,}700$; $P_{s1} = 29.92$ in **9.** $p = -0.93t + 93$ (approx) **11.** $V = 0.0758R + 2.1$ (approx); 2.1 mi/h to overcome friction **13.** $V = 0.602t + 331.4$ (approx)

Chapter 8

Exercise 1 (*page 205*): **1a.** $\log_2 8 = 3$ **1b.** $\log_2 1/64 = -6$ **1c.** $\log_7 1/49 = -2$ **3a.** $\log_5 625 = 4$ **3b.** $\log_3 1/27 = -3$ **3c.** $\log_{2/3} 8/27 = 3$ **5a.** $\log_3 1/81 = -4$ **5b.** $\log_6 36 = 2$ **5c.** $\log_{1/5} 25 = -2$ **7a.** $\log_{16} 8 = 3/4$ **7b.** $\log_{25} 5 = 1/2$ **7c.** $\log_{27} 9 = 2/3$ **9a.** $\log_{27} 1/3 = -1/3$ **9b.** $\log_{16} 1/32 = -5/4$ **9c.** $\log_{36} 1/216 = -3/2$

Exercise 2 (*page 206*): **1a.** 2 **1b.** 3 **1c.** 4 **3a.** $3/2$ **3b.** $4/3$ **3c.** $2/3$ **5a.** -3 **5b.** -3 **5c.** $-5/2$

Exercise 3 (*page 206*): **1a.** 8 **1b.** 25 **1c.** 81 **3a.** 100 **3b.** $1/9$ **3c.** 9 **5a.** 3 **5b.** 2 **5c.** 8 **7a.** 15 **7b.** any constant other than zero **7c.** 2 **9a.** $1/27$ **9b.** 0.1 **9c.** 8

Exercise 4 (*page 216*): **1d.** 8.61×10^3; 3.935 **1f.** 86,100; 8.61×10^4 **1h.** 0.861; 0.935 − 1 **1j.** 8.61×10^6; 6.935 **1l.** 0.00861; 8.61×10^{-3} **3a.** 0.549 − 2 **3b.** 0.549 − 1 **3c.** 3.902 **5a.** 354 **5b.** 79.8 **5c.** 0.0798 **7a.** 0.000354 **7b.** 7,980 **7c.** 0.00354

Exercise 5 (*page 217*): **1.** 3.49178 **3.** 2.49136 **5.** 4.49360 **7.** 0.49859 **9.** 6.49136 **11.** 1.49136

Exercise 6 (*page 218*): **1.** 0.49443 − 3 **3.** 0.49748 − 1 **5.** 0.50065 − 2 **7.** 0.50120 − 1 **9.** 0.50379 − 6 **11.** 0.49206 − 2 **13.** 31.03 **15.** 3167 **17.** 0.0032 **19.** 32,040 **21.** 311,100 **23.** 31.63

Exercise 7 (*page 218*): **1a.** 3.09132 **1c.** 0.09132 − 2 **1e.** 2.60032 **3a.** 2.25455 **3c.** 0.03743 − 2 **3e.** 0.84911 − 4 **5a.** 0.008605 **5c.** 400,000 **5e.** 57,550

Exercise 8 (*page 222*): **1a.** 2.42843 **1c.** 1.32950 **1e.** 0.61802 **3a.** 4.07766 **3c.** 0.89962 − 4 **3e.** 8.07266 **5a.** 0.0010071 **5c.** 0.00079367 **5e.** 139,700

Exercise 9 (*page 223*): **1.** 228,380 **3.** 4.4216 **5.** 9.5530 **7.** 6,999,200,000 **9.** 8,157,900,000

Exercise 10 (*page 224*): **1.** −8.0425 **3.** 0.077289 **5.** 0.081484 **7.** 0.27963 **9.** 24,476 **11.** 0.018578

Exercise 11 (*page 226*): **1.** 1.3430×10^9 **3.** 4,096.4

Exercise 12 (*page 229*): **1a.** 2,753.3 **1b.** −1,655.5 **1c.** 0.17116 **3a.** 0.042008 **3b.** 0.018105 **3c.** 0.00024273 **5a.** 0.37876 **5b.** 69.553 **5c.** 16.150 **7a.** 2.3428 **7b.** 29.829 **7c.** 0.31216

Exercise 13 (*page 230*): **1a.** 9.9058 **1b.** 4.5979 **1c.** 2.1341 **3a.** 8.5711 **3b.** 5.5195 **3c.** 7.4326 **5.** 317.93 **7.** 2,354.0 **9.** 195.72 **11.** 0.40880 **13.** 0.74308 **15.** −3.2836 **17.** 0.16014

Exercise 14 (*page 231*): **1.** 6.6257 **3.** 6.9078 **5.** 1.2987

Exercise 17 (*page 237*): **1.** 6.2288 **3.** 1.2027 **5.** 20.939 **7.** $7/4$ **9.** 7.3365 **11.** $3/2$

Exercise 18 (*page 240*): **1a.** \$112.00 **1b.** \$112.55 **1c.** \$112.68 **1d.** \$112.75 **3.** 11 years **5a.** 16 g **5b.** $W_0 = 54$ g; $C = 2/3$ **5c.** 21.25 g **5d.** 1.71 h **7.** 77.8° **9.** 13.2 h **11.** 27.2 percent; \$538.57 **17.** Approx 50 times as strong

Exercise 19 *(page 243)*: **1.** 6.17 in **3.** 177.2 **5.** 1.260 : 1 **7.** 1.124 : 1 **9.** 3.98 **11.** 4.77 **13.** Between 251 and 50 percent of normal power rating **15.** 2.0 W **17.** 18.85 **23.** 10.3 lb/in² **25.** 57.8L **27.** 1.30 **29.** 0.290 **31.** Log mean diam = 4.57 in; arithmetic mean diam = $4\frac{15}{16}$ in **33.** 3,020 ft approx **35.** 2,450°C **37.** 114.0 min **39.** 27 days 5 h approx **41.** Vel = 58.2 mi/min; period = 134 min

Chapter 9

Exercise 1 *(page 256)*: **1.** $x^4 + 12x^3y + 54x^2y^2 + 108xy^3 + 81y^4$ **3.** $w^8 + 2w^6x + \frac{3}{2}w^4x^2 + \frac{1}{2}w^2x^3 + \frac{1}{16}x^4$ **5.** $1{,}024x^5 + 640x^3 + 160x + \frac{20}{x} + \frac{5}{4x^3} + \frac{1}{32x^5}$ **7.** $\frac{x^6}{y^6} + \frac{6x^5}{y^4z} + \frac{15x^4}{y^2z^2} + \frac{20x^3}{z^3} + \frac{15x^2y^2}{z^4} + \frac{6xy^4}{z^5} + \frac{y^6}{z^6}$ **9.** $(100)^3 - 3(100)^2(2) + 3(100)(2)^2 - (2)^3 = 941{,}192$

Exercise 2 *(page 258)*: **1.** $1 - y + y^2 - y^3 + \cdots$ **3.** $1 + \frac{x}{4} + \frac{5x^2}{32} + \frac{15x^3}{128} + \cdots$ **5.** $a + \frac{b}{3a^2} - \frac{b^2}{9a^5} + \frac{5b^3}{81a^8} - \cdots$ **7.** 7.0711 **9.** 1.2247 **11.** 3.9149 **13.** 2.0362 **15.** 8.5499

Exercise 3 *(page 261)*: **1a.** 1.81482 **1c.** 0.67803 **1e.** 6.03309 **1g.** −4.44817 **2a.** 3.90661 **2c.** 8.18423 **3a.** 38.6 **3c.** 0.0496 **3e.** 79,500 **4a.** 59.6 **4c.** 0.001205 **4e.** 1973 **5a.** 44.70 **5c.** 0.2466 **5e.** 6.205 **5g.** 9.875 **6a.** 0.05734 **6c.** 77.95 **6e.** −0.07458

Exercise 4 *(page 263)*: **1a.** $\log x = 1.32133$ **1c.** $\log x = 0.10041 - 1$ **1e.** $\log x = 0.25710 - 1$ **2a.** $\ln x = 5.0045$ **2c.** $\ln x = -2.8861$ **2e.** $\ln x = -2.9370$ **3a.** 20.95 **3c.** 0.1260 **3e.** 0.1808 **4a.** 1.7618 **4c.** 9.2103 **4e.** −5.2035

Exercise 5 *(page 264)*: **1.** $1/0.693 = 1.443$ **2a.** $y = e^x$ **2c.** $y^a = e^x$ **3a.** $\ln z = w$ **3c.** $\ln(y/3) = -\frac{1}{2}$ (or $\ln y = 0.5986$) **4a.** 12.18 **4c.** 2.890 **5a.** $y = 5e^{0.47x}$ **5c.** $y = 3e^{3.465x}$ **6a.** $y = 0.63(14.88)^x$ **7a.** $(1/k)\ln(a/T)$ **7c.** $e^{-y/n}$ **8a.** 12 **8c.** 9 **9a.** $e^{3/2}$ **9c.** $2e$ **11.** 2.079 **13.** 1.099 **15.** 4.500 **17.** 1.386 **19.** 0.4343 − 1 **21.** 19.03 **23.** $\frac{1}{7}$

Exercise 6 *(page 265)*: **1.** $i = \frac{E}{R}e^{-t/RC}$ **3.** 0.398 A **5.** $i \approx 0$ **7a.** 0.114 A **9a.** $a = 0.173$ **9b.** 13.29 ft **11b.** 22.8 h **13.** $i = 0.054$ **15.** $i \approx E/R$ **17.** 63.2 percent **19a.** $k = 1.386 \times 10^{-4}$ **19b.** $k = 0.06935$ **21a.** 0.39 **21b.** 91.7 lb **21c.** 3.56 turns

Exercise 7 (*page 271*): **1.** 1.2214 **3a.** 16.069 **3b.** 6,482 **5a.** 29.92 in **5b.** 27.07 in **5c.** 16.42 in **6a.** 260.7 rpm at 5 min **6c.** 7.87 rpm at 15 min **7.** 15.83 g **8a.** 100.6° **9.** 49.2 percent

Chapter 10

Exercise 1 (*page 275*): **1.** $y = \pm 3$ **3.** $x = \pm 7$ **5.** $y = \pm 11$ **7.** $z = \pm 2\sqrt{2}$ **9.** $x = \pm\sqrt{30}$ **11.** $y = \pm 3a$ **13.** $w = a, 0$ **15.** $z = \pm(1/c)$ **17.** $x = \pm 1/4$ **19.** $w = \pm(\sqrt{3}/6)$ **21.** $w = \pm 11/2$ **23.** $x = \pm 12$ **25.** $y = \pm 2/7$ **27.** $x = \pm(m/5)$ **29.** $z = \pm 4$ **31.** $x = \pm 6$ **33.** $w = \pm 6$

Exercise 2 (*page 278*):

1.

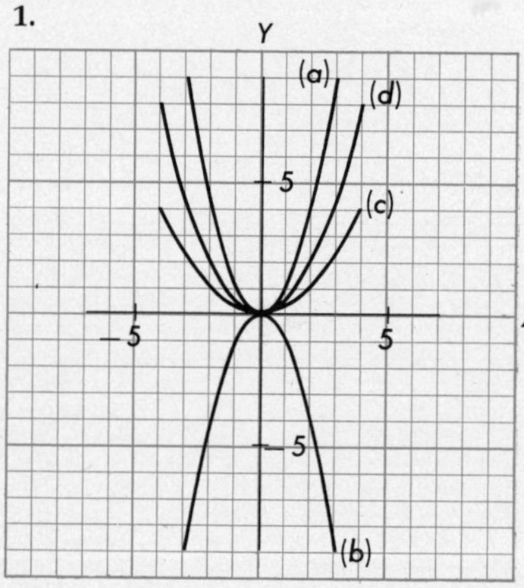

3.

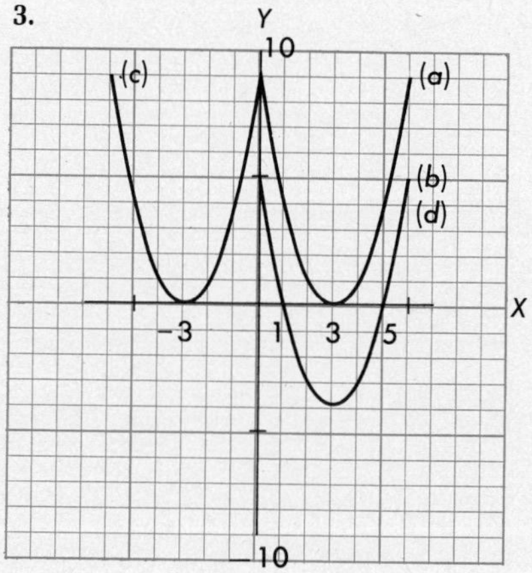

5a, b.

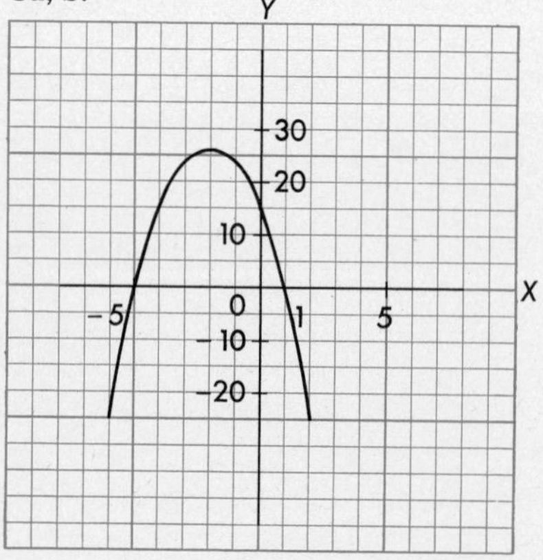

Exercise 3 (*page 278*): **1.** $x = 3, -1$ **3.** $x = 7, -8$ **5.** $x = 3, -8$ **7.** $x = 1, -\frac{2}{3}$ **9.** $x = 5, 3$

1.

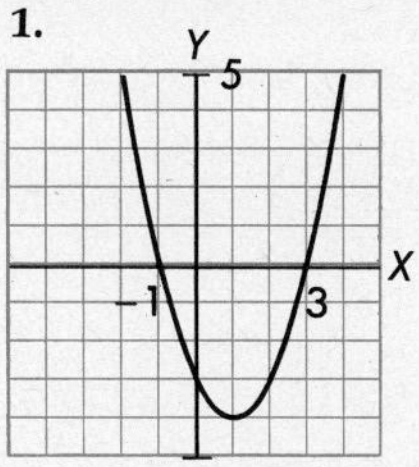

3.

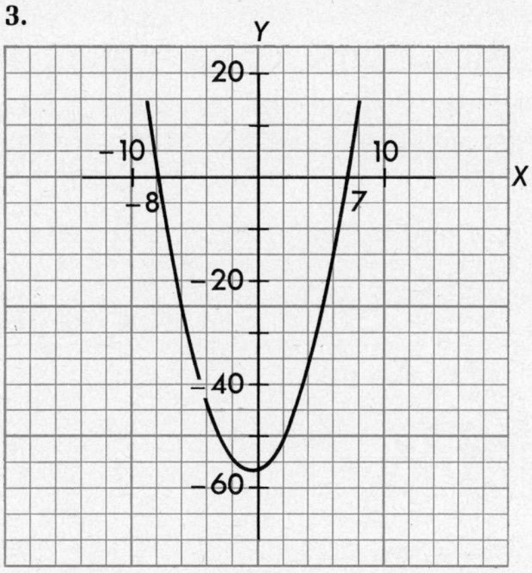

5.

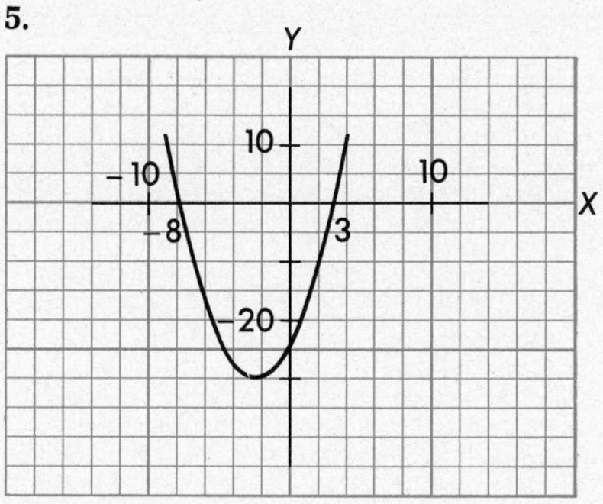

7.

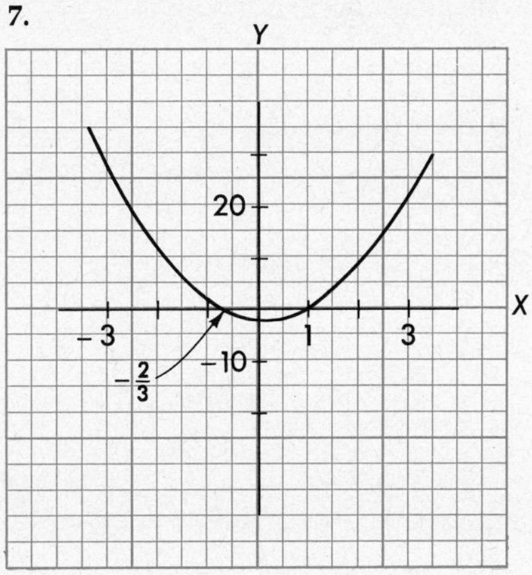

9.

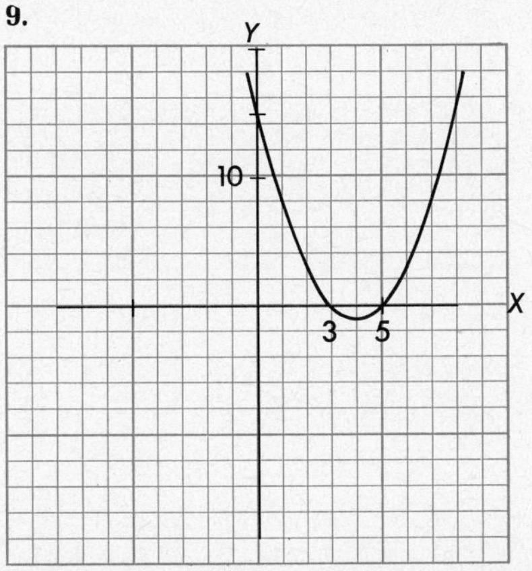

Exercise 4 (*page 279*): **1.** $x = 2, 2$ **3.** $x = 8, -9$ **5.** $x = -3, -4$ **7.** $x = 8, -6$ **9.** $x = 5, -8$ **11.** $x = -\frac{1}{2}, -1$ **13.** $x = \frac{3}{4}, -2$ **15.** $x = 8, 4$ **17.** $y = 3, 0$

Exercise 5 (*page 283*): **1.** $x = 1, -3$ **3.** $x = 1, -7$ **5.** $x = 2, -12$ **7.** $x = 13, -3$ **9.** $x = -b \pm a$ **11.** $x = 3b - 2a, -3b$ **13.** $x = \frac{2}{3}, -\frac{4}{3}$ **15.** $y = 10 \pm j\sqrt{5}$ **17.** $w = 2 \pm 2\sqrt{3}$ **19.** $y = -2, \frac{3}{2}$ **21.** $x = -4 \pm 4\sqrt{3}$ **23.** $x = 7 \pm j\sqrt{10}$

Exercise 6 (*page 285*): **1.** $x = 12, 5$ **3.** $x = 15, -11$ **5.** $y = 1, -\frac{1}{6}$

7. $x = \dfrac{-1 \pm j\sqrt{3}}{2}$ **9.** $w = \dfrac{3 \pm j\sqrt{6}}{3}$ **11.** $x = \frac{3}{4}, -\frac{4}{9}$ **13.** $w = \dfrac{-5 \pm j\sqrt{3}}{2}$

15. $p = \dfrac{3 \pm j\sqrt{11}}{10}$

Exercise 7 (*page 287*): **1.** $x = \dfrac{2m}{5}, -\dfrac{m}{3}$ **3.** $w = c, -a - b$ **5.** $y = \dfrac{a - b}{b - c}, 1$

7. $z = \dfrac{h \pm \sqrt{h^2 + 60}}{6}$ **9.** $x = h + k, 0$ **11.** $a = 2; b = -3m - 4; c = 8m - 2m^2$

Exercise 8 (*page 291*): **1.** $y = 2, -\frac{1}{2}$ **3.** $z = 24, -1$ **5.** $y = m, n$

7. $d = \dfrac{-7 \pm \sqrt{5}}{22}$ **9.** $h = 6, \frac{25}{6}$ **11.** $c = 4 \pm j4\sqrt{3}$ **13.** $y = a/3, -a/5$

15. $x = -n \pm \sqrt{n^2 + A/\pi}$ **17.** $m = 12$ **19.** $x = \dfrac{b - c}{c - a}, 1$ **21.** $x = \pm 4a$

23. $x = \dfrac{h \pm jh\sqrt{35}}{18}$

Exercise 9 (*page 292*): **1.** 64, real, rational, unequal **3.** 0, real, rational, equal **5.** 49, real, rational, unequal **7.** 49, real, rational, unequal **9.** 0, real, rational, equal **11.** 201, real, irrational, unequal **13.** 289, real, rational, unequal

Exercise 10 (*page 295*): **1.** Min; $1, -16$ **3.** Min; $-\frac{7}{2}, -\frac{25}{4}$ **5.** Max; $3, -1$ **7.** Max; $\frac{7}{12}, \frac{1}{24}$ **9.** Max; $-\frac{1}{2}, 16$ **11.** $a = -3; b = 16$; x intercept $= -1, 7$; y intercept $= -7$ **13.** 35×35 ft **15.** $h_{max} = 664$ ft **17.** $5\frac{1}{2}$ in

Exercise 11 (*page 298*): **1.** 14, 9 **3.** 13, 6 **5.** 8 **7.** 14, 16 **9.** 8 **11.** $2\frac{1}{2}$ s
13a.

t	−1	0	1	2	3	4	5	6	7	8
h	−68	+60	156	220	252	252	220	156	+60	−68

13c. $3\frac{1}{2}$ s; 256 ft **13d.** $7\frac{1}{2}$ s; $-\frac{1}{2}$ s **15.** 15 cm; 20 cm; 25 cm **17.** 10 **19.** 1.633 in **21.** 14Ω, 6Ω **23.** 65 × 72 m **25.** 1.7 ft **27.** 39.12 in **29.** 1.08 in **31.** 40.4°F **33.** 12.8 ft **35.** 8,720,000 mi from Mars **37.** 0.230 in **39.** 20 m; 21 m; 29 m **41.** 0.608 in **43.** 13.29 mi/h; 9.21 mi/h **45.** $a = 0.05$; $b = -1.3$; $c = -5$ **47.** $d = \sqrt{3h/2}$

Chapter 11

Exercise 1 (*page 309*): **1.** x intercept = −10; y intercept = 5 **3.** x intercept = ±6; y intercept = ±3 **5.** No intercepts **7.** No intercepts **9.** x intercept = $2 \pm \sqrt{24}$; y intercept = $-5 \pm \sqrt{45}$

Exercise 2 (*page 314*): **1.** Both axes, origin **3.** y axis **5.** $y = \pm x$, origin **7.** $x = 4$ **9.** y axis, $y = -3$ **11.** Origin

Exercise 3 (*page 323*): **1.** Intercepts $x = \pm 4$, $y = \pm 4$; symmetry both axes, origin; domain $|x| \leq 4$; range $|y| \leq 4$; no asymptotes **3.** Intercepts $y = \pm 3$; symmetry both axes, origin; domain unlimited, range $|y| \geq 3$; asymptotes $y = \pm x$ **5.** Intercept origin; domain and range unlimited **7.** Intercept $y = 15$; symmetry Y axis; domain unlimited, range $15 \geq y > 0$; asymptote X axis **9.** Intercepts $x = 1$, $y = -1$; no symmetry; discontinuities $x = -1$, $y = 1$; domain $x > -1$, $x < -1$, range $y > 1$, $y < 1$; asymptotes $x = -1$, $y = 1$ **11.** Intercepts $x = \pm 5$, $y = 5$; symmetry Y axis; domain $|x| \leq 5$, range $5 \geq y \geq 0$; no asymptotes **13.** Intercept $y = 10$; symmetry Y axis; domain unlimited, range $10 \geq y > 0$; asymptote X axis

1.

Equation $x^2 + y^2 = 16$

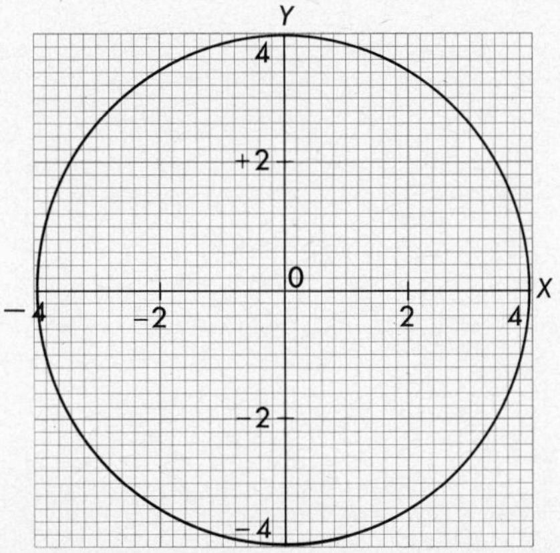

3.

$x^2 - y^2 = -9$

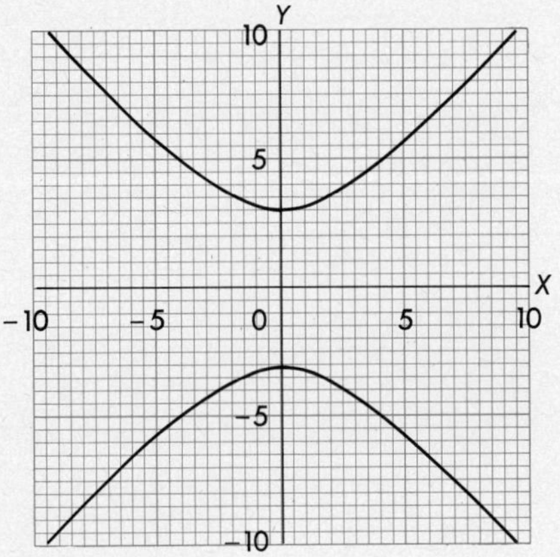

5.

$x = 4y$

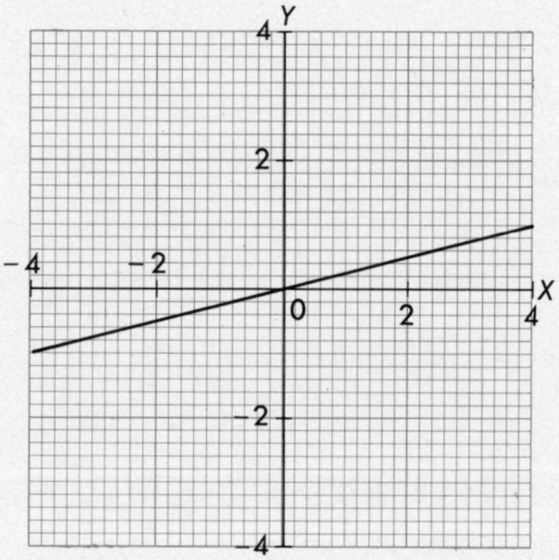

7.

$y = \frac{60}{x^2 + 4}$

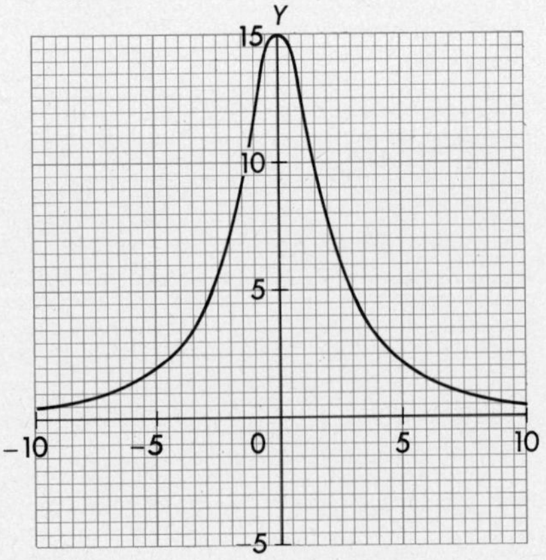

9.

$$y = \frac{x - 1}{x + 1}$$

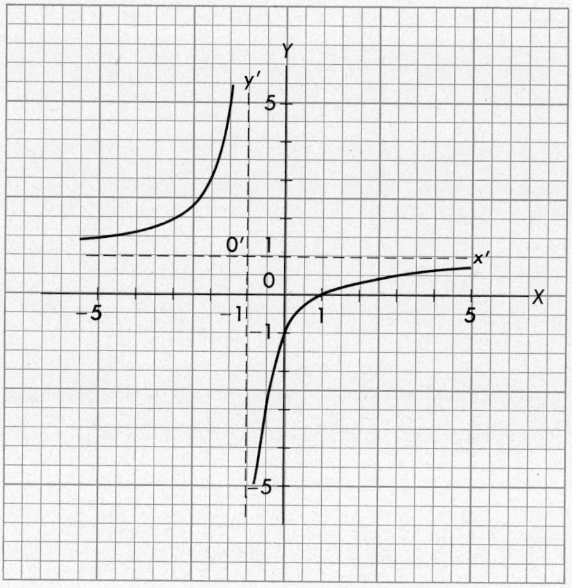

11.

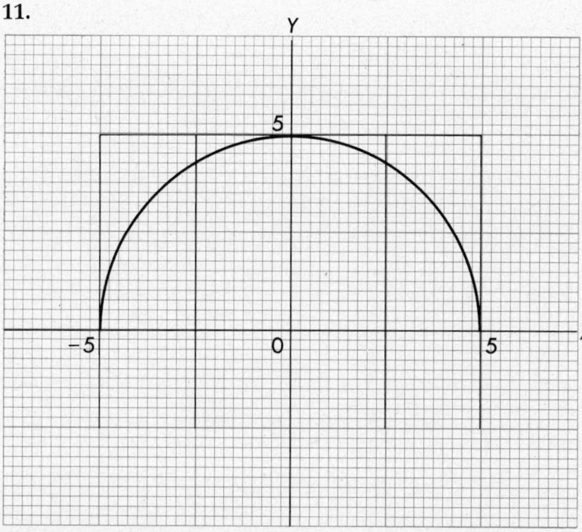

Semicircle
radius = 5
all y values
are positive.
$y = \sqrt{25 - x^2}$

13.

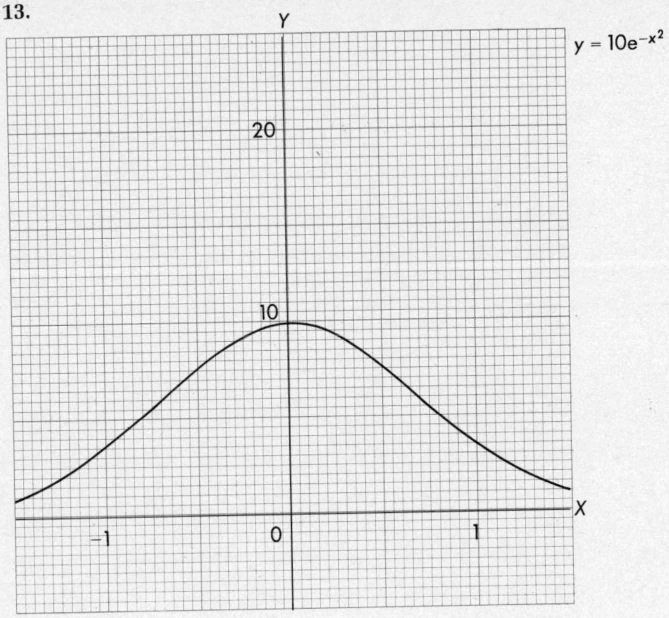

15.

$4x^2 - 9y^2 = k$

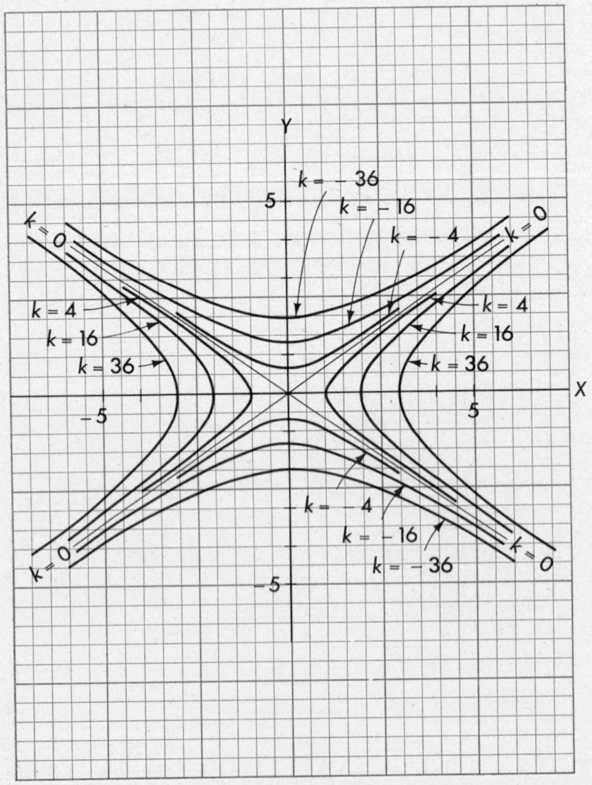

Exercise 4 *(page 325)*:

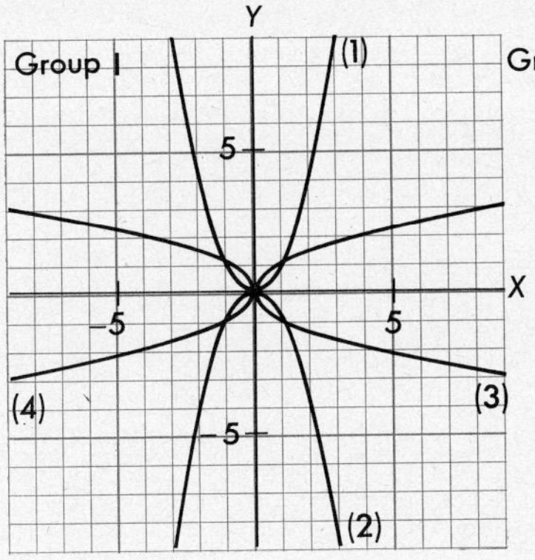

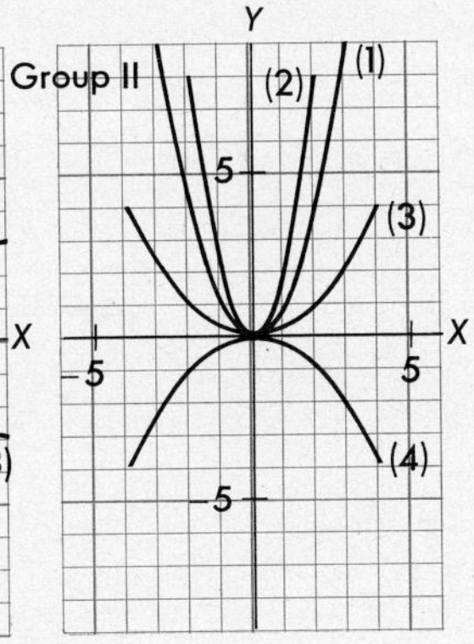

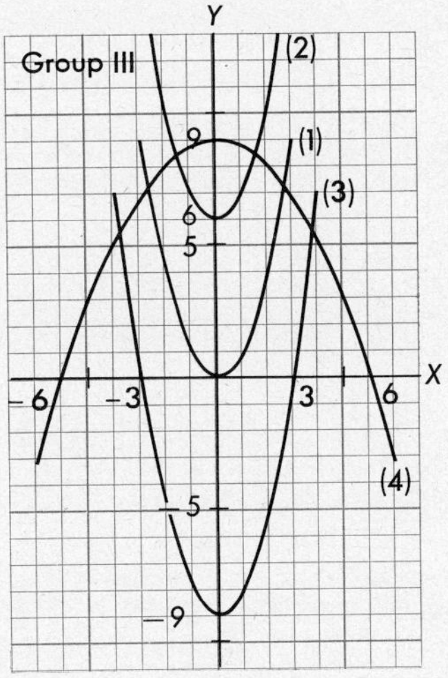

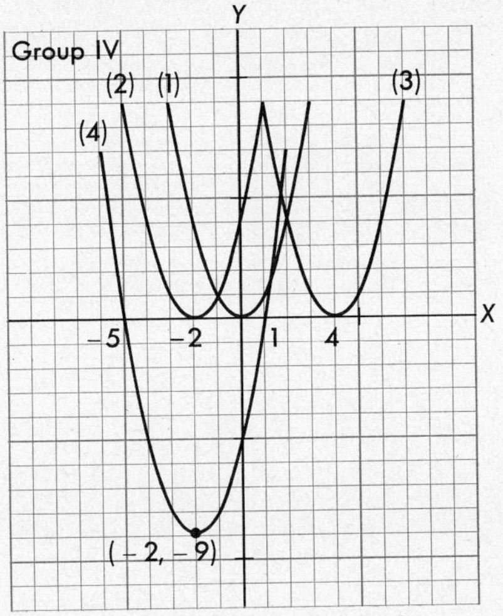

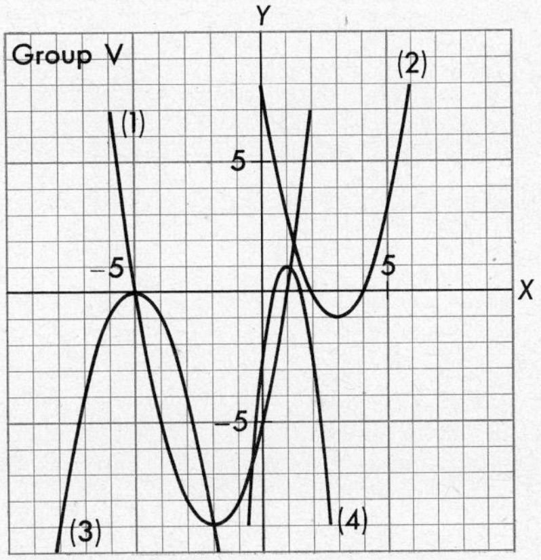

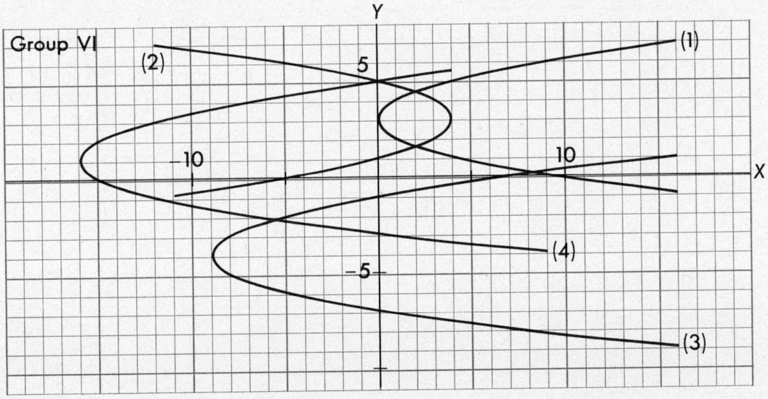

Exercise 5 (*page 337*): **1.** Basic equation $xy = 2$ **3.** Basic equation $y = x^2$ **5.** Basic equation $xy = 8$ **7.** Basic equation $y^2 = 9x$ **9.** Basic equation $x^2 + y^2 = 36$ **11.** Basic equation $x^2 + y^2 = 25/3$ **13.** 18.3 ft **15a.** $f = 1{,}010{,}000$ **15b.** $f = 20.2$

1.

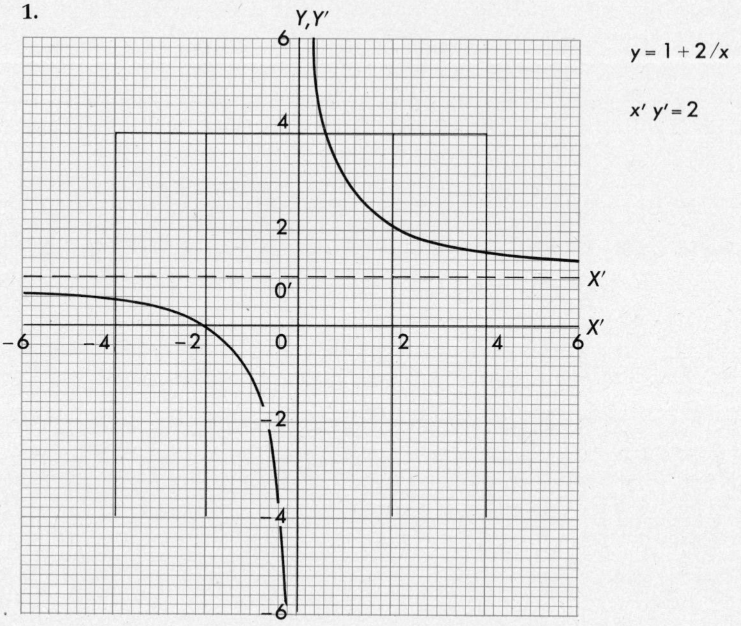

3.

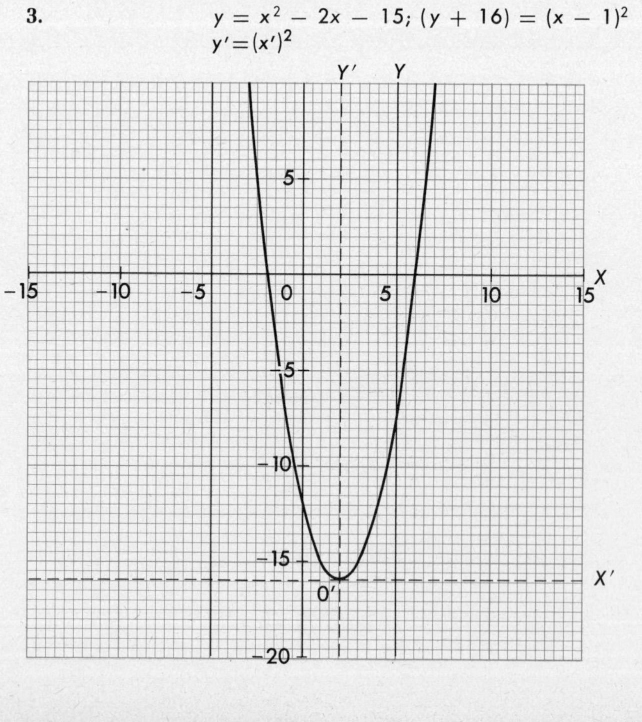

5. $(y-1)(x-2)=8$

$$y'x'=8$$

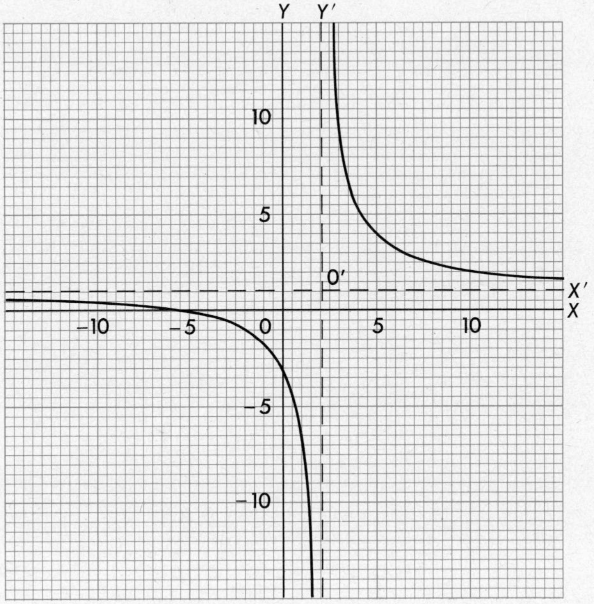

7. $y^2-4y-9x-23=0$

$$(y-2)^2=9(x+3)$$

$$(y')^2=9x'$$

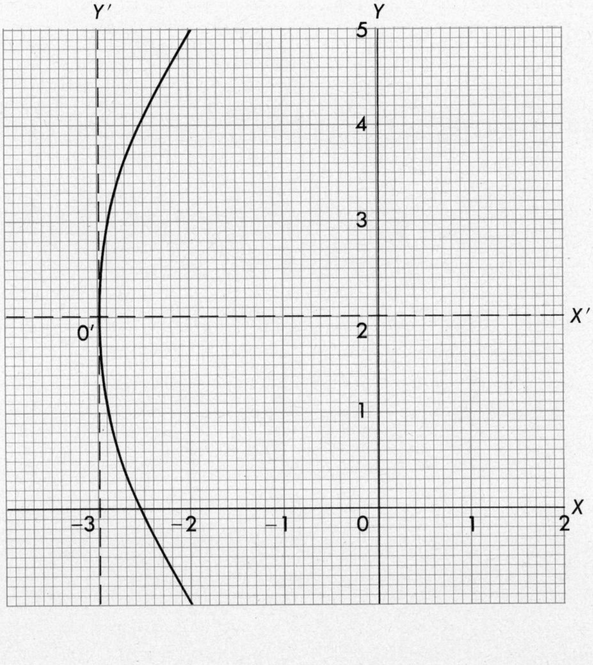

9. $x^2 + y^2 + 2x - 4y - 31 = 0$

$$(x + 1)^2 + (y - 2)^2 = 36$$

$$(x')^2 + (y')^2 = 36$$

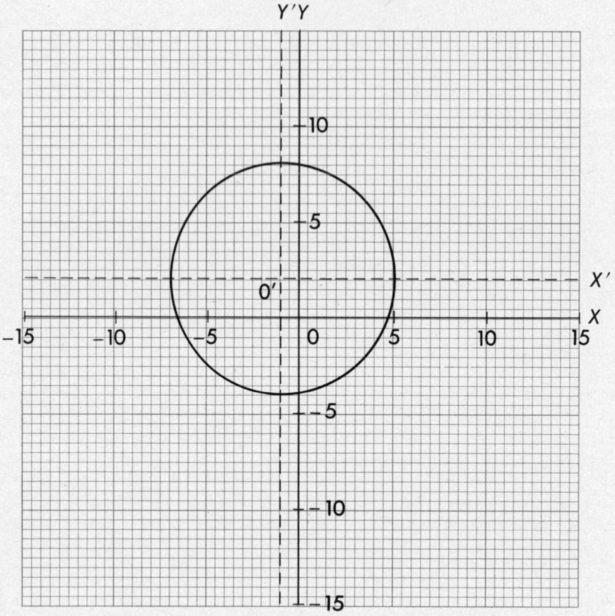

11. $3x^2 + 3y^2 - 12x + 12y - 1 = 0$

$$3(x - 2)^2 + 3(y + 2)^2 = 25$$

$$(x')^2 + (y')^2 = \frac{25}{3}$$

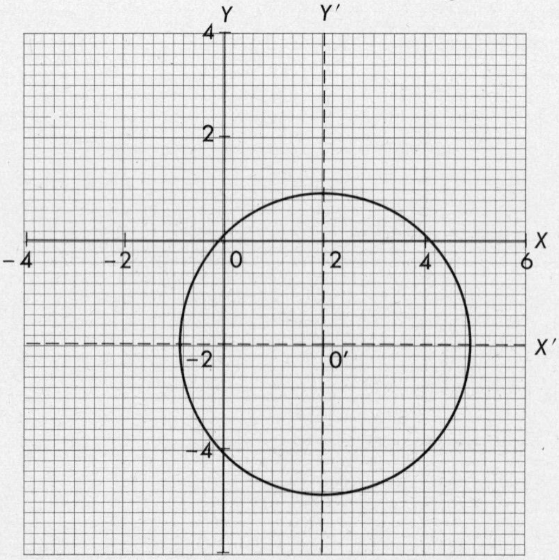

Circle radius $\frac{5\sqrt{3}}{3} = 2.89$

Center at $(2, -2)$

15a.

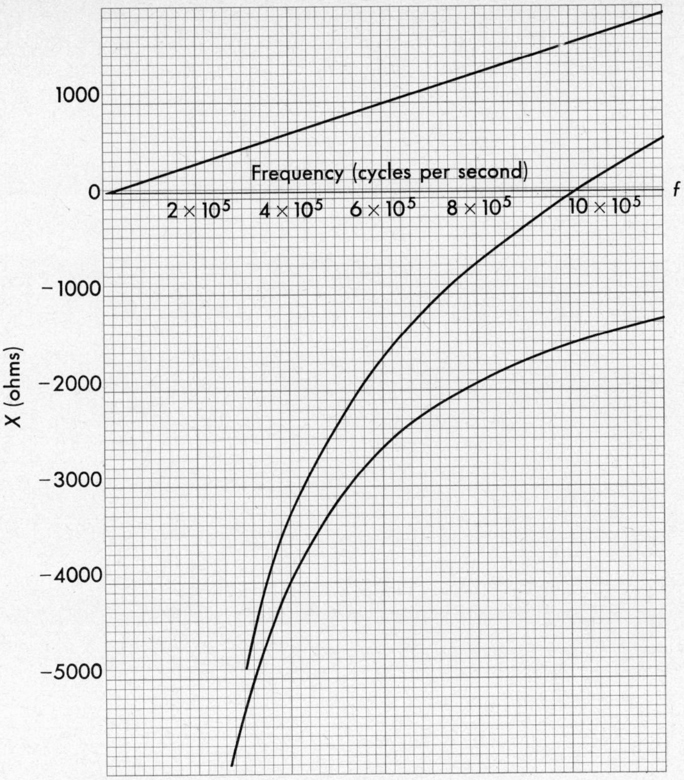
1000
0
−1000
−2000
−3000
−4000
−5000
X (ohms)
Frequency (cycles per second)
f
2 × 10^5
4 × 10^5
6 × 10^5
8 × 10^5
10 × 10^5

15b.

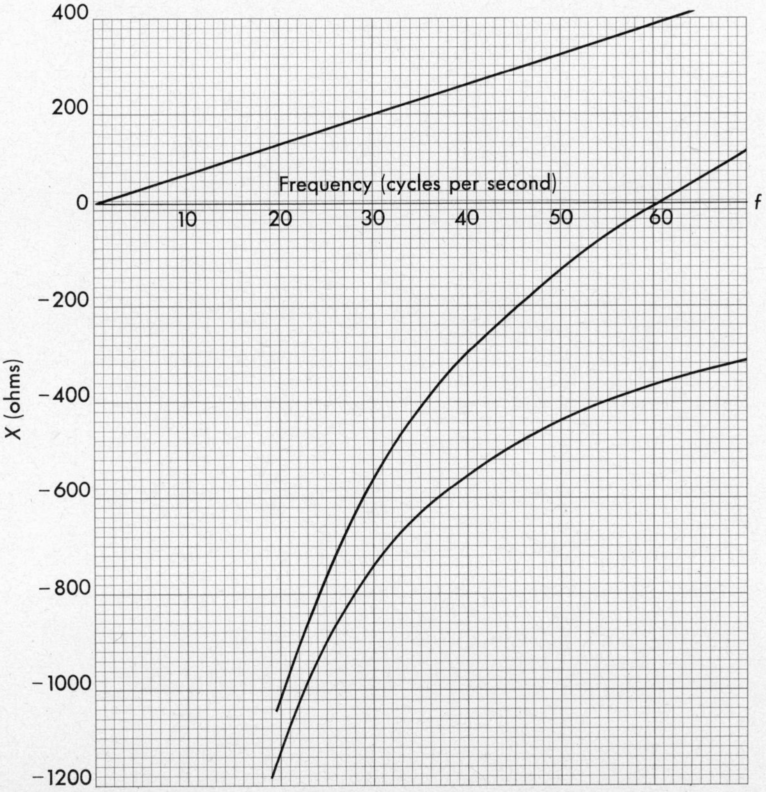
400
200
0
−200
−400
−600
−800
−1000
−1200
X (ohms)
Frequency (cycles per second)
f
10
20
30
40
50
60

Exercise 6 (*page 340*): **1.** $x = 3, -\frac{2}{3}$; $y = 2, -9$ **3.** $x = 1, 1$; $y = -4, -4$ **5.** $x = -5, -5$; $y = 4, 4$ **7.** $x = 1.9, -2.9$; $y = 3.1, -1.0$ **9.** $x = 3, -2, 1.8, -2.8$; $y = 3, -2, -2.8, 1.8$ **11.** Imaginary roots

1.

$xy = 6$

$3x - y = 7$

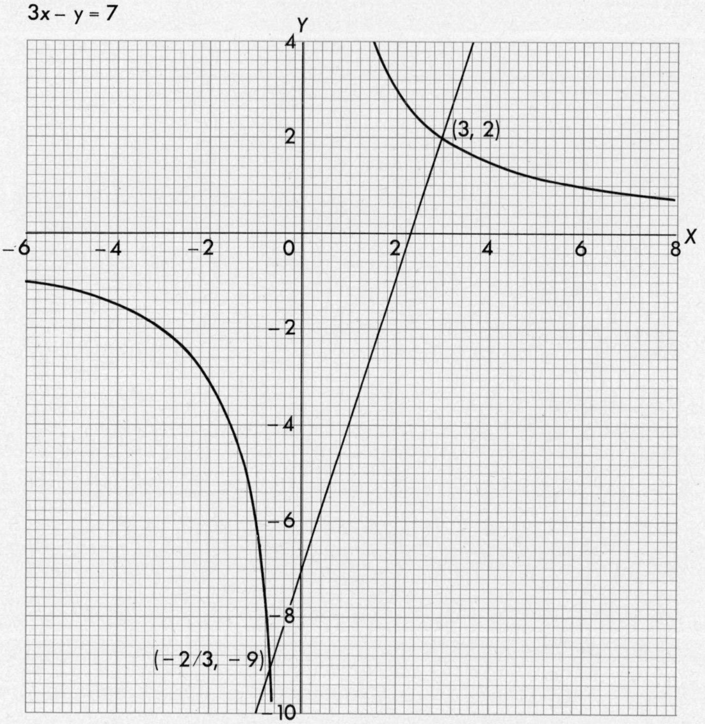

3. $y = x^2 - 4x - 1$
$2x + y = -2$

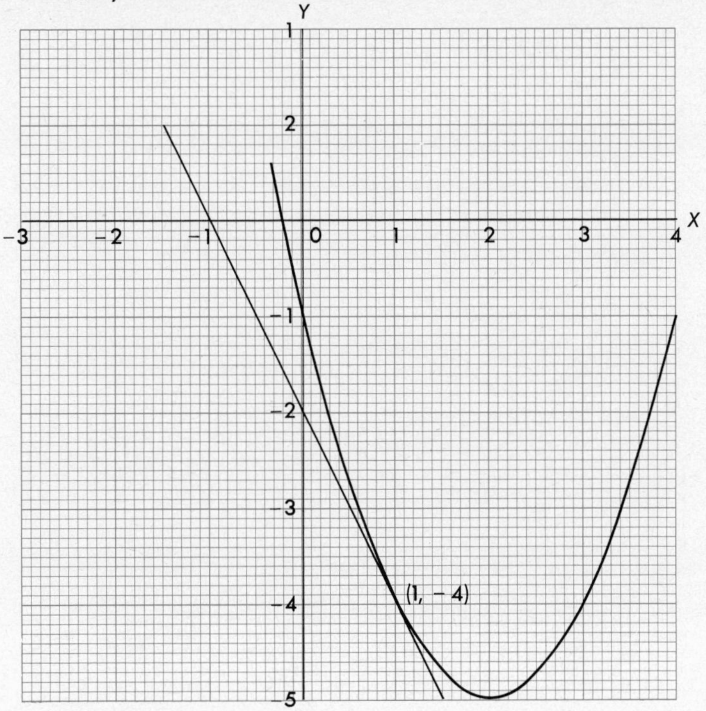

5. $x^2 - y^2 = 9$
$5x + 4y = -9$

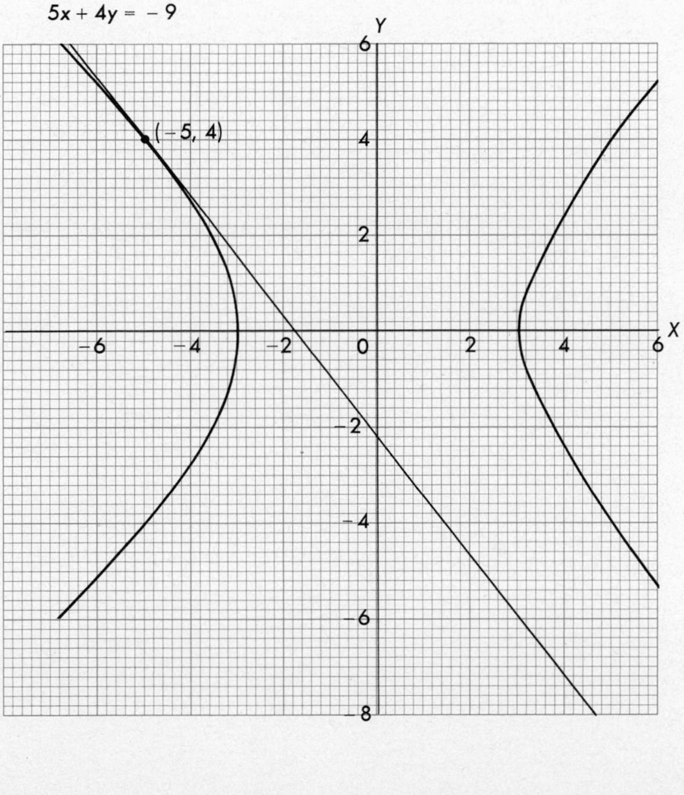

7. $x^2 + y^2 + 6x - 8y = 0$
$16x^2 + 9y^2 = 144$

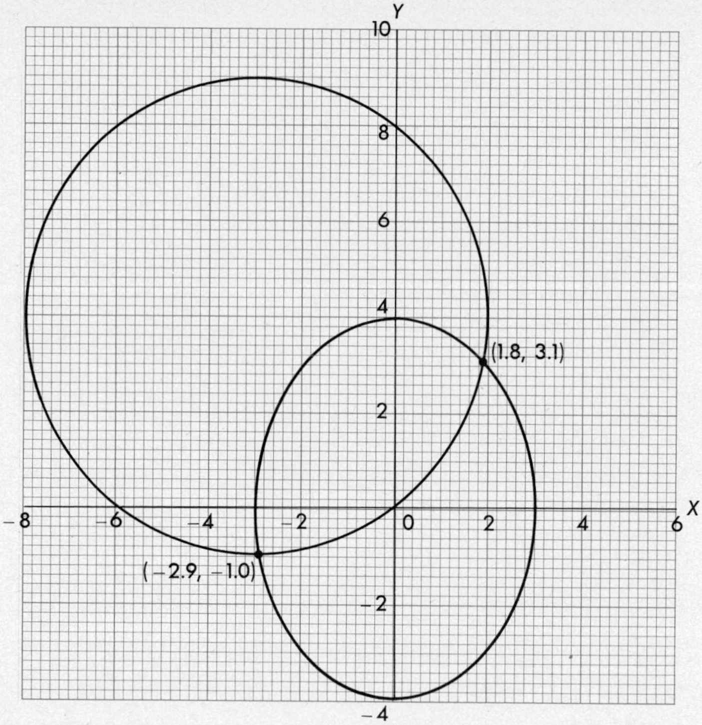

9. $y = x^2 - 6$
$x = y^2 - 6$

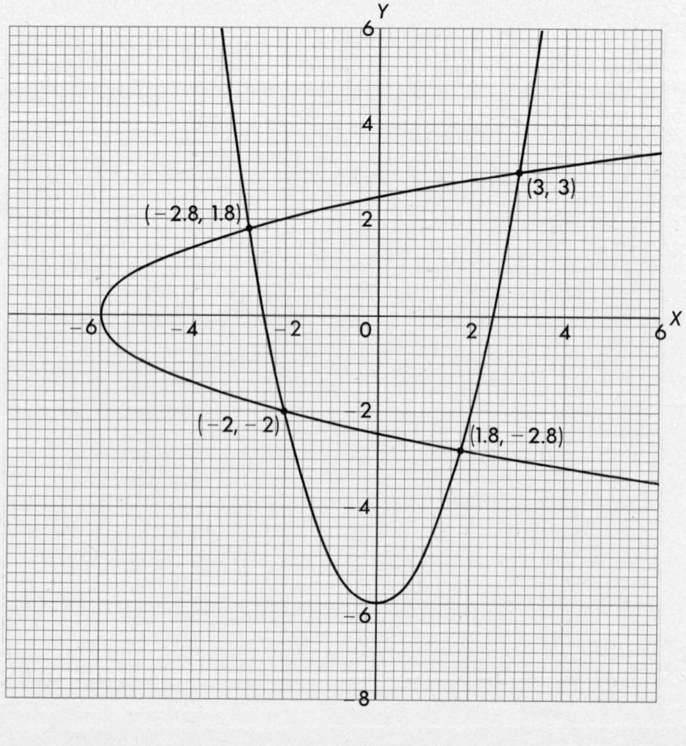

11. $4y^2 - x^2 = 25$
$x^2 + y^2 = 4$

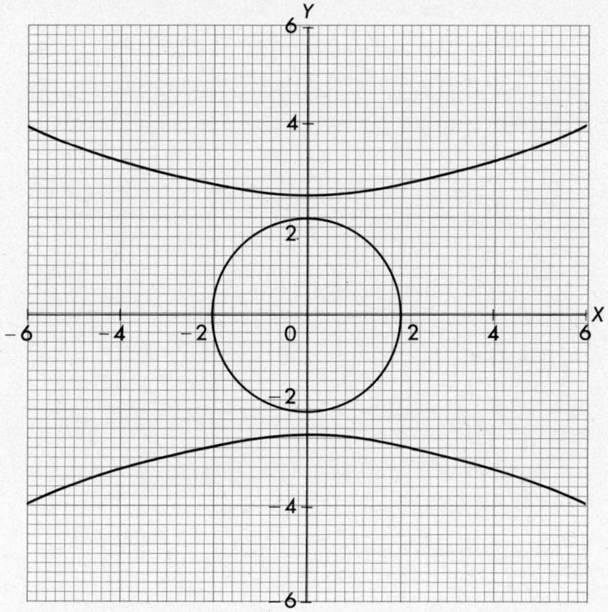

Exercise 7 (*page 341*): **1.** $x = 4, -4;\ y = 12, -12$ **3.** $x = 10, -10;\ y = 8, -8$ **5.** $x = 3, -4;\ y = -4, 3$ **7.** $x = 7, -\frac{47}{3};\ y = 3, \frac{43}{3}$ **9.** $x = 2, -\frac{22}{19};\ y = -4, \frac{74}{19}$

Exercise 8 (*page 343*): **1.** $x = 1, -1, 1, -1;\ y = 3, 3, -3, -3$ **3.** $x = 2, 2, -2, -2;$ $y = 0, 0, 0, 0$ **5.** $x = \sqrt{\frac{155}{44}}, -\sqrt{\frac{155}{44}}, \sqrt{\frac{155}{44}}, -\sqrt{\frac{155}{44}};$ $y = \sqrt{\frac{5}{22}}, \sqrt{\frac{5}{22}}, -\sqrt{\frac{5}{22}}, -\sqrt{\frac{5}{22}}$ **7.** $x = \frac{4}{7}\sqrt{21}, -\frac{4}{7}\sqrt{21}, \frac{4}{7}\sqrt{21}, -\frac{4}{7}\sqrt{21};$ $y = \frac{2}{7}\sqrt{91}, \frac{2}{7}\sqrt{91}, -\frac{2}{7}\sqrt{91}, -\frac{2}{7}\sqrt{91}$

Exercise 9 (*page 345*): **1.** $x = \frac{3}{13}\sqrt{13}, -\frac{3}{13}\sqrt{13};\ y = \frac{10}{13}\sqrt{13}, -\frac{10}{13}\sqrt{13}$

3. $x = 7, -7, 6, -6;\ y = 2, -2, 1, -1$ **5.** $x = 7, -7, \frac{j6}{5}\sqrt{3}, -\frac{j6}{5}\sqrt{3};$

$y = 2, -2, \frac{j14}{15}\sqrt{3}, -\frac{j14}{15}\sqrt{3}$ **7.** $x = 2, -2, \frac{4}{19}\sqrt{19}, -\frac{4}{19}\sqrt{19};$

$y = -5, 5, \frac{5}{19}\sqrt{19}, -\frac{5}{19}\sqrt{19}$ **9.** $K = \dfrac{D \pm \sqrt{D^2 - 4R^2}}{2R}$

Chapter 12

Exercise 1 *(page 347)*: **1.** $y = x^2 - 2x - 8$ **3.** $y = -x^2 + 3x + 28$
5. $y = 0.0172x^2 + 0.372x - 1.29$

Exercise 2 *(page 353)*:

1.

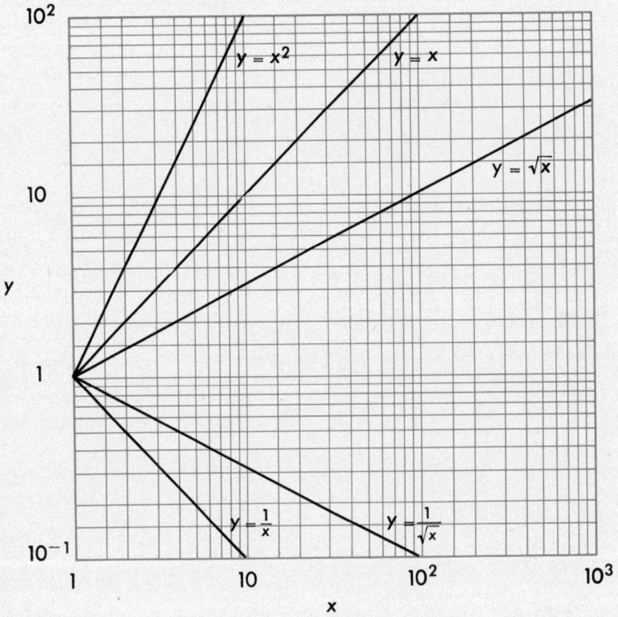

2.

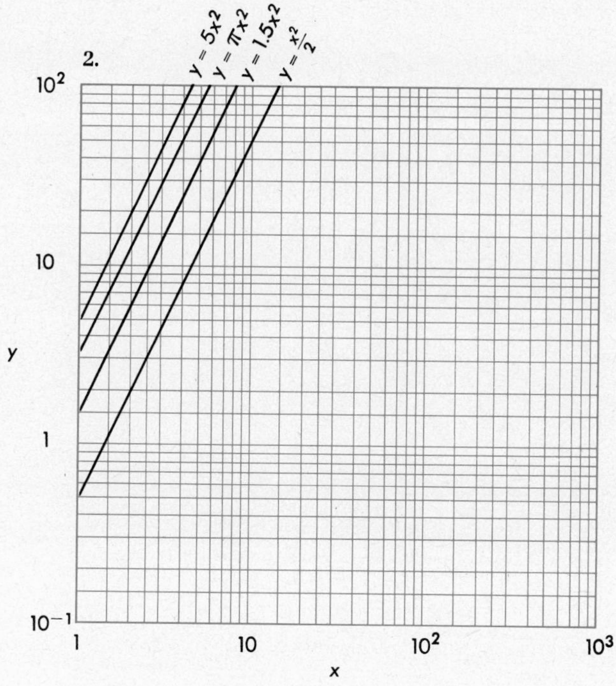

y = 5x2
y = πx2
y = 1.5x2
y = x²/2
10²
10
1
10⁻¹
y
1
10
10²
10³
x

3.

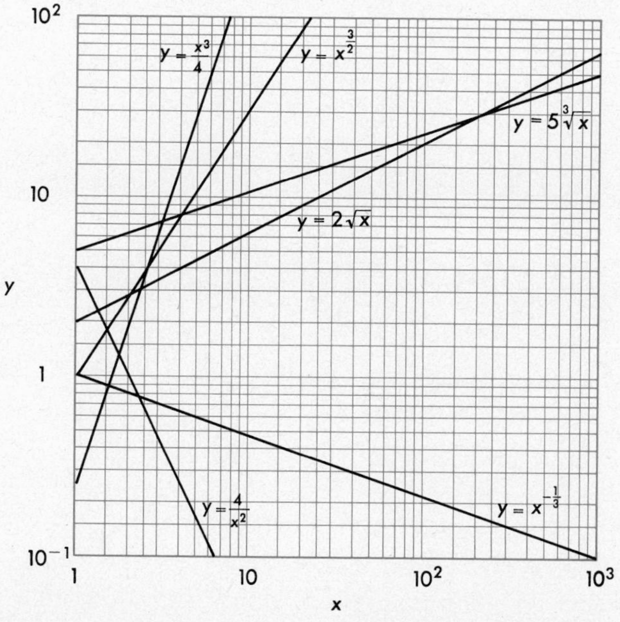

y = x³/4
y = x^(3/2)
y = 5∛x
y = 2√x
y = 4/x²
y = x^(-1/3)
10²
10
1
10⁻¹
y
1
10
10²
10³
x

Exercise 3

1.

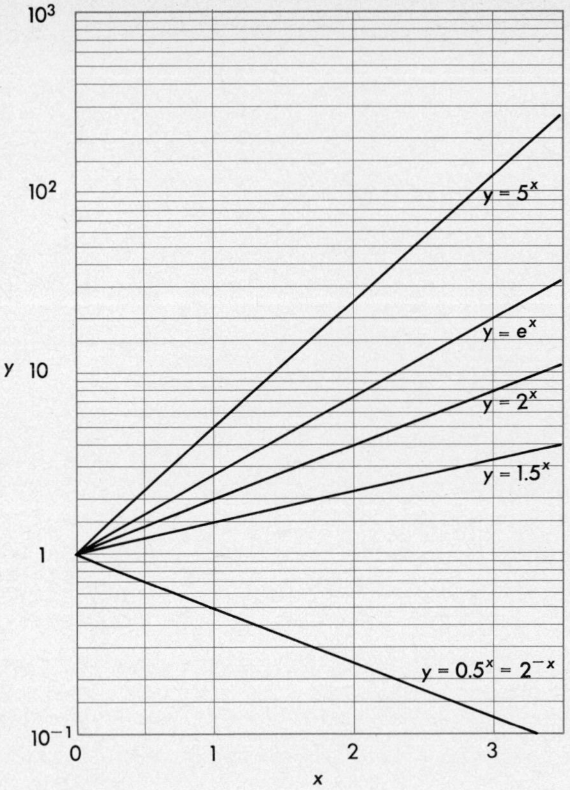

2.

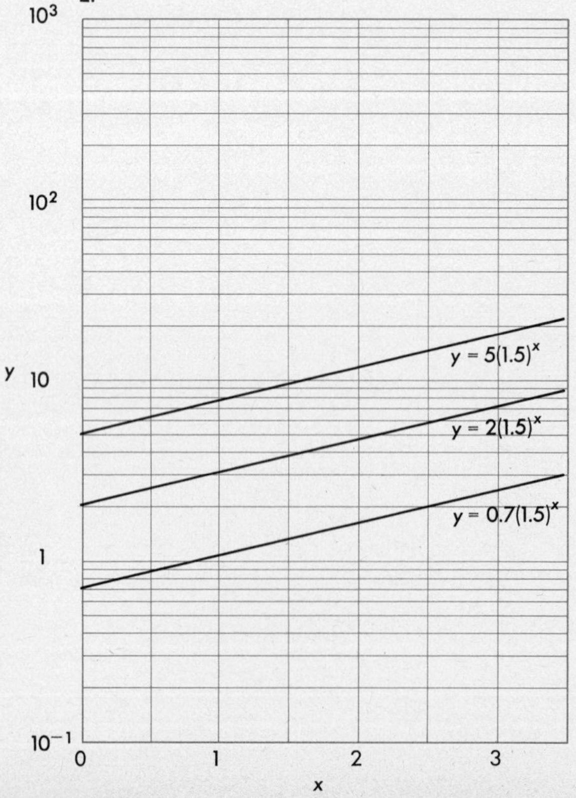

3.

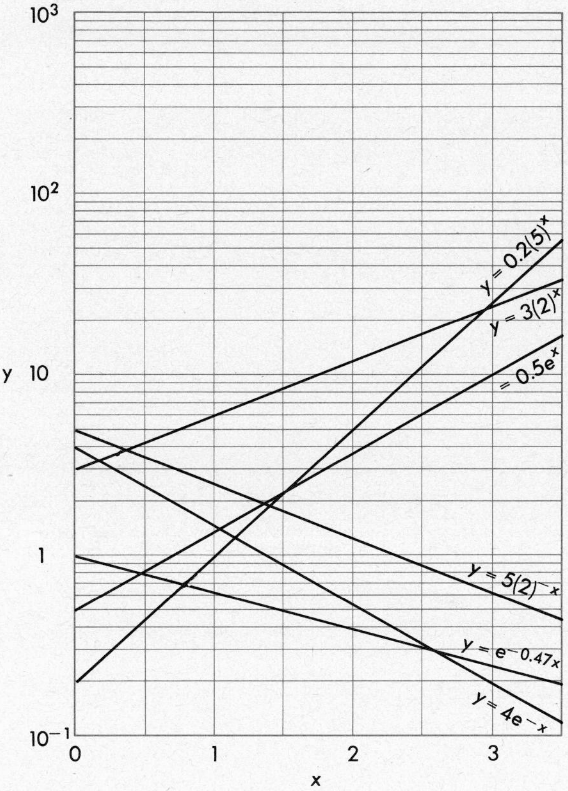

Exercise 4 (*page 359*): **a.** $y = x^2$ **c.** $y = 0.2x^2$ **e.** $y = 0.5\sqrt{x}$ **g.** $y = 1/x$ **i.** $y = 2^x$ **k.** $y = 0.1(3)^x$ **m.** $y = 10(5)^{-x} = 10(0.2)^x$

Exercise 5 (*page 360*): **1a.** $a = 1.38$; $b = 1.05$ **1b.** $y = 1.05e^{0.322x}$ **3.** $a = 0.532$; $b = 168$ **5.** $C = 3.31$; $n = 1.48$ **7a.** $N = 20.2(0.243)^t$ **7b.** $N = 20.2e^{-1.415t}$ **9.** $E = 4.04(10)^{-2}t + 3.36(10)^{-6}t^2 - 2.28(10)^{-9}t^3$ **11.** $y = 3.2(1.25)^x$ **13.** $V = 85.8p^{-0.938}$ **15.** $F = 690(4.8)^{-\theta}$ **17.** $E = 1.93$

Chapter 13

Exercise 1 (*page 369*): **1.** 0.47124 rad **3.** 4.38077 rad **5.** 77.9222° **7.** 210.2755°

Exercise 2 (*page 369*): **1.** 64 in **3.** 0.48 rad **5.** 22.9 in

Exercise 3 (*page 370*):

	Radians	*Degrees*	*Revolutions*
1.		143.24	0.39789
3.	17.453		2.7778
5.	2,513.3	144,000	
7.		72,000	200.00
9.	5.4977		0.87500

Exercise 4 (*page 374*):

	sin	cos	tan	cot	sec	csc
11.	0.35021	0.93667	0.37388	2.6746	1.0676	2.8555
13.	0.70690	0.70731	0.99942	1.0006	1.4138	1.4146
15.	0.43445	0.90070	0.48234	2.0732	1.1102	2.3018
17.	0.98619	0.16562	5.9545	0.16794	6.0379	1.0140
19.	0.00291	1.0000	0.00291	343.77	1.0000	343.78
21.	0.23203	0.97271	0.23854	4.1922	1.0281	4.3098
23.	0.82822	0.56040	1.4779	0.67663	1.7844	1.2074
25.	0.03054	0.99953	0.03055	32.730	1.0005	32.746

27. 10°24′ **29.** 48°57′ **31.** 44°03′ **33.** 21°16′ **35.** 3°06′ **37.** 50°29′ **39.** 55°35′ **41.** 48°03′ **43.** 25°05′ **45.** 11°10′ **47.** 67°25′ **49.** 50°08′ **51.** 41°06′ **53.** 29°15′ **55.** 5°10′

Exercise 5 (*page 379*):

	sin	cos	tan	cot	sec	cosec
1.	0.64279	−0.76604	−0.83910	−1.1918	−1.3054	1.5557
3.	0.99540	−0.09585	−10.385	−0.09629	−10.433	1.0046
5.	−0.91706	−0.39875	2.2998	0.43481	−2.5078	−1.0904
7.	−0.08455	0.99642	−0.08485	−11.875	1.0036	−11.828
9.	−0.00582	0.99998	−0.00582	−171.89	1.0000	−171.89

Exercise 6 (*page 381*): **1.** 0°20′ and 179°40′ **3.** 42°59′ and 137°01′ **5.** 268°53′ and 271°07′ **7.** 56°50′ and 303°10′ **9.** 99°44′ and 260°16′ **11.** 4°00′ and 184°00′ **13.** 24°51′ and 204°51′ **15.** 137°56′ and 317°56′ **17.** 29°10′ and 209°10′ **19.** 122°00′ and 302°00′ **21.** 11°10′ and 348°50′ **23.** 35°23′ and 324°37′ **25.** 132°40′ and 227°20′ **27.** 54°57′ and 125°03′ **29.** 9°18′ and 170°42′

Exercise 7 (*page 385*): **1.** 0, 0.500, 0.707, 0.866, 1.000, 0.866, 0.707, 0.500, 0, −0.500, −0.707, −0.866, −1.000, −0.866, −0.707, −0.500, 0 **3.** +1 and −1; +1 and −1: unlimited; unlimited; does not exist between +1 and −1, unlimited otherwise; does not exist between +1 and −1, unlimited otherwise 7. −0.707

Chapter 14

Exercise 1 (*page 388*): **1.** cos 70° **3.** sin 30° **5.** tan 73° **7.** sin 51.5° **9.** csc 65°

Exercise 2 (*page 394*): **1.** $a = 55.744$; $b = 76.072$; $B = 53°46'$ **3.** $a = 60.200$; $b = 117.47$; $A = 27°08'$ **5.** $a = 0.31011$; $b = 2.1698$; $B = 81°52'$ **7.** $a = 232.39$; $b = 92.168$; $B = 21°38'$ **9.** $a = 50.810$; $b = 39.389$; $A = 52°13'$ **11.** $b = 5{,}516.9$; $c = 40{,}998$; $B = 7°44'$ **13.** $b = 134.96$; $c = 143.04$; $B = 70°39'$ **15.** $b = 48.090$; $c = 50.103$; $B = 73°42'$ **17.** $b = 342.03$; $c = 463.29$; $A = 42°25'$ **19.** $a = 9{,}237.3$; $c = 12{,}302$; $B = 41°20'$ **21.** $A = 64°18'$; $B = 25°42'$; $c = 385.09$ **23.** $A = 69°25'$; $B = 20°35'$; $c = 71{,}707$ **25.** $A = 34°47'$; $B = 55°13'$; $c = 247.17$ **27.** $A = 18°10'$; $B = 71°50'$; $b = 2{,}556.9$ **29.** $A = 24°18'$; $B = 65°42'$; $b = 39{,}782$ **31.** $A = 21°20'$; $B = 68°40'$; $a = 4{,}082.8$ **33.** $A = 36°36'$; $B = 53°24'$; $a = 1{,}394.0$ **35.** $A = 16°49'$; $B = 73°11'$; $a = 297.70$

Exercise 3 (*page 397*):

	sin	cos	tan	cot	sec	csc
1.	0.04311	0.99907	0.04315	23.175	1.0009	23.196
3.	0.24678	0.96907	0.25466	3.9269	1.0319	4.0522
5.	0.64564	0.76365	0.84546	1.1827	1.3095	1.5489
7.	0.79646	0.60470	1.3172	0.75923	1.6538	1.2555
9.	0.98767	0.15653	6.3098	0.15848	6.3886	1.0125
11.	0.45795	0.88898	0.51514	1.9412	1.1249	2.1836
13.	0.95282	0.30354	3.1391	0.31856	3.2945	1.0495
15.	0.29674	0.95496	0.31073	3.2182	1.0472	3.3700

Exercise 4 (*page 397*): **1.** 6°04′06″ **3.** 35°04′20″ **5.** 46°35′24″ **7.** 12°01′10″ **9.** 88°37′48″ **11.** 40°59′27″ **13.** 24°54′20″ **15.** 46°16′30″ **17.** 86°23′12″ **19.** 32°52′07″ **21.** 87°30′45″ **23.** 51°24′30″ **25.** 64°44′48″ **27.** 6°08′51″ **29.** 46°17′30″

Exercise 5 (*page 398*): **1.** $a = 0.54882$; $b = 0.68148$; $B = 51°09'15''$ **3.** $a = 12.437$; $b = 9.1720$; $B = 36°24.5'$ **5.** $a = 2{,}517.9$; $b = 1{,}044.7$; $A = 67°27.9'$ **7.** $a = 6.3335$; $b = 8.5310$; $A = 36°35'26''$ **9.** $a = 6.8772$; $b = 12.194$; $A = 29°25'17''$ **11.** $b = 12{,}217$; $c = 12{,}281$; $B = 84°09'29''$ **13.** $b = 977.88$; $c = 1{,}389.3$; $B = 44°44.2'$ **15.** $b = 2{,}222.7$; $c = 2{,}334.5$; $B = 72°11.7'$ **17.** $a = 50.357$; $c = 757.90$; $A = 3°48.6'$ **19.** $a = 20.466$;

$c = 55.313$; $B = 68°17'02''$ **21.** $A = 27°45'34''$; $B = 62°14'26''$; $c = 42.941$ **23.** $A = 14°30'38''$; $B = 75°29'22''$; $c = 18.517$ **25.** $A = 25°13'12''$; $B = 64°46'48''$; $c = 196.42$ **27.** $A = 18°49'13''$; $B = 71°10'47''$; $c = 1{,}357.5$ **29.** $A = 34°58'13''$; $B = 55°01'47''$; $c = 54.523$ **31.** $A = 20°33'36''$; $B = 69°26'24''$; $b = 391.92$ **33.** $A = 67°37'33''$; $B = 22°22'27''$; $b = 16.358$ **35.** $A = 55°45'08''$; $B = 34°14'52''$; $b = 639.64$ **37.** $A = 65°21'30''$; $B = 24°38'30''$; $a = 272.50$ **39.** $A = 42°21'28''$; $B = 47°38'32''$; $a = 12.577$ **41.** 6.3351 in **43.** 0.9347 in

Exercise 6 (*page 401*): **1a.** 0.470 and 0.883 **1c.** 0.292 and 0.956 **1e.** 0.342 and 0.940 **1g.** 0.1253 and 0.99 **1i.** 0.442 and 0.897 **1k.** 0.288 and 0.958

Exercise 8 (*page 403*): **1a.** 0.364 **1c.** 0.972 **1e.** 0.283 **1g.** 0.894 **1i.** 0.762

Exercise 10 (*page 405*): **1.** $c = 247$, $A = 34.8°$, $B = 55.2°$ **3.** $a = 386$, $A = 58.0°$, $B = 32.0°$ **5.** $a = 9{,}220$, $c = 12{,}300$, $B = 41.33°$ **7.** $b = 342$, $c = 463$, $A = 42.42°$

Exercise 11 (*page 405*): **1.** $b = 3.26$, $c = 3.39$, $B = 73.93°$ **3.** $a = 310$, $b = 2{,}170$, $B = 81.87°$ **5.** $a = 60.2$, $b = 117.5$, $A = 27.13°$

Exercise 12 (*page 407*): **1.** $a = 89.488$; $b = 115.76$ **3.** $a = 47.868$; $b = 150.21$ **5.** $a = 0.65841$; $b = 1.2073$ **7.** $b = 0.42347$; $c = 15.364$ **9.** $a = 1{,}369{,}100$; $c = 1{,}369{,}200$ **11.** $A = 5°28'05''$; $b = 142.33$ **13.** $A = 30°07'41''$; $b = 9.3669$ **15.** $A = 38°39'08''$; $b = 0.45661$ **17.** $A = 84°47'01''$; $c = 96.028$ **19.** $A = 26°35'27''$; $c = 8.1702$

Exercise 13 (*page 409*): **1.** 10.719 in; 2.3694 in **3.** $47°09'24''$; $73°44'22''$ **5.** 0.828 in above **7.** 66.002 in^2

Exercise 14 (*page 411*): **1.** 4.95 in **3.** 10.04 in **5.** 6.93 in **7.** 2.00 in

Exercise 15 (*page 417*): **1.** $a = 7.02$ in **3.** $b = 2.013$ in **5.** $c = 37$ in **7.** $A = 39°11'$; $A' = 140°49'$

Exercise 16 (*page 423*): **3.** $a/\sin A = b$ **5.** $A = 28°05'$; $C = 106°15'$; $B = 45°40'$ **7.** $a = 7.3205$; $b = 5.1764$ **9.** $a = 1{,}000$; $b = 1{,}732.1$; $y = 866.03$ **11a.** $b = 66.913$ **11b.** $b = 17.365$ **13.** $a = 1.2007$; $c = 1.9355$; $B = 53°31'$ **15.** $a = 2.8438$; $c = 1.7307$; $B = 130°13'$ **17.** $a = 1.3670$; $c = 6.0563$; $B = 122°46'$ **19.** $a = 1.1165$; $b = 11.795$; $C = 90°46'$ **21.** $b = 4.9509$; $c = 2.9099$; $A = 104°30'$ **23.** $a = 11.080$; $b = 32.048$; $C = 128°12'$ **25.** $a = 1.2045$; $B = 86°55'$; $A = 44°44'$; $A' = 38°34'$; $B' = 93°05'$; $a' = 1.0669$ **27.** $c = 6.3591$; $B = 67°46'$; $C = 54°37'$; $c' = 1.3745$; $B' = 112°14'$; $C' = 10°09'$ **29.** $c = 3.418$; $B = 71°58'$; $C = 46°40'$; $c' = 0.8644$; $B' = 108°02'$; $C' = 10°36'$ **31.** $b = 2.0267$; $B = 32°51'$; $C = 84°38'$; $b' = 1.4067$; $B' = 22°07'$;

$C' = 95°22'$ **33.** $b = 2.7276$; $c = 4.3829$; $A = 59°12'$ **35.** $b = 20.678$; $c = 12.131$; $B = 87°44'31''$ **37.** $a = 56.356$; $b = 188.79$; $C = 10°13'15''$ **39.** $c = 30.238$; $A = 82°54'$; $C = 11°56'05''$ **41.** $a = 23.305$; $A = 42°20'10''$; $C = 28°26'34''$ **43.** $b = 10.002$; $A = 60°38'51''$; $B = 30°25'06''$ **45.** $b = 6.1150$; $c = 10.132$; $C = 65°51'09''$ **47.** $b = 43.227$; $c = 24.339$; $B = 130°19'$ **49.** $a = 13.398$; $c = 29.090$; $B = 111°36'58''$ **51.** $b = 7{,}363.2$; $c = 6{,}152.9$; $A = 56°54'48''$ **53.** $a = 61.048$; $c = 54.981$; $A = 107°26.7'$ **55.** $b = 1{,}964.2$; $c = 2{,}272.1$; $C = 122°45.7'$ **57.** $b = 413.14$; $c = 615.36$; $B = 30°45'51''$ **59.** $b = 96.050$; $c = 74.784$; $A = 113°50.8'$

Exercise 17 (*page 431*): **9.** 7.1414 **11.** 16.894 **13.** 10.890 **15.** 33.734 **17.** 13.416 **19.** $A = 46°23'49''$; $B = 104°15'00''$; $C = 29°21'09''$ **21.** $A = 61°55'39''$; $B = 81'12'10''$; $C = 36°52'11''$ **23.** $A = 34°02'53''$; $B = 44°24'54''$; $C = 101°32'13''$ **25.** $A = 44°24'54''$; $B = 57°07'18''$; $C = 78°27'47''$ **27.** $A = 42°32'13''$; $B = 56°18'45''$; $C = 81°09'00''$ **29.** $B = 15°35'00''$; $A = 29°03'21''$; $C = 135°21'37''$

Chapter 15

Exercise 1 (*page 438*): **1.** $\overrightarrow{AB}$, $\overrightarrow{GH}$ **3.** $\overrightarrow{AB}$, $\overrightarrow{GH}$, $\overrightarrow{KL}$, $\overrightarrow{EF}$, $\overrightarrow{IJ}$

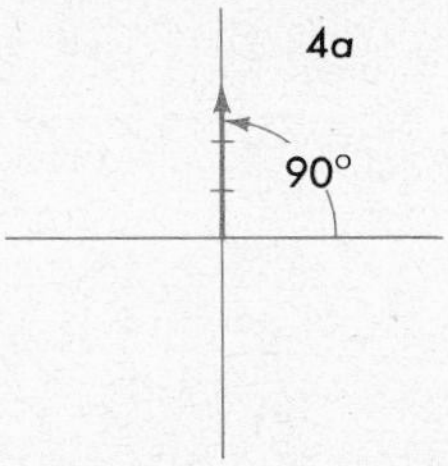

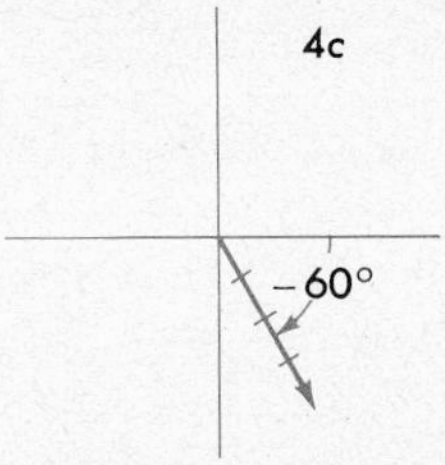

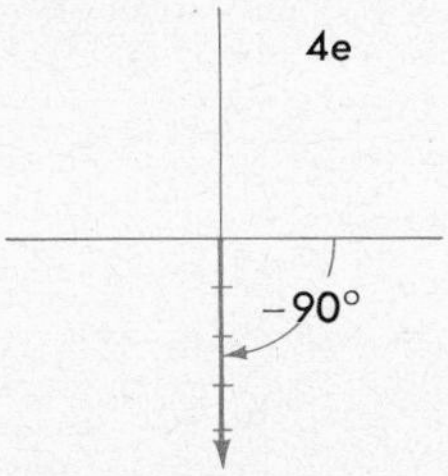

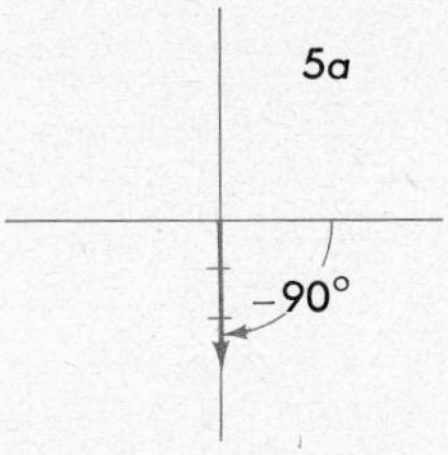

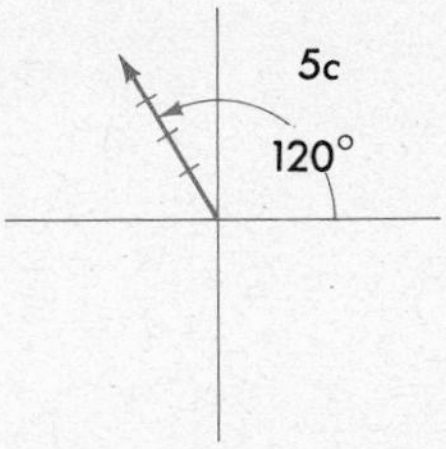

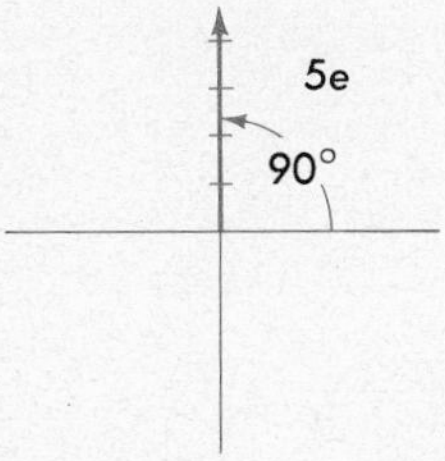

Exercise 2 (*page 442*): **1.** $(21.2, 1.21): 21.2\angle 3.27°$ **3.** $(-31.4, 15.13): 34.9\angle 154.28°$ **5.** $(37.4, 62.1): 72.5\angle 58.92°$ **7.** $(-300, 100): 316\angle 161.57°$ **9.** $(65.8, -38.0): 76\angle 330°$

Exercise 3 *(page 443)*:

	X projection	*Y projection*
1.	+ 2.67	+ 1.362
3.	− 8.66	+ 5.00
5.	0.00	+ 7.00
7.	+13.12	+ 7.27
9.	−14.14	−14.14
11.	− 1.532	− 1.286
13.	0.00	− 3.00
15.	+ 4.33	+ 2.50

Exercise 4 *(page 448)*: **1.** $21.2\underline{/3.27^\circ}$ **3.** $34.9\underline{/154.28^\circ}$ **5.** $72.5\underline{/58.92^\circ}$ **7.** $316\underline{/161.57^\circ}$ **9.** $76.0\underline{/330.00^\circ}$

Exercise 5 *(page 451)*: **1.** $R = 821.90$; $\phi = 5°35'33''$ **3.** 40°32′09″; 32°21′34″ **5.** $F_1 = 44.425$; $F_2 = 422.67$ **7.** F to submerge = 19.966; F horizontal = 15.045 **9.** Length BC = 31.855 ft; Force in BC = 740.81 lb; Force in AB = 976.73 lb

Chapter 16

Exercise 1 *(page 455)*: **1.** +0.868; +3.830; +1.710; −4.698; −4.330 **3.** Approximate slope = 1; tangent greater than sine

Exercise 2 *(page 457)*: **1a.** 8.55 **1b.** 25.00 **1c.** 19.15 **1d.** 0 **1e.** −12.50 **1f.** −25.00 **1g.** −21.65 **1h.** 0 **5.** 25.39 **7.** 45.6°; 134.4°; 225.6°; 314.4° **9.** 40°

3.

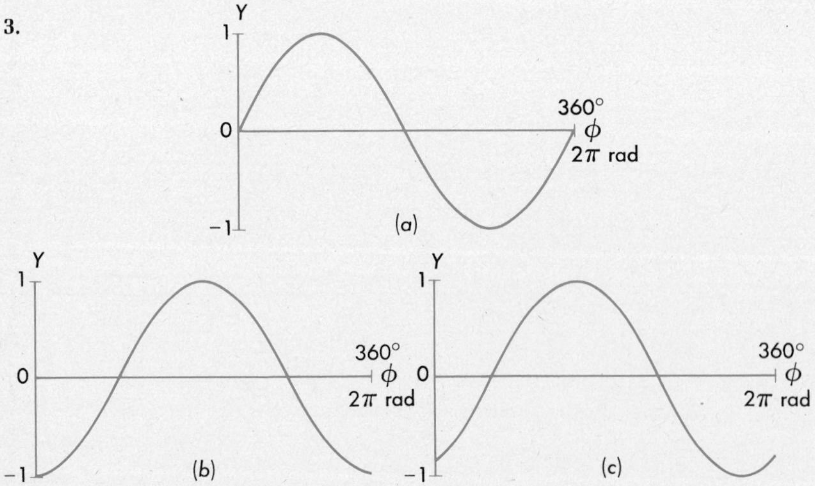

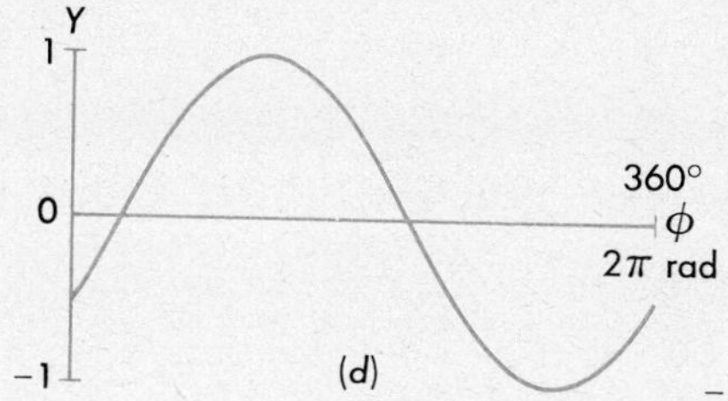

(d)

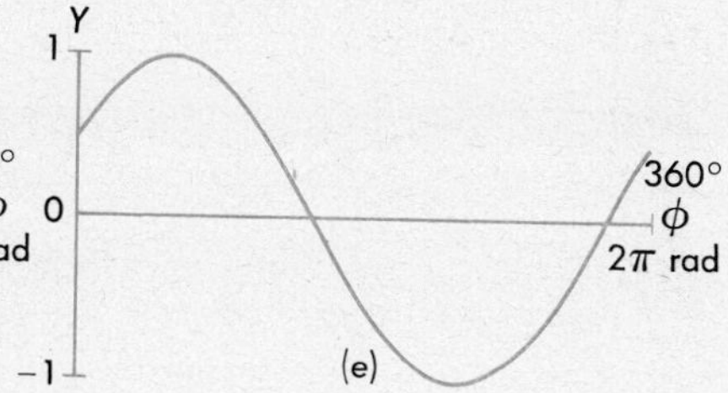

(e)

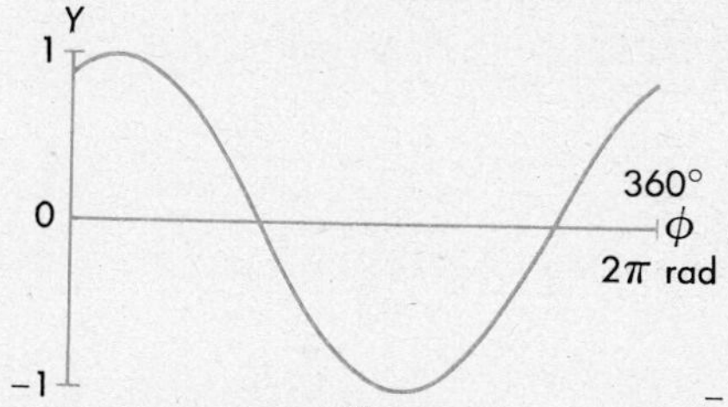

(f)

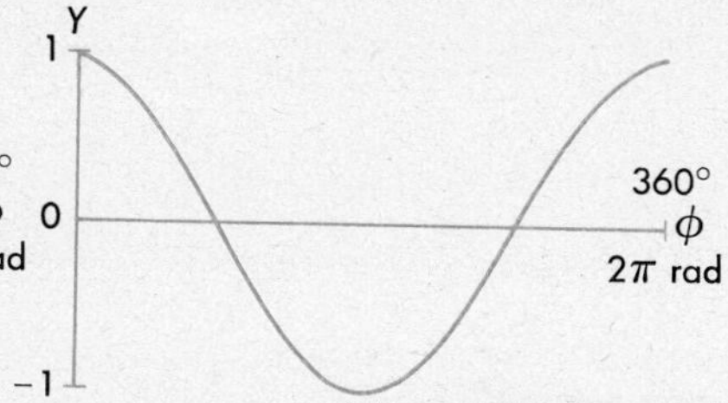

(g)

Exercise 3 (*page 463*):

1.

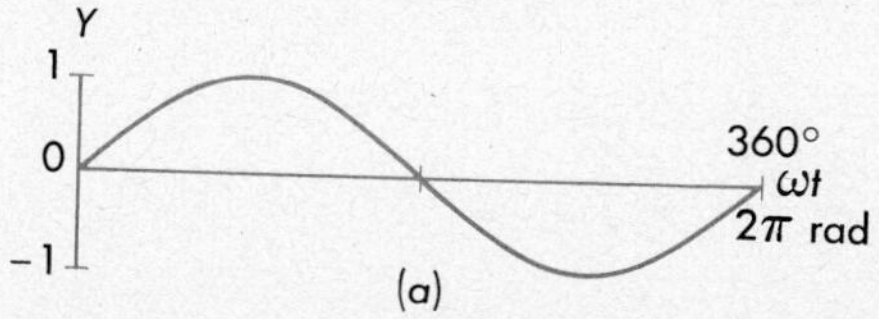

(a)

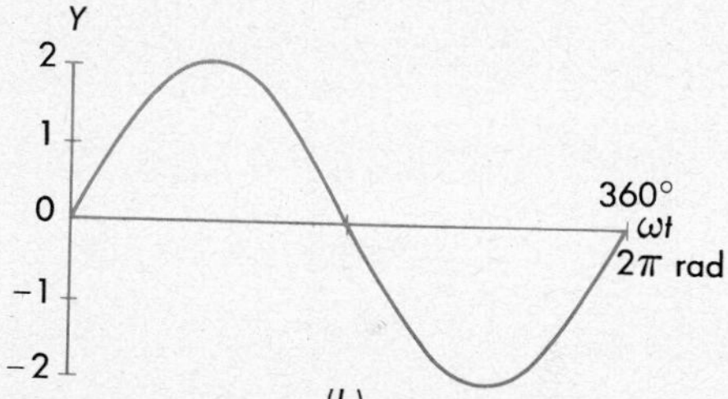

(b)

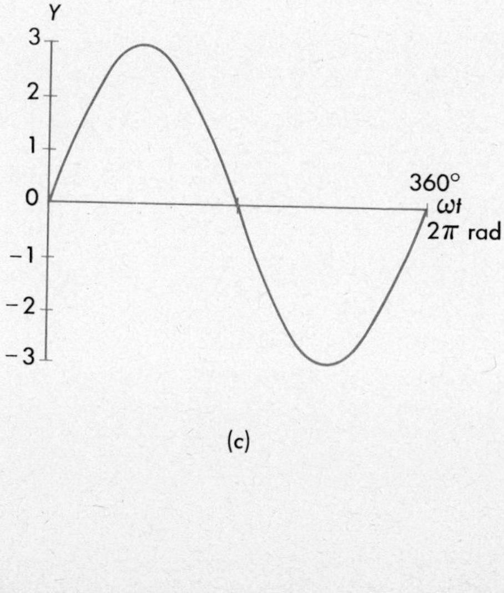

(c)

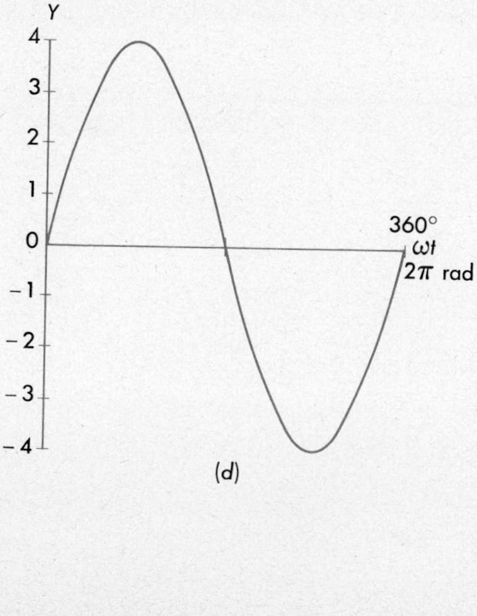

(d)

3.

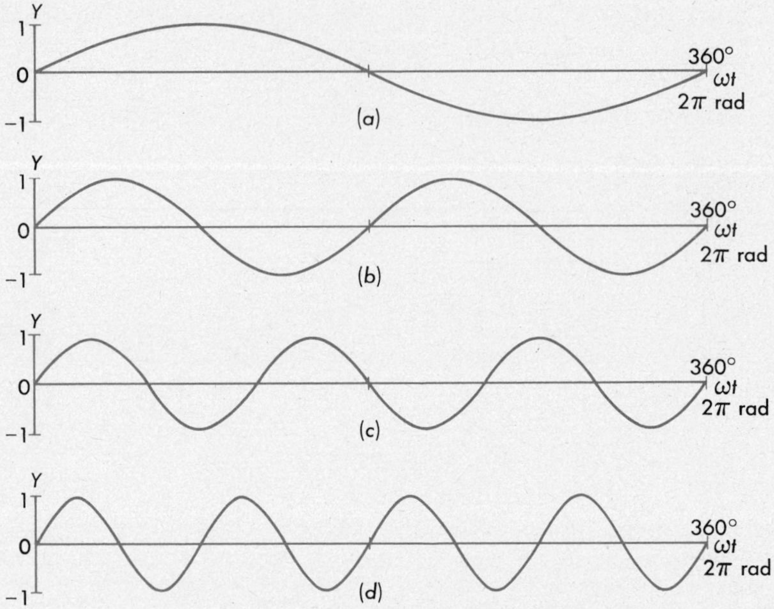

5.

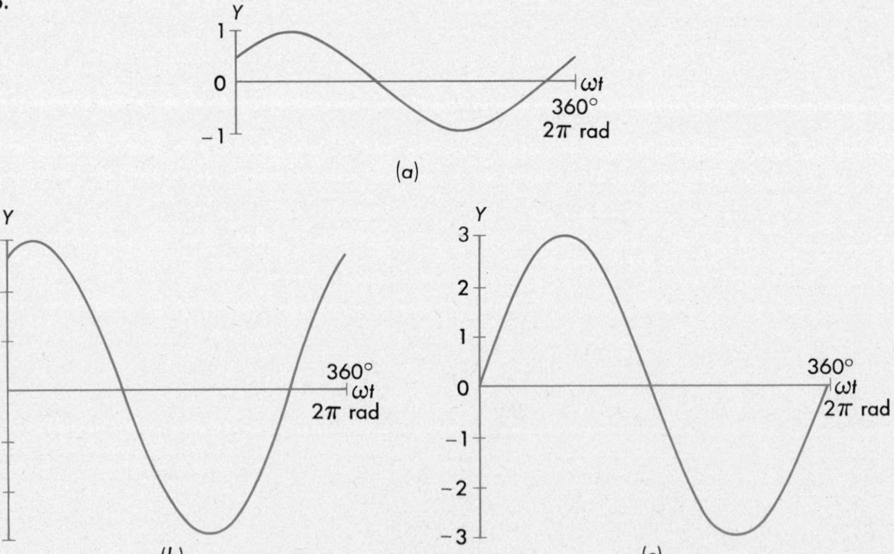

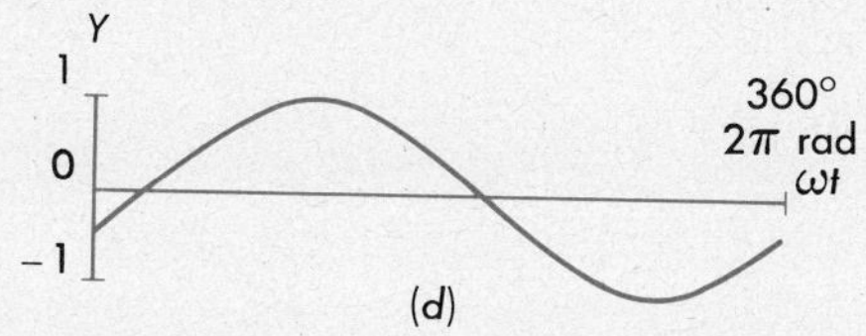

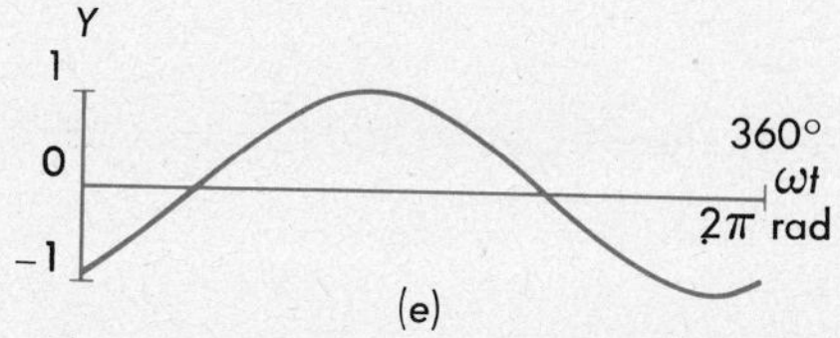

	Amplitude	*Frequency*	*Period*	*rad/s*	*deg/s*	*rad*	*deg*
6a.	23	50	0.02	100π	18,000	$\pi/6$	30
6c.	77	40	0.025	80π	14,400	$2\pi/7$	51.43
6e.	15	6×10^7	1.67×10^{-8}	$1.2\pi \times 10^8$	216×10^8	$-3\pi/5$	-108
6g.	200	1	1.00	2π	360	$-2\pi/5$	-72

7a. $y = 200 \sin (60\pi t - 5\pi/18)$ **7c.** $y = 5 \sin (2\pi \times 10^{12}t + \pi/2)$
7e. $y = 10 \sin (2{,}000\pi t - \pi/4)$ **7g.** $y = 20 \sin 50\pi t$ **7i.** $y = 100 \sin (100\pi t + \pi/2)$

Exercise 4 (*page 469*): **1.** Amplitude = 87; phase angle = +29.35° **3.** Amplitude = 7; phase angle = +34.06° **5.** Amplitude = 12; phase angle = −28.95°

Exercise 5 (*page 470*):

1.

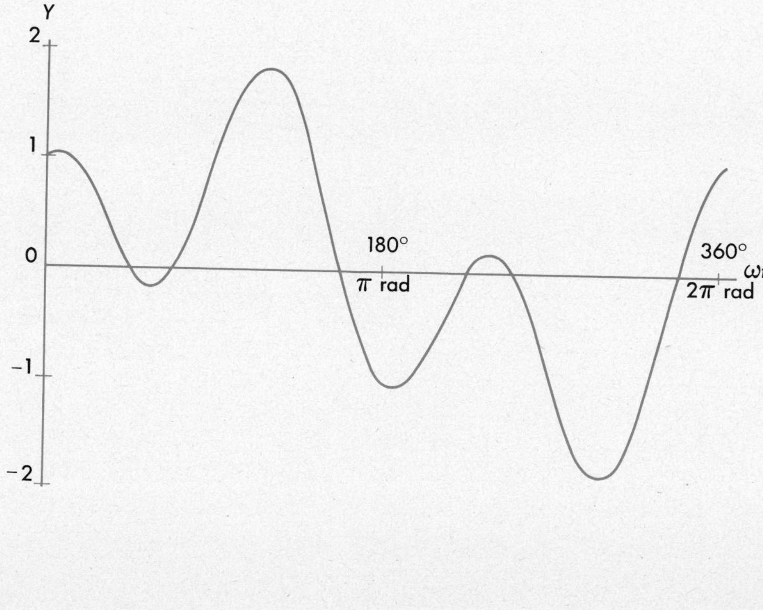

3.

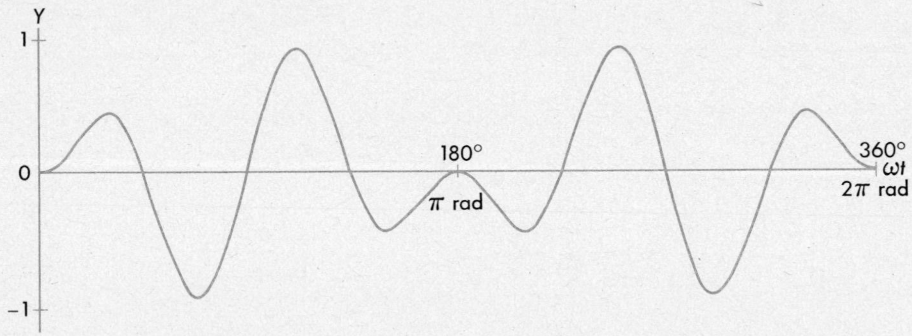

5.

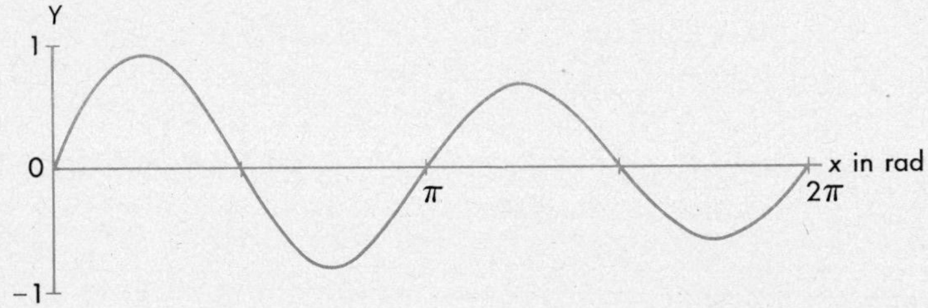

Exercise 6 (*page 475*):

1.

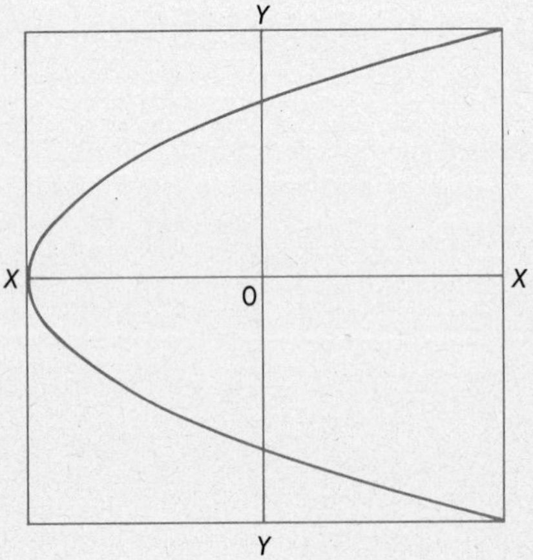

3.

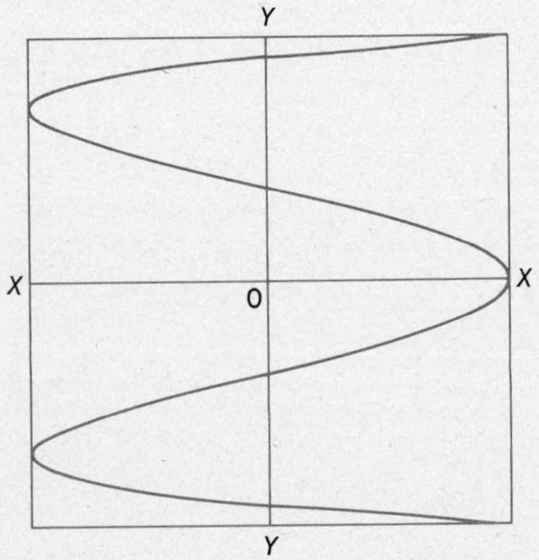

5.

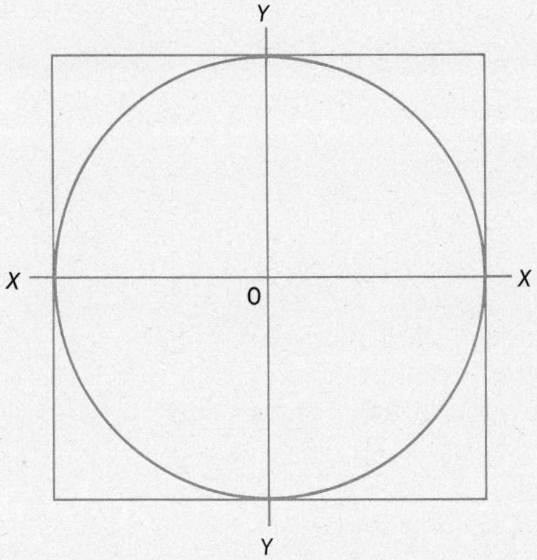

7.

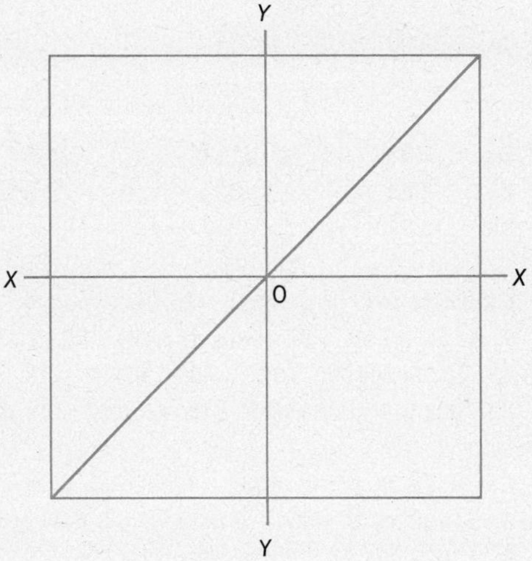

9.

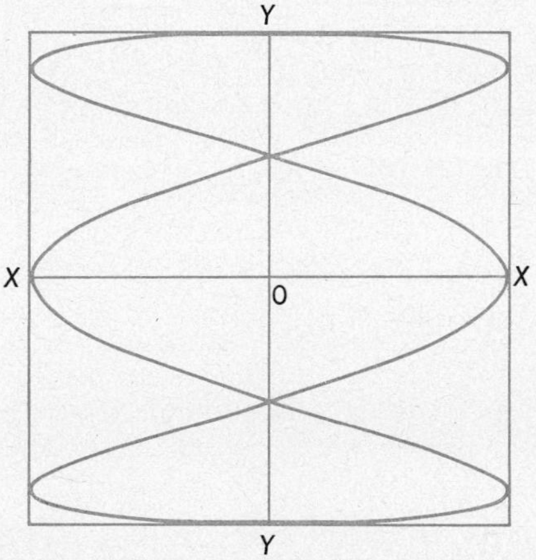

Chapter 17

Exercise 1 (*page 479*): **1a.** $+2.67 + j1.362$ **1c.** $-8.66 + j5.00$ **1e.** $0.00 + j7.00$ **1g.** $+13.12 + j7.27$ **1i.** $-14.14 - j14.14$ **1k.** $-1.532 - j1.286$ **1m.** $0.00 - j3.00$ **1o.** $+4.33 + j2.50$

	Modulus	*Argument*
2a.	5.00	53.1°
2c.	7.62	113.2°
2e.	5.00	306.9°
2g.	5.83	211.0°
2i.	2.83	135°
2k.	2.83	225°

Exercise 2 (*page 482*): **1.** $10.00\underline{/53.13^\circ}$ **3.** $7.21\underline{/33.69^\circ}$ **5.** $5.83\underline{/120.96^\circ}$ **7.** $11.70\underline{/19.98^\circ}$ **9.** $10.63\underline{/131.19^\circ}$ **11.** $8.06\underline{/209.74^\circ}$ **13.** $5.10\underline{/258.69^\circ}$ **15.** $16.55\underline{/244.98^\circ}$ **17.** $15.81\underline{/288.44^\circ}$ **19.** $8.02 + j13.25$ **21.** $10.62 + j24.8$ **23.** $10.13 + j11.84$ **25.** $2.02 + j2.37$ **27.** $37.1 - j17.31$ **29.** $-10.72 - j3.19$

Exercise 3 (*page 483*): **1.** $1 + j8$; $8.06\underline{/82.88^\circ}$ **3.** $-5 + j$; $5.10\underline{/168.69^\circ}$ **5.** $3 + j0$; $3\underline{/0^\circ}$ **7.** $-4.28 + j4.32$; $6.03\underline{/134.71^\circ}$ **9.** $7.59 - j11.75$; $13.99\underline{/302.86^\circ}$

Exercise 5 (*page 491*): **1.** $6(\cos 350^\circ + j \sin 350^\circ)$ **3.** $1{,}250(\cos 0^\circ + j \sin 0^\circ) = 1{,}250$ **5.** $9(\cos 23^\circ + j \sin 23^\circ)$ **7.** $5\underline{/100^\circ}$ **9.** $20\underline{/0^\circ}$ **11.** $1{,}250\underline{/0^\circ}$

Exercise 6 (*page 493*): **1.** $125\underline{/60^\circ}$ **3.** $16\underline{/240^\circ}$ **5.** $625\underline{/0^\circ}$

Exercise 7 (*page 495*): **1.** $2\underline{/10^\circ}$; $2\underline{/130^\circ}$; $2\underline{/250^\circ}$ **3.** $2\underline{/0^\circ}$; $2\underline{/180^\circ}$ **5.** $3\underline{/70^\circ}$; $3\underline{/160^\circ}$; $3\underline{/250^\circ}$; $3\underline{/340^\circ}$

Exercise 8 (*page 498*): **1.** 1; -1 **3.** 1; $(0.309 + j0.951)$; $(-0.809 + j0.588)$; $(-0.809 - j0.588)$; $(0.309 - j0.951)$

Exercise 9 (*page 499*): **1.** 3; $\left(-\frac{3}{2} + j\frac{3\sqrt{3}}{2}\right)$; $\left(-\frac{3}{2} - j\frac{3\sqrt{3}}{2}\right)$ **3.** $\left(\frac{3}{2} + j\frac{3\sqrt{3}}{2}\right)$; $\left(-\frac{3}{2} + j\frac{3\sqrt{3}}{2}\right)$; $(-3 + j0)$; $\left(-\frac{3}{2} - j\frac{3\sqrt{3}}{2}\right)$; $\left(\frac{3}{2} - j\frac{3\sqrt{3}}{2}\right)$; $(3 + j0)$

Exercise 10 (*page 500*):

	Amplitude	*Frequency*	*Period*	*Phase constant*
1.	10	60	0.0167	+60°
3.	10	60	0.0167	+60°
5.	25	400	0.0025	0

Chapter 18

Exercise 1 *(page 504)*: **1.** $-\sin x$ **3.** 1 **5.** 1 **7.** $\cos A$ **9.** $1 - \cos A$ **11.** 1 **13.** $2\cos^2 x$ **15.** $\sin x$ **17.** $\csc M$ **19.** $-\cos x$ **21.** $\cos x$ **23.** $1 + \sin x$ **25.** $\sec^2 \theta$ **27.** $\cot \phi$ **29.** 1 **31.** $\cot x$

Exercise 2 *(page 507)*: All odd-numbered problems are identities except Probs. 7, 23, and 25.

Exercise 3 *(page 513)*: All odd-numbered problems from Prob. 1 through Prob. 25 are identities except Probs. 1, 3, 5, and 11.

29. 0; 0.0025; 0.0446; 0.0797; 0.1048; 0.1348; 0.1680; 0.2056; 0.2500; 0.3048; 0.3779; 0.4866; 0.6882; 1.4626 **31a.** 1.000,076; 1.0174; 1.0713 **33.** $e = 62.91 \sin (120\pi t - 0.124)$ **35.** $e = 100 \sin 4{,}000{,}000t + 35 \sin 4{,}004{,}000t + 35 \sin 3{,}996{,}000t - 15 \sin 4{,}008{,}000t - 15 \sin 3{,}992{,}000t$ **37.** 89.686°

Exercise 4 *(page 522)*: **1.** 45°, 135° **3.** 60°, 300° **5.** 150°, 330° **7.** 0°, 45°, 180°, 225° **9.** 90°, 210°, 270°, 330° **11.** 90°, 210°, 270°, 330° **13.** 0°, 60°, 180°, 240° **15.** 0°, 90°, 270° **17.** 60°, 120° **19.** 0°, 180° **21.** 30°, 150°, 270° **23.** 45°, 225° **25.** No solution **27.** 78.46°, 281.54°

29. 35.25°, 144.75°, 215.25°, 324.75°

31b. $N = 2\cos^{-1}\dfrac{r+a}{r+b}$, $r = \dfrac{[b\cos (N/2)] - a}{1 - \cos (N/2)}$

33. $\theta = 35.43°$ **37.** 0, 0°45′, 7°30′, 22°05′, 32°08′, 40°39′, 48°46′

Chapter 19

Exercise 1 *(page 536)*: **1.** 0.74 **3.** $3\frac{1}{3}$ **5.** -1.14 **7.** $x = 1$, $y = 2.5$ **9.** $\Delta y = +0.0005$ **11.** -0.022

Exercise 2 *(page 540)*: **3a.** 1.00, 0.362, 0, -0.416, -1.00, -0.790, 0, 0.471, 0.961 **3b.** Same as **(a)** **3c.** $\dfrac{dy}{dx} = \cos x$

Exercise 3 *(page 545)*: **1.** 60

Exercise 4 (*page 545*): **1.** 2.8 m/s^2 **3.** 146 km/h **5.** 20 s **7.** 45 s

9.

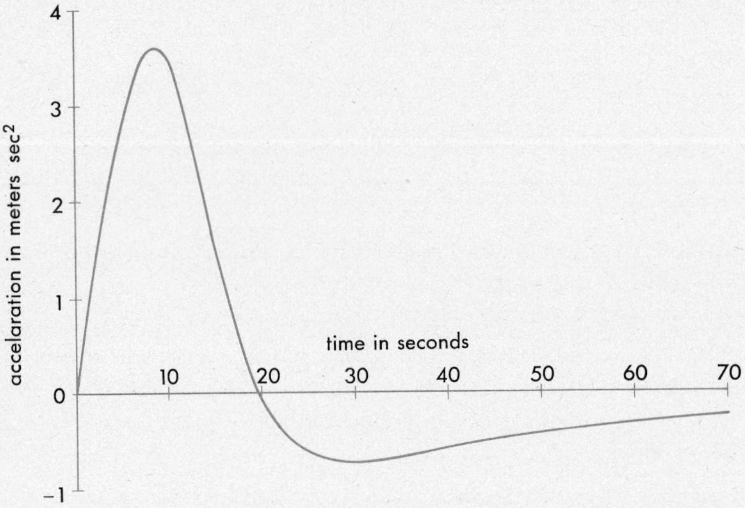

Exercise 5 (*page 546*): **1.** −1.35 deg/min **3.** −2.0 deg/min **5.** 3.5 min **7.** −3.9 deg/min **9.** −3.7 deg/min **11.** −6.0 deg/min **13.** −12.4° **15.** −0.045° **17.** 15.6° **19.** 20.6° **21.** −4.07 deg/min **23.** 0.01 min

25. −10, −8, −6, −4, −2 deg/min. The rate of change of temperature difference is directly proportional to the temperature difference itself.

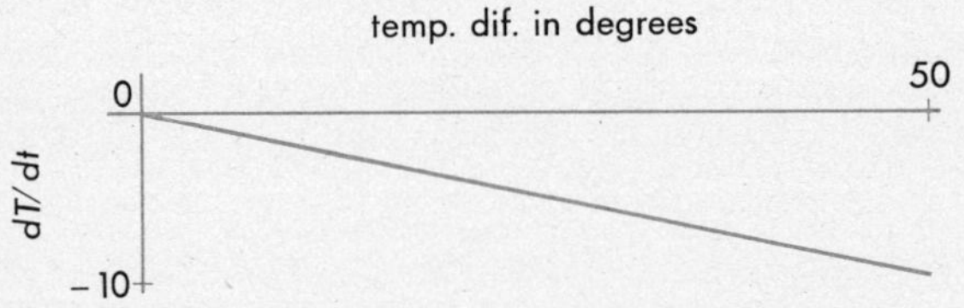

27. 5 min

Exercise 6 (*page 548*): **1.** −⅝ lb/ft **3.** −0.4 lb/ft **5.** −⅔ lb/ft; −⅗ ft/lb **9.** −2.5 lb/ft **11.** −0.0112 lb

Exercise 7 (*page 548*): **1.** 2,040 ft/s^2 **3.** 100.5 ft/s at 0.0625 s **5.** 2 ft

Exercise 8 (*page 549*): **1.** 200, 134, 89.9, 60.2, 40.4, 27.1, and 18.1 A/s **3.** 0.05 s
5.

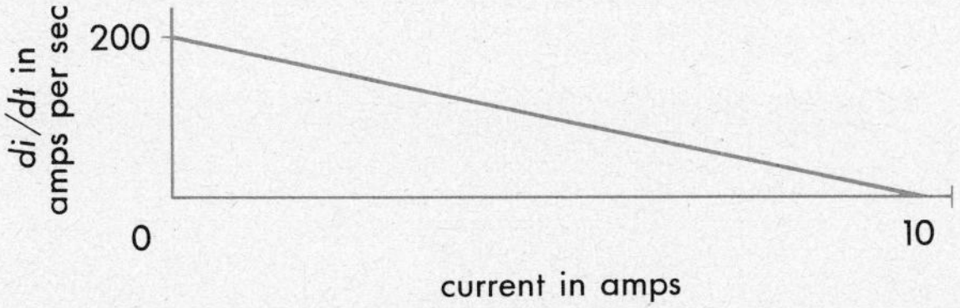

Exercise 9 (*page 551*): **5.** About 19,400 ft total movement **7.** −2,820 ft/s **9.** 437 s **11.** 75 ft/s^2 **13.** 66 s, 4,380 ft/s **15.** 206 s **17a.** 3,270 ft/s **17b.** 3,880 ft/s **17c.** −24 ft/s^2 **17d.** 75 ft/s^2 **17e.** 61,400 ft

Chapter 20

Exercise 1 (*page 556*): **1.** $\Delta y/\Delta x = 15x^2 + 15x(\Delta x) + 5(\Delta x)^2$

3. $\Delta y/\Delta x = 14x + 7(\Delta x)$ **5.** $\dfrac{\Delta w}{\Delta u} = 2u + \Delta u - 3$ **7.** $\dfrac{\Delta w}{\Delta z} = \dfrac{2z^2 + 2z(\Delta z) + 1}{z(z + \Delta z)}$

9. $\dfrac{\Delta w}{\Delta x} = \dfrac{1}{\sqrt{x + \Delta x} + \sqrt{x}}$ **11.** $\Delta V/\Delta R = \frac{4}{3}\pi[3R^2 + 3R(\Delta R) + (\Delta R)^2]$

Exercise 2 (*page 562*): **1.** 0 **3.** −9 **5.** −6 **7.** +2 **9.** No single limit

Exercise 3 (*page 566*):

1.

Number of pamphlets	*Total cost*	*Cost per pamphlet*
10	$10.50	$1.05
100	$15.00	$0.15
1,000	$60.00	$0.06
10,000	$510.00	$0.051
100,000	$5,010.00	$0.0501
1,000,000	$50,010.00	$0.05001

1c. $0.05 **3.** $15x^2$ **5.** $3x^2 - 2$ **7.** $-3/u^2$ **9.** $3/(t + 3)^2$

Exercise 4 (*page 574*): **1.** $y' = 6x$ **3.** $y' = 90x^8$ **5.** $y' = -6/x^3$ **7.** $y' = 8\sqrt[3]{x^2}/x$ **9.** $y' = -14/x^2$ **11.** $y' = 3\sqrt{x}/x$ **13.** $y' = 4\sqrt{x}/x^2$ **15.** $y' = 2.5\sqrt[4]{x}/x$ **17.** $y' = (4a/b)x^3$ **19.** $y' = -3\sqrt[4]{x}/(2x^2)$ **21.** $y' = -3\sqrt[4]{x}/(2\sqrt[4]{7}x^2)$ **23.** $y' = 0$ **25.** $y' = -2/\sqrt{x^3}$ **27.** −3.6 lb/ft **29.** −2.5 lb/ft **31.** $2\sqrt{5}$ lb

Exercise 5 (*page 581*): **1.** $2ax + b$ **3.** $12x - 13$ **5.** $(15x - 4)/(6x^3)$ **7.** $(n - 1)/(n\sqrt[n]{x})$ **9.** $-12/x^5$ **11.** $-104/x^5$ **13.** $-3k/x^4$ **15.** $15x^4$ **17.** $2\pi x$ **19.** $(3e - 2\pi x)/x^4$ **21.** 16 ft-lb/s **23.** 10.6 ft **25.** $a = 4$; $b = -2$

Exercise 6 (*page 585*): **1.** $8(3x + 1)(3x^2 + 2x + 5)^3$ **3.** $\dfrac{3 - 10x}{3(3x - 5x^2)^{2/3}}$

5. $\dfrac{-7t}{2(6 - 7t^2)^{3/4}}$ **7.** $\dfrac{-3t}{(1 - t^2)^{7/4}}$ **9.** $\dfrac{\sqrt{2}}{2t^{1/2}} + \dfrac{2}{3t^{2/3}}$ **11.** $\dfrac{8y}{3\sqrt[3]{1 + y^2}}$ **13.** $\dfrac{12x^2}{(1 - x^3)^2}$

15. $\dfrac{4t^2(3 - t^2)}{(5t^3 - t^5)^{4/5}}$ **17.** $\dfrac{dy}{dx} = -\dfrac{10}{(x + 3)^2}, -\dfrac{10}{9} = -1.1$

Exercise 7 (*page 590*): **1.** $\dfrac{2x^2 + 3}{\sqrt{3 + x^2}}$ **3.** $(x + 5)(3x^3 - 7)^2(33x^3 + 135x^2 - 14)$

5. $-\dfrac{14(x + 5)}{(x - 2)^3}$ **7.** $-\dfrac{2x^4 + x^2 + 5}{x^2(2x^2 + 5)^2}$ **9.** $-\dfrac{18}{(4x^2 - 9)^{3/2}}$

Exercise 8 (*page 600*): **1.** $x = -4$ (max); $x = +1$ (min) **3.** $x = 3$ (min); $x = -3$ (max) **5.** $x = -2$ (min) **7.** $x = 3/2$ (max); $x = -3/2$ (max) **11.** 5 in **13.** $d = [5B/(2A)]^{1/7}$ **15c2.** 949 articles/day **17.** $5/3$ by $5/3$ in **19.** 3 checks; 80 cents **21.** 38.65 ft **23.** $r = 3.325$ in; $h = 6.651$ in **25.** 1 to 1 **27.** 125′ **29.** $p_2/p_1 = [2/(k + 1)]^{k/(k-1)}$; 0.528 **31.** 7.16 ft

Exercise 9 (*page 611*): **1.** $4x^3 \cos x^4$ **3.** $4 \sin^3 x \cos x$ **5.** $-\frac{9}{2}\phi^{-1/4} \cos \phi^{3/4}$ **7.** $25 \cos x/(2\sqrt{\sin x})$ **9.** $-(\sqrt{3}/3)\phi^{-2/3} \sin \sqrt[3]{\phi}$ **11.** $(6/\phi^2) \sin (2/\phi)$

13. $-(1 + 1/x^2) \sin (x - 1/x)$ **15.** $4 \tan^3 x \sec^2 x$ **17.** $\left(1 - \dfrac{1}{x^2}\right) \sec^2 \left(x + \dfrac{1}{x}\right)$

19. $-\dfrac{\csc^2 \sqrt{\theta}}{2\sqrt{\theta}}$ **21.** $\dfrac{25 \sin x \sqrt{\cos x}}{2 \cos^2 x}$ **23.** $\dfrac{3 \sin \sqrt{x}}{2\sqrt{x} \cos^2 \sqrt{x}}$

25. $-\dfrac{12 \cos (3\phi + 2)}{\sin^2 (3\phi + 2)}$ **27.** 19.6 lb

29a. The equation has physical meaning only between $t = 0$ and $t = 1/8$ s.
29b. One revolution takes $1/8$ s.

Exercise 10 (*page 616*): **1.** $\dfrac{3}{\sqrt{9 - x^2}}$ **3.** $-\dfrac{5x^4}{\sqrt{1 - x^{10}}}$ **5.** $\dfrac{2}{\sqrt{16y - 15 - 4y^2}}$

Exercise 11 (*page 618*): **1.** $1/x$ **3.** $5/x$ **5.** $3/x$ **7.** $150/x$

Exercise 12 (*page 620*): **1.** $\dfrac{2x}{x^2 + 2}$ **3.** $\dfrac{8x}{x^2 + 3}$ **5.** $\dfrac{1}{3x - 4}$ **7.** $\dfrac{0.8686x}{x^2 - 4}$ **9.** $\dfrac{0.4343x}{9 - x^2}$

11. $\dfrac{0.8686}{2x - 3}$ **13.** $\dfrac{6x^2}{x^3 - 8} \ln (x^3 - 8)$ **15.** $0.4343 \cot (\theta + \pi)$

Exercise 13 (*page 623*): **1.** $10xe^{5x^2}$ **3.** e^{x+8} **5.** $-e^{\sqrt{1-x}}/(2\sqrt{1-x})$
7a. -1.35 deg/min **7c.** -2.0 deg/min **7e.** 3.47 min **7g.** -3.9 deg/min
7i. -3.64 deg/min **7k.** -6 deg/min **9a.** 200 A/s **9c.** 0.05 s

Exercise 14 (*page 629*): **1.** $a^x \ln a$ **3.** $\frac{2^{\sqrt{x}-1}}{\sqrt{x}} \ln 2$ **11.** $x \cdot 3^x(2 + x \ln 3)$

15. $-\frac{2(x^3 + 1)}{(x^2 - 2)^2}$ **17.** $\frac{x^2(9 - 2x^5)}{(x^5 + 3)^2}$ **19.** $\frac{e^x(3 + x)}{(4 + x)^2}$ **21.** $\frac{e^{2x}(1 + 4x)}{2\sqrt{x}}$

23. $x^{\sin x}\left(\frac{\sin x}{x} + \ln x \cos x\right)$

Exercise 15 (*page 629*): **1.** $e^x(\cos 2x - 2 \sin 2x)$ **3.** $3 \cos 6\theta$ **5.** $\ln x - 2x + 1$
7. $6(2 \sin 2\phi \sec^2 4\phi + \cos 2\phi \tan 4\phi)$ **9.** $10e^{3x^2} \tan x(3x \tan x + \sec^2 x)$

11. $21x^2\sqrt{2x^3 + 3x} \sin (14x^3 + 10) + \frac{3(2x^2 + 1) \sin^2 (7x^3 + 5)}{2\sqrt{2x^3 + 3x}}$

13. $-3e^{2x}\left(\frac{1}{x} + 2 \ln x\right)$ **15.** $-\frac{\sqrt{x} \sin \sqrt{x} + \cos \sqrt{x}}{2x\sqrt{x}}$ **17.** $\frac{\cos x - 2 \sin x}{e^{2x}}$

19. $\frac{1}{(x^2 - 9)^{3/2}}$ **21.** $\frac{(2x + 3) \ln x^2 - (2x + 6)}{\ln^2 x^2}$ **23.** $\frac{x \sin 8x - 8x^2 - 24}{2\sqrt{x^2 + 3}\,(\sin^2 4x)}$

25. $\frac{-9(3x - 6) \ln (3x - 6) \sin 3x - 9 \cos 3x}{(3x - 6) \ln^2 (3x - 6)}$ **27.** $\frac{20 - 100x}{(x + 0.2)^3}$

29. $\frac{AC - ABx^2}{(Ax + C + Bx^2)^2}$ **31.** $-\frac{5x^2 + 8x - 80}{(x + 0.8)^2}$

Exercise 16 (*page 630*): **1.** $\cot x$ **3.** $15 (\sin^2 5x)(\cos 5x)$ **5.** $\frac{1}{x^2(a + bx)}$

7. $\frac{x^3}{(x^2 + a^2)^{3/2}}$ **9.** $-\frac{2(x^3 + 2)}{(x^3 - 4)^2}$ **11.** $e^{-2x}(\cos x - 2 \sin x) + 2e^{2x}$ **13.** $-\frac{4}{(e^x - e^{-x})^2}$

15. $-\frac{10}{(1 - x)^3}$ **17.** $\frac{1}{x^2\sqrt{x^2 - 1}}$ **19.** $\sqrt{x^2 + a^2}$ **21.** $(16 - x^2)^{-3/2}$ **23.** $\frac{1}{x\sqrt{8x - 2x^2}}$

25. $\cos^2 x$ **27.** $x \sin^2 x$ **29.** $\tan^2 x$ **31.** $x \cos x$

Exercise 17 (*page 632*): **1.** 0.4; (−); decreasing **3.** 4; (−); decreasing
5. 2.5; (−); decreasing **7.** 4 (max); 1.45 (min); 6.1 (min) **9.** None (max); 3.85 (min)

Exercise 18 *(page 637)*:

	Max at:	Min at:	Point of inflection at:	Slope of primary curve at inflection point
1.	none	none	none	none
3.	$x = 0$	$x = +4$	$x = +2$	-12
5.	none	$x = 0.434$	none	none
7.	none	none	$x = +\sqrt[4]{3}$	$+3.51$
			$x = -\sqrt[4]{3}$	-3.51
9.	$x = 0$	$x = \pi/2$	$x = \pi/4$	-2
	$x = \pi$		$x = 3\pi/4$	$+2$
11.	$\theta = \pi/2$	$\theta = 0$	$\theta = \pi/4$	$+3/4$
	$\theta = 3\pi/2$	$\theta = \pi$	$\theta = 3\pi/4$	$-3/4$
		$\theta = 2\pi$	$\theta = 5\pi/4$	$+3/4$
			$\theta = 7\pi/4$	$-3/4$
13.	none	none	none	none
15.	none	$x = 1$	none	none
17.	$x = 1.47$ rad	$x = 4.61$ rad	2.94 rad	-0.75
			6.08 rad	$+0.52$

Exercise 19 *(page 638)*: **1.** $v = 72 - 32t$; $a = -32$ **3.** $t = 4$ s **5.** $t = 5.26$ in; $s = 8.51$ in **7.** 8.49 by 16.98 ft **9.** $V = wL/2 - wx$ **11.** 7.07 ft **13.** $\eta = E/(E + 2\sqrt{P_0 R})$ when $P_0 = I^2R$ **15.** 4.33 in **17.** 66° approx

19d.

ωt	dx/dt exact	dx/dt approx	d^2x/dt^2 exact	d^2x/dt^2 approx
0	0	0	0.30	0.30
$\pi/4$	0.40406	0.40355	0.17730	0.17678
$\pi/2$	0.5	0.5	-0.0510	-0.0500
π	0	0	-0.20	-0.20

19e. Max force $= 0.30m$

Exercise 20 *(page 647)*: **3.** $\dfrac{dy}{dx} = -\dfrac{5x}{3y}$ **5.** $\dfrac{dy}{dx} = \dfrac{15}{2y}$

7. $\dfrac{dy}{dx} = \dfrac{3x^2}{1 - 6y}$ **9.** $\dfrac{x^4(1 - y^5)}{y^4(x^5 - 1)}$

Exercise 21 (*page 648*): **1.** $-6\frac{2}{3}$ ft/min **3.** -4.734 ft/s **5.** $dy/dt = -x$
7. $2.4kD^2$ **9.** -12.7 lb/ft^2-s

Exercise 22 (*page 650*): **1.** 0.068″ **3.** 3.02 in^3 **7.** $dQ = 0.1b + 60c$ **11.** 0.056 Ω
13. 0.263″

Exercise 23 (*page 655*): **1.** $\dfrac{dx}{x^2\sqrt{1 - 9/x^2}}$ **3.** $\sqrt{a + bx}\,dx$ **5.** $\dfrac{x\,dx}{(a + bx)^3}$

7. $\dfrac{dx}{x^3\sqrt{x^2 - a^2}}$ **9a.** $dv = \dfrac{bv^3 - v^4}{pv^3 - av + ab}\,dp$

Chapter 21

Exercise 1 (*page 660*): **9.** $x^4/4 - 2x^3 + 250x^2 + 7x + C$ **11.** $\frac{5}{9}x^{3/2} + C$
13. $x^3 + x\sqrt{2} + C$ **15.** $-\frac{1}{4}x^{-4} + C$ **17.** $\pi x + \frac{7}{4}x^{12/7} + C$ **19.** $x^2 + C$
21. $\frac{1}{2}x^2 + C$ **23.** $-2x + C$ **25.** $\frac{3}{4}x^{4/3} + C$ **27.** $6\sqrt{x} + C$

Exercise 2 (*page 665*): **1.** $y = x^2 + 4$ **3.** $y = \frac{1}{2}x^2 + 12$ **5.** $y = -2x + 28$
7. $y = \frac{3}{4}x^{4/3} + 15.24$ **9.** $y = 6\sqrt{x} + 8$ **11.** -0.49″ **13.** The total energy is constant.

Exercise 3 (*page 668*): **1.** $-\frac{1}{5}(3 - t)^5 + C$ **3.** $-\frac{2}{3}(4 - m)^{3/2} + C$
5. $-\frac{1}{24}(3 - t^4)^6 + C$ **7.** $\sqrt{t^2 + 2t} + C$ **9.** $\frac{3}{4}(4x^2 - 9)^{5/2} + C$

Exercise 4 (*page 671*): **1.** 200 s **3.** -51.6 ft/s^2; 1.70 s **5.** $s = 0.008t^3 - 0.4t^2 + 10t$

Exercise 5 (*page 680*): **1.** $h = -16t^2 + h_0$; $v = -32t$ **3.** $h = -16t^2 + 100t + 192$;
$v = -32t + 100$ **5.** -149.6 in both cases **7.** 8 s

Exercise 6 (*page 692*): **1.** 78 **3.** 36 **5.** 7.5 **7.** $65\frac{1}{3}$ **9.** $b = 10.7$

Exercise 7 (*page 697*): **1.** $\bar{y} = 13$ **3.** $\bar{y} = 6$ **5.** $\bar{y} = 2.5$

Exercise 8 (*page 708*): **1.** $\frac{1}{3}$ **3.** 8 **5.** $20\frac{5}{6}$ **7.** $20\frac{5}{6}$ **9.** $41\frac{2}{3}$

Exercise 9 (*page 719*): **1.** $32{,}000\pi/3$ in^3 **3.** 20.8 in^3 **5.** $5{,}333\frac{1}{3}$ in^3 **7.** 2,044 in^3

Exercise 10 (*page 722*): **1.** 625π **3.** 500π **5.** 48π

Exercise 11 (*page 726*): **1.** 108 in-lb **3.** 96 in-lb **5.** 1.64 ft-lb **7.** 43,750 ft-lb
9. $450{,}000\pi$ ft-lb **11.** $54{,}000\pi$ ft-lb **15.** 186,500 ft-lb

Exercise 12 *(page 730)*: **1.** 1,302 lb **3.** 41,250 lb; 11 ft higher

Exercise 13 *(page 731)*: **1.** 8.72 ft-lb **3c.** $Q = 2E\left(\frac{CT}{\pi R}\right)^{1/2}$; $W = EQ$

5. $A = 0.000187t^2 + 0.251t + 182$ **7.** 1,750 cal; 1,591 cal

Exercise 14 *(page 735)*: **1.** 1.386 **3.** 3.128 **5.** 1.160 **7.** 1.086 **9.** 10.4
11. 3,550 ft-lb **13.** 2,330 ft-lb **15.** 13.5 ft/s; 4,733 ft

Exercise 15 *(page 739)*: **1.** $2 \sin 2\theta + C$ **3.** $\frac{1}{2} \sin x^2 + C$ **5.** $-\sin(4 - x) + C$

Exercise 16 *(page 742)*: **1a.** 0.268; 1.023 **1c.** 0.1038; 0.346 **1e.** 0.841; 0.841

1g. 1; 0.955 **3.** 216.5 W **5.** $\frac{2}{\pi}\left(I_1 + \frac{I_3}{3} + \frac{I_5}{5} + \cdots + \frac{I_k}{k}\right)$;

$0.707(I_1^2 + I_3^2 + I_5^2 + \cdots + I_k^2)^{1/2}$ **7.** $\bar{P} = 0.5(E_1 I_1 + E_3 I_3 + E_5 I_5 + \cdots + E_k I_k)$

9. $\frac{EI\pi^4 y_0^2}{64L^3}$

Exercise 17 *(page 747)*: **1.** $-\frac{1}{4}e^{1-4x} + C$ **3.** $\frac{e^{\pi x}}{\pi} + C$ **5.** $-\frac{e^{1/x}}{5} + C$

7. $\frac{e^{3x+1}}{3} + C$ **9.** $\frac{e^{2x}}{2} + 2e^{-x} - \frac{e^{-4x}}{4} + C$ **11.** $\frac{e^{6x}}{6} - \frac{2e^{3x-1}}{3} + \frac{x}{e^2} + C$

13. $\frac{e^{4x}}{4} - \frac{4e^{5x/2}}{5} + e^x + C$ **15.** $\frac{y_{n0} - Y_{n-1}}{EL}(e^{EL} - 1) + Y_{n-1}$

17. $\theta(x) = 0.819e^{-14.627x} + 0.106e^{-82.22x} + 0.0190e^{-212x} + 0.0559$ **19.** 17.1°

Exercise 18 *(page 760)*: **1.** 88.86 **3.** 0.03475 **5.** 9.620 **7.** 1.047 **9.** 4,981 **11.** 1.822
13. 42.30 **15.** 0.6467 **17.** 221.6 **19.** 0.5592 **21.** 88.86 **23.** 6.359; 5.823; 6.043
25. 3,822.9 lb

0° (180°) (359°) 179°

′	Sin	Tan	Ctn	Cos	Sec	Csc	′
0	.00000	.00000	———	1.0000	1.0000	———	60
1	.00029	.00029	3437.7	1.0000	1.0000	3437.7	59
2	.00058	.00058	1718.9	1.0000	1.0000	1718.9	58
3	.00087	.00087	1145.9	1.0000	1.0000	1145.9	57
4	.00116	.00116	859.44	1.0000	1.0000	859.44	56
5	.00145	.00145	687.55	1.0000	1.0000	687.55	55
6	.00175	.00175	572.96	1.0000	1.0000	572.96	54
7	.00204	.00204	491.11	1.0000	1.0000	491.11	53
8	.00233	.00233	429.72	1.0000	1.0000	429.72	52
9	.00262	.00262	381.97	1.0000	1.0000	381.97	51
10	.00291	.00291	343.77	1.0000	1.0000	343.78	50
11	.00320	.00320	312.52	.99999	1.0000	312.52	49
12	.00349	.00349	286.48	.99999	1.0000	286.48	48
13	.00378	.00378	264.44	.99999	1.0000	264.44	47
14	.00407	.00407	245.55	.99999	1.0000	245.55	46
15	.00436	.00436	229.18	.99999	1.0000	229.18	45
16	.00465	.00465	214.86	.99999	1.0000	214.86	44
17	.00495	.00495	202.22	.99999	1.0000	202.22	43
18	.00524	.00524	190.98	.99999	1.0000	190.99	42
19	.00553	.00553	180.93	.99998	1.0000	180.93	41
20	.00582	.00582	171.89	.99998	1.0000	171.89	40
21	.00611	.00611	163.70	.99998	1.0000	163.70	39
22	.00640	.00640	156.26	.99998	1.0000	156.26	38
23	.00669	.00669	149.47	.99998	1.0000	149.47	37
24	.00698	.00698	143.24	.99998	1.0000	143.24	36
25	.00727	.00727	137.51	.99997	1.0000	137.51	35
26	.00756	.00756	132.22	.99997	1.0000	132.22	34
27	.00785	.00785	127.32	.99997	1.0000	127.33	33
28	.00814	.00815	122.77	.99997	1.0000	122.78	32
29	.00844	.00844	118.54	.99996	1.0000	118.54	31
30	.00873	.00873	114.59	.99996	1.0000	114.59	30
31	.00902	.00902	110.89	.99996	1.0000	110.90	29
32	.00931	.00931	107.43	.99996	1.0000	107.43	28
33	.00960	.00960	104.17	.99995	1.0000	104.18	27
34	.00989	.00989	101.11	.99995	1.0000	101.11	26
35	.01018	.01018	98.218	.99995	1.0001	98.223	25
36	.01047	.01047	95.489	.99995	1.0001	95.495	24
37	.01076	.01076	92.908	.99994	1.0001	92.914	23
38	.01105	.01105	90.463	.99994	1.0001	90.469	22
39	.01134	.01135	88.144	.99994	1.0001	88.149	21
40	.01164	.01164	85.940	.99993	1.0001	85.946	20
41	.01193	.01193	83.844	.99993	1.0001	83.849	19
42	.01222	.01222	81.847	.99993	1.0001	81.853	18
43	.01251	.01251	79.943	.99992	1.0001	79.950	17
44	.01280	.01280	78.126	.99992	1.0001	78.133	16
45	.01309	.01309	76.390	.99991	1.0001	76.397	15
46	.01338	.01338	74.729	.99991	1.0001	74.736	14
47	.01367	.01367	73.139	.99991	1.0001	73.146	13
48	.01396	.01396	71.615	.99990	1.0001	71.622	12
49	.01425	.01425	70.153	.99990	1.0001	70.160	11
50	.01454	.01455	68.750	.99989	1.0001	68.757	10
51	.01483	.01484	67.402	.99989	1.0001	67.409	9
52	.01513	.01513	66.105	.99989	1.0001	66.113	8
53	.01542	.01542	64.858	.99988	1.0001	64.866	7
54	.01571	.01571	63.657	.99988	1.0001	63.665	6
55	.01600	.01600	62.499	.99987	1.0001	62.507	5
56	.01629	.01629	61.383	.99987	1.0001	61.391	4
57	.01658	.01658	60.306	.99986	1.0001	60.314	3
58	.01687	.01687	59.266	.99986	1.0001	59.274	2
59	.01716	.01716	58.261	.99985	1.0001	58.270	1
60	.01745	.01746	57.290	.99985	1.0002	57.299	0
′	Cos	Ctn	Tan	Sin	Csc	Sec	′

90° (270°) (269°) 89°

1° (181°) (358°) **178°**

′	Sin	Tan	Ctn	Cos	Sec	Csc	′
0	.01745	.01746	57.290	.99985	1.0002	57.299	60
1	.01774	.01775	56.351	.99984	1.0002	56.359	59
2	.01803	.01804	55.442	.99984	1.0002	55.451	58
3	.01832	.01833	54.561	.99983	1.0002	54.570	57
4	.01862	.01862	53.709	.99983	1.0002	53.718	56
5	.01891	.01891	52.882	.99982	1.0002	52.892	55
6	.01920	.01920	52.081	.99982	1.0002	52.090	54
7	.01949	.01949	51.303	.99981	1.0002	51.313	53
8	.01978	.01978	50.549	.99980	1.0002	50.558	52
9	.02007	.02007	49.816	.99980	1.0002	49.826	51
10	.02036	.02036	49.104	.99979	1.0002	49.114	50
11	.02065	.02066	48.412	.99979	1.0002	48.422	49
12	.02094	.02095	47.740	.99978	1.0002	47.750	48
13	.02123	.02124	47.085	.99977	1.0002	47.096	47
14	.02152	.02153	46.449	.99977	1.0002	46.460	46
15	.02181	.02182	45.829	.99976	1.0002	45.840	45
16	.02211	.02211	45.226	.99976	1.0002	45.237	44
17	.02240	.02240	44.639	.99975	1.0003	44.650	43
18	.02269	.02269	44.066	.99974	1.0003	44.077	42
19	.02298	.02298	43.508	.99974	1.0003	43.520	41
20	.02327	.02328	42.964	.99973	1.0003	42.976	40
21	.02356	.02357	42.433	.99972	1.0003	42.445	39
22	.02385	.02386	41.916	.99972	1.0003	41.928	38
23	.02414	.02415	41.411	.99971	1.0003	41.423	37
24	.02443	.02444	40.917	.99970	1.0003	40.930	36
25	.02472	.02473	40.436	.99969	1.0003	40.448	35
26	.02501	.02502	39.965	.99969	1.0003	39.978	34
27	.02530	.02531	39.506	.99968	1.0003	39.519	33
28	.02560	.02560	39.057	.99967	1.0003	39.070	32
29	.02589	.02589	38.618	.99966	1.0003	38.631	31
30	.02618	.02619	38.188	.99966	1.0003	38.202	30
31	.02647	.02648	37.769	.99965	1.0004	37.782	29
32	.02676	.02677	37.358	.99964	1.0004	37.371	28
33	.02705	.02706	36.956	.99963	1.0004	36.970	27
34	.02734	.02735	36.563	.99963	1.0004	36.576	26
35	.02763	.02764	36.178	.99962	1.0004	36.191	25
36	.02792	.02793	35.801	.99961	1.0004	35.815	24
37	.02821	.02822	35.431	.99960	1.0004	35.445	23
38	.02850	.02851	35.070	.99959	1.0004	35.084	22
39	.02879	.02881	34.715	.99959	1.0004	34.730	21
40	.02908	.02910	34.368	.99958	1.0004	34.382	20
41	.02938	.02939	34.027	.99957	1.0004	34.042	19
42	.02967	.02968	33.694	.99956	1.0004	33.708	18
43	.02996	.02997	33.366	.99955	1.0004	33.381	17
44	.03025	.03026	33.045	.99954	1.0005	33.060	16
45	.03054	.03055	32.730	.99953	1.0005	32.746	15
46	.03083	.03084	32.421	.99952	1.0005	32.437	14
47	.03112	.03114	32.118	.99952	1.0005	32.134	13
48	.03141	.03143	31.821	.99951	1.0005	31.836	12
49	.03170	.03172	31.528	.99950	1.0005	31.544	11
50	.03199	.03201	31.242	.99949	1.0005	31.258	10
51	.03228	.03230	30.960	.99948	1.0005	30.976	9
52	.03257	.03259	30.683	.99947	1.0005	30.700	8
53	.03286	.03288	30.412	.99946	1.0005	30.428	7
54	.03316	.03317	30.145	.99945	1.0006	30.161	6
55	.03345	.03346	29.882	.99944	1.0006	29.899	5
56	.03374	.03376	29.624	.99943	1.0006	29.641	4
57	.03403	.03405	29.371	.99942	1.0006	29.388	3
58	.03432	.03434	29.122	.99941	1.0006	29.139	2
59	.03461	.03463	28.877	.99940	1.0006	28.894	1
60	.03490	.03492	28.636	.99939	1.0006	28.654	0
′	Cos	Ctn	Tan	Sin	Csc	Sec	′

91° (271°) (268°) **88°**

*From Richard Stevens Burington, "Handbook of Mathematical Tables and Formulas," 4th ed., McGraw-Hill Book Company, New York, 1965. For degrees indicated at top (bottom) of page use column headings at top (bottom). With degrees at left (right) of each block (top or bottom), use minute column at left (right).

2° (182°) | **(357°) 177°**

′	Sin	Tan	Ctn	Cos	Sec	Csc	′
0	.03490	.03492	28.636	.99939	1.0006	28.654	60
1	.03519	.03521	28.399	.99938	1.0006	28.417	59
2	.03548	.03550	28.166	.99937	1.0006	28.184	58
3	.03577	.03579	27.937	.99936	1.0006	27.955	57
4	.03606	.03609	27.712	.99935	1.0007	27.730	56
5	.03635	.03638	27.490	.99934	1.0007	27.508	55
6	.03664	.03667	27.271	.99933	1.0007	27.290	54
7	.03693	.03696	27.057	.99932	1.0007	27.075	53
8	.03723	.03725	26.845	.99931	1.0007	26.864	52
9	.03752	.03754	26.637	.99930	1.0007	26.655	51
10	.03781	.03783	26.432	.99929	1.0007	26.451	50
11	.03810	.03812	26.230	.99927	1.0007	26.249	49
12	.03839	.03842	26.031	.99926	1.0007	26.050	48
13	.03868	.03871	25.835	.99925	1.0007	25.854	47
14	.03897	.03900	25.642	.99924	1.0008	25.661	46
15	.03926	.03929	25.452	.99923	1.0008	25.471	45
16	.03955	.03958	25.264	.99922	1.0008	25.284	44
17	.03984	.03987	25.080	.99921	1.0008	25.100	43
18	.04013	.04016	24.898	.99919	1.0008	24.918	42
19	.04042	.04046	24.719	.99918	1.0008	24.739	41
20	.04071	.04075	24.542	.99917	1.0008	24.562	40
21	.04100	.04104	24.368	.99916	1.0008	24.388	39
22	.04129	.04133	24.196	.99915	1.0009	24.216	38
23	.04159	.04162	24.026	.99913	1.0009	24.047	37
24	.04188	.04191	23.859	.99912	1.0009	23.880	36
25	.04217	.04220	23.695	.99911	1.0009	23.716	35
26	.04246	.04250	23.532	.99910	1.0009	23.553	34
27	.04275	.04279	23.372	.99909	1.0009	23.393	33
28	.04304	.04308	23.214	.99907	1.0009	23.235	32
29	.04333	.04337	23.058	.99906	1.0009	23.079	31
30	.04362	.04366	22.904	.99905	1.0010	22.926	30
31	.04391	.04395	22.752	.99904	1.0010	22.774	29
32	.04420	.04424	22.602	.99902	1.0010	22.624	28
33	.04449	.04454	22.454	.99901	1.0010	22.476	27
34	.04478	.04483	22.308	.99900	1.0010	22.330	26
35	.04507	.04512	22.164	.99898	1.0010	22.187	25
36	.04536	.04541	22.022	.99897	1.0010	22.044	24
37	.04565	.04570	21.881	.99896	1.0010	21.904	23
38	.04594	.04599	21.743	.99894	1.0011	21.766	22
39	.04623	.04628	21.606	.99893	1.0011	21.629	21
40	.04653	.04658	21.470	.99892	1.0011	21.494	20
41	.04682	.04687	21.337	.99890	1.0011	21.360	19
42	.04711	.04716	21.205	.99889	1.0011	21.229	18
43	.04740	.04745	21.075	.99888	1.0011	21.098	17
44	.04769	.04774	20.946	.99886	1.0011	20.970	16
45	.04798	.04803	20.819	.99885	1.0012	20.843	15
46	.04827	.04833	20.693	.99883	1.0012	20.717	14
47	.04856	.04862	20.569	.99882	1.0012	20.593	13
48	.04885	.04891	20.446	.99881	1.0012	20.471	12
49	.04914	.04920	20.325	.99879	1.0012	20.350	11
50	.04943	.04949	20.206	.99878	1.0012	20.230	10
51	.04972	.04978	20.087	.99876	1.0012	20.112	9
52	.05001	.05007	19.970	.99875	1.0013	19.995	8
53	.05030	.05037	19.855	.99873	1.0013	19.880	7
54	.05059	.05066	19.740	.99872	1.0013	19.766	6
55	.05088	.05095	19.627	.99870	1.0013	19.653	5
56	.05117	.05124	19.516	.99869	1.0013	19.541	4
57	.05146	.05153	19.405	.99867	1.0013	19.431	3
58	.05175	.05182	19.296	.99866	1.0013	19.322	2
59	.05205	.05212	19.188	.99864	1.0014	19.214	1
60	.05234	.05241	19.081	.99863	1.0014	19.107	0
′	Cos	Ctn	Tan	Sin	Csc	Sec	′

92° (272°) | **(267°) 87°**

3° (183°) | **(356°) 176°**

′	Sin	Tan	Ctn	Cos	Sec	Csc	′
0	.05234	.05241	19.081	.99863	1.0014	19.107	60
1	.05263	.05270	18.976	.99861	1.0014	19.002	59
2	.05292	.05299	18.871	.99860	1.0014	18.898	58
3	.05321	.05328	18.768	.99858	1.0014	18.794	57
4	.05350	.05357	18.666	.99857	1.0014	18.692	56
5	.05379	.05387	18.564	.99855	1.0014	18.591	55
6	.05408	.05416	18.464	.99854	1.0015	18.492	54
7	.05437	.05445	18.366	.99852	1.0015	18.393	53
8	.05466	.05474	18.268	.99851	1.0015	18.295	52
9	.05495	.05503	18.171	.99849	1.0015	18.198	51
10	.05524	.05533	18.075	.99847	1.0015	18.103	50
11	.05553	.05562	17.980	.99846	1.0015	18.008	49
12	.05582	.05591	17.886	.99844	1.0016	17.914	48
13	.05611	.05620	17.793	.99842	1.0016	17.822	47
14	.05640	.05649	17.702	.99841	1.0016	17.730	46
15	.05669	.05678	17.611	.99839	1.0016	17.639	45
16	.05698	.05708	17.521	.99838	1.0016	17.549	44
17	.05727	.05737	17.431	.99836	1.0016	17.460	43
18	.05756	.05766	17.343	.99834	1.0017	17.372	42
19	.05785	.05795	17.256	.99833	1.0017	17.285	41
20	.05814	.05824	17.169	.99831	1.0017	17.198	40
21	.05844	.05854	17.084	.99829	1.0017	17.113	39
22	.05873	.05883	16.999	.99827	1.0017	17.028	38
23	.05902	.05912	16.915	.99826	1.0017	16.945	37
24	.05931	.05941	16.832	.99824	1.0018	16.862	36
25	.05960	.05970	16.750	.99822	1.0018	16.779	35
26	.05989	.05999	16.668	.99821	1.0018	16.698	34
27	.06018	.06029	16.587	.99819	1.0018	16.618	33
28	.06047	.06058	16.507	.99817	1.0018	16.538	32
29	.06076	.06087	16.428	.99815	1.0019	16.459	31
30	.06105	.06116	16.350	.99813	1.0019	16.380	30
31	.06134	.06145	16.272	.99812	1.0019	16.303	29
32	.06163	.06175	16.195	.99810	1.0019	16.226	28
33	.06192	.06204	16.119	.99808	1.0019	16.150	27
34	.06221	.06233	16.043	.99806	1.0019	16.075	26
35	.06250	.06262	15.969	.99804	1.0020	16.000	25
36	.06279	.06291	15.895	.99803	1.0020	15.926	24
37	.06308	.06321	15.821	.99801	1.0020	15.853	23
38	.06337	.06350	15.748	.99799	1.0020	15.780	22
39	.06366	.06379	15.676	.99797	1.0020	15.708	21
40	.06395	.06408	15.605	.99795	1.0021	15.637	20
41	.06424	.06438	15.534	.99793	1.0021	15.566	19
42	.06453	.06467	15.464	.99792	1.0021	15.496	18
43	.06482	.06496	15.394	.99790	1.0021	15.427	17
44	.06511	.06525	15.325	.99788	1.0021	15.358	16
45	.06540	.06554	15.257	.99786	1.0021	15.290	15
46	.06569	.06584	15.189	.99784	1.0022	15.222	14
47	.06598	.06613	15.122	.99782	1.0022	15.155	13
48	.06627	.06642	15.056	.99780	1.0022	15.089	12
49	.06656	.06671	14.990	.99778	1.0022	15.023	11
50	.06685	.06700	14.924	.99776	1.0022	14.958	10
51	.06714	.06730	14.860	.99774	1.0023	14.893	9
52	.06743	.06759	14.795	.99772	1.0023	14.829	8
53	.06773	.06788	14.732	.99770	1.0023	14.766	7
54	.06802	.06817	14.669	.99768	1.0023	14.703	6
55	.06831	.06847	14.606	.99766	1.0023	14.640	5
56	.06860	.06876	14.544	.99764	1.0024	14.578	4
57	.06889	.06905	14.482	.99762	1.0024	14.517	3
58	.06918	.06934	14.421	.99760	1.0024	14.456	2
59	.06947	.06963	14.361	.99758	1.0024	14.395	1
60	.06976	.06993	14.301	.99756	1.0024	14.336	0
′	Cos	Ctn	Tan	Sin	Csc	Sec	′

93° (273°) | **(266°) 86°**

4° (184°) (355°) **175°**

′	Sin	Tan	Ctn	Cos	Sec	Csc	′
0	.06976	.06993	14.301	.99756	1.0024	14.336	60
1	.07005	.07022	14.241	.99754	1.0025	14.276	59
2	.07034	.07051	14.182	.99752	1.0025	14.217	58
3	.07063	.07080	14.124	.99750	1.0025	14.159	57
4	.07092	.07110	14.065	.99748	1.0025	14.101	56
5	.07121	.07139	14.008	.99746	1.0025	14.044	55
6	.07150	.07168	13.951	.99744	1.0026	13.987	54
7	.07179	.07197	13.894	.99742	1.0026	13.930	53
8	.07208	.07227	13.838	.99740	1.0026	13.874	52
9	.07237	.07256	13.782	.99738	1.0026	13.818	51
10	.07266	.07285	13.727	.99736	1.0027	13.763	50
11	.07295	.07314	13.672	.99734	1.0027	13.708	49
12	.07324	.07344	13.617	.99731	1.0027	13.654	48
13	.07353	.07373	13.563	.99729	1.0027	13.600	47
14	.07382	.07402	13.510	.99727	1.0027	13.547	46
15	.07411	.07431	13.457	.99725	1.0028	13.494	45
16	.07440	.07461	13.404	.99723	1.0028	13.441	44
17	.07469	.07490	13.352	.99721	1.0028	13.389	43
18	.07498	.07519	13.300	.99719	1.0028	13.337	42
19	.07527	.07548	13.248	.99716	1.0028	13.286	41
20	.07556	.07578	13.197	.99714	1.0029	13.235	40
21	.07585	.07607	13.146	.99712	1.0029	13.184	39
22	.07614	.07636	13.096	.99710	1.0029	13.134	38
23	.07643	.07665	13.046	.99708	1.0029	13.084	37
24	.07672	.07695	12.996	.99705	1.0030	13.035	36
25	.07701	.07724	12.947	.99703	1.0030	12.985	35
26	.07730	.07753	12.898	.99701	1.0030	12.937	34
27	.07759	.07782	12.850	.99699	1.0030	12.888	33
28	.07788	.07812	12.801	.99696	1.0030	12.840	32
29	.07817	.07841	12.754	.99694	1.0031	12.793	31
30	.07846	.07870	12.706	.99692	1.0031	12.745	30
31	.07875	.07899	12.659	.99689	1.0031	12.699	29
32	.07904	.07929	12.612	.99687	1.0031	12.652	28
33	.07933	.07958	12.566	.99685	1.0032	12.606	27
34	.07962	.07987	12.520	.99683	1.0032	12.560	26
35	.07991	.08017	12.474	.99680	1.0032	12.514	25
36	.08020	.08046	12.429	.99678	1.0032	12.469	24
37	.08049	.08075	12.384	.99676	1.0033	12.424	23
38	.08078	.08104	12.339	.99673	1.0033	12.379	22
39	.08107	.08134	12.295	.99671	1.0033	12.335	21
40	.08136	.08163	12.251	.99668	1.0033	12.291	20
41	.08165	.08192	12.207	.99666	1.0034	12.248	19
42	.08194	.08221	12.163	.99664	1.0034	12.204	18
43	.08223	.08251	12.120	.99661	1.0034	12.161	17
44	.08252	.08280	12.077	.99659	1.0034	12.119	16
45	.08281	.08309	12.035	.99657	1.0034	12.076	15
46	.08310	.08339	11.992	.99654	1.0035	12.034	14
47	.08339	.08368	11.950	.99652	1.0035	11.992	13
48	.08368	.08397	11.909	.99649	1.0035	11.951	12
49	.08397	.08427	11.867	.99647	1.0035	11.909	11
50	.08426	.08456	11.826	.99644	1.0036	11.868	10
51	.08455	.08485	11.785	.99642	1.0036	11.828	9
52	.08484	.08514	11.745	.99639	1.0036	11.787	8
53	.08513	.08544	11.705	.99637	1.0036	11.747	7
54	.08542	.08573	11.664	.99635	1.0037	11.707	6
55	.08571	.08602	11.625	.99632	1.0037	11.668	5
56	.08600	.08632	11.585	.99630	1.0037	11.628	4
57	.08629	.08661	11.546	.99627	1.0037	11.589	3
58	.08658	.08690	11.507	.99625	1.0038	11.551	2
59	.08687	.08720	11.468	.99622	1.0038	11.512	1
60	.08716	.08749	11.430	.99619	1.0038	11.474	0
′	Cos	Ctn	Tan	Sin	Csc	Sec	′

94° (274°) (265°) **85°**

5° (185°) (354°) **174°**

′	Sin	Tan	Ctn	Cos	Sec	Csc	′
0	.08716	.08749	11.430	.99619	1.0038	11.474	60
1	.08745	.08778	11.392	.99617	1.0038	11.436	59
2	.08774	.08807	11.354	.99614	1.0039	11.398	58
3	.08803	.08837	11.316	.99612	1.0039	11.360	57
4	.08831	.08866	11.279	.99609	1.0039	11.323	56
5	.08860	.08895	11.242	.99607	1.0039	11.286	55
6	.08889	.08925	11.205	.99604	1.0040	11.249	54
7	.08918	.08954	11.168	.99602	1.0040	11.213	53
8	.08947	.08983	11.132	.99599	1.0040	11.176	52
9	.08976	.09013	11.095	.99596	1.0041	11.140	51
10	.09005	.09042	11.059	.99594	1.0041	11.105	50
11	.09034	.09071	11.024	.99591	1.0041	11.069	49
12	.09063	.09101	10.988	.99588	1.0041	11.034	48
13	.09092	.09130	10.953	.99586	1.0042	10.998	47
14	.09121	.09159	10.918	.99583	1.0042	10.963	46
15	.09150	.09189	10.883	.99580	1.0042	10.929	45
16	.09179	.09218	10.848	.99578	1.0042	10.894	44
17	.09208	.09247	10.814	.99575	1.0043	10.860	43
18	.09237	.09277	10.780	.99572	1.0043	10.826	42
19	.09266	.09306	10.746	.99570	1.0043	10.792	41
20	.09295	.09335	10.712	.99567	1.0043	10.758	40
21	.09324	.09365	10.678	.99564	1.0044	10.725	39
22	.09353	.09394	10.645	.99562	1.0044	10.692	38
23	.09382	.09423	10.612	.99559	1.0044	10.659	37
24	.09411	.09453	10.579	.99556	1.0045	10.626	36
25	.09440	.09482	10.546	.99553	1.0045	10.593	35
26	.09469	.09511	10.514	.99551	1.0045	10.561	34
27	.09498	.09541	10.481	.99548	1.0045	10.529	33
28	.09527	.09570	10.449	.99545	1.0046	10.497	32
29	.09556	.09600	10.417	.99542	1.0046	10.465	31
30	.09585	.09629	10.385	.99540	1.0046	10.433	30
31	.09614	.09658	10.354	.99537	1.0047	10.402	29
32	.09642	.09688	10.322	.99534	1.0047	10.371	28
33	.09671	.09717	10.291	.99531	1.0047	10.340	27
34	.09700	.09746	10.260	.99528	1.0047	10.309	26
35	.09729	.09776	10.229	.99526	1.0048	10.278	25
36	.09758	.09805	10.199	.99523	1.0048	10.248	24
37	.09787	.09834	10.168	.99520	1.0048	10.217	23
38	.09816	.09864	10.138	.99517	1.0049	10.187	22
39	.09845	.09893	10.108	.99514	1.0049	10.157	21
40	.09874	.09923	10.078	.99511	1.0049	10.128	20
41	.09903	.09952	10.048	.99508	1.0049	10.098	19
42	.09932	.09981	10.019	.99506	1.0050	10.068	18
43	.09961	.10011	9.9893	.99503	1.0050	10.039	17
44	.09990	.10040	9.9601	.99500	1.0050	10.010	16
45	.10019	.10069	9.9310	.99497	1.0051	9.9812	15
46	.10048	.10099	9.9021	.99494	1.0051	9.9525	14
47	.10077	.10128	9.8734	.99491	1.0051	9.9239	13
48	.10106	.10158	9.8448	.99488	1.0051	9.8955	12
49	.10135	.10187	9.8164	.99485	1.0052	9.8672	11
50	.10164	.10216	9.7882	.99482	1.0052	9.8391	10
51	.10192	.10246	9.7601	.99479	1.0052	9.8112	9
52	.10221	.10275	9.7322	.99476	1.0053	9.7834	8
53	.10250	.10305	9.7044	.99473	1.0053	9.7558	7
54	.10279	.10334	9.6768	.99470	1.0053	9.7283	6
55	.10308	.10363	9.6493	.99467	1.0054	9.7010	5
56	.10337	.10393	9.6220	.99464	1.0054	9.6739	4
57	.10366	.10422	9.5949	.99461	1.0054	9.6469	3
58	.10395	.10452	9.5679	.99458	1.0054	9.6200	2
59	.10424	.10481	9.5411	.99455	1.0055	9.5933	1
60	.10453	.10510	9.5144	.99452	1.0055	9.5668	0
′	Cos	Ctn	Tan	Sin	Csc	Sec	′

95° (275°) (264°) **84°**

6° (186°) (353°) **173°**

′	Sin	Tan	Ctn	Cos	Sec	Csc	′
0	.10453	.10510	9.5144	.99452	1.0055	9.5668	60
1	.10482	.10540	9.4878	.99449	1.0055	9.5404	59
2	.10511	.10569	9.4614	.99446	1.0056	9.5141	58
3	.10540	.10599	9.4352	.99443	1.0056	9.4880	57
4	.10569	.10628	9.4090	.99440	1.0056	9.4620	56
5	.10597	.10657	9.3831	.99437	1.0057	9.4362	55
6	.10626	.10687	9.3572	.99434	1.0057	9.4105	54
7	.10655	.10716	9.3315	.99431	1.0057	9.3850	53
8	.10684	.10746	9.3060	.99428	1.0058	9.3596	52
9	.10713	.10775	9.2806	.99424	1.0058	9.3343	51
10	.10742	.10805	9.2553	.99421	1.0058	9.3092	50
11	.10771	.10834	9.2302	.99418	1.0059	9.2842	49
12	.10800	.10863	9.2052	.99415	1.0059	9.2593	48
13	.10829	.10893	9.1803	.99412	1.0059	9.2346	47
14	.10858	.10922	9.1555	.99409	1.0059	9.2100	46
15	.10887	.10952	9.1309	.99406	1.0060	9.1855	45
16	.10916	.10981	9.1065	.99402	1.0060	9.1612	44
17	.10945	.11011	9.0821	.99399	1.0060	9.1370	43
18	.10973	.11040	9.0579	.99396	1.0061	9.1129	42
19	.11002	.11070	9.0338	.99393	1.0061	9.0890	41
20	.11031	.11099	9.0098	.99390	1.0061	9.0652	40
21	.11060	.11128	8.9860	.99386	1.0062	9.0415	39
22	.11089	.11158	8.9623	.99383	1.0062	9.0179	38
23	.11118	.11187	8.9387	.99380	1.0062	8.9944	37
24	.11147	.11217	8.9152	.99377	1.0063	8.9711	36
25	.11176	.11246	8.8919	.99374	1.0063	8.9479	35
26	.11205	.11276	8.8686	.99370	1.0063	8.9248	34
27	.11234	.11305	8.8455	.99367	1.0064	8.9019	33
28	.11263	.11335	8.8225	.99364	1.0064	8.8790	32
29	.11291	.11364	8.7996	.99360	1.0064	8.8563	31
30	.11320	.11394	8.7769	.99357	1.0065	8.8337	30
31	.11349	.11423	8.7542	.99354	1.0065	8.8112	29
32	.11378	.11452	8.7317	.99351	1.0065	8.7888	28
33	.11407	.11482	8.7093	.99347	1.0066	8.7665	27
34	.11436	.11511	8.6870	.99344	1.0066	8.7444	26
35	.11465	.11541	8.6648	.99341	1.0066	8.7223	25
36	.11494	.11570	8.6427	.99337	1.0067	8.7004	24
37	.11523	.11600	8.6208	.99334	1.0067	8.6786	23
38	.11552	.11629	8.5989	.99331	1.0067	8.6569	22
39	.11580	.11659	8.5772	.99327	1.0068	8.6353	21
40	.11609	.11688	8.5555	.99324	1.0068	8.6138	20
41	.11638	.11718	8.5340	.99320	1.0068	8.5924	19
42	.11667	.11747	8.5126	.99317	1.0069	8.5711	18
43	.11696	.11777	8.4913	.99314	1.0069	8.5500	17
44	.11725	.11806	8.4701	.99310	1.0069	8.5289	16
45	.11754	.11836	8.4490	.99307	1.0070	8.5079	15
46	.11783	.11865	8.4280	.99303	1.0070	8.4871	14
47	.11812	.11895	8.4071	.99300	1.0070	8.4663	13
48	.11840	.11924	8.3863	.99297	1.0071	8.4457	12
49	.11869	.11954	8.3656	.99293	1.0071	8.4251	11
50	.11898	.11983	8.3450	.99290	1.0072	8.4047	10
51	.11927	.12013	8.3245	.99286	1.0072	8.3843	9
52	.11956	.12042	8.3041	.99283	1.0072	8.3641	8
53	.11985	.12072	8.2838	.99279	1.0073	8.3439	7
54	.12014	.12101	8.2636	.99276	1.0073	8.3238	6
55	.12043	.12131	8.2434	.99272	1.0073	8.3039	5
56	.12071	.12160	8.2234	.99269	1.0074	8.2840	4
57	.12100	.12190	8.2035	.99265	1.0074	8.2642	3
58	.12129	.12219	8.1837	.99262	1.0074	8.2446	2
59	.12158	.12249	8.1640	.99258	1.0075	8.2250	1
60	.12187	.12278	8.1443	.99255	1.0075	8.2055	0
′	Cos	Ctn	Tan	Sin	Csc	Sec	′

96° (276°) (263°) **83°**

7° (187°) (352°) **172°**

′	Sin	Tan	Ctn	Cos	Sec	Csc	′
0	.12187	.12278	8.1443	.99255	1.0075	8.2055	60
1	.12216	.12308	8.1248	.99251	1.0075	8.1861	59
2	.12245	.12338	8.1054	.99248	1.0076	8.1668	58
3	.12274	.12367	8.0860	.99244	1.0076	8.1476	57
4	.12302	.12397	8.0667	.99240	1.0077	8.1285	56
5	.12331	.12426	8.0476	.99237	1.0077	8.1095	55
6	.12360	.12456	8.0285	.99233	1.0077	8.0905	54
7	.12389	.12485	8.0095	.99230	1.0078	8.0717	53
8	.12418	.12515	7.9906	.99226	1.0078	8.0529	52
9	.12447	.12544	7.9718	.99222	1.0078	8.0342	51
10	.12476	.12574	7.9530	.99219	1.0079	8.0156	50
11	.12504	.12603	7.9344	.99215	1.0079	7.9971	49
12	.12533	.12633	7.9158	.99211	1.0079	7.9787	48
13	.12562	.12662	7.8973	.99208	1.0080	7.9604	47
14	.12591	.12692	7.8789	.99204	1.0080	7.9422	46
15	.12620	.12722	7.8606	.99200	1.0081	7.9240	45
16	.12649	.12751	7.8424	.99197	1.0081	7.9059	44
17	.12678	.12781	7.8243	.99193	1.0081	7.8879	43
18	.12706	.12810	7.8062	.99189	1.0082	7.8700	42
19	.12735	.12840	7.7882	.99186	1.0082	7.8522	41
20	.12764	.12869	7.7704	.99182	1.0082	7.8344	40
21	.12793	.12899	7.7525	.99178	1.0083	7.8168	39
22	.12822	.12929	7.7348	.99175	1.0083	7.7992	38
23	.12851	.12958	7.7171	.99171	1.0084	7.7817	37
24	.12880	.12988	7.6996	.99167	1.0084	7.7642	36
25	.12908	.13017	7.6821	.99163	1.0084	7.7469	35
26	.12937	.13047	7.6647	.99160	1.0085	7.7296	34
27	.12966	.13076	7.6473	.99156	1.0085	7.7124	33
28	.12995	.13106	7.6301	.99152	1.0086	7.6953	32
29	.13024	.13136	7.6129	.99148	1.0086	7.6783	31
30	.13053	.13165	7.5958	.99144	1.0086	7.6613	30
31	.13081	.13195	7.5787	.99141	1.0087	7.6444	29
32	.13110	.13224	7.5618	.99137	1.0087	7.6276	28
33	.13139	.13254	7.5449	.99133	1.0087	7.6109	27
34	.13168	.13284	7.5281	.99129	1.0088	7.5942	26
35	.13197	.13313	7.5113	.99125	1.0088	7.5776	25
36	.13226	.13343	7.4947	.99122	1.0089	7.5611	24
37	.13254	.13372	7.4781	.99118	1.0089	7.5446	23
38	.13283	.13402	7.4615	.99114	1.0089	7.5282	22
39	.13312	.13432	7.4451	.99110	1.0090	7.5119	21
40	.13341	.13461	7.4287	.99106	1.0090	7.4957	20
41	.13370	.13491	7.4124	.99102	1.0091	7.4795	19
42	.13399	.13521	7.3962	.99098	1.0091	7.4635	18
43	.13427	.13550	7.3800	.99094	1.0091	7.4474	17
44	.13456	.13580	7.3639	.99091	1.0092	7.4315	16
45	.13485	.13609	7.3479	.99087	1.0092	7.4156	15
46	.13514	.13639	7.3319	.99083	1.0093	7.3998	14
47	.13543	.13669	7.3160	.99079	1.0093	7.3840	13
48	.13572	.13698	7.3002	.99075	1.0093	7.3684	12
49	.13600	.13728	7.2844	.99071	1.0094	7.3527	11
50	.13629	.13758	7.2687	.99067	1.0094	7.3372	10
51	.13658	.13787	7.2531	.99063	1.0095	7.3217	9
52	.13687	.13817	7.2375	.99059	1.0095	7.3063	8
53	.13716	.13846	7.2220	.99055	1.0095	7.2909	7
54	.13744	.13876	7.2066	.99051	1.0096	7.2757	6
55	.13773	.13906	7.1912	.99047	1.0096	7.2604	5
56	.13802	.13935	7.1759	.99043	1.0097	7.2453	4
57	.13831	.13965	7.1607	.99039	1.0097	7.2302	3
58	.13860	.13995	7.1455	.99035	1.0097	7.2152	2
59	.13889	.14024	7.1304	.99031	1.0098	7.2002	1
60	.13917	.14054	7.1154	.99027	1.0098	7.1853	0
′	Cos	Ctn	Tan	Sin	Csc	Sec	′

97° (277°) (262°) **82°**

8° (188°) — (351°) **171°**

′	Sin	Tan	Ctn	Cos	Sec	Csc	′
0	.13917	.14054	7.1154	.99027	1.0098	7.1853	60
1	.13946	.14084	7.1004	.99023	1.0099	7.1705	59
2	.13975	.14113	7.0855	.99019	1.0099	7.1557	58
3	.14004	.14143	7.0706	.99015	1.0100	7.1410	57
4	.14033	.14173	7.0558	.99011	1.0100	7.1263	56
5	.14061	.14202	7.0410	.99006	1.0100	7.1117	55
6	.14090	.14232	7.0264	.99002	1.0101	7.0972	54
7	.14119	.14262	7.0117	.98998	1.0101	7.0827	53
8	.14148	.14291	6.9972	.98994	1.0102	7.0683	52
9	.14177	.14321	6.9827	.98990	1.0102	7.0539	51
10	.14205	.14351	6.9682	.98986	1.0102	7.0396	50
11	.14234	.14381	6.9538	.98982	1.0103	7.0254	49
12	.14263	.14410	6.9395	.98978	1.0103	7.0112	48
13	.14292	.14440	6.9252	.98973	1.0104	6.9971	47
14	.14320	.14470	6.9110	.98969	1.0104	6.9830	46
15	.14349	.14499	6.8969	.98965	1.0105	6.9690	45
16	.14378	.14529	6.8828	.98961	1.0105	6.9550	44
17	.14407	.14559	6.8687	.98957	1.0105	6.9411	43
18	.14436	.14588	6.8548	.98953	1.0106	6.9273	42
19	.14464	.14618	6.8408	.98948	1.0106	6.9135	41
20	.14493	.14648	6.8269	.98944	1.0107	6.8998	40
21	.14522	.14678	6.8131	.98940	1.0107	6.8861	39
22	.14551	.14707	6.7994	.98936	1.0108	6.8725	38
23	.14580	.14737	6.7856	.98931	1.0108	6.8589	37
24	.14608	.14767	6.7720	.98927	1.0108	6.8454	36
25	.14637	.14796	6.7584	.98923	1.0109	6.8320	35
26	.14666	.14826	6.7448	.98919	1.0109	6.8186	34
27	.14695	.14856	6.7313	.98914	1.0110	6.8052	33
28	.14723	.14886	6.7179	.98910	1.0110	6.7919	32
29	.14752	.14915	6.7045	.98906	1.0111	6.7787	31
30	.14781	.14945	6.6912	98902	1.0111	6.7655	30
31	.14810	.14975	6.6779	.98897	1.0112	6.7523	29
32	.14838	.15005	6.6646	.98893	1.0112	6.7392	28
33	.14867	.15034	6.6514	.98889	1.0112	6.7262	27
34	.14896	.15064	6.6383	.98884	1.0113	6.7132	26
35	.14925	.15094	6.6252	.98880	1.0113	6.7003	25
36	.14954	.15124	6.6122	.98876	1.0114	6.6874	24
37	.14982	.15153	6.5992	.98871	1.0114	6.6745	23
38	.15011	.15183	6.5863	.98867	1.0115	6.6618	22
39	.15040	.15213	6.5734	.98863	1.0115	6.6490	21
40	.15069	.15243	6.5606	.98858	1.0116	6.6363	20
41	.15097	.15272	6.5478	.98854	1.0116	6.6237	19
42	.15126	.15302	6.5350	.98849	1.0116	6.6111	18
43	.15155	.15332	6.5223	.98845	1.0117	6.5986	17
44	.15184	.15362	6.5097	.98841	1.0117	6.5861	16
45	.15212	.15391	6.4971	.98836	1.0118	6.5736	15
46	.15241	.15421	6.4846	.98832	1.0118	6.5612	14
47	.15270	.15451	6.4721	.98827	1.0119	6.5489	13
48	.15299	.15481	6.4596	.98823	1.0119	6.5366	12
49	.15327	.15511	6.4472	.98818	1.0120	6.5243	11
50	.15356	.15540	6.4348	.98814	1.0120	6.5121	10
51	.15385	.15570	6.4225	.98809	1.0120	6.4999	9
52	.15414	.15600	6.4103	.98805	1.0121	6.4878	8
53	.15442	.15630	6.3980	.98800	1.0121	6.4757	7
54	.15471	.15660	6.3859	.98796	1.0122	6.4637	6
55	.15500	.15689	6.3737	.98791	1.0122	6.4517	5
56	.15529	.15719	6.3617	.98787	1.0123	6.4398	4
57	.15557	.15749	6.3496	.98782	1.0123	6.4279	3
58	.15586	.15779	6.3376	.98778	1.0124	6.4160	2
59	.15615	.15809	6.3257	.98773	1.0124	6.4042	1
60	.15643	.15838	6.3138	.98769	1.0125	6.3925	0
′	Cos	Ctn	Tan	Sin	Csc	Sec	′

98° (278°) — (261°) **81°**

9° (189°) — (350°) **170°**

′	Sin	Tan	Ctn	Cos	Sec	Csc	′
0	.15643	.15838	6.3138	.98769	1.0125	6.3925	60
1	.15672	.15868	6.3019	.98764	1.0125	6.3807	59
2	.15701	.15898	6.2901	.98760	1.0126	6.3691	58
3	.15730	.15928	6.2783	.98755	1.0126	6.3574	57
4	.15758	.15958	6.2666	.98751	1.0127	6.3458	56
5	.15787	.15988	6.2549	.98746	1.0127	6.3343	55
6	.15816	.16017	6.2432	.98741	1.0127	6.3228	54
7	.15845	.16047	6.2316	.98737	1.0128	6.3113	53
8	.15873	.16077	6.2200	.98732	1.0128	6.2999	52
9	.15902	.16107	6.2085	.98728	1.0129	6.2885	51
10	.15931	.16137	6.1970	.98723	1.0129	6.2772	50
11	.15959	.16167	6.1856	.98718	1.0130	6.2659	49
12	.15988	.16196	6.1742	.98714	1.0130	6.2546	48
13	.16017	.16226	6.1628	.98709	1.0131	6.2434	47
14	.16046	.16256	6.1515	.98704	1.0131	6.2323	46
15	.16074	.16286	6.1402	.98700	1.0132	6.2211	45
16	.16103	.16316	6.1290	.98695	1.0132	6.2100	44
17	.16132	.16346	6.1178	.98690	1.0133	6.1990	43
18	.16160	.16376	6.1066	.98686	1.0133	6.1880	42
19	.16189	.16405	6.0955	.98681	1.0134	6.1770	41
20	.16218	.16435	6.0844	.98676	1.0134	6.1661	40
21	.16246	.16465	6.0734	.98671	1.0135	6.1552	39
22	.16275	.16495	6.0624	.98667	1.0135	6.1443	38
23	.16304	.16525	6.0514	.98662	1.0136	6.1335	37
24	.16333	.16555	6.0405	.98657	1.0136	6.1227	36
25	.16361	.16585	6.0296	.98652	1.0137	6.1120	35
26	.16390	.16615	6.0188	.98648	1.0137	6.1013	34
27	.16419	.16645	6.0080	.98643	1.0138	6.0906	33
28	.16447	.16674	5.9972	.98638	1.0138	6.0800	32
29	.16476	.16704	5.9865	.98633	1.0139	6.0694	31
30	.16505	.16734	5.9758	.98629	1.0139	6.0589	30
31	.16533	.16764	5.9651	.98624	1.0140	6.0483	29
32	.16562	.16794	5.9545	.98619	1.0140	6.0379	28
33	.16591	.16824	5.9439	.98614	1.0141	6.0274	27
34	.16620	.16854	5.9333	.98609	1.0141	6.0170	26
35	.16648	.16884	5.9228	.98604	1.0142	6.0067	25
36	.16677	.16914	5.9124	.98600	1.0142	5.9963	24
37	.16706	.16944	5.9019	.98595	1.0143	5.9860	23
38	.16734	.16974	5.8915	.98590	1.0143	5.9758	22
39	.16763	.17004	5.8811	.98585	1.0144	5.9656	21
40	.16792	.17033	5.8708	.98580	1.0144	5.9554	20
41	.16820	.17063	5.8605	.98575	1.0145	5.9452	19
42	.16849	.17093	5.8502	.98570	1.0145	5.9351	18
43	.16878	.17123	5.8400	.98565	1.0146	5.9250	17
44	.16906	.17153	5.8298	.98561	1.0146	5.9150	16
45	.16935	.17183	5.8197	.98556	1.0147	5.9049	15
46	.16964	.17213	5.8095	.98551	1.0147	5.8950	14
47	.16992	.17243	5.7994	.98546	1.0148	5.8850	13
48	.17021	.17273	5.7894	.98541	1.0148	5.8751	12
49	.17050	.17303	5.7794	.98536	1.0149	5.8652	11
50	.17078	.17333	5.7694	.98531	1.0149	5.8554	10
51	.17107	.17363	5.7594	.98526	1.0150	5.8456	9
52	.17136	.17393	5.7495	.98521	1.0150	5.8358	8
53	.17164	.17423	5.7396	.98516	1.0151	5.8261	7
54	.17193	.17453	5.7297	.98511	1.0151	5.8164	6
55	.17222	.17483	5.7199	.98506	1.0152	5.8067	5
56	.17250	.17513	5.7101	.98501	1.0152	5.7970	4
57	.17279	.17543	5.7004	.98496	1.0153	5.7874	3
58	.17308	.17573	5.6906	.98491	1.0153	5.7778	2
59	.17336	.17603	5.6809	.98486	1.0154	5.7683	1
60	.17365	.17633	5.6713	.98481	1.0154	5.7588	0
′	Cos	Ctn	Tan	Sin	Csc	Sec	′

99° (279°) — (260°) **80°**

10° (190°) (349°) **169°**

′	Sin	Tan	Ctn	Cos	Sec	Csc	′
0	.17365	.17633	5.6713	.98481	1.0154	5.7588	60
1	.17393	.17663	5.6617	.98476	1.0155	5.7493	59
2	.17422	.17693	5.6521	.98471	1.0155	5.7398	58
3	.17451	.17723	5.6425	.98466	1.0156	5.7304	57
4	.17479	.17753	5.6329	.98461	1.0156	5.7210	56
5	.17508	.17783	5.6234	.98455	1.0157	5.7117	55
6	.17537	.17813	5.6140	.98450	1.0157	5.7023	54
7	.17565	.17843	5.6045	.98445	1.0158	5.6930	53
8	.17594	.17873	5.5951	.98440	1.0158	5.6838	52
9	.17623	.17903	5.5857	.98435	1.0159	5.6745	51
10	.17651	.17933	5.5764	.98430	1.0160	5.6653	50
11	.17680	.17963	5.5671	.98425	1.0160	5.6562	49
12	.17708	.17993	5.5578	.98420	1.0161	5.6470	48
13	.17737	.18023	5.5485	.98414	1.0161	5.6379	47
14	.17766	.18053	5.5393	.98409	1.0162	5.6288	46
15	.17794	.18083	5.5301	.98404	1.0162	5.6198	45
16	.17823	.18113	5.5209	.98399	1.0163	5.6107	44
17	.17852	.18143	5.5118	.98394	1.0163	5.6017	43
18	.17880	.18173	5.5026	.98389	1.0164	5.5928	42
19	.17909	.18203	5.4936	.98383	1.0164	5.5838	41
20	.17937	.18233	5.4845	.98378	1.0165	5.5749	40
21	.17966	.18263	5.4755	.98373	1.0165	5.5660	39
22	.17995	.18293	5.4665	.98368	1.0166	5.5572	38
23	.18023	.18323	5.4575	.98362	1.0166	5.5484	37
24	.18052	.18353	5.4486	.98357	1.0167	5.5396	36
25	.18081	.18384	5.4397	.98352	1.0168	5.5308	35
26	.18109	.18414	5.4308	.98347	1.0168	5.5221	34
27	.18138	.18444	5.4219	.98341	1.0169	5.5134	33
28	.18166	.18474	5.4131	.98336	1.0169	5.5047	32
29	.18195	.18504	5.4043	.98331	1.0170	5.4960	31
30	.18224	.18534	5.3955	.98325	1.0170	5.4874	30
31	.18252	.18564	5.3868	.98320	1.0171	5.4788	29
32	.18281	.18594	5.3781	.98315	1.0171	5.4702	28
33	.18309	.18624	5.3694	.98310	1.0172	5.4617	27
34	.18338	.18654	5.3607	.98304	1.0173	5.4532	26
35	.18367	.18684	5.3521	.98299	1.0173	5.4447	25
36	.18395	.18714	5.3435	.98294	1.0174	5.4362	24
37	.18424	.18745	5.3349	.98288	1.0174	5.4278	23
38	.18452	.18775	5.3263	.98283	1.0175	5.4194	22
39	.18481	.18805	5.3178	.98277	1.0175	5.4110	21
40	.18509	.18835	5.3093	.98272	1.0176	5.4026	20
41	.18538	.18865	5.3008	.98267	1.0176	5.3943	19
42	.18567	.18895	5.2924	.98261	1.0177	5.3860	18
43	.18595	.18925	5.2839	.98256	1.0178	5.3777	17
44	.18624	.18955	5.2755	.98250	1.0178	5.3695	16
45	.18652	.18986	5.2672	.98245	1.0179	5.3612	15
46	.18681	.19016	5.2588	.98240	1.0179	5.3530	14
47	.18710	.19046	5.2505	.98234	1.0180	5.3449	13
48	.18738	.19076	5.2422	.98229	1.0180	5.3367	12
49	.18767	.19106	5.2339	.98223	1.0181	5.3286	11
50	.18795	.19136	5.2257	.98218	1.0181	5.3205	10
51	.18824	.19166	5.2174	.98212	1.0182	5.3124	9
52	.18852	.19197	5.2092	.98207	1.0183	5.3044	8
53	.18881	.19227	5.2011	.98201	1.0183	5.2963	7
54	.18910	.19257	5.1929	.98196	1.0184	5.2883	6
55	.18938	.19287	5.1848	.98190	1.0184	5.2804	5
56	.18967	.19317	5.1767	.98185	1.0185	5.2724	4
57	.18995	.19347	5.1686	.98179	1.0185	5.2645	3
58	.19024	.19378	5.1606	.98174	1.0186	5.2566	2
59	.19052	.19408	5.1526	.98168	1.0187	5.2487	1
60	.19081	.19438	5.1446	.98163	1.0187	5.2408	0
′	Cos	Ctn	Tan	Sin	Csc	Sec	′

100° (280°) (259°) **79°**

11° (191°) (348°) **168°**

′	Sin	Tan	Ctn	Cos	Sec	Csc	′
0	.19081	.19438	5.1446	.98163	1.0187	5.2408	60
1	.19109	.19468	5.1366	.98157	1.0188	5.2330	59
2	.19138	.19498	5.1286	.98152	1.0188	5.2252	58
3	.19167	.19529	5.1207	.98146	1.0189	5.2174	57
4	.19195	.19559	5.1128	.98140	1.0189	5.2097	56
5	.19224	.19589	5.1049	.98135	1.0190	5.2019	55
6	.19252	.19619	5.0970	.98129	1.0191	5.1942	54
7	.19281	.19649	5.0892	.98124	1.0191	5.1865	53
8	.19309	.19680	5.0814	.98118	1.0192	5.1789	52
9	.19338	.19710	5.0736	.98112	1.0192	5.1712	51
10	.19366	.19740	5.0658	.98107	1.0193	5.1636	50
11	.19395	.19770	5.0581	.98101	1.0194	5.1560	49
12	.19423	.19801	5.0504	.98096	1.0194	5.1484	48
13	.19452	.19831	5.0427	.98090	1.0195	5.1409	47
14	.19481	.19861	5.0350	.98084	1.0195	5.1333	46
15	.19509	.19891	5.0273	.98079	1.0196	5.1258	45
16	.19538	.19921	5.0197	.98073	1.0197	5.1183	44
17	.19566	.19952	5.0121	.98067	1.0197	5.1109	43
18	.19595	.19982	5.0045	.98061	1.0198	5.1034	42
19	.19623	.20012	4.9969	.98056	1.0198	5.0960	41
20	.19652	.20042	4.9894	.98050	1.0199	5.0886	40
21	.19680	.20073	4.9819	.98044	1.0199	5.0813	39
22	.19709	.20103	4.9744	.98039	1.0200	5.0739	38
23	.19737	.20133	4.9669	.98033	1.0201	5.0666	37
24	.19766	.20164	4.9594	.98027	1.0201	5.0593	36
25	.19794	.20194	4.9520	.98021	1.0202	5.0520	35
26	.19823	.20224	4.9446	.98016	1.0202	5.0447	34
27	.19851	.20254	4.9372	.98010	1.0203	5.0375	33
28	.19880	.20285	4.9298	.98004	1.0204	5.0302	32
29	.19908	.20315	4.9225	.97998	1.0204	5.0230	31
30	.19937	.20345	4.9152	.97992	1.0205	5.0159	30
31	.19965	.20376	4.9078	.97987	1.0205	5.0087	29
32	.19994	.20406	4.9006	.97981	1.0206	5.0016	28
33	.20022	.20436	4.8933	.97975	1.0207	4.9944	27
34	.20051	.20466	4.8860	.97969	1.0207	4.9873	26
35	.20079	.20497	4.8788	.97963	1.0208	4.9803	25
36	.20108	.20527	4.8716	.97958	1.0209	4.9732	24
37	.20136	.20557	4.8644	.97952	1.0209	4.9662	23
38	.20165	.20588	4.8573	.97946	1.0210	4.9591	22
39	.20193	.20618	4.8501	.97940	1.0210	4.9521	21
40	.20222	.20648	4.8430	.97934	1.0211	4.9452	20
41	.20250	.20679	4.8359	.97928	1.0212	4.9382	19
42	.20279	.20709	4.8288	.97922	1.0212	4.9313	18
43	.20307	.20739	4.8218	.97916	1.0213	4.9244	17
44	.20336	.20770	4.8147	.97910	1.0213	4.9175	16
45	.20364	.20800	4.8077	.97905	1.0214	4.9106	15
46	.20393	.20830	4.8007	.97899	1.0215	4.9037	14
47	.20421	.20861	4.7937	.97893	1.0215	4.8969	13
48	.20450	.20891	4.7867	.97887	1.0216	4.8901	12
49	.20478	.20921	4.7798	.97881	1.0217	4.8833	11
50	.20507	.20952	4.7729	.97875	1.0217	4.8765	10
51	.20535	.20982	4.7659	.97869	1.0218	4.8697	9
52	.20563	.21013	4.7591	.97863	1.0218	4.8630	8
53	.20592	.21043	4.7522	.97857	1.0219	4.8563	7
54	.20620	.21073	4.7453	.97851	1.0220	4.8496	6
55	.20649	.21104	4.7385	.97845	1.0220	4.8429	5
56	.20677	.21134	4.7317	.97839	1.0221	4.8362	4
57	.20706	.21164	4.7249	.97833	1.0222	4.8296	3
58	.20734	.21195	4.7181	.97827	1.0222	4.8229	2
59	.20763	.21225	4.7114	.97821	1.0223	4.8163	1
60	.20791	.21256	4.7046	.97815	1.0223	4.8097	0
′	Cos	Ctn	Tan	Sin	Csc	Sec	′

101° (281°) (258°) **78°**

12° (192°) (347°) **167°**

′	Sin	Tan	Ctn	Cos	Sec	Csc	′
0	.20791	.21256	4.7046	.97815	1.0223	4.8097	60
1	.20820	.21286	4.6979	.97809	1.0224	4.8032	59
2	.20848	.21316	4.6912	.97803	1.0225	4.7966	58
3	.20877	.21347	4.6845	.97797	1.0225	4.7901	57
4	.20905	.21377	4.6779	.97791	1.0226	4.7836	56
5	.20933	.21408	4.6712	.97784	1.0227	4.7771	55
6	.20962	.21438	4.6646	.97778	1.0227	4.7706	54
7	.20990	.21469	4.6580	.97772	1.0228	4.7641	53
8	.21019	.21499	4.6514	.97766	1.0228	4.7577	52
9	.21047	.21529	4.6448	.97760	1.0229	4.7512	51
10	.21076	.21560	4.6382	.97754	1.0230	4.7448	50
11	.21104	.21590	4.6317	.97748	1.0230	4.7384	49
12	.21132	.21621	4.6252	.97742	1.0231	4.7321	48
13	.21161	.21651	4.6187	.97735	1.0232	4.7257	47
14	.21189	.21682	4.6122	.97729	1.0232	4.7194	46
15	.21218	.21712	4.6057	.97723	1.0233	4.7130	45
16	.21246	.21743	4.5993	.97717	1.0234	4.7067	44
17	.21275	.21773	4.5928	.97711	1.0234	4.7004	43
18	.21303	.21804	4.5864	.97705	1.0235	4.6942	42
19	.21331	.21834	4.5800	.97698	1.0236	4.6879	41
20	.21360	.21864	4.5736	.97692	1.0236	4.6817	40
21	.21388	.21895	4.5673	.97686	1.0237	4.6755	39
22	.21417	.21925	4.5609	.97680	1.0238	4.6693	38
23	.21445	.21956	4.5546	.97673	1.0238	4.6631	37
24	.21474	.21986	4.5483	.97667	1.0239	4.6569	36
25	.21502	.22017	4.5420	.97661	1.0240	4.6507	35
26	.21530	.22047	4.5357	.97655	1.0240	4.6446	34
27	.21559	.22078	4.5294	.97648	1.0241	4.6385	33
28	.21587	.22108	4.5232	.97642	1.0241	4.6324	32
29	.21616	.22139	4.5169	.97636	1.0242	4.6263	31
30	.21644	.22169	4.5107	.97630	1.0243	4.6202	30
31	.21672	.22200	4.5045	.97623	1.0243	4.6142	29
32	.21701	.22231	4.4983	.97617	1.0244	4.6081	28
33	.21729	.22261	4.4922	.97611	1.0245	4.6021	27
34	.21758	.22292	4.4860	.97604	1.0245	4.5961	26
35	.21786	.22322	4.4799	.97598	1.0246	4.5901	25
36	.21814	.22353	4.4737	.97592	1.0247	4.5841	24
37	.21843	.22383	4.4676	.97585	1.0247	4.5782	23
38	.21871	.22414	4.4615	.97579	1.0248	4.5722	22
39	.21899	.22444	4.4555	.97573	1.0249	4.5663	21
40	.21928	.22475	4.4494	.97566	1.0249	4.5604	20
41	.21956	.22505	4.4434	.97560	1.0250	4.5545	19
42	.21985	.22536	4.4373	.97553	1.0251	4.5486	18
43	.22013	.22567	4.4313	.97547	1.0251	4.5428	17
44	.22041	.22597	4.4253	.97541	1.0252	4.5369	16
45	.22070	.22628	4.4194	.97534	1.0253	4.5311	15
46	.22098	.22658	4.4134	.97528	1.0253	4.5253	14
47	.22126	.22689	4.4075	.97521	1.0254	4.5195	13
48	.22155	.22719	4.4015	.97515	1.0255	4.5137	12
49	.22183	.22750	4.3956	.97508	1.0256	4.5079	11
50	.22212	.22781	4.3897	.97502	1.0256	4.5022	10
51	.22240	.22811	4.3838	.97496	1.0257	4.4964	9
52	.22268	.22842	4.3779	.97489	1.0258	4.4907	8
53	.22297	.22872	4.3721	.97483	1.0258	4.4850	7
54	.22325	.22903	4.3662	.97476	1.0259	4.4793	6
55	.22353	.22934	4.3604	.97470	1.0260	4.4736	5
56	.22382	.22964	4.3546	.97463	1.0260	4.4679	4
57	.22410	.22995	4.3488	.97457	1.0261	4.4623	3
58	.22438	.23026	4.3430	.97450	1.0262	4.4566	2
59	.22467	.23056	4.3372	.97444	1.0262	4.4510	1
60	.22495	.23087	4.3315	.97437	1.0263	4.4454	0
′	Cos	Ctn	Tan	Sin	Csc	Sec	′

102° (282°) (257°) **77°**

13° (193°) (346°) **166°**

′	Sin	Tan	Ctn	Cos	Sec	Csc	′
0	.22495	.23087	4.3315	.97437	1.0263	4.4454	60
1	.22523	.23117	4.3257	.97430	1.0264	4.4398	59
2	.22552	.23148	4.3200	.97424	1.0264	4.4342	58
3	.22580	.23179	4.3143	.97417	1.0265	4.4287	57
4	.22608	.23209	4.3086	.97411	1.0266	4.4231	56
5	.22637	.23240	4.3029	.97404	1.0266	4.4176	55
6	.22665	.23271	4.2972	.97398	1.0267	4.4121	54
7	.22693	.23301	4.2916	.97391	1.0268	4.4066	53
8	.22722	.23332	4.2859	.97384	1.0269	4.4011	52
9	.22750	.23363	4.2803	.97378	1.0269	4.3956	51
10	.22778	.23393	4.2747	.97371	1.0270	4.3901	50
11	.22807	.23424	4.2691	.97365	1.0271	4.3847	49
12	.22835	.23455	4.2635	.97358	1.0271	4.3792	48
13	.22863	.23485	4.2580	.97351	1.0272	4.3738	47
14	.22892	.23516	4.2524	.97345	1.0273	4.3684	46
15	.22920	.23547	4.2468	.97338	1.0273	4.3630	45
16	.22948	.23578	4.2413	.97331	1.0274	4.3576	44
17	.22977	.23608	4.2358	.97325	1.0275	4.3522	43
18	.23005	.23639	4.2303	.97318	1.0276	4.3469	42
19	.23033	.23670	4.2248	.97311	1.0276	4.3415	41
20	.23062	.23700	4.2193	.97304	1.0277	4.3362	40
21	.23090	.23731	4.2139	.97298	1.0278	4.3309	39
22	.23118	.23762	4.2084	.97291	1.0278	4.3256	38
23	.23146	.23793	4.2030	.97284	1.0279	4.3203	37
24	.23175	.23823	4.1976	.97278	1.0280	4.3150	36
25	.23203	.23854	4.1922	.97271	1.0281	4.3098	35
26	.23231	.23885	4.1868	.97264	1.0281	4.3045	34
27	.23260	.23916	4.1814	.97257	1.0282	4.2993	33
28	.23288	.23946	4.1760	.97251	1.0283	4.2941	32
29	.23316	.23977	4.1706	.97244	1.0283	4.2889	31
30	.23345	.24008	4.1653	.97237	1.0284	4.2837	30
31	.23373	.24039	4.1600	.97230	1.0285	4.2785	29
32	.23401	.24069	4.1547	.97223	1.0286	4.2733	28
33	.23429	.24100	4.1493	.97217	1.0286	4.2681	27
34	.23458	.24131	4.1441	.97210	1.0287	4.2630	26
35	.23486	.24162	4.1388	.97203	1.0288	4.2579	25
36	.23514	.24193	4.1335	.97196	1.0288	4.2527	24
37	.23542	.24223	4.1282	.97189	1.0289	4.2476	23
38	.23571	.24254	4.1230	.97182	1.0290	4.2425	22
39	.23599	.24285	4.1178	.97176	1.0291	4.2375	21
40	.23627	.24316	4.1126	.97169	1.0291	4.2324	20
41	.23656	.24347	4.1074	.97162	1.0292	4.2273	19
42	.23684	.24377	4.1022	.97155	1.0293	4.2223	18
43	.23712	.24408	4.0970	.97148	1.0294	4.2173	17
44	.23740	.24439	4.0918	.97141	1.0294	4.2122	16
45	.23769	.24470	4.0867	.97134	1.0295	4.2072	15
46	.23797	.24501	4.0815	.97127	1.0296	4.2022	14
47	.23825	.24532	4.0764	.97120	1.0297	4.1973	13
48	.23853	.24562	4.0713	.97113	1.0297	4.1923	12
49	.23882	.24593	4.0662	.97106	1.0298	4.1873	11
50	.23910	.24624	4.0611	.97100	1.0299	4.1824	10
51	.23938	.24655	4.0560	.97093	1.0299	4.1774	9
52	.23966	.24686	4.0509	.97086	1.0300	4.1725	8
53	.23995	.24717	4.0459	.97079	1.0301	4.1676	7
54	.24023	.24747	4.0408	.97072	1.0302	4.1627	6
55	.24051	.24778	4.0358	.97065	1.0302	4.1578	5
56	.24079	.24809	4.0308	.97058	1.0303	4.1529	4
57	.24108	.24840	4.0257	.97051	1.0304	4.1481	3
58	.24136	.24871	4.0207	.97044	1.0305	4.1432	2
59	.24164	.24902	4.0158	.97037	1.0305	4.1384	1
60	.24192	.24933	4.0108	.97030	1.0306	4.1336	0
′	Cos	Ctn	Tan	Sin	Csc	Sec	′

103° (283°) (256°) **76°**

14° (194°) (345°) **165°**

′	Sin	Tan	Ctn	Cos	Sec	Csc	′
0	.24192	.24933	4.0108	.97030	1.0306	4.1336	60
1	.24220	.24964	4.0058	.97023	1.0307	4.1287	59
2	.24249	.24995	4.0009	.97015	1.0308	4.1239	58
3	.24277	.25026	3.9959	.97008	1.0308	4.1191	57
4	.24305	.25056	3.9910	.97001	1.0309	4.1144	56
5	.24333	.25087	3.9861	.96994	1.0310	4.1096	55
6	.24362	.25118	3.9812	.96987	1.0311	4.1048	54
7	.24390	.25149	3.9763	.96980	1.0311	4.1001	53
8	.24418	.25180	3.9714	.96973	1.0312	4.0954	52
9	.24446	.25211	3.9665	.96966	1.0313	4.0906	51
10	.24474	.25242	3.9617	.96959	1.0314	4.0859	50
11	.24503	.25273	3.9568	.96952	1.0314	4.0812	49
12	.24531	.25304	3.9520	.96945	1.0315	4.0765	48
13	.24559	.25335	3.9471	.96937	1.0316	4.0718	47
14	.24587	.25366	3.9423	.96930	1.0317	4.0672	46
15	.24615	.25397	3.9375	.96923	1.0317	4.0625	45
16	.24644	.25428	3.9327	.96916	1.0318	4.0579	44
17	.24672	.25459	3.9279	.96909	1.0319	4.0532	43
18	.24700	.25490	3.9232	.96902	1.0320	4.0486	42
19	.24728	.25521	3.9184	.96894	1.0321	4.0440	41
20	.24756	.25552	3.9136	.96887	1.0321	4.0394	40
21	.24784	.25583	3.9089	.96880	1.0322	4.0348	39
22	.24813	.25614	3.9042	.96873	1.0323	4.0302	38
23	.24841	.25645	3.8995	.96866	1.0324	4.0256	37
24	.24869	.25676	3.8947	.96858	1.0324	4.0211	36
25	.24897	.25707	3.8900	.96851	1.0325	4.0165	35
26	.24925	.25738	3.8854	.96844	1.0326	4.0120	34
27	.24954	.25769	3.8807	.96837	1.0327	4.0075	33
28	.24982	.25800	3.8760	.96829	1.0327	4.0029	32
29	.25010	.25831	3.8714	.96822	1.0328	3.9984	31
30	.25038	.25862	3.8667	.96815	1.0329	3.9939	30
31	.25066	.25893	3.8621	.96807	1.0330	3.9894	29
32	.25094	.25924	3.8575	.96800	1.0331	3.9850	28
33	.25122	.25955	3.8528	.96793	1.0331	3.9805	27
34	.25151	.25986	3.8482	.96786	1.0332	3.9760	26
35	.25179	.26017	3.8436	.96778	1.0333	3.9716	25
36	.25207	.26048	3.8391	.96771	1.0334	3.9672	24
37	.25235	.26079	3.8345	.96764	1.0334	3.9627	23
38	.25263	.26110	3.8299	.96756	1.0335	3.9583	22
39	.25291	.26141	3.8254	.96749	1.0336	3.9539	21
40	.25320	.26172	3.8208	.96742	1.0337	3.9495	20
41	.25348	.26203	3.8163	.96734	1.0338	3.9451	19
42	.25376	.26235	3.8118	.96727	1.0338	3.9408	18
43	.25404	.26266	3.8073	.96719	1.0339	3.9364	17
44	.25432	.26297	3.8028	.96712	1.0340	3.9320	16
45	.25460	.26328	3.7983	.96705	1.0341	3.9277	15
46	.25488	.26359	3.7938	.96697	1.0342	3.9234	14
47	.25516	.26390	3.7893	.96690	1.0342	3.9190	13
48	.25545	.26421	3.7848	.96682	1.0343	3.9147	12
49	.25573	.26452	3.7804	.96675	1.0344	3.9104	11
50	.25601	.26483	3.7760	.96667	1.0345	3.9061	10
51	.25629	.26515	3.7715	.96660	1.0346	3.9018	9
52	.25657	.26546	3.7671	.96653	1.0346	3.8976	8
53	.25685	.26577	3.7627	.96645	1.0347	3.8933	7
54	.25713	.26608	3.7583	.96638	1.0348	3.8890	6
55	.25741	.26639	3.7539	.96630	1.0349	3.8848	5
56	.25769	.26670	3.7495	.96623	1.0350	3.8806	4
57	.25798	.26701	3.7451	.96615	1.0350	3.8763	3
58	.25826	.26733	3.7408	.96608	1.0351	3.8721	2
59	.25854	.26764	3.7364	.96600	1.0352	3.8679	1
60	.25882	.26795	3.7321	.96593	1.0353	3.8637	0
′	Cos	Ctn	Tan	Sin	Csc	Sec	′

104° (284°) (255°) **75°**

15° (195°) (344°) **164°**

′	Sin	Tan	Ctn	Cos	Sec	Csc	′
0	.25882	.26795	3.7321	.96593	1.0353	3.8637	60
1	.25910	.26826	3.7277	.96585	1.0354	3.8595	59
2	.25938	.26857	3.7234	.96578	1.0354	3.8553	58
3	.25966	.26888	3.7191	.96570	1.0355	3.8512	57
4	.25994	.26920	3.7148	.96562	1.0356	3.8470	56
5	.26022	.26951	3.7105	.96555	1.0357	3.8428	55
6	.26050	.26982	3.7062	.96547	1.0358	3.8387	54
7	.26079	.27013	3.7019	.96540	1.0358	3.8346	53
8	.26107	.27044	3.6976	.96532	1.0359	3.8304	52
9	.26135	.27076	3.6933	.96524	1.0360	3.8263	51
10	.26163	.27107	3.6891	.96517	1.0361	3.8222	50
11	.26191	.27138	3.6848	.96509	1.0362	3.8181	49
12	.26219	.27169	3.6806	.96502	1.0363	3.8140	48
13	.26247	.27201	3.6764	.96494	1.0363	3.8100	47
14	.26275	.27232	3.6722	.96486	1.0364	3.8059	46
15	.26303	.27263	3.6680	.96479	1.0365	3.8018	45
16	.26331	.27294	3.6638	.96471	1.0366	3.7978	44
17	.26359	.27326	3.6596	.96463	1.0367	3.7937	43
18	.26387	.27357	3.6554	.96456	1.0367	3.7897	42
19	.26415	.27388	3.6512	.96448	1.0368	3.7857	41
20	.26443	.27419	3.6470	.96440	1.0369	3.7817	40
21	.26471	.27451	3.6429	.96433	1.0370	3.7777	39
22	.26500	.27482	3.6387	.96425	1.0371	3.7737	38
23	.26528	.27513	3.6346	.96417	1.0372	3.7697	37
24	.26556	.27545	3.6305	.96410	1.0372	3.7657	36
25	.26584	.27576	3.6264	.96402	1.0373	3.7617	35
26	.26612	.27607	3.6222	.96394	1.0374	3.7577	34
27	.26640	.27638	3.6181	.96386	1.0375	3.7538	33
28	.26668	.27670	3.6140	.96379	1.0376	3.7498	32
29	.26696	.27701	3.6100	.96371	1.0377	3.7459	31
30	.26724	.27732	3.6059	.96363	1.0377	3.7420	30
31	.26752	.27764	3.6018	.96355	1.0378	3.7381	29
32	.26780	.27795	3.5978	.96347	1.0379	3.7341	28
33	.26808	.27826	3.5937	.96340	1.0380	3.7302	27
34	.26836	.27858	3.5897	.96332	1.0381	3.7263	26
35	.26864	.27889	3.5856	.96324	1.0382	3.7225	25
36	.26892	.27921	3.5816	.96316	1.0382	3.7186	24
37	.26920	.27952	3.5776	.96308	1.0383	3.7147	23
38	.26948	.27983	3.5736	.96301	1.0384	3.7108	22
39	.26976	.28015	3.5696	.96293	1.0385	3.7070	21
40	.27004	.28046	3.5656	.96285	1.0386	3.7032	20
41	.27032	.28077	3.5616	.96277	1.0387	3.6993	19
42	.27060	.28109	3.5576	.96269	1.0388	3.6955	18
43	.27088	.28140	3.5536	.96261	1.0388	3.6917	17
44	.27116	.28172	3.5497	.96253	1.0389	3.6879	16
45	.27144	.28203	3.5457	.96246	1.0390	3.6840	15
46	.27172	.28234	3.5418	.96238	1.0391	3.6803	14
47	.27200	.28266	3.5379	.96230	1.0392	3.6765	13
48	.27228	.28297	3.5339	.96222	1.0393	3.6727	12
49	.27256	.28329	3.5300	.96214	1.0394	3.6689	11
50	.27284	.28360	3.5261	.96206	1.0394	3.6652	10
51	.27312	.28391	3.5222	.96198	1.0395	3.6614	9
52	.27340	.28423	3.5183	.96190	1.0396	3.6576	8
53	.27368	.28454	3.5144	.96182	1.0397	3.6539	7
54	.27396	.28486	3.5105	.96174	1.0398	3.6502	6
55	.27424	.28517	3.5067	.96166	1.0399	3.6465	5
56	.27452	.28549	3.5028	.96158	1.0400	3.6427	4
57	.27480	.28580	3.4989	.96150	1.0400	3.6390	3
58	.27508	.28612	3.4951	.96142	1.0401	3.6353	2
59	.27536	.28643	3.4912	.96134	1.0402	3.6316	1
60	.27564	.28675	3.4874	.96126	1.0403	3.6280	0
′	Cos	Ctn	Tan	Sin	Csc	Sec	′

105° (285°) (254°) **74°**

16° (196°) (343°) **163°**

′	Sin	Tan	Ctn	Cos	Sec	Csc	′
0	.27564	.28675	3.4874	.96126	1.0403	3.6280	60
1	.27592	.28706	3.4836	.96118	1.0404	3.6243	59
2	.27620	.28738	3.4798	.96110	1.0405	3.6206	58
3	.27648	.28769	3.4760	.96102	1.0406	3.6169	57
4	.27676	.28801	3.4722	.96094	1.0406	3.6133	56
5	.27704	.28832	3.4684	.96086	1.0407	3.6097	55
6	.27731	.28864	3.4646	.96078	1.0408	3.6060	54
7	.27759	.28895	3.4608	.96070	1.0409	3.6024	53
8	.27787	.28927	3.4570	.96062	1.0410	3.5988	52
9	.27815	.28958	3.4533	.96054	1.0411	3.5951	51
10	.27843	.28990	3.4495	.96046	1.0412	3.5915	50
11	.27871	.29021	3.4458	.96037	1.0413	3.5879	49
12	.27899	.29053	3.4420	.96029	1.0413	3.5843	48
13	.27927	.29084	3.4383	.96021	1.0414	3.5808	47
14	.27955	.29116	3.4346	.96013	1.0415	3.5772	46
15	.27983	.29147	3.4308	.96005	1.0416	3.5736	45
16	.28011	.29179	3.4271	.95997	1.0417	3.5700	44
17	.28039	.29210	3.4234	.95989	1.0418	3.5665	43
18	.28067	.29242	3.4197	.95981	1.0419	3.5629	42
19	.28095	.29274	3.4160	.95972	1.0420	3.5594	41
20	.28123	.29305	3.4124	.95964	1.0421	3.5559	40
21	.28150	.29337	3.4087	.95956	1.0421	3.5523	39
22	.28178	.29368	3.4050	.95948	1.0422	3.5488	38
23	.28206	.29400	3.4014	.95940	1.0423	3.5453	37
24	.28234	.29432	3.3977	.95931	1.0424	3.5418	36
25	.28262	.29463	3.3941	.95923	1.0425	3.5383	35
26	.28290	.29495	3.3904	.95915	1.0426	3.5348	34
27	.28318	.29526	3.3868	.95907	1.0427	3.5313	33
28	.28346	.29558	3.3832	.95898	1.0428	3.5279	32
29	.28374	.29590	3.3796	.95890	1.0429	3.5244	31
30	.28402	.29621	3.3759	.95882	1.0429	3.5209	30
31	.28429	.29653	3.3723	.95874	1.0430	3.5175	29
32	.28457	.29685	3.3687	.95865	1.0431	3.5140	28
33	.28485	.29716	3.3652	.95857	1.0432	3.5106	27
34	.28513	.29748	3.3616	.95849	1.0433	3.5072	26
35	.28541	.29780	3.3580	.95841	1.0434	3.5037	25
36	.28569	.29811	3.3544	.95832	1.0435	3.5003	24
37	.28597	.29843	3.3509	.95824	1.0436	3.4969	23
38	.28625	.29875	3.3473	.95816	1.0437	3.4935	22
39	.28652	.29906	3.3438	.95807	1.0438	3.4901	21
40	.28680	.29938	3.3402	.95799	1.0439	3.4867	20
41	.28708	.29970	3.3367	.95791	1.0439	3.4833	19
42	.28736	.30001	3.3332	.95782	1.0440	3.4799	18
43	.28764	.30033	3.3297	.95774	1.0441	3.4766	17
44	.28792	.30065	3.3261	.95766	1.0442	3.4732	16
45	.28820	.30097	3.3226	.95757	1.0443	3.4699	15
46	.28847	.30128	3.3191	.95749	1.0444	3.4665	14
47	.28875	.30160	3.3156	.95740	1.0445	3.4632	13
48	.28903	.30192	3.3122	.95732	1.0446	3.4598	12
49	.28931	.30224	3.3087	.95724	1.0447	3.4565	11
50	.28959	.30255	3.3052	.95715	1.0448	3.4532	10
51	.28987	.30287	3.3017	.95707	1.0449	3.4499	9
52	.29015	.30319	3.2983	.95698	1.0450	3.4465	8
53	.29042	.30351	3.2948	.95690	1.0450	3.4432	7
54	.29070	.30382	3.2914	.95681	1.0451	3.4399	6
55	.29098	.30414	3.2879	.95673	1.0452	3.4367	5
56	.29126	.30446	3.2845	.95664	1.0453	3.4334	4
57	.29154	.30478	3.2811	.95656	1.0454	3.4301	3
58	.29182	.30509	3.2777	.95647	1.0455	3.4268	2
59	.29209	.30541	3.2743	.95639	1.0456	3.4236	1
60	.29237	.30573	3.2709	.95630	1.0457	3.4203	0
′	Cos	Ctn	Tan	Sin	Csc	Sec	′

106° (286°) (253°) **73°**

17° (197°) (342°) **162°**

′	Sin	Tan	Ctn	Cos	Sec	Csc	′
0	.29237	.30573	3.2709	.95630	1.0457	3.4203	60
1	.29265	.30605	3.2675	.95622	1.0458	3.4171	59
2	.29293	.30637	3.2641	.95613	1.0459	3.4138	58
3	.29321	.30669	3.2607	.95605	1.0460	3.4106	57
4	.29348	.30700	3.2573	.95596	1.0461	3.4073	56
5	.29376	.30732	3.2539	.95588	1.0462	3.4041	55
6	.29404	.30764	3.2506	.95579	1.0463	3.4009	54
7	.29432	.30796	3.2472	.95571	1.0463	3.3977	53
8	.29460	.30828	3.2438	.95562	1.0464	3.3945	52
9	.29487	.30860	3.2405	.95554	1.0465	3.3913	51
10	.29515	.30891	3.2371	.95545	1.0466	3.3881	50
11	.29543	.30923	3.2338	.95536	1.0467	3.3849	49
12	.29571	.30955	3.2305	.95528	1.0468	3.3817	48
13	.29599	.30987	3.2272	.95519	1.0469	3.3785	47
14	.29626	.31019	3.2238	.95511	1.0470	3.3754	46
15	.29654	.31051	3.2205	.95502	1.0471	3.3722	45
16	.29682	.31083	3.2172	.95493	1.0472	3.3691	44
17	.29710	.31115	3.2139	.95485	1.0473	3.3659	43
18	.29737	.31147	3.2106	.95476	1.0474	3.3628	42
19	.29765	.31178	3.2073	.95467	1.0475	3.3596	41
20	.29793	.31210	3.2041	.95459	1.0476	3.3565	40
21	.29821	.31242	3.2008	.95450	1.0477	3.3534	39
22	.29849	.31274	3.1975	.95441	1.0478	3.3502	38
23	.29876	.31306	3.1943	.95433	1.0479	3.3471	37
24	.29904	.31338	3.1910	.95424	1.0480	3.3440	36
25	.29932	.31370	3.1878	.95415	1.0480	3.3409	35
26	.29960	.31402	3.1845	.95407	1.0481	3.3378	34
27	.29987	.31434	3.1813	.95398	1.0482	3.3347	33
28	.30015	.31466	3.1780	.95389	1.0483	3.3317	32
29	.30043	.31498	3.1748	.95380	1.0484	3.3286	31
30	.30071	.31530	3.1716	.95372	1.0485	3.3255	30
31	.30098	.31562	3.1684	.95363	1.0486	3.3224	29
32	.30126	.31594	3.1652	.95354	1.0487	3.3194	28
33	.30154	.31626	3.1620	.95345	1.0488	3.3163	27
34	.30182	.31658	3.1588	.95337	1.0489	3.3133	26
35	.30209	.31690	3.1556	.95328	1.0490	3.3102	25
36	.30237	.31722	3.1524	.95319	1.0491	3.3072	24
37	.30265	.31754	3.1492	.95310	1.0492	3.3042	23
38	.30292	.31786	3.1460	.95301	1.0493	3.3012	22
39	.30320	.31818	3.1429	.95293	1.0494	3.2981	21
40	.30348	.31850	3.1397	.95284	1.0495	3.2951	20
41	.30376	.31882	3.1366	.95275	1.0496	3.2921	19
42	.30403	.31914	3.1334	.95266	1.0497	3.2891	18
43	.30431	.31946	3.1303	.95257	1.0498	3.2861	17
44	.30459	.31978	3.1271	.95248	1.0499	3.2831	16
45	.30486	.32010	3.1240	.95240	1.0500	3.2801	15
46	.30514	.32042	3.1209	.95231	1.0501	3.2772	14
47	.30542	.32074	3.1178	.95222	1.0502	3.2742	13
48	.30570	.32106	3.1146	.95213	1.0503	3.2712	12
49	.30597	.32139	3.1115	.95204	1.0504	3.2683	11
50	.30625	.32171	3.1084	.95195	1.0505	3.2653	10
51	.30653	.32203	3.1053	.95186	1.0506	3.2624	9
52	.30680	.32235	3.1022	.95177	1.0507	3.2594	8
53	.30708	.32267	3.0991	.95168	1.0508	3.2565	7
54	.30736	.32299	3.0961	.95159	1.0509	3.2535	6
55	.30763	.32331	3.0930	.95150	1.0510	3.2506	5
56	.30791	.32363	3.0899	.95142	1.0511	3.2477	4
57	.30819	.32396	3.0868	.95133	1.0512	3.2448	3
58	.30846	.32428	3.0838	.95124	1.0513	3.2419	2
59	.30874	.32460	3.0807	.95115	1.0514	3.2390	1
60	.30902	.32492	3.0777	.95106	1.0515	3.2361	0
′	Cos	Ctn	Tan	Sin	Csc	Sec	′

107° (287°) (252°) **72°**

18° (198°) (341°) **161°**

′	Sin	Tan	Ctn	Cos	Sec	Csc	′
0	.30902	.32492	3.0777	.95106	1.0515	3.2361	60
1	.30929	.32524	3.0746	.95097	1.0516	3.2332	59
2	.30957	.32556	3.0716	.95088	1.0517	3.2303	58
3	.30985	.32588	3.0686	.95079	1.0518	3.2274	57
4	.31012	.32621	3.0655	.95070	1.0519	3.2245	56
5	.31040	.32653	3.0625	.95061	1.0520	3.2217	55
6	.31068	.32685	3.0595	.95052	1.0521	3.2188	54
7	.31095	.32717	3.0565	.95043	1.0522	3.2159	53
8	.31123	.32749	3.0535	.95033	1.0523	3.2131	52
9	.31151	.32782	3.0505	.95024	1.0524	3.2102	51
10	.31178	.32814	3.0475	.95015	1.0525	3.2074	50
11	.31206	.32846	3.0445	.95006	1.0526	3.2045	49
12	.31233	.32878	3.0415	.94997	1.0527	3.2017	48
13	.31261	.32911	3.0385	.94988	1.0528	3.1989	47
14	.31289	.32943	3.0356	.94979	1.0529	3.1960	46
15	.31316	.32975	3.0326	.94970	1.0530	3.1932	45
16	.31344	.33007	3.0296	.94961	1.0531	3.1904	44
17	.31372	.33040	3.0267	.94952	1.0532	3.1876	43
18	.31399	.33072	3.0237	.94943	1.0533	3.1848	42
19	.31427	.33104	3.0208	.94933	1.0534	3.1820	41
20	.31454	.33136	3.0178	.94924	1.0535	3.1792	40
21	.31482	.33169	3.0149	.94915	1.0536	3.1764	39
22	.31510	.33201	3.0120	.94906	1.0537	3.1736	38
23	.31537	.33233	3.0090	.94897	1.0538	3.1708	37
24	.31565	.33266	3.0061	.94888	1.0539	3.1681	36
25	.31593	.33298	3.0032	.94878	1.0540	3.1653	35
26	.31620	.33330	3.0003	.94869	1.0541	3.1625	34
27	.31648	.33363	2.9974	.94860	1.0542	3.1598	33
28	.31675	.33395	2.9945	.94851	1.0543	3.1570	32
29	.31703	.33427	2.9916	.94842	1.0544	3.1543	31
30	.31730	.33460	2.9887	.94832	1.0545	3.1515	30
31	.31758	.33492	2.9858	.94823	1.0546	3.1488	29
32	.31786	.33524	2.9829	.94814	1.0547	3.1461	28
33	.31813	.33557	2.9800	.94805	1.0548	3.1433	27
34	.31841	.33589	2.9772	.94795	1.0549	3.1406	26
35	.31868	.33621	2.9743	.94786	1.0550	3.1379	25
36	.31896	.33654	2.9714	.94777	1.0551	3.1352	24
37	.31923	.33686	2.9686	.94768	1.0552	3.1325	23
38	.31951	.33718	2.9657	.94758	1.0553	3.1298	22
39	.31979	.33751	2.9629	.94749	1.0554	3.1271	21
40	.32006	.33783	2.9600	.94740	1.0555	3.1244	20
41	.32034	.33816	2.9572	.94730	1.0556	3.1217	19
42	.32061	.33848	2.9544	.94721	1.0557	3.1190	18
43	.32089	.33881	2.9515	.94712	1.0558	3.1163	17
44	.32116	.33913	2.9487	.94702	1.0559	3.1137	16
45	.32144	.33945	2.9459	.94693	1.0560	3.1110	15
46	.32171	.33978	2.9431	.94684	1.0561	3.1083	14
47	.32199	.34010	2.9403	.94674	1.0563	3.1057	13
48	.32227	.34043	2.9375	.94665	1.0564	3.1030	12
49	.32254	.34075	2.9347	.94656	1.0565	3.1004	11
50	.32282	.34108	2.9319	.94646	1.0566	3.0977	10
51	.32309	.34140	2.9291	.94637	1.0567	3.0951	9
52	.32337	.34173	2.9263	.94627	1.0568	3.0925	8
53	.32364	.34205	2.9235	.94618	1.0569	3.0898	7
54	.32392	.34238	2.9208	.94609	1.0570	3.0872	6
55	.32419	.34270	2.9180	.94599	1.0571	3.0846	5
56	.32447	.34303	2.9152	.94590	1.0572	3.0820	4
57	.32474	.34335	2.9125	.94580	1.0573	3.0794	3
58	.32502	.34368	2.9097	.94571	1.0574	3.0768	2
59	.32529	.34400	2.9070	.94561	1.0575	3.0742	1
60	.32557	.34433	2.9042	.94552	1.0576	3.0716	0
′	Cos	Ctn	Tan	Sin	Csc	Sec	′

108° (288°) (251°) **71°**

19° (199°) (340°) **160°**

′	Sin	Tan	Ctn	Cos	Sec	Csc	′
0	.32557	.34433	2.9042	.94552	1.0576	3.0716	60
1	.32584	.34465	2.9015	.94542	1.0577	3.0690	59
2	.32612	.34498	2.8987	.94533	1.0578	3.0664	58
3	.32639	.34530	2.8960	.94523	1.0579	3.0638	57
4	.32667	.34563	2.8933	.94514	1.0580	3.0612	56
5	.32694	.34596	2.8905	.94504	1.0582	3.0586	55
6	.32722	.34628	2.8878	.94495	1.0583	3.0561	54
7	.32749	.34661	2.8851	.94485	1.0584	3.0535	53
8	.32777	.34693	2.8824	.94476	1.0585	3.0509	52
9	.32804	.34726	2.8797	.94466	1.0586	3.0484	51
10	.32832	.34758	2.8770	.94457	1.0587	3.0458	50
11	.32859	.34791	2.8743	.94447	1.0588	3.0433	49
12	.32887	.34824	2.8716	.94438	1.0589	3.0407	48
13	.32914	.34856	2.8689	.94428	1.0590	3.0382	47
14	.32942	.34889	2.8662	.94418	1.0591	3.0357	46
15	.32969	.34922	2.8636	.94409	1.0592	3.0331	45
16	.32997	.34954	2.8609	.94399	1.0593	3.0306	44
17	.33024	.34987	2.8582	.94390	1.0594	3.0281	43
18	.33051	.35020	2.8556	.94380	1.0595	3.0256	42
19	.33079	.35052	2.8529	.94370	1.0597	3.0231	41
20	.33106	.35085	2.8502	.94361	1.0598	3.0206	40
21	.33134	.35118	2.8476	.94351	1.0599	3.0181	39
22	.33161	.35150	2.8449	.94342	1.0600	3.0156	38
23	.33189	.35183	2.8423	.94332	1.0601	3.0131	37
24	.33216	.35216	2.8397	.94322	1.0602	3.0106	36
25	.33244	.35248	2.8370	.94313	1.0603	3.0081	35
26	.33271	.35281	2.8344	.94303	1.0604	3.0056	34
27	.33298	.35314	2.8318	.94293	1.0605	3.0031	33
28	.33326	.35346	2.8291	.94284	1.0606	3.0007	32
29	.33353	.35379	2.8265	.94274	1.0607	2.9982	31
30	.33381	.35412	2.8239	.94264	1.0608	2.9957	30
31	.33408	.35445	2.8213	.94254	1.0610	2.9933	29
32	.33436	.35477	2.8187	.94245	1.0611	2.9908	28
33	.33463	.35510	2.8161	.94235	1.0612	2.9884	27
34	.33490	.35543	2.8135	.94225	1.0613	2.9859	26
35	.33518	.35576	2.8109	.94215	1.0614	2.9835	25
36	.33545	.35608	2.8083	.94206	1.0615	2.9811	24
37	.33573	.35641	2.8057	.94196	1.0616	2.9786	23
38	.33600	.35674	2.8032	.94186	1.0617	2.9762	22
39	.33627	.35707	2.8006	.94176	1.0618	2.9738	21
40	.33655	.35740	2.7980	.94167	1.0619	2.9713	20
41	.33682	.35772	2.7955	.94157	1.0621	2.9689	19
42	.33710	.35805	2.7929	.94147	1.0622	2.9665	18
43	.33737	.35838	2.7903	.94137	1.0623	2.9641	17
44	.33764	.35871	2.7878	.94127	1.0624	2.9617	16
45	.33792	.35904	2.7852	.94118	1.0625	2.9593	15
46	.33819	.35937	2.7827	.94108	1.0626	2.9569	14
47	.33846	.35969	2.7801	.94098	1.0627	2.9545	13
48	.33874	.36002	2.7776	.94088	1.0628	2.9521	12
49	.33901	.36035	2.7751	.94078	1.0629	2.9498	11
50	.33929	.36068	2.7725	.94068	1.0631	2.9474	10
51	.33956	.36101	2.7700	.94058	1.0632	2.9450	9
52	.33983	.36134	2.7675	.94049	1.0633	2.9426	8
53	.34011	.36167	2.7650	.94039	1.0634	2.9403	7
54	.34038	.36199	2.7625	.94029	1.0635	2.9379	6
55	.34065	.36232	2.7600	.94019	1.0636	2.9355	5
56	.34093	.36265	2.7575	.94009	1.0637	2.9332	4
57	.34120	.36298	2.7550	.93999	1.0638	2.9308	3
58	.34147	.36331	2.7525	.93989	1.0640	2.9285	2
59	.34175	.36364	2.7500	.93979	1.0641	2.9261	1
60	.34202	.36397	2.7475	.93969	1.0642	2.9238	0
′	Cos	Ctn	Tan	Sin	Csc	Sec	′

109° (289°) (250°) **70°**

20° (200°) (339°) **159°**

′	Sin	Tan	Ctn	Cos	Sec	Csc	′
0	.34202	.36397	2.7475	.93969	1.0642	2.9238	60
1	.34229	.36430	2.7450	.93959	1.0643	2.9215	59
2	.34257	.36463	2.7425	.93949	1.0644	2.9191	58
3	.34284	.36496	2.7400	.93939	1.0645	2.9168	57
4	.34311	.36529	2.7376	.93929	1.0646	2.9145	56
5	.34339	.36562	2.7351	.93919	1.0647	2.9122	55
6	.34366	.36595	2.7326	.93909	1.0649	2.9099	54
7	.34393	.36628	2.7302	.93899	1.0650	2.9075	53
8	.34421	.36661	2.7277	.93889	1.0651	2.9052	52
9	.34448	.36694	2.7253	.93879	1.0652	2.9029	51
10	.34475	.36727	2.7228	.93869	1.0653	2.9006	50
11	.34503	.36760	2.7204	.93859	1.0654	2.8983	49
12	.34530	.36793	2.7179	.93849	1.0655	2.8960	48
13	.34557	.36826	2.7155	.93839	1.0657	2.8938	47
14	.34584	.36859	2.7130	.93829	1.0658	2.8915	46
15	.34612	.36892	2.7106	.93819	1.0659	2.8892	45
16	.34639	.36925	2.7082	.93809	1.0660	2.8869	44
17	.34666	.36958	2.7058	.93799	1.0661	2.8846	43
18	.34694	.36991	2.7034	.93789	1.0662	2.8824	42
19	.34721	.37024	2.7009	.93779	1.0663	2.8801	41
20	.34748	.37057	2.6985	.93769	1.0665	2.8779	40
21	.34775	.37090	2.6961	.93759	1.0666	2.8756	39
22	.34803	.37123	2.6937	.93748	1.0667	2.8733	38
23	.34830	.37157	2.6913	.93738	1.0668	2.8711	37
24	.34857	.37190	2.6889	.93728	1.0669	2.8688	36
25	.34884	.37223	2.6865	.93718	1.0670	2.8666	35
26	.34912	.37256	2.6841	.93708	1.0671	2.8644	34
27	.34939	.37289	2.6818	.93698	1.0673	2.8621	33
28	.34966	.37322	2.6794	.93688	1.0674	2.8599	32
29	.34993	.37355	2.6770	.93677	1.0675	2.8577	31
30	.35021	.37388	2.6746	.93667	1.0676	2.8555	30
31	.35048	.37422	2.6723	.93657	1.0677	2.8532	29
32	.35075	.37455	2.6699	.93647	1.0678	2.8510	28
33	.35102	.37488	2.6675	.93637	1.0680	2.8488	27
34	.35130	.37521	2.6652	.93626	1.0681	2.8466	26
35	.35157	.37554	2.6628	.93616	1.0682	2.8444	25
36	.35184	.37588	2.6605	.93606	1.0683	2.8422	24
37	.35211	.37621	2.6581	.93596	1.0684	2.8400	23
38	.35239	.37654	2.6558	.93585	1.0685	2.8378	22
39	.35266	.37687	2.6534	.93575	1.0687	2.8356	21
40	.35293	.37720	2.6511	.93565	1.0688	2.8334	20
41	.35320	.37754	2.6488	.93555	1.0689	2.8312	19
42	.35347	.37787	2.6464	.93544	1.0690	2.8291	18
43	.35375	.37820	2.6441	.93534	1.0691	2.8269	17
44	.35402	.37853	2.6418	.93524	1.0692	2.8247	16
45	.35429	.37887	2.6395	.93514	1.0694	2.8225	15
46	.35456	.37920	2.6371	.93503	1.0695	2.8204	14
47	.35484	.37953	2.6348	.93493	1.0696	2.8182	13
48	.35511	.37986	2.6325	.93483	1.0697	2.8161	12
49	.35538	.38020	2.6302	.93472	1.0698	2.8139	11
50	.35565	.38053	2.6279	.93462	1.0700	2.8117	10
51	.35592	.38086	2.6256	.93452	1.0701	2.8096	9
52	.35619	.38120	2.6233	.93441	1.0702	2.8075	8
53	.35647	.38153	2.6210	.93431	1.0703	2.8053	7
54	.35674	.38186	2.6187	.93420	1.0704	2.8032	6
55	.35701	.38220	2.6165	.93410	1.0705	2.8010	5
56	.35728	.38253	2.6142	.93400	1.0707	2.7989	4
57	.35755	.38286	2.6119	.93389	1.0708	2.7968	3
58	.35782	.38320	2.6096	.93379	1.0709	2.7947	2
59	.35810	.38353	2.6074	.93368	1.0710	2.7925	1
60	.35837	.38386	2.6051	.93358	1.0711	2.7904	0
′	Cos	Ctn	Tan	Sin	Csc	Sec	′

110° (290°) (249°) **69°**

21° (201°) (338°) **158°**

′	Sin	Tan	Ctn	Cos	Sec	Csc	′
0	.35837	.38386	2.6051	.93358	1.0711	2.7904	60
1	.35864	.38420	2.6028	.93348	1.0713	2.7883	59
2	.35891	.38453	2.6006	.93337	1.0714	2.7862	58
3	.35918	.38487	2.5983	.93327	1.0715	2.7841	57
4	.35945	.38520	2.5961	.93316	1.0716	2.7820	56
5	.35973	.38553	2.5938	.93306	1.0717	2.7799	55
6	.36000	.38587	2.5916	.93295	1.0719	2.7778	54
7	.36027	.38620	2.5893	.93285	1.0720	2.7757	53
8	.36054	.38654	2.5871	.93274	1.0721	2.7736	52
9	.36081	.38687	2.5848	.93264	1.0722	2.7715	51
10	.36108	.38721	2.5826	.93253	1.0723	2.7695	50
11	.36135	.38754	2.5804	.93243	1.0725	2.7674	49
12	.36162	.38787	2.5782	.93232	1.0726	2.7653	48
13	.36190	.38821	2.5759	.93222	1.0727	2.7632	47
14	.36217	.38854	2.5737	.93211	1.0728	2.7612	46
15	.36244	.38888	2.5715	.93201	1.0730	2.7591	45
16	.36271	.38921	2.5693	.93190	1.0731	2.7570	44
17	.36298	.38955	2.5671	.93180	1.0732	2.7550	43
18	.36325	.38988	2.5649	.93169	1.0733	2.7529	42
19	.36352	.39022	2.5627	.93159	1.0734	2.7509	41
20	.36379	.39055	2.5605	.93148	1.0736	2.7488	40
21	.36406	.39089	2.5583	.93137	1.0737	2.7468	39
22	.36434	.39122	2.5561	.93127	1.0738	2.7447	38
23	.36461	.39156	2.5539	.93116	1.0739	2.7427	37
24	.36488	.39190	2.5517	.93106	1.0740	2.7407	36
25	.36515	.39223	2.5495	.93095	1.0742	2.7386	35
26	.36542	.39257	2.5473	.93084	1.0743	2.7366	34
27	.36569	.39290	2.5452	.93074	1.0744	2.7346	33
28	.36596	.39324	2.5430	.93063	1.0745	2.7325	32
29	.36623	.39357	2.5408	.93052	1.0747	2.7305	31
30	.36650	.39391	2.5386	.93042	1.0748	2.7285	30
31	.36677	.39425	2.5365	.93031	1.0749	2.7265	29
32	.36704	.39458	2.5343	.93020	1.0750	2.7245	28
33	.36731	.39492	2.5322	.93010	1.0752	2.7225	27
34	.36758	.39526	2.5300	.92999	1.0753	2.7205	26
35	.36785	.39559	2.5279	.92988	1.0754	2.7185	25
36	.36812	.39593	2.5257	.92978	1.0755	2.7165	24
37	.36839	.39626	2.5236	.92967	1.0757	2.7145	23
38	.36867	.39660	2.5214	.92956	1.0758	2.7125	22
39	.36894	.39694	2.5193	.92945	1.0759	2.7105	21
40	.36921	.39727	2.5172	.92935	1.0760	2.7085	20
41	.36948	.39761	2.5150	.92924	1.0761	2.7065	19
42	.36975	.39795	2.5129	.92913	1.0763	2.7046	18
43	.37002	.39829	2.5108	.92902	1.0764	2.7026	17
44	.37029	.39862	2.5086	.92892	1.0765	2.7006	16
45	.37056	.39896	2.5065	.92881	1.0766	2.6986	15
46	.37083	.39930	2.5044	.92870	1.0768	2.6967	14
47	.37110	.39963	2.5023	.92859	1.0769	2.6947	13
48	.37137	.39997	2.5002	.92849	1.0770	2.6927	12
49	.37164	.40031	2.4981	.92838	1.0771	2.6908	11
50	.37191	.40065	2.4960	.92827	1.0773	2.6888	10
51	.37218	.40098	2.4939	.92816	1.0774	2.6869	9
52	.37245	.40132	2.4918	.92805	1.0775	2.6849	8
53	.37272	.40166	2.4897	.92794	1.0777	2.6830	7
54	.37299	.40200	2.4876	.92784	1.0778	2.6811	6
55	.37326	.40234	2.4855	.92773	1.0779	2.6791	5
56	.37353	.40267	2.4834	.92762	1.0780	2.6772	4
57	.37380	.40301	2.4813	.92751	1.0782	2.6752	3
58	.37407	.40335	2.4792	.92740	1.0783	2.6733	2
59	.37434	.40369	2.4772	.92729	1.0784	2.6714	1
60	.37461	.40403	2.4751	.92718	1.0785	2.6695	0
′	Cos	Ctn	Tan	Sin	Csc	Sec	′

111° (291°) (248°) **68°**

22° (202°) (337°) **157°**

′	Sin	Tan	Ctn	Cos	Sec	Csc	′
0	.37461	.40403	2.4751	.92718	1.0785	2.6695	60
1	.37488	.40436	2.4730	.92707	1.0787	2.6675	59
2	.37515	.40470	2.4709	.92697	1.0788	2.6656	58
3	.37542	.40504	2.4689	.92686	1.0789	2.6637	57
4	.37569	.40538	2.4668	.92675	1.0790	2.6618	56
5	.37595	.40572	2.4648	.92664	1.0792	2.6599	55
6	.37622	.40606	2.4627	.92653	1.0793	2.6580	54
7	.37649	.40640	2.4606	.92642	1.0794	2.6561	53
8	.37676	.40674	2.4586	.92631	1.0796	2.6542	52
9	.37703	.40707	2.4566	.92620	1.0797	2.6523	51
10	.37730	.40741	2.4545	.92609	1.0798	2.6504	50
11	.37757	.40775	2.4525	.92598	1.0799	2.6485	49
12	.37784	.40809	2.4504	.92587	1.0801	2.6466	48
13	.37811	.40843	2.4484	.92576	1.0802	2.6447	47
14	.37838	.40877	2.4464	.92565	1.0803	2.6429	46
15	.37865	.40911	2.4443	.92554	1.0804	2.6410	45
16	.37892	.40945	2.4423	.92543	1.0806	2.6391	44
17	.37919	.40979	2.4403	.92532	1.0807	2.6372	43
18	.37946	.41013	2.4383	.92521	1.0808	2.6354	42
19	.37973	.41047	2.4362	.92510	1.0810	2.6335	41
20	.37999	.41081	2.4342	.92499	1.0811	2.6316	40
21	.38026	.41115	2.4322	.92488	1.0812	2.6298	39
22	.38053	.41149	2.4302	.92477	1.0814	2.6279	38
23	.38080	.41183	2.4282	.92466	1.0815	2.6260	37
24	.38107	.41217	2.4262	.92455	1.0816	2.6242	36
25	.38134	.41251	2.4242	.92444	1.0817	2.6223	35
26	.38161	.41285	2.4222	.92432	1.0819	2.6205	34
27	.38188	.41319	2.4202	.92421	1.0820	2.6186	33
28	.38215	.41353	2.4182	.92410	1.0821	2.6168	32
29	.38241	.41387	2.4162	.92399	1.0823	2.6150	31
30	.38268	.41421	2.4142	.92388	1.0824	2.6131	30
31	.38295	.41455	2.4122	.92377	1.0825	2.6113	29
32	.38322	.41490	2.4102	.92366	1.0827	2.6095	28
33	.38349	.41524	2.4083	.92355	1.0828	2.6076	27
34	.38376	.41558	2.4063	.92343	1.0829	2.6058	26
35	.38403	.41592	2.4043	.92332	1.0830	2.6040	25
36	.38430	.41626	2.4023	.92321	1.0832	2.6022	24
37	.38456	.41660	2.4004	.92310	1.0833	2.6003	23
38	.38483	.41694	2.3984	.92299	1.0834	2.5985	22
39	.38510	.41728	2.3964	.92287	1.0836	2.5967	21
40	.38537	.41763	2.3945	.92276	1.0837	2.5949	20
41	.38564	.41797	2.3925	.92265	1.0838	2.5931	19
42	.38591	.41831	2.3906	.92254	1.0840	2.5913	18
43	.38617	.41865	2.3886	.92243	1.0841	2.5895	17
44	.38644	.41899	2.3867	.92231	1.0842	2.5877	16
45	.38671	.41933	2.3847	.92220	1.0844	2.5859	15
46	.38698	.41968	2.3828	.92209	1.0845	2.5841	14
47	.38725	.42002	2.3808	.92198	1.0846	2.5823	13
48	.38752	.42036	2.3789	.92186	1.0848	2.5805	12
49	.38778	.42070	2.3770	.92175	1.0849	2.5788	11
50	.38805	.42105	2.3750	.92164	1.0850	2.5770	10
51	.38832	.42139	2.3731	.92152	1.0852	2.5752	9
52	.38859	.42173	2.3712	.92141	1.0853	2.5734	8
53	.38886	.42207	2.3693	.92130	1.0854	2.5716	7
54	.38912	.42242	2.3673	.92119	1.0856	2.5699	6
55	.38939	.42276	2.3654	.92107	1.0857	2.5681	5
56	.38966	.42310	2.3635	.92096	1.0858	2.5663	4
57	.38993	.42345	2.3616	.92085	1.0860	2.5646	3
58	.39020	.42379	2.3597	.92073	1.0861	2.5628	2
59	.39046	.42413	2.3578	.92062	1.0862	2.5611	1
60	.39073	.42447	2.3559	.92050	1.0864	2.5593	0
′	Cos	Ctn	Tan	Sin	Csc	Sec	′

112° (292°) (247°) **67°**

23° (203°) (336°) **156°**

′	Sin	Tan	Ctn	Cos	Sec	Csc	′
0	.39073	.42447	2.3559	.92050	1.0864	2.5593	60
1	.39100	.42482	2.3539	.92039	1.0865	2.5576	59
2	.39127	.42516	2.3520	.92028	1.0866	2.5558	58
3	.39153	.42551	2.3501	.92016	1.0868	2.5541	57
4	.39180	.42585	2.3483	.92005	1.0869	2.5523	56
5	.39207	.42619	2.3464	.91994	1.0870	2.5506	55
6	.39234	.42654	2.3445	.91982	1.0872	2.5488	54
7	.39260	.42688	2.3426	.91971	1.0873	2.5471	53
8	.39287	.42722	2.3407	.91959	1.0874	2.5454	52
9	.39314	.42757	2.3388	.91948	1.0876	2.5436	51
10	.39341	.42791	2.3369	.91936	1.0877	2.5419	50
11	.39367	.42826	2.3351	.91925	1.0878	2.5402	49
12	.39394	.42860	2.3332	.91914	1.0880	2.5384	48
13	.39421	.42894	2.3313	.91902	1.0881	2.5367	47
14	.39448	.42929	2.3294	.91891	1.0883	2.5350	46
15	.39474	.42963	2.3276	.91879	1.0884	2.5333	45
16	.39501	.42998	2.3257	.91868	1.0885	2.5316	44
17	.39528	.43032	2.3238	.91856	1.0887	2.5299	43
18	.39555	.43067	2.3220	.91845	1.0888	2.5282	42
19	.39581	.43101	2.3201	.91833	1.0889	2.5264	41
20	.39608	.43136	2.3183	.91822	1.0891	2.5247	40
21	.39635	.43170	2.3164	.91810	1.0892	2.5230	39
22	.39661	.43205	2.3146	.91799	1.0893	2.5213	38
23	.39688	.43239	2.3127	.91787	1.0895	2.5196	37
24	.39715	.43274	2.3109	.91775	1.0896	2.5180	36
25	.39741	.43308	2.3090	.91764	1.0898	2.5163	35
26	.39768	.43343	2.3072	.91752	1.0899	2.5146	34
27	.39795	.43378	2.3053	.91741	1.0900	2.5129	33
28	.39822	.43412	2.3035	.91729	1.0902	2.5112	32
29	.39848	.43447	2.3017	.91718	1.0903	2.5095	31
30	.39875	.43481	2.2998	.91706	1.0904	2.5078	30
31	.39902	.43516	2.2980	.91694	1.0906	2.5062	29
32	.39928	.43550	2.2962	.91683	1.0907	2.5045	28
33	.39955	.43585	2.2944	.91671	1.0909	2.5028	27
34	.39982	.43620	2.2925	.91660	1.0910	2.5012	26
35	.40008	.43654	2.2907	.91648	1.0911	2.4995	25
36	.40035	.43689	2.2889	.91636	1.0913	2.4978	24
37	.40062	.43724	2.2871	.91625	1.0914	2.4962	23
38	.40088	.43758	2.2853	.91613	1.0915	2.4945	22
39	.40115	.43793	2.2835	.91601	1.0917	2.4928	21
40	.40141	.43828	2.2817	.91590	1.0918	2.4912	20
41	.40168	.43862	2.2799	.91578	1.0920	2.4895	19
42	.40195	.43897	2.2781	.91566	1.0921	2.4879	18
43	.40221	.43932	2.2763	.91555	1.0922	2.4862	17
44	.40248	.43966	2.2745	.91543	1.0924	2.4846	16
45	.40275	.44001	2.2727	.91531	1.0925	2.4830	15
46	.40301	.44036	2.2709	.91519	1.0927	2.4813	14
47	.40328	.44071	2.2691	.91508	1.0928	2.4797	13
48	.40355	.44105	2.2673	.91496	1.0929	2.4780	12
49	.40381	.44140	2.2655	.91484	1.0931	2.4764	11
50	.40408	.44175	2.2637	.91472	1.0932	2.4748	10
51	.40434	.44210	2.2620	.91461	1.0934	2.4731	9
52	.40461	.44244	2.2602	.91449	1.0935	2.4715	8
53	.40488	.44279	2.2584	.91437	1.0936	2.4699	7
54	.40514	.44314	2.2566	.91425	1.0938	2.4683	6
55	.40541	.44349	2.2549	.91414	1.0939	2.4667	5
56	.40567	.44384	2.2531	.91402	1.0941	2.4650	4
57	.40594	.44418	2.2513	.91390	1.0942	2.4634	3
58	.40621	.44453	2.2496	.91378	1.0944	2.4618	2
59	.40647	.44488	2.2478	.91366	1.0945	2.4602	1
60	.40674	.44523	2.2460	.91355	1.0946	2.4586	0
′	Cos	Ctn	Tan	Sin	Csc	Sec	′

113° (293°) (246°) **66°**

24° (204°) (335°) **155°**

′	Sin	Tan	Ctn	Cos	Sec	Csc	′
0	.40674	.44523	2.2460	.91355	1.0946	2.4586	60
1	.40700	.44558	2.2443	.91343	1.0948	2.4570	59
2	.40727	.44593	2.2425	.91331	1.0949	2.4554	58
3	.40753	.44627	2.2408	.91319	1.0951	2.4538	57
4	.40780	.44662	2.2390	.91307	1.0952	2.4522	56
5	.40806	.44697	2.2373	.91295	1.0953	2.4506	55
6	.40833	.44732	2.2355	.91283	1.0955	2.4490	54
7	.40860	.44767	2.2338	.91272	1.0956	2.4474	53
8	.40886	.44802	2.2320	.91260	1.0958	2.4458	52
9	.40913	.44837	2.2303	.91248	1.0959	2.4442	51
10	.40939	.44872	2.2286	.91236	1.0961	2.4426	50
11	.40966	.44907	2.2268	.91224	1.0962	2.4411	49
12	.40992	.44942	2.2251	.91212	1.0963	2.4395	48
13	.41019	.44977	2.2234	.91200	1.0965	2.4379	47
14	.41045	.45012	2.2216	.91188	1.0966	2.4363	46
15	.41072	.45047	2.2199	.91176	1.0968	2.4348	45
16	.41098	.45082	2.2182	.91164	1.0969	2.4332	44
17	.41125	.45117	2.2165	.91152	1.0971	2.4316	43
18	.41151	.45152	2.2148	.91140	1.0972	2.4300	42
19	.41178	.45187	2.2130	.91128	1.0974	2.4285	41
20	.41204	.45222	2.2113	.91116	1.0975	2.4269	40
21	.41231	.45257	2.2096	.91104	1.0976	2.4254	39
22	.41257	.45292	2.2079	.91092	1.0978	2.4238	38
23	.41284	.45327	2.2062	.91080	1.0979	2.4222	37
24	.41310	.45362	2.2045	.91068	1.0981	2.4207	36
25	.41337	.45397	2.2028	.91056	1.0982	2.4191	35
26	.41363	.45432	2.2011	.91044	1.0984	2.4176	34
27	.41390	.45467	2.1994	.91032	1.0985	2.4160	33
28	.41416	.45502	2.1977	.91020	1.0987	2.4145	32
29	.41443	.45538	2.1960	.91008	1.0988	2.4130	31
30	.41469	.45573	2.1943	.90996	1.0989	2.4114	30
31	.41496	.45608	2.1926	.90984	1.0991	2.4099	29
32	.41522	.45643	2.1909	.90972	1.0992	2.4083	28
33	.41549	.45678	2.1892	.90960	1.0994	2.4068	27
34	.41575	.45713	2.1876	.90948	1.0995	2.4053	26
35	.41602	.45748	2.1859	.90936	1.0997	2.4038	25
36	.41628	.45784	2.1842	.90924	1.0998	2.4022	24
37	.41655	.45819	2.1825	.90911	1.1000	2.4007	23
38	.41681	.45854	2.1808	.90899	1.1001	2.3992	22
39	.41707	.45889	2.1792	.90887	1.1003	2.3977	21
40	.41734	.45924	2.1775	.90875	1.1004	2.3961	20
41	.41760	.45960	2.1758	.90863	1.1006	2.3946	19
42	.41787	.45995	2.1742	.90851	1.1007	2.3931	18
43	.41813	.46030	2.1725	.90839	1.1009	2.3916	17
44	.41840	.46065	2.1708	.90826	1.1010	2.3901	16
45	.41866	.46101	2.1692	.90814	1.1011	2.3886	15
46	.41892	.46136	2.1675	.90802	1.1013	2.3871	14
47	.41919	.46171	2.1659	.90790	1.1014	2.3856	13
48	.41945	.46206	2.1642	.90778	1.1016	2.3841	12
49	.41972	.46242	2.1625	.90766	1.1017	2.3826	11
50	.41998	.46277	2.1609	.90753	1.1019	2.3811	10
51	.42024	.46312	2.1592	.90741	1.1020	2.3796	9
52	.42051	.46348	2.1576	.90729	1.1022	2.3781	8
53	.42077	.46383	2.1560	.90717	1.1023	2.3766	7
54	.42104	.46418	2.1543	.90704	1.1025	2.3751	6
55	.42130	.46454	2.1527	.90692	1.1026	2.3736	5
56	.42156	.46489	2.1510	.90680	1.1028	2.3721	4
57	.42183	.46525	2.1494	.90668	1.1029	2.3706	3
58	.42209	.46560	2.1478	.90655	1.1031	2.3692	2
59	.42235	.46595	2.1461	.90643	1.1032	2.3677	1
60	.42262	.46631	2.1445	.90631	1.1034	2.3662	0
′	Cos	Ctn	Tan	Sin	Csc	Sec	′

114° (294°) (245°) **65°**

25° (205°) (334°) **154°**

′	Sin	Tan	Ctn	Cos	Sec	Csc	′
0	.42262	.46631	2.1445	.90631	1.1034	2.3662	60
1	.42288	.46666	2.1429	.90618	1.1035	2.3647	59
2	.42315	.46702	2.1413	.90606	1.1037	2.3633	58
3	.42341	.46737	2.1396	.90594	1.1038	2.3618	57
4	.42367	.46772	2.1380	.90582	1.1040	2.3603	56
5	.42394	.46808	2.1364	.90569	1.1041	2.3588	55
6	.42420	.46843	2.1348	.90557	1.1043	2.3574	54
7	.42446	.46879	2.1332	.90545	1.1044	2.3559	53
8	.42473	.46914	2.1315	.90532	1.1046	2.3545	52
9	.42499	.46950	2.1299	.90520	1.1047	2.3530	51
10	.42525	.46985	2.1283	.90507	1.1049	2.3515	50
11	.42552	.47021	2.1267	.90495	1.1050	2.3501	49
12	.42578	.47056	2.1251	.90483	1.1052	2.3486	48
13	.42604	.47092	2.1235	.90470	1.1053	2.3472	47
14	.42631	.47128	2.1219	.90458	1.1055	2.3457	46
15	.42657	.47163	2.1203	.90446	1.1056	2.3443	45
16	.42683	.47199	2.1187	.90433	1.1058	2.3428	44
17	.42709	.47234	2.1171	.90421	1.1059	2.3414	43
18	.42736	.47270	2.1155	.90408	1.1061	2.3400	42
19	.42762	.47305	2.1139	.90396	1.1062	2.3385	41
20	.42788	.47341	2.1123	.90383	1.1064	2.3371	40
21	.42815	.47377	2.1107	.90371	1.1066	2.3356	39
22	.42841	.47412	2.1092	.90358	1.1067	2.3342	38
23	.42867	.47448	2.1076	.90346	1.1069	2.3328	37
24	.42894	.47483	2.1060	.90334	1.1070	2.3314	36
25	.42920	.47519	2.1044	.90321	1.1072	2.3299	35
26	.42946	.47555	2.1028	.90309	1.1073	2.3285	34
27	.42972	.47590	2.1013	.90296	1.1075	2.3271	33
28	.42999	.47626	2.0997	.90284	1.1076	2.3257	32
29	.43025	.47662	2.0981	.90271	1.1078	2.3242	31
30	.43051	.47698	2.0965	.90259	1.1079	2.3228	30
31	.43077	.47733	2.0950	.90246	1.1081	2.3214	29
32	.43104	.47769	2.0934	.90233	1.1082	2.3200	28
33	.43130	.47805	2.0918	.90221	1.1084	2.3186	27
34	.43156	.47840	2.0903	.90208	1.1085	2.3172	26
35	.43182	.47876	2.0887	.90196	1.1087	2.3158	25
36	.43209	.47912	2.0872	.90183	1.1089	2.3144	24
37	.43235	.47948	2.0856	.90171	1.1090	2.3130	23
38	.43261	.47984	2.0840	.90158	1.1092	2.3115	22
39	.43287	.48019	2.0825	.90146	1.1093	2.3101	21
40	.43313	.48055	2.0809	.90133	1.1095	2.3088	20
41	.43340	.48091	2.0794	.90120	1.1096	2.3074	19
42	.43366	.48127	2.0778	.90108	1.1098	2.3060	18
43	.43392	.48163	2.0763	.90095	1.1099	2.3046	17
44	.43418	.48198	2.0748	.90082	1.1101	2.3032	16
45	.43445	.48234	2.0732	.90070	1.1102	2.3018	15
46	.43471	.48270	2.0717	.90057	1.1104	2.3004	14
47	.43497	.48306	2.0701	.90045	1.1106	2.2990	13
48	.43523	.48342	2.0686	.90032	1.1107	2.2976	12
49	.43549	.48378	2.0671	.90019	1.1109	2.2962	11
50	.43575	.48414	2.0655	.90007	1.1110	2.2949	10
51	.43602	.48450	2.0640	.89994	1.1112	2.2935	9
52	.43628	.48486	2.0625	.89981	1.1113	2.2921	8
53	.43654	.48521	2.0609	.89968	1.1115	2.2907	7
54	.43680	.48557	2.0594	.89956	1.1117	2.2894	6
55	.43706	.48593	2.0579	.89943	1.1118	2.2880	5
56	.43733	.48629	2.0564	.89930	1.1120	2.2866	4
57	.43759	.48665	2.0549	.89918	1.1121	2.2853	3
58	.43785	.48701	2.0533	.89905	1.1123	2.2839	2
59	.43811	.48737	2.0518	.89892	1.1124	2.2825	1
60	.43837	.48773	2.0503	.89879	1.1126	2.2812	0
′	Cos	Ctn	Tan	Sin	Csc	Sec	′

115° (295°) (244°) **64°**

26° (206°) (333°) **153°**

′	Sin	Tan	Ctn	Cos	Sec	Csc	′
0	.43837	.48773	2.0503	.89879	1.1126	2.2812	60
1	.43863	.48809	2.0488	.89867	1.1128	2.2798	59
2	.43889	.48845	2.0473	.89854	1.1129	2.2785	58
3	.43916	.48881	2.0458	.89841	1.1131	2.2771	57
4	.43942	.48917	2.0443	.89828	1.1132	2.2757	56
5	.43968	.48953	2.0428	.89816	1.1134	2.2744	55
6	.43994	.48989	2.0413	.89803	1.1136	2.2730	54
7	.44020	.49026	2.0398	.89790	1.1137	2.2717	53
8	.44046	.49062	2.0383	.89777	1.1139	2.2703	52
9	.44072	.49098	2.0368	.89764	1.1140	2.2690	51
10	.44098	.49134	2.0353	.89752	1.1142	2.2677	50
11	.44124	.49170	2.0338	.89739	1.1143	2.2663	49
12	.44151	.49206	2.0323	.89726	1.1145	2.2650	48
13	.44177	.49242	2.0308	.89713	1.1147	2.2636	47
14	.44203	.49278	2.0293	.89700	1.1148	2.2623	46
15	.44229	.49315	2.0278	.89687	1.1150	2.2610	45
16	.44255	.49351	2.0263	.89674	1.1151	2.2596	44
17	.44281	.49387	2.0248	.89662	1.1153	2.2583	43
18	.44307	.49423	2.0233	.89649	1.1155	2.2570	42
19	.44333	.49459	2.0219	.89636	1.1156	2.2556	41
20	.44359	.49495	2.0204	.89623	1.1158	2.2543	40
21	.44385	.49532	2.0189	.89610	1.1159	2.2530	39
22	.44411	.49568	2.0174	.89597	1.1161	2.2517	38
23	.44437	.49604	2.0160	.89584	1.1163	2.2504	37
24	.44464	.49640	2.0145	.89571	1.1164	2.2490	36
25	.44490	.49677	2.0130	.89558	1.1166	2.2477	35
26	.44516	.49713	2.0115	.89545	1.1168	2.2464	34
27	.44542	.49749	2.0101	.89532	1.1169	2.2451	33
28	.44568	.49786	2.0086	.89519	1.1171	2.2438	32
29	.44594	.49822	2.0072	.89506	1.1172	2.2425	31
30	.44620	.49858	2.0057	.89493	1.1174	2.2412	30
31	.44646	.49894	2.0042	.89480	1.1176	2.2399	29
32	.44672	.49931	2.0028	.89467	1.1177	2.2385	28
33	.44698	.49967	2.0013	.89454	1.1179	2.2372	27
34	.44724	.50004	1.9999	.89441	1.1180	2.2359	26
35	.44750	.50040	1.9984	.89428	1.1182	2.2346	25
36	.44776	.50076	1.9970	.89415	1.1184	2.2333	24
37	.44802	.50113	1.9955	.89402	1.1185	2.2320	23
38	.44828	.50149	1.9941	.89389	1.1187	2.2308	22
39	.44854	.50185	1.9926	.89376	1.1189	2.2295	21
40	.44880	.50222	1.9912	.89363	1.1190	2.2282	20
41	.44906	.50258	1.9897	.89350	1.1192	2.2269	19
42	.44932	.50295	1.9883	.89337	1.1194	2.2256	18
43	.44958	.50331	1.9868	.89324	1.1195	2.2243	17
44	.44984	.50368	1.9854	.89311	1.1197	2.2230	16
45	.45010	.50404	1.9840	.89298	1.1198	2.2217	15
46	.45036	.50441	1.9825	.89285	1.1200	2.2205	14
47	.45062	.50477	1.9811	.89272	1.1202	2.2192	13
48	.45088	.50514	1.9797	.89259	1.1203	2.2179	12
49	.45114	.50550	1.9782	.89245	1.1205	2.2166	11
50	.45140	.50587	1.9768	.89232	1.1207	2.2153	10
51	.45166	.50623	1.9754	.89219	1.1208	2.2141	9
52	.45192	.50660	1.9740	.89206	1.1210	2.2128	8
53	.45218	.50696	1.9725	.89193	1.1212	2.2115	7
54	.45243	.50733	1.9711	.89180	1.1213	2.2103	6
55	.45269	.50769	1.9697	.89167	1.1215	2.2090	5
56	.45295	.50806	1.9683	.89153	1.1217	2.2077	4
57	.45321	.50843	1.9669	.89140	1.1218	2.2065	3
58	.45347	.50879	1.9654	.89127	1.1220	2.2052	2
59	.45373	.50916	1.9640	.89114	1.1222	2.2039	1
60	.45399	.50953	1.9626	.89101	1.1223	2.2027	0
′	Cos	Ctn	Tan	Sin	Csc	Sec	′

116° (296°) (243°) **63°**

27° (207°) (332°) **152°**

′	Sin	Tan	Ctn	Cos	Sec	Csc	′
0	.45399	.50953	1.9626	.89101	1.1223	2.2027	60
1	.45425	.50989	1.9612	.89087	1.1225	2.2014	59
2	.45451	.51026	1.9598	.89074	1.1227	2.2002	58
3	.45477	.51063	1.9584	.89061	1.1228	2.1989	57
4	.45503	.51099	1.9570	.89048	1.1230	2.1977	56
5	.45529	.51136	1.9556	.89035	1.1232	2.1964	55
6	.45554	.51173	1.9542	.89021	1.1233	2.1952	54
7	.45580	.51209	1.9528	.89008	1.1235	2.1939	53
8	.45606	.51246	1.9514	.88995	1.1237	2.1927	52
9	.45632	.51283	1.9500	.88981	1.1238	2.1914	51
10	.45658	.51319	1.9486	.88968	1.1240	2.1902	50
11	.45684	.51356	1.9472	.88955	1.1242	2.1890	49
12	.45710	.51393	1.9458	.88942	1.1243	2.1877	48
13	.45736	.51430	1.9444	.88928	1.1245	2.1865	47
14	.45762	.51467	1.9430	.88915	1.1247	2.1852	46
15	.45787	.51503	1.9416	.88902	1.1248	2.1840	45
16	.45813	.51540	1.9402	.88888	1.1250	2.1828	44
17	.45839	.51577	1.9388	.88875	1.1252	2.1815	43
18	.45865	.51614	1.9375	.88862	1.1253	2.1803	42
19	.45891	.51651	1.9361	.88848	1.1255	2.1791	41
20	.45917	.51688	1.9347	.88835	1.1257	2.1779	40
21	.45942	.51724	1.9333	.88822	1.1259	2.1766	39
22	.45968	.51761	1.9319	.88808	1.1260	2.1754	38
23	.45994	.51798	1.9306	.88795	1.1262	2.1742	37
24	.46020	.51835	1.9292	.88782	1.1264	2.1730	36
25	.46046	.51872	1.9278	.88768	1.1265	2.1718	35
26	.46072	.51909	1.9265	.88755	1.1267	2.1705	34
27	.46097	.51946	1.9251	.88741	1.1269	2.1693	33
28	.46123	.51983	1.9237	.88728	1.1270	2.1681	32
29	.46149	.52020	1.9223	.88715	1.1272	2.1669	31
30	.46175	.52057	1.9210	.88701	1.1274	2.1657	30
31	.46201	.52094	1.9196	.88688	1.1276	2.1645	29
32	.46226	.52131	1.9183	.88674	1.1277	2.1633	28
33	.46252	.52168	1.9169	.88661	1.1279	2.1621	27
34	.46278	.52205	1.9155	.88647	1.1281	2.1609	26
35	.46304	.52242	1.9142	.88634	1.1282	2.1596	25
36	.46330	.52279	1.9128	.88620	1.1284	2.1584	24
37	.46355	.52316	1.9115	.88607	1.1286	2.1572	23
38	.46381	.52353	1.9101	.88593	1.1288	2.1560	22
39	.46407	.52390	1.9088	.88580	1.1289	2.1549	21
40	.46433	.52427	1.9074	.88566	1.1291	2.1537	20
41	.46458	.52464	1.9061	.88553	1.1293	2.1525	19
42	.46484	.52501	1.9047	.88539	1.1294	2.1513	18
43	.46510	.52538	1.9034	.88526	1.1296	2.1501	17
44	.46536	.52575	1.9020	.88512	1.1298	2.1489	16
45	.46561	.52613	1.9007	.88499	1.1300	2.1477	15
46	.46587	.52650	1.8993	.88485	1.1301	2.1465	14
47	.46613	.52687	1.8980	.88472	1.1303	2.1453	13
48	.46639	.52724	1.8967	.88458	1.1305	2.1441	12
49	.46664	.52761	1.8953	.88445	1.1307	2.1430	11
50	.46690	.52798	1.8940	.88431	1.1308	2.1418	10
51	.46716	.52836	1.8927	.88417	1.1310	2.1406	9
52	.46742	.52873	1.8913	.88404	1.1312	2.1394	8
53	.46767	.52910	1.8900	.88390	1.1313	2.1382	7
54	.46793	.52947	1.8887	.88377	1.1315	2.1371	6
55	.46819	.52985	1.8873	.88363	1.1317	2.1359	5
56	.46844	.53022	1.8860	.88349	1.1319	2.1347	4
57	.46870	.53059	1.8847	.88336	1.1320	2.1336	3
58	.46896	.53096	1.8834	.88322	1.1322	2.1324	2
59	.46921	.53134	1.8820	.88308	1.1324	2.1312	1
60	.46947	.53171	1.8807	.88295	1.1326	2.1301	0
′	Cos	Ctn	Tan	Sin	Csc	Sec	′

117° (297°) (242°) **62°**

28° (208°) (331°) **151°**

′	Sin	Tan	Ctn	Cos	Sec	Csc	′
0	.46947	.53171	1.8807	.88295	1.1326	2.1301	60
1	.46973	.53208	1.8794	.88281	1.1327	2.1289	59
2	.46999	.53246	1.8781	.88267	1.1329	2.1277	58
3	.47024	.53283	1.8768	.88254	1.1331	2.1266	57
4	.47050	.53320	1.8755	.88240	1.1333	2.1254	56
5	.47076	.53358	1.8741	.88226	1.1334	2.1242	55
6	.47101	.53395	1.8728	.88213	1.1336	2.1231	54
7	.47127	.53432	1.8715	.88199	1.1338	2.1219	53
8	.47153	.53470	1.8702	.88185	1.1340	2.1208	52
9	.47178	.53507	1.8689	.88172	1.1342	2.1196	51
10	.47204	.53545	1.8676	.88158	1.1343	2.1185	50
11	.47229	.53582	1.8663	.88144	1.1345	2.1173	49
12	.47255	.53620	1.8650	.88130	1.1347	2.1162	48
13	.47281	.53657	1.8637	.88117	1.1349	2.1150	47
14	.47306	.53694	1.8624	.88103	1.1350	2.1139	46
15	.47332	.53732	1.8611	.88089	1.1352	2.1127	45
16	.47358	.53769	1.8598	.88075	1.1354	2.1116	44
17	.47383	.53807	1.8585	.88062	1.1356	2.1105	43
18	.47409	.53844	1.8572	.88048	1.1357	2.1093	42
19	.47434	.53882	1.8559	.88034	1.1359	2.1082	41
20	.47460	.53920	1.8546	.88020	1.1361	2.1070	40
21	.47486	.53957	1.8533	.88006	1.1363	2.1059	39
22	.47511	.53995	1.8520	.87993	1.1365	2.1048	38
23	.47537	.54032	1.8507	.87979	1.1366	2.1036	37
24	.47562	.54070	1.8495	.87965	1.1368	2.1025	36
25	.47588	.54107	1.8482	.87951	1.1370	2.1014	35
26	.47614	.54145	1.8469	.87937	1.1372	2.1002	34
27	.47639	.54183	1.8456	.87923	1.1374	2.0991	33
28	.47665	.54220	1.8443	.87909	1.1375	2.0980	32
29	.47690	.54258	1.8430	.87896	1.1377	2.0969	31
30	.47716	.54296	1.8418	.87882	1.1379	2.0957	30
31	.47741	.54333	1.8405	.87868	1.1381	2.0946	29
32	.47767	.54371	1.8392	.87854	1.1383	2.0935	28
33	.47793	.54409	1.8379	.87840	1.1384	2.0924	27
34	.47818	.54446	1.8367	.87826	1.1386	2.0913	26
35	.47844	.54484	1.8354	.87812	1.1388	2.0901	25
36	.47869	.54522	1.8341	.87798	1.1390	2.0890	24
37	.47895	.54560	1.8329	.87784	1.1392	2.0879	23
38	.47920	.54597	1.8316	.87770	1.1393	2.0868	22
39	.47946	.54635	1.8303	.87756	1.1395	2.0857	21
40	.47971	.54673	1.8291	.87743	1.1397	2.0846	20
41	.47997	.54711	1.8278	.87729	1.1399	2.0835	19
42	.48022	.54748	1.8265	.87715	1.1401	2.0824	18
43	.48048	.54786	1.8253	.87701	1.1402	2.0813	17
44	.48073	.54824	1.8240	.87687	1.1404	2.0802	16
45	.48099	.54862	1.8228	.87673	1.1406	2.0791	15
46	.48124	.54900	1.8215	.87659	1.1408	2.0779	14
47	.48150	.54938	1.8202	.87645	1.1410	2.0768	13
48	.48175	.54975	1.8190	.87631	1.1412	2.0757	12
49	.48201	.55013	1.8177	.87617	1.1413	2.0747	11
50	.48226	.55051	1.8165	.87603	1.1415	2.0736	10
51	.48252	.55089	1.8152	.87589	1.1417	2.0725	9
52	.48277	.55127	1.8140	.87575	1.1419	2.0714	8
53	.48303	.55165	1.8127	.87561	1.1421	2.0703	7
54	.48328	.55203	1.8115	.87546	1.1423	2.0692	6
55	.48354	.55241	1.8103	.87532	1.1424	2.0681	5
56	.48379	.55279	1.8090	.87518	1.1426	2.0670	4
57	.48405	.55317	1.8078	.87504	1.1428	2.0659	3
58	.48430	.55355	1.8065	.87490	1.1430	2.0648	2
59	.48456	.55393	1.8053	.87476	1.1432	2.0637	1
60	.48481	.55431	1.8040	.87462	1.1434	2.0627	0
′	Cos	Ctn	Tan	Sin	Csc	Sec	′

118° (298°) (241°) **61°**

29° (209°) (330°) **150°**

′	Sin	Tan	Ctn	Cos	Sec	Csc	′
0	.48481	.55431	1.8040	.87462	1.1434	2.0627	60
1	.48506	.55469	1.8028	.87448	1.1435	2.0616	59
2	.48532	.55507	1.8016	.87434	1.1437	2.0605	58
3	.48557	.55545	1.8003	.87420	1.1439	2.0594	57
4	.48583	.55583	1.7991	.87406	1.1441	2.0583	56
5	.48608	.55621	1.7979	.87391	1.1443	2.0573	55
6	.48634	.55659	1.7966	.87377	1.1445	2.0562	54
7	.48659	.55697	1.7954	.87363	1.1446	2.0551	53
8	.48684	.55736	1.7942	.87349	1.1448	2.0540	52
9	.48710	.55774	1.7930	.87335	1.1450	2.0530	51
10	.48735	.55812	1.7917	.87321	1.1452	2.0519	50
11	.48761	.55850	1.7905	.87306	1.1454	2.0508	49
12	.48786	.55888	1.7893	.87292	1.1456	2.0498	48
13	.48811	.55926	1.7881	.87278	1.1458	2.0487	47
14	.48837	.55964	1.7868	.87264	1.1460	2.0476	46
15	.48862	.56003	1.7856	.87250	1.1461	2.0466	45
16	.48888	.56041	1.7844	.87235	1.1463	2.0455	44
17	.48913	.56079	1.7832	.87221	1.1465	2.0445	43
18	.48938	.56117	1.7820	.87207	1.1467	2.0434	42
19	.48964	.56156	1.7808	.87193	1.1469	2.0423	41
20	.48989	.56194	1.7796	.87178	1.1471	2.0413	40
21	.49014	.56232	1.7783	.87164	1.1473	2.0402	39
22	.49040	.56270	1.7771	.87150	1.1474	2.0392	38
23	.49065	.56309	1.7759	.87136	1.1476	2.0381	37
24	.49090	.56347	1.7747	.87121	1.1478	2.0371	36
25	.49116	.56385	1.7735	.87107	1.1480	2.0360	35
26	.49141	.56424	1.7723	.87093	1.1482	2.0350	34
27	.49166	.56462	1.7711	.87079	1.1484	2.0339	33
28	.49192	.56501	1.7699	.87064	1.1486	2.0329	32
29	.49217	.56539	1.7687	.87050	1.1488	2.0318	31
30	.49242	.56577	1.7675	.87036	1.1490	2.0308	30
31	.49268	.56616	1.7663	.87021	1.1491	2.0297	29
32	.49293	.56654	1.7651	.87007	1.1493	2.0287	28
33	.49318	.56693	1.7639	.86993	1.1495	2.0276	27
34	.49344	.56731	1.7627	.86978	1.1497	2.0266	26
35	.49369	.56769	1.7615	.86964	1.1499	2.0256	25
36	.49394	.56808	1.7603	.86949	1.1501	2.0245	24
37	.49419	.56846	1.7591	.86935	1.1503	2.0235	23
38	.49445	.56885	1.7579	.86921	1.1505	2.0225	22
39	.49470	.56923	1.7567	.86906	1.1507	2.0214	21
40	.49495	.56962	1.7556	.86892	1.1509	2.0204	20
41	.49521	.57000	1.7544	.86878	1.1510	2.0194	19
42	.49546	.57039	1.7532	.86863	1.1512	2.0183	18
43	.49571	.57078	1.7520	.86849	1.1514	2.0173	17
44	.49596	.57116	1.7508	.86834	1.1516	2.0163	16
45	.49622	.57155	1.7496	.86820	1.1518	2.0152	15
46	.49647	.57193	1.7485	.86805	1.1520	2.0142	14
47	.49672	.57232	1.7473	.86791	1.1522	2.0132	13
48	.49697	.57271	1.7461	.86777	1.1524	2.0122	12
49	.49723	.57309	1.7449	.86762	1.1526	2.0112	11
50	.49748	.57348	1.7437	.86748	1.1528	2.0101	10
51	.49773	.57386	1.7426	.86733	1.1530	2.0091	9
52	.49798	.57425	1.7414	.86719	1.1532	2.0081	8
53	.49824	.57464	1.7402	.86704	1.1533	2.0071	7
54	.49849	.57503	1.7391	.86690	1.1535	2.0061	6
55	.49874	.57541	1.7379	.86675	1.1537	2.0051	5
56	.49899	.57580	1.7367	.86661	1.1539	2.0040	4
57	.49924	.57619	1.7355	.86646	1.1541	2.0030	3
58	.49950	.57657	1.7344	.86632	1.1543	2.0020	2
59	.49975	.57696	1.7332	.86617	1.1545	2.0010	1
60	.50000	.57735	1.7321	.86603	1.1547	2.0000	0
′	Cos	Ctn	Tan	Sin	Csc	Sec	′

119° (299°) (240°) **60°**

30° (210°) (329°) **149°**

′	Sin	Tan	Ctn	Cos	Sec	Csc	′
0	.50000	.57735	1.7321	.86603	1.1547	2.0000	60
1	.50025	.57774	1.7309	.86588	1.1549	1.9990	59
2	.50050	.57813	1.7297	.86573	1.1551	1.9980	58
3	.50076	.57851	1.7286	.86559	1.1553	1.9970	57
4	.50101	.57890	1.7274	.86544	1.1555	1.9960	56
5	.50126	.57929	1.7262	.86530	1.1557	1.9950	55
6	.50151	.57968	1.7251	.86515	1.1559	1.9940	54
7	.50176	.58007	1.7239	.86501	1.1561	1.9930	53
8	.50201	.58046	1.7228	.86486	1.1563	1.9920	52
9	.50227	.58085	1.7216	.86471	1.1565	1.9910	51
10	.50252	.58124	1.7205	.86457	1.1566	1.9900	50
11	.50277	.58162	1.7193	.86442	1.1568	1.9890	49
12	.50302	.58201	1.7182	.86427	1.1570	1.9880	48
13	.50327	.58240	1.7170	.86413	1.1572	1.9870	47
14	.50352	.58279	1.7159	.86398	1.1574	1.9860	46
15	.50377	.58318	1.7147	.86384	1.1576	1.9850	45
16	.50403	.58357	1.7136	.86369	1.1578	1.9840	44
17	.50428	.58396	1.7124	.86354	1.1580	1.9830	43
18	.50453	.58435	1.7113	.86340	1.1582	1.9821	42
19	.50478	.58474	1.7102	.86325	1.1584	1.9811	41
20	.50503	.58513	1.7090	.86310	1.1586	1.9801	40
21	.50528	.58552	1.7079	.86295	1.1588	1.9791	39
22	.50553	.58591	1.7067	.86281	1.1590	1.9781	38
23	.50578	.58631	1.7056	.86266	1.1592	1.9771	37
24	.50603	.58670	1.7045	.86251	1.1594	1.9762	36
25	.50628	.58709	1.7033	.86237	1.1596	1.9752	35
26	.50654	.58748	1.7022	.86222	1.1598	1.9742	34
27	.50679	.58787	1.7011	.86207	1.1600	1.9732	33
28	.50704	.58826	1.6999	.86192	1.1602	1.9722	32
29	.50729	.58865	1.6988	.86178	1.1604	1.9713	31
30	.50754	.58905	1.6977	.86163	1.1606	1.9703	30
31	.50779	.58944	1.6965	.86148	1.1608	1.9693	29
32	.50804	.58983	1.6954	.86133	1.1610	1.9684	28
33	.50829	.59022	1.6943	.86119	1.1612	1.9674	27
34	.50854	.59061	1.6932	.86104	1.1614	1.9664	26
35	.50879	.59101	1.6920	.86089	1.1616	1.9654	25
36	.50904	.59140	1.6909	.86074	1.1618	1.9645	24
37	.50929	.59179	1.6898	.86059	1.1620	1.9635	23
38	.50954	.59218	1.6887	.86045	1.1622	1.9625	22
39	.50979	.59258	1.6875	.86030	1.1624	1.9616	21
40	.51004	.59297	1.6864	.86015	1.1626	1.9606	20
41	.51029	.59336	1.6853	.86000	1.1628	1.9597	19
42	.51054	.59376	1.6842	.85985	1.1630	1.9587	18
43	.51079	.59415	1.6831	.85970	1.1632	1.9577	17
44	.51104	.59454	1.6820	.85956	1.1634	1.9568	16
45	.51129	.59494	1.6808	.85941	1.1636	1.9558	15
46	.51154	.59533	1.6797	.85926	1.1638	1.9549	14
47	.51179	.59573	1.6786	.85911	1.1640	1.9539	13
48	.51204	.59612	1.6775	.85896	1.1642	1.9530	12
49	.51229	.59651	1.6764	.85881	1.1644	1.9520	11
50	.51254	.59691	1.6753	.85866	1.1646	1.9511	10
51	.51279	.59730	1.6742	.85851	1.1648	1.9501	9
52	.51304	.59770	1.6731	.85836	1.1650	1.9492	8
53	.51329	.59809	1.6720	.85821	1.1652	1.9482	7
54	.51354	.59849	1.6709	.85806	1.1654	1.9473	6
55	.51379	.59888	1.6698	.85792	1.1656	1.9463	5
56	.51404	.59928	1.6687	.85777	1.1658	1.9454	4
57	.51429	.59967	1.6676	.85762	1.1660	1.9444	3
58	.51454	.60007	1.6665	.85747	1.1662	1.9435	2
59	.51479	.60046	1.6654	.85732	1.1664	1.9425	1
60	.51504	.60086	1.6643	.85717	1.1666	1.9416	0
′	Cos	Ctn	Tan	Sin	Csc	Sec	′

120° (300°) (239°) **59°**

31° (211°) (328°) **148°**

′	Sin	Tan	Ctn	Cos	Sec	Csc	′
0	.51504	.60086	1.6643	.85717	1.1666	1.9416	60
1	.51529	.60126	1.6632	.85702	1.1668	1.9407	59
2	.51554	.60165	1.6621	.85687	1.1670	1.9397	58
3	.51579	.60205	1.6610	.85672	1.1672	1.9388	57
4	.51604	.60245	1.6599	.85657	1.1675	1.9379	56
5	.51628	.60284	1.6588	.85642	1.1677	1.9369	55
6	.51653	.60324	1.6577	.85627	1.1679	1.9360	54
7	.51678	.60364	1.6566	.85612	1.1681	1.9351	53
8	.51703	.60403	1.6555	.85597	1.1683	1.9341	52
9	.51728	.60443	1.6545	.85582	1.1685	1.9332	51
10	.51753	.60483	1.6534	.85567	1.1687	1.9323	50
11	.51778	.60522	1.6523	.85551	1.1689	1.9313	49
12	.51803	.60562	1.6512	.85536	1.1691	1.9304	48
13	.51828	.60602	1.6501	.85521	1.1693	1.9295	47
14	.51852	.60642	1.6490	.85506	1.1695	1.9285	46
15	.51877	.60681	1.6479	.85491	1.1697	1.9276	45
16	.51902	.60721	1.6469	.85476	1.1699	1.9267	44
17	.51927	.60761	1.6458	.85461	1.1701	1.9258	43
18	.51952	.60801	1.6447	.85446	1.1703	1.9249	42
19	.51977	.60841	1.6436	.85431	1.1705	1.9239	41
20	.52002	.60881	1.6426	.85416	1.1707	1.9230	40
21	.52026	.60921	1.6415	.85401	1.1710	1.9221	39
22	.52051	.60960	1.6404	.85385	1.1712	1.9212	38
23	.52076	.61000	1.6393	.85370	1.1714	1.9203	37
24	.52101	.61040	1.6383	.85355	1.1716	1.9194	36
25	.52126	.61080	1.6372	.85340	1.1718	1.9184	35
26	.52151	.61120	1.6361	.85325	1.1720	1.9175	34
27	.52175	.61160	1.6351	.85310	1.1722	1.9166	33
28	.52200	.61200	1.6340	.85294	1.1724	1.9157	32
29	.52225	.61240	1.6329	.85279	1.1726	1.9148	31
30	.52250	.61280	1.6319	.85264	1.1728	1.9139	30
31	.52275	.61320	1.6308	.85249	1.1730	1.9130	29
32	.52299	.61360	1.6297	.85234	1.1732	1.9121	28
33	.52324	.61400	1.6287	.85218	1.1735	1.9112	27
34	.52349	.61440	1.6276	.85203	1.1737	1.9103	26
35	.52374	.61480	1.6265	.85188	1.1739	1.9094	25
36	.52399	.61520	1.6255	.85173	1.1741	1.9084	24
37	.52423	.61561	1.6244	.85157	1.1743	1.9075	23
38	.52448	.61601	1.6234	.85142	1.1745	1.9066	22
39	.52473	.61641	1.6223	.85127	1.1747	1.9057	21
40	.52498	.61681	1.6212	.85112	1.1749	1.9048	20
41	.52522	.61721	1.6202	.85096	1.1751	1.9039	19
42	.52547	.61761	1.6191	.85081	1.1753	1.9031	18
43	.52572	.61801	1.6181	.85066	1.1756	1.9022	17
44	.52597	.61842	1.6170	.85051	1.1758	1.9013	16
45	.52621	.61882	1.6160	.85035	1.1760	1.9004	15
46	.52646	.61922	1.6149	.85020	1.1762	1.8995	14
47	.52671	.61962	1.6139	.85005	1.1764	1.8986	13
48	.52696	.62003	1.6128	.84989	1.1766	1.8977	12
49	.52720	.62043	1.6118	.84974	1.1768	1.8968	11
50	.52745	.62083	1.6107	.84959	1.1770	1.8959	10
51	.52770	.62124	1.6097	.84943	1.1773	1.8950	9
52	.52794	.62164	1.6087	.84928	1.1775	1.8941	8
53	.52819	.62204	1.6076	.84913	1.1777	1.8933	7
54	.52844	.62245	1.6066	.84897	1.1779	1.8924	6
55	.52869	.62285	1.6055	.84882	1.1781	1.8915	5
56	.52893	.62325	1.6045	.84866	1.1783	1.8906	4
57	.52918	.62366	1.6034	.84851	1.1785	1.8897	3
58	.52943	.62406	1.6024	.84836	1.1788	1.8888	2
59	.52967	.62446	1.6014	.84820	1.1790	1.8880	1
60	.52992	.62487	1.6003	.84805	1.1792	1.8871	0
′	Cos	Ctn	Tan	Sin	Csc	Sec	′

121° (301°) (238°) **58°**

32° (212°) (327°) **147°**

′	Sin	Tan	Ctn	Cos	Sec	Csc	′
0	.52992	.62487	1.6003	.84805	1.1792	1.8871	60
1	.53017	.62527	1.5993	.84789	1.1794	1.8862	59
2	.53041	.62568	1.5983	.84774	1.1796	1.8853	58
3	.53066	.62608	1.5972	.84759	1.1798	1.8844	57
4	.53091	.62649	1.5962	.84743	1.1800	1.8836	56
5	.53115	.62689	1.5952	.84728	1.1803	1.8827	55
6	.53140	.62730	1.5941	.84712	1.1805	1.8818	54
7	.53164	.62770	1.5931	.84697	1.1807	1.8810	53
8	.53189	.62811	1.5921	.84681	1.1809	1.8801	52
9	.53214	.62852	1.5911	.84666	1.1811	1.8792	51
10	.53238	.62892	1.5900	.84650	1.1813	1.8783	50
11	.53263	.62933	1.5890	.84635	1.1815	1.8775	49
12	.53288	.62973	1.5880	.84619	1.1818	1.8766	48
13	.53312	.63014	1.5869	.84604	1.1820	1.8757	47
14	.53337	.63055	1.5859	.84588	1.1822	1.8749	46
15	.53361	.63095	1.5849	.84573	1.1824	1.8740	45
16	.53386	.63136	1.5839	.84557	1.1826	1.8731	44
17	.53411	.63177	1.5829	.84542	1.1828	1.8723	43
18	.53435	.63217	1.5818	.84526	1.1831	1.8714	42
19	.53460	.63258	1.5808	.84511	1.1833	1.8706	41
20	.53484	.63299	1.5798	.84495	1.1835	1.8697	40
21	.53509	.63340	1.5788	.84480	1.1837	1.8688	39
22	.53534	.63380	1.5778	.84464	1.1839	1.8680	38
23	.53558	.63421	1.5768	.84448	1.1842	1.8671	37
24	.53583	.63462	1.5757	.84433	1.1844	1.8663	36
25	.53607	.63503	1.5747	.84417	1.1846	1.8654	35
26	.53632	.63544	1.5737	.84402	1.1848	1.8646	34
27	.53656	.63584	1.5727	.84386	1.1850	1.8637	33
28	.53681	.63625	1.5717	.84370	1.1852	1.8629	32
29	.53705	.63666	1.5707	.84355	1.1855	1.8620	31
30	.53730	.63707	1.5697	.84339	1.1857	1.8612	30
31	.53754	.63748	1.5687	.84324	1.1859	1.8603	29
32	.53779	.63789	1.5677	.84308	1.1861	1.8595	28
33	.53804	.63830	1.5667	.84292	1.1863	1.8586	27
34	.53828	.63871	1.5657	.84277	1.1866	1.8578	26
35	.53853	.63912	1.5647	.84261	1.1868	1.8569	25
36	.53877	.63953	1.5637	.84245	1.1870	1.8561	24
37	.53902	.63994	1.5627	.84230	1.1872	1.8552	23
38	.53926	.64035	1.5617	.84214	1.1875	1.8544	22
39	.53951	.64076	1.5607	.84198	1.1877	1.8535	21
40	.53975	.64117	1.5597	.84182	1.1879	1.8527	20
41	.54000	.64158	1.5587	.84167	1.1881	1.8519	19
42	.54024	.64199	1.5577	.84151	1.1883	1.8510	18
43	.54049	.64240	1.5567	.84135	1.1886	1.8502	17
44	.54073	.64281	1.5557	.84120	1.1888	1.8494	16
45	.54097	.64322	1.5547	.84104	1.1890	1.8485	15
46	.54122	.64363	1.5537	.84088	1.1892	1.8477	14
47	.54146	.64404	1.5527	.84072	1.1895	1.8468	13
48	.54171	.64446	1.5517	.84057	1.1897	1.8460	12
49	.54195	.64487	1.5507	.84041	1.1899	1.8452	11
50	.54220	.64528	1.5497	.84025	1.1901	1.8443	10
51	.54244	.64569	1.5487	.84009	1.1903	1.8435	9
52	.54269	.64610	1.5477	.83994	1.1906	1.8427	8
53	.54293	.64652	1.5468	.83978	1.1908	1.8419	7
54	.54317	.64693	1.5458	.83962	1.1910	1.8410	6
55	.54342	.64734	1.5448	.83946	1.1912	1.8402	5
56	.54366	.64775	1.5438	.83930	1.1915	1.8394	4
57	.54391	.64817	1.5428	.83915	1.1917	1.8385	3
58	.54415	.64858	1.5418	.83899	1.1919	1.8377	2
59	.54440	.64899	1.5408	.83883	1.1921	1.8369	1
60	.54464	.64941	1.5399	.83867	1.1924	1.8361	0
′	Cos	Ctn	Tan	Sin	Csc	Sec	′

122° (302°) (237°) **57°**

33° (213°) (326°) **146°**

′	Sin	Tan	Ctn	Cos	Sec	Csc	′
0	.54464	.64941	1.5399	.83867	1.1924	1.8361	60
1	.54488	.64982	1.5389	.83851	1.1926	1.8353	59
2	.54513	.65024	1.5379	.83835	1.1928	1.8344	58
3	.54537	.65065	1.5369	.83819	1.1930	1.8336	57
4	.54561	.65106	1.5359	.83804	1.1933	1.8328	56
5	.54586	.65148	1.5350	.83788	1.1935	1.8320	55
6	.54610	.65189	1.5340	.83772	1.1937	1.8312	54
7	.54635	.65231	1.5330	.83756	1.1939	1.8303	53
8	.54659	.65272	1.5320	.83740	1.1942	1.8295	52
9	.54683	.65314	1.5311	.83724	1.1944	1.8287	51
10	.54708	.65355	1.5301	.83708	1.1946	1.8279	50
11	.54732	.65397	1.5291	.83692	1.1949	1.8271	49
12	.54756	.65438	1.5282	.83676	1.1951	1.8263	48
13	.54781	.65480	1.5272	.83660	1.1953	1.8255	47
14	.54805	.65521	1.5262	.83645	1.1955	1.8247	46
15	.54829	.65563	1.5253	.83629	1.1958	1.8238	45
16	.54854	.65604	1.5243	.83613	1.1960	1.8230	44
17	.54878	.65646	1.5233	.83597	1.1962	1.8222	43
18	.54902	.65688	1.5224	.83581	1.1964	1.8214	42
19	.54927	.65729	1.5214	.83565	1.1967	1.8206	41
20	.54951	.65771	1.5204	.83549	1.1969	1.8198	40
21	.54975	.65813	1.5195	.83533	1.1971	1.8190	39
22	.54999	.65854	1.5185	.83517	1.1974	1.8182	38
23	.55024	.65896	1.5175	.83501	1.1976	1.8174	37
24	.55048	.65938	1.5166	.83485	1.1978	1.8166	36
25	.55072	.65980	1.5156	.83469	1.1981	1.8158	35
26	.55097	.66021	1.5147	.83453	1.1983	1.8150	34
27	.55121	.66063	1.5137	.83437	1.1985	1.8142	33
28	.55145	.66105	1.5127	.83421	1.1987	1.8134	32
29	.55169	.66147	1.5118	.83405	1.1990	1.8126	31
30	.55194	.66189	1.5108	.83389	1.1992	1.8118	30
31	.55218	.66230	1.5099	.83373	1.1994	1.8110	29
32	.55242	.66272	1.5089	.83356	1.1997	1.8102	28
33	.55266	.66314	1.5080	.83340	1.1999	1.8094	27
34	.55291	.66356	1.5070	.83324	1.2001	1.8086	26
35	.55315	.66398	1.5061	.83308	1.2004	1.8078	25
36	.55339	.66440	1.5051	.83292	1.2006	1.8070	24
37	.55363	.66482	1.5042	.83276	1.2008	1.8062	23
38	.55388	.66524	1.5032	.83260	1.2011	1.8055	22
39	.55412	.66566	1.5023	.83244	1.2013	1.8047	21
40	.55436	.66608	1.5013	.83228	1.2015	1.8039	20
41	.55460	.66650	1.5004	.83212	1.2018	1.8031	19
42	.55484	.66692	1.4994	.83195	1.2020	1.8023	18
43	.55509	.66734	1.4985	.83179	1.2022	1.8015	17
44	.55533	.66776	1.4975	.83163	1.2025	1.8007	16
45	.55557	.66818	1.4966	.83147	1.2027	1.8000	15
46	.55581	.66860	1.4957	.83131	1.2029	1.7992	14
47	.55605	.66902	1.4947	.83115	1.2032	1.7984	13
48	.55630	.66944	1.4938	.83098	1.2034	1.7976	12
49	.55654	.66986	1.4928	.83082	1.2036	1.7968	11
50	.55678	.67028	1.4919	.83066	1.2039	1.7960	10
51	.55702	.67071	1.4910	.83050	1.2041	1.7953	9
52	.55726	.67113	1.4900	.83034	1.2043	1.7945	8
53	.55750	.67155	1.4891	.83017	1.2046	1.7937	7
54	.55775	.67197	1.4882	.83001	1.2048	1.7929	6
55	.55799	.67239	1.4872	.82985	1.2050	1.7922	5
56	.55823	.67282	1.4863	.82969	1.2053	1.7914	4
57	.55847	.67324	1.4854	.82953	1.2055	1.7906	3
58	.55871	.67366	1.4844	.82936	1.2057	1.7898	2
59	.55895	.67409	1.4835	.82920	1.2060	1.7891	1
60	.55919	.67451	1.4826	.82904	1.2062	1.7883	0
′	Cos	Ctn	Tan	Sin	Csc	Sec	′

123° (303°) (236°) **56°**

34° (214°) (325°) **145°**

′	Sin	Tan	Ctn	Cos	Sec	Csc	′
0	.55919	.67451	1.4826	.82904	1.2062	1.7883	60
1	.55943	.67493	1.4816	.82887	1.2065	1.7875	59
2	.55968	.67536	1.4807	.82871	1.2067	1.7868	58
3	.55992	.67578	1.4798	.82855	1.2069	1.7860	57
4	.56016	.67620	1.4788	.82839	1.2072	1.7852	56
5	.56040	.67663	1.4779	.82822	1.2074	1.7844	55
6	.56064	.67705	1.4770	.82806	1.2076	1.7837	54
7	.56088	.67748	1.4761	.82790	1.2079	1.7829	53
8	.56112	.67790	1.4751	.82773	1.2081	1.7821	52
9	.56136	.67832	1.4742	.82757	1.2084	1.7814	51
10	.56160	.67875	1.4733	.82741	1.2086	1.7806	50
11	.56184	.67917	1.4724	.82724	1.2088	1.7799	49
12	.56208	.67960	1.4715	.82708	1.2091	1.7791	48
13	.56232	.68002	1.4705	.82692	1.2093	1.7783	47
14	.56256	.68045	1.4696	.82675	1.2096	1.7776	46
15	.56280	.68088	1.4687	.82659	1.2098	1.7768	45
16	.56305	.68130	1.4678	.82643	1.2100	1.7761	44
17	.56329	.68173	1.4669	.82626	1.2103	1.7753	43
18	.56353	.68215	1.4659	.82610	1.2105	1.7745	42
19	.56377	.68258	1.4650	.82593	1.2108	1.7738	41
20	.56401	.68301	1.4641	.82577	1.2110	1.7730	40
21	.56425	.68343	1.4632	.82561	1.2112	1.7723	39
22	.56449	.68386	1.4623	.82544	1.2115	1.7715	38
23	.56473	.68429	1.4614	.82528	1.2117	1.7708	37
24	.56497	.68471	1.4605	.82511	1.2120	1.7700	36
25	.56521	.68514	1.4596	.82495	1.2122	1.7693	35
26	.56545	.68557	1.4586	.82478	1.2124	1.7685	34
27	.56569	.68600	1.4577	.82462	1.2127	1.7678	33
28	.56593	.68642	1.4568	.82446	1.2129	1.7670	32
29	.56617	.68685	1.4559	.82429	1.2132	1.7663	31
30	.56641	.68728	1.4550	.82413	1.2134	1.7655	30
31	.56665	.68771	1.4541	.82396	1.2136	1.7648	29
32	.56689	.68814	1.4532	.82380	1.2139	1.7640	28
33	.56713	.68857	1.4523	.82363	1.2141	1.7633	27
34	.56736	.68900	1.4514	.82347	1.2144	1.7625	26
35	.56760	.68942	1.4505	.82330	1.2146	1.7618	25
36	.56784	.68985	1.4496	.82314	1.2149	1.7610	24
37	.56808	.69028	1.4487	.82297	1.2151	1.7603	23
38	.56832	.69071	1.4478	.82281	1.2154	1.7596	22
39	.56856	.69114	1.4469	.82264	1.2156	1.7588	21
40	.56880	.69157	1.4460	.82248	1.2158	1.7581	20
41	.56904	.69200	1.4451	.82231	1.2161	1.7573	19
42	.56928	.69243	1.4442	.82214	1.2163	1.7566	18
43	.56952	.69286	1.4433	.82198	1.2166	1.7559	17
44	.56976	.69329	1.4424	.82181	1.2168	1.7551	16
45	.57000	.69372	1.4415	.82165	1.2171	1.7544	15
46	.57024	.69416	1.4406	.82148	1.2173	1.7537	14
47	.57047	.69459	1.4397	.82132	1.2176	1.7529	13
48	.57071	.69502	1.4388	.82115	1.2178	1.7522	12
49	.57095	.69545	1.4379	.82098	1.2181	1.7515	11
50	.57119	.69588	1.4370	.82082	1.2183	1.7507	10
51	.57143	.69631	1.4361	.82065	1.2185	1.7500	9
52	.57167	.69675	1.4352	.82048	1.2188	1.7493	8
53	.57191	.69718	1.4344	.82032	1.2190	1.7485	7
54	.57215	.69761	1.4335	.82015	1.2193	1.7478	6
55	.57238	.69804	1.4326	.81999	1.2195	1.7471	5
56	.57262	.69847	1.4317	.81982	1.2198	1.7463	4
57	.57286	.69891	1.4308	.81965	1.2200	1.7456	3
58	.57310	.69934	1.4299	.81949	1.2203	1.7449	2
59	.57334	.69977	1.4290	.81932	1.2205	1.7442	1
60	.57358	.70021	1.4281	.81915	1.2208	1.7434	0
′	Cos	Ctn	Tan	Sin	Csc	Sec	′

124° (304°) (235°) **55°**

35° (215°) (324°) **144°**

′	Sin	Tan	Ctn	Cos	Sec	Csc	′
0	.57358	.70021	1.4281	.81915	1.2208	1.7434	60
1	.57381	.70064	1.4273	.81899	1.2210	1.7427	59
2	.57405	.70107	1.4264	.81882	1.2213	1.7420	58
3	.57429	.70151	1.4255	.81865	1.2215	1.7413	57
4	.57453	.70194	1.4246	.81848	1.2218	1.7406	56
5	.57477	.70238	1.4237	.81832	1.2220	1.7398	55
6	.57501	.70281	1.4229	.81815	1.2223	1.7391	54
7	.57524	.70325	1.4220	.81798	1.2225	1.7384	53
8	.57548	.70368	1.4211	.81782	1.2228	1.7377	52
9	.57572	.70412	1.4202	.81765	1.2230	1.7370	51
10	.57596	.70455	1.4193	.81748	1.2233	1.7362	50
11	.57619	.70499	1.4185	.81731	1.2235	1.7355	49
12	.57643	.70542	1.4176	.81714	1.2238	1.7348	48
13	.57667	.70586	1.4167	.81698	1.2240	1.7341	47
14	.57691	.70629	1.4158	.81681	1.2243	1.7334	46
15	.57715	.70673	1.4150	.81664	1.2245	1.7327	45
16	.57738	.70717	1.4141	.81647	1.2248	1.7320	44
17	.57762	.70760	1.4132	.81631	1.2250	1.7312	43
18	.57786	.70804	1.4124	.81614	1.2253	1.7305	42
19	.57810	.70848	1.4115	.81597	1.2255	1.7298	41
20	.57833	.70891	1.4106	.81580	1.2258	1.7291	40
21	.57857	.70935	1.4097	.81563	1.2260	1.7284	39
22	.57881	.70979	1.4089	.81546	1.2263	1.7277	38
23	.57904	.71023	1.4080	.81530	1.2265	1.7270	37
24	.57928	.71066	1.4071	.81513	1.2268	1.7263	36
25	.57952	.71110	1.4063	.81496	1.2271	1.7256	35
26	.57976	.71154	1.4054	.81479	1.2273	1.7249	34
27	.57999	.71198	1.4045	.81462	1.2276	1.7242	33
28	.58023	.71242	1.4037	.81445	1.2278	1.7235	32
29	.58047	.71285	1.4028	.81428	1.2281	1.7228	31
30	.58070	.71329	1.4019	.81412	1.2283	1.7221	30
31	.58094	.71373	1.4011	.81395	1.2286	1.7213	29
32	.58118	.71417	1.4002	.81378	1.2288	1.7206	28
33	.58141	.71461	1.3994	.81361	1.2291	1.7199	27
34	.58165	.71505	1.3985	.81344	1.2293	1.7192	26
35	.58189	.71549	1.3976	.81327	1.2296	1.7185	25
36	.58212	.71593	1.3968	.81310	1.2299	1.7179	24
37	.58236	.71637	1.3959	.81293	1.2301	1.7172	23
38	.58260	.71681	1.3951	.81276	1.2304	1.7165	22
39	.58283	.71725	1.3942	.81259	1.2306	1.7158	21
40	.58307	.71769	1.3934	.81242	1.2309	1.7151	20
41	.58330	.71813	1.3925	.81225	1.2311	1.7144	19
42	.58354	.71857	1.3916	.81208	1.2314	1.7137	18
43	.58378	.71901	1.3908	.81191	1.2317	1.7130	17
44	.58401	.71946	1.3899	.81174	1.2319	1.7123	16
45	.58425	.71990	1.3891	.81157	1.2322	1.7116	15
46	.58449	.72034	1.3882	.81140	1.2324	1.7109	14
47	.58472	.72078	1.3874	.81123	1.2327	1.7102	13
48	.58496	.72122	1.3865	.81106	1.2329	1.7095	12
49	.58519	.72167	1.3857	.81089	1.2332	1.7088	11
50	.58543	.72211	1.3848	.81072	1.2335	1.7081	10
51	.58567	.72255	1.3840	.81055	1.2337	1.7075	9
52	.58590	.72299	1.3831	.81038	1.2340	1.7068	8
53	.58614	.72344	1.3823	.81021	1.2342	1.7061	7
54	.58637	.72388	1.3814	.81004	1.2345	1.7054	6
55	.58661	.72432	1.3806	.80987	1.2348	1.7047	5
56	.58684	.72477	1.3798	.80970	1.2350	1.7040	4
57	.58708	.72521	1.3789	.80953	1.2353	1.7033	3
58	.58731	.72565	1.3781	.80936	1.2355	1.7027	2
59	.58755	.72610	1.3772	.80919	1.2358	1.7020	1
60	.58779	.72654	1.3764	.80902	1.2361	1.7013	0
′	Cos	Ctn	Tan	Sin	Csc	Sec	′

125° (305°) (234°) **54°**

36° (216°) (323°) **143°**

′	Sin	Tan	Ctn	Cos	Sec	Csc	′
0	.58779	.72654	1.3764	.80902	1.2361	1.7013	60
1	.58802	.72699	1.3755	.80885	1.2363	1.7006	59
2	.58826	.72743	1.3747	.80867	1.2366	1.6999	58
3	.58849	.72788	1.3739	.80850	1.2369	1.6993	57
4	.58873	.72832	1.3730	.80833	1.2371	1.6986	56
5	.58896	.72877	1.3722	.80816	1.2374	1.6979	55
6	.58920	.72921	1.3713	.80799	1.2376	1.6972	54
7	.58943	.72966	1.3705	.80782	1.2379	1.6966	53
8	.58967	.73010	1.3697	.80765	1.2382	1.6959	52
9	.58990	.73055	1.3688	.80748	1.2384	1.6952	51
10	.59014	.73100	1.3680	.80730	1.2387	1.6945	50
11	.59037	.73144	1.3672	.80713	1.2390	1.6939	49
12	.59061	.73189	1.3663	.80696	1.2392	1.6932	48
13	.59084	.73234	1.3655	.80679	1.2395	1.6925	47
14	.59108	.73278	1.3647	.80662	1.2397	1.6918	46
15	.59131	.73323	1.3638	.80644	1.2400	1.6912	45
16	.59154	.73368	1.3630	.80627	1.2403	1.6905	44
17	.59178	.73413	1.3622	.80610	1.2405	1.6898	43
18	.59201	.73457	1.3613	.80593	1.2408	1.6892	42
19	.59225	.73502	1.3605	.80576	1.2411	1.6885	41
20	.59248	.73547	1.3597	.80558	1.2413	1.6878	40
21	.59272	.73592	1.3588	.80541	1.2416	1.6871	39
22	.59295	.73637	1.3580	.80524	1.2419	1.6865	38
23	.59318	.73681	1.3572	.80507	1.2421	1.6858	37
24	.59342	.73726	1.3564	.80489	1.2424	1.6852	36
25	.59365	.73771	1.3555	.80472	1.2427	1.6845	35
26	.59389	.73816	1.3547	.80455	1.2429	1.6838	34
27	.59412	.73861	1.3539	.80438	1.2432	1.6832	33
28	.59436	.73906	1.3531	.80420	1.2435	1.6825	32
29	.59459	.73951	1.3522	.80403	1.2437	1.6818	31
30	.59482	.73996	1.3514	.80386	1.2440	1.6812	30
31	.59506	.74041	1.3506	.80368	1.2443	1.6805	29
32	.59529	.74086	1.3498	.80351	1.2445	1.6799	28
33	.59552	.74131	1.3490	.80334	1.2448	1.6792	27
34	.59576	.74176	1.3481	.80316	1.2451	1.6785	26
35	.59599	.74221	1.3473	.80299	1.2453	1.6779	25
36	.59622	.74267	1.3465	.80282	1.2456	1.6772	24
37	.59646	.74312	1.3457	.80264	1.2459	1.6766	23
38	.59669	.74357	1.3449	.80247	1.2462	1.6759	22
39	.59693	.74402	1.3440	.80230	1.2464	1.6753	21
40	.59716	.74447	1.3432	.80212	1.2467	1.6746	20
41	.59739	.74492	1.3424	.80195	1.2470	1.6739	19
42	.59763	.74538	1.3416	.80178	1.2472	1.6733	18
43	.59786	.74583	1.3408	.80160	1.2475	1.6726	17
44	.59809	.74628	1.3400	.80143	1.2478	1.6720	16
45	.59832	.74674	1.3392	.80125	1.2480	1.6713	15
46	.59856	.74719	1.3384	.80108	1.2483	1.6707	14
47	.59879	.74764	1.3375	.80091	1.2486	1.6700	13
48	.59902	.74810	1.3367	.80073	1.2489	1.6694	12
49	.59926	.74855	1.3359	.80056	1.2491	1.6687	11
50	.59949	.74900	1.3351	.80038	1.2494	1.6681	10
51	.59972	.74946	1.3343	.80021	1.2497	1.6674	9
52	.59995	.74991	1.3335	.80003	1.2499	1.6668	8
53	.60019	.75037	1.3327	.79986	1.2502	1.6661	7
54	.60042	.75082	1.3319	.79968	1.2505	1.6655	6
55	.60065	.75128	1.3311	.79951	1.2508	1.6649	5
56	.60089	.75173	1.3303	.79934	1.2510	1.6642	4
57	.60112	.75219	1.3295	.79916	1.2513	1.6636	3
58	.60135	.75264	1.3287	.79899	1.2516	1.6629	2
59	.60158	.75310	1.3278	.79881	1.2519	1.6623	1
60	.60182	.75355	1.3270	.79864	1.2521	1.6616	0
′	Cos	Ctn	Tan	Sin	Csc	Sec	′

126° (306°) (233°) **53°**

37° (217°) (322°) **142°**

′	Sin	Tan	Ctn	Cos	Sec	Csc	′
0	.60182	.75355	1.3270	.79864	1.2521	1.6616	60
1	.60205	.75401	1.3262	.79846	1.2524	1.6610	59
2	.60228	.75447	1.3254	.79829	1.2527	1.6604	58
3	.60251	.75492	1.3246	.79811	1.2530	1.6597	57
4	.60274	.75538	1.3238	.79793	1.2532	1.6591	56
5	.60298	.75584	1.3230	.79776	1.2535	1.6584	55
6	.60321	.75629	1.3222	.79758	1.2538	1.6578	54
7	.60344	.75675	1.3214	.79741	1.2541	1.6572	53
8	.60367	.75721	1.3206	.79723	1.2543	1.6565	52
9	.60390	.75767	1.3198	.79706	1.2546	1.6559	51
10	.60414	.75812	1.3190	.79688	1.2549	1.6553	50
11	.60437	.75858	1.3182	.79671	1.2552	1.6546	49
12	.60460	.75904	1.3175	.79653	1.2554	1.6540	48
13	.60483	.75950	1.3167	.79635	1.2557	1.6534	47
14	.60506	.75996	1.3159	.79618	1.2560	1.6527	46
15	.60529	.76042	1.3151	.79600	1.2563	1.6521	45
16	.60553	.76088	1.3143	.79583	1.2566	1.6515	44
17	.60576	.76134	1.3135	.79565	1.2568	1.6508	43
18	.60599	.76180	1.3127	.79547	1.2571	1.6502	42
19	.60622	.76226	1.3119	.79530	1.2574	1.6496	41
20	.60645	.76272	1.3111	.79512	1.2577	1.6489	40
21	.60668	.76318	1.3103	.79494	1.2579	1.6483	39
22	.60691	.76364	1.3095	.79477	1.2582	1.6477	38
23	.60714	.76410	1.3087	.79459	1.2585	1.6471	37
24	.60738	.76456	1.3079	.79441	1.2588	1.6464	36
25	.60761	.76502	1.3072	.79424	1.2591	1.6458	35
26	.60784	.76548	1.3064	.79406	1.2593	1.6452	34
27	.60807	.76594	1.3056	.79388	1.2596	1.6446	33
28	.60830	.76640	1.3048	.79371	1.2599	1.6439	32
29	.60853	.76686	1.3040	.79353	1.2602	1.6433	31
30	.60876	.76733	1.3032	.79335	1.2605	1.6427	30
31	.60899	.76779	1.3024	.79318	1.2608	1.6421	29
32	.60922	.76825	1.3017	.79300	1.2610	1.6414	28
33	.60945	.76871	1.3009	.79282	1.2613	1.6408	27
34	.60968	.76918	1.3001	.79264	1.2616	1.6402	26
35	.60991	.76964	1.2993	.79247	1.2619	1.6396	25
36	.61015	.77010	1.2985	.79229	1.2622	1.6390	24
37	.61038	.77057	1.2977	.79211	1.2624	1.6383	23
38	.61061	.77103	1.2970	.79193	1.2627	1.6377	22
39	.61084	.77149	1.2962	.79176	1.2630	1.6371	21
40	.61107	.77196	1.2954	.79158	1.2633	1.6365	20
41	.61130	.77242	1.2946	.79140	1.2636	1.6359	19
42	.61153	.77289	1.2938	.79122	1.2639	1.6353	18
43	.61176	.77335	1.2931	.79105	1.2641	1.6346	17
44	.61199	.77382	1.2923	.79087	1.2644	1.6340	16
45	.61222	.77428	1.2915	.79069	1.2647	1.6334	15
46	.61245	.77475	1.2907	.79051	1.2650	1.6328	14
47	.61268	.77521	1.2900	.79033	1.2653	1.6322	13
48	.61291	.77568	1.2892	.79016	1.2656	1.6316	12
49	.61314	.77615	1.2884	.78998	1.2659	1.6310	11
50	.61337	.77661	1.2876	.78980	1.2661	1.6303	10
51	.61360	.77708	1.2869	.78962	1.2664	1.6297	9
52	.61383	.77754	1.2861	.78944	1.2667	1.6291	8
53	.61406	.77801	1.2853	.78926	1.2670	1.6285	7
54	.61429	.77848	1.2846	.78908	1.2673	1.6279	6
55	.61451	.77895	1.2838	.78891	1.2676	1.6273	5
56	.61474	.77941	1.2830	.78873	1.2679	1.6267	4
57	.61497	.77988	1.2822	.78855	1.2682	1.6261	3
58	.61520	.78035	1.2815	.78837	1.2684	1.6255	2
59	.61543	.78082	1.2807	.78819	1.2687	1.6249	1
60	.61566	.78129	1.2799	.78801	1.2690	1.6243	0
′	Cos	Ctn	Tan	Sin	Csc	Sec	′

127° (307°) (232°) **52°**

38° (218°) (321°) **141°**

′	Sin	Tan	Ctn	Cos	Sec	Csc	′
0	.61566	.78129	1.2799	.78801	1.2690	1.6243	60
1	.61589	.78175	1.2792	.78783	1.2693	1.6237	59
2	.61612	.78222	1.2784	.78765	1.2696	1.6231	58
3	.61635	.78269	1.2776	.78747	1.2699	1.6225	57
4	.61658	.78316	1.2769	.78729	1.2702	1.6219	56
5	.61681	.78363	1.2761	.78711	1.2705	1.6213	55
6	.61704	.78410	1.2753	.78694	1.2708	1.6207	54
7	.61726	.78457	1.2746	.78676	1.2710	1.6201	53
8	.61749	.78504	1.2738	.78658	1.2713	1.6195	52
9	.61772	.78551	1.2731	.78640	1.2716	1.6189	51
10	.61795	.78598	1.2723	.78622	1.2719	1.6183	50
11	.61818	.78645	1.2715	.78604	1.2722	1.6177	49
12	.61841	.78692	1.2708	.78586	1.2725	1.6171	48
13	.61864	.78739	1.2700	.78568	1.2728	1.6165	47
14	.61887	.78786	1.2693	.78550	1.2731	1.6159	46
15	.61909	.78834	1.2685	.78532	1.2734	1.6153	45
16	.61932	.78881	1.2677	.78514	1.2737	1.6147	44
17	.61955	.78928	1.2670	.78496	1.2740	1.6141	43
18	.61978	.78975	1.2662	.78478	1.2742	1.6135	42
19	.62001	.79022	1.2655	.78460	1.2745	1.6129	41
20	.62024	.79070	1.2647	.78442	1.2748	1.6123	40
21	.62046	.79117	1.2640	.78424	1.2751	1.6117	39
22	.62069	.79164	1.2632	.78405	1.2754	1.6111	38
23	.62092	.79212	1.2624	.78387	1.2757	1.6105	37
24	.62115	.79259	1.2617	.78369	1.2760	1.6099	36
25	.62138	.79306	1.2609	.78351	1.2763	1.6093	35
26	.62160	.79354	1.2602	.78333	1.2766	1.6087	34
27	.62183	.79401	1.2594	.78315	1.2769	1.6082	33
28	.62206	.79449	1.2587	.78297	1.2772	1.6076	32
29	.62229	.79496	1.2579	.78279	1.2775	1.6070	31
30	.62251	.79544	1.2572	.78261	1.2778	1.6064	30
31	.62274	.79591	1.2564	.78243	1.2781	1.6058	29
32	.62297	.79639	1.2557	.78225	1.2784	1.6052	28
33	.62320	.79686	1.2549	.78206	1.2787	1.6046	27
34	.62342	.79734	1.2542	.78188	1.2790	1.6040	26
35	.62365	.79781	1.2534	.78170	1.2793	1.6035	25
36	.62388	.79829	1.2527	.78152	1.2796	1.6029	24
37	.62411	.79877	1.2519	.78134	1.2799	1.6023	23
38	.62433	.79924	1.2512	.78116	1.2802	1.6017	22
39	.62456	.79972	1.2504	.78098	1.2804	1.6011	21
40	.62479	.80020	1.2497	.78079	1.2807	1.6005	20
41	.62502	.80067	1.2489	.78061	1.2810	1.6000	19
42	.62524	.80115	1.2482	.78043	1.2813	1.5994	18
43	.62547	.80163	1.2475	.78025	1.2816	1.5988	17
44	.62570	.80211	1.2467	.78007	1.2819	1.5982	16
45	.62592	.80258	1.2460	.77988	1.2822	1.5976	15
46	.62615	.80306	1.2452	.77970	1.2825	1.5971	14
47	.62638	.80354	1.2445	.77952	1.2828	1.5965	13
48	.62660	.80402	1.2437	.77934	1.2831	1.5959	12
49	.62683	.80450	1.2430	.77916	1.2834	1.5953	11
50	.62706	.80498	1.2423	.77897	1.2837	1.5948	10
51	.62728	.80546	1.2415	.77879	1.2840	1.5942	9
52	.62751	.80594	1.2408	.77861	1.2843	1.5936	8
53	.62774	.80642	1.2401	.77843	1.2846	1.5930	7
54	.62796	.80690	1.2393	.77824	1.2849	1.5925	6
55	.62819	.80738	1.2386	.77806	1.2852	1.5919	5
56	.62842	.80786	1.2378	.77788	1.2855	1.5913	4
57	.62864	.80834	1.2371	.77769	1.2859	1.5907	3
58	.62887	.80882	1.2364	.77751	1.2862	1.5902	2
59	.62909	.80930	1.2356	.77733	1.2865	1.5896	1
60	.62932	.80978	1.2349	.77715	1.2868	1.5890	0
′	Cos	Ctn	Tan	Sin	Csc	Sec	′

128° (308°) (231°) **51°**

39° (219°) (320°) **140°**

′	Sin	Tan	Ctn	Cos	Sec	Csc	′
0	.62932	.80978	1.2349	.77715	1.2868	1.5890	60
1	.62955	.81027	1.2342	.77696	1.2871	1.5884	59
2	.62977	.81075	1.2334	.77678	1.2874	1.5879	58
3	.63000	.81123	1.2327	.77660	1.2877	1.5873	57
4	.63022	.81171	1.2320	.77641	1.2880	1.5867	56
5	.63045	.81220	1.2312	.77623	1.2883	1.5862	55
6	.63068	.81268	1.2305	.77605	1.2886	1.5856	54
7	.63090	.81316	1.2298	.77586	1.2889	1.5850	53
8	.63113	.81364	1.2290	.77568	1.2892	1.5845	52
9	.63135	.81413	1.2283	.77550	1.2895	1.5839	51
10	.63158	.81461	1.2276	.77531	1.2898	1.5833	50
11	.63180	.81510	1.2268	.77513	1.2901	1.5828	49
12	.63203	.81558	1.2261	.77494	1.2904	1.5822	48
13	.63225	.81606	1.2254	.77476	1.2907	1.5816	47
14	.63248	.81655	1.2247	.77458	1.2910	1.5811	46
15	.63271	.81703	1.2239	.77439	1.2913	1.5805	45
16	.63293	.81752	1.2232	.77421	1.2916	1.5800	44
17	.63316	.81800	1.2225	.77402	1.2919	1.5794	43
18	.63338	.81849	1.2218	.77384	1.2923	1.5788	42
19	.63361	.81898	1.2210	.77366	1.2926	1.5783	41
20	.63383	.81946	1.2203	.77347	1.2929	1.5777	40
21	.63406	.81995	1.2196	.77329	1.2932	1.5771	39
22	.63428	.82044	1.2189	.77310	1.2935	1.5766	38
23	.63451	.82092	1.2181	.77292	1.2938	1.5760	37
24	.63473	.82141	1.2174	.77273	1.2941	1.5755	36
25	.63496	.82190	1.2167	.77255	1.2944	1.5749	35
26	.63518	.82238	1.2160	.77236	1.2947	1.5744	34
27	.63540	.82287	1.2153	.77218	1.2950	1.5738	33
28	.63563	.82336	1.2145	.77199	1.2953	1.5732	32
29	.63585	.82385	1.2138	.77181	1.2957	1.5727	31
30	.63608	.82434	1.2131	.77162	1.2960	1.5721	30
31	.63630	.82483	1.2124	.77144	1.2963	1.5716	29
32	.63653	.82531	1.2117	.77125	1.2966	1.5710	28
33	.63675	.82580	1.2109	.77107	1.2969	1.5705	27
34	.63698	.82629	1.2102	.77088	1.2972	1.5699	26
35	.63720	.82678	1.2095	.77070	1.2975	1.5694	25
36	.63742	.82727	1.2088	.77051	1.2978	1.5688	24
37	.63765	.82776	1.2081	.77033	1.2981	1.5683	23
38	.63787	.82825	1.2074	.77014	1.2985	1.5677	22
39	.63810	.82874	1.2066	.76996	1.2988	1.5672	21
40	.63832	.82923	1.2059	.76977	1.2991	1.5666	20
41	.63854	.82972	1.2052	.76959	1.2994	1.5661	19
42	.63877	.83022	1.2045	.76940	1.2997	1.5655	18
43	.63899	.83071	1.2038	.76921	1.3000	1.5650	17
44	.63922	.83120	1.2031	.76903	1.3003	1.5644	16
45	.63944	.83169	1.2024	.76884	1.3007	1.5639	15
46	.63966	.83218	1.2017	.76866	1.3010	1.5633	14
47	.63989	.83268	1.2009	.76847	1.3013	1.5628	13
48	.64011	.83317	1.2002	.76828	1.3016	1.5622	12
49	.64033	.83366	1.1995	.76810	1.3019	1.5617	11
50	.64056	.83415	1.1988	.76791	1.3022	1.5611	10
51	.64078	.83465	1.1981	.76772	1.3026	1.5606	9
52	.64100	.83514	1.1974	.76754	1.3029	1.5601	8
53	.64123	.83564	1.1967	.76735	1.3032	1.5595	7
54	.64145	.83613	1.1960	.76717	1.3035	1.5590	6
55	.64167	.83662	1.1953	.76698	1.3038	1.5584	5
56	.64190	.83712	1.1946	.76679	1.3041	1.5579	4
57	.64212	.83761	1.1939	.76661	1.3045	1.5573	3
58	.64234	.83811	1.1932	.76642	1.3048	1.5568	2
59	.64256	.83860	1.1925	.76623	1.3051	1.5563	1
60	.64279	.83910	1.1918	.76604	1.3054	1.5557	0
′	Cos	Ctn	Tan	Sin	Csc	Sec	′

129° (309°) (230°) **50°**

40° (220°) (319°) **139°**

′	Sin	Tan	Ctn	Cos	Sec	Csc	′
0	.64279	.83910	1.1918	.76604	1.3054	1.5557	60
1	.64301	.83960	1.1910	.76586	1.3057	1.5552	59
2	.64323	.84009	1.1903	.76567	1.3060	1.5546	58
3	.64346	.84059	1.1896	.76548	1.3064	1.5541	57
4	.64368	.84108	1.1889	.76530	1.3067	1.5536	56
5	.64390	.84158	1.1882	.76511	1.3070	1.5530	55
6	.64412	.84208	1.1875	.76492	1.3073	1.5525	54
7	.64435	.84258	1.1868	.76473	1.3076	1.5520	53
8	.64457	.84307	1.1861	.76455	1.3080	1.5514	52
9	.64479	.84357	1.1854	.76436	1.3083	1.5509	51
10	.64501	.84407	1.1847	.76417	1.3086	1.5504	50
11	.64524	.84457	1.1840	.76398	1.3089	1.5498	49
12	.64546	.84507	1.1833	.76380	1.3093	1.5493	48
13	.64568	.84556	1.1826	.76361	1.3096	1.5488	47
14	.64590	.84606	1.1819	.76342	1.3099	1.5482	46
15	.64612	.84656	1.1812	.76323	1.3102	1.5477	45
16	.64635	.84706	1.1806	.76304	1.3105	1.5472	44
17	.64657	.84756	1.1799	.76286	1.3109	1.5466	43
18	.64679	.84806	1.1792	.76267	1.3112	1.5461	42
19	.64701	.84856	1.1785	.76248	1.3115	1.5456	41
20	.64723	.84906	1.1778	.76229	1.3118	1.5450	40
21	.64746	.84956	1.1771	.76210	1.3122	1.5445	39
22	.64768	.85006	1.1764	.76192	1.3125	1.5440	38
23	.64790	.85057	1.1757	.76173	1.3128	1.5435	37
24	.64812	.85107	1.1750	.76154	1.3131	1.5429	36
25	.64834	.85157	1.1743	.76135	1.3135	1.5424	35
26	.64856	.85207	1.1736	.76116	1.3138	1.5419	34
27	.64878	.85257	1.1729	.76097	1.3141	1.5413	33
28	.64901	.85308	1.1722	.76078	1.3144	1.5408	32
29	.64923	.85358	1.1715	.76059	1.3148	1.5403	31
30	.64945	.85408	1.1708	.76041	1.3151	1.5398	30
31	.64967	.85458	1.1702	.76022	1.3154	1.5392	29
32	.64989	.85509	1.1695	.76003	1.3157	1.5387	28
33	.65011	.85559	1.1688	.75984	1.3161	1.5382	27
34	.65033	.85609	1.1681	.75965	1.3164	1.5377	26
35	.65055	.85660	1.1674	.75946	1.3167	1.5372	25
36	.65077	.85710	1.1667	.75927	1.3171	1.5366	24
37	.65100	.85761	1.1660	.75908	1.3174	1.5361	23
38	.65122	.85811	1.1653	.75889	1.3177	1.5356	22
39	.65144	.85862	1.1647	.75870	1.3180	1.5351	21
40	.65166	.85912	1.1640	.75851	1.3184	1.5345	20
41	.65188	.85963	1.1633	.75832	1.3187	1.5340	19
42	.65210	.86014	1.1626	.75813	1.3190	1.5335	18
43	.65232	.86064	1.1619	.75794	1.3194	1.5330	17
44	.65254	.86115	1.1612	.75775	1.3197	1.5325	16
45	.65276	.86166	1.1606	.75756	1.3200	1.5320	15
46	.65298	.86216	1.1599	.75738	1.3203	1.5314	14
47	.65320	.86267	1.1592	.75719	1.3207	1.5309	13
48	.65342	.86318	1.1585	.75700	1.3210	1.5304	12
49	.65364	.86368	1.1578	.75680	1.3213	1.5299	11
50	.65386	.86419	1.1571	.75661	1.3217	1.5294	10
51	.65408	.86470	1.1565	.75642	1.3220	1.5289	9
52	.65430	.86521	1.1558	.75623	1.3223	1.5283	8
53	.65452	.86572	1.1551	.75604	1.3227	1.5278	7
54	.65474	.86623	1.1544	.75585	1.3230	1.5273	6
55	.65496	.86674	1.1538	.75566	1.3233	1.5268	5
56	.65518	.86725	1.1531	.75547	1.3237	1.5263	4
57	.65540	.86776	1.1524	.75528	1.3240	1.5258	3
58	.65562	.86827	1.1517	.75509	1.3243	1.5253	2
59	.65584	.86878	1.1510	.75490	1.3247	1.5248	1
60	.65606	.86929	1.1504	.75471	1.3250	1.5243	0
′	Cos	Ctn	Tan	Sin	Csc	Sec	′

130° (310°) (229°) **49°**

41° (221°) (318°) **138°**

′	Sin	Tan	Ctn	Cos	Sec	Csc	′
0	.65606	.86929	1.1504	.75471	1.3250	1.5243	60
1	.65628	.86980	1.1497	.75452	1.3253	1.5237	59
2	.65650	.87031	1.1490	.75433	1.3257	1.5232	58
3	.65672	.87082	1.1483	.75414	1.3260	1.5227	57
4	.65694	.87133	1.1477	.75395	1.3264	1.5222	56
5	.65716	.87184	1.1470	.75375	1.3267	1.5217	55
6	.65738	.87236	1.1463	.75356	1.3270	1.5212	54
7	.65759	.87287	1.1456	.75337	1.3274	1.5207	53
8	.65781	.87338	1.1450	.75318	1.3277	1.5202	52
9	.65803	.87389	1.1443	.75299	1.3280	1.5197	51
10	.65825	.87441	1.1436	.75280	1.3284	1.5192	50
11	.65847	.87492	1.1430	.75261	1.3287	1.5187	49
12	.65869	.87543	1.1423	.75241	1.3291	1.5182	48
13	.65891	.87595	1.1416	.75222	1.3294	1.5177	47
14	.65913	.87646	1.1410	.75203	1.3297	1.5172	46
15	.65935	.87698	1.1403	.75184	1.3301	1.5167	45
16	.65956	.87749	1.1396	.75165	1.3304	1.5162	44
17	.65978	.87801	1.1389	.75146	1.3307	1.5156	43
18	.66000	.87852	1.1383	.75126	1.3311	1.5151	42
19	.66022	.87904	1.1376	.75107	1.3314	1.5146	41
20	.66044	.87955	1.1369	.75088	1.3318	1.5141	40
21	.66066	.88007	1.1363	.75069	1.3321	1.5136	39
22	.66088	.88059	1.1356	.75050	1.3325	1.5131	38
23	.66109	.88110	1.1349	.75030	1.3328	1.5126	37
24	.66131	.88162	1.1343	.75011	1.3331	1.5121	36
25	.66153	.88214	1.1336	.74992	1.3335	1.5116	35
26	.66175	.88265	1.1329	.74973	1.3338	1.5111	34
27	.66197	.88317	1.1323	.74953	1.3342	1.5107	33
28	.66218	.88369	1.1316	.74934	1.3345	1.5102	32
29	.66240	.88421	1.1310	.74915	1.3348	1.5097	31
30	.66262	.88473	1.1303	.74896	1.3352	1.5092	30
31	.66284	.88524	1.1296	.74876	1.3355	1.5087	29
32	.66306	.88576	1.1290	.74857	1.3359	1.5082	28
33	.66327	.88628	1.1283	.74838	1.3362	1.5077	27
34	.66349	.88680	1.1276	.74818	1.3366	1.5072	26
35	.66371	.88732	1.1270	.74799	1.3369	1.5067	25
36	.66393	.88784	1.1263	.74780	1.3373	1.5062	24
37	.66414	.88836	1.1257	.74760	1.3376	1.5057	23
38	.66436	.88888	1.1250	.74741	1.3380	1.5052	22
39	.66458	.88940	1.1243	.74722	1.3383	1.5047	21
40	.66480	.88992	1.1237	.74703	1.3386	1.5042	20
41	.66501	.89045	1.1230	.74683	1.3390	1.5037	19
42	.66523	.89097	1.1224	.74664	1.3393	1.5032	18
43	.66545	.89149	1.1217	.74644	1.3397	1.5027	17
44	.66566	.89201	1.1211	.74625	1.3400	1.5023	16
45	.66588	.89253	1.1204	.74606	1.3404	1.5018	15
46	.66610	.89306	1.1197	.74586	1.3407	1.5013	14
47	.66632	.89358	1.1191	.74567	1.3411	1.5008	13
48	.66653	.89410	1.1184	.74548	1.3414	1.5003	12
49	.66675	.89463	1.1178	.74528	1.3418	1.4998	11
50	.66697	.89515	1.1171	.74509	1.3421	1.4993	10
51	.66718	.89567	1.1165	.74489	1.3425	1.4988	9
52	.66740	.89620	1.1158	.74470	1.3428	1.4984	8
53	.66762	.89672	1.1152	.74451	1.3432	1.4979	7
54	.66783	.89725	1.1145	.74431	1.3435	1.4974	6
55	.66805	.89777	1.1139	.74412	1.3439	1.4969	5
56	.66827	.89830	1.1132	.74392	1.3442	1.4964	4
57	.66848	.89883	1.1126	.74373	1.3446	1.4959	3
58	.66870	.89935	1.1119	.74353	1.3449	1.4954	2
59	.66891	.89988	1.1113	.74334	1.3453	1.4950	1
60	.66913	.90040	1.1106	.74314	1.3456	1.4945	0
′	Cos	Ctn	Tan	Sin	Csc	Sec	′

131° (311°) (228°) **48°**

42° (222°) (317°) **137°**

′	Sin	Tan	Ctn	Cos	Sec	Csc	′
0	.66913	.90040	1.1106	.74314	1.3456	1.4945	60
1	.66935	.90093	1.1100	.74295	1.3460	1.4940	59
2	.66956	.90146	1.1093	.74276	1.3463	1.4935	58
3	.66978	.90199	1.1087	.74256	1.3467	1.4930	57
4	.66999	.90251	1.1080	.74237	1.3470	1.4925	56
5	.67021	.90304	1.1074	.74217	1.3474	1.4921	55
6	.67043	.90357	1.1067	.74198	1.3478	1.4916	54
7	.67064	.90410	1.1061	.74178	1.3481	1.4911	53
8	.67086	.90463	1.1054	.74159	1.3485	1.4906	52
9	.67107	.90516	1.1048	.74139	1.3488	1.4901	51
10	.67129	.90569	1.1041	.74120	1.3492	1.4897	50
11	.67151	.90621	1.1035	.74100	1.3495	1.4892	49
12	.67172	.90674	1.1028	.74080	1.3499	1.4887	48
13	.67194	.90727	1.1022	.74061	1.3502	1.4882	47
14	.67215	.90781	1.1016	.74041	1.3506	1.4878	46
15	.67237	.90834	1.1009	.74022	1.3510	1.4873	45
16	.67258	.90887	1.1003	.74002	1.3513	1.4868	44
17	.67280	.90940	1.0996	.73983	1.3517	1.4863	43
18	.67301	.90993	1.0990	.73963	1.3520	1.4859	42
19	.67323	.91046	1.0983	.73944	1.3524	1.4854	41
20	.67344	.91099	1.0977	.73924	1.3527	1.4849	40
21	.67366	.91153	1.0971	.73904	1.3531	1.4844	39
22	.67387	.91206	1.0964	.73885	1.3535	1.4840	38
23	.67409	.91259	1.0958	.73865	1.3538	1.4835	37
24	.67430	.91313	1.0951	.73846	1.3542	1.4830	36
25	.67452	.91366	1.0945	.73826	1.3545	1.4825	35
26	.67473	.91419	1.0939	.73806	1.3549	1.4821	34
27	.67495	.91473	1.0932	.73787	1.3553	1.4816	33
28	.67516	.91526	1.0926	.73767	1.3556	1.4811	32
29	.67538	.91580	1.0919	.73747	1.3560	1.4807	31
30	.67559	.91633	1.0913	.73728	1.3563	1.4802	30
31	.67580	.91687	1.0907	.73708	1.3567	1.4797	29
32	.67602	.91740	1.0900	.73688	1.3571	1.4792	28
33	.67623	.91794	1.0894	.73669	1.3574	1.4788	27
34	.67645	.91847	1.0888	.73649	1.3578	1.4783	26
35	.67666	.91901	1.0881	.73629	1.3582	1.4778	25
36	.67688	.91955	1.0875	.73610	1.3585	1.4774	24
37	.67709	.92008	1.0869	.73590	1.3589	1.4769	23
38	.67730	.92062	1.0862	.73570	1.3592	1.4764	22
39	.67752	.92116	1.0856	.73551	1.3596	1.4760	21
40	.67773	.92170	1.0850	.73531	1.3600	1.4755	20
41	.67795	.92224	1.0843	.73511	1.3603	1.4750	19
42	.67816	.92277	1.0837	.73491	1.3607	1.4746	18
43	.67837	.92331	1.0831	.73472	1.3611	1.4741	17
44	.67859	.92385	1.0824	.73452	1.3614	1.4737	16
45	.67880	.92439	1.0818	.73432	1.3618	1.4732	15
46	.67901	.92493	1.0812	.73413	1.3622	1.4727	14
47	.67923	.92547	1.0805	.73393	1.3625	1.4723	13
48	.67944	.92601	1.0799	.73373	1.3629	1.4718	12
49	.67965	.92655	1.0793	.73353	1.3633	1.4713	11
50	.67987	.92709	1.0786	.73333	1.3636	1.4709	10
51	.68008	.92763	1.0780	.73314	1.3640	1.4704	9
52	.68029	.92817	1.0774	.73294	1.3644	1.4700	8
53	.68051	.92872	1.0768	.73274	1.3647	1.4695	7
54	.68072	.92926	1.0761	.73254	1.3651	1.4690	6
55	.68093	.92980	1.0755	.73234	1.3655	1.4686	5
56	.68115	.93034	1.0749	.73215	1.3658	1.4681	4
57	.68136	.93088	1.0742	.73195	1.3662	1.4677	3
58	.68157	.93143	1.0736	.73175	1.3666	1.4672	2
59	.68179	.93197	1.0730	.73155	1.3670	1.4667	1
60	.68200	.93252	1.0724	.73135	1.3673	1.4663	0
′	Cos	Ctn	Tan	Sin	Csc	Sec	′

132° (312°) (227°) **47°**

43° (223°) (316°) **136°**

′	Sin	Tan	Ctn	Cos	Sec	Csc	′
0	.68200	.93252	1.0724	.73135	1.3673	1.4663	60
1	.68221	.93306	1.0717	.73116	1.3677	1.4658	59
2	.68242	.93360	1.0711	.73096	1.3681	1.4654	58
3	.68264	.93415	1.0705	.73076	1.3684	1.4649	57
4	.68285	.93469	1.0699	.73056	1.3688	1.4645	56
5	.68306	.93524	1.0692	.73036	1.3692	1.4640	55
6	.68327	.93578	1.0686	.73016	1.3696	1.4635	54
7	.68349	.93633	1.0680	.72996	1.3699	1.4631	53
8	.68370	.93688	1.0674	.72976	1.3703	1.4626	52
9	.68391	.93742	1.0668	.72957	1.3707	1.4622	51
10	.68412	.93797	1.0661	.72937	1.3711	1.4617	50
11	.68434	.93852	1.0655	.72917	1.3714	1.4613	49
12	.68455	.93906	1.0649	.72897	1.3718	1.4608	48
13	.68476	.93961	1.0643	.72877	1.3722	1.4604	47
14	.68497	.94016	1.0637	.72857	1.3726	1.4599	46
15	.68518	.94071	1.0630	.72837	1.3729	1.4595	45
16	.68539	.94125	1.0624	.72817	1.3733	1.4590	44
17	.68561	.94180	1.0618	.72797	1.3737	1.4586	43
18	.68582	.94235	1.0612	.72777	1.3741	1.4581	42
19	.68603	.94290	1.0606	.72757	1.3744	1.4577	41
20	.68624	.94345	1.0599	.72737	1.3748	1.4572	40
21	.68645	.94400	1.0593	.72717	1.3752	1.4568	39
22	.68666	.94455	1.0587	.72697	1.3756	1.4563	38
23	.68688	.94510	1.0581	.72677	1.3759	1.4559	37
24	.68709	.94565	1.0575	.72657	1.3763	1.4554	36
25	.68730	.94620	1.0569	.72637	1.3767	1.4550	35
26	.68751	.94676	1.0562	.72617	1.3771	1.4545	34
27	.68772	.94731	1.0556	.72597	1.3775	1.4541	33
28	.68793	.94786	1.0550	.72577	1.3778	1.4536	32
29	.68814	.94841	1.0544	.72557	1.3782	1.4532	31
30	.68835	.94896	1.0538	.72537	1.3786	1.4527	30
31	.68857	.94952	1.0532	.72517	1.3790	1.4523	29
32	.68878	.95007	1.0526	.72497	1.3794	1.4518	28
33	.68899	.95062	1.0519	.72477	1.3797	1.4514	27
34	.68920	.95118	1.0513	.72457	1.3801	1.4510	26
35	.68941	.95173	1.0507	.72437	1.3805	1.4505	25
36	.68962	.95229	1.0501	.72417	1.3809	1.4501	24
37	.68983	.95284	1.0495	.72397	1.3813	1.4496	23
38	.69004	.95340	1.0489	.72377	1.3817	1.4492	22
39	.69025	.95395	1.0483	.72357	1.3820	1.4487	21
40	.69046	.95451	1.0477	.72337	1.3824	1.4483	20
41	.69067	.95506	1.0470	.72317	1.3828	1.4479	19
42	.69088	.95562	1.0464	.72297	1.3832	1.4474	18
43	.69109	.95618	1.0458	.72277	1.3836	1.4470	17
44	.69130	.95673	1.0452	.72257	1.3840	1.4465	16
45	.69151	.95729	1.0446	.72236	1.3843	1.4461	15
46	.69172	.95785	1.0440	.72216	1.3847	1.4457	14
47	.69193	.95841	1.0434	.72196	1.3851	1.4452	13
48	.69214	.95897	1.0428	.72176	1.3855	1.4448	12
49	.69235	.95952	1.0422	.72156	1.3859	1.4443	11
50	.69256	.96008	1.0416	.72136	1.3863	1.4439	10
51	.69277	.96064	1.0410	.72116	1.3867	1.4435	9
52	.69298	.96120	1.0404	.72095	1.3871	1.4430	8
53	.69319	.96176	1.0398	.72075	1.3874	1.4426	7
54	.69340	.96232	1.0392	.72055	1.3878	1.4422	6
55	.69361	.96288	1.0385	.72035	1.3882	1.4417	5
56	.69382	.96344	1.0379	.72015	1.3886	1.4413	4
57	.69403	.96400	1.0373	.71995	1.3890	1.4409	3
58	.69424	.96457	1.0367	.71974	1.3894	1.4404	2
59	.69445	.96513	1.0361	.71954	1.3898	1.4400	1
60	.69466	.96569	1.0355	.71934	1.3902	1.4396	0
′	Cos	Ctn	Tan	Sin	Csc	Sec	′

133° (313°) (226°) **46°**

44° (224°) (315°) **135°**

′	Sin	Tan	Ctn	Cos	Sec	Csc	′
0	.69466	.96569	1.0355	.71934	1.3902	1.4396	60
1	.69487	.96625	1.0349	.71914	1.3906	1.4391	59
2	.69508	.96681	1.0343	.71894	1.3909	1.4387	58
3	.69529	.96738	1.0337	.71873	1.3913	1.4383	57
4	.69549	.96794	1.0331	.71853	1.3917	1.4378	56
5	.69570	.96850	1.0325	.71833	1.3921	1.4374	55
6	.69591	.96907	1.0319	.71813	1.3925	1.4370	54
7	.69612	.96963	1.0313	.71792	1.3929	1.4365	53
8	.69633	.97020	1.0307	.71772	1.3933	1.4361	52
9	.69654	.97076	1.0301	.71752	1.3937	1.4357	51
10	.69675	.97133	1.0295	.71732	1.3941	1.4352	50
11	.69696	.97189	1.0289	.71711	1.3945	1.4348	49
12	.69717	.97246	1.0283	.71691	1.3949	1.4344	48
13	.69737	.97302	1.0277	.71671	1.3953	1.4340	47
14	.69758	.97359	1.0271	.71650	1.3957	1.4335	46
15	.69779	.97416	1.0265	.71630	1.3961	1.4331	45
16	.69800	.97472	1.0259	.71610	1.3965	1.4327	44
17	.69821	.97529	1.0253	.71590	1.3969	1.4322	43
18	.69842	.97586	1.0247	.71569	1.3972	1.4318	42
19	.69862	.97643	1.0241	.71549	1.3976	1.4314	41
20	.69883	.97700	1.0235	.71529	1.3980	1.4310	40
21	.69904	.97756	1.0230	.71508	1.3984	1.4305	39
22	.69925	.97813	1.0224	.71488	1.3988	1.4301	38
23	.69946	.97870	1.0218	.71468	1.3992	1.4297	37
24	.69966	.97927	1.0212	.71447	1.3996	1.4293	36
25	.69987	.97984	1.0206	.71427	1.4000	1.4288	35
26	.70008	.98041	1.0200	.71407	1.4004	1.4284	34
27	.70029	.98098	1.0194	.71386	1.4008	1.4280	33
28	.70049	.98155	1.0188	.71366	1.4012	1.4276	32
29	.70070	.98213	1.0182	.71345	1.4016	1.4271	31
30	.70091	.98270	1.0176	.71325	1.4020	1.4267	30
31	.70112	.98327	1.0170	.71305	1.4024	1.4263	29
32	.70132	.98384	1.0164	.71284	1.4028	1.4259	28
33	.70153	.98441	1.0158	.71264	1.4032	1.4255	27
34	.70174	.98499	1.0152	.71243	1.4036	1.4250	26
35	.70195	.98556	1.0147	.71223	1.4040	1.4246	25
36	.70215	.98613	1.0141	.71203	1.4044	1.4242	24
37	.70236	.98671	1.0135	.71182	1.4048	1.4238	23
38	.70257	.98728	1.0129	.71162	1.4052	1.4234	22
39	.70277	.98786	1.0123	.71141	1.4057	1.4229	21
40	.70298	.98843	1.0117	.71121	1.4061	1.4225	20
41	.70319	.98901	1.0111	.71100	1.4065	1.4221	19
42	.70339	.98958	1.0105	.71080	1.4069	1.4217	18
43	.70360	.99016	1.0099	.71059	1.4073	1.4213	17
44	.70381	.99073	1.0094	.71039	1.4077	1.4208	16
45	.70401	.99131	1.0088	.71019	1.4081	1.4204	15
46	.70422	.99189	1.0082	.70998	1.4085	1.4200	14
47	.70443	.99247	1.0076	.70978	1.4089	1.4196	13
48	.70463	.99304	1.0070	.70957	1.4093	1.4192	12
49	.70484	.99362	1.0064	.70937	1.4097	1.4188	11
50	.70505	.99420	1.0058	.70916	1.4101	1.4183	10
51	.70525	.99478	1.0052	.70896	1.4105	1.4179	9
52	.70546	.99536	1.0047	.70875	1.4109	1.4175	8
53	.70567	.99594	1.0041	.70855	1.4113	1.4171	7
54	.70587	.99652	1.0035	.70834	1.4118	1.4167	6
55	.70608	.99710	1.0029	.70813	1.4122	1.4163	5
56	.70628	.99768	1.0023	.70793	1.4126	1.4159	4
57	.70649	.99826	1.0017	.70772	1.4130	1.4154	3
58	.70670	.99884	1.0012	.70752	1.4134	1.4150	2
59	.70690	.99942	1.0006	.70731	1.4138	1.4146	1
60	.70711	1.0000	1.0000	.70711	1.4142	1.4142	0
′	Cos	Ctn	Tan	Sin	Csc	Sec	′

134° (314°) (225°) **45°**

100-150

N.	0	1	2	3	4	5	6	7	8	9
100	00 000	043	087	130	173	217	260	303	346	389
101	432	475	518	561	604	647	689	732	775	817
102	860	903	945	988	*030	*072	*115	*157	*199	*242
103	01 284	326	368	410	452	494	536	578	620	662
104	703	745	787	828	870	912	953	995	*036	*078
105	02 119	160	202	243	284	325	366	407	449	490
106	531	572	612	653	694	735	776	816	857	898
107	938	979	*019	*060	*100	*141	*181	*222	*262	*302
108	03 342	383	423	463	503	543	583	623	663	703
109	743	782	822	862	902	941	981	*021	*060	*100
110	04 139	179	218	258	297	336	376	415	454	493
111	532	571	610	650	689	727	766	805	844	883
112	922	961	999	*038	*077	*115	*154	*192	*231	*269
113	05 308	346	385	423	461	500	538	576	614	652
114	690	729	767	805	843	881	918	956	994	*032
115	06 070	108	145	183	221	258	296	333	371	408
116	446	483	521	558	595	633	670	707	744	781
117	819	856	893	930	967	*004	*041	*078	*115	*151
118	07 188	225	262	298	335	372	408	445	482	518
119	555	591	628	664	700	737	773	809	846	882
120	918	954	990	*027	*063	*099	*135	*171	*207	*243
121	08 279	314	350	386	422	458	493	529	565	600
122	636	672	707	743	778	814	849	884	920	955
123	991	*026	*061	*096	*132	*167	*202	*237	*272	*307
124	09 342	377	412	447	482	517	552	587	621	656
125	691	726	760	795	830	864	899	934	968	*003
126	10 037	072	106	140	175	209	243	278	312	346
127	380	415	449	483	517	551	585	619	653	687
128	721	755	789	823	857	890	924	958	992	*025
129	11 059	093	126	160	193	227	261	294	327	361
130	394	428	461	494	528	561	594	628	661	694
131	727	760	793	826	860	893	926	959	992	*024
132	12 057	090	123	156	189	222	254	287	320	352
133	385	418	450	483	516	548	581	613	646	678
134	710	743	775	808	840	872	905	937	969	*001
135	13 033	066	098	130	162	194	226	258	290	322
136	354	386	418	450	481	513	545	577	609	640
137	672	704	735	767	799	830	862	893	925	956
138	988	*019	*051	*082	*114	*145	*176	*208	*239	*270
139	14 301	333	364	395	426	457	489	520	551	582
140	613	644	675	706	737	768	799	829	860	891
141	922	953	983	*014	*045	*076	*106	*137	*168	*198
142	15 229	259	290	320	351	381	412	442	473	503
143	534	564	594	625	655	685	715	746	776	806
144	836	866	897	927	957	987	*017	*047	*077	*107
145	16 137	167	197	227	256	286	316	346	376	406
146	435	465	495	524	554	584	613	643	673	702
147	732	761	791	820	850	879	909	938	967	997
148	17 026	056	085	114	143	173	202	231	260	289
149	319	348	377	406	435	464	493	522	551	580
150	609	638	667	696	725	754	782	811	840	869
N.	**0**	**1**	**2**	**3**	**4**	**5**	**6**	**7**	**8**	**9**

Prop. Pts.

	44	43	42
1	4.4	4.3	4.2
2	8.8	8.6	8.4
3	13.2	12.9	12.6
4	17.6	17.2	16.8
5	22.0	21.5	21.0
6	26.4	25.8	25.2
7	30.8	30.1	29.4
8	35.2	34.4	33.6
9	39.6	38.7	37.8

	41	40	39
1	4.1	4.0	3.9
2	8.2	8.0	7.8
3	12.3	12.0	11.7
4	16.4	16.0	15.6
5	20.5	20.0	19.5
6	24.6	24.0	23.4
7	28.7	28.0	27.3
8	32.8	32.0	31.2
9	36.9	36.0	35.1

	38	37	36
1	3.8	3.7	3.6
2	7.6	7.4	7.2
3	11.4	11.1	10.8
4	15.2	14.8	14.4
5	19.0	18.5	18.0
6	22.8	22.2	21.6
7	26.6	25.9	25.2
8	30.4	29.6	28.8
9	34.2	33.3	32.4

	35	34	33
1	3.5	3.4	3.3
2	7.0	6.8	6.6
3	10.5	10.2	9.9
4	14.0	13.6	13.2
5	17.5	17.0	16.5
6	21.0	20.4	19.8
7	24.5	23.8	23.1
8	28.0	27.2	26.4
9	31.5	30.6	29.7

	32	31	30
1	3.2	3.1	3.0
2	6.4	6.2	6.0
3	9.6	9.3	9.0
4	12.8	12.4	12.0
5	16.0	15.5	15.0
6	19.2	18.6	18.0
7	22.4	21.7	21.0
8	25.6	24.8	24.0
9	28.8	27.9	27.0

Prop. Pts.

*From E. Richard Heineman, "Plane Trigonometry with Tables," 3d ed., McGraw-Hill Book Company, New York, 1964.

150-200

N.	0	1	2	3	4	5	6	7	8	9
150	17 609	638	667	696	725	754	782	811	840	869
151	898	926	955	984	*013	*041	*070	*099	*127	*156
152	18 184	213	241	270	298	327	355	384	412	441
153	469	498	526	554	583	611	639	667	696	724
154	752	780	808	837	865	893	921	949	977	*005
155	19 033	061	089	117	145	173	201	229	257	285
156	312	340	368	396	424	451	479	507	535	562
157	590	618	645	673	700	728	756	783	811	838
158	866	893	921	948	976	*003	*030	*058	*085	*112
159	20 140	167	194	222	249	276	303	330	358	385
160	412	439	466	493	520	548	575	602	629	656
161	683	710	737	763	790	817	844	871	898	925
162	952	978	*005	*032	*059	*085	*112	*139	*165	*192
163	21 219	245	272	299	325	352	378	405	431	458
164	484	511	537	564	590	617	643	669	696	722
165	748	775	801	827	854	880	906	932	958	985
166	22 011	037	063	089	115	141	167	194	220	246
167	272	298	324	350	376	401	427	453	479	505
168	531	557	583	608	634	660	686	712	737	763
169	789	814	840	866	891	917	943	968	994	*019
170	23 045	070	096	121	147	172	198	223	249	274
171	300	325	350	376	401	426	452	477	502	528
172	553	578	603	629	654	679	704	729	754	779
173	805	830	855	880	905	930	955	980	*005	*030
174	24 055	080	105	130	155	180	204	229	254	279
175	304	329	353	378	403	428	452	477	502	527
176	551	576	601	625	650	674	699	724	748	773
177	797	822	846	871	895	920	944	969	993	*018
178	25 042	066	091	115	139	164	188	212	237	261
179	285	310	334	358	382	406	431	455	479	503
180	527	551	575	600	624	648	672	696	720	744
181	768	792	816	840	864	888	912	935	959	983
182	26 007	031	055	079	102	126	150	174	198	221
183	245	269	293	316	340	364	387	411	435	458
184	482	505	529	553	576	600	623	647	670	694
185	717	741	764	788	811	834	858	881	905	928
186	951	975	998	*021	*045	*068	*091	*114	*138	*161
187	27 184	207	231	254	277	300	323	346	370	393
188	416	439	462	485	508	531	554	577	600	623
189	646	669	692	715	738	761	784	807	830	852
190	875	898	921	944	967	989	*012	*035	*058	*081
191	28 103	126	149	171	194	217	240	262	285	307
192	330	353	375	398	421	443	466	488	511	533
193	556	578	601	623	646	668	691	713	735	758
194	780	803	825	847	870	892	914	937	959	981
195	29 003	026	048	070	092	115	137	159	181	203
196	226	248	270	292	314	336	358	380	403	425
197	447	469	491	513	535	557	579	601	623	645
198	667	688	710	732	754	776	798	820	842	863
199	885	907	929	951	973	994	*016	*038	*060	*081
200	30 103	125	146	168	190	211	233	255	276	298
N.	**0**	**1**	**2**	**3**	**4**	**5**	**6**	**7**	**8**	**9**

Prop. Pts.

	29	**28**
1	2.9	2.8
2	5.8	5.6
3	8.7	8.4
4	11.6	11.2
5	14.5	14.0
6	17.4	16.8
7	20.3	19.6
8	23.2	22.4
9	26.1	25.2

	27	**26**
1	2.7	2.6
2	5.4	5.2
3	8.1	7.8
4	10.8	10.4
5	13.5	13.0
6	16.2	15.6
7	18.9	18.2
8	21.6	20.8
9	24.3	23.4

	25
1	2.5
2	5.0
3	7.5
4	10.0
5	12.5
6	15.0
7	17.5
8	20.0
9	22.5

	24	**23**
1	2.4	2.3
2	4.8	4.6
3	7.2	6.9
4	9.6	9.2
5	12.0	11.5
6	14.4	13.8
7	16.8	16.1
8	19.2	18.4
9	21.6	20.7

	22	**21**
1	2.2	2.1
2	4.4	4.2
3	6.6	6.3
4	8.8	8.4
5	11.0	10.5
6	13.2	12.6
7	15.4	14.7
8	17.6	16.8
9	19.8	18.9

200-250

N.		0	1	2	3	4	5	6	7	8	9
200	30	103	125	146	168	190	211	233	255	276	298
201		320	341	363	384	406	428	449	471	492	514
202		535	557	578	600	621	643	664	685	707	728
203		750	771	792	814	835	856	878	899	920	942
204		963	984	*006	*027	*048	*069	*091	*112	*133	*154
205	31	175	197	218	239	260	281	302	323	345	366
206		387	408	429	450	471	492	513	534	555	576
207		597	618	639	660	681	702	723	744	765	785
208		806	827	848	869	890	911	931	952	973	994
209	32	015	035	056	077	098	118	139	160	181	201
210		222	243	263	284	305	325	346	366	387	408
211		428	449	469	490	510	531	552	572	593	613
212		634	654	675	695	715	736	756	777	797	818
213		838	858	879	899	919	940	960	980	*001	*021
214	33	041	062	082	102	122	143	163	183	203	224
215		244	264	284	304	325	345	365	385	405	425
216		445	465	486	506	526	546	566	586	606	626
217		646	666	686	706	726	746	766	786	806	826
218		846	866	885	905	925	945	965	985	*005	*025
219	34	044	064	084	104	124	143	163	183	203	223
220		242	262	282	301	321	341	361	380	400	420
221		439	459	479	498	518	537	557	577	596	616
222		635	655	674	694	713	733	753	772	792	811
223		830	850	869	889	908	928	947	967	986	*005
224	35	025	044	064	083	102	122	141	160	180	199
225		218	238	257	276	295	315	334	353	372	392
226		411	430	449	468	488	507	526	545	564	583
227		603	622	641	660	679	698	717	736	755	774
228		793	813	832	851	870	889	908	927	946	965
229		984	*003	*021	*040	*059	*078	*097	*116	*135	*154
230	36	173	192	211	229	248	267	286	305	324	342
231		361	380	399	418	436	455	474	493	511	530
232		549	568	586	605	624	642	661	680	698	717
233		736	754	773	791	810	829	847	866	884	903
234		922	940	959	977	996	*014	*033	*051	*070	*088
235	37	107	125	144	162	181	199	218	236	254	273
236		291	310	328	346	365	383	401	420	438	457
237		475	493	511	530	548	566	585	603	621	639
238		658	676	694	712	731	749	767	785	803	822
239		840	858	876	894	912	931	949	967	985	*003
240	38	021	039	057	075	093	112	130	148	166	184
241		202	220	238	256	274	292	310	328	346	364
242		382	399	417	435	453	471	489	507	525	543
243		561	578	596	614	632	650	668	686	703	721
244		739	757	775	792	810	828	846	863	881	899
245		917	934	952	970	987	*005	*023	*041	*058	*076
246	39	094	111	129	146	164	182	199	217	235	252
247		270	287	305	322	340	358	375	393	410	428
248		445	463	480	498	515	533	550	568	585	602
249		620	637	655	672	690	707	724	742	759	777
250		794	811	829	846	863	881	898	915	933	950
N.		**0**	**1**	**2**	**3**	**4**	**5**	**6**	**7**	**8**	**9**

Prop. Pts.

	22	21
1	2.2	2.1
2	4.4	4.2
3	6.6	6.3
4	8.8	8.4
5	11.0	10.5
6	13.2	12.6
7	15.4	14.7
8	17.6	16.8
9	19.8	18.9

	20
1	2.0
2	4.0
3	6.0
4	8.0
5	10.0
6	12.0
7	14.0
8	16.0
9	18.0

	19
1	1.9
2	3.8
3	5.7
4	7.6
5	9.5
6	11.4
7	13.3
8	15.2
9	17.1

	18
1	1.8
2	3.6
3	5.4
4	7.2
5	9.0
6	10.8
7	12.6
8	14.4
9	16.2

	17
1	1.7
2	3.4
3	5.1
4	6.8
5	8.5
6	10.2
7	11.9
8	13.6
9	15.3

Prop. Pts.

250-300

N.		0	1	2	3	4	5	6	7	8	9
250	39	794	811	829	846	863	881	898	915	933	950
251		967	985	*002	*019	*037	*054	*071	*088	*106	*123
252	40	140	157	175	192	209	226	243	261	278	295
253		312	329	346	364	381	398	415	432	449	466
254		483	500	518	535	552	569	586	603	620	637
255		654	671	688	705	722	739	756	773	790	807
256		824	841	858	875	892	909	926	943	960	976
257		993	*010	*027	*044	*061	*078	*095	*111	*128	*145
258	41	162	179	196	212	229	246	263	280	296	313
259		330	347	363	380	397	414	430	447	464	481
260		497	514	531	547	564	581	597	614	631	647
261		664	681	697	714	731	747	764	780	797	814
262		830	847	863	880	896	913	929	946	963	979
263		996	*012	*029	*045	*062	*078	*095	*111	*127	*144
264	42	160	177	193	210	226	243	259	275	292	308
265		325	341	357	374	390	406	423	439	455	472
266		488	504	521	537	553	570	586	602	619	635
267		651	667	684	700	716	732	749	765	781	797
268		813	830	846	862	878	894	911	927	943	959
269		975	991	*008	*024	*040	*056	*072	*088	*104	*120
270	43	136	152	169	185	201	217	233	249	265	281
271		297	313	329	345	361	377	393	409	425	441
272		457	473	489	505	521	537	553	569	584	600
273		616	632	648	664	680	696	712	727	743	759
274		775	791	807	823	838	854	870	886	902	917
275		933	949	965	981	996	*012	*028	*044	*059	*075
276	44	091	107	122	138	154	170	185	201	217	232
277		248	264	279	295	311	326	342	358	373	389
278		404	420	436	451	467	483	498	514	529	545
279		560	576	592	607	623	638	654	669	685	700
280		716	731	747	762	778	793	809	824	840	855
281		871	886	902	917	932	948	963	979	994	*010
282	45	025	040	056	071	086	102	117	133	148	163
283		179	194	209	225	240	255	271	286	301	317
284		332	347	362	378	393	408	423	439	454	469
285		484	500	515	530	545	561	576	591	606	621
286		637	652	667	682	697	712	728	743	758	773
287		788	803	818	834	849	864	879	894	909	924
288		939	954	969	984	*000	*015	*030	*045	*060	*075
289	46	090	105	120	135	150	165	180	195	210	225
290		240	255	270	285	300	315	330	345	359	374
291		389	404	419	434	449	464	479	494	509	523
292		538	553	568	583	598	613	627	642	657	672
293		687	702	716	731	746	761	776	790	805	820
294		835	850	864	879	894	909	923	938	953	967
295		982	997	*012	*026	*041	*056	*070	*085	*100	*114
296	47	129	144	159	173	188	202	217	232	246	261
297		276	290	305	319	334	349	363	378	392	407
298		422	436	451	465	480	494	509	524	538	553
299		567	582	596	611	625	640	654	669	683	698
300		712	727	741	756	770	784	799	813	828	842
N.		**0**	**1**	**2**	**3**	**4**	**5**	**6**	**7**	**8**	**9**

Prop. Pts.

	18	17	16	15	14
1	1.8	1.7	1.6	1.5	1.4
2	3.6	3.4	3.2	3.0	2.8
3	5.4	5.1	4.8	4.5	4.2
4	7.2	6.8	6.4	6.0	5.6
5	9.0	8.5	8.0	7.5	7.0
6	10.8	10.2	9.6	9.0	8.4
7	12.6	11.9	11.2	10.5	9.8
8	14.4	13.6	12.8	12.0	11.2
9	16.2	15.3	14.4	13.5	12.6

log e = 0.43429

300-350

N.	0	1	2	3	4	5	6	7	8	9
300	47 712	727	741	756	770	784	799	813	828	842
301	857	871	885	900	914	929	943	958	972	986
302	48 001	015	029	044	058	073	087	101	116	130
303	144	159	173	187	202	216	230	244	259	273
304	287	302	316	330	344	359	373	387	401	416
305	430	444	458	473	487	501	515	530	544	558
306	572	586	601	615	629	643	657	671	686	700
307	714	728	742	756	770	785	799	813	827	841
308	855	869	883	897	911	926	940	954	968	982
309	996	*010	*024	*038	*052	*066	*080	*094	*108	*122
310	49 136	150	164	178	192	206	220	234	248	262
311	276	290	304	318	332	346	360	374	388	402
312	415	429	443	457	471	485	499	513	527	541
313	554	568	582	596	610	624	638	651	665	679
314	693	707	721	734	748	762	776	790	803	817
315	831	845	859	872	886	900	914	927	941	955
316	969	982	996	*010	*024	*037	*051	*065	*079	*092
317	50 106	120	133	147	161	174	188	202	215	229
318	243	256	270	284	297	311	325	338	352	365
319	379	393	406	420	433	447	461	474	488	501
320	515	529	542	556	569	583	596	610	623	637
321	651	664	678	691	705	718	732	745	759	772
322	786	799	813	826	840	853	866	880	893	907
323	920	934	947	961	974	987	*001	*014	*028	*041
324	51 055	068	081	095	108	121	135	148	162	175
325	188	202	215	228	242	255	268	282	295	308
326	322	335	348	362	375	388	402	415	428	441
327	455	468	481	495	508	521	534	548	561	574
328	587	601	614	627	640	654	667	680	693	706
329	720	733	746	759	772	786	799	812	825	838
330	851	865	878	891	904	917	930	943	957	970
331	983	996	*009	*022	*035	*048	*061	*075	*088	*101
332	52 114	127	140	153	166	179	192	205	218	231
333	244	257	270	284	297	310	323	336	349	362
334	375	388	401	414	427	440	453	466	479	492
335	504	517	530	543	556	569	582	595	608	621
336	634	647	660	673	686	699	711	724	737	750
337	763	776	789	802	815	827	840	853	866	879
338	892	905	917	930	943	956	969	982	994	*007
339	53 020	033	046	058	071	084	097	110	122	135
340	148	161	173	186	199	212	224	237	250	263
341	275	288	301	314	326	339	352	364	377	390
342	403	415	428	441	453	466	479	491	504	517
343	529	542	555	567	580	593	605	618	631	643
344	656	668	681	694	706	719	732	744	757	769
345	782	794	807	820	832	845	857	870	882	895
346	908	920	933	945	958	970	983	995	*008	*020
347	54 033	045	058	070	083	095	108	120	133	145
348	158	170	183	195	208	220	233	245	258	270
349	283	295	307	320	332	345	357	370	382	394
350	407	419	432	444	456	469	481	494	506	518

N. 0 1 2 3 4 5 6 7 8 9 Prop. Pts.

Prop. Pts.

	15
1	1.5
2	3.0
3	4.5
4	6.0
5	7.5
6	9.0
7	10.5
8	12.0
9	13.5

log π = 0.49715

	14
1	1.4
2	2.8
3	4.2
4	5.6
5	7.0
6	8.4
7	9.8
8	11.2
9	12.6

	13
1	1.3
2	2.6
3	3.9
4	5.2
5	6.5
6	7.8
7	9.1
8	10.4
9	11.7

	12
1	1.2
2	2.4
3	3.6
4	4.8
5	6.0
6	7.2
7	8.4
8	9.6
9	10.8

350-400

N.	0	1	2	3	4	5	6	7	8	9
350	54 407	419	432	444	456	469	481	494	506	518
351	531	543	555	568	580	593	605	617	630	642
352	654	667	679	691	704	716	728	741	753	765
353	777	790	802	814	827	839	851	864	876	888
354	900	913	925	937	949	962	974	986	998	*011
355	55 023	035	047	060	072	084	096	108	121	133
356	145	157	169	182	194	206	218	230	242	255
357	267	279	291	303	315	328	340	352	364	376
358	388	400	413	425	437	449	461	473	485	497
359	509	522	534	546	558	570	582	594	606	618
360	630	642	654	666	678	691	703	715	727	739
361	751	763	775	787	799	811	823	835	847	859
362	871	883	895	907	919	931	943	955	967	979
363	991	*003	*015	*027	*038	*050	*062	*074	*086	*098
364	56 110	122	134	146	158	170	182	194	205	217
365	229	241	253	265	277	289	301	312	324	336
366	348	360	372	384	396	407	419	431	443	455
367	467	478	490	502	514	526	538	549	561	573
368	585	597	608	620	632	644	656	667	679	691
369	703	714	726	738	750	761	773	785	797	808
370	820	832	844	855	867	879	891	902	914	926
371	937	949	961	972	984	996	*008	*019	*031	*043
372	57 054	066	078	089	101	113	124	136	148	159
373	171	183	194	206	217	229	241	252	264	276
374	287	299	310	322	334	345	357	368	380	392
375	403	415	426	438	449	461	473	484	496	507
376	519	530	542	553	565	576	588	600	611	623
377	634	646	657	669	680	692	703	715	726	738
378	749	761	772	784	795	807	818	830	841	852
379	864	875	887	898	910	921	933	944	955	967
380	978	990	*001	*013	*024	*035	*047	*058	*070	*081
381	58 092	104	115	127	138	149	161	172	184	195
382	206	218	229	240	252	263	274	286	297	309
383	320	331	343	354	365	377	388	399	410	422
384	433	444	456	467	478	490	501	512	524	535
385	546	557	569	580	591	602	614	625	636	647
386	659	670	681	692	704	715	726	737	749	760
387	771	782	794	805	816	827	838	850	861	872
388	883	894	906	917	928	939	950	961	973	984
389	995	*006	*017	*028	*040	*051	*062	*073	*084	*095
390	59 106	118	129	140	151	162	173	184	195	207
391	218	229	240	251	262	273	284	295	306	318
392	329	340	351	362	373	384	395	406	417	428
393	439	450	461	472	483	494	506	517	528	539
394	550	561	572	583	594	605	616	627	638	649
395	660	671	682	693	704	715	726	737	748	759
396	770	780	791	802	813	824	835	846	857	868
397	879	890	901	912	923	934	945	956	966	977
398	988	999	*010	*021	*032	*043	*054	*065	*076	*086
399	60 097	108	119	130	141	152	163	173	184	195
400	206	217	228	239	249	260	271	282	293	304
N.	**0**	**1**	**2**	**3**	**4**	**5**	**6**	**7**	**8**	**9**

Prop. Pts.

	13
1	1.3
2	2.6
3	3.9
4	5.2
5	6.5
6	7.8
7	9.1
8	10.4
9	11.7

	12
1	1.2
2	2.4
3	3.6
4	4.8
5	6.0
6	7.2
7	8.4
8	9.6
9	10.8

	11
1	1.1
2	2.2
3	3.3
4	4.4
5	5.5
6	6.6
7	7.7
8	8.8
9	9.9

	10
1	1.0
2	2.0
3	3.0
4	4.0
5	5.0
6	6.0
7	7.0
8	8.0
9	9.0

400-450

N.	0	1	2	3	4	5	6	7	8	9
400	60 206	217	228	239	249	260	271	282	293	304
401	314	325	336	347	358	369	379	390	401	412
402	423	433	444	455	466	477	487	498	509	520
403	531	541	552	563	574	584	595	606	617	627
404	638	649	660	670	681	692	703	713	724	735
405	746	756	767	778	788	799	810	821	831	842
406	853	863	874	885	895	906	917	927	938	949
407	959	970	981	991	*002	*013	*023	*034	*045	*055
408	61 066	077	087	098	109	119	130	140	151	162
409	172	183	194	204	215	225	236	247	257	268
410	278	289	300	310	321	331	342	352	363	374
411	384	395	405	416	426	437	448	458	469	479
412	490	500	511	521	532	542	553	563	574	584
413	595	606	616	627	637	648	658	669	679	690
414	700	711	721	731	742	752	763	773	784	794
415	805	815	826	836	847	857	868	878	888	899
416	909	920	930	941	951	962	972	982	993	*003
417	62 014	024	034	045	055	066	076	086	097	107
418	118	128	138	149	159	170	180	190	201	211
419	221	232	242	252	263	273	284	294	304	315
420	325	335	346	356	366	377	387	397	408	418
421	428	439	449	459	469	480	490	500	511	521
422	531	542	552	562	572	583	593	603	613	624
423	634	644	655	665	675	685	696	706	716	726
424	737	747	757	767	778	788	798	808	818	829
425	839	849	859	870	880	890	900	910	921	931
426	941	951	961	972	982	992	*002	*012	*022	*033
427	63 043	053	063	073	083	094	104	114	124	134
428	144	155	165	175	185	195	205	215	225	236
429	246	256	266	276	286	296	306	317	327	337
430	347	357	367	377	387	397	407	417	428	438
431	448	458	468	478	488	498	508	518	528	538
432	548	558	568	579	589	599	609	619	629	639
433	649	659	669	679	689	699	709	719	729	739
434	749	759	769	779	789	799	809	819	829	839
435	849	859	869	879	889	899	909	919	929	939
436	949	959	969	979	988	998	*008	*018	*028	*038
437	64 048	058	068	078	088	098	108	118	128	137
438	147	157	167	177	187	197	207	217	227	237
439	246	256	266	276	286	296	306	316	326	335
440	345	355	365	375	385	395	404	414	424	434
441	444	454	464	473	483	493	503	513	523	532
442	542	552	562	572	582	591	601	611	621	631
443	640	650	660	670	680	689	699	709	719	729
444	738	748	758	768	777	787	797	807	816	826
445	836	846	856	865	875	885	895	904	914	924
446	933	943	953	963	972	982	992	*002	*011	*021
447	65 031	040	050	060	070	079	089	099	108	118
448	128	137	147	157	167	176	186	196	205	215
449	225	234	244	254	263	273	283	292	302	312
450	321	331	341	350	360	369	379	389	398	408
N.	0	1	2	3	4	5	6	7	8	9

Prop. Pts.

	11
1	1.1
2	2.2
3	3.3
4	4.4
5	5.5
6	6.6
7	7.7
8	8.8
9	9.9

	10
1	1.0
2	2.0
3	3.0
4	4.0
5	5.0
6	6.0
7	7.0
8	8.0
9	9.0

	9
1	0.9
2	1.8
3	2.7
4	3.6
5	4.5
6	5.4
7	6.3
8	7.2
9	8.1

Prop. Pts.

450-500

N.		0	1	2	3	4	5	6	7	8	9
450	65	321	331	341	350	360	369	379	389	398	408
451		418	427	437	447	456	466	475	485	495	504
452		514	523	533	543	552	562	571	581	591	600
453		610	619	629	639	648	658	667	677	686	696
454		706	715	725	734	744	753	763	772	782	792
455		801	811	820	830	839	849	858	868	877	887
456		896	906	916	925	935	944	954	963	973	982
457		992	*001	*011	*020	*030	*039	*049	*058	*068	*077
458	66	087	096	106	115	124	134	143	153	162	172
459		181	191	200	210	219	229	238	247	257	266
460		276	285	295	304	314	323	332	342	351	361
461		370	380	389	398	408	417	427	436	445	455
462		464	474	483	492	502	511	521	530	539	549
463		558	567	577	586	596	605	614	624	633	642
464		652	661	671	680	689	699	708	717	727	736
465		745	755	764	773	783	792	801	811	820	829
466		839	848	857	867	876	885	894	904	913	922
467		932	941	950	960	969	978	987	997	*006	*015
468	67	025	034	043	052	062	071	080	089	099	108
469		117	127	136	145	154	164	173	182	191	201
470		210	219	228	237	247	256	265	274	284	293
471		302	311	321	330	339	348	357	367	376	385
472		394	403	413	422	431	440	449	459	468	477
473		486	495	504	514	523	532	541	550	560	569
474		578	587	596	605	614	624	633	642	651	660
475		669	679	688	697	706	715	724	733	742	752
476		761	770	779	788	797	806	815	825	834	843
477		852	861	870	879	888	897	906	916	925	934
478		943	952	961	970	979	988	997	*006	*015	*024
479	68	034	043	052	061	070	079	088	097	106	115
480		124	133	142	151	160	169	178	187	196	205
481		215	224	233	242	251	260	269	278	287	296
482		305	314	323	332	341	350	359	368	377	386
483		395	404	413	422	431	440	449	458	467	476
484		485	494	502	511	520	529	538	547	556	565
485		574	583	592	601	610	619	628	637	646	655
486		664	673	681	690	699	708	717	726	735	744
487		753	762	771	780	789	797	806	815	824	833
488		842	851	860	869	878	886	895	904	913	922
489		931	940	949	958	966	975	984	993	*002	*011
490	69	020	028	037	046	055	064	073	082	090	099
491		108	117	126	135	144	152	161	170	179	188
492		197	205	214	223	232	241	249	258	267	276
493		285	294	302	311	320	329	338	346	355	364
494		373	381	390	399	408	417	425	434	443	452
495		461	469	478	487	496	504	513	522	531	539
496		548	557	566	574	583	592	601	609	618	627
497		636	644	653	662	671	679	688	697	705	714
498		723	732	740	749	758	767	775	784	793	801
499		810	819	827	836	845	854	862	871	880	888
500		897	906	914	923	932	940	949	958	966	975
N.		**0**	**1**	**2**	**3**	**4**	**5**	**6**	**7**	**8**	**9**

Prop. Pts.

	10
1	1.0
2	2.0
3	3.0
4	4.0
5	5.0
6	6.0
7	7.0
8	8.0
9	9.0

	9
1	0.9
2	1.8
3	2.7
4	3.6
5	4.5
6	5.4
7	6.3
8	7.2
9	8.1

	8
1	0.8
2	1.6
3	2.4
4	3.2
5	4.0
6	4.8
7	5.6
8	6.4
9	7.2

Prop. Pts.

500-550

N.	0	1	2	3	4	5	6	7	8	9
500	69 897	906	914	923	932	940	949	958	966	975
501	984	992	*001	*010	*018	*027	*036	*044	*053	*062
502	70 070	079	088	096	105	114	122	131	140	148
503	157	165	174	183	191	200	209	217	226	234
504	243	252	260	269	278	286	295	303	312	321
505	329	338	346	355	364	372	381	389	398	406
506	415	424	432	441	449	458	467	475	484	492
507	501	509	518	526	535	544	552	561	569	578
508	586	595	603	612	621	629	638	646	655	663
509	672	680	689	697	706	714	723	731	740	749
510	757	766	774	783	791	800	808	817	825	834
511	842	851	859	868	876	885	893	902	910	919
512	927	935	944	952	961	969	978	986	995	*003
513	71 012	020	029	037	046	054	063	071	079	088
514	096	105	113	122	130	139	147	155	164	172
515	181	189	198	206	214	223	231	240	248	257
516	265	273	282	290	299	307	315	324	332	341
517	349	357	366	374	383	391	399	408	416	425
518	433	441	450	458	466	475	483	492	500	508
519	517	525	533	542	550	559	567	575	584	592
520	600	609	617	625	634	642	650	659	667	675
521	684	692	700	709	717	725	734	742	750	759
522	767	775	784	792	800	809	817	825	834	842
523	850	858	867	875	883	892	900	908	917	925
524	933	941	950	958	966	975	983	991	999	*008
525	72 016	024	032	041	049	057	066	074	082	090
526	099	107	115	123	132	140	148	156	165	173
527	181	189	198	206	214	222	230	239	247	255
528	263	272	280	288	296	304	313	321	329	337
529	346	354	362	370	378	387	395	403	411	419
530	428	436	444	452	460	469	477	485	493	501
531	509	518	526	534	542	550	558	567	575	583
532	591	599	607	616	624	632	640	648	656	665
533	673	681	689	697	705	713	722	730	738	746
534	754	762	770	779	787	795	803	811	819	827
535	835	843	852	860	868	876	884	892	900	908
536	916	925	933	941	949	957	965	973	981	989
537	997	*006	*014	*022	*030	*038	*046	*054	*062	*070
538	73 078	086	094	102	111	119	127	135	143	151
539	159	167	175	183	191	199	207	215	223	231
540	239	247	255	263	272	280	288	296	304	312
541	320	328	336	344	352	360	368	376	384	392
542	400	408	416	424	432	440	448	456	464	472
543	480	488	496	504	512	520	528	536	544	552
544	560	568	576	584	592	600	608	616	624	632
545	640	648	656	664	672	679	687	695	703	711
546	719	727	735	743	751	759	767	775	783	791
547	799	807	815	823	830	838	846	854	862	870
548	878	886	894	902	910	918	926	933	941	949
549	957	965	973	981	989	997	*005	*013	*020	*028
550	74 036	044	052	060	068	076	084	092	099	107
N.	0	1	2	3	4	5	6	7	8	9

Prop. Pts.

	9
1	0.9
2	1.8
3	2.7
4	3.6
5	4.5
6	5.4
7	6.3
8	7.2
9	8.1

	8
1	0.8
2	1.6
3	2.4
4	3.2
5	4.0
6	4.8
7	5.6
8	6.4
9	7.2

	7
1	0.7
2	1.4
3	2.1
4	2.8
5	3.5
6	4.2
7	4.9
8	5.6
9	6.3

550-600

N.	0	1	2	3	4	5	6	7	8	9
550	74 036	044	052	060	068	076	084	092	099	107
551	115	123	131	139	147	155	162	170	178	186
552	194	202	210	218	225	233	241	249	257	265
553	273	280	288	296	304	312	320	327	335	343
554	351	359	367	374	382	390	398	406	414	421
555	429	437	445	453	461	468	476	484	492	500
556	507	515	523	531	539	547	554	562	570	578
557	586	593	601	609	617	624	632	640	648	656
558	663	671	679	687	695	702	710	718	726	733
559	741	749	757	764	772	780	788	796	803	811
560	819	827	834	842	850	858	865	873	881	889
561	896	904	912	920	927	935	943	950	958	966
562	974	981	989	997	*005	*012	*020	*028	*035	*043
563	75 051	059	066	074	082	089	097	105	113	120
564	128	136	143	151	159	166	174	182	189	197
565	205	213	220	228	236	243	251	259	266	274
566	282	289	297	305	312	320	328	335	343	351
567	358	366	374	381	389	397	404	412	420	427
568	435	442	450	458	465	473	481	488	496	504
569	511	519	526	534	542	549	557	565	572	580
570	587	595	603	610	618	626	633	641	648	656
571	664	671	679	686	694	702	709	717	724	732
572	740	747	755	762	770	778	785	793	800	808
573	815	823	831	838	846	853	861	868	876	884
574	891	899	906	914	921	929	937	944	952	959
575	967	974	982	989	997	*005	*012	*020	*027	*035
576	76 042	050	057	065	072	080	087	095	103	110
577	118	125	133	140	148	155	163	170	178	185
578	193	200	208	215	223	230	238	245	253	260
579	268	275	283	290	298	305	313	320	328	335
580	343	350	358	365	373	380	388	395	403	410
581	418	425	433	440	448	455	462	470	477	485
582	492	500	507	515	522	530	537	545	552	559
583	567	574	582	589	597	604	612	619	626	634
584	641	649	656	664	671	678	686	693	701	708
585	716	723	730	738	745	753	760	768	775	782
586	790	797	805	812	819	827	834	842	849	856
587	864	871	879	886	893	901	908	916	923	930
588	938	945	953	960	967	975	982	989	997	*004
589	77 012	019	026	034	041	048	056	063	070	078
590	085	093	100	107	115	122	129	137	144	151
591	159	166	173	181	188	195	203	210	217	225
592	232	240	247	254	262	269	276	283	291	298
593	305	313	320	327	335	342	349	357	364	371
594	379	386	393	401	408	415	422	430	437	444
595	452	459	466	474	481	488	495	503	510	517
596	525	532	539	546	554	561	568	576	583	590
597	597	605	612	619	627	634	641	648	656	663
598	670	677	685	692	699	706	714	721	728	735
599	743	750	757	764	772	779	786	793	801	808
600	815	822	830	837	844	851	859	866	873	880
N.	**0**	**1**	**2**	**3**	**4**	**5**	**6**	**7**	**8**	**9**

Prop. Pts.

	8
1	0.8
2	1.6
3	2.4
4	3.2
5	4.0
6	4.8
7	5.6
8	6.4
9	7.2

	7
1	0.7
2	1.4
3	2.1
4	2.8
5	3.5
6	4.2
7	4.9
8	5.6
9	6.3

600-650

N.	0	1	2	3	4	5	6	7	8	9
600	77 815	822	830	837	844	851	859	866	873	880
601	887	895	902	909	916	924	931	938	945	952
602	960	967	974	981	988	996	*003	*010	*017	*025
603	78 032	039	046	053	061	068	075	082	089	097
604	104	111	118	125	132	140	147	154	161	168
605	176	183	190	197	204	211	219	226	233	240
606	247	254	262	269	276	283	290	297	305	312
607	319	326	333	340	347	355	362	369	376	383
608	390	398	405	412	419	426	433	440	447	455
609	462	469	476	483	490	497	504	512	519	526
610	533	540	547	554	561	569	576	583	590	597
611	604	611	618	625	633	640	647	654	661	668
612	675	682	689	696	704	711	718	725	732	739
613	746	753	760	767	774	781	789	796	803	810
614	817	824	831	838	845	852	859	866	873	880
615	888	895	902	909	916	923	930	937	944	951
616	958	965	972	979	986	993	*000	*007	*014	*021
617	79 029	036	043	050	057	064	071	078	085	092
618	099	106	113	120	127	134	141	148	155	162
619	169	176	183	190	197	204	211	218	225	232
620	239	246	253	260	267	274	281	288	295	302
621	309	316	323	330	337	344	351	358	365	372
622	379	386	393	400	407	414	421	428	435	442
623	449	456	463	470	477	484	491	498	505	511
624	518	525	532	539	546	553	560	567	574	581
625	588	595	602	609	616	623	630	637	644	650
626	657	664	671	678	685	692	699	706	713	720
627	727	734	741	748	754	761	768	775	782	789
628	796	803	810	817	824	831	837	844	851	858
629	865	872	879	886	893	900	906	913	920	927
630	934	941	948	955	962	969	975	982	989	996
631	80 003	010	017	024	030	037	044	051	058	065
632	072	079	085	092	099	106	113	120	127	134
633	140	147	154	161	168	175	182	188	195	202
634	209	216	223	229	236	243	250	257	264	271
635	277	284	291	298	305	312	318	325	332	339
636	346	353	359	366	373	380	387	393	400	407
637	414	421	428	434	441	448	455	462	468	475
638	482	489	496	502	509	516	523	530	536	543
639	550	557	564	570	577	584	591	598	604	611
640	618	625	632	638	645	652	659	665	672	679
641	686	693	699	706	713	720	726	733	740	747
642	754	760	767	774	781	787	794	801	808	814
643	821	828	835	841	848	855	862	868	875	882
644	889	895	902	909	916	922	929	936	943	949
645	956	963	969	976	983	990	996	*003	*010	*017
646	81 023	030	037	043	050	057	064	070	077	084
647	090	097	104	111	117	124	131	137	144	151
648	158	164	171	178	184	191	198	204	211	218
649	224	231	238	245	251	258	265	271	278	285
650	291	298	305	311	318	325	331	338	345	351
N.	**0**	**1**	**2**	**3**	**4**	**5**	**6**	**7**	**8**	**9**

Prop. Pts.

	8
1	0.8
2	1.6
3	2.4
4	3.2
5	4.0
6	4.8
7	5.6
8	6.4
9	7.2

	7
1	0.7
2	1.4
3	2.1
4	2.8
5	3.5
6	4.2
7	4.9
8	5.6
9	6.3

	6
1	0.6
2	1.2
3	1.8
4	2.4
5	3.0
6	3.6
7	4.2
8	4.8
9	5.4

Prop. Pts.

650-700

N.	0	1	2	3	4	5	6	7	8	9
650	81 291	298	305	311	318	325	331	338	345	351
651	358	365	371	378	385	391	398	405	411	418
652	425	431	438	445	451	458	465	471	478	485
653	491	498	505	511	518	525	531	538	544	551
654	558	564	571	578	584	591	598	604	611	617
655	624	631	637	644	651	657	664	671	677	684
656	690	697	704	710	717	723	730	737	743	750
657	757	763	770	776	783	790	796	803	809	816
658	823	829	836	842	849	856	862	869	875	882
659	889	895	902	908	915	921	928	935	941	948
660	954	961	968	974	981	987	994	*000	*007	*014
661	82 020	027	033	040	046	053	060	066	073	079
662	086	092	099	105	112	119	125	132	138	145
663	151	158	164	171	178	184	191	197	204	210
664	217	223	230	236	243	249	256	263	269	276
665	282	289	295	302	308	315	321	328	334	341
666	347	354	360	367	373	380	387	393	400	406
667	413	419	426	432	439	445	452	458	465	471
668	478	484	491	497	504	510	517	523	530	536
669	543	549	556	562	569	575	582	588	595	601
670	607	614	620	627	633	640	646	653	659	666
671	672	679	685	692	698	705	711	718	724	730
672	737	743	750	756	763	769	776	782	789	795
673	802	808	814	821	827	834	840	847	853	860
674	866	872	879	885	892	898	905	911	918	924
675	930	937	943	950	956	963	969	975	982	988
676	995	*001	*008	*014	*020	*027	*033	*040	*046	*052
677	83 059	065	072	078	085	091	097	104	110	117
678	123	129	136	142	149	155	161	168	174	181
679	187	193	200	206	213	219	225	232	238	245
680	251	257	264	270	276	283	289	296	302	308
681	315	321	327	334	340	347	353	359	366	372
682	378	385	391	398	404	410	417	423	429	436
683	442	448	455	461	467	474	480	487	493	499
684	506	512	518	525	531	537	544	550	556	563
685	569	575	582	588	594	601	607	613	620	626
686	632	639	645	651	658	664	670	677	683	689
687	696	702	708	715	721	727	734	740	746	753
688	759	765	771	778	784	790	797	803	809	816
689	822	828	835	841	847	853	860	866	872	879
690	885	891	897	904	910	916	923	929	935	942
691	948	954	960	967	973	979	985	992	998	*004
692	84 011	017	023	029	036	042	048	055	061	067
693	073	080	086	092	098	105	111	117	123	130
694	136	142	148	155	161	167	173	180	186	192
695	198	205	211	217	223	230	236	242	248	255
696	261	267	273	280	286	292	298	305	311	317
697	323	330	336	342	348	354	361	367	373	379
698	386	392	398	404	410	417	423	429	435	442
699	448	454	460	466	473	479	485	491	497	504
700	510	516	522	528	535	541	547	553	559	566
N.	**0**	**1**	**2**	**3**	**4**	**5**	**6**	**7**	**8**	**9**

Prop. Pts.

	7
1	0.7
2	1.4
3	2.1
4	2.8
5	3.5
6	4.2
7	4.9
8	5.6
9	6.3

	6
1	0.6
2	1.2
3	1.8
4	2.4
5	3.0
6	3.6
7	4.2
8	4.8
9	5.4

Prop. Pts.

700-750

N.	0	1	2	3	4	5	6	7	8	9
700	84 510	516	522	528	535	541	547	553	559	566
701	572	578	584	590	597	603	609	615	621	628
702	634	640	646	652	658	665	671	677	683	689
703	696	702	708	714	720	726	733	739	745	751
704	757	763	770	776	782	788	794	800	807	813
705	819	825	831	837	844	850	856	862	868	874
706	880	887	893	899	905	911	917	924	930	936
707	942	948	954	960	967	973	979	985	991	997
708	85 003	009	016	022	028	034	040	046	052	058
709	065	071	077	083	089	095	101	107	114	120
710	126	132	138	144	150	156	163	169	175	181
711	187	193	199	205	211	217	224	230	236	242
712	248	254	260	266	272	278	285	291	297	303
713	309	315	321	327	333	339	345	352	358	364
714	370	376	382	388	394	400	406	412	418	425
715	431	437	443	449	455	461	467	473	479	485
716	491	497	503	509	516	522	528	534	540	546
717	552	558	564	570	576	582	588	594	600	606
718	612	618	625	631	637	643	649	655	661	667
719	673	679	685	691	697	703	709	715	721	727
720	733	739	745	751	757	763	769	775	781	788
721	794	800	806	812	818	824	830	836	842	848
722	854	860	866	872	878	884	890	896	902	908
723	914	920	926	932	938	944	950	956	962	968
724	974	980	986	992	998	*004	*010	*016	*022	*028
725	86 034	040	046	052	058	064	070	076	082	088
726	094	100	106	112	118	124	130	136	141	147
727	153	159	165	171	177	183	189	195	201	207
728	213	219	225	231	237	243	249	255	261	267
729	273	279	285	291	297	303	308	314	320	326
730	332	338	344	350	356	362	368	374	380	386
731	392	398	404	410	415	421	427	433	439	445
732	451	457	463	469	475	481	487	493	499	504
733	510	516	522	528	534	540	546	552	558	564
734	570	576	581	587	593	599	605	611	617	623
735	629	635	641	646	652	658	664	670	676	682
736	688	694	700	705	711	717	723	729	735	741
737	747	753	759	764	770	776	782	788	794	800
738	806	812	817	823	829	835	841	847	853	859
739	864	870	876	882	888	894	900	906	911	917
740	923	929	935	941	947	953	958	964	970	976
741	982	988	994	999	*005	*011	*017	*023	*029	*035
742	87 040	046	052	058	064	070	075	081	087	093
743	099	105	111	116	122	128	134	140	146	151
744	157	163	169	175	181	186	192	198	204	210
745	216	221	227	233	239	245	251	256	262	268
746	274	280	286	291	297	303	309	315	320	326
747	332	338	344	349	355	361	367	373	379	384
748	390	396	402	408	413	419	425	431	437	442
749	448	454	460	466	471	477	483	489	495	500
750	506	512	518	523	529	535	541	547	552	558
N.	**0**	**1**	**2**	**3**	**4**	**5**	**6**	**7**	**8**	**9**

Prop. Pts.

	7
1	0.7
2	1.4
3	2.1
4	2.8
5	3.5
6	4.2
7	4.9
8	5.6
9	6.3

	6
1	0.6
2	1.2
3	1.8
4	2.4
5	3.0
6	3.6
7	4.2
8	4.8
9	5.4

	5
1	0.5
2	1.0
3	1.5
4	2.0
5	2.5
6	3.0
7	3.5
8	4.0
9	4.5

750-800

N.	0	1	2	3	4	5	6	7	8	9
750	87 506	512	518	523	529	535	541	547	552	558
751	564	570	576	581	587	593	599	604	610	616
752	622	628	633	639	645	651	656	662	668	674
753	679	685	691	697	703	708	714	720	726	731
754	737	743	749	754	760	766	772	777	783	789
755	795	800	806	812	818	823	829	835	841	846
756	852	858	864	869	875	881	887	892	898	904
757	910	915	921	927	933	938	944	950	955	961
758	967	973	978	984	990	996	*001	*007	*013	*018
759	88 024	030	036	041	047	053	058	064	070	076
760	081	087	093	098	104	110	116	121	127	133
761	138	144	150	156	161	167	173	178	184	190
762	195	201	207	213	218	224	230	235	241	247
763	252	258	264	270	275	281	287	292	298	304
764	309	315	321	326	332	338	343	349	355	360
765	366	372	377	383	389	395	400	406	412	417
766	423	429	434	440	446	451	457	463	468	474
767	480	485	491	497	502	508	513	519	525	530
768	536	542	547	553	559	564	570	576	581	587
769	593	598	604	610	615	621	627	632	638	643
770	649	655	660	666	672	677	683	689	694	700
771	705	711	717	722	728	734	739	745	750	756
772	762	767	773	779	784	790	795	801	807	812
773	818	824	829	835	840	846	852	857	863	868
774	874	880	885	891	897	902	908	913	919	925
775	930	936	941	947	953	958	964	969	975	981
776	986	992	997	*003	*009	*014	*020	*025	*031	*037
777	89 042	048	053	059	064	070	076	081	087	092
778	098	104	109	115	120	126	131	137	143	148
779	154	159	165	170	176	182	187	193	198	204
780	209	215	221	226	232	237	243	248	254	260
781	265	271	276	282	287	293	298	304	310	315
782	321	326	332	337	343	348	354	360	365	371
783	376	382	387	393	398	404	409	415	421	426
784	432	437	443	448	454	459	465	470	476	481
785	487	492	498	504	509	515	520	526	531	537
786	542	548	553	559	564	570	575	581	586	592
787	597	603	609	614	620	625	631	636	642	647
788	653	658	664	669	675	680	686	691	697	702
789	708	713	719	724	730	735	741	746	752	757
790	763	768	774	779	785	790	796	801	807	812
791	818	823	829	834	840	845	851	856	862	867
792	873	878	883	889	894	900	905	911	916	922
793	927	933	938	944	949	955	960	966	971	977
794	982	988	993	998	*004	*009	*015	*020	*026	*031
795	90 037	042	048	053	059	064	069	075	080	086
796	091	097	102	108	113	119	124	129	135	140
797	146	151	157	162	168	173	179	184	189	195
798	200	206	211	217	222	227	233	238	244	249
799	255	260	266	271	276	282	287	293	298	304
800	309	314	320	325	331	336	342	347	352	358
N.	**0**	**1**	**2**	**3**	**4**	**5**	**6**	**7**	**8**	**9**

Prop. Pts.

	6
1	0.6
2	1.2
3	1.8
4	2.4
5	3.0
6	3.6
7	4.2
8	4.8
9	5.4

	5
1	0.5
2	1.0
3	1.5
4	2.0
5	2.5
6	3.0
7	3.5
8	4.0
9	4.5

800-850

N.	0	1	2	3	4	5	6	7	8	9	Prop. Pts.
800	90 309	314	320	325	331	336	342	347	352	358	
801	363	369	374	380	385	390	396	401	407	412	
802	417	423	428	434	439	445	450	455	461	466	
803	472	477	482	488	493	499	504	509	515	520	
804	526	531	536	542	547	553	558	563	569	574	
805	580	585	590	596	601	607	612	617	623	628	
806	634	639	644	650	655	660	666	671	677	682	
807	687	693	698	703	709	714	720	725	730	736	
808	741	747	752	757	763	768	773	779	784	789	
809	795	800	806	811	816	822	827	832	838	843	
810	849	854	859	865	870	875	881	886	891	897	
811	902	907	913	918	924	929	934	940	945	950	
812	956	961	966	972	977	982	988	993	998	*004	
813	91 009	014	020	025	030	036	041	046	052	057	
814	062	068	073	078	084	089	094	100	105	110	
815	116	121	126	132	137	142	148	153	158	164	
816	169	174	180	185	190	196	201	206	212	217	
817	222	228	233	238	243	249	254	259	265	270	
818	275	281	286	291	297	302	307	312	318	323	
819	328	334	339	344	350	355	360	365	371	376	
820	381	387	392	397	403	408	413	418	424	429	
821	434	440	445	450	455	461	466	471	477	482	
822	487	492	498	503	508	514	519	524	529	535	
823	540	545	551	556	561	566	572	577	582	587	
824	593	598	603	609	614	619	624	630	635	640	
825	645	651	656	661	666	672	677	682	687	693	
826	698	703	709	714	719	724	730	735	740	745	
827	751	756	761	766	772	777	782	787	793	798	
828	803	808	814	819	824	829	834	840	845	850	
829	855	861	866	871	876	882	887	892	897	903	
830	908	913	918	924	929	934	939	944	950	955	
831	960	965	971	976	981	986	991	997	*002	*007	
832	92 012	018	023	028	033	038	044	049	054	059	
833	065	070	075	080	085	091	096	101	106	111	
834	117	122	127	132	137	143	148	153	158	163	
835	169	174	179	184	189	195	200	205	210	215	
836	221	226	231	236	241	247	252	257	262	267	
837	273	278	283	288	293	298	304	309	314	319	
838	324	330	335	340	345	350	355	361	366	371	
839	376	381	387	392	397	402	407	412	418	423	
840	428	433	438	443	449	454	459	464	469	474	
841	480	485	490	495	500	505	511	516	521	526	
842	531	536	542	547	552	557	562	567	572	578	
843	583	588	593	598	603	609	614	619	624	629	
844	634	639	645	650	655	660	665	670	675	681	
845	686	691	696	701	706	711	716	722	727	732	
846	737	742	747	752	758	763	768	773	778	783	
847	788	793	799	804	809	814	819	824	829	834	
848	840	845	850	855	860	865	870	875	881	886	
849	891	896	901	906	911	916	921	927	932	937	
850	942	947	952	957	962	967	973	978	983	988	
N.	**0**	**1**	**2**	**3**	**4**	**5**	**6**	**7**	**8**	**9**	**Prop. Pts.**

Prop. Pts.

	6
1	0.6
2	1.2
3	1.8
4	2.4
5	3.0
6	3.6
7	4.2
8	4.8
9	5.4

	5
1	0.5
2	1.0
3	1.5
4	2.0
5	2.5
6	3.0
7	3.5
8	4.0
9	4.5

850-900

N.	0	1	2	3	4	5	6	7	8	9
850	92 942	947	952	957	962	967	973	978	983	988
851	993	998	*003	*008	*013	*018	*024	*029	*034	*039
852	93 044	049	054	059	064	069	075	080	085	090
853	095	100	105	110	115	120	125	131	136	141
854	146	151	156	161	166	171	176	181	186	192
855	197	202	207	212	217	222	227	232	237	242
856	247	252	258	263	268	273	278	283	288	293
857	298	303	308	313	318	323	328	334	339	344
858	349	354	359	364	369	374	379	384	389	394
859	399	404	409	414	420	425	430	435	440	445
860	450	455	460	465	470	475	480	485	490	495
861	500	505	510	515	520	526	531	536	541	546
862	551	556	561	566	571	576	581	586	591	596
863	601	606	611	616	621	626	631	636	641	646
864	651	656	661	666	671	676	682	687	692	697
865	702	707	712	717	722	727	732	737	742	747
866	752	757	762	767	772	777	782	787	792	797
867	802	807	812	817	822	827	832	837	842	847
868	852	857	862	867	872	877	882	887	892	897
869	902	907	912	917	922	927	932	937	942	947
870	952	957	962	967	972	977	982	987	992	997
871	94 002	007	012	017	022	027	032	037	042	047
872	052	057	062	067	072	077	082	086	091	096
873	101	106	111	116	121	126	131	136	141	146
874	151	156	161	166	171	176	181	186	191	196
875	201	206	211	216	221	226	231	236	240	245
876	250	255	260	265	270	275	280	285	290	295
877	300	305	310	315	320	325	330	335	340	345
878	349	354	359	364	369	374	379	384	389	394
879	399	404	409	414	419	424	429	433	438	443
880	448	453	458	463	468	473	478	483	488	493
881	498	503	507	512	517	522	527	532	537	542
882	547	552	557	562	567	571	576	581	586	591
883	596	601	606	611	616	621	626	630	635	640
884	645	650	655	660	665	670	675	680	685	689
885	694	699	704	709	714	719	724	729	734	738
886	743	748	753	758	763	768	773	778	783	787
887	792	797	802	807	812	817	822	827	832	836
888	841	846	851	856	861	866	871	876	880	885
889	890	895	900	905	910	915	919	924	929	934
890	939	944	949	954	959	963	968	973	978	983
891	988	993	998	*002	*007	*012	*017	*022	*027	*032
892	95 036	041	046	051	056	061	066	071	075	080
893	085	090	095	100	105	109	114	119	124	129
894	134	139	143	148	153	158	163	168	173	177
895	182	187	192	197	202	207	211	216	221	226
896	231	236	240	245	250	255	260	265	270	274
897	279	284	289	294	299	303	308	313	318	323
898	328	332	337	342	347	352	357	361	366	371
899	376	381	386	390	395	400	405	410	415	419
900	424	429	434	439	444	448	453	458	463	468
N.	**0**	**1**	**2**	**3**	**4**	**5**	**6**	**7**	**8**	**9**

Prop. Pts.

	6
1	0.6
2	1.2
3	1.8
4	2.4
5	3.0
6	3.6
7	4.2
8	4.8
9	5.4

	5
1	0.5
2	1.0
3	1.5
4	2.0
5	2.5
6	3.0
7	3.5
8	4.0
9	4.5

	4
1	0.4
2	0.8
3	1.2
4	1.6
5	2.0
6	2.4
7	2.8
8	3.2
9	3.6

Prop. Pts.

900-950

N.	0	1	2	3	4	5	6	7	8	9	Prop. Pts.
900	95 424	429	434	439	444	448	453	458	463	468	
901	472	477	482	487	492	497	501	506	511	516	
902	521	525	530	535	540	545	550	554	559	564	
903	569	574	578	583	588	593	598	602	607	612	
904	617	622	626	631	636	641	646	650	655	660	
905	665	670	674	679	684	689	694	698	703	708	
906	713	718	722	727	732	737	742	746	751	756	
907	761	766	770	775	780	785	789	794	799	804	
908	809	813	818	823	828	832	837	842	847	852	
909	856	861	866	871	875	880	885	890	895	899	
910	904	909	914	918	923	928	933	938	942	947	
911	952	957	961	966	971	976	980	985	990	995	
912	999	*004	*009	*014	*019	*023	*028	*033	*038	*042	
913	96 047	052	057	061	066	071	076	080	085	090	
914	095	099	104	109	114	118	123	128	133	137	
915	142	147	152	156	161	166	171	175	180	185	
916	190	194	199	204	209	213	218	223	227	232	
917	237	242	246	251	256	261	265	270	275	280	
918	284	289	294	298	303	308	313	317	322	327	
919	332	336	341	346	350	355	360	365	369	374	
920	379	384	388	393	398	402	407	412	417	421	
921	426	431	435	440	445	450	454	459	464	468	
922	473	478	483	487	492	497	501	506	511	515	
923	520	525	530	534	539	544	548	553	558	562	
924	567	572	577	581	586	591	595	600	605	609	
925	614	619	624	628	633	638	642	647	652	656	
926	661	666	670	675	680	685	689	694	699	703	
927	708	713	717	722	727	731	736	741	745	750	
928	755	759	764	769	774	778	783	788	792	797	
929	802	806	811	816	820	825	830	834	839	844	
930	848	853	858	862	867	872	876	881	886	890	
931	895	900	904	909	914	918	923	928	932	937	
932	942	946	951	956	960	965	970	974	979	984	
933	988	993	997	*002	*007	*011	*016	*021	*025	*030	
934	97 035	039	044	049	053	058	063	067	072	077	
935	081	086	090	095	100	104	109	114	118	123	
936	128	132	137	142	146	151	155	160	165	169	
937	174	179	183	188	192	197	202	206	211	216	
938	220	225	230	234	239	243	248	253	257	262	
939	267	271	276	280	285	290	294	299	304	308	
940	313	317	322	327	331	336	340	345	350	354	
941	359	364	368	373	377	382	387	391	396	400	
942	405	410	414	419	424	428	433	437	442	447	
943	451	456	460	465	470	474	479	483	488	493	
944	497	502	506	511	516	520	525	529	534	539	
945	543	548	552	557	562	566	571	575	580	585	
946	589	594	598	603	607	612	617	621	626	630	
947	635	640	644	649	653	658	663	667	672	676	
948	681	685	690	695	699	704	708	713	717	722	
949	727	731	736	740	745	749	754	759	763	768	
950	772	777	782	786	791	795	800	804	809	813	
N.	**0**	**1**	**2**	**3**	**4**	**5**	**6**	**7**	**8**	**9**	**Prop. Pts.**

Prop. Pts.:

	5
1	0.5
2	1.0
3	1.5
4	2.0
5	2.5
6	3.0
7	3.5
8	4.0
9	4.5

	4
1	0.4
2	0.8
3	1.2
4	1.6
5	2.0
6	2.4
7	2.8
8	3.2
9	3.6

950-1000

N.	0	1	2	3	4	5	6	7	8	9	Prop. Pts.
950	97 772	777	782	786	791	795	800	804	809	813	
951	818	823	827	832	836	841	845	850	855	859	
952	864	868	873	877	882	886	891	896	900	905	
953	909	914	918	923	928	932	937	941	946	950	
954	955	959	964	968	973	978	982	987	991	996	
955	98 000	005	009	014	019	023	028	032	037	041	
956	046	050	055	059	064	068	073	078	082	087	
957	091	096	100	105	109	114	118	123	127	132	
958	137	141	146	150	155	159	164	168	173	177	
959	182	186	191	195	200	204	209	214	218	223	
960	227	232	236	241	245	250	254	259	263	268	
961	272	277	281	286	290	295	299	304	308	313	
962	318	322	327	331	336	340	345	349	354	358	
963	363	367	372	376	381	385	390	394	399	403	
964	408	412	417	421	426	430	435	439	444	448	
965	453	457	462	466	471	475	480	484	489	493	
966	498	502	507	511	516	520	525	529	534	538	
967	543	547	552	556	561	565	570	574	579	583	
968	588	592	597	601	605	610	614	619	623	628	
969	632	637	641	646	650	655	659	664	668	673	
970	677	682	686	691	695	700	704	709	713	717	
971	722	726	731	735	740	744	749	753	758	762	
972	767	771	776	780	784	789	793	798	802	807	
973	811	816	820	825	829	834	838	843	847	851	
974	856	860	865	869	874	878	883	887	892	896	
975	900	905	909	914	918	923	927	932	936	941	
976	945	949	954	958	963	967	972	976	981	985	
977	989	994	998	*003	*007	*012	*016	*021	*025	*029	
978	99 034	038	043	047	052	056	061	065	069	074	
979	078	083	087	092	096	100	105	109	114	118	
980	123	127	131	136	140	145	149	154	158	162	
981	167	171	176	180	185	189	193	198	202	207	
982	211	216	220	224	229	233	238	242	247	251	
983	255	260	264	269	273	277	282	286	291	295	
984	300	304	308	313	317	322	326	330	335	339	
985	344	348	352	357	361	366	370	374	379	383	
986	388	392	396	401	405	410	414	419	423	427	
987	432	436	441	445	449	454	458	463	467	471	
988	476	480	484	489	493	498	502	506	511	515	
989	520	524	528	533	537	542	546	550	555	559	
990	564	568	572	577	581	585	590	594	599	603	
991	607	612	616	621	625	629	634	638	642	647	
992	651	656	660	664	669	673	677	682	686	691	
993	695	699	704	708	712	717	721	726	730	734	
994	739	743	747	752	756	760	765	769	774	778	
995	782	787	791	795	800	804	808	813	817	822	
996	826	830	835	839	843	848	852	856	861	865	
997	870	874	878	883	887	891	896	900	904	909	
998	913	917	922	926	930	935	939	944	948	952	
999	957	961	965	970	974	978	983	987	991	996	
1000	00 000	004	009	013	017	022	026	030	035	039	
N.	**0**	**1**	**2**	**3**	**4**	**5**	**6**	**7**	**8**	**9**	**Prop. Pts.**

Prop. Pts.

	5
1	0.5
2	1.0
3	1.5
4	2.0
5	2.5
6	3.0
7	3.5
8	4.0
9	4.5

	4
1	0.4
2	0.8
3	1.2
4	1.6
5	2.0
6	2.4
7	2.8
8	3.2
9	3.6

*TABLE 3. AUXILIARY TABLE OF S AND T FOR A IN MINUTES (COMMON LOGARITHMS)**

$$S = \log \sin A - \log A' \text{ and } T = \log \tan A - \log A'$$

$$A' = \text{number of minutes in } A \text{ and } (90^\circ - A)' = \text{number of minutes in } 90^\circ - A$$

A'	S
0 to 13	6.46373 — 10
14 to 42	72 — 10
43 to 58	71 — 10
59 to 71	6.46370 — 10
72 to 81	69 — 10
82 to 91	68 — 10
92 to 99	6.46367 — 10
100 to 107	66 — 10
108 to 115	65 — 10
116 to 121	6.46364 — 10
122 to 128	63 — 10
129 to 134	62 — 10
135 to 140	6.46361 — 10
141 to 146	60 — 10
147 to 151	59 — 10
152 to 157	6.46358 — 10
158 to 162	57 — 10
163 to 167	56 — 10
168 to 171	6.46355 — 10
172 to 176	54 — 10
177 to 181	53 — 10

A'	T
0 to 26	6.46373 — 10
27 to 39	74 — 10
40 to 48	75 — 10
49 to 56	6.46376 — 10
57 to 63	77 — 10
64 to 69	78 — 10
70 to 74	6.46379 — 10
75 to 80	80 — 10
81 to 85	81 — 10
86 to 89	6.46382 — 10
90 to 94	83 — 10
95 to 98	84 — 10
99 to 102	6.46385 — 10
103 to 106	86 — 10
107 to 110	87 — 10
111 to 113	6.46388 — 10
114 to 117	89 — 10
118 to 120	90 — 10
121 to 124	6.46391 — 10
125 to 127	92 — 10
128 to 130	93 — 10

A'	T
131 to 133	6.46394 — 10
134 to 136	95 — 10
137 to 139	96 — 10
140 to 142	6.46397 — 10
143 to 145	98 — 10
146 to 148	99 — 10
149 to 150	6.46400 — 10
151 to 153	01 — 10
154 to 156	02 — 10
157 to 158	6.46403 — 10
159 to 161	04 — 10
162 to 163	05 — 10
164 to 166	6.46406 — 10
167 to 168	07 — 10
169 to 171	08 — 10
172 to 173	6.46409 — 10
174 to 175	10 — 10
176 to 178	11 — 10
179 to 180	6.46412 — 10
181 to 182	13 — 10
183 to 184	14 — 10

For small angles, $\log \sin A = \log A' + S$ and $\log \tan A = \log A' + T$; for angles near 90°, $\log \cos A = \log (90^\circ - A)' + S$ and $\log \text{ctn } A = \log (90^\circ - A)' + T$.

*From Richard Stevens Burington, "Handbook of Mathematical Tables and Formulas," 4th ed., McGraw-Hill Book Company, New York, 1965.

Rationale of the Use of Table 3

This procedure makes use of the series $\sin A = x - x^3/3! + x^5/5! \cdots$ where x is in radians. For very small angles ($A < 14'$) it is sufficient to write $\sin A = x = A'k$, where A' = number of minutes in A and k = radians/min = $\pi/[(180)(60)] = 0.0002909$ and $\log k = 6.46373 - 10$.

Then $\log \sin A = \log A' + \log k = \log A' + S$ (since $\log k$ is represented by S in the table). It follows, then, that

$$\log \sin A = \log A' + 6.46373 - 10$$

For somewhat larger angles (0°14′ to 3°0′) it is necessary to include the second term of the sine series and write $\sin A = x - x^3/3!$. This refinement is incorporated in a reduced value of S which is $6.46368 - 10$ at $A' = 90'$ and $6.46353 - 10$ at $A' = 180'$.

For example, to find log sin 1°16′42″ convert 1°16′42″ to $76.7' = A'$. From Table 3, $S = 6.46369 - 10$. Therefore $\log \sin 1°16'42'' = \log 76.7 + 6.46369 - 10 = 1.88480 + 6.46369 - 10 = 8.34849 - 10$.

A similar reasoning applies to the determination of the tangent of very small angles. The series is $\tan A = x + x^3/3 + 2x^5/15 + \cdots$. With $0' \leq A \leq 26'$ sufficient accuracy is obtained by using the equation $\tan A = x = A'k$ from which we arrive at the equation

$$\log \tan A = \log A' + T = \log A' + 6.46373 - 10$$

With $26' \leq A \leq 180'$ we find that the second term of the tangent series must be included to write $\tan A = x + x^3/3$ the effect of which is to increase T being $6.46383 - 10$ at $A' = 90'$ and $6.46412 - 10$ at $A' = 180'$.

The −10 portion of the characteristic of the logarithm is not printed but must be written down whenever such a logarithm is used.

0° (180°) (359°) **179°**

′	L Sin	d	L Tan	c d	L Ctn	L Cos	′
0	—		—		—	10.00 000	60
1	6.46 373	30103	6.46 373	30103	13.53 627	10.00 000	59
2	6.76 476	17609	6.76 476	17609	13.23 524	10.00 000	58
3	6.94 085	12494	6.94 085	12494	13.05 915	10.00 000	57
4	7.06 579	9691	7.06 579	9691	12.93 421	10.00 000	56
5	7.16 270	7918	7.16 270	7918	12.83 730	10.00 000	55
6	7.24 188	6694	7.24 188	6694	12.75 812	10.00 000	54
7	7.30 882	5800	7.30 882	5800	12.69 118	10.00 000	53
8	7.36 682	5115	7.36 682	5115	12.63 318	10.00 000	52
9	7.41 797	4576	7.41 797	4576	12.58 203	10.00 000	51
10	7.46 373	4139	7.46 373	4139	12.53 627	10.00 000	50
11	7.50 512	3779	7.50 512	3779	12.49 488	10.00 000	49
12	7.54 291	3476	7.54 291	3476	12.45 709	10.00 000	48
13	7.57 767	3218	7.57 767	3219	12.42 233	10.00 000	47
14	7.60 985	2997	7.60 986	2996	12.39 014	10.00 000	46
15	7.63 982	2802	7.63 982	2803	12.36 018	10.00 000	45
16	7.66 784	2633	7.66 785	2633	12.33 215	10.00 000	44
17	7.69 417	2483	7.69 418	2482	12.30 582	9.99 999	43
18	7.71 900	2348	7.71 900	2348	12.28 100	9.99 999	42
19	7.74 248	2227	7.74 248	2228	12.25 752	9.99 999	41
20	7.76 475	2119	7.76 476	2119	12.23 524	9.99 999	40
21	7.78 594	2021	7.78 595	2020	12.21 405	9.99 999	39
22	7.80 615	1930	7.80 615	1931	12.19 385	9.99 999	38
23	7.82 545	1848	7.82 546	1848	12.17 454	9.99 999	37
24	7.84 393	1773	7.84 394	1773	12.15 606	9.99 999	36
25	7.86 166	1704	7.86 167	1704	12.13 833	9.99 999	35
26	7.87 870	1639	7.87 871	1639	12.12 129	9.99 999	34
27	7.89 509	1579	7.89 510	1579	12.10 490	9.99 999	33
28	7.91 088	1524	7.91 089	1524	12.08 911	9.99 999	32
29	7.92 612	1472	7.92 613	1473	12.07 387	9.99 998	31
30	7.94 084	1424	7.94 086	1424	12.05 914	9.99 998	30
31	7.95 508	1379	7.95 510	1379	12.04 490	9.99 998	29
32	7.96 887	1336	7.96 889	1336	12.03 111	9.99 998	28
33	7.98 223	1297	7.98 225	1297	12.01 775	9.99 998	27
34	7.99 520	1259	7.99 522	1259	12.00 478	9.99 998	26
35	8.00 779	1223	8.00 781	1223	11.99 219	9.99 998	25
36	8.02 002	1190	8.02 004	1190	11.97 996	9.99 998	24
37	8.03 192	1158	8.03 194	1159	11.96 806	9.99 997	23
38	8.04 350	1128	8.04 353	1128	11.95 647	9.99 997	22
39	8.05 478	1100	8.05 481	1100	11.94 519	9.99 997	21
40	8.06 578	1072	8.06 581	1072	11.93 419	9.99 997	20
41	8.07 650	1046	8.07 653	1047	11.92 347	9.99 997	19
42	8.08 696	1022	8.08 700	1022	11.91 300	9.99 997	18
43	8.09 718	999	8.09 722	998	11.90 278	9.99 997	17
44	8.10 717	976	8.10 720	976	11.89 280	9.99 996	16
45	8.11 693	954	8.11 696	955	11.88 304	9.99 996	15
46	8.12 647	934	8.12 651	934	11.87 349	9.99 996	14
47	8.13 581	914	8.13 585	915	11.86 415	9.99 996	13
48	8.14 495	896	8.14 500	895	11.85 500	9.99 996	12
49	8.15 391	877	8.15 395	878	11.84 605	9.99 996	11
50	8.16 268	860	8.16 273	860	11.83 727	9.99 995	10
51	8.17 128	843	8.17 133	843	11.82 867	9.99 995	9
52	8.17 971	827	8.17 976	828	11.82 024	9.99 995	8
53	8.18 798	812	8.18 804	812	11.81 196	9.99 995	7
54	8.19 610	797	8.19 616	797	11.80 384	9.99 995	6
55	8.20 407	782	8.20 413	782	11.79 587	9.99 994	5
56	8.21 189	769	8.21 195	769	11.78 805	9.99 994	4
57	8.21 958	755	8.21 964	756	11.78 036	9.99 994	3
58	8.22 713	743	8.22 720	742	11.77 280	9.99 994	2
59	8.23 456	730	8.23 462	730	11.76 538	9.99 994	1
60	8.24 186		8.24 192		11.75 808	9.99 993	0
′	L Cos	d	L Ctn	c d	L Tan	L Sin	′

90° (270°) (269°) **89°**

For more accurate values of L sin and L tan for interpolated values of angles less than 3° (or L cos or L ctn of angles greater than 87°) use Table 3, page 884.

*From Richard Stevens Burington, "Handbook of Mathematical Tables and Formulas," 4th ed., McGraw-Hill Book Company, New York, 1965.

The −10 portion of the characteristic of the logarithm is not printed but must be written down whenever such a logarithm is used.

1° (181°) (358°) **178°**

′	L Sin	d	L Tan	c d	L Ctn	L Cos	′
0	8.24 186	717	8.24 192	718	11.75 808	9.99 993	60
1	8.24 903	706	8.24 910	706	11.75 090	9.99 993	59
2	8.25 609	695	8.25 616	696	11.74 384	9.99 993	58
3	8.26 304	684	8.26 312	684	11.73 688	9.99 993	57
4	8.26 988	673	8.26 996	673	11.73 004	9.99 992	56
5	8.27 661	663	8.27 669	663	11.72 331	9.99 992	55
6	8.28 324	653	8.28 332	654	11.71 668	9.99 992	54
7	8.28 977	644	8.28 986	643	11.71 014	9.99 992	53
8	8.29 621	634	8.29 629	634	11.70 371	9.99 992	52
9	8.30 255	624	8.30 263	625	11.69 737	9.99 991	51
10	8.30 879	616	8.30 888	617	11.69 112	9.99 991	50
11	8.31 495	608	8.31 505	607	11.68 495	9.99 991	49
12	8.32 103	599	8.32 112	599	11.67 888	9.99 990	48
13	8.32 702	590	8.32 711	591	11.67 289	9.99 990	47
14	8.33 292	583	8.33 302	584	11.66 698	9.99 990	46
15	8.33 875	575	8.33 886	575	11.66 114	9.99 990	45
16	8.34 450	568	8.34 461	568	11.65 539	9.99 989	44
17	8.35 018	560	8.35 029	561	11.64 971	9.99 989	43
18	8.35 578	553	8.35 590	553	11.64 410	9.99 989	42
19	8.36 131	547	8.36 143	546	11.63 857	9.99 989	41
20	8.36 678	539	8.36 689	540	11.63 311	9.99 988	40
21	8.37 217	533	8.37 229	533	11.62 771	9.99 988	39
22	8.37 750	526	8.37 762	527	11.62 238	9.99 988	38
23	8.38 276	520	8.38 289	520	11.61 711	9.99 987	37
24	8.38 796	514	8.38 809	514	11.61 191	9.99 987	36
25	8.39 310	508	8.39 323	509	11.60 677	9.99 987	35
26	8.39 818	502	8.39 832	502	11.60 168	9.99 986	34
27	8.40 320	496	8.40 334	496	11.59 666	9.99 986	33
28	8.40 816	491	8.40 830	491	11.59 170	9.99 986	32
29	8.41 307	485	8.41 321	486	11.58 679	9.99 985	31
30	8.41 792	480	8.41 807	480	11.58 193	9.99 985	30
31	8.42 272	474	8.42 287	475	11.57 713	9.99 985	29
32	8.42 746	470	8.42 762	470	11.57 238	9.99 984	28
33	8.43 216	464	8.43 232	464	11.56 768	9.99 984	27
34	8.43 680	459	8.43 696	460	11.56 304	9.99 984	26
35	8.44 139	455	8.44 156	455	11.55 844	9.99 983	25
36	8.44 594	450	8.44 611	450	11.55 389	9.99 983	24
37	8.45 044	445	8.45 061	446	11.54 939	9.99 983	23
38	8.45 489	441	8.45 507	441	11.54 493	9.99 982	22
39	8.45 930	436	8.45 948	437	11.54 052	9.99 982	21
40	8.46 366	433	8.46 385	432	11.53 615	9.99 982	20
41	8.46 799	427	8.46 817	428	11.53 183	9.99 981	19
42	8.47 226	424	8.47 245	424	11.52 755	9.99 981	18
43	8.47 650	419	8.47 669	420	11.52 331	9.99 981	17
44	8.48 069	416	8.48 089	416	11.51 911	9.99 980	16
45	8.48 485	411	8.48 505	412	11.51 495	9.99 980	15
46	8.48 896	408	8.48 917	408	11.51 083	9.99 979	14
47	8.49 304	404	8.49 325	404	11.50 675	9.99 979	13
48	8.49 708	400	8.49 729	401	11.50 271	9.99 979	12
49	8.50 108	396	8.50 130	397	11.49 870	9.99 978	11
50	8.50 504	393	8.50 527	393	11.49 473	9.99 978	10
51	8.50 897	390	8.50 920	390	11.49 080	9.99 977	9
52	8.51 287	386	8.51 310	386	11.48 690	9.99 977	8
53	8.51 673	382	8.51 696	383	11.48 304	9.99 977	7
54	8.52 055	379	8.52 079	380	11.47 921	9.99 976	6
55	8.52 434	376	8.52 459	376	11.47 541	9.99 976	5
56	8.52 810	373	8.52 835	373	11.47 165	9.99 975	4
57	8.53 183	369	8.53 208	370	11.46 792	9.99 975	3
58	8.53 552	367	8.53 578	367	11.46 422	9.99 974	2
59	8.53 919	363	8.53 945	363	11.46 055	9.99 974	1
60	8.54 282		8.54 308		11.45 692	9.99 974	0
′	L Cos	d	L Ctn	c d	L Tan	L Sin	′

91° (271°) (268°) **88°**

For more accurate values of L sin and L tan for interpolated values of angles less than 3° (or L cos or L ctn of angles greater than 87°) use Table 3, page 884.

The −10 portion of the characteristic of the logarithm is not printed but must be written down whenever such a logarithm is used.

2° (182°) (357°) **177°**

′	L Sin	d	L Tan	c d	L Ctn	L Cos	′
0	8.54 282	360	8.54 308	361	11.45 692	9.99 974	60
1	8.54 642	357	8.54 669	358	11.45 331	9.99 973	59
2	8.54 999	355	8.55 027	355	11.44 973	9.99 973	58
3	8.55 354	351	8.55 382	352	11.44 618	9.99 972	57
4	8.55 705	349	8.55 734	349	11.44 266	9.99 972	56
5	8.56 054	346	8.56 083	346	11.43 917	9.99 971	55
6	8.56 400	343	8.56 429	344	11.43 571	9.99 971	54
7	8.56 743	341	8.56 773	341	11.43 227	9.99 970	53
8	8.57 084	337	8.57 114	338	11.42 886	9.99 970	52
9	8.57 421	336	8.57 452	336	11.42 548	9.99 969	51
10	8.57 757	332	8.57 788	333	11.42 212	9.99 969	50
11	8.58 089	330	8.58 121	330	11.41 879	9.99 968	49
12	8.58 419	328	8.58 451	328	11.41 549	9.99 968	48
13	8.58 747	325	8.58 779	326	11.41 221	9.99 967	47
14	8.59 072	323	8.59 105	323	11.40 895	9.99 967	46
15	8.59 395	320	8.59 428	321	11.40 572	9.99 967	45
16	8.59 715	318	8.59 749	319	11.40 251	9.99 966	44
17	8.60 033	316	8.60 068	316	11.39 932	9.99 966	43
18	8.60 349	313	8.60 384	314	11.39 616	9.99 965	42
19	8.60 662	311	8.60 698	311	11.39 302	9.99 964	41
20	8.60 973	309	8.61 009	310	11.38 991	9.99 964	40
21	8.61 282	307	8.61 319	307	11.38 681	9.99 963	39
22	8.61 589	305	8.61 626	305	11.38 374	9.99 963	38
23	8.61 894	302	8.61 931	303	11.38 069	9.99 962	37
24	8.62 196	301	8.62 234	301	11.37 766	9.99 962	36
25	8.62 497	298	8.62 535	299	11.37 465	9.99 961	35
26	8.62 795	296	8.62 834	297	11.37 166	9.99 961	34
27	8.63 091	294	8.63 131	295	11.36 869	9.99 960	33
28	8.63 385	293	8.63 426	292	11.36 574	9.99 960	32
29	8.63 678	290	8.63 718	291	11.36 282	9.99 959	31
30	8.63 968	288	8.64 009	289	11.35 991	9.99 959	30
31	8.64 256	287	8.64 298	287	11.35 702	9.99 958	29
32	8.64 543	284	8.64 585	285	11.35 415	9.99 958	28
33	8.64 827	283	8.64 870	284	11.35 130	9.99 957	27
34	8.65 110	281	8.65 154	281	11.34 846	9.99 956	26
35	8.65 391	279	8.65 435	280	11.34 565	9.99 956	25
36	8.65 670	277	8.65 715	278	11.34 285	9.99 955	24
37	8.65 947	276	8.65 993	276	11.34 007	9.99 955	23
38	8.66 223	274	8.66 269	274	11.33 731	9.99 954	22
39	8.66 497	272	8.66 543	273	11.33 457	9.99 954	21
40	8.66 769	270	8.66 816	271	11.33 184	9.99 953	20
41	8.67 039	269	8.67 087	269	11.32 913	9.99 952	19
42	8.67 308	267	8.67 356	268	11.32 644	9.99 952	18
43	8.67 575	266	8.67 624	266	11.32 376	9.99 951	17
44	8.67 841	263	8.67 890	264	11.32 110	9.99 951	16
45	8.68 104	263	8.68 154	263	11.31 846	9.99 950	15
46	8.68 367	260	8.68 417	261	11.31 583	9.99 949	14
47	8.68 627	259	8.68 678	260	11.31 322	9.99 949	13
48	8.68 886	258	8.68 938	258	11.31 062	9.99 948	12
49	8.69 144	256	8.69 196	257	11.30 804	9.99 948	11
50	8.69 400	254	8.69 453	255	11.30 547	9.99 947	10
51	8.69 654	253	8.69 708	254	11.30 292	9.99 946	9
52	8.69 907	252	8.69 962	252	11.30 038	9.99 946	8
53	8.70 159	250	8.70 214	251	11.29 786	9.99 945	7
54	8.70 409	249	8.70 465	249	11.29 535	9.99 944	6
55	8.70 658	247	8.70 714	248	11.29 286	9.99 944	5
56	8.70 905	246	8.70 962	246	11.29 038	9.99 943	4
57	8.71 151	244	8.71 208	245	11.28 792	9.99 942	3
58	8.71 395	243	8.71 453	244	11.28 547	9.99 942	2
59	8.71 638	242	8.71 697	243	11.28 303	9.99 941	1
60	8.71 880		8.71 940		11.28 060	9.99 940	0
′	L Cos	d	L Ctn	c d	L Tan	L Sin	′

92° (272°) (267°) **87°**

For more accurate values of L sin and L tan for interpolated values of angles less than 3° (or L cos or L ctn of angles greater than 87°) use Table 3, page 884.

The −10 portion of the characteristic of the logarithm is not printed but must be written down whenever such a logarithm is used.

3° (183°) (356°) **176°**

′	L Sin	d	L Tan	c d	L Ctn	L Cos	′
0	8.71 880	240	8.71 940	241	11.28 060	9.99 940	60
1	8.72 120	239	8.72 181	239	11.27 819	9.99 940	59
2	8.72 359	238	8.72 420	239	11.27 580	9.99 939	58
3	8.72 597	237	8.72 659	237	11.27 341	9.99 938	57
4	8.72 834	235	8.72 896	236	11.27 104	9.99 938	56
5	8.73 069	234	8.73 132	234	11.26 868	9.99 937	55
6	8.73 303	232	8.73 366	234	11.26 634	9.99 936	54
7	8.73 535	232	8.73 600	232	11.26 400	9.99 936	53
8	8.73 767	230	8.73 832	231	11.26 168	9.99 935	52
9	8.73 997	229	8.74 063	229	11.25 937	9.99 934	51
10	8.74 226	228	8.74 292	229	11.25 708	9.99 934	50
11	8.74 454	226	8.74 521	227	11.25 479	9.99 933	49
12	8.74 680	226	8.74 748	226	11.25 252	9.99 932	48
13	8.74 906	224	8.74 974	225	11.25 026	9.99 932	47
14	8.75 130	223	8.75 199	224	11.24 801	9.99 931	46
15	8.75 353	222	8.75 423	222	11.24 577	9.99 930	45
16	8.75 575	220	8.75 645	222	11.24 355	9.99 929	44
17	8.75 795	220	8.75 867	220	11.24 133	9.99 929	43
18	8.76 015	219	8.76 087	219	11.23 913	9.99 928	42
19	8.76 234	217	8.76 306	219	11.23 694	9.99 927	41
20	8.76 451	216	8.76 525	217	11.23 475	9.99 926	40
21	8.76 667	216	8.76 742	216	11.23 258	9.99 926	39
22	8.76 883	214	8.76 958	215	11.23 042	9.99 925	38
23	8.77 097	213	8.77 173	214	11.22 827	9.99 924	37
24	8.77 310	212	8.77 387	213	11.22 613	9.99 923	36
25	8.77 522	211	8.77 600	211	11.22 400	9.99 923	35
26	8.77 733	210	8.77 811	211	11.22 189	9.99 922	34
27	8.77 943	209	8.78 022	210	11.21 978	9.99 921	33
28	8.78 152	208	8.78 232	209	11.21 768	9.99 920	32
29	8.78 360	208	8.78 441	208	11.21 559	9.99 920	31
30	8.78 568	206	8.78 649	206	11.21 351	9.99 919	30
31	8.78 774	205	8.78 855	206	11.21 145	9.99 918	29
32	8.78 979	204	8.79 061	205	11.20 939	9.99 917	28
33	8.79 183	203	8.79 266	204	11.20 734	9.99 917	27
34	8.79 386	202	8.79 470	203	11.20 530	9.99 916	26
35	8.79 588	201	8.79 673	202	11.20 327	9.99 915	25
36	8.79 789	201	8.79 875	201	11.20 125	9.99 914	24
37	8.79 990	199	8.80 076	201	11.19 924	9.99 913	23
38	8.80 189	199	8.80 277	199	11.19 723	9.99 913	22
39	8.80 388	197	8.80 476	198	11.19 524	9.99 912	21
40	8.80 585	197	8.80 674	198	11.19 326	9.99 911	20
41	8.80 782	196	8.80 872	196	11.19 128	9.99 910	19
42	8.80 978	195	8.81 068	196	11.18 932	9.99 909	18
43	8.81 173	194	8.81 264	195	11.18 736	9.99 909	17
44	8.81 367	193	8.81 459	194	11.18 541	9.99 908	16
45	8.81 560	192	8.81 653	193	11.18 347	9.99 907	15
46	8.81 752	192	8.81 846	192	11.18 154	9.99 906	14
47	8.81 944	190	8.82 038	192	11.17 962	9.99 905	13
48	8.82 134	190	8.82 230	190	11.17 770	9.99 904	12
49	8.82 324	189	8.82 420	190	11.17 580	9.99 904	11
50	8.82 513	188	8.82 610	189	11.17 390	9.99 903	10
51	8.82 701	187	8.82 799	188	11.17 201	9.99 902	9
52	8.82 888	187	8.82 987	188	11.17 013	9.99 901	8
53	8.83 075	186	8.83 175	186	11.16 825	9.99 900	7
54	8.83 261	185	8.83 361	186	11.16 639	9.99 899	6
55	8.83 446	184	8.83 547	185	11.16 453	9.99 898	5
56	8.83 630	183	8.83 732	184	11.16 268	9.99 898	4
57	8.83 813	183	8.83 916	184	11.16 084	9.99 897	3
58	8.83 996	181	8.84 100	182	11.15 900	9.99 896	2
59	8.84 177	181	8.84 282	182	11.15 718	9.99 895	1
60	8.84 358		8.84 464		11.15 536	9.99 894	0
′	L Cos	d	L Ctn	c d	L Tan	L Sin	′

Proportional parts

″	241	239	237	235	234
1	4.0	4.0	4.0	3.9	3.9
2	8.0	8.0	7.9	7.8	7.8
3	12.0	12.0	11.8	11.8	11.7
4	16.1	15.9	15.8	15.7	15.6
5	20.1	19.9	19.8	19.6	19.5
6	24.1	23.9	23.7	23.5	23.4
7	28.1	27.9	27.6	27.4	27.3
8	32.1	31.9	31.6	31.3	31.2
9	36.2	35.8	35.6	35.2	35.1
″	232	229	227	225	223
1	3.9	3.8	3.8	3.8	3.7
2	7.7	7.6	7.6	7.5	7.4
3	11.6	11.4	11.4	11.2	11.2
4	15.5	15.3	15.1	15.0	14.9
5	19.3	19.1	18.9	18.8	18.6
6	23.2	22.9	22.7	22.5	22.3
7	27.1	26.7	26.5	26.2	26.0
8	30.9	30.5	30.3	30.0	29.7
9	34.8	34.4	34.0	33.8	33.4
″	222	220	217	215	213
1	3.7	3.7	3.6	3.6	3.6
2	7.4	7.3	7.2	7.2	7.1
3	11.1	11.0	10.8	10.8	10.6
4	14.8	14.7	14.5	14.3	14.2
5	18.5	18.3	18.1	17.9	17.8
6	22.2	22.0	21.7	21.5	21.3
7	25.9	25.7	25.3	25.1	24.8
8	29.6	29.3	28.9	28.7	28.4
9	33.3	33.0	32.6	32.2	32.0
″	211	208	206	203	201
1	3.5	3.5	3.4	3.4	3.4
2	7.0	6.9	6.9	6.8	6.7
3	10.6	10.4	10.3	10.2	10.0
4	14.1	13.9	13.7	13.5	13.4
5	17.6	17.3	17.2	16.9	16.8
6	21.1	20.8	20.6	20.3	20.1
7	24.6	24.3	24.0	23.7	23.4
8	28.1	27.7	27.5	27.1	26.8
9	31.6	31.2	30.9	30.4	30.2
″	199	197	195	193	192
1	3.3	3.3	3.2	3.2	3.2
2	6.6	6.6	6.5	6.4	6.4
3	10.0	9.8	9.8	9.6	9.6
4	13.3	13.1	13.0	12.9	12.8
5	16.6	16.4	16.2	16.1	16.0
6	19.9	19.7	19.5	19.3	19.2
7	23.2	23.0	22.8	22.5	22.4
8	26.5	26.3	26.0	25.7	25.6
9	29.8	29.6	29.2	29.0	28.8
″	189	187	185	183	181
1	3.2	3.1	3.1	3.0	3.0
2	6.3	6.2	6.2	6.1	6.0
3	9.4	9.4	9.2	9.2	9.0
4	12.6	12.5	12.3	12.2	12.1
5	15.8	15.6	15.4	15.2	15.1
6	18.9	18.7	18.5	18.3	18.1
7	22.0	21.8	21.6	21.4	21.1
8	25.2	24.9	24.7	24.4	24.1
9	28.4	28.0	27.8	27.4	27.2

Proportional parts

93° (273°) (266°) **86°**

The −10 portion of the characteristic of the logarithm is not printed but must be written down whenever such a logarithm is used.

4° (184°) (355°) **175°**

′	L Sin	d	L Tan	c d	L Ctn	L Cos	′
0	8.84 358	181	8.84 464	182	11.15 536	9.99 894	60
1	8.84 539	179	8.84 646	180	11.15 354	9.99 893	59
2	8.84 718	179	8.84 826	180	11.15 174	9.99 892	58
3	8.84 897	178	8.85 006	179	11.14 994	9.99 891	57
4	8.85 075	177	8.85 185	178	11.14 815	9.99 891	56
5	8.85 252	177	8.85 363	177	11.14 637	9.99 890	55
6	8.85 429	176	8.85 540	177	11.14 460	9.99 889	54
7	8.85 605	175	8.85 717	176	11.14 283	9.99 888	53
8	8.85 780	175	8.85 893	176	11.14 107	9.99 887	52
9	8.85 955	173	8.86 069	174	11.13 931	9.99 886	51
10	8.86 128	173	8.86 243	174	11.13 757	9.99 885	50
11	8.86 301	173	8.86 417	174	11.13 583	9.99 884	49
12	8.86 474	171	8.86 591	172	11.13 409	9.99 883	48
13	8.86 645	171	8.86 763	172	11.13 237	9.99 882	47
14	8.86 816	171	8.86 935	171	11.13 065	9.99 881	46
15	8.86 987	169	8.87 106	171	11.12 894	9.99 880	45
16	8.87 156	169	8.87 277	170	11.12 723	9.99 879	44
17	8.87 325	169	8.87 447	169	11.12 553	9.99 879	43
18	8.87 494	167	8.87 616	169	11.12 384	9.99 878	42
19	8.87 661	168	8.87 785	168	11.12 215	9.99 877	41
20	8.87 829	166	8.87 953	167	11.12 047	9.99 876	40
21	8.87 995	166	8.88 120	167	11.11 880	9.99 875	39
22	8.88 161	165	8.88 287	166	11.11 713	9.99 874	38
23	8.88 326	164	8.88 453	165	11.11 547	9.99 873	37
24	8.88 490	164	8.88 618	165	11.11 382	9.99 872	36
25	8.88 654	163	8.88 783	165	11.11 217	9.99 871	35
26	8.88 817	163	8.88 948	163	11.11 052	9.99 870	34
27	8.88 980	162	8.89 111	163	11.10 889	9.99 869	33
28	8.89 142	162	8.89 274	163	11.10 726	9.99 868	32
29	8.89 304	160	8.89 437	161	11.10 563	9.99 867	31
30	8.89 464	161	8.89 598	162	11.10 402	9.99 866	30
31	8.89 625	159	8.89 760	160	11.10 240	9.99 865	29
32	8.89 784	159	8.89 920	160	11.10 080	9.99 864	28
33	8.89 943	159	8.90 080	160	11.09 920	9.99 863	27
34	8.90 102	158	8.90 240	159	11.09 760	9.99 862	26
35	8.90 260	157	8.90 399	158	11.09 601	9.99 861	25
36	8.90 417	157	8.90 557	158	11.09 443	9.99 860	24
37	8.90 574	156	8.90 715	157	11.09 285	9.99 859	23
38	8.90 730	155	8.90 872	157	11.09 128	9.99 858	22
39	8.90 885	155	8.91 029	156	11.08 971	9.99 857	21
40	8.91 040	155	8.91 185	155	11.08 815	9.99 856	20
41	8.91 195	154	8.91 340	155	11.08 660	9.99 855	19
42	8.91 349	153	8.91 495	155	11.08 505	9.99 854	18
43	8.91 502	153	8.91 650	153	11.08 350	9.99 853	17
44	8.91 655	152	8.91 803	154	11.08 197	9.99 852	16
45	8.91 807	152	8.91 957	153	11.08 043	9.99 851	15
46	8.91 959	151	8.92 110	152	11.07 890	9.99 850	14
47	8.92 110	151	8.92 262	152	11.07 738	9.99 848	13
48	8.92 261	150	8.92 414	151	11.07 586	9.99 847	12
49	8.92 411	150	8.92 565	151	11.07 435	9.99 846	11
50	8.92 561	149	8.92 716	150	11.07 284	9.99 845	10
51	8.92 710	149	8.92 866	150	11.07 134	9.99 844	9
52	8.92 859	148	8.93 016	149	11.06 984	9.99 843	8
53	8.93 007	147	8.93 165	148	11.06 835	9.99 842	7
54	8.93 154	147	8.93 313	149	11.06 687	9.99 841	6
55	8.93 301	147	8.93 462	147	11.06 538	9.99 840	5
56	8.93 448	146	8.93 609	147	11.06 391	9.99 839	4
57	8.93 594	146	8.93 756	147	11.06 244	9.99 838	3
58	8.93 740	145	8.93 903	146	11.06 097	9.99 837	2
59	8.93 885	145	8.94 049	146	11.05 951	9.99 836	1
60	8.94 030		8.94 195		11.05 805	9.99 834	0
′	L Cos	d	L Ctn	c d	L Tan	L Sin	′

Proportional parts

″	182	181	179	178	177
1	3.0	3.0	3.0	3.0	3.0
2	6.1	6.0	6.0	5.9	5.9
3	9.1	9.0	9.0	8.9	8.8
4	12.1	12.1	11.9	11.9	11.8
5	15.2	15.1	14.9	14.8	14.8
6	18.2	18.1	17.9	17.8	17.7
7	21.2	21.1	20.9	20.8	20.6
8	24.3	24.1	23.9	23.7	23.6
9	27.3	27.2	26.8	26.7	26.6

″	176	175	174	173	172
1	2.9	2.9	2.9	2.9	2.9
2	5.9	5.8	5.8	5.8	5.7
3	8.8	8.8	8.7	8.6	8.6
4	11.7	11.7	11.6	11.5	11.5
5	14.7	14.6	14.5	14.4	14.3
6	17.6	17.5	17.4	17.3	17.2
7	20.5	20.4	20.3	20.2	20.1
8	23.5	23.3	23.2	23.1	22.9
9	26.4	26.2	26.1	26.0	25.8

″	171	170	169	168	167
1	2.8	2.8	2.8	2.8	2.8
2	5.7	5.7	5.6	5.6	5.6
3	8.6	8.5	8.4	8.4	8.4
4	11.4	11.3	11.3	11.2	11.1
5	14.2	14.2	14.1	14.0	13.9
6	17.1	17.0	16.9	16.8	16.7
7	20.0	19.8	19.7	19.6	19.5
8	22.8	22.7	22.5	22.4	22.3
9	25.6	25.5	25.4	25.2	25.0

″	166	165	164	163	162
1	2.8	2.8	2.7	2.7	2.7
2	5.5	5.5	5.5	5.4	5.4
3	8.3	8.2	8.2	8.2	8.1
4	11.1	11.0	10.9	10.9	10.8
5	13.8	13.8	13.7	13.6	13.5
6	16.6	16.5	16.4	16.3	16.2
7	19.4	19.2	19.1	19.0	18.9
8	22.1	22.0	21.9	21.7	21.6
9	24.9	24.8	24.6	24.4	24.3

″	161	160	159	158	157
1	2.7	2.7	2.6	2.6	2.6
2	5.4	5.3	5.3	5.3	5.2
3	8.0	8.0	8.0	7.9	7.8
4	10.7	10.7	10.6	10.5	10.5
5	13.4	13.3	13.2	13.2	13.1
6	16.1	16.0	15.9	15.8	15.7
7	18.8	18.7	18.6	18.4	18.3
8	21.5	21.3	21.2	21.1	20.9
9	24.2	24.0	23.8	23.7	23.6

″	156	155	154	153	152
1	2.6	2.6	2.6	2.6	2.5
2	5.2	5.2	5.1	5.1	5.1
3	7.8	7.8	7.7	7.6	7.6
4	10.4	10.3	10.3	10.2	10.1
5	13.0	12.9	12.8	12.8	12.7
6	15.6	15.5	15.4	15.3	15.2
7	18.2	18.1	18.0	17.8	17.7
8	20.8	20.7	20.5	20.4	20.3
9	23.4	23.2	23.1	23.0	22.8

Proportional parts

94° (274°) (265°) **85°**

The −10 portion of the characteristic of the logarithm is not printed but must be written down whenever such a logarithm is used.

5° (185°) (354°) **174°**

′	L Sin	d	L Tan	c d	L Ctn	L Cos	′
0	8.94 030	144	8.94 195	145	11.05 805	9.99 834	60
1	8.94 174	143	8.94 340	145	11.05 660	9.99 833	59
2	8.94 317	144	8.94 485	145	11.05 515	9.99 832	58
3	8.94 461	142	8.94 630	143	11.05 370	9.99 831	57
4	8.94 603	143	8.94 773	144	11.05 227	9.99 830	56
5	8.94 746	141	8.94 917	143	11.05 083	9.99 829	55
6	8.94 887	142	8.95 060	142	11.04 940	9.99 828	54
7	8.95 029	141	8.95 202	142	11.04 798	9.99 827	53
8	8.95 170	140	8.95 344	142	11.04 656	9.99 825	52
9	8.95 310	140	8.95 486	141	11.04 514	9.99 824	51
10	8.95 450	139	8.95 627	140	11.04 373	9.99 823	50
11	8.95 589	139	8.95 767	141	11.04 233	9.99 822	49
12	8.95 728	139	8.95 908	139	11.04 092	9.99 821	48
13	8.95 867	138	8.96 047	140	11.03 953	9.99 820	47
14	8.96 005	138	8.96 187	138	11.03 813	9.99 819	46
15	8.96 143	137	8.96 325	139	11.03 675	9.99 817	45
16	8.96 280	137	8.96 464	138	11.03 536	9.99 816	44
17	8.96 417	136	8.96 602	137	11.03 398	9.99 815	43
18	8.96 553	136	8.96 739	138	11.03 261	9.99 814	42
19	8.96 689	136	8.96 877	136	11.03 123	9.99 813	41
20	8.96 825	135	8.97 013	137	11.02 987	9.99 812	40
21	8.96 960	135	8.97 150	135	11.02 850	9.99 810	39
22	8.97 095	134	8.97 285	136	11.02 715	9.99 809	38
23	8.97 229	134	8.97 421	135	11.02 579	9.99 808	37
24	8.97 363	133	8.97 556	135	11.02 444	9.99 807	36
25	8.97 496	133	8.97 691	134	11.02 309	9.99 806	35
26	8.97 629	133	8.97 825	134	11.02 175	9.99 804	34
27	8.97 762	132	8.97 959	133	11.02 041	9.99 803	33
28	8.97 894	132	8.98 092	133	11.01 908	9.99 802	32
29	8.98 026	131	8.98 225	133	11.01 775	9.99 801	31
30	8.98 157	131	8.98 358	132	11.01 642	9.99 800	30
31	8.98 288	131	8.98 490	132	11.01 510	9.99 798	29
32	8.98 419	130	8.98 622	131	11.01 378	9.99 797	28
33	8.98 549	130	8.98 753	131	11.01 247	9.99 796	27
34	8.98 679	129	8.98 884	131	11.01 116	9.99 795	26
35	8.98 808	129	8.99 015	130	11.00 985	9.99 793	25
36	8.98 937	129	8.99 145	130	11.00 855	9.99 792	24
37	8.99 066	128	8.99 275	130	11.00 725	9.99 791	23
38	8.99 194	128	8.99 405	129	11.00 595	9.99 790	22
39	8.99 322	128	8.99 534	128	11.00 466	9.99 788	21
40	8.99 450	127	8.99 662	129	11.00 338	9.99 787	20
41	8.99 577	127	8.99 791	128	11.00 209	9.99 786	19
42	8.99 704	126	8.99 919	127	11.00 081	9.99 785	18
43	8.99 830	126	9.00 046	128	10.99 954	9.99 783	17
44	8.99 956	126	9.00 174	127	10.99 826	9.99 782	16
45	9.00 082	125	9.00 301	126	10.99 699	9.99 781	15
46	9.00 207	125	9.00 427	126	10.99 573	9.99 780	14
47	9.00 332	124	9.00 553	126	10.99 447	9.99 778	13
48	9.00 456	125	9.00 679	126	10.99 321	9.99 777	12
49	9.00 581	123	9.00 805	125	10.99 195	9.99 776	11
50	9.00 704	124	9.00 930	125	10.99 070	9.99 775	10
51	9.00 828	123	9.01 055	124	10.98 945	9.99 773	9
52	9.00 951	123	9.01 179	124	10.98 821	9.99 772	8
53	9.01 074	122	9.01 303	124	10.98 697	9.99 771	7
54	9.01 196	122	9.01 427	123	10.98 573	9.99 769	6
55	9.01 318	122	9.01 550	123	10.98 450	9.99 768	5
56	9.01 440	121	9.01 673	123	10.98 327	9.99 767	4
57	9.01 561	121	9.01 796	122	10.98 204	9.99 765	3
58	9.01 682	121	9.01 918	122	10.98 082	9.99 764	2
59	9.01 803	120	9.02 040	122	10.97 960	9.99 763	1
60	9.01 923		9.02 162		10.97 838	9.99 761	0
′	L Cos	d	L Ctn	c d	L Tan	L Sin	′

Proportional parts

″	151	149	148	147	146
1	2.5	2.5	2.5	2.4	2.4
2	5.0	5.0	4.9	4.9	4.9
3	7.6	7.4	7.4	7.4	7.3
4	10.1	9.9	9.9	9.8	9.7
5	12.6	12.4	12.3	12.2	12.2
6	15.1	14.9	14.8	14.7	14.6
7	17.6	17.4	17.3	17.2	17.0
8	20.1	19.9	19.7	19.6	19.5
9	22.6	22.4	22.2	22.0	21.9

″	145	144	143	142	141
1	2.4	2.4	2.4	2.4	2.4
2	4.8	4.8	4.8	4.7	4.7
3	7.2	7.2	7.2	7.1	7.0
4	9.7	9.6	9.5	9.5	9.4
5	12.1	12.0	11.9	11.8	11.8
6	14.5	14.4	14.3	14.2	14.1
7	16.9	16.8	16.7	16.6	16.4
8	19.3	19.2	19.1	18.9	18.8
9	21.8	21.6	21.4	21.3	21.2

″	140	139	138	137	136
1	2.3	2.3	2.3	2.3	2.3
2	4.7	4.6	4.6	4.6	4.5
3	7.0	7.0	6.9	6.8	6.8
4	9.3	9.3	9.2	9.1	9.1
5	11.7	11.6	11.5	11.4	11.3
6	14.0	13.9	13.8	13.7	13.6
7	16.3	16.2	16.1	16.0	15.9
8	18.7	18.5	18.4	18.3	18.1
9	21.0	20.8	20.7	20.6	20.4

″	135	134	133	132	131
1	2.2	2.2	2.2	2.2	2.2
2	4.5	4.5	4.4	4.4	4.4
3	6.8	6.7	6.6	6.6	6.6
4	9.0	8.9	8.9	8.8	8.7
5	11.2	11.2	11.1	11.0	10.9
6	13.5	13.4	13.3	13.2	13.1
7	15.8	15.6	15.5	15.4	15.3
8	18.0	17.9	17.7	17.6	17.5
9	20.2	20.1	20.0	19.8	19.6

″	130	129	128	127	126
1	2.2	2.2	2.1	2.1	2.1
2	4.3	4.3	4.3	4.2	4.2
3	6.5	6.4	6.4	6.4	6.3
4	8.7	8.6	8.5	8.5	8.4
5	10.8	10.8	10.7	10.6	10.5
6	13.0	12.9	12.8	12.7	12.6
7	15.2	15.0	14.9	14.8	14.7
8	17.3	17.2	17.1	16.9	16.8
9	19.5	19.4	19.2	19.0	18.9

″	125	124	123	122	121
1	2.1	2.1	2.0	2.0	2.0
2	4.2	4.1	4.1	4.1	4.0
3	6.2	6.2	6.2	6.1	6.0
4	8.3	8.3	8.2	8.1	8.1
5	10.4	10.3	10.2	10.2	10.1
6	12.5	12.4	12.3	12.2	12.1
7	14.6	14.5	14.4	14.2	14.1
8	16.7	16.5	16.4	16.3	16.1
9	18.8	18.6	18.4	18.3	18.2

Proportional parts

95° (275°) (264°) **84°**

The −10 portion of the characteristic of the logarithm is not printed but must be written down whenever such a logarithm is used.

6° (186°) (353°) **173°**

′	L Sin	d	L Tan	c d	L Ctn	L Cos	′
0	9.01 923	120	9.02 162	121	10.97 838	9.99 761	60
1	9.02 043	120	9.02 283	121	10.97 717	9.99 760	59
2	9.02 163	120	9.02 404	121	10.97 596	9.99 759	58
3	9.02 283	119	9.02 525	120	10.97 475	9.99 757	57
4	9.02 402	118	9.02 645	121	10.97 355	9.99 756	56
5	9.02 520	119	9.02 766	119	10.97 234	9.99 755	55
6	9.02 639	118	9.02 885	120	10.97 115	9.99 753	54
7	9.02 757	117	9.03 005	119	10.96 995	9.99 752	53
8	9.02 874	118	9.03 124	118	10.96 876	9.99 751	52
9	9.02 992	117	9.03 242	119	10.96 758	9.99 749	51
10	9.03 109	117	9.03 361	118	10.96 639	9.99 748	50
11	9.03 226	116	9.03 479	118	10.96 521	9.99 747	49
12	9.03 342	116	9.03 597	117	10.96 403	9.99 745	48
13	9.03 458	116	9.03 714	118	10.96 286	9.99 744	47
14	9.03 574	116	9.03 832	116	10.96 168	9.99 742	46
15	9.03 690	115	9.03 948	117	10.96 052	9.99 741	45
16	9.03 805	115	9.04 065	116	10.95 935	9.99 740	44
17	9.03 920	114	9.04 181	116	10.95 819	9.99 738	43
18	9.04 034	115	9.04 297	116	10.95 703	9.99 737	42
19	9.04 149	113	9.04 413	115	10.95 587	9.99 736	41
20	9.04 262	114	9.04 528	115	10.95 472	9.99 734	40
21	9.04 376	114	9.04 643	115	10.95 357	9.99 733	39
22	9.04 490	113	9.04 758	115	10.95 242	9.99 731	38
23	9.04 603	112	9.04 873	114	10.95 127	9.99 730	37
24	9.04 715	113	9.04 987	114	10.95 013	9.99 728	36
25	9.04 828	112	9.05 101	113	10.94 899	9.99 727	35
26	9.04 940	112	9.05 214	114	10.94 786	9.99 726	34
27	9.05 052	112	9.05 328	113	10.94 672	9.99 724	33
28	9.05 164	111	9.05 441	112	10.94 559	9.99 723	32
29	9.05 275	111	9.05 553	113	10.94 447	9.99 721	31
30	9.05 386	111	9.05 666	112	10.94 334	9.99 720	30
31	9.05 497	110	9.05 778	112	10.94 222	9.99 718	29
32	9.05 607	110	9.05 890	112	10.94 110	9.99 717	28
33	9.05 717	110	9.06 002	111	10.93 998	9.99 716	27
34	9.05 827	110	9.06 113	111	10.93 887	9.99 714	26
35	9.05 937	109	9.06 224	111	10.93 776	9.99 713	25
36	9.06 046	109	9.06 335	110	10.93 665	9.99 711	24
37	9.06 155	109	9.06 445	111	10.93 555	9.99 710	23
38	9.06 264	108	9.06 556	110	10.93 444	9.99 708	22
39	9.06 372	109	9.06 666	109	10.93 334	9.99 707	21
40	9.06 481	108	9.06 775	110	10.93 225	9.99 705	20
41	9.06 589	107	9.06 885	109	10.93 115	9.99 704	19
42	9.06 696	108	9.06 994	109	10.93 006	9.99 702	18
43	9.06 804	107	9.07 103	108	10.92 897	9.99 701	17
44	9.06 911	107	9.07 211	109	10.92 789	9.99 699	16
45	9.07 018	106	9.07 320	108	10.92 680	9.99 698	15
46	9.07 124	107	9.07 428	108	10.92 572	9.99 696	14
47	9.07 231	106	9.07 536	107	10.92 464	9.99 695	13
48	9.07 337	105	9.07 643	108	10.92 357	9.99 693	12
49	9.07 442	106	9.07 751	107	10.92 249	9.99 692	11
50	9.07 548	105	9.07 858	106	10.92 142	9.99 690	10
51	9.07 653	105	9.07 964	107	10.92 036	9.99 689	9
52	9.07 758	105	9.08 071	106	10.91 929	9.99 687	8
53	9.07 863	105	9.08 177	106	10.91 823	9.99 686	7
54	9.07 968	104	9.08 283	106	10.91 717	9.99 684	6
55	9.08 072	104	9.08 389	106	10.91 611	9.99 683	5
56	9.08 176	104	9.08 495	105	10.91 505	9.99 681	4
57	9.08 280	103	9.08 600	105	10.91 400	9.99 680	3
58	9.08 383	103	9.08 705	105	10.91 295	9.99 678	2
59	9.08 486	103	9.08 810	104	10.91 190	9.99 677	1
60	9.08 589		9.08 914		10.91 086	9.99 675	0
′	L Cos	d	L Ctn	c d	L Tan	L Sin	′

Proportional parts

″	121	120	119	118
1	2.0	2.0	2.0	2.0
2	4.0	4.0	4.0	3.9
3	6.0	6.0	6.0	5.9
4	8.1	8.0	7.9	7.9
5	10.1	10.0	9.9	9.8
6	12.1	12.0	11.9	11.8
7	14.1	14.0	13.9	13.8
8	16.1	16.0	15.9	15.7
9	18.2	18.0	17.8	17.7
10	20.2	20.0	19.8	19.7
20	40.3	40.0	39.7	39.3
30	60.5	60.0	59.5	59.0
40	80.7	80.0	79.3	78.7
50	100.8	100.0	99.2	98.3

″	117	116	115	114
1	2.0	1.9	1.9	1.9
2	3.9	3.9	3.8	3.8
3	5.8	5.8	5.8	5.7
4	7.8	7.7	7.7	7.6
5	9.8	9.7	9.6	9.5
6	11.7	11.6	11.5	11.4
7	13.6	13.5	13.4	13.3
8	15.6	15.5	15.3	15.2
9	17.6	17.4	17.2	17.1
10	19.5	19.3	19.2	19.0
20	39.0	38.7	38.3	38.0
30	58.5	58.0	57.5	57.0
40	78.0	77.3	76.7	76.0
50	97.5	96.7	95.8	95.0

″	113	112	111	110
1	1.9	1.9	1.8	1.8
2	3.8	3.7	3.7	3.7
3	5.6	5.6	5.6	5.5
4	7.5	7.5	7.4	7.3
5	9.4	9.3	9.2	9.2
6	11.3	11.2	11.1	11.0
7	13.2	13.1	13.0	12.8
8	15.1	14.9	14.8	14.7
9	17.0	16.8	16.6	16.5
10	18.8	18.7	18.5	18.3
20	37.7	37.3	37.0	36.7
30	56.5	56.0	55.5	55.0
40	75.3	74.7	74.0	73.3
50	94.2	93.3	92.5	91.7

″	109	108	107	106
1	1.8	1.8	1.8	1.8
2	3.6	3.6	3.6	3.5
3	5.4	5.4	5.4	5.3
4	7.3	7.2	7.1	7.1
5	9.1	9.0	8.9	8.8
6	10.9	10.8	10.7	10.6
7	12.7	12.6	12.5	12.4
8	14.5	14.4	14.3	14.1
9	16.4	16.2	16.0	15.9
10	18.2	18.0	17.8	17.7
20	36.3	36.0	35.7	35.3
30	54.5	54.0	53.5	53.0
40	72.7	72.0	71.3	70.7
50	90.8	90.0	89.2	88.3

Proportional parts

96° (276°) (263°) **83°**

The −10 portion of the characteristic of the logarithm is not printed but must be written down whenever such a logarithm is used.

7° (187°) (352°) **172°**

′	L Sin	d	L Tan	c d	L Ctn	L Cos	′
0	9.08 589	103	9.08 914	105	10.91 086	9.99 675	60
1	9.08 692	103	9.09 019	104	10.90 981	9.99 674	59
2	9.08 795	102	9.09 123	104	10.90 877	9.99 672	58
3	9.08 897	102	9.09 227	103	10.90 773	9.99 670	57
4	9.08 999	102	9.09 330	104	10.90 670	9.99 669	56
5	9.09 101	101	9.09 434	103	10.90 566	9.99 667	55
6	9.09 202	102	9.09 537	103	10.90 463	9.99 666	54
7	9.09 304	101	9.09 640	102	10.90 360	9.99 664	53
8	9.09 405	101	9.09 742	103	10.90 258	9.99 663	52
9	9.09 506	100	9.09 845	102	10.90 155	9.99 661	51
10	9.09 606	101	9.09 947	102	10.90 053	9.99 659	50
11	9.09 707	100	9.10 049	101	10.89 951	9.99 658	49
12	9.09 807	100	9.10 150	102	10.89 850	9.99 656	48
13	9.09 907	99	9.10 252	101	10.89 748	9.99 655	47
14	9.10 006	100	9.10 353	101	10.89 647	9.99 653	46
15	9.10 106	99	9.10 454	101	10.89 546	9.99 651	45
16	9.10 205	99	9.10 555	101	10.89 445	9.99 650	44
17	9.10 304	98	9.10 656	100	10.89 344	9.99 648	43
18	9.10 402	99	9.10 756	100	10.89 244	9.99 647	42
19	9.10 501	98	9.10 856	100	10.89 144	9.99 645	41
20	9.10 599	98	9.10 956	100	10.89 044	9.99 643	40
21	9.10 697	98	9.11 056	99	10.88 944	9.99 642	39
22	9.10 795	98	9.11 155	99	10.88 845	9.99 640	38
23	9.10 893	97	9.11 254	99	10.88 746	9.99 638	37
24	9.10 990	97	9.11 353	99	10.88 647	9.99 637	36
25	9.11 087	97	9.11 452	99	10.88 548	9.99 635	35
26	9.11 184	97	9.11 551	98	10.88 449	9.99 633	34
27	9.11 281	96	9.11 649	98	10.88 351	9.99 632	33
28	9.11 377	97	9.11 747	98	10.88 253	9.99 630	32
29	9.11 474	96	9.11 845	98	10.88 155	9.99 629	31
30	9.11 570	96	9.11 943	97	10.88 057	9.99 627	30
31	9.11 666	95	9.12 040	98	10.87 960	9.99 625	29
32	9.11 761	96	9.12 138	97	10.87 862	9.99 624	28
33	9.11 857	95	9.12 235	97	10.87 765	9.99 622	27
34	9.11 952	95	9.12 332	96	10.87 668	9.99 620	26
35	9.12 047	95	9.12 428	97	10.87 572	9.99 618	25
36	9.12 142	94	9.12 525	96	10.87 475	9.99 617	24
37	9.12 236	95	9.12 621	96	10.87 379	9.99 615	23
38	9.12 331	94	9.12 717	96	10.87 283	9.99 613	22
39	9.12 425	94	9.12 813	96	10.87 187	9.99 612	21
40	9.12 519	93	9.12 909	95	10.87 091	9.99 610	20
41	9.12 612	94	9.13 004	95	10.86 996	9.99 608	19
42	9.12 706	93	9.13 099	95	10.86 901	9.99 607	18
43	9.12 799	93	9.13 194	95	10.86 806	9.99 605	17
44	9.12 892	93	9.13 289	95	10.86 711	9.99 603	16
45	9.12 985	93	9.13 384	94	10.86 616	9.99 601	15
46	9.13 078	93	9.13 478	95	10.86 522	9.99 600	14
47	9.13 171	92	9.13 573	94	10.86 427	9.99 598	13
48	9.13 263	92	9.13 667	94	10.86 333	9.99 596	12
49	9.13 355	92	9.13 761	93	10.86 239	9.99 595	11
50	9.13 447	92	9.13 854	94	10.86 146	9.99 593	10
51	9.13 539	91	9.13 948	93	10.86 052	9.99 591	9
52	9.13 630	92	9.14 041	93	10.85 959	9.99 589	8
53	9.13 722	91	9.14 134	93	10.85 866	9.99 588	7
54	9.13 813	91	9.14 227	93	10.85 773	9.99 586	6
55	9.13 904	90	9.14 320	92	10.85 680	9.99 584	5
56	9.13 994	91	9.14 412	92	10.85 588	9.99 582	4
57	9.14 085	90	9.14 504	93	10.85 496	9.99 581	3
58	9.14 175	91	9.14 597	91	10.85 403	9.99 579	2
59	9.14 266	90	9.14 688	92	10.85 312	9.99 577	1
60	9.14 356		9.14 780		10.85 220	9.99 575	0
′	L Cos	d	L Ctn	c d	L Tan	L Sin	′

Proportional parts

″	105	104	103	102
1	1.8	1.7	1.7	1.7
2	3.5	3.5	3.4	3.4
3	5.2	5.2	5.2	5.1
4	7.0	6.9	6.9	6.8
5	8.8	8.7	8.6	8.5
6	10.5	10.4	10.3	10.2
7	12.2	12.1	12.0	11.9
8	14.0	13.9	13.7	13.6
9	15.8	15.6	15.4	15.3
10	17.5	17.3	17.2	17.0
20	35.0	34.7	34.3	34.0
30	52.5	52.0	51.5	51.0
40	70.0	69.3	68.7	68.0
50	87.5	86.7	85.8	85.0

″	101	100	99	98
1	1.7	1.7	1.6	1.6
2	3.4	3.3	3.3	3.3
3	5.0	5.0	5.0	4.9
4	6.7	6.7	6.6	6.5
5	8.4	8.3	8.2	8.2
6	10.1	10.0	9.9	9.8
7	11.8	11.7	11.6	11.4
8	13.5	13.3	13.2	13.1
9	15.2	15.0	14.8	14.7
10	16.8	16.7	16.5	16.3
20	33.7	33.3	33.0	32.7
30	50.5	50.0	49.5	49.0
40	67.3	66.7	66.0	65.3
50	84.2	83.3	82.5	81.7

″	97	96	95	94
1	1.6	1.6	1.6	1.6
2	3.2	3.2	3.2	3.1
3	4.8	4.8	4.8	4.7
4	6.5	6.4	6.3	6.3
5	8.1	8.0	7.9	7.8
6	9.7	9.6	9.5	9.4
7	11.3	11.2	11.1	11.0
8	12.9	12.8	12.7	12.5
9	14.6	14.4	14.2	14.1
10	16.2	16.0	15.8	15.7
20	32.3	32.0	31.7	31.3
30	48.5	48.0	47.5	47.0
40	64.7	64.0	63.3	62.7
50	80.8	80.0	79.2	78.3

″	93	92	91	90
1	1.6	1.5	1.5	1.5
2	3.1	3.1	3.0	3.0
3	4.6	4.6	4.6	4.5
4	6.2	6.1	6.1	6.0
5	7.8	7.7	7.6	7.5
6	9.3	9.2	9.1	9.0
7	10.8	10.7	10.6	10.5
8	12.4	12.3	12.1	12.0
9	14.0	13.8	13.6	13.5
10	15.5	15.3	15.2	15.0
20	31.0	30.7	30.3	30.0
30	46.5	46.0	45.5	45.0
40	62.0	61.3	60.7	60.0
50	77.5	76.7	75.8	75.0

Proportional parts

97° (277°) (262°) **82°**

The −10 portion of the characteristic of the logarithm is not printed but must be written down whenever such a logarithm is used.

8° (188°) (351°) **171°**

′	L Sin	d	L Tan	c d	L Ctn	L Cos	′
0	9.14 356	89	9.14 780	92	10.85 220	9.99 575	60
1	9.14 445	90	9.14 872	91	10.85 128	9.99 574	59
2	9.14 535	89	9.14 963	91	10.85 037	9.99 572	58
3	9.14 624	90	9.15 054	91	10.84 946	9.99 570	57
4	9.14 714	89	9.15 145	91	10.84 855	9.99 568	56
5	9.14 803	88	9.15 236	91	10.84 764	9.99 566	55
6	9.14 891	89	9.15 327	90	10.84 673	9.99 565	54
7	9.14 980	89	9.15 417	91	10.84 583	9.99 563	53
8	9.15 069	88	9.15 508	90	10.84 492	9.99 561	52
9	9.15 157	88	9.15 598	90	10.84 402	9.99 559	51
10	9.15 245	88	9.15 688	89	10.84 312	9.99 557	50
11	9.15 333	88	9.15 777	90	10.84 223	9.99 556	49
12	9.15 421	87	9.15 867	89	10.84 133	9.99 554	48
13	9.15 508	88	9.15 956	90	10.84 044	9.99 552	47
14	9.15 596	87	9.16 046	89	10.83 954	9.99 550	46
15	9.15 683	87	9.16 135	89	10.83 865	9.99 548	45
16	9.15 770	87	9.16 224	88	10.83 776	9.99 546	44
17	9.15 857	87	9.16 312	89	10.83 688	9.99 545	43
18	9.15 944	86	9.16 401	88	10.83 599	9.99 543	42
19	9.16 030	86	9.16 489	88	10.83 511	9.99 541	41
20	9.16 116	87	9.16 577	88	10.83 423	9.99 539	40
21	9.16 203	86	9.16 665	88	10.83 335	9.99 537	39
22	9.16 289	85	9.16 753	88	10.83 247	9.99 535	38
23	9.16 374	86	9.16 841	87	10.83 159	9.99 533	37
24	9.16 460	85	9.16 928	88	10.83 072	9.99 532	36
25	9.16 545	86	9.17 016	87	10.82 984	9.99 530	35
26	9.16 631	85	9.17 103	87	10.82 897	9.99 528	34
27	9.16 716	85	9.17 190	87	10.82 810	9.99 526	33
28	9.16 801	85	9.17 277	86	10.82 723	9.99 524	32
29	9.16 886	84	9.17 363	87	10.82 637	9.99 522	31
30	9.16 970	85	9.17 450	86	10.82 550	9.99 520	30
31	9.17 055	84	9.17 536	86	10.82 464	9.99 518	29
32	9.17 139	84	9.17 622	86	10.82 378	9.99 517	28
33	9.17 223	84	9.17 708	86	10.82 292	9.99 515	27
34	9.17 307	84	9.17 794	86	10.82 206	9.99 513	26
35	9.17 391	83	9.17 880	85	10.82 120	9.99 511	25
36	9.17 474	84	9.17 965	86	10.82 035	9.99 509	24
37	9.17 558	83	9.18 051	85	10.81 949	9.99 507	23
38	9.17 641	83	9.18 136	85	10.81 864	9.99 505	22
39	9.17 724	83	9.18 221	85	10.81 779	9.99 503	21
40	9.17 807	83	9.18 306	85	10.81 694	9.99 501	20
41	9.17 890	83	9.18 391	84	10.81 609	9.99 499	19
42	9.17 973	82	9.18 475	85	10.81 525	9.99 497	18
43	9.18 055	82	9.18 560	84	10.81 440	9.99 495	17
44	9.18 137	83	9.18 644	84	10.81 356	9.99 494	16
45	9.18 220	82	9.18 728	84	10.81 272	9.99 492	15
46	9.18 302	81	9.18 812	84	10.81 188	9.99 490	14
47	9.18 383	82	9.18 896	83	10.81 104	9.99 488	13
48	9.18 465	82	9.18 979	84	10.81 021	9.99 486	12
49	9.18 547	81	9.19 063	83	10.80 937	9.99 484	11
50	9.18 628	81	9.19 146	83	10.80 854	9.99 482	10
51	9.18 709	81	9.19 229	83	10.80 771	9.99 480	9
52	9.18 790	81	9.19 312	83	10.80 688	9.99 478	8
53	9.18 871	81	9.19 395	83	10.80 605	9.99 476	7
54	9.18 952	81	9.19 478	83	10.80 522	9.99 474	6
55	9.19 033	80	9.19 561	82	10.80 439	9.99 472	5
56	9.19 113	80	9.19 643	82	10.80 357	9.99 470	4
57	9.19 193	80	9.19 725	82	10.80 275	9.99 468	3
58	9.19 273	80	9.19 807	82	10.80 193	9.99 466	2
59	9.19 353	80	9.19 889	82	10.80 111	9.99 464	1
60	9.19 433		9.19 971		10.80 029	9.99 462	0
′	L Cos	d	L Ctn	c d	L Tan	L Sin	′

Proportional parts

″	92	91	90
1	1.5	1.5	1.5
2	3.1	3.0	3.0
3	4.6	4.6	4.5
4	6.1	6.1	6.0
5	7.7	7.6	7.5
6	9.2	9.1	9.0
7	10.7	10.6	10.5
8	12.3	12.1	12.0
9	13.8	13.6	13.5
10	15.3	15.2	15.0
20	30.7	30.3	30.0
30	46.0	45.5	45.0
40	61.3	60.7	60.0
50	76.7	75.8	75.0

″	89	88	87
1	1.5	1.5	1.4
2	3.0	2.9	2.9
3	4.4	4.4	4.4
4	5.9	5.9	5.8
5	7.4	7.3	7.2
6	8.9	8.8	8.7
7	10.4	10.3	10.2
8	11.9	11.7	11.6
9	13.4	13.2	13.0
10	14.8	14.7	14.5
20	29.7	29.3	29.0
30	44.5	44.0	43.5
40	59.3	58.7	58.0
50	74.2	73.3	72.5

″	86	85	84
1	1.4	1.4	1.4
2	2.9	2.8	2.8
3	4.3	4.2	4.2
4	5.7	5.7	5.6
5	7.2	7.1	7.0
6	8.6	8.5	8.4
7	10.0	9.9	9.8
8	11.5	11.3	11.2
9	12.9	12.8	12.6
10	14.3	14.2	14.0
20	28.7	28.3	28.0
30	43.0	42.5	42.0
40	57.3	56.7	56.0
50	71.7	70.8	70.0

″	83	82	81
1	1.4	1.4	1.4
2	2.8	2.7	2.7
3	4.2	4.1	4.0
4	5.5	5.5	5.4
5	6.9	6.8	6.8
6	8.3	8.2	8.1
7	9.7	9.6	9.4
8	11.1	10.9	10.8
9	12.4	12.3	12.2
10	13.8	13.7	13.5
20	27.7	27.3	27.0
30	41.5	41.0	40.5
40	55.3	54.7	54.0
50	69.2	68.3	67.5

Proportional parts

98° (278°) (261°) **81°**

The −10 portion of the characteristic of the logarithm is not printed but must be written down whenever such a logarithm is used.

9° (189°) (350°) **170°**

′	L Sin	d	L Tan	c d	L Ctn	L Cos	′
0	9.19 433	80	9.19 971	82	10.80 029	9.99 462	60
1	9.19 513	79	9.20 053	81	10.79 947	9.99 460	59
2	9.19 592	80	9.20 134	82	10.79 866	9.99 458	58
3	9.19 672	79	9.20 216	81	10.79 784	9.99 456	57
4	9.19 751	79	9.20 297	81	10.79 703	9.99 454	56
5	9.19 830	79	9.20 378	81	10.79 622	9.99 452	55
6	9.19 909	79	9.20 459	81	10.79 541	9.99 450	54
7	9.19 988	79	9.20 540	81	10.79 460	9.99 448	53
8	9.20 067	78	9.20 621	80	10.79 379	9.99 446	52
9	9.20 145	78	9.20 701	81	10.79 299	9.99 444	51
10	9.20 223	79	9.20 782	80	10.79 218	9.99 442	50
11	9.20 302	78	9.20 862	80	10.79 138	9.99 440	49
12	9.20 380	78	9.20 942	80	10.79 058	9.99 438	48
13	9.20 458	77	9.21 022	80	10.78 978	9.99 436	47
14	9.20 535	78	9.21 102	80	10.78 898	9.99 434	46
15	9.20 613	78	9.21 182	79	10.78 818	9.99 432	45
16	9.20 691	77	9.21 261	80	10.78 739	9.99 429	44
17	9.20 768	77	9.21 341	79	10.78 659	9.99 427	43
18	9.20 845	77	9.21 420	79	10.78 580	9.99 425	42
19	9.20 922	77	9.21 499	79	10.78 501	9.99 423	41
20	9.20 999	77	9.21 578	79	10.78 422	9.99 421	40
21	9.21 076	77	9.21 657	79	10.78 343	9.99 419	39
22	9.21 153	76	9.21 736	78	10.78 264	9.99 417	38
23	9.21 229	77	9.21 814	79	10.78 186	9.99 415	37
24	9.21 306	76	9.21 893	78	10.78 107	9.99 413	36
25	9.21 382	76	9.21 971	78	10.78 029	9.99 411	35
26	9.21 458	76	9.22 049	78	10.77 951	9.99 409	34
27	9.21 534	76	9.22 127	78	10.77 873	9.99 407	33
28	9.21 610	75	9.22 205	78	10.77 795	9.99 404	32
29	9.21 685	76	9.22 283	78	10.77 717	9.99 402	31
30	9.21 761	75	9.22 361	77	10.77 639	9.99 400	30
31	9.21 836	76	9.22 438	78	10.77 562	9.99 398	29
32	9.21 912	75	9.22 516	77	10.77 484	9.99 396	28
33	9.21 987	75	9.22 593	77	10.77 407	9.99 394	27
34	9.22 062	75	9.22 670	77	10.77 330	9.99 392	26
35	9.22 137	74	9.22 747	77	10.77 253	9.99 390	25
36	9.22 211	75	9.22 824	77	10.77 176	9.99 388	24
37	9.22 286	75	9.22 901	76	10.77 099	9.99 385	23
38	9.22 361	74	9.22 977	77	10.77 023	9.99 383	22
39	9.22 435	74	9.23 054	76	10.76 946	9.99 381	21
40	9.22 509	74	9.23 130	76	10.76 870	9.99 379	20
41	9.22 583	74	9.23 206	77	10.76 794	9.99 377	19
42	9.22 657	74	9.23 283	76	10.76 717	9.99 375	18
43	9.22 731	74	9.23 359	76	10.76 641	9.99 372	17
44	9.22 805	73	9.23 435	75	10.76 565	9.99 370	16
45	9.22 878	74	9.23 510	76	10.76 490	9.99 368	15
46	9.22 952	73	9.23 586	75	10.76 414	9.99 366	14
47	9.23 025	73	9.23 661	76	10.76 339	9.99 364	13
48	9.23 098	73	9.23 737	75	10.76 263	9.99 362	12
49	9.23 171	73	9.23 812	75	10.76 188	9.99 359	11
50	9.23 244	73	9.23 887	75	10.76 113	9.99 357	10
51	9.23 317	73	9.23 962	75	10.76 038	9.99 355	9
52	9.23 390	72	9.24 037	75	10.75 963	9.99 353	8
53	9.23 462	73	9.24 112	74	10.75 888	9.99 351	7
54	9.23 535	72	9.24 186	75	10.75 814	9.99 348	6
55	9.23 607	72	9.24 261	74	10.75 739	9.99 346	5
56	9.23 679	73	9.24 335	75	10.75 665	9.99 344	4
57	9.23 752	71	9.24 410	74	10.75 590	9.99 342	3
58	9.23 823	72	9.24 484	74	10.75 516	9.99 340	2
59	9.23 895	72	9.24 558	74	10.75 442	9.99 337	1
60	9.23 967		9.24 632		10.75 368	9.99 335	0
′	L Cos	d	L Ctn	c d	L Tan	L Sin	′

Proportional parts

″	80	79	78	77
1	1.3	1.3	1.3	1.3
2	2.7	2.6	2.6	2.6
3	4.0	4.0	3.9	3.8
4	5.3	5.3	5.2	5.1
5	6.7	6.6	6.5	6.4
6	8.0	7.9	7.8	7.7
7	9.3	9.2	9.1	9.0
8	10.7	10.5	10.4	10.3
9	12.0	11.8	11.7	11.6
10	13.3	13.2	13.0	12.8
20	26.7	26.3	26.0	25.7
30	40.0	39.5	39.0	38.5
40	53.3	52.7	52.0	51.3
50	66.7	65.8	65.0	64.2

″	76	75	74	73
1	1.3	1.2	1.2	1.2
2	2.5	2.5	2.5	2.4
3	3.8	3.8	3.7	3.6
4	5.1	5.0	4.9	4.9
5	6.3	6.2	6.2	6.1
6	7.6	7.5	7.4	7.3
7	8.9	8.8	8.6	8.5
8	10.1	10.0	9.9	9.7
9	11.4	11.2	11.1	11.0
10	12.7	12.5	12.3	12.2
20	25.3	25.0	24.7	24.3
30	38.0	37.5	37.0	36.5
40	50.7	50.0	49.3	48.7
50	63.3	62.5	61.7	60.8

″	72	71	3	2
1	1.2	1.2	0.0	0.0
2	2.4	2.4	0.1	0.1
3	3.6	3.6	0.2	0.1
4	4.8	4.7	0.2	0.1
5	6.0	5.9	0.2	0.2
6	7.2	7.1	0.3	0.2
7	8.4	8.3	0.4	0.2
8	9.6	9.5	0.4	0.3
9	10.8	10.6	0.4	0.3
10	12.0	11.8	0.5	0.3
20	24.0	23.7	1.0	0.7
30	36.0	35.5	1.5	1.0
40	48.0	47.3	2.0	1.3
50	60.0	59.2	2.5	1.7

Proportional parts

99° (279°) (260°) **80°**

The −10 portion of the characteristic of the logarithm is not printed but must be written down whenever such a logarithm is used.

10° (190°) (349°) **169°**

′	L Sin	d	L Tan	c d	L Ctn	L Cos	d	′
0	9.23 967	72	9.24 632	74	10.75 368	9.99 335	2	60
1	9.24 039	71	9.24 706	73	10.75 294	9.99 333	2	59
2	9.24 110	71	9.24 779	74	10.75 221	9.99 331	3	58
3	9.24 181	72	9.24 853	73	10.75 147	9.99 328	2	57
4	9.24 253	71	9.24 926	74	10.75 074	9.99 326	2	56
5	9.24 324	71	9.25 000	73	10.75 000	9.99 324	2	55
6	9.24 395	71	9.25 073	73	10.74 927	9.99 322	3	54
7	9.24 466	70	9.25 146	73	10.74 854	9.99 319	2	53
8	9.24 536	71	9.25 219	73	10.74 781	9.99 317	2	52
9	9.24 607	70	9.25 292	73	10.74 708	9.99 315	2	51
10	9.24 677	71	9.25 365	72	10.74 635	9.99 313	3	50
11	9.24 748	70	9.25 437	73	10.74 563	9.99 310	2	49
12	9.24 818	70	9.25 510	72	10.74 490	9.99 308	2	48
13	9.24 888	70	9.25 582	73	10.74 418	9.99 306	2	47
14	9.24 958	70	9.25 655	72	10.74 345	9.99 304	3	46
15	9.25 028	70	9.25 727	72	10.74 273	9.99 301	2	45
16	9.25 098	70	9.25 799	72	10.74 201	9.99 299	2	44
17	9.25 168	69	9.25 871	72	10.74 129	9.99 297	3	43
18	9.25 237	70	9.25 943	72	10.74 057	9.99 294	2	42
19	9.25 307	69	9.26 015	71	10.73 985	9.99 292	2	41
20	9.25 376	69	9.26 086	72	10.73 914	9.99 290	2	40
21	9.25 445	69	9.26 158	71	10.73 842	9.99 288	3	39
22	9.25 514	69	9.26 229	72	10.73 771	9.99 285	2	38
23	9.25 583	69	9.26 301	71	10.73 699	9.99 283	2	37
24	9.25 652	69	9.26 372	71	10.73 628	9.99 281	3	36
25	9.25 721	69	9.26 443	71	10.73 557	9.99 278	2	35
26	9.25 790	68	9.26 514	71	10.73 486	9.99 276	2	34
27	9.25 858	69	9.26 585	70	10.73 415	9.99 274	3	33
28	9.25 927	68	9.26 655	71	10.73 345	9.99 271	2	32
29	9.25 995	68	9.26 726	71	10.73 274	9.99 269	2	31
30	9.26 063	68	9.26 797	70	10.73 203	9.99 267	3	30
31	9.26 131	68	9.26 867	70	10.73 133	9.99 264	2	29
32	9.26 199	68	9.26 937	71	10.73 063	9.99 262	2	28
33	9.26 267	68	9.27 008	70	10.72 992	9.99 260	3	27
34	9.26 335	68	9.27 078	70	10.72 922	9.99 257	2	26
35	9.26 403	67	9.27 148	70	10.72 852	9.99 255	3	25
36	9.26 470	68	9.27 218	70	10.72 782	9.99 252	2	24
37	9.26 538	67	9.27 288	69	10.72 712	9.99 250	2	23
38	9.26 605	67	9.27 357	70	10.72 643	9.99 248	3	22
39	9.26 672	67	9.27 427	69	10.72 573	9.99 245	2	21
40	9.26 739	67	9.27 496	70	10.72 504	9.99 243	2	20
41	9.26 806	67	9.27 566	69	10.72 434	9.99 241	3	19
42	9.26 873	67	9.27 635	69	10.72 365	9.99 238	2	18
43	9.26 940	67	9.27 704	69	10.72 296	9.99 236	3	17
44	9.27 007	66	9.27 773	69	10.72 227	9.99 233	2	16
45	9.27 073	67	9.27 842	69	10.72 158	9.99 231	2	15
46	9.27 140	66	9.27 911	69	10.72 089	9.99 229	3	14
47	9.27 206	67	9.27 980	69	10.72 020	9.99 226	2	13
48	9.27 273	66	9.28 049	68	10.71 951	9.99 224	3	12
49	9.27 339	66	9.28 117	69	10.71 883	9.99 221	2	11
50	9.27 405	66	9.28 186	68	10.71 814	9.99 219	2	10
51	9.27 471	66	9.28 254	69	10.71 746	9.99 217	3	9
52	9.27 537	65	9.28 323	68	10.71 677	9.99 214	2	8
53	9.27 602	66	9.28 391	68	10.71 609	9.99 212	3	7
54	9.27 668	66	9.28 459	68	10.71 541	9.99 209	2	6
55	9.27 734	65	9.28 527	68	10.71 473	9.99 207	3	5
56	9.27 799	65	9.28 595	67	10.71 405	9.99 204	2	4
57	9.27 864	66	9.28 662	68	10.71 338	9.99 202	2	3
58	9.27 930	65	9.28 730	68	10.71 270	9.99 200	3	2
59	9.27 995	65	9.28 798	67	10.71 202	9.99 197	2	1
60	9.28 060		9.28 865		10.71 135	9.99 195		0
′	L Cos	d	L Ctn	c d	L Tan	L Sin	d	′

Proportional parts

″	74	73	72
1	1.2	1.2	1.2
2	2.5	2.4	2.4
3	3.7	3.6	3.6
4	4.9	4.9	4.8
5	6.2	6.1	6.0
6	7.4	7.3	7.2
7	8.6	8.5	8.4
8	9.9	9.7	9.6
9	11.1	11.0	10.8
10	12.3	12.2	12.0
20	24.7	24.3	24.0
30	37.0	36.5	36.0
40	49.3	48.7	48.0
50	61.7	60.8	60.0

″	71	70	69
1	1.2	1.2	1.2
2	2.4	2.3	2.3
3	3.6	3.5	3.4
4	4.7	4.7	4.6
5	5.9	5.8	5.8
6	7.1	7.0	6.9
7	8.3	8.2	8.0
8	9.5	9.3	9.2
9	10.6	10.5	10.4
10	11.8	11.7	11.5
20	23.7	23.3	23.0
30	35.5	35.0	34.5
40	47.3	46.7	46.0
50	59.2	58.3	57.5

″	68	67	66
1	1.1	1.1	1.1
2	2.3	2.2	2.2
3	3.4	3.4	3.3
4	4.5	4.5	4.4
5	5.7	5.6	5.5
6	6.8	6.7	6.6
7	7.9	7.8	7.7
8	9.1	8.9	8.8
9	10.2	10.0	9.9
10	11.3	11.2	11.0
20	22.7	22.3	22.0
30	34.0	33.5	33.0
40	45.3	44.7	44.0
50	56.7	55.8	55.0

Proportional parts

100° (280°) (259°) **79°**

The −10 portion of the characteristic of the logarithm is not printed but must be written down whenever such a logarithm is used.

11° (191°) (348°) **168°**

′	L Sin	d	L Tan	c d	L Ctn	L Cos	d	′
0	9.28 060	65	9.28 865	68	10.71 135	9.99 195	3	60
1	9.28 125	65	9.28 933	67	10.71 067	9.99 192	2	59
2	9.28 190	64	9.29 000	67	10.71 000	9.99 190	3	58
3	9.28 254	65	9.29 067	67	10.70 933	9.99 187	2	57
4	9.28 319	65	9.29 134	67	10.70 866	9.99 185	3	56
5	9.28 384	64	9.29 201	67	10.70 799	9.99 182	2	55
6	9.28 448	64	9.29 268	67	10.70 732	9.99 180	3	54
7	9.28 512	65	9.29 335	67	10.70 665	9.99 177	2	53
8	9.28 577	64	9.29 402	66	10.70 598	9.99 175	3	52
9	9.28 641	64	9.29 468	67	10.70 532	9.99 172	2	51
10	9.28 705	64	9.29 535	66	10.70 465	9.99 170	3	50
11	9.28 769	64	9.29 601	67	10.70 399	9.99 167	2	49
12	9.28 833	63	9.29 668	66	10.70 332	9.99 165	3	48
13	9.28 896	64	9.29 734	66	10.70 266	9.99 162	2	47
14	9.28 960	64	9.29 800	66	10.70 200	9.99 160	3	46
15	9.29 024	63	9.29 866	66	10.70 134	9.99 157	2	45
16	9.29 087	63	9.29 932	66	10.70 068	9.99 155	3	44
17	9.29 150	64	9.29 998	66	10.70 002	9.99 152	2	43
18	9.29 214	63	9.30 064	66	10.69 936	9.99 150	3	42
19	9.29 277	63	9.30 130	65	10.69 870	9.99 147	2	41
20	9.29 340	63	9.30 195	66	10.69 805	9.99 145	3	40
21	9.29 403	63	9.30 261	65	10.69 739	9.99 142	2	39
22	9.29 466	63	9.30 326	65	10.69 674	9.99 140	3	38
23	9.29 529	62	9.30 391	66	10.69 609	9.99 137	2	37
24	9.29 591	63	9.30 457	65	10.69 543	9.99 135	3	36
25	9.29 654	62	9.30 522	65	10.69 478	9.99 132	2	35
26	9.29 716	63	9.30 587	65	10.69 413	9.99 130	3	34
27	9.29 779	62	9.30 652	65	10.69 348	9.99 127	3	33
28	9.29 841	62	9.30 717	65	10.69 283	9.99 124	2	32
29	9.29 903	63	9.30 782	64	10.69 218	9.99 122	3	31
30	9.29 966	62	9.30 846	65	10.69 154	9.99 119	2	30
31	9.30 028	62	9.30 911	64	10.69 089	9.99 117	3	29
32	9.30 090	61	9.30 975	65	10.69 025	9.99 114	2	28
33	9.30 151	62	9.31 040	64	10.68 960	9.99 112	3	27
34	9.30 213	62	9.31 104	64	10.68 896	9.99 109	3	26
35	9.30 275	61	9.31 168	65	10.68 832	9.99 106	2	25
36	9.30 336	62	9.31 233	64	10.68 767	9.99 104	3	24
37	9.30 398	61	9.31 297	64	10.68 703	9.99 101	2	23
38	9.30 459	62	9.31 361	64	10.68 639	9.99 099	3	22
39	9.30 521	61	9.31 425	64	10.68 575	9.99 096	3	21
40	9.30 582	61	9.31 489	63	10.68 511	9.99 093	2	20
41	9.30 643	61	9.31 552	64	10.68 448	9.99 091	3	19
42	9.30 704	61	9.31 616	63	10.68 384	9.99 088	2	18
43	9.30 765	61	9.31 679	64	10.68 321	9.99 086	3	17
44	9.30 826	61	9.31 743	63	10.68 257	9.99 083	3	16
45	9.30 887	60	9.31 806	64	10.68 194	9.99 080	2	15
46	9.30 947	61	9.31 870	63	10.68 130	9.99 078	3	14
47	9.31 008	60	9.31 933	63	10.68 067	9.99 075	3	13
48	9.31 068	61	9.31 996	63	10.68 004	9.99 072	2	12
49	9.31 129	60	9.32 059	63	10.67 941	9.99 070	3	11
50	9.31 189	61	9.32 122	63	10.67 878	9.99 067	3	10
51	9.31 250	60	9.32 185	63	10.67 815	9.99 064	2	9
52	9.31 310	60	9.32 248	63	10.67 752	9.99 062	3	8
53	9.31 370	60	9.32 311	62	10.67 689	9.99 059	3	7
54	9.31 430	60	9.32 373	63	10.67 627	9.99 056	2	6
55	9.31 490	59	9.32 436	62	10.67 564	9.99 054	3	5
56	9.31 549	60	9.32 498	63	10.67 502	9.99 051	3	4
57	9.31 609	60	9.32 561	62	10.67 439	9.99 048	2	3
58	9.31 669	59	9.32 623	62	10.67 377	9.99 046	3	2
59	9.31 728	60	9.32 685	62	10.67 315	9.99 043	3	1
60	9.31 788		9.32 747		10.67 253	9.99 040		0
′	L Cos	d	L Ctn	c d	L Tan	L Sin	d	′

Proportional parts

″	65	64	63
1	1.1	1.1	1.0
2	2.2	2.1	2.1
3	3.2	3.2	3.2
4	4.3	4.3	4.2
5	5.4	5.3	5.2
6	6.5	6.4	6.3
7	7.6	7.5	7.4
8	8.7	8.5	8.4
9	9.8	9.6	9.4
10	10.8	10.7	10.5
20	21.7	21.3	21.0
30	32.5	32.0	31.5
40	43.3	42.7	42.0
50	54.2	53.3	52.5

″	62	61	60
1	1.0	1.0	1.0
2	2.1	2.0	2.0
3	3.1	3.0	3.0
4	4.1	4.1	4.0
5	5.2	5.1	5.0
6	6.2	6.1	6.0
7	7.2	7.1	7.0
8	8.3	8.1	8.0
9	9.3	9.2	9.0
10	10.3	10.2	10.0
20	20.7	20.3	20.0
30	31.0	30.5	30.0
40	41.3	40.7	40.0
50	51.7	50.8	50.0

″	59	3	2
1	1.0	0.0	0.0
2	2.0	0.1	0.1
3	3.0	0.2	0.1
4	3.9	0.2	0.1
5	4.9	0.2	0.2
6	5.9	0.3	0.2
7	6.9	0.4	0.2
8	7.9	0.4	0.3
9	8.8	0.4	0.3
10	9.8	0.5	0.3
20	19.7	1.0	0.7
30	29.5	1.5	1.0
40	39.3	2.0	1.3
50	49.2	2.5	1.7

Proportional parts

101° (281°) (258°) **78°**

The −10 portion of the characteristic of the logarithm is not printed but must be written down whenever such a logarithm is used.

12° (192°) (347°) **167°**

′	L Sin	d	L Tan	c d	L Ctn	L Cos	d	′
0	9.31 788	59	9.32 747	63	10.67 253	9.99 040	2	60
1	9.31 847	60	9.32 810	62	10.67 190	9.99 038	3	59
2	9.31 907	59	9.32 872	61	10.67 128	9.99 035	3	58
3	9.31 966	59	9.32 933	62	10.67 067	9.99 032	2	57
4	9.32 025	59	9.32 995	62	10.67 005	9.99 030	3	56
5	9.32 084	59	9.33 057	62	10.66 943	9.99 027	3	55
6	9.32 143	59	9.33 119	61	10.66 881	9.99 024	2	54
7	9.32 202	59	9.33 180	62	10.66 820	9.99 022	3	53
8	9.32 261	58	9.33 242	61	10.66 758	9.99 019	3	52
9	9.32 319	59	9.33 303	62	10.66 697	9.99 016	3	51
10	9.32 378	59	9.33 365	61	10.66 635	9.99 013	2	50
11	9.32 437	58	9.33 426	61	10.66 574	9.99 011	3	49
12	9.32 495	58	9.33 487	61	10.66 513	9.99 008	3	48
13	9.32 553	59	9.33 548	61	10.66 452	9.99 005	3	47
14	9.32 612	58	9.33 609	61	10.66 391	9.99 002	2	46
15	9.32 670	58	9.33 670	61	10.66 330	9.99 000	3	45
16	9.32 728	58	9.33 731	61	10.66 269	9.98 997	3	44
17	9.32 786	58	9.33 792	61	10.66 208	9.98 994	3	43
18	9.32 844	58	9.33 853	60	10.66 147	9.98 991	2	42
19	9.32 902	58	9.33 913	61	10.66 087	9.98 989	3	41
20	9.32 960	58	9.33 974	60	10.66 026	9.98 986	3	40
21	9.33 018	57	9.34 034	61	10.65 966	9.98 983	3	39
22	9.33 075	58	9.34 095	60	10.65 905	9.98 980	2	38
23	9.33 133	57	9.34 155	60	10.65 845	9.98 978	3	37
24	9.33 190	58	9.34 215	61	10.65 785	9.98 975	3	36
25	9.33 248	57	9.34 276	60	10.65 724	9.98 972	3	35
26	9.33 305	57	9.34 336	60	10.65 664	9.98 969	2	34
27	9.33 362	58	9.34 396	60	10.65 604	9.98 967	3	33
28	9.33 420	57	9.34 456	60	10.65 544	9.98 964	3	32
29	9.33 477	57	9.34 516	60	10.65 484	9.98 961	3	31
30	9.33 534	57	9.34 576	59	10.65 424	9.98 958	3	30
31	9.33 591	56	9.34 635	60	10.65 365	9.98 955	2	29
32	9.33 647	57	9.34 695	60	10.65 305	9.98 953	3	28
33	9.33 704	57	9.34 755	59	10.65 245	9.98 950	3	27
34	9.33 761	57	9.34 814	60	10.65 186	9.98 947	3	26
35	9.33 818	56	9.34 874	59	10.65 126	9.98 944	3	25
36	9.33 874	57	9.34 933	59	10.65 067	9.98 941	3	24
37	9.33 931	56	9.34 992	59	10.65 008	9.98 938	2	23
38	9.33 987	56	9.35 051	60	10.64 949	9.98 936	3	22
39	9.34 043	57	9.35 111	59	10.64 889	9.98 933	3	21
40	9.34 100	56	9.35 170	59	10.64 830	9.98 930	3	20
41	9.34 156	56	9.35 229	59	10.64 771	9.98 927	3	19
42	9.34 212	56	9.35 288	59	10.64 712	9.98 924	3	18
43	9.34 268	56	9.35 347	58	10.64 653	9.98 921	2	17
44	9.34 324	56	9.35 405	59	10.64 595	9.98 919	3	16
45	9.34 380	56	9.35 464	59	10.64 536	9.98 916	3	15
46	9.34 436	55	9.35 523	58	10.64 477	9.98 913	3	14
47	9.34 491	56	9.35 581	59	10.64 419	9.98 910	3	13
48	9.34 547	55	9.35 640	58	10.64 360	9.98 907	3	12
49	9.34 602	56	9.35 698	59	10.64 302	9.98 904	3	11
50	9.34 658	55	9.35 757	58	10.64 243	9.98 901	3	10
51	9.34 713	56	9.35 815	58	10.64 185	9.98 898	2	9
52	9.34 769	55	9.35 873	58	10.64 127	9.98 896	3	8
53	9.34 824	55	9.35 931	58	10.64 069	9.98 893	3	7
54	9.34 879	55	9.35 989	58	10.64 011	9.98 890	3	6
55	9.34 934	55	9.36 047	58	10.63 953	9.98 887	3	5
56	9.34 989	55	9.36 105	58	10.63 895	9.98 884	3	4
57	9.35 044	55	9.36 163	58	10.63 837	9.98 881	3	3
58	9.35 099	55	9.36 221	58	10.63 779	9.98 878	3	2
59	9.35 154	55	9.36 279	57	10.63 721	9.98 875	3	1
60	9.35 209		9.36 336		10.63 664	9.98 872		0
′	L Cos	d	L Ctn	c d	L Tan	L Sin	d	′

Proportional parts

″	63	62	61
1	1.0	1.0	1.0
2	2.1	2.1	2.0
3	3.2	3.1	3.0
4	4.2	4.1	4.1
5	5.2	5.2	5.1
6	6.3	6.2	6.1
7	7.4	7.2	7.1
8	8.4	8.3	8.1
9	9.4	9.3	9.2
10	10.5	10.3	10.2
20	21.0	20.7	20.3
30	31.5	31.0	30.5
40	42.0	41.3	40.7
50	52.5	51.7	50.8

″	60	59	58
1	1.0	1.0	1.0
2	2.0	2.0	1.9
3	3.0	3.0	2.9
4	4.0	3.9	3.9
5	5.0	4.9	4.8
6	6.0	5.9	5.8
7	7.0	6.9	6.8
8	8.0	7.9	7.7
9	9.0	8.8	8.7
10	10.0	9.8	9.7
20	20.0	19.7	19.3
30	30.0	29.5	29.0
40	40.0	39.3	38.7
50	50.0	49.2	48.3

″	57	56	55
1	1.0	0.9	0.9
2	1.9	1.9	1.8
3	2.8	2.8	2.8
4	3.8	3.7	3.7
5	4.8	4.7	4.6
6	5.7	5.6	5.5
7	6.6	6.5	6.4
8	7.6	7.5	7.3
9	8.6	8.4	8.2
10	9.5	9.3	9.2
20	19.0	18.7	18.3
30	28.5	28.0	27.5
40	38.0	37.3	36.7
50	47.5	46.7	45.8

Proportional parts

102° (282°) (257°) **77°**

The −10 portion of the characteristic of the logarithm is not printed but must be written down whenever such a logarithm is used.

13° (193°) (346°) **166°**

′	L Sin	d	L Tan	c d	L Ctn	L Cos	d	′
0	9.35 209	54	9.36 336	58	10.63 664	9.98 872	3	60
1	9.35 263	55	9.36 394	58	10.63 606	9.98 869	2	59
2	9.35 318	55	9.36 452	57	10.63 548	9.98 867	3	58
3	9.35 373	54	9.36 509	57	10.63 491	9.98 864	3	57
4	9.35 427	54	9.36 566	58	10.63 434	9.98 861	3	56
5	9.35 481	55	9.36 624	57	10.63 376	9.98 858	3	55
6	9.35 536	54	9.36 681	57	10.63 319	9.98 855	3	54
7	9.35 590	54	9.36 738	57	10.63 262	9.98 852	3	53
8	9.35 644	54	9.36 795	57	10.63 205	9.98 849	3	52
9	9.35 698	54	9.36 852	57	10.63 148	9.98 846	3	51
10	9.35 752	54	9.36 909	57	10.63 091	9.98 843	3	50
11	9.35 806	54	9.36 966	57	10.63 034	9.98 840	3	49
12	9.35 860	54	9.37 023	57	10.62 977	9.98 837	3	48
13	9.35 914	54	9.37 080	57	10.62 920	9.98 834	3	47
14	9.35 968	54	9.37 137	56	10.62 863	9.98 831	3	46
15	9.36 022	53	9.37 193	57	10.62 807	9.98 828	3	45
16	9.36 075	54	9.37 250	56	10.62 750	9.98 825	3	44
17	9.36 129	53	9.37 306	57	10.62 694	9.98 822	3	43
18	9.36 182	54	9.37 363	56	10.62 637	9.98 819	3	42
19	9.36 236	53	9.37 419	57	10.62 581	9.98 816	3	41
20	9.36 289	53	9.37 476	56	10.62 524	9.98 813	3	40
21	9.36 342	53	9.37 532	56	10.62 468	9.98 810	3	39
22	9.36 395	54	9.37 588	56	10.62 412	9.98 807	3	38
23	9.36 449	53	9.37 644	56	10.62 356	9.98 804	3	37
24	9.36 502	53	9.37 700	56	10.62 300	9.98 801	3	36
25	9.36 555	53	9.37 756	56	10.62 244	9.98 798	3	35
26	9.36 608	52	9.37 812	56	10.62 188	9.98 795	3	34
27	9.36 660	53	9.37 868	56	10.62 132	9.98 792	3	33
28	9.36 713	53	9.37 924	56	10.62 076	9.98 789	3	32
29	9.36 766	53	9.37 980	55	10.62 020	9.98 786	3	31
30	9.36 819	52	9.38 035	56	10.61 965	9.98 783	3	30
31	9.36 871	53	9.38 091	56	10.61 909	9.98 780	3	29
32	9.36 924	52	9.38 147	55	10.61 853	9.98 777	3	28
33	9.36 976	52	9.38 202	55	10.61 798	9.98 774	3	27
34	9.37 028	53	9.38 257	56	10.61 743	9.98 771	3	26
35	9.37 081	52	9.38 313	55	10.61 687	9.98 768	3	25
36	9.37 133	52	9.38 368	55	10.61 632	9.98 765	3	24
37	9.37 185	52	9.38 423	56	10.61 577	9.98 762	3	23
38	9.37 237	52	9.38 479	55	10.61 521	9.98 759	3	22
39	9.37 289	52	9.38 534	55	10.61 466	9.98 756	3	21
40	9.37 341	52	9.38 589	55	10.61 411	9.98 753	3	20
41	9.37 393	52	9.38 644	55	10.61 356	9.98 750	4	19
42	9.37 445	52	9.38 699	55	10.61 301	9.98 746	3	18
43	9.37 497	52	9.38 754	54	10.61 246	9.98 743	3	17
44	9.37 549	51	9.38 808	55	10.61 192	9.98 740	3	16
45	9.37 600	52	9.38 863	55	10.61 137	9.98 737	3	15
46	9.37 652	51	9.38 918	54	10.61 082	9.98 734	3	14
47	9.37 703	52	9.38 972	55	10.61 028	9.98 731	3	13
48	9.37 755	51	9.39 027	55	10.60 973	9.98 728	3	12
49	9.37 806	52	9.39 082	54	10.60 918	9.98 725	3	11
50	9.37 858	51	9.39 136	54	10.60 864	9.98 722	3	10
51	9.37 909	51	9.39 190	55	10.60 810	9.98 719	4	9
52	9.37 960	51	9.39 245	54	10.60 755	9.98 715	3	8
53	9.38 011	51	9.39 299	54	10.60 701	9.98 712	3	7
54	9.38 062	51	9.39 353	54	10.60 647	9.98 709	3	6
55	9.38 113	51	9.39 407	54	10.60 593	9.98 706	3	5
56	9.38 164	51	9.39 461	54	10.60 539	9.98 703	3	4
57	9.38 215	51	9.39 515	54	10.60 485	9.98 700	3	3
58	9.38 266	51	9.39 569	54	10.60 431	9.98 697	3	2
59	9.38 317	51	9.39 623	54	10.60 377	9.98 694	4	1
60	9.38 368		9.39 677		10.60 323	9.98 690		0
′	L Cos	d	L Ctn	c d	L Tan	L Sin	d	′

Proportional parts

″	57	56	55
1	1.0	0.9	0.9
2	1.9	1.9	1.8
3	2.8	2.8	2.8
4	3.8	3.7	3.7
5	4.8	4.7	4.6
6	5.7	5.6	5.5
7	6.6	6.5	6.4
8	7.6	7.5	7.3
9	8.6	8.4	8.2
10	9.5	9.3	9.2
20	19.0	18.7	18.3
30	28.5	28.0	27.5
40	38.0	37.3	36.7
50	47.5	46.7	45.8

″	54	53	52
1	0.9	0.9	0.9
2	1.8	1.8	1.7
3	2.7	2.6	2.6
4	3.6	3.5	3.5
5	4.5	4.4	4.3
6	5.4	5.3	5.2
7	6.3	6.2	6.1
8	7.2	7.1	6.9
9	8.1	8.0	7.8
10	9.0	8.8	8.7
20	18.0	17.7	17.3
30	27.0	26.5	26.0
40	36.0	35.3	34.7
50	45.0	44.2	43.3

″	51	4	3	2
1	0.8	0.1	0.0	0.0
2	1.7	0.1	0.1	0.1
3	2.6	0.2	0.2	0.1
4	3.4	0.3	0.2	0.1
5	4.2	0.3	0.2	0.2
6	5.1	0.4	0.3	0.2
7	6.0	0.5	0.4	0.2
8	6.8	0.5	0.4	0.3
9	7.6	0.6	0.4	0.3
10	8.5	0.7	0.5	0.3
20	17.0	1.3	1.0	0.7
30	25.5	2.0	1.5	1.0
40	34.0	2.7	2.0	1.3
50	42.5	3.3	2.5	1.7

Proportional parts

103° (283°) (256°) **76°**

The −10 portion of the characteristic of the logarithm is not printed but must be written down whenever such a logarithm is used.

14° (194°) (345°) **165°**

′	L Sin	d	L Tan	c d	L Ctn	L Cos	d	′
0	9.38 368	50	9.39 677	54	10.60 323	9.98 690	3	60
1	9.38 418	51	9.39 731	54	10.60 269	9.98 687	3	59
2	9.38 469	50	9.39 785	53	10.60 215	9.98 684	3	58
3	9.38 519	51	9.39 838	54	10.60 162	9.98 681	3	57
4	9.38 570	50	9.39 892	53	10.60 108	9.98 678	3	56
5	9.38 620	50	9.39 945	54	10.60 055	9.98 675	4	55
6	9.38 670	51	9.39 999	53	10.60 001	9.98 671	3	54
7	9.38 721	50	9.40 052	54	10.59 948	9.98 668	3	53
8	9.38 771	50	9.40 106	53	10.59 894	9.98 665	3	52
9	9.38 821	50	9.40 159	53	10.59 841	9.98 662	3	51
10	9.38 871	50	9.40 212	54	10.59 788	9.98 659	3	50
11	9.38 921	50	9.40 266	53	10.59 734	9.98 656	4	49
12	9.38 971	50	9.40 319	53	10.59 681	9.98 652	3	48
13	9.39 021	50	9.40 372	53	10.59 628	9.98 649	3	47
14	9.39 071	50	9.40 425	53	10.59 575	9.98 646	3	46
15	9.39 121	49	9.40 478	53	10.59 522	9.98 643	3	45
16	9.39 170	50	9.40 531	53	10.59 469	9.98 640	4	44
17	9.39 220	50	9.40 584	52	10.59 416	9.98 636	3	43
18	9.39 270	49	9.40 636	53	10.59 364	9.98 633	3	42
19	9.39 319	50	9.40 689	53	10.59 311	9.98 630	3	41
20	9.39 369	49	9.40 742	53	10.59 258	9.98 627	4	40
21	9.39 418	49	9.40 795	52	10.59 205	9.98 623	3	39
22	9.39 467	50	9.40 847	53	10.59 153	9.98 620	3	38
23	9.39 517	49	9.40 900	52	10.59 100	9.98 617	3	37
24	9.39 566	49	9.40 952	53	10.59 048	9.98 614	4	36
25	9.39 615	49	9.41 005	52	10.58 995	9.98 610	3	35
26	9.39 664	49	9.41 057	52	10.58 943	9.98 607	3	34
27	9.39 713	49	9.41 109	52	10.58 891	9.98 604	3	33
28	9.39 762	49	9.41 161	53	10.58 839	9.98 601	4	32
29	9.39 811	49	9.41 214	52	10.58 786	9.98 597	3	31
30	9.39 860	49	9.41 266	52	10.58 734	9.98 594	3	30
31	9.39 909	49	9.41 318	52	10.58 682	9.98 591	3	29
32	9.39 958	48	9.41 370	52	10.58 630	9.98 588	4	28
33	9.40 006	49	9.41 422	52	10.58 578	9.98 584	3	27
34	9.40 055	48	9.41 474	52	10.58 526	9.98 581	3	26
35	9.40 103	49	9.41 526	52	10.58 474	9.98 578	4	25
36	9.40 152	48	9.41 578	51	10.58 422	9.98 574	3	24
37	9.40 200	49	9.41 629	52	10.58 371	9.98 571	3	23
38	9.40 249	48	9.41 681	52	10.58 319	9.98 568	3	22
39	9.40 297	49	9.41 733	51	10.58 267	9.98 565	4	21
40	9.40 346	48	9.41 784	52	10.58 216	9.98 561	3	20
41	9.40 394	48	9.41 836	51	10.58 164	9.98 558	3	19
42	9.40 442	48	9.41 887	52	10.58 113	9.98 555	4	18
43	9.40 490	48	9.41 939	51	10.58 061	9.98 551	3	17
44	9.40 538	48	9.41 990	51	10.58 010	9.98 548	3	16
45	9.40 586	48	9.42 041	52	10.57 959	9.98 545	4	15
46	9.40 634	48	9.42 093	51	10.57 907	9.98 541	3	14
47	9.40 682	48	9.42 144	51	10.57 856	9.98 538	3	13
48	9.40 730	48	9.42 195	51	10.57 805	9.98 535	4	12
49	9.40 778	47	9.42 246	51	10.57 754	9.98 531	3	11
50	9.40 825	48	9.42 297	51	10.57 703	9.98 528	3	10
51	9.40 873	48	9.42 348	51	10.57 652	9.98 525	4	9
52	9.40 921	47	9.42 399	51	10.57 601	9.98 521	3	8
53	9.40 968	48	9.42 450	51	10.57 550	9.98 518	3	7
54	9.41 016	47	9.42 501	51	10.57 499	9.98 515	4	6
55	9.41 063	48	9.42 552	51	10.57 448	9.98 511	3	5
56	9.41 111	47	9.42 603	50	10.57 397	9.98 508	3	4
57	9.41 158	47	9.42 653	51	10.57 347	9.98 505	4	3
58	9.41 205	47	9.42 704	51	10.57 296	9.98 501	3	2
59	9.41 252	48	9.42 755	50	10.57 245	9.98 498	4	1
60	9.41 300		9.42 805		10.57 195	9.98 494		0
′	L Cos	d	L Ctn	c d	L Tan	L Sin	d	′

104° (284°) (255°) **75°**

Proportional parts

″	54	53	52
1	0.9	0.9	0.9
2	1.8	1.8	1.7
3	2.7	2.6	2.6
4	3.6	3.5	3.5
5	4.5	4.4	4.3
6	5.4	5.3	5.2
7	6.3	6.2	6.1
8	7.2	7.1	6.9
9	8.1	8.0	7.8
10	9.0	8.8	8.7
20	18.0	17.7	17.3
30	27.0	26.5	26.0
40	36.0	35.3	34.7
50	45.0	44.2	43.3

″	51	50	49
1	0.8	0.8	0.8
2	1.7	1.7	1.6
3	2.6	2.5	2.4
4	3.4	3.3	3.3
5	4.2	4.2	4.1
6	5.1	5.0	4.9
7	6.0	5.8	5.7
8	6.8	6.7	6.5
9	7.6	7.5	7.4
10	8.5	8.3	8.2
20	17.0	16.7	16.3
30	25.5	25.0	24.5
40	34.0	33.3	32.7
50	42.5	41.7	40.8

″	48	47	4	3
1	0.8	0.8	0.1	0.0
2	1.6	1.6	0.1	0.1
3	2.4	2.4	0.2	0.2
4	3.2	3.1	0.3	0.2
5	4.0	3.9	0.3	0.2
6	4.8	4.7	0.4	0.3
7	5.6	5.5	0.5	0.4
8	6.4	6.3	0.5	0.4
9	7.2	7.0	0.6	0.4
10	8.0	7.8	0.7	0.5
20	16.0	15.7	1.3	1.0
30	24.0	23.5	2.0	1.5
40	32.0	31.3	2.7	2.0
50	40.0	39.2	3.3	2.5

Proportional parts

The −10 portion of the characteristic of the logarithm is not printed but must be written down whenever such a logarithm is used.

15° (195°) (344°) **164°**

′	L Sin	d	L Tan	c d	L Ctn	L Cos	d	′
0	9.41 300	47	9.42 805	51	10.57 195	9.98 494	3	60
1	9.41 347	47	9.42 856	50	10.57 144	9.98 491	3	59
2	9.41 394	47	9.42 906	51	10.57 094	9.98 488	4	58
3	9.41 441	47	9.42 957	50	10.57 043	9.98 484	3	57
4	9.41 488	47	9.43 007	50	10.56 993	9.98 481	4	56
5	9.41 535	47	9.43 057	51	10.56 943	9.98 477	3	55
6	9.41 582	46	9.43 108	50	10.56 892	9.98 474	3	54
7	9.41 628	47	9.43 158	50	10.56 842	9.98 471	4	53
8	9.41 675	47	9.43 208	50	10.56 792	9.98 467	3	52
9	9.41 722	46	9.43 258	50	10.56 742	9.98 464	4	51
10	9.41 768	47	9.43 308	50	10.56 692	9.98 460	3	50
11	9.41 815	46	9.43 358	50	10.56 642	9.98 457	4	49
12	9.41 861	47	9.43 408	50	10.56 592	9.98 453	3	48
13	9.41 908	46	9.43 458	50	10.56 542	9.98 450	3	47
14	9.41 954	47	9.43 508	50	10.56 492	9.98 447	4	46
15	9.42 001	46	9.43 558	49	10.56 442	9.98 443	3	45
16	9.42 047	46	9.43 607	50	10.56 393	9.98 440	4	44
17	9.42 093	47	9.43 657	50	10.56 343	9.98 436	3	43
18	9.42 140	46	9.43 707	49	10.56 293	9.98 433	4	42
19	9.42 186	46	9.43 756	50	10.56 244	9.98 429	3	41
20	9.42 232	46	9.43 806	49	10.56 194	9.98 426	4	40
21	9.42 278	46	9.43 855	50	10.56 145	9.98 422	3	39
22	9.42 324	46	9.43 905	49	10.56 095	9.98 419	4	38
23	9.42 370	46	9.43 954	50	10.56 046	9.98 415	3	37
24	9.42 416	45	9.44 004	49	10.55 996	9.98 412	3	36
25	9.42 461	46	9.44 053	49	10.55 947	9.98 409	4	35
26	9.42 507	46	9.44 102	49	10.55 898	9.98 405	3	34
27	9.42 553	46	9.44 151	50	10.55 849	9.98 402	4	33
28	9.42 599	45	9.44 201	49	10.55 799	9.98 398	3	32
29	9.42 644	46	9.44 250	49	10.55 750	9.98 395	4	31
30	9.42 690	45	9.44 299	49	10.55 701	9.98 391	3	30
31	9.42 735	46	9.44 348	49	10.55 652	9.98 388	4	29
32	9.42 781	45	9.44 397	49	10.55 603	9.98 384	3	28
33	9.42 826	46	9.44 446	49	10.55 554	9.98 381	4	27
34	9.42 872	45	9.44 495	49	10.55 505	9.98 377	4	26
35	9.42 917	45	9.44 544	48	10.55 456	9.98 373	3	25
36	9.42 962	46	9.44 592	49	10.55 408	9.98 370	4	24
37	9.43 008	45	9.44 641	49	10.55 359	9.98 366	3	23
38	9.43 053	45	9.44 690	48	10.55 310	9.98 363	4	22
39	9.43 098	45	9.44 738	49	10.55 262	9.98 359	3	21
40	9.43 143	45	9.44 787	49	10.55 213	9.98 356	4	20
41	9.43 188	45	9.44 836	48	10.55 164	9.98 352	3	19
42	9.43 233	45	9.44 884	49	10.55 116	9.98 349	4	18
43	9.43 278	45	9.44 933	48	10.55 067	9.98 345	3	17
44	9.43 323	44	9.44 981	48	10.55 019	9.98 342	4	16
45	9.43 367	45	9.45 029	49	10.54 971	9.98 338	4	15
46	9.43 412	45	9.45 078	48	10.54 922	9.98 334	3	14
47	9.43 457	45	9.45 126	48	10.54 874	9.98 331	4	13
48	9.43 502	44	9.45 174	48	10.54 826	9.98 327	3	12
49	9.43 546	45	9.45 222	49	10.54 778	9.98 324	4	11
50	9.43 591	44	9.45 271	48	10.54 729	9.98 320	3	10
51	9.43 635	45	9.45 319	48	10.54 681	9.98 317	4	9
52	9.43 680	44	9.45 367	48	10.54 633	9.98 313	4	8
53	9.43 724	45	9.45 415	48	10.54 585	9.98 309	3	7
54	9.43 769	44	9.45 463	48	10.54 537	9.98 306	4	6
55	9.43 813	44	9.45 511	48	10.54 489	9.98 302	3	5
56	9.43 857	44	9.45 559	47	10.54 441	9.98 299	4	4
57	9.43 901	45	9.45 606	48	10.54 394	9.98 295	4	3
58	9.43 946	44	9.45 654	48	10.54 346	9.98 291	3	2
59	9.43 990	44	9.45 702	48	10.54 298	9.98 288	4	1
60	9.44 034		9.45 750		10.54 250	9.98 284		0
′	L Cos	d	L Ctn	c d	L Tan	L Sin	d	′

Proportional parts

″	51	50	49
1	0.8	0.8	0.8
2	1.7	1.7	1.6
3	2.6	2.5	2.4
4	3.4	3.3	3.3
5	4.2	4.2	4.1
6	5.1	5.0	4.9
7	6.0	5.8	5.7
8	6.8	6.7	6.5
9	7.6	7.5	7.4
10	8.5	8.3	8.2
20	17.0	16.7	16.3
30	25.5	25.0	24.5
40	34.0	33.3	32.7
50	42.5	41.7	40.8

″	48	47	46
1	0.8	0.8	0.8
2	1.6	1.6	1.5
3	2.4	2.4	2.3
4	3.2	3.1	3.1
5	4.0	3.9	3.8
6	4.8	4.7	4.6
7	5.6	5.5	5.4
8	6.4	6.3	6.1
9	7.2	7.0	6.9
10	8.0	7.8	7.7
20	16.0	15.7	15.3
30	24.0	23.5	23.0
40	32.0	31.3	30.7
50	40.0	39.2	38.3

″	45	44	4	3
1	0.8	0.7	0.1	0.0
2	1.5	1.5	0.1	0.1
3	2.2	2.2	0.2	0.2
4	3.0	2.9	0.3	0.2
5	3.8	3.7	0.3	0.2
6	4.5	4.4	0.4	0.3
7	5.2	5.1	0.5	0.4
8	6.0	5.9	0.5	0.4
9	6.8	6.6	0.6	0.4
10	7.5	7.3	0.7	0.5
20	15.0	14.7	1.3	1.0
30	22.5	22.0	2.0	1.5
40	30.0	29.3	2.7	2.0
50	37.5	36.7	3.3	2.5

Proportional parts

105° (285°) (254°) **74°**

The −10 portion of the characteristic of the logarithm is not printed but must be written down whenever such a logarithm is used.

16° (196°) (343°) **163°**

′	L Sin	d	L Tan	c d	L Ctn	L Cos	d	′
0	9.44 034	44	9.45 750	47	10.54 250	9.98 284	3	60
1	9.44 078	44	9.45 797	48	10.54 203	9.98 281	4	59
2	9.44 122	44	9.45 845	47	10.54 155	9.98 277	4	58
3	9.44 166	44	9.45 892	48	10.54 108	9.98 273	3	57
4	9.44 210	43	9.45 940	47	10.54 060	9.98 270	4	56
5	9.44 253	44	9.45 987	48	10.54 013	9.98 266	4	55
6	9.44 297	44	9.46 035	47	10.53 965	9.98 262	3	54
7	9.44 341	44	9.46 082	48	10.53 918	9.98 259	4	53
8	9.44 385	43	9.46 130	47	10.53 870	9.98 255	4	52
9	9.44 428	44	9.46 177	47	10.53 823	9.98 251	3	51
10	9.44 472	44	9.46 224	47	10.53 776	9.98 248	4	50
11	9.44 516	43	9.46 271	48	10.53 729	9.98 244	4	49
12	9.44 559	43	9.46 319	47	10.53 681	9.98 240	3	48
13	9.44 602	44	9.46 366	47	10.53 634	9.98 237	4	47
14	9.44 646	43	9.46 413	47	10.53 587	9.98 233	4	46
15	9.44 689	44	9.46 460	47	10.53 540	9.98 229	3	45
16	9.44 733	43	9.46 507	47	10.53 493	9.98 226	4	44
17	9.44 776	43	9.46 554	47	10.53 446	9.98 222	4	43
18	9.44 819	43	9.46 601	47	10.53 399	9.98 218	3	42
19	9.44 862	43	9.46 648	46	10.53 352	9.98 215	4	41
20	9.44 905	43	9.46 694	47	10.53 306	9.98 211	4	40
21	9.44 948	44	9.46 741	47	10.53 259	9.98 207	3	39
22	9.44 992	43	9.46 788	47	10.53 212	9.98 204	4	38
23	9.45 035	42	9.46 835	46	10.53 165	9.98 200	4	37
24	9.45 077	43	9.46 881	47	10.53 119	9.98 196	4	36
25	9.45 120	43	9.46 928	47	10.53 072	9.98 192	3	35
26	9.45 163	43	9.46 975	46	10.53 025	9.98 189	4	34
27	9.45 206	43	9.47 021	47	10.52 979	9.98 185	4	33
28	9.45 249	43	9.47 068	46	10.52 932	9.98 181	4	32
29	9.45 292	42	9.47 114	46	10.52 886	9.98 177	3	31
30	9.45 334	43	9.47 160	47	10.52 840	9.98 174	4	30
31	9.45 377	42	9.47 207	46	10.52 793	9.98 170	4	29
32	9.45 419	43	9.47 253	46	10.52 747	9.98 166	4	28
33	9.45 462	42	9.47 299	47	10.52 701	9.98 162	3	27
34	9.45 504	43	9.47 346	46	10.52 654	9.98 159	4	26
35	9.45 547	42	9.47 392	46	10.52 608	9.98 155	4	25
36	9.45 589	43	9.47 438	46	10.52 562	9.98 151	4	24
37	9.45 632	42	9.47 484	46	10.52 516	9.98 147	3	23
38	9.45 674	42	9.47 530	46	10.52 470	9.98 144	4	22
39	9.45 716	42	9.47 576	46	10.52 424	9.98 140	4	21
40	9.45 758	43	9.47 622	46	10.52 378	9.98 136	4	20
41	9.45 801	42	9.47 668	46	10.52 332	9.98 132	3	19
42	9.45 843	42	9.47 714	46	10.52 286	9.98 129	4	18
43	9.45 885	42	9.47 760	46	10.52 240	9.98 125	4	17
44	9.45 927	42	9.47 806	46	10.52 194	9.98 121	4	16
45	9.45 969	42	9.47 852	45	10.52 148	9.98 117	4	15
46	9.46 011	42	9.47 897	46	10.52 103	9.98 113	3	14
47	9.46 053	42	9.47 943	46	10.52 057	9.98 110	4	13
48	9.46 095	41	9.47 989	46	10.52 011	9.98 106	4	12
49	9.46 136	42	9.48 035	45	10.51 965	9.98 102	4	11
50	9.46 178	42	9.48 080	46	10.51 920	9.98 098	4	10
51	9.46 220	42	9.48 126	45	10.51 874	9.98 094	4	9
52	9.46 262	41	9.48 171	46	10.51 829	9.98 090	3	8
53	9.46 303	42	9.48 217	45	10.51 783	9.98 087	4	7
54	9.46 345	41	9.48 262	45	10.51 738	9.98 083	4	6
55	9.46 386	42	9.48 307	46	10.51 693	9.98 079	4	5
56	9.46 428	41	9.48 353	45	10.51 647	9.98 075	4	4
57	9.46 469	42	9.48 398	45	10.51 602	9.98 071	4	3
58	9.46 511	41	9.48 443	46	10.51 557	9.98 067	4	2
59	9.46 552	42	9.48 489	45	10.51 511	9.98 063	3	1
60	9.46 594		9.48 534		10.51 466	9.98 060		0
′	L Cos	d	L Ctn	c d	L Tan	L Sin	d	′

Proportional parts

″	48	47	46
1	0.8	0.8	0.8
2	1.6	1.6	1.5
3	2.4	2.4	2.3
4	3.2	3.1	3.1
5	4.0	3.9	3.8
6	4.8	4.7	4.6
7	5.6	5.5	5.4
8	6.4	6.3	6.1
9	7.2	7.0	6.9
10	8.0	7.8	7.7
20	16.0	15.7	15.3
30	24.0	23.5	23.0
40	32.0	31.3	30.7
50	40.0	39.2	38.3

″	45	44	43
1	0.8	0.7	0.7
2	1.5	1.5	1.4
3	2.2	2.2	2.2
4	3.0	2.9	2.9
5	3.8	3.7	3.6
6	4.5	4.4	4.3
7	5.2	5.1	5.0
8	6.0	5.9	5.7
9	6.8	6.6	6.4
10	7.5	7.3	7.2
20	15.0	14.7	14.3
30	22.5	22.0	21.5
40	30.0	29.3	28.7
50	37.5	36.7	35.8

″	42	41	4	3
1	0.7	0.7	0.1	0.0
2	1.4	1.4	0.1	0.1
3	2.1	2.0	0.2	0.2
4	2.8	2.7	0.3	0.2
5	3.5	3.4	0.3	0.2
6	4.2	4.1	0.4	0.3
7	4.9	4.8	0.5	0.4
8	5.6	5.5	0.5	0.4
9	6.3	6.2	0.6	0.4
10	7.0	6.8	0.7	0.5
20	14.0	13.7	1.3	1.0
30	21.0	20.5	2.0	1.5
40	28.0	27.3	2.7	2.0
50	35.0	34.2	3.3	2.5

Proportional parts

106° (286°) (253°) **73°**

The −10 portion of the characteristic of the logarithm is not printed but must be written down whenever such a logarithm is used.

17° (197°) (342°) **162°**

′	L Sin	d	L Tan	c d	L Ctn	L Cos	d	′
0	9.46 594	41	9.48 534	45	10.51 466	9.98 060	4	60
1	9.46 635	41	9.48 579	45	10.51 421	9.98 056	4	59
2	9.46 676	41	9.48 624	45	10.51 376	9.98 052	4	58
3	9.46 717	41	9.48 669	45	10.51 331	9.98 048	4	57
4	9.46 758	42	9.48 714	45	10.51 286	9.98 044	4	56
5	9.46 800	41	9.48 759	45	10.51 241	9.98 040	4	55
6	9.46 841	41	9.48 804	45	10.51 196	9.98 036	4	54
7	9.46 882	41	9.48 849	45	10.51 151	9.98 032	3	53
8	9.46 923	41	9.48 894	45	10.51 106	9.98 029	4	52
9	9.46 964	41	9.48 939	45	10.51 061	9.98 025	4	51
10	9.47 005	40	9.48 984	45	10.51 016	9.98 021	4	50
11	9.47 045	41	9.49 029	44	10.50 971	9.98 017	4	49
12	9.47 086	41	9.49 073	45	10.50 927	9.98 013	4	48
13	9.47 127	41	9.49 118	45	10.50 882	9.98 009	4	47
14	9.47 168	41	9.49 163	44	10.50 837	9.98 005	4	46
15	9.47 209	40	9.49 207	45	10.50 793	9.98 001	4	45
16	9.47 249	41	9.49 252	44	10.50 748	9.97 997	4	44
17	9.47 290	40	9.49 296	45	10.50 704	9.97 993	4	43
18	9.47 330	41	9.49 341	44	10.50 659	9.97 989	3	42
19	9.47 371	40	9.49 385	45	10.50 615	9.97 986	4	41
20	9.47 411	41	9.49 430	44	10.50 570	9.97 982	4	40
21	9.47 452	40	9.49 474	45	10.50 526	9.97 978	4	39
22	9.47 492	41	9.49 519	44	10.50 481	9.97 974	4	38
23	9.47 533	40	9.49 563	44	10.50 437	9.97 970	4	37
24	9.47 573	40	9.49 607	45	10.50 393	9.97 966	4	36
25	9.47 613	41	9.49 652	44	10.50 348	9.97 962	4	35
26	9.47 654	40	9.49 696	44	10.50 304	9.97 958	4	34
27	9.47 694	40	9.49 740	44	10.50 260	9.97 954	4	33
28	9.47 734	40	9.49 784	44	10.50 216	9.97 950	4	32
29	9.47 774	40	9.49 828	44	10.50 172	9.97 946	4	31
30	9.47 814	40	9.49 872	44	10.50 128	9.97 942	4	30
31	9.47 854	40	9.49 916	44	10.50 084	9.97 938	4	29
32	9.47 894	40	9.49 960	44	10.50 040	9.97 934	4	28
33	9.47 934	40	9.50 004	44	10.49 996	9.97 930	4	27
34	9.47 974	40	9.50 048	44	10.49 952	9.97 926	4	26
35	9.48 014	40	9.50 092	44	10.49 908	9.97 922	4	25
36	9.48 054	40	9.50 136	44	10.49 864	9.97 918	4	24
37	9.48 094	39	9.50 180	43	10.49 820	9.97 914	4	23
38	9.48 133	40	9.50 223	44	10.49 777	9.97 910	4	22
39	9.48 173	40	9.50 267	44	10.49 733	9.97 906	4	21
40	9.48 213	39	9.50 311	44	10.49 689	9.97 902	4	20
41	9.48 252	40	9.50 355	43	10.49 645	9.97 898	4	19
42	9.48 292	40	9.50 398	44	10.49 602	9.97 894	4	18
43	9.48 332	39	9.50 442	43	10.49 558	9.97 890	4	17
44	9.48 371	40	9.50 485	44	10.49 515	9.97 886	4	16
45	9.48 411	39	9.50 529	43	10.49 471	9.97 882	4	15
46	9.48 450	40	9.50 572	44	10.49 428	9.97 878	4	14
47	9.48 490	39	9.50 616	43	10.49 384	9.97 874	4	13
48	9.48 529	39	9.50 659	44	10.49 341	9.97 870	4	12
49	9.48 568	39	9.50 703	43	10.49 297	9.97 866	5	11
50	9.48 607	40	9.50 746	43	10.49 254	9.97 861	4	10
51	9.48 647	39	9.50 789	44	10.49 211	9.97 857	4	9
52	9.48 686	39	9.50 833	43	10.49 167	9.97 853	4	8
53	9.48 725	39	9.50 876	43	10.49 124	9.97 849	4	7
54	9.48 764	39	9.50 919	43	10.49 081	9.97 845	4	6
55	9.48 803	39	9.50 962	43	10.49 038	9.97 841	4	5
56	9.48 842	39	9.51 005	43	10.48 995	9.97 837	4	4
57	9.48 881	39	9.51 048	44	10.48 952	9.97 833	4	3
58	9.48 920	39	9.51 092	43	10.48 908	9.97 829	4	2
59	9.48 959	39	9.51 135	43	10.48 865	9.97 825	4	1
60	9.48 998		9.51 178		10.48 822	9.97 821		0
′	L Cos	d	L Ctn	c d	L Tan	L Sin	d	′

107° (287°) (252°) **72°**

Proportional parts

″	45	44	43
1	0.8	0.7	0.7
2	1.5	1.5	1.4
3	2.2	2.2	2.2
4	3.0	2.9	2.9
5	3.8	3.7	3.6
6	4.5	4.4	4.3
7	5.2	5.1	5.0
8	6.0	5.9	5.7
9	6.8	6.6	6.4
10	7.5	7.3	7.2
20	15.0	14.7	14.3
30	22.5	22.0	21.5
40	30.0	29.3	28.7
50	37.5	36.7	35.8

″	42	41	40
1	0.7	0.7	0.7
2	1.4	1.4	1.3
3	2.1	2.0	2.0
4	2.8	2.7	2.7
5	3.5	3.4	3.3
6	4.2	4.1	4.0
7	4.9	4.8	4.7
8	5.6	5.5	5.3
9	6.3	6.2	6.0
10	7.0	6.8	6.7
20	14.0	13.7	13.3
30	21.0	20.5	20.0
40	28.0	27.3	26.7
50	35.0	34.2	33.3

″	39	5	4	3
1	0.6	0.1	0.1	0.0
2	1.3	0.2	0.1	0.1
3	2.0	0.2	0.2	0.2
4	2.6	0.3	0.3	0.2
5	3.2	0.4	0.3	0.2
6	3.9	0.5	0.4	0.3
7	4.6	0.6	0.5	0.4
8	5.2	0.7	0.5	0.4
9	5.8	0.8	0.6	0.4
10	6.5	0.8	0.7	0.5
20	13.0	1.7	1.3	1.0
30	19.5	2.5	2.0	1.5
40	26.0	3.3	2.7	2.0
50	32.5	4.2	3.3	2.5

Proportional parts

The −10 portion of the characteristic of the logarithm is not printed but must be written down whenever such a logarithm is used.

18° (198°) (341°) **161°**

′	L Sin	d	L Tan	c d	L Ctn	L Cos	d	′
0	9.48 998	39	9.51 178	43	10.48 822	9.97 821	4	60
1	9.49 037	39	9.51 221	43	10.48 779	9.97 817	5	59
2	9.49 076	39	9.51 264	42	10.48 736	9.97 812	4	58
3	9.49 115	38	9.51 306	43	10.48 694	9.97 808	4	57
4	9.49 153	39	9.51 349	43	10.48 651	9.97 804	4	56
5	9.49 192	39	9.51 392	43	10.48 608	9.97 800	4	55
6	9.49 231	38	9.51 435	43	10.48 565	9.97 796	4	54
7	9.49 269	39	9.51 478	42	10.48 522	9.97 792	4	53
8	9.49 308	39	9.51 520	43	10.48 480	9.97 788	4	52
9	9.49 347	38	9.51 563	43	10.48 437	9.97 784	5	51
10	9.49 385	39	9.51 606	42	10.48 394	9.97 779	4	50
11	9.49 424	38	9.51 648	43	10.48 352	9.97 775	4	49
12	9.49 462	38	9.51 691	43	10.48 309	9.97 771	4	48
13	9.49 500	39	9.51 734	42	10.48 266	9.97 767	4	47
14	9.49 539	38	9.51 776	43	10.48 224	9.97 763	4	46
15	9.49 577	38	9.51 819	42	10.48 181	9.97 759	5	45
16	9.49 615	39	9.51 861	42	10.48 139	9.97 754	4	44
17	9.49 654	38	9.51 903	43	10.48 097	9.97 750	4	43
18	9.49 692	38	9.51 946	42	10.48 054	9.97 746	4	42
19	9.49 730	38	9.51 988	43	10.48 012	9.97 742	4	41
20	9.49 768	38	9.52 031	42	10.47 969	9.97 738	4	40
21	9.49 806	38	9.52 073	42	10.47 927	9.97 734	5	39
22	9.49 844	38	9.52 115	42	10.47 885	9.97 729	4	38
23	9.49 882	38	9.52 157	43	10.47 843	9.97 725	4	37
24	9.49 920	38	9.52 200	42	10.47 800	9.97 721	4	36
25	9.49 958	38	9.52 242	42	10.47 758	9.97 717	4	35
26	9.49 996	38	9.52 284	42	10.47 716	9.97 713	5	34
27	9.50 034	38	9.52 326	42	10.47 674	9.97 708	4	33
28	9.50 072	38	9.52 368	42	10.47 632	9.97 704	4	32
29	9.50 110	38	9.52 410	42	10.47 590	9.97 700	4	31
30	9.50 148	37	9.52 452	42	10.47 548	9.97 696	5	30
31	9.50 185	38	9.52 494	42	10.47 506	9.97 691	4	29
32	9.50 223	38	9.52 536	42	10.47 464	9.97 687	4	28
33	9.50 261	37	9.52 578	42	10.47 422	9.97 683	4	27
34	9.50 298	38	9.52 620	41	10.47 380	9.97 679	5	26
35	9.50 336	38	9.52 661	42	10.47 339	9.97 674	4	25
36	9.50 374	37	9.52 703	42	10.47 297	9.97 670	4	24
37	9.50 411	38	9.52 745	42	10.47 255	9.97 666	4	23
38	9.50 449	37	9.52 787	42	10.47 213	9.97 662	5	22
39	9.50 486	37	9.52 829	41	10.47 171	9.97 657	4	21
40	9.50 523	38	9.52 870	42	10.47 130	9.97 653	4	20
41	9.50 561	37	9.52 912	41	10.47 088	9.97 649	4	19
42	9.50 598	37	9.52 953	42	10.47 047	9.97 645	5	18
43	9.50 635	38	9.52 995	42	10.47 005	9.97 640	4	17
44	9.50 673	37	9.53 037	41	10.46 963	9.97 636	4	16
45	9.50 710	37	9.53 078	42	10.46 922	9.97 632	4	15
46	9.50 747	37	9.53 120	41	10.46 880	9.97 628	5	14
47	9.50 784	37	9.53 161	41	10.46 839	9.97 623	4	13
48	9.50 821	37	9.53 202	42	10.46 798	9.97 619	4	12
49	9.50 858	38	9.53 244	41	10.46 756	9.97 615	5	11
50	9.50 896	37	9.53 285	42	10.46 715	9.97 610	4	10
51	9.50 933	37	9.53 327	41	10.46 673	9.97 606	4	9
52	9.50 970	37	9.53 368	41	10.46 632	9.97 602	5	8
53	9.51 007	36	9.53 409	41	10.46 591	9.97 597	4	7
54	9.51 043	37	9.53 450	42	10.46 550	9.97 593	4	6
55	9.51 080	37	9.53 492	41	10.46 508	9.97 589	5	5
56	9.51 117	37	9.53 533	41	10.46 467	9.97 584	4	4
57	9.51 154	37	9.53 574	41	10.46 426	9.97 580	4	3
58	9.51 191	36	9.53 615	41	10.46 385	9.97 576	5	2
59	9.51 227	37	9.53 656	41	10.46 344	9.97 571	4	1
60	9.51 264		9.53 697		10.46 303	9.97 567		0
′	L Cos	d	L Ctn	c d	L Tan	L Sin	d	′

108° (288°) (251°) **71°**

Proportional parts

″	43	42	41
1	0.7	0.7	0.7
2	1.4	1.4	1.4
3	2.2	2.1	2.0
4	2.9	2.8	2.7
5	3.6	3.5	3.4
6	4.3	4.2	4.1
7	5.0	4.9	4.8
8	5.7	5.6	5.5
9	6.4	6.3	6.2
10	7.2	7.0	6.8
20	14.3	14.0	13.7
30	21.5	21.0	20.5
40	28.7	28.0	27.3
50	35.8	35.0	34.2

″	39	38	37
1	0.6	0.6	0.6
2	1.3	1.3	1.2
3	2.0	1.9	1.8
4	2.6	2.5	2.5
5	3.2	3.2	3.1
6	3.9	3.8	3.7
7	4.6	4.4	4.3
8	5.2	5.1	4.9
9	5.8	5.7	5.6
10	6.5	6.3	6.2
20	13.0	12.7	12.3
30	19.5	19.0	18.5
40	26.0	25.3	24.7
50	32.5	31.7	30.8

″	36	5	4
1	0.6	0.1	0.1
2	1.2	0.2	0.1
3	1.8	0.2	0.2
4	2.4	0.3	0.3
5	3.0	0.4	0.3
6	3.6	0.5	0.4
7	4.2	0.6	0.5
8	4.8	0.7	0.5
9	5.4	0.8	0.6
10	6.0	0.8	0.7
20	12.0	1.7	1.3
30	18.0	2.5	2.0
40	24.0	3.3	2.7
50	30.0	4.2	3.3

Proportional parts

The −10 portion of the characteristic of the logarithm is not printed but must be written down whenever such a logarithm is used.

19° (199°) (340°) **160°**

′	L Sin	d	L Tan	c d	L Ctn	L Cos	d	′
0	9.51 264	37	9.53 697	41	10.46 303	9.97 567	4	60
1	9.51 301	37	9.53 738	41	10.46 262	9.97 563	5	59
2	9.51 338	36	9.53 779	41	10.46 221	9.97 558	4	58
3	9.51 374	37	9.53 820	41	10.46 180	9.97 554	4	57
4	9.51 411	36	9.53 861	41	10.46 139	9.97 550	5	56
5	9.51 447	37	9.53 902	41	10.46 098	9.97 545	4	55
6	9.51 484	36	9.53 943	41	10.46 057	9.97 541	5	54
7	9.51 520	37	9.53 984	41	10.46 016	9.97 536	4	53
8	9.51 557	36	9.54 025	40	10.45 975	9.97 532	4	52
9	9.51 593	36	9.54 065	41	10.45 935	9.97 528	5	51
10	9.51 629	37	9.54 106	41	10.45 894	9.97 523	4	50
11	9.51 666	36	9.54 147	40	10.45 853	9.97 519	4	49
12	9.51 702	36	9.54 187	41	10.45 813	9.97 515	5	48
13	9.51 738	36	9.54 228	41	10.45 772	9.97 510	4	47
14	9.51 774	37	9.54 269	40	10.45 731	9.97 506	5	46
15	9.51 811	36	9.54 309	41	10.45 691	9.97 501	4	45
16	9.51 847	36	9.54 350	40	10.45 650	9.97 497	5	44
17	9.51 883	36	9.54 390	41	10.45 610	9.97 492	4	43
18	9.51 919	36	9.54 431	40	10.45 569	9.97 488	4	42
19	9.51 955	36	9.54 471	41	10.45 529	9.97 484	5	41
20	9.51 991	36	9.54 512	40	10.45 488	9.97 479	4	40
21	9.52 027	36	9.54 552	41	10.45 448	9.97 475	5	39
22	9.52 063	36	9.54 593	40	10.45 407	9.97 470	4	38
23	9.52 099	36	9.54 633	40	10.45 367	9.97 466	5	37
24	9.52 135	36	9.54 673	41	10.45 327	9.97 461	4	36
25	9.52 171	36	9.54 714	40	10.45 286	9.97 457	4	35
26	9.52 207	35	9.54 754	40	10.45 246	9.97 453	5	34
27	9.52 242	36	9.54 794	41	10.45 206	9.97 448	4	33
28	9.52 278	36	9.54 835	40	10.45 165	9.97 444	5	32
29	9.52 314	36	9.54 875	40	10.45 125	9.97 439	4	31
30	9.52 350	35	9.54 915	40	10.45 085	9.97 435	5	30
31	9.52 385	36	9.54 955	40	10.45 045	9.97 430	4	29
32	9.52 421	35	9.54 995	40	10.45 005	9.97 426	5	28
33	9.52 456	36	9.55 035	40	10.44 965	9.97 421	4	27
34	9.52 492	35	9.55 075	40	10.44 925	9.97 417	5	26
35	9.52 527	36	9.55 115	40	10.44 885	9.97 412	4	25
36	9.52 563	35	9.55 155	40	10.44 845	9.97 408	5	24
37	9.52 598	36	9.55 195	40	10.44 805	9.97 403	4	23
38	9.52 634	35	9.55 235	40	10.44 765	9.97 399	5	22
39	9.52 669	36	9.55 275	40	10.44 725	9.97 394	4	21
40	9.52 705	35	9.55 315	40	10.44 685	9.97 390	5	20
41	9.52 740	35	9.55 355	40	10.44 645	9.97 385	4	19
42	9.52 775	36	9.55 395	39	10.44 605	9.97 381	5	18
43	9.52 811	35	9.55 434	40	10.44 566	9.97 376	4	17
44	9.52 846	35	9.55 474	40	10.44 526	9.97 372	5	16
45	9.52 881	35	9.55 514	40	10.44 486	9.97 367	4	15
46	9.52 916	35	9.55 554	39	10.44 446	9.97 363	5	14
47	9.52 951	35	9.55 593	40	10.44 407	9.97 358	5	13
48	9.52 986	35	9.55 633	40	10.44 367	9.97 353	4	12
49	9.53 021	35	9.55 673	39	10.44 327	9.97 349	5	11
50	9.53 056	36	9.55 712	40	10.44 288	9.97 344	4	10
51	9.53 092	34	9.55 752	39	10.44 248	9.97 340	5	9
52	9.53 126	35	9.55 791	40	10.44 209	9.97 335	4	8
53	9.53 161	35	9.55 831	39	10.44 169	9.97 331	5	7
54	9.53 196	35	9.55 870	40	10.44 130	9.97 326	4	6
55	9.53 231	35	9.55 910	39	10.44 090	9.97 322	5	5
56	9.53 266	35	9.55 949	40	10.44 051	9.97 317	5	4
57	9.53 301	35	9.55 989	39	10.44 011	9.97 312	4	3
58	9.53 336	34	9.56 028	39	10.43 972	9.97 308	5	2
59	9.53 370	35	9.56 067	40	10.43 933	9.97 303	4	1
60	9.53 405		9.56 107		10.43 893	9.97 299		0
′	L Cos	d	L Ctn	c d	L Tan	L Sin	d	′

Proportional parts

″	41	40	39
1	0.7	0.7	0.6
2	1.4	1.3	1.3
3	2.0	2.0	2.0
4	2.7	2.7	2.6
5	3.4	3.3	3.2
6	4.1	4.0	3.9
7	4.8	4.7	4.6
8	5.5	5.3	5.2
9	6.2	6.0	5.8
10	6.8	6.7	6.5
20	13.7	13.3	13.0
30	20.5	20.0	19.5
40	27.3	26.7	26.0
50	34.2	33.3	32.5

″	37	36	35
1	0.6	0.6	0.6
2	1.2	1.2	1.2
3	1.8	1.8	1.8
4	2.5	2.4	2.3
5	3.1	3.0	2.9
6	3.7	3.6	3.5
7	4.3	4.2	4.1
8	4.9	4.8	4.7
9	5.6	5.4	5.2
10	6.2	6.0	5.8
20	12.3	12.0	11.7
30	18.5	18.0	17.5
40	24.7	24.0	23.3
50	30.8	30.0	29.2

″	34	5	4
1	0.6	0.1	0.1
2	1.1	0.2	0.1
3	1.7	0.2	0.2
4	2.3	0.3	0.3
5	2.8	0.4	0.3
6	3.4	0.5	0.4
7	4.0	0.6	0.5
8	4.5	0.7	0.5
9	5.1	0.8	0.6
10	5.7	0.8	0.7
20	11.3	1.7	1.3
30	17.0	2.5	2.0
40	22.7	3.3	2.7
50	28.3	4.2	3.3

Proportional parts

109° (289°) (250°) **70°**

The −10 portion of the characteristic of the logarithm is not printed but must be written down whenever such a logarithm is used.

20° (200°) (339°) **159°**

′	L Sin	d	L Tan	c d	L Ctn	L Cos	d	′
0	9.53 405	35	9.56 107	39	10.43 893	9.97 299	5	60
1	9.53 440	35	9.56 146	39	10.43 854	9.97 294	5	59
2	9.53 475	34	9.56 185	39	10.43 815	9.97 289	4	58
3	9.53 509	35	9.56 224	40	10.43 776	9.97 285	5	57
4	9.53 544	34	9.56 264	39	10.43 736	9.97 280	4	56
5	9.53 578	35	9.56 303	39	10.43 697	9.97 276	5	55
6	9.53 613	34	9.56 342	39	10.43 658	9.97 271	5	54
7	9.53 647	35	9.56 381	39	10.43 619	9.97 266	4	53
8	9.53 682	34	9.56 420	39	10.43 580	9.97 262	5	52
9	9.53 716	35	9.56 459	39	10.43 541	9.97 257	5	51
10	9.53 751	34	9.56 498	39	10.43 502	9.97 252	4	50
11	9.53 785	34	9.56 537	39	10.43 463	9.97 248	5	49
12	9.53 819	35	9.56 576	39	10.43 424	9.97 243	5	48
13	9.53 854	34	9.56 615	39	10.43 385	9.97 238	4	47
14	9.53 888	34	9.56 654	39	10.43 346	9.97 234	5	46
15	9.53 922	35	9.56 693	39	10.43 307	9.97 229	5	45
16	9.53 957	34	9.56 732	39	10.43 268	9.97 224	4	44
17	9.53 991	34	9.56 771	39	10.43 229	9.97 220	5	43
18	9.54 025	34	9.56 810	39	10.43 190	9.97 215	5	42
19	9.54 059	34	9.56 849	38	10.43 151	9.97 210	4	41
20	9.54 093	34	9.56 887	39	10.43 113	9.97 206	5	40
21	9.54 127	34	9.56 926	39	10.43 074	9.97 201	5	39
22	9.54 161	34	9.56 965	39	10.43 035	9.97 196	4	38
23	9.54 195	34	9.57 004	38	10.42 996	9.97 192	5	37
24	9.54 229	34	9.57 042	39	10.42 958	9.97 187	5	36
25	9.54 263	34	9.57 081	39	10.42 919	9.97 182	4	35
26	9.54 297	34	9.57 120	38	10.42 880	9.97 178	5	34
27	9.54 331	34	9.57 158	39	10.42 842	9.97 173	5	33
28	9.54 365	34	9.57 197	38	10.42 803	9.97 168	5	32
29	9.54 399	34	9.57 235	39	10.42 765	9.97 163	4	31
30	9.54 433	33	9.57 274	38	10.42 726	9.97 159	5	30
31	9.54 466	34	9.57 312	39	10.42 688	9.97 154	5	29
32	9.54 500	34	9.57 351	38	10.42 649	9.97 149	4	28
33	9.54 534	33	9.57 389	39	10.42 611	9.97 145	5	27
34	9.54 567	34	9.57 428	38	10.42 572	9.97 140	5	26
35	9.54 601	34	9.57 466	38	10.42 534	9.97 135	5	25
36	9.54 635	33	9.57 504	39	10.42 496	9.97 130	4	24
37	9.54 668	34	9.57 543	38	10.42 457	9.97 126	5	23
38	9.54 702	33	9.57 581	38	10.42 419	9.97 121	5	22
39	9.54 735	34	9.57 619	39	10.42 381	9.97 116	5	21
40	9.54 769	33	9.57 658	38	10.42 342	9.97 111	4	20
41	9.54 802	34	9.57 696	38	10.42 304	9.97 107	5	19
42	9.54 836	33	9.57 734	38	10.42 266	9.97 102	5	18
43	9.54 869	34	9.57 772	38	10.42 228	9.97 097	5	17
44	9.54 903	33	9.57 810	39	10.42 190	9.97 092	5	16
45	9.54 936	33	9.57 849	38	10.42 151	9.97 087	4	15
46	9.54 969	34	9.57 887	38	10.42 113	9.97 083	5	14
47	9.55 003	33	9.57 925	38	10.42 075	9.97 078	5	13
48	9.55 036	33	9.57 963	38	10.42 037	9.97 073	5	12
49	9.55 069	33	9.58 001	38	10.41 999	9.97 068	5	11
50	9.55 102	34	9.58 039	38	10.41 961	9.97 063	4	10
51	9.55 136	33	9.58 077	38	10.41 923	9.97 059	5	9
52	9.55 169	33	9.58 115	38	10.41 885	9.97 054	5	8
53	9.55 202	33	9.58 153	38	10.41 847	9.97 049	5	7
54	9.55 235	33	9.58 191	38	10.41 809	9.97 044	5	6
55	9.55 268	33	9.58 229	38	10.41 771	9.97 039	4	5
56	9.55 301	33	9.58 267	37	10.41 733	9.97 035	5	4
57	9.55 334	33	9.58 304	38	10.41 696	9.97 030	5	3
58	9.55 367	33	9.58 342	38	10.41 658	9.97 025	5	2
59	9.55 400	33	9.58 380	38	10.41 620	9.97 020	5	1
60	9.55 433		9.58 418		10.41 582	9.97 015		0
′	L Cos	d	L Ctn	c d	L Tan	L Sin	d	′

Proportional parts

″	40	39	38
1	0.7	0.6	0.6
2	1.3	1.3	1.3
3	2.0	2.0	1.9
4	2.7	2.6	2.5
5	3.3	3.2	3.2
6	4.0	3.9	3.8
7	4.7	4.6	4.4
8	5.3	5.2	5.1
9	6.0	5.8	5.7
10	6.7	6.5	6.3
20	13.3	13.0	12.7
30	20.0	19.5	19.0
40	26.7	26.0	25.3
50	33.3	32.5	31.7

″	37	35	34
1	0.6	0.6	0.6
2	1.2	1.2	1.1
3	1.8	1.8	1.7
4	2.5	2.3	2.3
5	3.1	2.9	2.8
6	3.7	3.5	3.4
7	4.3	4.1	4.0
8	4.9	4.7	4.5
9	5.6	5.2	5.1
10	6.2	5.8	5.7
20	12.3	11.7	11.3
30	18.5	17.5	17.0
40	24.7	23.3	22.7
50	30.8	29.2	28.3

″	33	5	4
1	0.6	0.1	0.1
2	1.1	0.2	0.1
3	1.6	0.2	0.2
4	2.2	0.3	0.3
5	2.8	0.4	0.3
6	3.3	0.5	0.4
7	3.8	0.6	0.5
8	4.4	0.7	0.5
9	5.0	0.8	0.6
10	5.5	0.8	0.7
20	11.0	1.7	1.3
30	16.5	2.5	2.0
40	22.0	3.3	2.7
50	27.5	4.2	3.3

Proportional parts

110° (290°) (249°) **69°**

The −10 portion of the characteristic of the logarithm is not printed but must be written down whenever such a logarithm is used.

21° (201°) (338°) **158°**

′	L Sin	d	L Tan	c d	L Ctn	L Cos	d	′
0	9.55 433	33	9.58 418	37	10.41 582	9.97 015	5	60
1	9.55 466	33	9.58 455	38	10.41 545	9.97 010	5	59
2	9.55 499	33	9.58 493	38	10.41 507	9.97 005	4	58
3	9.55 532	32	9.58 531	38	10.41 469	9.97 001	5	57
4	9.55 564	33	9.58 569	37	10.41 431	9.96 996	5	56
5	9.55 597	33	9.58 606	38	10.41 394	9.96 991	5	55
6	9.55 630	33	9.58 644	37	10.41 356	9.96 986	5	54
7	9.55 663	32	9.58 681	38	10.41 319	9.96 981	5	53
8	9.55 695	33	9.58 719	38	10.41 281	9.96 976	5	52
9	9.55 728	33	9.58 757	37	10.41 243	9.96 971	5	51
10	9.55 761	32	9.58 794	38	10.41 206	9.96 966	4	50
11	9.55 793	33	9.58 832	37	10.41 168	9.96 962	5	49
12	9.55 826	32	9.58 869	38	10.41 131	9.96 957	5	48
13	9.55 858	33	9.58 907	37	10.41 093	9.96 952	5	47
14	9.55 891	32	9.58 944	37	10.41 056	9.96 947	5	46
15	9.55 923	33	9.58 981	38	10.41 019	9.96 942	5	45
16	9.55 956	32	9.59 019	37	10.40 981	9.96 937	5	44
17	9.55 988	33	9.59 056	38	10.40 944	9.96 932	5	43
18	9.56 021	32	9.59 094	37	10.40 906	9.96 927	5	42
19	9.56 053	32	9.59 131	37	10.40 869	9.96 922	5	41
20	9.56 085	33	9.59 168	37	10.40 832	9.96 917	5	40
21	9.56 118	32	9.59 205	38	10.40 795	9.96 912	5	39
22	9.56 150	32	9.59 243	37	10.40 757	9.96 907	4	38
23	9.56 182	33	9.59 280	37	10.40 720	9.96 903	5	37
24	9.56 215	32	9.59 317	37	10.40 683	9.96 898	5	36
25	9.56 247	32	9.59 354	37	10.40 646	9.96 893	5	35
26	9.56 279	32	9.59 391	38	10.40 609	9.96 888	5	34
27	9.56 311	32	9.59 429	37	10.40 571	9.96 883	5	33
28	9.56 343	32	9.59 466	37	10.40 534	9.96 878	5	32
29	9.56 375	33	9.59 503	37	10.40 497	9.96 873	5	31
30	9.56 408	32	9.59 540	37	10.40 460	9.96 868	5	30
31	9.56 440	32	9.59 577	37	10.40 423	9.96 863	5	29
32	9.56 472	32	9.59 614	37	10.40 386	9.96 858	5	28
33	9.56 504	32	9.59 651	37	10.40 349	9.96 853	5	27
34	9.56 536	32	9.59 688	37	10.40 312	9.96 848	5	26
35	9.56 568	31	9.59 725	37	10.40 275	9.96 843	5	25
36	9.56 599	32	9.59 762	37	10.40 238	9.96 838	5	24
37	9.56 631	32	9.59 799	36	10.40 201	9.96 833	5	23
38	9.56 663	32	9.59 835	37	10.40 165	9.96 828	5	22
39	9.56 695	32	9.59 872	37	10.40 128	9.96 823	5	21
40	9.56 727	32	9.59 909	37	10.40 091	9.96 818	5	20
41	9.56 759	31	9.59 946	37	10.40 054	9.96 813	5	19
42	9.56 790	32	9.59 983	36	10.40 017	9.96 808	5	18
43	9.56 822	32	9.60 019	37	10.39 981	9.96 803	5	17
44	9.56 854	32	9.60 056	37	10.39 944	9.96 798	5	16
45	9.56 886	31	9.60 093	37	10.39 907	9.96 793	5	15
46	9.56 917	32	9.60 130	36	10.39 870	9.96 788	5	14
47	9.56 949	31	9.60 166	37	10.39 834	9.96 783	5	13
48	9.56 980	32	9.60 203	37	10.39 797	9.96 778	6	12
49	9.57 012	32	9.60 240	36	10.39 760	9.96 772	5	11
50	9.57 044	31	9.60 276	37	10.39 724	9.96 767	5	10
51	9.57 075	32	9.60 313	36	10.39 687	9.96 762	5	9
52	9.57 107	31	9.60 349	37	10.39 651	9.96 757	5	8
53	9.57 138	31	9.60 386	36	10.39 614	9.96 752	5	7
54	9.57 169	32	9.60 422	37	10.39 578	9.96 747	5	6
55	9.57 201	31	9.60 459	36	10.39 541	9.96 742	5	5
56	9.57 232	32	9.60 495	37	10.39 505	9.96 737	5	4
57	9.57 264	31	9.60 532	36	10.39 468	9.96 732	5	3
58	9.57 295	31	9.60 568	37	10.39 432	9.96 727	5	2
59	9.57 326	32	9.60 605	36	10.39 395	9.96 722	5	1
60	9.57 358		9.60 641		10.39 359	9.96 717		0
′	L Cos	d	L Ctn	c d	L Tan	L Sin	d	′

Proportional parts

″	38	37	36
1	0.6	0.6	0.6
2	1.3	1.2	1.2
3	1.9	1.8	1.8
4	2.5	2.5	2.4
5	3.2	3.1	3.0
6	3.8	3.7	3.6
7	4.4	4.3	4.2
8	5.1	4.9	4.8
9	5.7	5.6	5.4
10	6.3	6.2	6.0
20	12.7	12.3	12.0
30	19.0	18.5	18.0
40	25.3	24.7	24.0
50	31.7	30.8	30.0

″	33	32	31
1	0.6	0.5	0.5
2	1.1	1.1	1.0
3	1.6	1.6	1.6
4	2.2	2.1	2.1
5	2.8	2.7	2.6
6	3.3	3 2	3.1
7	3.8	3.7	3.6
8	4.4	4.3	4.1
9	5.0	4.8	4.6
10	5.5	5.3	5.2
20	11.0	10.7	10.3
30	16.5	16.0	15.5
40	22.0	21.3	20.7
50	27.5	26.7	25.8

″	6	5	4
1	0.1	0.1	0.1
2	0.2	0.2	0.1
3	0.3	0.2	0.2
4	0.4	0.3	0.3
5	0.5	0.4	0.3
6	0.6	0.5	0.4
7	0.7	0.6	0.5
8	0.8	0.7	0.5
9	0.9	0.8	0.6
10	1.0	0.8	0.7
20	2.0	1.7	1.3
30	3.0	2.5	2.0
40	4.0	3.3	2.7
50	5.0	4.2	3.3

Proportional parts

111° (291°) (248°) **68°**

The −10 portion of the characteristic of the logarithm is not printed but must be written down whenever such a logarithm is used.

22° (202°) | (337°) **157°**

′	L Sin	d	L Tan	c d	L Ctn	L Cos	d	′
0	9.57 358	31	9.60 641	36	10.39 359	9.96 717	6	60
1	9.57 389	31	9.60 677	37	10.39 323	9.96 711	5	59
2	9.57 420	31	9.60 714	36	10.39 286	9.96 706	5	58
3	9.57 451	31	9.60 750	36	10.39 250	9.96 701	5	57
4	9.57 482	32	9.60 786	37	10.39 214	9.96 696	5	56
5	9.57 514	31	9.60 823	36	10.39 177	9.96 691	5	55
6	9.57 545	31	9.60 859	36	10.39 141	9.96 686	5	54
7	9.57 576	31	9.60 895	36	10.39 105	9.96 681	5	53
8	9.57 607	31	9.60 931	36	10.39 069	9.96 676	6	52
9	9.57 638	31	9.60 967	37	10.39 033	9.96 670	5	51
10	9.57 669	31	9.61 004	36	10.38 996	9.96 665	5	50
11	9.57 700	31	9.61 040	36	10.38 960	9.96 660	5	49
12	9.57 731	31	9.61 076	36	10.38 924	9.96 655	5	48
13	9.57 762	31	9.61 112	36	10.38 888	9.96 650	5	47
14	9.57 793	31	9.61 148	36	10.38 852	9.96 645	5	46
15	9.57 824	31	9.61 184	36	10.38 816	9.96 640	6	45
16	9.57 855	30	9.61 220	36	10.38 780	9.96 634	5	44
17	9.57 885	31	9.61 256	36	10.38 744	9.96 629	5	43
18	9.57 916	31	9.61 292	36	10.38 708	9.96 624	5	42
19	9.57 947	31	9.61 328	36	10.38 672	9.96 619	5	41
20	9.57 978	30	9.61 364	36	10.38 636	9.96 614	6	40
21	9.58 008	31	9.61 400	36	10.38 600	9.96 608	5	39
22	9.58 039	31	9.61 436	36	10.38 564	9.96 603	5	38
23	9.58 070	31	9.61 472	36	10.38 528	9.96 598	5	37
24	9.58 101	30	9.61 508	36	10.38 492	9.96 593	5	36
25	9.58 131	31	9.61 544	35	10.38 456	9.96 588	6	35
26	9.58 162	30	9.61 579	36	10.38 421	9.96 582	5	34
27	9.58 192	31	9.61 615	36	10.38 385	9.96 577	5	33
28	9.58 223	30	9.61 651	36	10.38 349	9.96 572	5	32
29	9.58 253	31	9.61 687	35	10.38 313	9.96 567	5	31
30	9.58 284	30	9.61 722	36	10.38 278	9.96 562	6	30
31	9.58 314	31	9.61 758	36	10.38 242	9.96 556	5	29
32	9.58 345	30	9.61 794	36	10.38 206	9.96 551	5	28
33	9.58 375	31	9.61 830	35	10.38 170	9.96 546	5	27
34	9.58 406	30	9.61 865	36	10.38 135	9.96 541	6	26
35	9.58 436	31	9.61 901	35	10.38 099	9.96 535	5	25
36	9.58 467	30	9.61 936	36	10.38 064	9.96 530	5	24
37	9.58 497	30	9.61 972	36	10.38 028	9.96 525	5	23
38	9.58 527	30	9.62 008	35	10.37 992	9.96 520	6	22
39	9.58 557	31	9.62 043	36	10.37 957	9.96 514	5	21
40	9.58 588	30	9.62 079	35	10.37 921	9.96 509	5	20
41	9.58 618	30	9.62 114	36	10.37 886	9.96 504	6	19
42	9.58 648	30	9.62 150	35	10.37 850	9.96 498	5	18
43	9.58 678	31	9.62 185	36	10.37 815	9.96 493	5	17
44	9.58 709	30	9.62 221	35	10.37 779	9.96 488	5	16
45	9.58 739	30	9.62 256	36	10.37 744	9.96 483	6	15
46	9.58 769	30	9.62 292	35	10.37 708	9.96 477	5	14
47	9.58 799	30	9.62 327	35	10.37 673	9.96 472	5	13
48	9.58 829	30	9.62 362	36	10.37 638	9.96 467	6	12
49	9.58 859	30	9.62 398	35	10.37 602	9.96 461	5	11
50	9.58 889	30	9.62 433	35	10.37 567	9.96 456	5	10
51	9.58 919	30	9.62 468	36	10.37 532	9.96 451	6	9
52	9.58 949	30	9.62 504	35	10.37 496	9.96 445	5	8
53	9.58 979	30	9.62 539	35	10.37 461	9.96 440	5	7
54	9.59 009	30	9.62 574	35	10.37 426	9.96 435	6	6
55	9.59 039	30	9.62 609	36	10.37 391	9.96 429	5	5
56	9.59 069	29	9.62 645	35	10.37 355	9.96 424	5	4
57	9.59 098	30	9.62 680	35	10.37 320	9.96 419	6	3
58	9.59 128	30	9.62 715	35	10.37 285	9.96 413	5	2
59	9.59 158	30	9.62 750	35	10.37 250	9.96 408	5	1
60	9.59 188		9.62 785		10.37 215	9.96 403		0
′	L Cos	d	L Ctn	c d	L Tan	L Sin	d	′

112° (292°) | (247°) **67°**

Proportional parts

″	37	36	35
1	0.6	0.6	0.6
2	1.2	1.2	1.2
3	1.8	1.8	1.8
4	2.5	2.4	2.3
5	3.1	3.0	2.9
6	3.7	3.6	3.5
7	4.3	4.2	4.1
8	4.9	4.8	4.7
9	5.6	5.4	5.2
10	6.2	6.0	5.8
20	12.3	12.0	11.7
30	18.5	18.0	17.5
40	24.7	24.0	23.3
50	30.8	30.0	29.2
″	32	31	30
1	0.5	0.5	0.5
2	1.1	1.0	1.0
3	1.6	1.6	1.5
4	2.1	2.1	2.0
5	2.7	2.6	2.5
6	3.2	3.1	3.0
7	3.7	3.6	3.5
8	4.3	4.1	4.0
9	4.8	4.6	4.5
10	5.3	5.2	5.0
20	10.7	10.3	10.0
30	16.0	15.5	15.0
40	21.3	20.7	20.0
50	26.7	25.8	25.0
″	29	6	5
1	0.5	0.1	0.1
2	1.0	0.2	0.2
3	1.4	0.3	0.2
4	1.9	0.4	0.3
5	2.4	0.5	0.4
6	2.9	0.6	0.5
7	3.4	0.7	0.6
8	3.9	0.8	0.7
9	4.4	0.9	0.8
10	4.8	1.0	0.8
20	9.7	2.0	1.7
30	14.5	3.0	2.5
40	19.3	4.0	3.3
50	24.2	5.0	4.2

Proportional parts

The −10 portion of the characteristic of the logarithm is not printed but must be written down whenever such a logarithm is used.

23° (203°) (336°) **156°**

′	L Sin	d	L Tan	c d	L Ctn	L Cos	d	′
0	9.59 188	30	9.62 785	35	10.37 215	9.96 403	6	60
1	9.59 218	29	9.62 820	35	10.37 180	9.96 397	5	59
2	9.59 247	30	9.62 855	35	10.37 145	9.96 392	5	58
3	9.59 277	30	9.62 890	36	10.37 110	9.96 387	6	57
4	9.59 307	29	9.62 926	35	10.37 074	9.96 381	5	56
5	9.59 336	30	9.62 961	35	10.37 039	9.96 376	6	55
6	9.59 366	30	9.62 996	35	10.37 004	9.96 370	5	54
7	9.59 396	29	9.63 031	35	10.36 969	9.96 365	5	53
8	9.59 425	30	9.63 066	35	10.36 934	9.96 360	6	52
9	9.59 455	29	9.63 101	34	10.36 899	9.96 354	5	51
10	9.59 484	30	9.63 135	35	10.36 865	9.96 349	6	50
11	9.59 514	29	9.63 170	35	10.36 830	9.96 343	5	49
12	9.59 543	30	9.63 205	35	10.36 795	9.96 338	5	48
13	9.59 573	29	9.63 240	35	10.36 760	9.96 333	6	47
14	9.59 602	30	9.63 275	35	10.36 725	9.96 327	5	46
15	9.59 632	29	9.63 310	35	10.36 690	9.96 322	6	45
16	9.59 661	29	9.63 345	34	10.36 655	9.96 316	5	44
17	9.59 690	30	9.63 379	35	10.36 621	9.96 311	6	43
18	9.59 720	29	9.63 414	35	10.36 586	9.96 305	5	42
19	9.59 749	29	9.63 449	35	10.36 551	9.96 300	6	41
20	9.59 778	30	9.63 484	35	10.36 516	9.96 294	5	40
21	9.59 808	29	9.63 519	34	10.36 481	9.96 289	5	39
22	9.59 837	29	9.63 553	35	10.36 447	9.96 284	6	38
23	9.59 866	29	9.63 588	35	10.36 412	9.96 278	5	37
24	9.59 895	29	9.63 623	34	10.36 377	9.96 273	6	36
25	9.59 924	30	9.63 657	35	10.36 343	9.96 267	5	35
26	9.59 954	29	9.63 692	34	10.36 308	9.96 262	6	34
27	9.59 983	29	9.63 726	35	10.36 274	9.96 256	5	33
28	9.60 012	29	9.63 761	35	10.36 239	9.96 251	6	32
29	9.60 041	29	9.63 796	34	10.36 204	9.96 245	5	31
30	9.60 070	29	9.63 830	35	10.36 170	9.96 240	6	30
31	9.60 099	29	9.63 865	34	10.36 135	9.96 234	5	29
32	9.60 128	29	9.63 899	35	10.36 101	9.96 229	6	28
33	9.60 157	29	9.63 934	34	10.36 066	9.96 223	5	27
34	9.60 186	29	9.63 968	35	10.36 032	9.96 218	6	26
35	9.60 215	29	9.64 003	34	10.35 997	9.96 212	5	25
36	9.60 244	29	9.64 037	35	10.35 963	9.96 207	6	24
37	9.60 273	29	9.64 072	34	10.35 928	9.96 201	5	23
38	9.60 302	29	9.64 106	34	10.35 894	9.96 196	6	22
39	9.60 331	28	9.64 140	35	10.35 860	9.96 190	5	21
40	9.60 359	29	9.64 175	34	10.35 825	9.96 185	6	20
41	9.60 388	29	9.64 209	34	10.35 791	9.96 179	5	19
42	9.60 417	29	9.64 243	35	10.35 757	9.96 174	6	18
43	9.60 446	28	9.64 278	34	10.35 722	9.96 168	6	17
44	9.60 474	29	9.64 312	34	10.35 688	9.96 162	5	16
45	9.60 503	29	9.64 346	35	10.35 654	9.96 157	6	15
46	9.60 532	29	9.64 381	34	10.35 619	9.96 151	5	14
47	9.60 561	28	9.64 415	34	10.35 585	9.96 146	6	13
48	9.60 589	29	9.64 449	34	10.35 551	9.96 140	5	12
49	9.60 618	28	9.64 483	34	10.35 517	9.96 135	6	11
50	9.60 646	29	9.64 517	35	10.35 483	9.96 129	6	10
51	9.60 675	29	9.64 552	34	10.35 448	9.96 123	5	9
52	9.60 704	28	9.64 586	34	10.35 414	9.96 118	6	8
53	9.60 732	29	9.64 620	34	10.35 380	9.96 112	5	7
54	9.60 761	28	9.64 654	34	10.35 346	9.96 107	6	6
55	9.60 789	29	9.64 688	34	10.35 312	9.96 101	6	5
56	9.60 818	28	9.64 722	34	10.35 278	9.96 095	5	4
57	9.60 846	29	9.64 756	34	10.35 244	9.96 090	6	3
58	9.60 875	28	9.64 790	34	10.35 210	9.96 084	5	2
59	9.60 903	28	9.64 824	34	10.35 176	9.96 079	6	1
60	9.60 931		9.64 858		10.35 142	9.96 073		0
′	L Cos	d	L Ctn	c d	L Tan	L Sin	d	′

Proportional parts

″	36	35	34
1	0.6	0.6	0.6
2	1.2	1.2	1.1
3	1.8	1.8	1.7
4	2.4	2.3	2.3
5	3.0	2.9	2.8
6	3.6	3.5	3.4
7	4.2	4.1	4.0
8	4.8	4.7	4.5
9	5.4	5.2	5.1
10	6.0	5.8	5.7
20	12.0	11.7	11.3
30	18.0	17.5	17.0
40	24.0	23.3	22.7
50	30.0	29.2	28.3

″	30	29	28
1	0.5	0.5	0.5
2	1.0	1.0	0.9
3	1.5	1.4	1.4
4	2.0	1.9	1.9
5	2.5	2.4	2.3
6	3.0	2.9	2.8
7	3.5	3.4	3.3
8	4.0	3.9	3.7
9	4.5	4.4	4.2
10	5.0	4.8	4.7
20	10.0	9.7	9.3
30	15.0	14.5	14.0
40	20.0	19.3	18.7
50	25.0	24.2	23.3

″	6	5
1	0.1	0.1
2	0.2	0.2
3	0.3	0.2
4	0.4	0.3
5	0.5	0.4
6	0.6	0.5
7	0.7	0.6
8	0.8	0.7
9	0.9	0.8
10	1.0	0.8
20	2.0	1.7
30	3.0	2.5
40	4.0	3.3
50	5.0	4.2

Proportional parts

113° (293°) (246°) **66°**

The −10 portion of the characteristic of the logarithm is not printed but must be written down whenever such a logarithm is used.

24° (204°) (335°) **155°**

′	L Sin	d	L Tan	c d	L Ctn	L Cos	d	′
0	9.60 931	29	9.64 858	34	10.35 142	9.96 073	6	60
1	9.60 960	28	9.64 892	34	10.35 108	9.96 067	5	59
2	9.60 988	28	9.64 926	34	10.35 074	9.96 062	6	58
3	9.61 016	29	9.64 960	34	10.35 040	9.96 056	6	57
4	9.61 045	28	9.64 994	34	10.35 006	9.96 050	5	56
5	9.61 073	28	9.65 028	34	10.34 972	9.96 045	6	55
6	9.61 101	28	9.65 062	34	10.34 938	9.96 039	5	54
7	9.61 129	29	9.65 096	34	10.34 904	9.96 034	6	53
8	9.61 158	28	9.65 130	34	10.34 870	9.96 028	6	52
9	9.61 186	28	9.65 164	33	10.34 836	9.96 022	5	51
10	9.61 214	28	9.65 197	34	10.34 803	9.96 017	6	50
11	9.61 242	28	9.65 231	34	10.34 769	9.96 011	6	49
12	9.61 270	28	9.65 265	34	10.34 735	9.96 005	5	48
13	9.61 298	28	9.65 299	34	10.34 701	9.96 000	6	47
14	9.61 326	28	9.65 333	33	10.34 667	9.95 994	6	46
15	9.61 354	28	9.65 366	34	10.34 634	9.95 988	6	45
16	9.61 382	29	9.65 400	34	10.34 600	9.95 982	5	44
17	9.61 411	27	9.65 434	33	10.34 566	9.95 977	6	43
18	9.61 438	28	9.65 467	34	10.34 533	9.95 971	6	42
19	9.61 466	28	9.65 501	34	10.34 499	9.95 965	5	41
20	9.61 494	28	9.65 535	33	10.34 465	9.95 960	6	40
21	9.61 522	28	9.65 568	34	10.34 432	9.95 954	6	39
22	9.61 550	28	9.65 602	34	10.34 398	9.95 948	6	38
23	9.61 578	28	9.65 636	33	10.34 364	9.95 942	5	37
24	9.61 606	28	9.65 669	34	10.34 331	9.95 937	6	36
25	9.61 634	28	9.65 703	33	10.34 297	9.95 931	6	35
26	9.61 662	27	9.65 736	34	10.34 264	9.95 925	5	34
27	9.61 689	28	9.65 770	33	10.34 230	9.95 920	6	33
28	9.61 717	28	9.65 803	34	10.34 197	9.95 914	6	32
29	9.61 745	28	9.65 837	33	10.34 163	9.95 908	6	31
30	9.61 773	27	9.65 870	34	10.34 130	9.95 902	5	30
31	9.61 800	28	9.65 904	33	10.34 096	9.95 897	6	29
32	9.61 828	28	9.65 937	34	10.34 063	9.95 891	6	28
33	9.61 856	27	9.65 971	33	10.34 029	9.95 885	6	27
34	9.61 883	28	9.66 004	34	10.33 996	9.95 879	6	26
35	9.61 911	28	9.66 038	33	10.33 962	9.95 873	5	25
36	9.61 939	27	9.66 071	33	10.33 929	9.95 868	6	24
37	9.61 966	28	9.66 104	34	10.33 896	9.95 862	6	23
38	9.61 994	27	9.66 138	33	10.33 862	9.95 856	6	22
39	9.62 021	28	9.66 171	33	10.33 829	9.95 850	6	21
40	9.62 049	27	9.66 204	34	10.33 796	9.95 844	5	20
41	9.62 076	28	9.66 238	33	10.33 762	9.95 839	6	19
42	9.62 104	27	9.66 271	33	10.33 729	9.95 833	6	18
43	9.62 131	28	9.66 304	33	10.33 696	9.95 827	6	17
44	9.62 159	27	9.66 337	34	10.33 663	9.95 821	6	16
45	9.62 186	28	9.66 371	33	10.33 629	9.95 815	5	15
46	9.62 214	27	9.66 404	33	10.33 596	9.95 810	6	14
47	9.62 241	27	9.66 437	33	10.33 563	9.95 804	6	13
48	9.62 268	28	9.66 470	33	10.33 530	9.95 798	6	12
49	9.62 296	27	9.66 503	34	10.33 497	9.95 792	6	11
50	9.62 323	27	9.66 537	33	10.33 463	9.95 786	6	10
51	9.62 350	27	9.66 570	33	10.33 430	9.95 780	5	9
52	9.62 377	28	9.66 603	33	10.33 397	9.95 775	6	8
53	9.62 405	27	9.66 636	33	10.33 364	9.95 769	6	7
54	9.62 432	27	9.66 669	33	10.33 331	9.95 763	6	6
55	9.62 459	27	9.66 702	33	10.33 298	9.95 757	6	5
56	9.62 486	27	9.66 735	33	10.33 265	9.95 751	6	4
57	9.62 513	28	9.66 768	33	10.33 232	9.95 745	6	3
58	9.62 541	27	9.66 801	33	10.33 199	9.95 739	6	2
59	9.62 568	27	9.66 834	33	10.33 166	9.95 733	5	1
60	9.62 595		9.66 867		10.33 133	9.95 728		0
′	L Cos	d	L Ctn	c d	L Tan	L Sin	d	′

Proportional parts

″	34	33
1	0.6	0.6
2	1.1	1.1
3	1.7	1.6
4	2.3	2.2
5	2.8	2.8
6	3.4	3.3
7	4.0	3.8
8	4.5	4.4
9	5.1	5.0
10	5.7	5.5
20	11.3	11.0
30	17.0	16.5
40	22.7	22.0
50	28.3	27.5

″	29	28	27
1	0.5	0.5	0.4
2	1.0	0.9	0.9
3	1.4	1.4	1.4
4	1.9	1.9	1.8
5	2.4	2.3	2.2
6	2.9	2.8	2.7
7	3.4	3.3	3.2
8	3.9	3.7	3.6
9	4.4	4.2	4.0
10	4.8	4.7	4.5
20	9.7	9.3	9.0
30	14.5	14.0	13.5
40	19.3	18.7	18.0
50	24.2	23.3	22.5

″	6	5
1	0.1	0.1
2	0.2	0.2
3	0.3	0.2
4	0.4	0.3
5	0.5	0.4
6	0.6	0.5
7	0.7	0.6
8	0.8	0.7
9	0.9	0.8
10	1.0	0.8
20	2.0	1.7
30	3.0	2.5
40	4.0	3.3
50	5.0	4.2

114° (294°) (245°) **65°**

The −10 portion of the characteristic of the logarithm is not printed but must be written down whenever such a logarithm is used.

25° (205°) (334°) **154°**

′	L Sin	d	L Tan	c d	L Ctn	L Cos	d	′
0	9.62 595	27	9.66 867	33	10.33 133	9.95 728	6	60
1	9.62 622	27	9.66 900	33	10.33 100	9.95 722	6	59
2	9.62 649	27	9.66 933	33	10.33 067	9.95 716	6	58
3	9.62 676	27	9.66 966	33	10.33 034	9.95 710	6	57
4	9.62 703	27	9.66 999	33	10.33 001	9.95 704	6	56
5	9.62 730	27	9.67 032	33	10.32 968	9.95 698	6	55
6	9.62 757	27	9.67 065	33	10.32 935	9.95 692	6	54
7	9.62 784	27	9.67 098	33	10.32 902	9.95 686	6	53
8	9.62 811	27	9.67 131	32	10.32 869	9.95 680	6	52
9	9.62 838	27	9.67 163	33	10.32 837	9.95 674	6	51
10	9.62 865	27	9.67 196	33	10.32 804	9.95 668	5	50
11	9.62 892	26	9.67 229	33	10.32 771	9.95 663	6	49
12	9.62 918	27	9.67 262	33	10.32 738	9.95 657	6	48
13	9.62 945	27	9.67 295	32	10.32 705	9.95 651	6	47
14	9.62 972	27	9.67 327	33	10.32 673	9.95 645	6	46
15	9.62 999	27	9.67 360	33	10.32 640	9.95 639	6	45
16	9.63 026	26	9.67 393	33	10.32 607	9.95 633	6	44
17	9.63 052	27	9.67 426	32	10.32 574	9.95 627	6	43
18	9.63 079	27	9.67 458	33	10.32 542	9.95 621	6	42
19	9.63 106	27	9.67 491	33	10.32 509	9.95 615	6	41
20	9.63 133	26	9.67 524	32	10.32 476	9.95 609	6	40
21	9.63 159	27	9.67 556	33	10.32 444	9.95 603	6	39
22	9.63 186	27	9.67 589	33	10.32 411	9.95 597	6	38
23	9.63 213	26	9.67 622	32	10.32 378	9.95 591	6	37
24	9.63 239	27	9.67 654	33	10.32 346	9.95 585	6	36
25	9.63 266	26	9.67 687	32	10.32 313	9.95 579	6	35
26	9.63 292	27	9.67 719	33	10.32 281	9.95 573	6	34
27	9.63 319	26	9.67 752	33	10.32 248	9.95 567	6	33
28	9.63 345	27	9.67 785	32	10.32 215	9.95 561	6	32
29	9.63 372	26	9.67 817	33	10.32 183	9.95 555	6	31
30	9.63 398	27	9.67 850	32	10.32 150	9.95 549	6	30
31	9.63 425	26	9.67 882	33	10.32 118	9.95 543	6	29
32	9.63 451	27	9.67 915	32	10.32 085	9.95 537	6	28
33	9.63 478	26	9.67 947	33	10.32 053	9.95 531	6	27
34	9.63 504	27	9.67 980	32	10.32 020	9.95 525	6	26
35	9.63 531	26	9.68 012	32	10.31 988	9.95 519	6	25
36	9.63 557	26	9.68 044	33	10.31 956	9.95 513	6	24
37	9.63 583	27	9.68 077	32	10.31 923	9.95 507	7	23
38	9.63 610	26	9.68 109	33	10.31 891	9.95 500	6	22
39	9.63 636	26	9.68 142	32	10.31 858	9.95 494	6	21
40	9.63 662	27	9.68 174	32	10.31 826	9.95 488	6	20
41	9.63 689	26	9.68 206	33	10.31 794	9.95 482	6	19
42	9.63 715	26	9.68 239	32	10.31 761	9.95 476	6	18
43	9.63 741	26	9.68 271	32	10.31 729	9.95 470	6	17
44	9.63 767	27	9.68 303	33	10.31 697	9.95 464	6	16
45	9.63 794	26	9.68 336	32	10.31 664	9.95 458	6	15
46	9.63 820	26	9.68 368	32	10.31 632	9.95 452	6	14
47	9.63 846	26	9.68 400	32	10.31 600	9.95 446	6	13
48	9.63 872	26	9.68 432	33	10.31 568	9.95 440	6	12
49	9.63 898	26	9.68 465	32	10.31 535	9.95 434	7	11
50	9.63 924	26	9.68 497	32	10.31 503	9.95 427	6	10
51	9.63 950	26	9.68 529	32	10.31 471	9.95 421	6	9
52	9.63 976	26	9.68 561	32	10.31 439	9.95 415	6	8
53	9.64 002	26	9.68 593	33	10.31 407	9.95 409	6	7
54	9.64 028	26	9.68 626	32	10.31 374	9.95 403	6	6
55	9.64 054	26	9.68 658	32	10.31 342	9.95 397	6	5
56	9.64 080	26	9.68 690	32	10.31 310	9.95 391	7	4
57	9.64 106	26	9.68 722	32	10.31 278	9.95 384	6	3
58	9.64 132	26	9.68 754	32	10.31 246	9.95 378	6	2
59	9.64 158	26	9.68 786	32	10.31 214	9.95 372	6	1
60	9.64 184		9.68 818		10.31 182	9.95 366		0
′	L Cos	d	L Ctn	c d	L Tan	L Sin	d	′

Proportional parts

″	33	32
1	0.6	0.5
2	1.1	1.1
3	1.6	1.6
4	2.2	2.1
5	2.8	2.7
6	3.3	3.2
7	3.8	3.7
8	4.4	4.3
9	5.0	4.8
10	5.5	5.3
20	11.0	10.7
30	16.5	16.0
40	22.0	21.3
50	27.5	26.7

″	27	26
1	0.4	0.4
2	0.9	0.9
3	1.4	1.3
4	1.8	1.7
5	2.2	2.2
6	2.7	2.6
7	3.2	3.0
8	3.6	3.5
9	4.0	3.9
10	4.5	4.3
20	9.0	8.7
30	13.5	13.0
40	18.0	17.3
50	22.5	21.7

″	7	6	5
1	0.1	0.1	0.1
2	0.2	0.2	0.2
3	0.4	0.3	0.2
4	0.5	0.4	0.3
5	0.6	0.5	0.4
6	0.7	0.6	0.5
7	0.8	0.7	0.6
8	0.9	0.8	0.7
9	1.0	0.9	0.8
10	1.2	1.0	0.8
20	2.3	2.0	1.7
30	3.5	3.0	2.5
40	4.7	4.0	3.3
50	5.8	5.0	4.2

Proportional parts

115° (295°) (244°) **64°**

The −10 portion of the characteristic of the logarithm is not printed but must be written down whenever such a logarithm is used.

26° (206°) (333°) **153°**

′	L Sin	d	L Tan	c d	L Ctn	L Cos	d	′
0	9.64 184	26	9.68 818	32	10.31 182	9.95 366	6	60
1	9.64 210	26	9.68 850	32	10.31 150	9.95 360	6	59
2	9.64 236	26	9.68 882	32	10.31 118	9.95 354	6	58
3	9.64 262	26	9.68 914	32	10.31 086	9.95 348	7	57
4	9.64 288	25	9.68 946	32	10.31 054	9.95 341	6	56
5	9.64 313	26	9.68 978	32	10.31 022	9.95 335	6	55
6	9.64 339	26	9.69 010	32	10.30 990	9.95 329	6	54
7	9.64 365	26	9.69 042	32	10.30 958	9.95 323	6	53
8	9.64 391	26	9.69 074	32	10.30 926	9.95 317	7	52
9	9.64 417	25	9.69 106	32	10.30 894	9.95 310	6	51
10	9.64 442	26	9.69 138	32	10.30 862	9.95 304	6	50
11	9.64 468	26	9.69 170	32	10.30 830	9.95 298	6	49
12	9.64 494	25	9.69 202	32	10.30 798	9.95 292	6	48
13	9.64 519	26	9.69 234	32	10.30 766	9.95 286	7	47
14	9.64 545	26	9.69 266	32	10.30 734	9.95 279	6	46
15	9.64 571	25	9.69 298	31	10.30 702	9.95 273	6	45
16	9.64 596	26	9.69 329	32	10.30 671	9.95 267	6	44
17	9.64 622	25	9.69 361	32	10.30 639	9.95 261	7	43
18	9.64 647	26	9.69 393	32	10.30 607	9.95 254	6	42
19	9.64 673	25	9.69 425	32	10.30 575	9.95 248	6	41
20	9.64 698	26	9.69 457	31	10.30 543	9.95 242	6	40
21	9.64 724	25	9.69 488	32	10.30 512	9.95 236	7	39
22	9.64 749	26	9.69 520	32	10.30 480	9.95 229	6	38
23	9.64 775	25	9.69 552	32	10.30 448	9.95 223	6	37
24	9.64 800	26	9.69 584	31	10.30 416	9.95 217	6	36
25	9.64 826	25	9.69 615	32	10.30 385	9.95 211	7	35
26	9.64 851	26	9.69 647	32	10.30 353	9.95 204	6	34
27	9.64 877	25	9.69 679	31	10.30 321	9.95 198	6	33
28	9.64 902	25	9.69 710	32	10.30 290	9.95 192	7	32
29	9.64 927	26	9.69 742	32	10.30 258	9.95 185	6	31
30	9.64 953	25	9.69 774	31	10.30 226	9.95 179	6	30
31	9.64 978	25	9.69 805	32	10.30 195	9.95 173	6	29
32	9.65 003	26	9.69 837	31	10.30 163	9.95 167	7	28
33	9.65 029	25	9.69 868	32	10.30 132	9.95 160	6	27
34	9.65 054	25	9.69 900	32	10.30 100	9.95 154	6	26
35	9.65 079	25	9.69 932	31	10.30 068	9.95 148	7	25
36	9.65 104	26	9.69 963	32	10.30 037	9.95 141	6	24
37	9.65 130	25	9.69 995	31	10.30 005	9.95 135	6	23
38	9.65 155	25	9.70 026	32	10.29 974	9.95 129	7	22
39	9.65 180	25	9.70 058	31	10.29 942	9.95 122	6	21
40	9.65 205	25	9.70 089	32	10.29 911	9.95 116	6	20
41	9.65 230	25	9.70 121	31	10.29 879	9.95 110	7	19
42	9.65 255	26	9.70 152	32	10.29 848	9.95 103	6	18
43	9.65 281	25	9.70 184	31	10.29 816	9.95 097	7	17
44	9.65 306	25	9.70 215	32	10.29 785	9.95 090	6	16
45	9.65 331	25	9.70 247	31	10.29 753	9.95 084	6	15
46	9.65 356	25	9.70 278	31	10.29 722	9.95 078	7	14
47	9.65 381	25	9.70 309	32	10.29 691	9.95 071	6	13
48	9.65 406	25	9.70 341	31	10.29 659	9.95 065	6	12
49	9.65 431	25	9.70 372	32	10.29 628	9.95 059	7	11
50	9.65 456	25	9.70 404	31	10.29 596	9.95 052	6	10
51	9.65 481	25	9.70 435	31	10.29 565	9.95 046	7	9
52	9.65 506	25	9.70 466	32	10.29 534	9.95 039	6	8
53	9.65 531	25	9.70 498	31	10.29 502	9.95 033	6	7
54	9.65 556	24	9.70 529	31	10.29 471	9.95 027	7	6
55	9.65 580	25	9.70 560	32	10.29 440	9.95 020	6	5
56	9.65 605	25	9.70 592	31	10.29 408	9.95 014	7	4
57	9.65 630	25	9.70 623	31	10.29 377	9.95 007	6	3
58	9.65 655	25	9.70 654	31	10.29 346	9.95 001	6	2
59	9.65 680	25	9.70 685	32	10.29 315	9.94 995	7	1
60	9.65 705		9.70 717		10.29 283	9.94 988		0
′	L Cos	d	L Ctn	c d	L Tan	L Sin	d	′

Proportional parts

″	32	31
1	0.5	0.5
2	1.1	1.0
3	1.6	1.6
4	2.1	2.1
5	2.7	2.6
6	3.2	3.1
7	3.7	3.6
8	4.3	4.1
9	4.8	4.6
10	5.3	5.2
20	10.7	10.3
30	16.0	15.5
40	21.3	20.7
50	26.7	25.8

″	26	25	24
1	0.4	0.4	0.4
2	0.9	0.8	0.8
3	1.3	1.2	1.2
4	1.7	1.7	1.6
5	2.2	2.1	2.0
6	2.6	2.5	2.4
7	3.0	2.9	2.8
8	3.5	3.3	3.2
9	3.9	3.8	3.6
10	4.3	4.2	4.0
20	8.7	8.3	8.0
30	13.0	12.5	12.0
40	17.3	16.7	16.0
50	21.7	20.8	20.0

″	7	6
1	0.1	0.1
2	0.2	0.2
3	0.4	0.3
4	0.5	0.4
5	0.6	0.5
6	0.7	0.6
7	0.8	0.7
8	0.9	0.8
9	1.0	0.9
10	1.2	1.0
20	2.3	2.0
30	3.5	3.0
40	4.7	4.0
50	5.8	5.0

Proportional parts

116° (296°) (243°) **63°**

The −10 portion of the characteristic of the logarithm is not printed but must be written down whenever such a logarithm is used.

27° (207°) (332°) **152°**

′	L Sin	d	L Tan	c d	L Ctn	L Cos	d	′
0	9.65 705	24	9.70 717	31	10.29 283	9.94 988	6	60
1	9.65 729	25	9.70 748	31	10.29 252	9.94 982	7	59
2	9.65 754	25	9.70 779	31	10.29 221	9.94 975	6	58
3	9.65 779	25	9.70 810	31	10.29 190	9.94 969	7	57
4	9.65 804	24	9.70 841	32	10.29 159	9.94 962	6	56
5	9.65 828	25	9.70 873	31	10.29 127	9.94 956	7	55
6	9.65 853	25	9.70 904	31	10.29 096	9.94 949	6	54
7	9.65 878	24	9.70 935	31	10.29 065	9.94 943	7	53
8	9.65 902	25	9.70 966	31	10.29 034	9.94 936	6	52
9	9.65 927	25	9.70 997	31	10.29 003	9.94 930	7	51
10	9.65 952	24	9.71 028	31	10.28 972	9.94 923	6	50
11	9.65 976	25	9.71 059	31	10.28 941	9.94 917	6	49
12	9.66 001	24	9.71 090	31	10.28 910	9.94 911	7	48
13	9.66 025	25	9.71 121	32	10.28 879	9.94 904	6	47
14	9.66 050	25	9.71 153	31	10.28 847	9.94 898	7	46
15	9.66 075	24	9.71 184	31	10.28 816	9.94 891	6	45
16	9.66 099	25	9.71 215	31	10.28 785	9.94 885	7	44
17	9.66 124	24	9.71 246	31	10.28 754	9.94 878	7	43
18	9.66 148	25	9.71 277	31	10.28 723	9.94 871	6	42
19	9.66 173	24	9.71 308	31	10.28 692	9.94 865	7	41
20	9.66 197	24	9.71 339	31	10.28 661	9.94 858	6	40
21	9.66 221	25	9.71 370	31	10.28 630	9.94 852	7	39
22	9.66 246	24	9.71 401	30	10.28 599	9.94 845	6	38
23	9.66 270	25	9.71 431	31	10.28 569	9.94 839	7	37
24	9.66 295	24	9.71 462	31	10.28 538	9.94 832	6	36
25	9.66 319	24	9.71 493	31	10.28 507	9.94 826	7	35
26	9.66 343	25	9.71 524	31	10.28 476	9.94 819	6	34
27	9.66 368	24	9.71 555	31	10.28 445	9.94 813	7	33
28	9.66 392	24	9.71 586	31	10.28 414	9.94 806	7	32
29	9.66 416	25	9.71 617	31	10.28 383	9.94 799	6	31
30	9.66 441	24	9.71 648	31	10.28 352	9.94 793	7	30
31	9.66 465	24	9.71 679	30	10.28 321	9.94 786	6	29
32	9.66 489	24	9.71 709	31	10.28 291	9.94 780	7	28
33	9.66 513	24	9.71 740	31	10.28 260	9.94 773	6	27
34	9.66 537	25	9.71 771	31	10.28 229	9.94 767	7	26
35	9.66 562	24	9.71 802	31	10.28 198	9.94 760	7	25
36	9.66 586	24	9.71 833	30	10.28 167	9.94 753	6	24
37	9.66 610	24	9.71 863	31	10.28 137	9.94 747	7	23
38	9.66 634	24	9.71 894	31	10.28 106	9.94 740	6	22
39	9.66 658	24	9.71 925	30	10.28 075	9.94 734	7	21
40	9.66 682	24	9.71 955	31	10.28 045	9.94 727	7	20
41	9.66 706	25	9.71 986	31	10.28 014	9.94 720	6	19
42	9.66 731	24	9.72 017	31	10.27 983	9.94 714	7	18
43	9.66 755	24	9.72 048	30	10.27 952	9.94 707	7	17
44	9.66 779	24	9.72 078	31	10.27 922	9.94 700	6	16
45	9.66 803	24	9.72 109	31	10.27 891	9.94 694	7	15
46	9.66 827	24	9.72 140	30	10.27 860	9.94 687	7	14
47	9.66 851	24	9.72 170	31	10.27 830	9.94 680	6	13
48	9.66 875	24	9.72 201	30	10.27 799	9.94 674	7	12
49	9.66 899	23	9.72 231	31	10.27 769	9.94 667	7	11
50	9.66 922	24	9.72 262	31	10.27 738	9.94 660	6	10
51	9.66 946	24	9.72 293	30	10.27 707	9.94 654	7	9
52	9.66 970	24	9.72 323	31	10.27 677	9.94 647	7	8
53	9.66 994	24	9.72 354	30	10.27 646	9.94 640	6	7
54	9.67 018	24	9.72 384	31	10.27 616	9.94 634	7	6
55	9.67 042	24	9.72 415	30	10.27 585	9.94 627	7	5
56	9.67 066	24	9.72 445	31	10.27 555	9.94 620	6	4
57	9.67 090	23	9.72 476	30	10.27 524	9.94 614	7	3
58	9.67 113	24	9.72 506	31	10.27 494	9.94 607	7	2
59	9.67 137	24	9.72 537	30	10.27 463	9.94 600	7	1
60	9.67 161		9.72 567		10.27 433	9.94 593		0
′	L Cos	d	L Ctn	c d	L Tan	L Sin	d	′

Proportional parts

″	32	31	30
1	0.5	0.5	0.5
2	1.1	1.0	1.0
3	1.6	1.6	1.5
4	2.1	2.1	2.0
5	2.7	2.6	2.5
6	3.2	3.1	3.0
7	3.7	3.6	3.5
8	4.3	4.1	4.0
9	4.8	4.6	4.5
10	5.3	5.2	5.0
20	10.7	10.3	10.0
30	16.0	15.5	15.0
40	21.3	20.7	20.0
50	26.7	25.8	25.0

″	25	24	23
1	0.4	0.4	0.4
2	0.8	0.8	0.8
3	1.2	1.2	1.2
4	1.7	1.6	1.5
5	2.1	2.0	1.9
6	2.5	2.4	2.3
7	2.9	2.8	2.7
8	3.3	3.2	3.1
9	3.8	3.6	3.4
10	4.2	4.0	3.8
20	8.3	8.0	7.7
30	12.5	12.0	11.5
40	16.7	16.0	15.3
50	20.8	20.0	19.2

″	7	6
1	0.1	0.1
2	0.2	0.2
3	0.4	0.3
4	0.5	0.4
5	0.6	0.5
6	0.7	0.6
7	0.8	0.7
8	0.9	0.8
9	1.0	0.9
10	1.2	1.0
20	2.3	2.0
30	3.5	3.0
40	4.7	4.0
50	5.8	5.0

Proportional parts

117° (297°) (242°) **62°**

The -10 portion of the characteristic of the logarithm is not printed but must be written down whenever such a logarithm is used.

28° (208°) (331°) **151°**

′	L Sin	d	L Tan	c d	L Ctn	L Cos	d	′
0	9.67 161	24	9.72 567	31	10.27 433	9.94 593	6	60
1	9.67 185	23	9.72 598	30	10.27 402	9.94 587	7	59
2	9.67 208	24	9.72 628	31	10.27 372	9.94 580	7	58
3	9.67 232	24	9.72 659	30	10.27 341	9.94 573	6	57
4	9.67 256	24	9.72 689	31	10.27 311	9.94 567	7	56
5	9.67 280	23	9.72 720	30	10.27 280	9.94 560	7	55
6	9.67 303	24	9.72 750	30	10.27 250	9.94 553	7	54
7	9.67 327	23	9.72 780	31	10.27 220	9.94 546	6	53
8	9.67 350	24	9.72 811	30	10.27 189	9.94 540	7	52
9	9.67 374	24	9.72 841	31	10.27 159	9.94 533	7	51
10	9.67 398	23	9.72 872	30	10.27 128	9.94 526	7	50
11	9.67 421	24	9.72 902	30	10.27 098	9.94 519	6	49
12	9.67 445	23	9.72 932	31	10.27 068	9.94 513	7	48
13	9.67 468	24	9.72 963	30	10.27 037	9.94 506	7	47
14	9.67 492	23	9.72 993	30	10.27 007	9.94 499	7	46
15	9.67 515	24	9.73 023	31	10.26 977	9.94 492	7	45
16	9.67 539	23	9.73 054	30	10.26 946	9.94 485	6	44
17	9.67 562	24	9.73 084	30	10.26 916	9.94 479	7	43
18	9.67 586	23	9.73 114	30	10.26 886	9.94 472	7	42
19	9.67 609	24	9.73 144	31	10.26 856	9.94 465	7	41
20	9.67 633	23	9.73 175	30	10.26 825	9.94 458	7	40
21	9.67 656	24	9.73 205	30	10.26 795	9.94 451	6	39
22	9.67 680	23	9.73 235	30	10.26 765	9.94 445	7	38
23	9.67 703	23	9.73 265	30	10.26 735	9.94 438	7	37
24	9.67 726	24	9.73 295	31	10.26 705	9.94 431	7	36
25	9.67 750	23	9.73 326	30	10.26 674	9.94 424	7	35
26	9.67 773	23	9.73 356	30	10.26 644	9.94 417	7	34
27	9.67 796	24	9.73 386	30	10.26 614	9.94 410	6	33
28	9.67 820	23	9.73 416	30	10.26 584	9.94 404	7	32
29	9.67 843	23	9.73 446	30	10.26 554	9.94 397	7	31
30	9.67 866	24	9.73 476	31	10.26 524	9.94 390	7	30
31	9.67 890	23	9.73 507	30	10.26 493	9.94 383	7	29
32	9.67 913	23	9.73 537	30	10.26 463	9.94 376	7	28
33	9.67 936	23	9.73 567	30	10.26 433	9.94 369	7	27
34	9.67 959	23	9.73 597	30	10.26 403	9.94 362	7	26
35	9.67 982	24	9.73 627	30	10.26 373	9.94 355	6	25
36	9.68 006	23	9.73 657	30	10.26 343	9.94 349	7	24
37	9.68 029	23	9.73 687	30	10.26 313	9.94 342	7	23
38	9.68 052	23	9.73 717	30	10.26 283	9.94 335	7	22
39	9.68 075	23	9.73 747	30	10.26 253	9.94 328	7	21
40	9.68 098	23	9.73 777	30	10.26 223	9.94 321	7	20
41	9.68 121	23	9.73 807	30	10.26 193	9.94 314	7	19
42	9.68 144	23	9.73 837	30	10.26 163	9.94 307	7	18
43	9.68 167	23	9.73 867	30	10.26 133	9.94 300	7	17
44	9.68 190	23	9.73 897	30	10.26 103	9.94 293	7	16
45	9.68 213	24	9.73 927	30	10.26 073	9.94 286	7	15
46	9.68 237	23	9.73 957	30	10.26 043	9.94 279	6	14
47	9.68 260	23	9.73 987	30	10.26 013	9.94 273	7	13
48	9.68 283	22	9.74 017	30	10.25 983	9.94 266	7	12
49	9.68 305	23	9.74 047	30	10.25 953	9.94 259	7	11
50	9.68 328	23	9.74 077	30	10.25 923	9.94 252	7	10
51	9.68 351	23	9.74 107	30	10.25 893	9.94 245	7	9
52	9.68 374	23	9.74 137	29	10.25 863	9.94 238	7	8
53	9.68 397	23	9.74 166	30	10.25 834	9.94 231	7	7
54	9.68 420	23	9.74 196	30	10.25 804	9.94 224	7	6
55	9.68 443	23	9.74 226	30	10.25 774	9.94 217	7	5
56	9.68 466	23	9.74 256	30	10.25 744	9.94 210	7	4
57	9.68 489	23	9.74 286	30	10.25 714	9.94 203	7	3
58	9.68 512	22	9.74 316	29	10.25 684	9.94 196	7	2
59	9.68 534	23	9.74 345	30	10.25 655	9.94 189	7	1
60	9.68 557		9.74 375		10.25 625	9.94 182		0
′	L Cos	d	L Ctn	c d	L Tan	L Sin	d	′

Proportional parts

″	31	30	29
1	0.5	0.5	0.5
2	1.0	1.0	1.0
3	1.6	1.5	1.4
4	2.1	2.0	1.9
5	2.6	2.5	2.4
6	3.1	3.0	2.9
7	3.6	3.5	3.4
8	4.1	4.0	3.9
9	4.6	4.5	4.4
10	5.2	5.0	4.8
20	10.3	10.0	9.7
30	15.5	15.0	14.5
40	20.7	20.0	19.3
50	25.8	25.0	24.2

″	24	23	22
1	0.4	0.4	0.4
2	0.8	0.8	0.7
3	1.2	1.2	1.1
4	1.6	1.5	1.5
5	2.0	1.9	1.8
6	2.4	2.3	2.2
7	2.8	2.7	2.6
8	3.2	3.1	2.9
9	3.6	3.4	3.3
10	4.0	3.8	3.7
20	8.0	7.7	7.3
30	12.0	11.5	11.0
40	16.0	15.3	14.7
50	20.0	19.2	18.3

″	7	6
1	0.1	0.1
2	0.2	0.2
3	0.4	0.3
4	0.5	0.4
5	0.6	0.5
6	0.7	0.6
7	0.8	0.7
8	0.9	0.8
9	1.0	0.9
10	1.2	1.0
20	2.3	2.0
30	3.5	3.0
40	4.7	4.0
50	5.8	5.0

Proportional parts

118° (298°) (241°) **61°**

The −10 portion of the characteristic of the logarithm is not printed but must be written down whenever such a logarithm is used.

29° (209°) (330°) **150°**

′	L Sin	d	L Tan	c d	L Ctn	L Cos	d	′
0	9.68 557	23	9.74 375	30	10.25 625	9.94 182	7	60
1	9.68 580	23	9.74 405	30	10.25 595	9.94 175	7	59
2	9.68 603	22	9.74 435	30	10.25 565	9.94 168	7	58
3	9.68 625	23	9.74 465	29	10.25 535	9.94 161	7	57
4	9.68 648	23	9.74 494	30	10.25 506	9.94 154	7	56
5	9.68 671	23	9.74 524	30	10.25 476	9.94 147	7	55
6	9.68 694	22	9.74 554	29	10.25 446	9.94 140	7	54
7	9.68 716	23	9.74 583	30	10.25 417	9.94 133	7	53
8	9.68 739	23	9.74 613	30	10.25 387	9.94 126	7	52
9	9.68 762	22	9.74 643	30	10.25 357	9.94 119	7	51
10	9.68 784	23	9.74 673	29	10.25 327	9.94 112	7	50
11	9.68 807	22	9.74 702	30	10.25 298	9.94 105	7	49
12	9.68 829	23	9.74 732	30	10.25 268	9.94 098	8	48
13	9.68 852	23	9.74 762	29	10.25 238	9.94 090	7	47
14	9.68 875	22	9.74 791	30	10.25 209	9.94 083	7	46
15	9.68 897	23	9.74 821	30	10.25 179	9.94 076	7	45
16	9.68 920	22	9.74 851	29	10.25 149	9.94 069	7	44
17	9.68 942	23	9.74 880	30	10.25 120	9.94 062	7	43
18	9.68 965	22	9.74 910	29	10.25 090	9.94 055	7	42
19	9.68 987	23	9.74 939	30	10.25 061	9.94 048	7	41
20	9.69 010	22	9.74 969	29	10.25 031	9.94 041	7	40
21	9.69 032	23	9.74 998	30	10.25 002	9.94 034	7	39
22	9.69 055	22	9.75 028	30	10.24 972	9.94 027	7	38
23	9.69 077	23	9.75 058	29	10.24 942	9.94 020	8	37
24	9.69 100	22	9.75 087	30	10.24 913	9.94 012	7	36
25	9.69 122	22	9.75 117	29	10.24 883	9.94 005	7	35
26	9.69 144	23	9.75 146	30	10.24 854	9.93 998	7	34
27	9.69 167	22	9.75 176	29	10.24 824	9.93 991	7	33
28	9.69 189	23	9.75 205	30	10.24 795	9.93 984	7	32
29	9.69 212	22	9.75 235	29	10.24 765	9.93 977	7	31
30	9.69 234	22	9.75 264	30	10.24 736	9.93 970	7	30
31	9.69 256	23	9.75 294	29	10.24 706	9.93 963	8	29
32	9.69 279	22	9.75 323	30	10.24 677	9.93 955	7	28
33	9.69 301	22	9.75 353	29	10.24 647	9.93 948	7	27
34	9.69 323	22	9.75 382	29	10.24 618	9.93 941	7	26
35	9.69 345	23	9.75 411	30	10.24 589	9.93 934	7	25
36	9.69 368	22	9.75 441	29	10.24 559	9.93 927	7	24
37	9.69 390	22	9.75 470	30	10.24 530	9.93 920	8	23
38	9.69 412	22	9.75 500	29	10.24 500	9.93 912	7	22
39	9.69 434	22	9.75 529	29	10.24 471	9.93 905	7	21
40	9.69 456	23	9.75 558	30	10.24 442	9.93 898	7	20
41	9.69 479	22	9.75 588	29	10.24 412	9.93 891	7	19
42	9.69 501	22	9.75 617	30	10.24 383	9.93 884	8	18
43	9.69 523	22	9.75 647	29	10.24 353	9.93 876	7	17
44	9.69 545	22	9.75 676	29	10.24 324	9.93 869	7	16
45	9.69 567	22	9.75 705	30	10.24 295	9.93 862	7	15
46	9.69 589	22	9.75 735	29	10.24 265	9.93 855	8	14
47	9.69 611	22	9.75 764	29	10.24 236	9.93 847	7	13
48	9.69 633	22	9.75 793	29	10.24 207	9.93 840	7	12
49	9.69 655	22	9.75 822	30	10.24 178	9.93 833	7	11
50	9.69 677	22	9.75 852	29	10.24 148	9.93 826	7	10
51	9.69 699	22	9.75 881	29	10.24 119	9.93 819	8	9
52	9.69 721	22	9.75 910	29	10.24 090	9.93 811	7	8
53	9.69 743	22	9.75 939	30	10.24 061	9.93 804	7	7
54	9.69 765	22	9.75 969	29	10.24 031	9.93 797	8	6
55	9.69 787	22	9.75 998	29	10.24 002	9.93 789	7	5
56	9.69 809	22	9.76 027	29	10.23 973	9.93 782	7	4
57	9.69 831	22	9.76 056	30	10.23 944	9.93 775	7	3
58	9.69 853	22	9.76 086	29	10.23 914	9.93 768	8	2
59	9.69 875	22	9.76 115	29	10.23 885	9.93 760	7	1
60	9.69 897		9.76 144		10.23 856	9.93 753		0
′	L Cos	d	L Ctn	c d	L Tan	L Sin	d	′

Proportional parts

″	30	29	23
1	0.5	0.5	0.4
2	1.0	1.0	0.8
3	1.5	1.4	1.2
4	2.0	1.9	1.5
5	2.5	2.4	1.9
6	3.0	2.9	2.3
7	3.5	3.4	2.7
8	4.0	3.9	3.1
9	4.5	4.4	3.4
10	5.0	4.8	3.8
20	10.0	9.7	7.7
30	15.0	14.5	11.5
40	20.0	19.3	15.3
50	25.0	24.2	19.2

″	22	8	7
1	0.4	0.1	0.1
2	0.7	0.3	0.2
3	1.1	0.4	0.4
4	1.5	0.5	0.5
5	1.8	0.7	0.6
6	2.2	0.8	0.7
7	2.6	0.9	0.8
8	2.9	1.1	0.9
9	3.3	1.2	1.0
10	3.7	1.3	1.2
20	7.3	2.7	2.3
30	11.0	4.0	3.5
40	14.7	5.3	4.7
50	18.3	6.7	5.8

Proportional parts

119° (299) (240°) **60°**

The −10 portion of the characteristic of the logarithm is not printed but must be written down whenever such a logarithm is used.

30° (210°) (329°) **149°**

′	L Sin	d	L Tan	c d	L Ctn	L Cos	d	′
0	9.69 897	22	9.76 144	29	10.23 856	9.93 753	7	60
1	9.69 919	22	9.76 173	29	10.23 827	9.93 746	8	59
2	9.69 941	22	9.76 202	29	10.23 798	9.93 738	7	58
3	9.69 963	21	9.76 231	30	10.23 769	9.93 731	7	57
4	9.69 984	22	9.76 261	29	10.23 739	9.93 724	7	56
5	9.70 006	22	9.76 290	29	10.23 710	9.93 717	8	55
6	9.70 028	22	9.76 319	29	10.23 681	9.93 709	7	54
7	9.70 050	22	9.76 348	29	10.23 652	9.93 702	7	53
8	9.70 072	21	9.76 377	29	10.23 623	9.93 695	8	52
9	9.70 093	22	9.76 406	29	10.23 594	9.93 687	7	51
10	9.70 115	22	9.76 435	29	10.23 565	9.93 680	7	50
11	9.70 137	22	9.76 464	29	10.23 536	9.93 673	8	49
12	9.70 159	21	9.76 493	29	10.23 507	9.93 665	7	48
13	9.70 180	22	9.76 522	29	10.23 478	9.93 658	8	47
14	9.70 202	22	9.76 551	29	10.23 449	9.93 650	7	46
15	9.70 224	21	9.76 580	29	10.23 420	9.93 643	7	45
16	9.70 245	22	9.76 609	30	10.23 391	9.93 636	8	44
17	9.70 267	21	9.76 639	29	10.23 361	9.93 628	7	43
18	9.70 288	22	9.76 668	29	10.23 332	9.93 621	7	42
19	9.70 310	22	9.76 697	28	10.23 303	9.93 614	8	41
20	9.70 332	21	9.76 725	29	10.23 275	9.93 606	7	40
21	9.70 353	22	9.76 754	29	10.23 246	9.93 599	8	39
22	9.70 375	21	9.76 783	29	10.23 217	9.93 591	7	38
23	9.70 396	22	9.76 812	29	10.23 188	9.93 584	7	37
24	9.70 418	21	9.76 841	29	10.23 159	9.93 577	8	36
25	9.70 439	22	9.76 870	29	10.23 130	9.93 569	7	35
26	9.70 461	21	9.76 899	29	10.23 101	9.93 562	8	34
27	9.70 482	22	9.76 928	29	10.23 072	9.93 554	7	33
28	9.70 504	21	9.76 957	29	10.23 043	9.93 547	8	32
29	9.70 525	22	9.76 986	29	10.23 014	9.93 539	7	31
30	9.70 547	21	9.77 015	29	10.22 985	9.93 532	7	30
31	9.70 568	22	9.77 044	29	10.22 956	9.93 525	8	29
32	9.70 590	21	9.77 073	28	10.22 927	9.93 517	7	28
33	9.70 611	22	9.77 101	29	10.22 899	9.93 510	8	27
34	9.70 633	21	9.77 130	29	10.22 870	9.93 502	7	26
35	9.70 654	21	9.77 159	29	10.22 841	9.93 495	8	25
36	9.70 675	22	9.77 188	29	10.22 812	9.93 487	7	24
37	9.70 697	21	9.77 217	29	10.22 783	9.93 480	8	23
38	9.70 718	21	9.77 246	28	10.22 754	9.93 472	7	22
39	9.70 739	22	9.77 274	29	10.22 726	9.93 465	8	21
40	9.70 761	21	9.77 303	29	10.22 697	9.93 457	7	20
41	9.70 782	21	9.77 332	29	10.22 668	9.93 450	8	19
42	9.70 803	21	9.77 361	29	10.22 639	9.93 442	7	18
43	9.70 824	22	9.77 390	28	10.22 610	9.93 435	8	17
44	9.70 846	21	9.77 418	29	10.22 582	9.93 427	7	16
45	9.70 867	21	9.77 447	29	10.22 553	9.93 420	8	15
46	9.70 888	21	9.77 476	29	10.22 524	9.93 412	7	14
47	9.70 909	22	9.77 505	28	10.22 495	9.93 405	8	13
48	9.70 931	21	9.77 533	29	10.22 467	9.93 397	7	12
49	9.70 952	21	9.77 562	29	10.22 438	9.93 390	8	11
50	9.70 973	21	9.77 591	28	10.22 409	9.93 382	7	10
51	9.70 994	21	9.77 619	29	10.22 381	9.93 375	8	9
52	9.71 015	21	9.77 648	29	10.22 352	9.93 367	7	8
53	9.71 036	22	9.77 677	29	10.22 323	9.93 360	8	7
54	9.71 058	21	9.77 706	28	10.22 294	9.93 352	8	6
55	9.71 079	21	9.77 734	29	10.22 266	9.93 344	7	5
56	9.71 100	21	9.77 763	28	10.22 237	9.93 337	8	4
57	9.71 121	21	9.77 791	29	10.22 209	9.93 329	7	3
58	9.71 142	21	9.77 820	29	10.22 180	9.93 322	8	2
59	9.71 163	21	9.77 849	28	10.22 151	9.93 314	7	1
60	9.71 184		9.77 877		10.22 123	9.93 307		0
′	L Cos	d	L Ctn	c d	L Tan	L Sin	d	′

Proportional parts

″	30	29	28
1	0.5	0.5	0.5
2	1.0	1.0	0.9
3	1.5	1.4	1.4
4	2.0	1.9	1.9
5	2.5	2.4	2.3
6	3.0	2.9	2.8
7	3.5	3.4	3.3
8	4.0	3.9	3.7
9	4.5	4.4	4.2
10	5.0	4.8	4.7
20	10.0	9.7	9.3
30	15.0	14.5	14.0
40	20.0	19.3	18.7
50	25.0	24.2	23.3

″	22	21
1	0.4	0.4
2	0.7	0.7
3	1.1	1.0
4	1.5	1.4
5	1.8	1.8
6	2.2	2.1
7	2.6	2.4
8	2.9	2.8
9	3.3	3.2
10	3.7	3.5
20	7.3	7.0
30	11.0	10.5
40	14.7	14.0
50	18.3	17.5

″	8	7
1	0.1	0.1
2	0.3	0.2
3	0.4	0.4
4	0.5	0.5
5	0.7	0.6
6	0.8	0.7
7	0.9	0.8
8	1.1	0.9
9	1.2	1.0
10	1.3	1.2
20	2.7	2.3
30	4.0	3.5
40	5.3	4.7
50	6.7	5.8

Proportional parts

120° (300°) (239°) **59°**

The −10 portion of the characteristic of the logarithm is not printed but must be written down whenever such a logarithm is used.

31° (211°) (328°) **148°**

′	L Sin	d	L Tan	c d	L Ctn	L Cos	d	′
0	9.71 184	21	9.77 877	29	10.22 123	9.93 307	8	60
1	9.71 205	21	9.77 906	29	10.22 094	9.93 299	8	59
2	9.71 226	21	9.77 935	28	10.22 065	9.93 291	7	58
3	9.71 247	21	9.77 963	29	10.22 037	9.93 284	8	57
4	9.71 268	21	9.77 992	28	10.22 008	9.93 276	7	56
5	9.71 289	21	9.78 020	29	10.21 980	9.93 269	8	55
6	9.71 310	21	9.78 049	28	10.21 951	9.93 261	8	54
7	9.71 331	21	9.78 077	29	10.21 923	9.93 253	7	53
8	9.71 352	21	9.78 106	29	10.21 894	9.93 246	8	52
9	9.71 373	20	9.78 135	28	10.21 865	9.93 238	8	51
10	9.71 393	21	9.78 163	29	10.21 837	9.93 230	7	50
11	9.71 414	21	9.78 192	28	10.21 808	9.93 223	8	49
12	9.71 435	21	9.78 220	29	10.21 780	9.93 215	8	48
13	9.71 456	21	9.78 249	28	10.21 751	9.93 207	7	47
14	9.71 477	21	9.78 277	29	10.21 723	9.93 200	8	46
15	9.71 498	21	9.78 306	28	10.21 694	9.93 192	8	45
16	9.71 519	20	9.78 334	29	10.21 666	9.93 184	7	44
17	9.71 539	21	9.78 363	28	10.21 637	9.93 177	8	43
18	9.71 560	21	9.78 391	28	10.21 609	9.93 169	8	42
19	9.71 581	21	9.78 419	29	10.21 581	9.93 161	7	41
20	9.71 602	20	9.78 448	28	10.21 552	9.93 154	8	40
21	9.71 622	21	9.78 476	29	10.21 524	9.93 146	8	39
22	9.71 643	21	9.78 505	28	10.21 495	9.93 138	7	38
23	9.71 664	21	9.78 533	29	10.21 467	9.93 131	8	37
24	9.71 685	20	9.78 562	28	10.21 438	9.93 123	8	36
25	9.71 705	21	9.78 590	28	10.21 410	9.93 115	7	35
26	9.71 726	21	9.78 618	29	10.21 382	9.93 108	8	34
27	9.71 747	20	9.78 647	28	10.21 353	9.93 100	8	33
28	9.71 767	21	9.78 675	29	10.21 325	9.93 092	8	32
29	9.71 788	21	9.78 704	28	10.21 296	9.93 084	7	31
30	9.71 809	20	9.78 732	28	10.21 268	9.93 077	8	30
31	9.71 829	21	9.78 760	29	10.21 240	9.93 069	8	29
32	9.71 850	20	9.78 789	28	10.21 211	9.93 061	8	28
33	9.71 870	21	9.78 817	28	10.21 183	9.93 053	7	27
34	9.71 891	20	9.78 845	29	10.21 155	9.93 046	8	26
35	9.71 911	21	9.78 874	28	10.21 126	9.93 038	8	25
36	9.71 932	20	9.78 902	28	10.21 098	9.93 030	8	24
37	9.71 952	21	9.78 930	29	10.21 070	9.93 022	8	23
38	9.71 973	21	9.78 959	28	10.21 041	9.93 014	7	22
39	9.71 994	20	9.78 987	28	10.21 013	9.93 007	8	21
40	9.72 014	20	9.79 015	28	10.20 985	9.92 999	8	20
41	9.72 034	21	9.79 043	29	10.20 957	9.92 991	8	19
42	9.72 055	20	9.79 072	28	10.20 928	9.92 983	7	18
43	9.72 075	21	9.79 100	28	10.20 900	9.92 976	8	17
44	9.72 096	20	9.79 128	28	10.20 872	9.92 968	8	16
45	9.72 116	21	9.79 156	29	10.20 844	9.92 960	8	15
46	9.72 137	20	9.79 185	28	10.20 815	9.92 952	8	14
47	9.72 157	20	9.79 213	28	10.20 787	9.92 944	8	13
48	9.72 177	21	9.79 241	28	10.20 759	9.92 936	7	12
49	9.72 198	20	9.79 269	28	10.20 731	9.92 929	8	11
50	9.72 218	20	9.79 297	29	10.20 703	9.92 921	8	10
51	9.72 238	21	9.79 326	28	10.20 674	9.92 913	8	9
52	9.72 259	20	9.79 354	28	10.20 646	9.92 905	8	8
53	9.72 279	20	9.79 382	28	10.20 618	9.92 897	8	7
54	9.72 299	21	9.79 410	28	10.20 590	9.92 889	8	6
55	9.72 320	20	9.79 438	28	10.20 562	9.92 881	7	5
56	9.72 340	20	9.79 466	29	10.20 534	9.92 874	8	4
57	9.72 360	21	9.79 495	28	10.20 505	9.92 866	8	3
58	9.72 381	20	9.79 523	28	10.20 477	9.92 858	8	2
59	9.72 401	20	9.79 551	28	10.20 449	9.92 850	8	1
60	9.72 421		9.79 579		10.20 421	9.92 842		0
′	L Cos	d	L Ctn	c d	L Tan	L Sin	d	′

Proportional parts

″	29	28
1	0.5	0.5
2	1.0	0.9
3	1.4	1.4
4	1.9	1.9
5	2.4	2.3
6	2.9	2.8
7	3.4	3.3
8	3.9	3.7
9	4.4	4.2
10	4.8	4.7
20	9.7	9.3
30	14.5	14.0
40	19.3	18.7
50	24.2	23.3

″	21	20
1	0.4	0.3
2	0.7	0.7
3	1.0	1.0
4	1.4	1.3
5	1.8	1.7
6	2.1	2.0
7	2.4	2.3
8	2.8	2.7
9	3.2	3.0
10	3.5	3.3
20	7.0	6.7
30	10.5	10.0
40	14.0	13.3
50	17.5	16.7

″	8	7
1	0.1	0.1
2	0.3	0.2
3	0.4	0.4
4	0.5	0.5
5	0.7	0.6
6	0.8	0.7
7	0.9	0.8
8	1.1	0.9
9	1.2	1.0
10	1.3	1.2
20	2.7	2.3
30	4.0	3.5
40	5.3	4.7
50	6.7	5.8

Proportional parts

121° (301°) (238°) **58°**

The −10 portion of the characteristic of the logarithm is not printed but must be written down whenever such a logarithm is used.

32° (212°) (327°) **147°**

′	L Sin	d	L Tan	c d	L Ctn	L Cos	d	′
0	9.72 421	20	9.79 579	28	10.20 421	9.92 842	8	60
1	9.72 441	20	9.79 607	28	10.20 393	9.92 834	8	59
2	9.72 461	21	9.79 635	28	10.20 365	9.92 826	8	58
3	9.72 482	20	9.79 663	28	10.20 337	9.92 818	8	57
4	9.72 502	20	9.79 691	28	10.20 309	9.92 810	7	56
5	9.72 522	20	9.79 719	28	10.20 281	9.92 803	8	55
6	9.72 542	20	9.79 747	29	10.20 253	9.92 795	8	54
7	9.72 562	20	9.79 776	28	10.20 224	9.92 787	8	53
8	9.72 582	20	9.79 804	28	10.20 196	9.92 779	8	52
9	9.72 602	20	9.79 832	28	10.20 168	9.92 771	8	51
10	9.72 622	21	9.79 860	28	10.20 140	9.92 763	8	50
11	9.72 643	20	9.79 888	28	10.20 112	9.92 755	8	49
12	9.72 663	20	9.79 916	28	10.20 084	9.92 747	8	48
13	9.72 683	20	9.79 944	28	10.20 056	9.92 739	8	47
14	9.72 703	20	9.79 972	28	10.20 028	9.92 731	8	46
15	9.72 723	20	9.80 000	28	10.20 000	9.92 723	8	45
16	9.72 743	20	9.80 028	28	10.19 972	9.92 715	8	44
17	9.72 763	20	9.80 056	28	10.19 944	9.92 707	8	43
18	9.72 783	20	9.80 084	28	10.19 916	9.92 699	8	42
19	9.72 803	20	9.80 112	28	10.19 888	9.92 691	8	41
20	9.72 823	20	9.80 140	28	10.19 860	9.92 683	8	40
21	9.72 843	20	9.80 168	27	10.19 832	9.92 675	8	39
22	9.72 863	20	9.80 195	28	10.19 805	9.92 667	8	38
23	9.72 883	19	9.80 223	28	10.19 777	9.92 659	8	37
24	9.72 902	20	9.80 251	28	10.19 749	9.92 651	8	36
25	9.72 922	20	9.80 279	28	10.19 721	9.92 643	8	35
26	9.72 942	20	9.80 307	28	10.19 693	9.92 635	8	34
27	9.72 962	20	9.80 335	28	10.19 665	9.92 627	8	33
28	9.72 982	20	9.80 363	28	10.19 637	9.92 619	8	32
29	9.73 002	20	9.80 391	28	10.19 609	9.92 611	8	31
30	9.73 022	19	9.80 419	28	10.19 581	9.92 603	8	30
31	9.73 041	20	9.80 447	27	10.19 553	9.92 595	8	29
32	9.73 061	20	9.80 474	28	10.19 526	9.92 587	8	28
33	9.73 081	20	9.80 502	28	10.19 498	9.92 579	8	27
34	9.73 101	20	9.80 530	28	10.19 470	9.92 571	8	26
35	9.73 121	19	9.80 558	28	10.19 442	9.92 563	8	25
36	9.73 140	20	9.80 586	28	10.19 414	9.92 555	9	24
37	9.73 160	20	9.80 614	28	10.19 386	9.92 546	8	23
38	9.73 180	20	9.80 642	27	10.19 358	9.92 538	8	22
39	9.73 200	19	9.80 669	28	10.19 331	9.92 530	8	21
40	9.73 219	20	9.80 697	28	10.19 303	9.92 522	8	20
41	9.73 239	20	9.80 725	28	10.19 275	9.92 514	8	19
42	9.73 259	19	9.80 753	28	10.19 247	9.92 506	8	18
43	9.73 278	20	9.80 781	27	10.19 219	9.92 498	8	17
44	9.73 298	20	9.80 808	28	10.19 192	9.92 490	8	16
45	9.73 318	19	9.80 836	28	10.19 164	9.92 482	9	15
46	9.73 337	20	9.80 864	28	10.19 136	9.92 473	8	14
47	9.73 357	20	9.80 892	27	10.19 108	9.92 465	8	13
48	9.73 377	19	9.80 919	28	10.19 081	9.92 457	8	12
49	9.73 396	20	9.80 947	28	10.19 053	9.92 449	8	11
50	9.73 416	19	9.80 975	28	10.19 025	9.92 441	8	10
51	9.73 435	20	9.81 003	27	10.18 997	9.92 433	8	9
52	9.73 455	19	9.81 030	28	10.18 970	9.92 425	9	8
53	9.73 474	20	9.81 058	28	10.18 942	9.92 416	8	7
54	9.73 494	19	9.81 086	27	10.18 914	9.92 408	8	6
55	9.73 513	20	9.81 113	28	10.18 887	9.92 400	8	5
56	9.73 533	19	9.81 141	28	10.18 859	9.92 392	8	4
57	9.73 552	20	9.81 169	27	10.18 831	9.92 384	8	3
58	9.73 572	19	9.81 196	28	10.18 804	9.92 376	9	2
59	9.73 591	20	9.81 224	28	10.18 776	9.92 367	8	1
60	9.73 611		9.81 252		10.18 748	9.92 359		0
′	L Cos	d	L Ctn	c d	L Tan	L Sin	d	′

Proportional parts

″	29	28	27
1	0.5	0.5	0.4
2	1.0	0.9	0.9
3	1.4	1.4	1.4
4	1.9	1.9	1.8
5	2.4	2.3	2.2
6	2.9	2.8	2.7
7	3.4	3.3	3.2
8	3.9	3.7	3.6
9	4.4	4.2	4.0
10	4.8	4.7	4.5
20	9.7	9.3	9.0
30	14.5	14.0	13.5
40	19.3	18.7	18.0
50	24.2	23.3	22.5

″	21	20	19
1	0.4	0.3	0.3
2	0.7	0.7	0.6
3	1.0	1.0	1.0
4	1.4	1.3	1.3
5	1.8	1.7	1.6
6	2.1	2.0	1.9
7	2.4	2.3	2.2
8	2.8	2.7	2.5
9	3.2	3.0	2.8
10	3.5	3.3	3.2
20	7.0	6.7	6.3
30	10.5	10.0	9.5
40	14.0	13.3	12.7
50	17.5	16.7	15.8

″	9	8	7
1	0.2	0.1	0.1
2	0.3	0.3	0.2
3	0.4	0.4	0.4
4	0.6	0.5	0.5
5	0.8	0.7	0.6
6	0.9	0.8	0.7
7	1.0	0.9	0.8
8	1.2	1.1	0.9
9	1.4	1.2	1.0
10	1.5	1.3	1.2
20	3.0	2.7	2.3
30	4.5	4.0	3.5
40	6.0	5.3	4.7
50	7.5	6.7	5.8

Proportional parts

122° (302°) (237°) **57°**

The −10 portion of the characteristic of the logarithm is not printed but must be written down whenever such a logarithm is used.

33° (213°) (326°) **146°**

′	L Sin	d	L Tan	c d	L Ctn	L Cos	d	′
0	9.73 611	19	9.81 252	27	10.18 748	9.92 359	8	60
1	9.73 630	20	9.81 279	28	10.18 721	9.92 351	8	59
2	9.73 650	19	9.81 307	28	10.18 693	9.92 343	8	58
3	9.73 669	20	9.81 335	27	10.18 665	9.92 335	9	57
4	9.73 689	19	9.81 362	28	10.18 638	9.92 326	8	56
5	9.73 708	19	9.81 390	28	10.18 610	9.92 318	8	55
6	9.73 727	20	9.81 418	27	10.18 582	9.92 310	8	54
7	9.73 747	19	9.81 445	28	10.18 555	9.92 302	9	53
8	9.73 766	19	9.81 473	27	10.18 527	9.92 293	8	52
9	9.73 785	20	9.81 500	28	10.18 500	9.92 285	8	51
10	9.73 805	19	9.81 528	28	10.18 472	9.92 277	8	50
11	9.73 824	19	9.81 556	27	10.18 444	9.92 269	9	49
12	9.73 843	20	9.81 583	28	10.18 417	9.92 260	8	48
13	9.73 863	19	9.81 611	27	10.18 389	9.92 252	8	47
14	9.73 882	19	9.81 638	28	10.18 362	9.92 244	9	46
15	9.73 901	20	9.81 666	27	10.18 334	9.92 235	8	45
16	9.73 921	19	9.81 693	28	10.18 307	9.92 227	8	44
17	9.73 940	19	9.81 721	27	10.18 279	9.92 219	8	43
18	9.73 959	19	9.81 748	28	10.18 252	9.92 211	9	42
19	9.73 978	19	9.81 776	27	10.18 224	9.92 202	8	41
20	9.73 997	20	9.81 803	28	10.18 197	9.92 194	8	40
21	9.74 017	19	9.81 831	27	10.18 169	9.92 186	9	39
22	9.74 036	19	9.81 858	28	10.18 142	9.92 177	8	38
23	9.74 055	19	9.81 886	27	10.18 114	9.92 169	8	37
24	9.74 074	19	9.81 913	28	10.18 087	9.92 161	9	36
25	9.74 093	20	9.81 941	27	10.18 059	9.92 152	8	35
26	9.74 113	19	9.81 968	28	10.18 032	9.92 144	8	34
27	9.74 132	19	9.81 996	27	10.18 004	9.92 136	9	33
28	9.74 151	19	9.82 023	28	10.17 977	9.92 127	8	32
29	9.74 170	19	9.82 051	27	10.17 949	9.92 119	8	31
30	9.74 189	19	9.82 078	28	10.17 922	9.92 111	9	30
31	9.74 208	19	9.82 106	27	10.17 894	9.92 102	8	29
32	9.74 227	19	9.82 133	28	10.17 867	9.92 094	8	28
33	9.74 246	19	9.82 161	27	10.17 839	9.92 086	9	27
34	9.74 265	19	9.82 188	27	10.17 812	9.92 077	8	26
35	9.74 284	19	9.82 215	28	10.17 785	9.92 069	9	25
36	9.74 303	19	9.82 243	27	10.17 757	9.92 060	8	24
37	9.74 322	19	9.82 270	28	10.17 730	9.92 052	8	23
38	9.74 341	19	9.82 298	27	10.17 702	9.92 044	9	22
39	9.74 360	19	9.82 325	27	10.17 675	9.92 035	8	21
40	9.74 379	19	9.82 352	28	10.17 648	9.92 027	9	20
41	9.74 398	19	9.82 380	27	10.17 620	9.92 018	8	19
42	9.74 417	19	9.82 407	28	10.17 593	9.92 010	8	18
43	9.74 436	19	9.82 435	27	10.17 565	9.92 002	9	17
44	9.74 455	19	9.82 462	27	10.17 538	9.91 993	8	16
45	9.74 474	19	9.82 489	28	10.17 511	9.91 985	9	15
46	9.74 493	19	9.82 517	27	10.17 483	9.91 976	8	14
47	9.74 512	19	9.82 544	27	10.17 456	9.91 968	9	13
48	9.74 531	18	9.82 571	28	10.17 429	9.91 959	8	12
49	9.74 549	19	9.82 599	27	10.17 401	9.91 951	9	11
50	9.74 568	19	9.82 626	27	10.17 374	9.91 942	8	10
51	9.74 587	19	9.82 653	28	10.17 347	9.91 934	9	9
52	9.74 606	19	9.82 681	27	10.17 319	9.91 925	8	8
53	9.74 625	19	9.82 708	27	10.17 292	9.91 917	9	7
54	9.74 644	18	9.82 735	27	10.17 265	9.91 908	8	6
55	9.74 662	19	9.82 762	28	10.17 238	9.91 900	9	5
56	9.74 681	19	9.82 790	27	10.17 210	9.91 891	8	4
57	9.74 700	19	9.82 817	27	10.17 183	9.91 883	9	3
58	9.74 719	18	9.82 844	27	10.17 156	9.91 874	8	2
59	9.74 737	19	9.82 871	28	10.17 129	9.91 866	9	1
60	9.74 756		9.82 899		10.17 101	9.91 857		0
′	L Cos	d	L Ctn	c d	L Tan	L Sin	d	′

Proportional parts

″	28	27
1	0.5	0.4
2	0.9	0.9
3	1.4	1.4
4	1.9	1.8
5	2.3	2.2
6	2.8	2.7
7	3.3	3.2
8	3.7	3.6
9	4.2	4.0
10	4.7	4.5
20	9.3	9.0
30	14.0	13.5
40	18.7	18.0
50	23.3	22.5

″	20	19	18
1	0.3	0.3	0.3
2	0.7	0.6	0.6
3	1.0	1.0	0.9
4	1.3	1.3	1.2
5	1.7	1.6	1.5
6	2.0	1.9	1.8
7	2.3	2.2	2.1
8	2.7	2.5	2.4
9	3.0	2.8	2.7
10	3.3	3.2	3.0
20	6.7	6.3	6.0
30	10.0	9.5	9.0
40	13.3	12.7	12.0
50	16.7	15.8	15.0

″	9	8
1	0.2	0.1
2	0.3	0.3
3	0.4	0.4
4	0.6	0.5
5	0.8	0.7
6	0.9	0.8
7	1.0	0.9
8	1.2	1.1
9	1.4	1.2
10	1.5	1.3
20	3.0	2.7
30	4.5	4.0
40	6.0	5.3
50	7.5	6.7

Proportional parts

123° (303°) (236°) **56°**

The −10 portion of the characteristic of the logarithm is not printed but must be written down whenever such a logarithm is used.

34° (214°) (325°) **145°**

′	L Sin	d	L Tan	c d	L Ctn	L Cos	d	′
0	9.74 756	19	9.82 899	27	10.17 101	9.91 857	8	60
1	9.74 775	19	9.82 926	27	10.17 074	9.91 849	9	59
2	9.74 794	18	9.82 953	27	10.17 047	9.91 840	8	58
3	9.74 812	19	9.82 980	28	10.17 020	9.91 832	9	57
4	9.74 831	19	9.83 008	27	10.16 992	9.91 823	8	56
5	9.74 850	18	9.83 035	27	10.16 965	9.91 815	9	55
6	9.74 868	19	9.83 062	27	10.16 938	9.91 806	8	54
7	9.74 887	19	9.83 089	28	10.16 911	9.91 798	9	53
8	9.74 906	18	9.83 117	27	10.16 883	9.91 789	8	52
9	9.74 924	19	9.83 144	27	10.16 856	9.91 781	9	51
10	9.74 943	18	9.83 171	27	10.16 829	9.91 772	9	50
11	9.74 961	19	9.83 198	27	10.16 802	9.91 763	8	49
12	9.74 980	19	9.83 225	27	10.16 775	9.91 755	9	48
13	9.74 999	18	9.83 252	28	10.16 748	9.91 746	8	47
14	9.75 017	19	9.83 280	27	10.16 720	9.91 738	9	46
15	9.75 036	18	9.83 307	27	10.16 693	9.91 729	9	45
16	9.75 054	19	9.83 334	27	10.16 666	9.91 720	8	44
17	9.75 073	18	9.83 361	27	10.16 639	9.91 712	9	43
18	9.75 091	19	9.83 388	27	10.16 612	9.91 703	8	42
19	9.75 110	18	9.83 415	27	10.16 585	9.91 695	9	41
20	9.75 128	19	9.83 442	28	10.16 558	9.91 686	9	40
21	9.75 147	18	9.83 470	27	10.16 530	9.91 677	8	39
22	9.75 165	19	9.83 497	27	10.16 503	9.91 669	9	38
23	9.75 184	18	9.83 524	27	10.16 476	9.91 660	9	37
24	9.75 202	19	9.83 551	27	10.16 449	9.91 651	8	36
25	9.75 221	18	9.83 578	27	10.16 422	9.91 643	9	35
26	9.75 239	19	9.83 605	27	10.16 395	9.91 634	9	34
27	9.75 258	18	9.83 632	27	10.16 368	9.91 625	8	33
28	9.75 276	18	9.83 659	27	10.16 341	9.91 617	9	32
29	9.75 294	19	9.83 686	27	10.16 314	9.91 608	9	31
30	9.75 313	18	9.83 713	27	10.16 287	9.91 599	8	30
31	9.75 331	19	9.83 740	28	10.16 260	9.91 591	9	29
32	9.75 350	18	9.83 768	27	10.16 232	9.91 582	9	28
33	9.75 368	18	9.83 795	27	10.16 205	9.91 573	8	27
34	9.75 386	19	9.83 822	27	10.16 178	9.91 565	9	26
35	9.75 405	18	9.83 849	27	10.16 151	9.91 556	9	25
36	9.75 423	18	9.83 876	27	10.16 124	9.91 547	9	24
37	9.75 441	18	9.83 903	27	10.16 097	9.91 538	8	23
38	9.75 459	19	9.83 930	27	10.16 070	9.91 530	9	22
39	9.75 478	18	9.83 957	27	10.16 043	9.91 521	9	21
40	9.75 496	18	9.83 984	27	10.16 016	9.91 512	8	20
41	9.75 514	19	9.84 011	27	10.15 989	9.91 504	9	19
42	9.75 533	18	9.84 038	27	10.15 962	9.91 495	9	18
43	9.75 551	18	9.84 065	27	10.15 935	9.91 486	9	17
44	9.75 569	18	9.84 092	27	10.15 908	9.91 477	8	16
45	9.75 587	18	9.84 119	27	10.15 881	9.91 469	9	15
46	9.75 605	19	9.84 146	27	10.15 854	9.91 460	9	14
47	9.75 624	18	9.84 173	27	10.15 827	9.91 451	9	13
48	9.75 642	18	9.84 200	27	10.15 800	9.91 442	9	12
49	9.75 660	18	9.84 227	27	10.15 773	9.91 433	8	11
50	9.75 678	18	9.84 254	26	10.15 746	9.91 425	9	10
51	9.75 696	18	9.84 280	27	10.15 720	9.91 416	9	9
52	9.75 714	19	9.84 307	27	10.15 693	9.91 407	9	8
53	9.75 733	18	9.84 334	27	10.15 666	9.91 398	9	7
54	9.75 751	18	9.84 361	27	10.15 639	9.91 389	8	6
55	9.75 769	18	9.84 388	27	10.15 612	9.91 381	9	5
56	9.75 787	18	9.84 415	27	10.15 585	9.91 372	9	4
57	9.75 805	18	9.84 442	27	10.15 558	9.91 363	9	3
58	9.75 823	18	9.84 469	27	10.15 531	9.91 354	9	2
59	9.75 841	18	9.84 496	27	10.15 504	9.91 345	9	1
60	9.75 859		9.84 523		10.15 477	9.91 336		0
′	L Cos	d	L Ctn	c d	L Tan	L Sin	d	′

Proportional parts

″	28	27	26
1	0.5	0.4	0.4
2	0.9	0.9	0.9
3	1.4	1.4	1.3
4	1.9	1.8	1.7
5	2.3	2.2	2.2
6	2.8	2.7	2.6
7	3.3	3.2	3.0
8	3.7	3.6	3.5
9	4.2	4.0	3.9
10	4.7	4.5	4.3
20	9.3	9.0	8.7
30	14.0	13.5	13.0
40	18.7	18.0	17.3
50	23.3	22.5	21.7

″	19	18
1	0.3	0.3
2	0.6	0.6
3	1.0	0.9
4	1.3	1.2
5	1.6	1.5
6	1.9	1.8
7	2.2	2.1
8	2.5	2.4
9	2.8	2.7
10	3.2	3.0
20	6.3	6.0
30	9.5	9.0
40	12.7	12.0
50	15.8	15.0

″	9	8
1	0.2	0.1
2	0.3	0.3
3	0.4	0.4
4	0.6	0.5
5	0.8	0.7
6	0.9	0.8
7	1.0	0.9
8	1.2	1.1
9	1.4	1.2
10	1.5	1.3
20	3.0	2.7
30	4.5	4.0
40	6.0	5.3
50	7.5	6.7

Proportional parts

124° (304°) (235°) **55°**

The −10 portion of the characteristic of the logarithm is not printed but must be written down whenever such a logarithm is used.

35° (215°) (324°) **144°**

′	L Sin	d	L Tan	c d	L Ctn	L Cos	d	′
0	9.75 859	18	9.84 523	27	10.15 477	9.91 336	8	60
1	9.75 877	18	9.84 550	26	10.15 450	9.91 328	9	59
2	9.75 895	18	9.84 576	27	10.15 424	9.91 319	9	58
3	9.75 913	18	9.84 603	27	10.15 397	9.91 310	9	57
4	9.75 931	18	9.84 630	27	10.15 370	9.91 301	9	56
5	9.75 949	18	9.84 657	27	10.15 343	9.91 292	9	55
6	9.75 967	18	9.84 684	27	10.15 316	9.91 283	9	54
7	9.75 985	18	9.84 711	27	10.15 289	9.91 274	8	53
8	9.76 003	18	9.84 738	26	10.15 262	9.91 266	9	52
9	9.76 021	18	9.84 764	27	10.15 236	9.91 257	9	51
10	9.76 039	18	9.84 791	27	10.15 209	9.91 248	9	50
11	9.76 057	18	9.84 818	27	10.15 182	9.91 239	9	49
12	9.76 075	18	9.84 845	27	10.15 155	9.91 230	9	48
13	9.76 093	18	9.84 872	27	10.15 128	9.91 221	9	47
14	9.76 111	18	9.84 899	26	10.15 101	9.91 212	9	46
15	9.76 129	17	9.84 925	27	10.15 075	9.91 203	9	45
16	9.76 146	18	9.84 952	27	10.15 048	9.91 194	9	44
17	9.76 164	18	9.84 979	27	10.15 021	9.91 185	9	43
18	9.76 182	18	9.85 006	27	10.14 994	9.91 176	9	42
19	9.76 200	18	9.85 033	26	10.14 967	9.91 167	9	41
20	9.76 218	18	9.85 059	27	10.14 941	9.91 158	9	40
21	9.76 236	17	9.85 086	27	10.14 914	9.91 149	8	39
22	9.76 253	18	9.85 113	27	10.14 887	9.91 141	9	38
23	9.76 271	18	9.85 140	26	10.14 860	9.91 132	9	37
24	9.76 289	18	9.85 166	27	10.14 834	9.91 123	9	36
25	9.76 307	17	9.85 193	27	10.14 807	9.91 114	9	35
26	9.76 324	18	9.85 220	27	10.14 780	9.91 105	9	34
27	9.76 342	18	9.85 247	26	10.14 753	9.91 096	9	33
28	9.76 360	18	9.85 273	27	10.14 727	9.91 087	9	32
29	9.76 378	17	9.85 300	27	10.14 700	9.91 078	9	31
30	9.76 395	18	9.85 327	27	10.14 673	9.91 069	9	30
31	9.76 413	18	9.85 354	26	10.14 646	9.91 060	9	29
32	9.76 431	17	9.85 380	27	10.14 620	9.91 051	9	28
33	9.76 448	18	9.85 407	27	10.14 593	9.91 042	9	27
34	9.76 466	18	9.85 434	26	10.14 566	9.91 033	10	26
35	9.76 484	17	9.85 460	27	10.14 540	9.91 023	9	25
36	9.76 501	18	9.85 487	27	10.14 513	9.91 014	9	24
37	9.76 519	18	9.85 514	26	10.14 486	9.91 005	9	23
38	9.76 537	17	9.85 540	27	10.14 460	9.90 996	9	22
39	9.76 554	18	9.85 567	27	10.14 433	9.90 987	9	21
40	9.76 572	18	9.85 594	26	10.14 406	9.90 978	9	20
41	9.76 590	17	9.85 620	27	10.14 380	9.90 969	9	19
42	9.76 607	18	9.85 647	27	10.14 353	9.90 960	9	18
43	9.76 625	17	9.85 674	26	10.14 326	9.90 951	9	17
44	9.76 642	18	9.85 700	27	10.14 300	9.90 942	9	16
45	9.76 660	17	9.85 727	27	10.14 273	9.90 933	9	15
46	9.76 677	18	9.85 754	26	10.14 246	9.90 924	9	14
47	9.76 695	17	9.85 780	27	10.14 220	9.90 915	9	13
48	9.76 712	18	9.85 807	27	10.14 193	9.90 906	10	12
49	9.76 730	17	9.85 834	26	10.14 166	9.90 896	9	11
50	9.76 747	18	9.85 860	27	10.14 140	9.90 887	9	10
51	9.76 765	17	9.85 887	26	10.14 113	9.90 878	9	9
52	9.76 782	18	9.85 913	27	10.14 087	9.90 869	9	8
53	9.76 800	17	9.85 940	27	10.14 060	9.90 860	9	7
54	9.76 817	18	9.85 967	26	10.14 033	9.90 851	9	6
55	9.76 835	17	9.85 993	27	10.14 007	9.90 842	10	5
56	9.76 852	18	9.86 020	26	10.13 980	9.90 832	9	4
57	9.76 870	17	9.86 046	27	10.13 954	9.90 823	9	3
58	9.76 887	17	9.86 073	27	10.13 927	9.90 814	9	2
59	9.76 904	18	9.86 100	26	10.13 900	9.90 805	9	1
60	9.76 922		9.86 126		10.13 874	9.90 796		0
′	L Cos	d	L Ctn	c d	L Tan	L Sin	d	′

Proportional parts

″	27	26	18
1	0.4	0.4	0.3
2	0.9	0.9	0.6
3	1.4	1.3	0.9
4	1.8	1.7	1.2
5	2.2	2.2	1.5
6	2.7	2.6	1.8
7	3.2	3.0	2.1
8	3.6	3.5	2.4
9	4.0	3.9	2.7
10	4.5	4.3	3.0
20	9.0	8.7	6.0
30	13.5	13.0	9.0
40	18.0	17.3	12.0
50	22.5	21.7	15.0

″	17	10
1	0.3	0.2
2	0.6	0.3
3	0.8	0.5
4	1.1	0.7
5	1.4	0.8
6	1.7	1.0
7	2.0	1.2
8	2.3	1.3
9	2.6	1.5
10	2.8	1.7
20	5.7	3.3
30	8.5	5.0
40	11.3	6.7
50	14.2	8.3

″	9	8
1	0.2	0.1
2	0.3	0.3
3	0.4	0.4
4	0.6	0.5
5	0.8	0.7
6	0.9	0.8
7	1.0	0.9
8	1.2	1.1
9	1.4	1.2
10	1.5	1.3
20	3.0	2.7
30	4.5	4.0
40	6.0	5.3
50	7.5	6.7

Proportional parts

125° (305°) (234°) **54°**

The −10 portion of the characteristic of the logarithm is not printed but must be written down whenever such a logarithm is used.

36° (216°) (323°) **143°**

′	L Sin	d	L Tan	c d	L Ctn	L Cos	d	′
0	9.76 922	17	9.86 126	27	10.13 874	9.90 796	9	60
1	9.76 939	18	9.86 153	26	10.13 847	9.90 787	10	59
2	9.76 957	17	9.86 179	27	10.13 821	9.90 777	9	58
3	9.76 974	17	9.86 206	26	10.13 794	9.90 768	9	57
4	9.76 991	18	9.86 232	27	10.13 768	9.90 759	9	56
5	9.77 009	17	9.86 259	26	10.13 741	9.90 750	9	55
6	9.77 026	17	9.86 285	27	10.13 715	9.90 741	10	54
7	9.77 043	18	9.86 312	26	10.13 688	9.90 731	9	53
8	9.77 061	17	9.86 338	27	10.13 662	9.90 722	9	52
9	9.77 078	17	9.86 365	27	10.13 635	9.90 713	9	51
10	9.77 095	17	9.86 392	26	10.13 608	9.90 704	10	50
11	9.77 112	18	9.86 418	27	10.13 582	9.90 694	9	49
12	9.77 130	17	9.86 445	26	10.13 555	9.90 685	9	48
13	9.77 147	17	9.86 471	27	10.13 529	9.90 676	9	47
14	9.77 164	17	9.86 498	26	10.13 502	9.90 667	10	46
15	9.77 181	18	9.86 524	27	10.13 476	9.90 657	9	45
16	9.77 199	17	9.86 551	26	10.13 449	9.90 648	9	44
17	9.77 216	17	9.86 577	26	10.13 423	9.90 639	9	43
18	9.77 233	17	9.86 603	27	10.13 397	9.90 630	10	42
19	9.77 250	18	9.86 630	26	10.13 370	9.90 620	9	41
20	9.77 268	17	9.86 656	27	10.13 344	9.90 611	9	40
21	9.77 285	17	9.86 683	26	10.13 317	9.90 602	10	39
22	9.77 302	17	9.86 709	27	10.13 291	9.90 592	9	38
23	9.77 319	17	9.86 736	26	10.13 264	9.90 583	9	37
24	9.77 336	17	9.86 762	27	10.13 238	9.90 574	9	36
25	9.77 353	17	9.86 789	26	10.13 211	9.90 565	10	35
26	9.77 370	17	9.86 815	27	10.13 185	9.90 555	9	34
27	9.77 387	18	9.86 842	26	10.13 158	9.90 546	9	33
28	9.77 405	17	9.86 868	26	10.13 132	9.90 537	10	32
29	9.77 422	17	9.86 894	27	10.13 106	9.90 527	9	31
30	9.77 439	17	9.86 921	26	10.13 079	9.90 518	9	30
31	9.77 456	17	9.86 947	27	10.13 053	9.90 509	10	29
32	9.77 473	17	9.86 974	26	10.13 026	9.90 499	9	28
33	9.77 490	17	9.87 000	27	10.13 000	9.90 490	10	27
34	9.77 507	17	9.87 027	26	10.12 973	9.90 480	9	26
35	9.77 524	17	9.87 053	26	10.12 947	9.90 471	9	25
36	9.77 541	17	9.87 079	27	10.12 921	9.90 462	10	24
37	9.77 558	17	9.87 106	26	10.12 894	9.90 452	9	23
38	9.77 575	17	9.87 132	26	10.12 868	9.90 443	9	22
39	9.77 592	17	9.87 158	27	10.12 842	9.90 434	10	21
40	9.77 609	17	9.87 185	26	10.12 815	9.90 424	9	20
41	9.77 626	17	9.87 211	27	10.12 789	9.90 415	10	19
42	9.77 643	17	9.87 238	26	10.12 762	9.90 405	9	18
43	9.77 660	17	9.87 264	26	10.12 736	9.90 396	10	17
44	9.77 677	17	9.87 290	27	10.12 710	9.90 386	9	16
45	9.77 694	17	9.87 317	26	10.12 683	9.90 377	9	15
46	9.77 711	17	9.87 343	26	10.12 657	9.90 368	10	14
47	9.77 728	16	9.87 369	27	10.12 631	9.90 358	9	13
48	9.77 744	17	9.87 396	26	10.12 604	9.90 349	10	12
49	9.77 761	17	9.87 422	26	10.12 578	9.90 339	9	11
50	9.77 778	17	9.87 448	27	10.12 552	9.90 330	10	10
51	9.77 795	17	9.87 475	26	10.12 525	9.90 320	9	9
52	9.77 812	17	9.87 501	26	10.12 499	9.90 311	10	8
53	9.77 829	17	9.87 527	27	10.12 473	9.90 301	9	7
54	9.77 846	16	9.87 554	26	10.12 446	9.90 292	10	6
55	9.77 862	17	9.87 580	26	10.12 420	9.90 282	9	5
56	9.77 879	17	9.87 606	27	10.12 394	9.90 273	10	4
57	9.77 896	17	9.87 633	26	10.12 367	9.90 263	9	3
58	9.77 913	17	9.87 659	26	10.12 341	9.90 254	10	2
59	9.77 930	16	9.87 685	26	10.12 315	9.90 244	9	1
60	9.77 946		9.87 711		10.12 289	9.90 235		0
′	L Cos	d	L Ctn	c d	L Tan	L Sin	d	′

Proportional parts

″	27	26
1	0.4	0.4
2	0.9	0.9
3	1.4	1.3
4	1.8	1.7
5	2.2	2.2
6	2.7	2.6
7	3.2	3.0
8	3.6	3.5
9	4.0	3.9
10	4.5	4.3
20	9.0	8.7
30	13.5	13.0
40	18.0	17.3
50	22.5	21.7

″	18	17	16
1	0.3	0.3	0.3
2	0.6	0.6	0.5
3	0.9	0.8	0.8
4	1.2	1.1	1.1
5	1.5	1.4	1.3
6	1.8	1.7	1.6
7	2.1	2.0	1.9
8	2.4	2.3	2.1
9	2.7	2.6	2.4
10	3.0	2.8	2.7
20	6.0	5.7	5.3
30	9.0	8.5	8.0
40	12.0	11.3	10.7
50	15.0	14.2	13.3

″	10	9
1	0.2	0.2
2	0.3	0.3
3	0.5	0.4
4	0.7	0.6
5	0.8	0.8
6	1.0	0.9
7	1.2	1.0
8	1.3	1.2
9	1.5	1.4
10	1.7	1.5
20	3.3	3.0
30	5.0	4.5
40	6.7	6.0
50	8.3	7.5

Proportional parts

126° (306°) (233°) **53°**

The −10 portion of the characteristic of the logarithm is not printed but must be written down whenever such a logarithm is used.

37° (217°) (322°) **142°**

′	L Sin	d	L Tan	c d	L Ctn	L Cos	d	′
0	9.77 946	17	9.87 711	27	10.12 289	9.90 235	10	60
1	9.77 963	17	9.87 738	26	10.12 262	9.90 225	9	59
2	9.77 980	17	9.87 764	26	10.12 236	9.90 216	10	58
3	9.77 997	16	9.87 790	27	10.12 210	9.90 206	9	57
4	9.78 013	17	9.87 817	26	10.12 183	9.90 197	10	56
5	9.78 030	17	9.87 843	26	10.12 157	9.90 187	9	55
6	9.78 047	16	9.87 869	26	10.12 131	9.90 178	10	54
7	9.78 063	17	9.87 895	27	10.12 105	9.90 168	9	53
8	9.78 080	17	9.87 922	26	10.12 078	9.90 159	10	52
9	9.78 097	16	9.87 948	26	10.12 052	9.90 149	10	51
10	9.78 113	17	9.87 974	26	10.12 026	9.90 139	9	50
11	9.78 130	17	9.88 000	27	10.12 000	9.90 130	10	49
12	9.78 147	16	9.88 027	26	10.11 973	9.90 120	9	48
13	9.78 163	17	9.88 053	26	10.11 947	9.90 111	10	47
14	9.78 180	17	9.88 079	26	10.11 921	9.90 101	10	46
15	9.78 197	16	9.88 105	26	10.11 895	9.90 091	9	45
16	9.78 213	17	9.88 131	27	10.11 869	9.90 082	10	44
17	9.78 230	16	9.88 158	26	10.11 842	9.90 072	9	43
18	9.78 246	17	9.88 184	26	10.11 816	9.90 063	10	42
19	9.78 263	17	9.88 210	26	10.11 790	9.90 053	10	41
20	9.78 280	16	9.88 236	26	10.11 764	9.90 043	9	40
21	9.78 296	17	9.88 262	27	10.11 738	9.90 034	10	39
22	9.78 313	16	9.88 289	26	10.11 711	9.90 024	10	38
23	9.78 329	17	9.88 315	26	10.11 685	9.90 014	9	37
24	9.78 346	16	9.88 341	26	10.11 659	9.90 005	10	36
25	9.78 362	17	9.88 367	26	10.11 633	9.89 995	10	35
26	9.78 379	16	9.88 393	27	10.11 607	9.89 985	9	34
27	9.78 395	17	9.88 420	26	10.11 580	9.89 976	10	33
28	9.78 412	16	9.88 446	26	10.11 554	9.89 966	10	32
29	9.78 428	17	9.88 472	26	10.11 528	9.89 956	9	31
30	9.78 445	16	9.88 498	26	10.11 502	9.89 947	10	30
31	9.78 461	17	9.88 524	26	10.11 476	9.89 937	10	29
32	9.78 478	16	9.88 550	27	10.11 450	9.89 927	9	28
33	9.78 494	16	9.88 577	26	10.11 423	9.89 918	10	27
34	9.78 510	17	9.88 603	26	10.11 397	9.89 908	10	26
35	9.78 527	16	9.88 629	26	10.11 371	9.89 898	10	25
36	9.78 543	17	9.88 655	26	10.11 345	9.89 888	9	24
37	9.78 560	16	9.88 681	26	10.11 319	9.89 879	10	23
38	9.78 576	16	9.88 707	26	10.11 293	9.89 869	10	22
39	9.78 592	17	9.88 733	26	10.11 267	9.89 859	10	21
40	9.78 609	16	9.88 759	27	10.11 241	9.89 849	9	20
41	9.78 625	17	9.88 786	26	10.11 214	9.89 840	10	19
42	9.78 642	16	9.88 812	26	10.11 188	9.89 830	10	18
43	9.78 658	16	9.88 838	26	10.11 162	9.89 820	10	17
44	9.78 674	17	9.88 864	26	10.11 136	9.89 810	9	16
45	9.78 691	16	9.88 890	26	10.11 110	9.89 801	10	15
46	9.78 707	16	9.88 916	26	10.11 084	9.89 791	10	14
47	9.78 723	16	9.88 942	26	10.11 058	9.89 781	10	13
48	9.78 739	17	9.88 968	26	10.11 032	9.89 771	10	12
49	9.78 756	16	9.88 994	26	10.11 006	9.89 761	9	11
50	9.78 772	16	9.89 020	26	10.10 980	9.89 752	10	10
51	9.78 788	17	9.89 046	27	10.10 954	9.89 742	10	9
52	9.78 805	16	9.89 073	26	10.10 927	9.89 732	10	8
53	9.78 821	16	9.89 099	26	10.10 901	9.89 722	10	7
54	9.78 837	16	9.89 125	26	10.10 875	9.89 712	10	6
55	9.78 853	16	9.89 151	26	10.10 849	9.89 702	9	5
56	9.78 869	17	9.89 177	26	10.10 823	9.89 693	10	4
57	9.78 886	16	9.89 203	26	10.10 797	9.89 683	10	3
58	9.78 902	16	9.89 229	26	10.10 771	9.89 673	10	2
59	9.78 918	16	9.89 255	26	10.10 745	9.89 663	10	1
60	9.78 934		9.89 281		10.10 719	9.89 653		0
′	L Cos	d	L Ctn	c d	L Tan	L Sin	d	′

Proportional parts

″	27	26	17	16	10	9
1	0.4	0.4	0.3	0.3	0.2	0.2
2	0.9	0.9	0.6	0.5	0.3	0.3
3	1.4	1.3	0.8	0.8	0.5	0.4
4	1.8	1.7	1.1	1.1	0.7	0.6
5	2.2	2.2	1.4	1.3	0.8	0.8
6	2.7	2.6	1.7	1.6	1.0	0.9
7	3.2	3.0	2.0	1.9	1.2	1.0
8	3.6	3.5	2.3	2.1	1.3	1.2
9	4.0	3.9	2.6	2.4	1.5	1.4
10	4.5	4.3	2.8	2.7	1.7	1.5
20	9.0	8.7	5.7	5.3	3.3	3.0
30	13.5	13.0	8.5	8.0	5.0	4.5
40	18.0	17.3	11.3	10.7	6.7	6.0
50	22.5	21.7	14.2	13.3	8.3	7.5

Proportional parts

127° (307°) (232°) **52°**

The −10 portion of the characteristic of the logarithm is not printed but must be written down whenever such a logarithm is used.

38° (218°) (321°) **141°**

′	L Sin	d	L Tan	c d	L Ctn	L Cos	d	′
0	9.78 934	16	9.89 281	26	10.10 719	9.89 653	10	60
1	9.78 950	17	9.89 307	26	10.10 693	9.89 643	10	59
2	9.78 967	16	9.89 333	26	10.10 667	9.89 633	9	58
3	9.78 983	16	9.89 359	26	10.10 641	9.89 624	10	57
4	9.78 999	16	9.89 385	26	10.10 615	9.89 614	10	56
5	9.79 015	16	9.89 411	26	10.10 589	9.89 604	10	55
6	9.79 031	16	9.89 437	26	10.10 563	9.89 594	10	54
7	9.79 047	16	9.89 463	26	10.10 537	9.89 584	10	53
8	9.79 063	16	9.89 489	26	10.10 511	9.89 574	10	52
9	9.79 079	16	9.89 515	26	10.10 485	9.89 564	10	51
10	9.79 095	16	9.89 541	26	10.10 459	9.89 554	10	50
11	9.79 111	17	9.89 567	26	10.10 433	9.89 544	10	49
12	9.79 128	16	9.89 593	26	10.10 407	9.89 534	10	48
13	9.79 144	16	9.89 619	26	10.10 381	9.89 524	10	47
14	9.79 160	16	9.89 645	26	10.10 355	9.89 514	10	46
15	9.79 176	16	9.89 671	26	10.10 329	9.89 504	9	45
16	9.79 192	16	9.89 697	26	10.10 303	9.89 495	10	44
17	9.79 208	16	9.89 723	26	10.10 277	9.89 485	10	43
18	9.79 224	16	9.89 749	26	10.10 251	9.89 475	10	42
19	9.79 240	16	9.89 775	26	10.10 225	9.89 465	10	41
20	9.79 256	16	9.89 801	26	10.10 199	9.89 455	10	40
21	9.79 272	16	9.89 827	26	10.10 173	9.89 445	10	39
22	9.79 288	16	9.89 853	26	10.10 147	9.89 435	10	38
23	9.79 304	15	9.89 879	26	10.10 121	9.89 425	10	37
24	9.79 319	16	9.89 905	26	10.10 095	9.89 415	10	36
25	9.79 335	16	9.89 931	26	10.10 069	9.89 405	10	35
26	9.79 351	16	9.89 957	26	10.10 043	9.89 395	10	34
27	9.79 367	16	9.89 983	26	10.10 017	9.89 385	10	33
28	9.79 383	16	9.90 009	26	10.09 991	9.89 375	11	32
29	9.79 399	16	9.90 035	26	10.09 965	9.89 364	10	31
30	9.79 415	16	9.90 061	25	10.09 939	9.89 354	10	30
31	9.79 431	16	9.90 086	26	10.09 914	9.89 344	10	29
32	9.79 447	16	9.90 112	26	10.09 888	9.89 334	10	28
33	9.79 463	15	9.90 138	26	10.09 862	9.89 324	10	27
34	9.79 478	16	9.90 164	26	10.09 836	9.89 314	10	26
35	9.79 494	16	9.90 190	26	10.09 810	9.89 304	10	25
36	9.79 510	16	9.90 216	26	10.09 784	9.89 294	10	24
37	9.79 526	16	9.90 242	26	10.09 758	9.89 284	10	23
38	9.79 542	16	9.90 268	26	10.09 732	9.89 274	10	22
39	9.79 558	15	9.90 294	26	10.09 706	9.89 264	10	21
40	9.79 573	16	9.90 320	26	10.09 680	9.89 254	10	20
41	9.79 589	16	9.90 346	25	10.09 654	9.89 244	11	19
42	9.79 605	16	9.90 371	26	10.09 629	9.89 233	10	18
43	9.79 621	15	9.90 397	26	10.09 603	9.89 223	10	17
44	9.79 636	16	9.90 423	26	10.09 577	9.89 213	10	16
45	9.79 652	16	9.90 449	26	10.09 551	9.89 203	10	15
46	9.79 668	16	9.90 475	26	10.09 525	9.89 193	10	14
47	9.79 684	15	9.90 501	26	10.09 499	9.89 183	10	13
48	9.79 699	16	9.90 527	26	10.09 473	9.89 173	11	12
49	9.79 715	16	9.90 553	25	10.09 447	9.89 162	10	11
50	9.79 731	15	9.90 578	26	10.09 422	9.89 152	10	10
51	9.79 746	16	9.90 604	26	10.09 396	9.89 142	10	9
52	9.79 762	16	9.90 630	26	10.09 370	9.89 132	10	8
53	9.79 778	15	9.90 656	26	10.09 344	9.89 122	10	7
54	9.79 793	16	9.90 682	26	10.09 318	9.89 112	11	6
55	9.79 809	16	9.90 708	26	10.09 292	9.89 101	10	5
56	9.79 825	15	9.90 734	25	10.09 266	9.89 091	10	4
57	9.79 840	16	9.90 759	26	10.09 241	9.89 081	10	3
58	9.79 856	16	9.90 785	26	10.09 215	9.89 071	11	2
59	9.79 872	15	9.90 811	26	10.09 189	9.89 060	10	1
60	9.79 887		9.90 837		10.09 163	9.89 050		0
′	L Cos	d	L Ctn	c d	L Tan	L Sin	d	′

Proportional parts

″	26	25
1	0.4	0.4
2	0.9	0.8
3	1.3	1.2
4	1.7	1.7
5	2.2	2.1
6	2.6	2.5
7	3.0	2.9
8	3.5	3.3
9	3.9	3.8
10	4.3	4.2
20	8.7	8.3
30	13.0	12.5
40	17.3	16.7
50	21.7	20.8

″	17	16	15
1	0.3	0.3	0.2
2	0.6	0.5	0.5
3	0.8	0.8	0.8
4	1.1	1.1	1.0
5	1.4	1.3	1.2
6	1.7	1.6	1.5
7	2.0	1.9	1.8
8	2.3	2.1	2.0
9	2.6	2.4	2.2
10	2.8	2.7	2.5
20	5.7	5.3	5.0
30	8.5	8.0	7.5
40	11.3	10.7	10.0
50	14.2	13.3	12.5

″	11	10	9
1	0.2	0.2	0.2
2	0.4	0.3	0.3
3	0.6	0.5	0.4
4	0.7	0.7	0.6
5	0.9	0.8	0.8
6	1.1	1.0	0.9
7	1.3	1.2	1.0
8	1.5	1.3	1.2
9	1.6	1.5	1.4
10	1.8	1.7	1.5
20	3.7	3.3	3.0
30	5.5	5.0	4.5
40	7.3	6.7	6.0
50	9.2	8.3	7.5

Proportional parts

128° (308°) (231°) **51°**

The −10 portion of the characteristic of the logarithm is not printed but must be written down whenever such a logarithm is used.

39° (219°) (320°) **140°**

′	L Sin	d	L Tan	c d	L Ctn	L Cos	d	′
0	9.79 887	16	9.90 837	26	10.09 163	9.89 050	10	60
1	9.79 903	15	9.90 863	26	10.09 137	9.89 040	10	59
2	9.79 918	16	9.90 889	25	10.09 111	9.89 030	10	58
3	9.79 934	16	9.90 914	26	10.09 086	9.89 020	11	57
4	9.79 950	15	9.90 940	26	10.09 060	9.89 009	10	56
5	9.79 965	16	9.90 966	26	10.09 034	9.88 999	10	55
6	9.79 981	15	9.90 992	26	10.09 008	9.88 989	11	54
7	9.79 996	16	9.91 018	25	10.08 982	9.88 978	10	53
8	9.80 012	15	9.91 043	26	10.08 957	9.88 968	10	52
9	9.80 027	16	9.91 069	26	10.08 931	9.88 958	10	51
10	9.80 043	15	9.91 095	26	10.08 905	9.88 948	11	50
11	9.80 058	16	9.91 121	26	10.08 879	9.88 937	10	49
12	9.80 074	15	9.91 147	25	10.08 853	9.88 927	10	48
13	9.80 089	16	9.91 172	26	10.08 828	9.88 917	11	47
14	9.80 105	15	9.91 198	26	10.08 802	9.88 906	10	46
15	9.80 120	16	9.91 224	26	10.08 776	9.88 896	10	45
16	9.80 136	15	9.91 250	26	10.08 750	9.88 886	11	44
17	9.80 151	15	9.91 276	25	10.08 724	9.88 875	10	43
18	9.80 166	16	9.91 301	26	10.08 699	9.88 865	10	42
19	9.80 182	15	9.91 327	26	10.08 673	9.88 855	11	41
20	9.80 197	16	9.91 353	26	10.08 647	9.88 844	10	40
21	9.80 213	15	9.91 379	25	10.08 621	9.88 834	10	39
22	9.80 228	16	9.91 404	26	10.08 596	9.88 824	11	38
23	9.80 244	15	9.91 430	26	10.08 570	9.88 813	10	37
24	9.80 259	15	9.91 456	26	10.08 544	9.88 803	10	36
25	9.80 274	16	9.91 482	25	10.08 518	9.88 793	11	35
26	9.80 290	15	9.91 507	26	10.08 493	9.88 782	10	34
27	9.80 305	15	9.91 533	26	10.08 467	9.88 772	11	33
28	9.80 320	16	9.91 559	26	10.08 441	9.88 761	10	32
29	9.80 336	15	9.91 585	25	10.08 415	9.88 751	10	31
30	9.80 351	15	9.91 610	26	10.08 390	9.88 741	11	30
31	9.80 366	16	9.91 636	26	10.08 364	9.88 730	10	29
32	9.80 382	15	9.91 662	26	10.08 338	9.88 720	11	28
33	9.80 397	15	9.91 688	25	10.08 312	9.88 709	10	27
34	9.80 412	16	9.91 713	26	10.08 287	9.88 699	11	26
35	9.80 428	15	9.91 739	26	10.08 261	9.88 688	10	25
36	9.80 443	15	9.91 765	26	10.08 235	9.88 678	10	24
37	9.80 458	15	9.91 791	25	10.08 209	9.88 668	11	23
38	9.80 473	16	9.91 816	26	10.08 184	9.88 657	10	22
39	9.80 489	15	9.91 842	26	10.08 158	9.88 647	11	21
40	9.80 504	15	9.91 868	25	10.08 132	9.88 636	10	20
41	9.80 519	15	9.91 893	26	10.08 107	9.88 626	11	19
42	9.80 534	16	9.91 919	26	10.08 081	9.88 615	10	18
43	9.80 550	15	9.91 945	26	10.08 055	9.88 605	11	17
44	9.80 565	15	9.91 971	25	10.08 029	9.88 594	10	16
45	9.80 580	15	9.91 996	26	10.08 004	9.88 584	11	15
46	9.80 595	15	9.92 022	26	10.07 978	9.88 573	10	14
47	9.80 610	15	9.92 048	25	10.07 952	9.88 563	11	13
48	9.80 625	16	9.92 073	26	10.07 927	9.88 552	10	12
49	9.80 641	15	9.92 099	26	10.07 901	9.88 542	11	11
50	9.80 656	15	9.92 125	25	10.07 875	9.88 531	10	10
51	9.80 671	15	9.92 150	26	10.07 850	9.88 521	11	9
52	9.80 686	15	9.92 176	26	10.07 824	9.88 510	11	8
53	9.80 701	15	9.92 202	25	10.07 798	9.88 499	10	7
54	9.80 716	15	9.92 227	26	10.07 773	9.88 489	11	6
55	9.80 731	15	9.92 253	26	10.07 747	9.88 478	10	5
56	9.80 746	16	9.92 279	25	10.07 721	9.88 468	11	4
57	9.80 762	15	9.92 304	26	10.07 696	9.88 457	10	3
58	9.80 777	15	9.92 330	26	10.07 670	9.88 447	11	2
59	9.80 792	15	9.92 356	25	10.07 644	9.88 436	11	1
60	9.80 807		9.92 381		10.07 619	9.88 425		0
′	L Cos	d	L Ctn	c d	L Tan	L Sin	d	′

Proportional parts

″	26	25	″	16	15	″	11	10
1	0.4	0.4	1	0.3	0.2	1	0.2	0.2
2	0.9	0.8	2	0.5	0.5	2	0.4	0.3
3	1.3	1.2	3	0.8	0.8	3	0.6	0.5
4	1.7	1.7	4	1.1	1.0	4	0.7	0.7
5	2.2	2.1	5	1.3	1.2	5	0.9	0.8
6	2.6	2.5	6	1.6	1.5	6	1.1	1.0
7	3.0	2.9	7	1.9	1.8	7	1.3	1.2
8	3.5	3.3	8	2.1	2.0	8	1.5	1.3
9	3.9	3.8	9	2.4	2.2	9	1.6	1.5
10	4.3	4.2	10	2.7	2.5	10	1.8	1.7
20	8.7	8.3	20	5.3	5.0	20	3.7	3.3
30	13.0	12.5	30	8.0	7.5	30	5.5	5.0
40	17.3	16.7	40	10.7	10.0	40	7.3	6.7
50	21.7	20.8	50	13.3	12.5	50	9.2	8.3

129° (309°) (230°) **50°**

The −10 portion of the characteristic of the logarithm is not printed but must be written down whenever such a logarithm is used.

40° (220°) (319°) **139°**

′	L Sin	d	L Tan	c d	L Ctn	L Cos	d	′
0	9.80 807	15	9.92 381	26	10.07 619	9.88 425	10	60
1	9.80 822	15	9.92 407	26	10.07 593	9.88 415	11	59
2	9.80 837	15	9.92 433	25	10.07 567	9.88 404	10	58
3	9.80 852	15	9.92 458	26	10.07 542	9.88 394	11	57
4	9.80 867	15	9.92 484	26	10.07 516	9.88 383	11	56
5	9.80 882	15	9.92 510	25	10.07 490	9.88 372	10	55
6	9.80 897	15	9.92 535	26	10.07 465	9.88 362	11	54
7	9.80 912	15	9.92 561	26	10.07 439	9.88 351	11	53
8	9.80 927	15	9.92 587	25	10.07 413	9.88 340	10	52
9	9.80 942	15	9.92 612	26	10.07 388	9.88 330	11	51
10	9.80 957	15	9.92 638	25	10.07 362	9.88 319	11	50
11	9.80 972	15	9.92 663	26	10.07 337	9.88 308	10	49
12	9.80 987	15	9.92 689	26	10.07 311	9.88 298	11	48
13	9.81 002	15	9.92 715	25	10.07 285	9.88 287	11	47
14	9.81 017	15	9.92 740	26	10.07 260	9.88 276	10	46
15	9.81 032	15	9.92 766	26	10.07 234	9.88 266	11	45
16	9.81 047	14	9.92 792	25	10.07 208	9.88 255	11	44
17	9.81 061	15	9.92 817	26	10.07 183	9.88 244	10	43
18	9.81 076	15	9.92 843	25	10.07 157	9.88 234	11	42
19	9.81 091	15	9.92 868	26	10.07 132	9.88 223	11	41
20	9.81 106	15	9.92 894	26	10.07 106	9.88 212	11	40
21	9.81 121	15	9.92 920	25	10.07 080	9.88 201	10	39
22	9.81 136	15	9.92 945	26	10.07 055	9.88 191	11	38
23	9.81 151	15	9.92 971	25	10.07 029	9.88 180	11	37
24	9.81 166	14	9.92 996	26	10.07 004	9.88 169	11	36
25	9.81 180	15	9.93 022	26	10.06 978	9.88 158	10	35
26	9.81 195	15	9.93 048	25	10.06 952	9.88 148	11	34
27	9.81 210	15	9.93 073	26	10.06 927	9.88 137	11	33
28	9.81 225	15	9.93 099	25	10.06 901	9.88 126	11	32
29	9.81 240	14	9.93 124	26	10.06 876	9.88 115	10	31
30	9.81 254	15	9.93 150	25	10.06 850	9.88 105	11	30
31	9.81 269	15	9.93 175	26	10.06 825	9.88 094	11	29
32	9.81 284	15	9.93 201	26	10.06 799	9.88 083	11	28
33	9.81 299	15	9.93 227	25	10.06 773	9.88 072	11	27
34	9.81 314	14	9.93 252	26	10.06 748	9.88 061	10	26
35	9.81 328	15	9.93 278	25	10.06 722	9.88 051	11	25
36	9.81 343	15	9.93 303	26	10.06 697	9.88 040	11	24
37	9.81 358	14	9.93 329	25	10.06 671	9.88 029	11	23
38	9.81 372	15	9.93 354	26	10.06 646	9.88 018	11	22
39	9.81 387	15	9.93 380	26	10.06 620	9.88 007	11	21
40	9.81 402	15	9.93 406	25	10.06 594	9.87 996	11	20
41	9.81 417	14	9.93 431	26	10.06 569	9.87 985	10	19
42	9.81 431	15	9.93 457	25	10.06 543	9.87 975	11	18
43	9.81 446	15	9.93 482	26	10.06 518	9.87 964	11	17
44	9.81 461	14	9.93 508	25	10.06 492	9.87 953	11	16
45	9.81 475	15	9.93 533	26	10.06 467	9.87 942	11	15
46	9.81 490	15	9.93 559	25	10.06 441	9.87 931	11	14
47	9.81 505	14	9.93 584	26	10.06 416	9.87 920	11	13
48	9.81 519	15	9.93 610	26	10.06 390	9.87 909	11	12
49	9.81 534	15	9.93 636	25	10.06 364	9.87 898	11	11
50	9.81 549	14	9.93 661	26	10.06 339	9.87 887	10	10
51	9.81 563	15	9.93 687	25	10.06 313	9.87 877	11	9
52	9.81 578	14	9.93 712	26	10.06 288	9.87 866	11	8
53	9.81 592	15	9.93 738	25	10.06 262	9.87 855	11	7
54	9.81 607	15	9.93 763	26	10.06 237	9.87 844	11	6
55	9.81 622	14	9.93 789	25	10.06 211	9.87 833	11	5
56	9.81 636	15	9.93 814	26	10.06 186	9.87 822	11	4
57	9.81 651	14	9.93 840	25	10.06 160	9.87 811	11	3
58	9.81 665	15	9.93 865	26	10.06 135	9.87 800	11	2
59	9.81 680	14	9.93 891	25	10.06 109	9.87 789	11	1
60	9.81 694		9.93 916		10.06 084	9.87 778		0
′	L Cos	d	L Ctn	c d	L Tan	L Sin	d	′

Proportional parts

″	26	25
1	0.4	0.4
2	0.9	0.8
3	1.3	1.2
4	1.7	1.7
5	2.2	2.1
6	2.6	2.5
7	3.0	2.9
8	3.5	3.3
9	3.9	3.8
10	4.3	4.2
20	8.7	8.3
30	13.0	12.5
40	17.3	16.7
50	21.7	20.8

″	15	14
1	0.2	0.2
2	0.5	0.5
3	0.8	0.7
4	1.0	0.9
5	1.2	1.2
6	1.5	1.4
7	1.8	1.6
8	2.0	1.9
9	2.2	2.1
10	2.5	2.3
20	5.0	4.7
30	7.5	7.0
40	10.0	9.3
50	12.5	11.7

″	11	10
1	0.2	0.2
2	0.4	0.3
3	0.6	0.5
4	0.7	0.7
5	0.9	0.8
6	1.1	1.0
7	1.3	1.2
8	1.5	1.3
9	1.6	1.5
10	1.8	1.7
20	3.7	3.3
30	5.5	5.0
40	7.3	6.7
50	9.2	8.3

Proportional parts

130° (310°) (229°) **49°**

The −10 portion of the characteristic of the logarithm is not printed but must be written down whenever such a logarithm is used.

41° (221°) (318°) **138°**

′	L Sin	d	L Tan	c d	L Ctn	L Cos	d	′
0	9.81 694	15	9.93 916	26	10.06 084	9.87 778	11	60
1	9.81 709	14	9.93 942	25	10.06 058	9.87 767	11	59
2	9.81 723	15	9.93 967	26	10.06 033	9.87 756	11	58
3	9.81 738	14	9.93 993	25	10.06 007	9.87 745	11	57
4	9.81 752	15	9.94 018	26	10.05 982	9.87 734	11	56
5	9.81 767	14	9.94 044	25	10.05 956	9.87 723	11	55
6	9.81 781	15	9.94 069	26	10.05 931	9.87 712	11	54
7	9.81 796	14	9.94 095	25	10.05 905	9.87 701	11	53
8	9.81 810	15	9.94 120	26	10.05 880	9.87 690	11	52
9	9.81 825	14	9.94 146	25	10.05 854	9.87 679	11	51
10	9.81 839	15	9.94 171	26	10.05 829	9.87 668	11	50
11	9.81 854	14	9.94 197	25	10.05 803	9.87 657	11	49
12	9.81 868	14	9.94 222	26	10.05 778	9.87 646	11	48
13	9.81 882	15	9.94 248	25	10.05 752	9.87 635	11	47
14	9.81 897	14	9.94 273	26	10.05 727	9.87 624	11	46
15	9.81 911	15	9.94 299	25	10.05 701	9.87 613	12	45
16	9.81 926	14	9.94 324	26	10.05 676	9.87 601	11	44
17	9.81 940	15	9.94 350	25	10.05 650	9.87 590	11	43
18	9.81 955	14	9.94 375	26	10.05 625	9.87 579	11	42
19	9.81 969	14	9.94 401	25	10.05 599	9.87 568	11	41
20	9.81 983	15	9.94 426	26	10.05 574	9.87 557	11	40
21	9.81 998	14	9.94 452	25	10.05 548	9.87 546	11	39
22	9.82 012	14	9.94 477	26	10.05 523	9.87 535	11	38
23	9.82 026	15	9.94 503	25	10.05 497	9.87 524	11	37
24	9.82 041	14	9.94 528	26	10.05 472	9.87 513	12	36
25	9.82 055	14	9.94 554	25	10.05 446	9.87 501	11	35
26	9.82 069	15	9.94 579	25	10.05 421	9.87 490	11	34
27	9.82 084	14	9.94 604	26	10.05 396	9.87 479	11	33
28	9.82 098	14	9.94 630	25	10.05 370	9.87 468	11	32
29	9.82 112	14	9.94 655	26	10.05 345	9.87 457	11	31
30	9.82 126	15	9.94 681	25	10.05 319	9.87 446	12	30
31	9.82 141	14	9.94 706	26	10.05 294	9.87 434	11	29
32	9.82 155	14	9.94 732	25	10.05 268	9.87 423	11	28
33	9.82 169	15	9.94 757	26	10.05 243	9.87 412	11	27
34	9.82 184	14	9.94 783	25	10.05 217	9.87 401	11	26
35	9.82 198	14	9.94 808	26	10.05 192	9.87 390	12	25
36	9.82 212	14	9.94 834	25	10.05 166	9.87 378	11	24
37	9.82 226	14	9.94 859	25	10.05 141	9.87 367	11	23
38	9.82 240	15	9.94 884	26	10.05 116	9.87 356	11	22
39	9.82 255	14	9.94 910	25	10.05 090	9.87 345	11	21
40	9.82 269	14	9.94 935	26	10.05 065	9.87 334	12	20
41	9.82 283	14	9.94 961	25	10.05 039	9.87 322	11	19
42	9.82 297	14	9.94 986	26	10.05 014	9.87 311	11	18
43	9.82 311	15	9.95 012	25	10.04 988	9.87 300	12	17
44	9.82 326	14	9.95 037	25	10.04 963	9.87 288	11	16
45	9.82 340	14	9.95 062	26	10.04 938	9.87 277	11	15
46	9.82 354	14	9.95 088	25	10.04 912	9.87 266	11	14
47	9.82 368	14	9.95 113	26	10.04 887	9.87 255	12	13
48	9.82 382	14	9.95 139	25	10.04 861	9.87 243	11	12
49	9.82 396	14	9.95 164	26	10.04 836	9.87 232	11	11
50	9.82 410	14	9.95 190	25	10.04 810	9.87 221	12	10
51	9.82 424	15	9.95 215	25	10.04 785	9.87 209	11	9
52	9.82 439	14	9.95 240	26	10.04 760	9.87 198	11	8
53	9.82 453	14	9.95 266	25	10.04 734	9.87 187	12	7
54	9.82 467	14	9.95 291	26	10.04 709	9.87 175	11	6
55	9.82 481	14	9.95 317	25	10.04 683	9.87 164	11	5
56	9.82 495	14	9.95 342	26	10.04 658	9.87 153	12	4
57	9.82 509	14	9.95 368	25	10.04 632	9.87 141	11	3
58	9.82 523	14	9.95 393	25	10.04 607	9.87 130	11	2
59	9.82 537	14	9.95 418	26	10.04 582	9.87 119	12	1
60	9.82 551		9.95 444		10.04 556	9.87 107		0
′	L Cos	d	L Ctn	c d	L Tan	L Sin	d	′

Proportional parts

″	26	25
1	0.4	0.4
2	0.9	0.8
3	1.3	1.2
4	1.7	1.7
5	2.2	2.1
6	2.6	2.5
7	3.0	2.9
8	3.5	3.3
9	3.9	3.8
10	4.3	4.2
20	8.7	8.3
30	13.0	12.5
40	17.3	16.7
50	21.7	20.8

″	15	14
1	0.2	0.2
2	0.5	0.5
3	0.8	0.7
4	1.0	0.9
5	1.2	1.2
6	1.5	1.4
7	1.8	1.6
8	2.0	1.9
9	2.2	2.1
10	2.5	2.3
20	5.0	4.7
30	7.5	7.0
40	10.0	9.3
50	12.5	11.7

″	12	11
1	0.2	0.2
2	0.4	0.4
3	0.6	0.6
4	0.8	0.7
5	1.0	0.9
6	1.2	1.1
7	1.4	1.3
8	1.6	1.5
9	1.8	1.6
10	2.0	1.8
20	4.0	3.7
30	6.0	5.5
40	8.0	7.3
50	10.0	9.2

Proportional parts

131° (311°) (228°) **48°**

The −10 portion of the characteristic of the logarithm is not printed but must be written down whenever such a logarithm is used.

42° (222°) (317°) **137°**

′	L Sin	d	L Tan	c d	L Ctn	L Cos	d	′
0	9.82 551	14	9.95 444	25	10.04 556	9.87 107	11	60
1	9.82 565	14	9.95 469	26	10.04 531	9.87 096	11	59
2	9.82 579	14	9.95 495	25	10.04 505	9.87 085	12	58
3	9.82 593	14	9.95 520	25	10.04 480	9.87 073	11	57
4	9.82 607	14	9.95 545	26	10.04 455	9.87 062	12	56
5	9.82 621	14	9.95 571	25	10.04 429	9.87 050	11	55
6	9.82 635	14	9.95 596	26	10.04 404	9.87 039	11	54
7	9.82 649	14	9.95 622	25	10.04 378	9.87 028	12	53
8	9.82 663	14	9.95 647	25	10.04 353	9.87 016	11	52
9	9.82 677	14	9.95 672	26	10.04 328	9.87 005	12	51
10	9.82 691	14	9.95 698	25	10.04 302	9.86 993	11	50
11	9.82 705	14	9.95 723	25	10.04 277	9.86 982	12	49
12	9.82 719	14	9.95 748	26	10.04 252	9.86 970	11	48
13	9.82 733	14	9.95 774	25	10.04 226	9.86 959	12	47
14	9.82 747	14	9.95 799	26	10.04 201	9.86 947	11	46
15	9.82 761	14	9.95 825	25	10.04 175	9.86 936	12	45
16	9.82 775	13	9.95 850	25	10.04 150	9.86 924	11	44
17	9.82 788	14	9.95 875	26	10.04 125	9.86 913	11	43
18	9.82 802	14	9.95 901	25	10.04 099	9.86 902	12	42
19	9.82 816	14	9.95 926	26	10.04 074	9.86 890	11	41
20	9.82 830	14	9.95 952	25	10.04 048	9.86 879	12	40
21	9.82 844	14	9.95 977	25	10.04 023	9.86 867	12	39
22	9.82 858	14	9.96 002	26	10.03 998	9.86 855	11	38
23	9.82 872	13	9.96 028	25	10.03 972	9.86 844	12	37
24	9.82 885	14	9.96 053	25	10.03 947	9.86 832	11	36
25	9.82 899	14	9.96 078	26	10.03 922	9.86 821	12	35
26	9.82 913	14	9.96 104	25	10.03 896	9.86 809	11	34
27	9.82 927	14	9.96 129	26	10.03 871	9.86 798	12	33
28	9.82 941	14	9.96 155	25	10.03 845	9.86 786	11	32
29	9.82 955	13	9.96 180	25	10.03 820	9.86 775	12	31
30	9.82 968	14	9.96 205	26	10.03 795	9.86 763	11	30
31	9.82 982	14	9.96 231	25	10.03 769	9.86 752	12	29
32	9.82 996	14	9.96 256	25	10.03 744	9.86 740	12	28
33	9.83 010	13	9.96 281	26	10.03 719	9.86 728	11	27
34	9.83 023	14	9.96 307	25	10.03 693	9.86 717	12	26
35	9.83 037	14	9.96 332	25	10.03 668	9.86 705	11	25
36	9.83 051	14	9.96 357	26	10.03 643	9.86 694	12	24
37	9.83 065	13	9.96 383	25	10.03 617	9.86 682	12	23
38	9.83 078	14	9.96 408	25	10.03 592	9.86 670	11	22
39	9.83 092	14	9.96 433	26	10.03 567	9.86 659	12	21
40	9.83 106	14	9.96 459	25	10.03 541	9.86 647	12	20
41	9.83 120	13	9.96 484	26	10.03 516	9.86 635	11	19
42	9.83 133	14	9.96 510	25	10.03 490	9.86 624	12	18
43	9.83 147	14	9.96 535	25	10.03 465	9.86 612	12	17
44	9.83 161	13	9.96 560	26	10.03 440	9.86 600	11	16
45	9.83 174	14	9.96 586	25	10.03 414	9.86 589	12	15
46	9.83 188	14	9.96 611	25	10.03 389	9.86 577	12	14
47	9.83 202	13	9.96 636	26	10.03 364	9.86 565	11	13
48	9.83 215	14	9.96 662	25	10.03 338	9.86 554	12	12
49	9.83 229	13	9.96 687	25	10.03 313	9.86 542	12	11
50	9.83 242	14	9.96 712	26	10.03 288	9.86 530	12	10
51	9.83 256	14	9.96 738	25	10.03 262	9.86 518	11	9
52	9.83 270	13	9.96 763	25	10.03 237	9.86 507	12	8
53	9.83 283	14	9.96 788	26	10.03 212	9.86 495	12	7
54	9.83 297	13	9.96 814	25	10.03 186	9.86 483	11	6
55	9.83 310	14	9.96 839	25	10.03 161	9.86 472	12	5
56	9.83 324	14	9.96 864	26	10.03 136	9.86 460	12	4
57	9.83 338	13	9.96 890	25	10.03 110	9.86 448	12	3
58	9.83 351	14	9.96 915	25	10.03 085	9.86 436	11	2
59	9.83 365	13	9.96 940	26	10.03 060	9.86 425	12	1
60	9.83 378		9.96 966		10.03 034	9.86 413		0
′	L Cos	d	L Ctn	c d	LTan	L Sin	d	′

132° (312°) (227°) **47°**

Proportional parts

″	26	25
1	0.4	0.4
2	0.9	0.8
3	1.3	1.2
4	1.7	1.7
5	2.2	2.1
6	2.6	2.5
7	3.0	2.9
8	3.5	3.3
9	3.9	3.8
10	4.3	4.2
20	8.7	8.3
30	13.0	12.5
40	17.3	16.7
50	21.7	20.8

″	14	13
1	0.2	0.2
2	0.5	0.4
3	0.7	0.6
4	0.9	0.9
5	1.2	1.1
6	1.4	1.3
7	1.6	1.5
8	1.9	1.7
9	2.1	2.0
10	2.3	2.2
20	4.7	4.3
30	7.0	6.5
40	9.3	8.7
50	11.7	10.8

″	12	11
1	0.2	0.2
2	0.4	0.4
3	0.6	0.6
4	0.8	0.7
5	1.0	0.9
6	1.2	1.1
7	1.4	1.3
8	1.6	1.5
9	1.8	1.6
10	2.0	1.8
20	4.0	3.7
30	6.0	5.5
40	8.0	7.3
50	10.0	9.2

Proportional parts

The −10 portion of the characteristic of the logarithm is not printed but must be written down whenever such a logarithm is used.

43° (223°) (316°) **136°**

′	L Sin	d	L Tan	c d	L Ctn	L Cos	d	′
0	9.83 378	14	9.96 966	25	10.03 034	9.86 413	12	60
1	9.83 392	13	9.96 991	25	10.03 009	9.86 401	12	59
2	9.83 405	14	9.97 016	26	10.02 984	9.86 389	12	58
3	9.83 419	13	9.97 042	25	10.02 958	9.86 377	11	57
4	9.83 432	14	9.97 067	25	10.02 933	9.86 366	12	56
5	9.83 446	13	9.97 092	26	10.02 908	9.86 354	12	55
6	9.83 459	14	9.97 118	25	10.02 882	9.86 342	12	54
7	9.83 473	13	9.97 143	25	10.02 857	9.86 330	12	53
8	9.83 486	14	9.97 168	25	10.02 832	9.86 318	12	52
9	9.83 500	13	9.97 193	26	10.02 807	9.86 306	11	51
10	9.83 513	14	9.97 219	25	10.02 781	9.86 295	12	50
11	9.83 527	13	9.97 244	25	10.02 756	9.86 283	12	49
12	9.83 540	14	9.97 269	26	10.02 731	9.86 271	12	48
13	9.83 554	13	9.97 295	25	10.02 705	9.86 259	12	47
14	9.83 567	14	9.97 320	25	10.02 680	9.86 247	12	46
15	9.83 581	13	9.97 345	26	10.02 655	9.86 235	12	45
16	9.83 594	14	9.97 371	25	10.02 629	9.86 223	12	44
17	9.83 608	13	9.97 396	25	10.02 604	9.86 211	11	43
18	9.83 621	13	9.97 421	26	10.02 579	9.86 200	12	42
19	9.83 634	14	9.97 447	25	10.02 553	9.86 188	12	41
20	9.83 648	13	9.97 472	25	10.02 528	9.86 176	12	40
21	9.83 661	13	9.97 497	26	10.02 503	9.86 164	12	39
22	9.83 674	14	9.97 523	25	10.02 477	9.86 152	12	38
23	9.83 688	13	9.97 548	25	10.02 452	9.86 140	12	37
24	9.83 701	14	9.97 573	25	10.02 427	9.86 128	12	36
25	9.83 715	13	9.97 598	26	10.02 402	9.86 116	12	35
26	9.83 728	13	9.97 624	25	10.02 376	9.86 104	12	34
27	9.83 741	14	9.97 649	25	10.02 351	9.86 092	12	33
28	9.83 755	13	9.97 674	26	10.02 326	9.86 080	12	32
29	9.83 768	13	9.97 700	25	10.02 300	9.86 068	12	31
30	9.83 781	14	9.97 725	25	10.02 275	9.86 056	12	30
31	9.83 795	13	9.97 750	26	10.02 250	9.86 044	12	29
32	9.83 808	13	9.97 776	25	10.02 224	9.86 032	12	28
33	9.83 821	13	9.97 801	25	10.02 199	9.86 020	12	27
34	9.83 834	14	9.97 826	25	10.02 174	9.86 008	12	26
35	9.83 848	13	9.97 851	26	10.02 149	9.85 996	12	25
36	9.83 861	13	9.97 877	25	10.02 123	9.85 984	12	24
37	9.83 874	13	9.97 902	25	10.02 098	9.85 972	12	23
38	9.83 887	14	9.97 927	26	10.02 073	9.85 960	12	22
39	9.83 901	13	9.97 953	25	10.02 047	9.85 948	12	21
40	9.83 914	13	9.97 978	25	10.02 022	9.85 936	12	20
41	9.83 927	13	9.98 003	26	10.01 997	9.85 924	12	19
42	9.83 940	14	9.98 029	25	10.01 971	9.85 912	12	18
43	9.83 954	13	9.98 054	25	10.01 946	9.85 900	12	17
44	9.83 967	13	9.98 079	25	10.01 921	9.85 888	12	16
45	9.83 980	13	9.98 104	26	10.01 896	9.85 876	12	15
46	9.83 993	13	9.98 130	25	10.01 870	9.85 864	13	14
47	9.84 006	14	9.98 155	25	10.01 845	9.85 851	12	13
48	9.84 020	13	9.98 180	26	10.01 820	9.85 839	12	12
49	9.84 033	13	9.98 206	25	10.01 794	9.85 827	12	11
50	9.84 046	13	9.98 231	25	10.01 769	9.85 815	12	10
51	9.84 059	13	9.98 256	25	10.01 744	9.85 803	12	9
52	9.84 072	13	9.98 281	26	10.01 719	9.85 791	12	8
53	9.84 085	13	9.98 307	25	10.01 693	9.85 779	13	7
54	9.84 098	14	9.98 332	25	10.01 668	9.85 766	12	6
55	9.84 112	13	9.98 357	26	10.01 643	9.85 754	12	5
56	9.84 125	13	9.98 383	25	10.01 617	9.85 742	12	4
57	9.84 138	13	9.98 408	25	10.01 592	9.85 730	12	3
58	9.84 151	13	9.98 433	25	10.01 567	9.85 718	12	2
59	9.84 164	13	9.98 458	26	10.01 542	9.85 706	13	1
60	9.84 177		9.98 484		10.01 516	9.85 693		0
′	L Cos	d	L Ctn	c d	L Tan	L Sin	d	′

133° (313°) (226°) **46°**

Proportional parts

″	26	25
1	0.4	0.4
2	0.9	0.8
3	1.3	1.2
4	1.7	1.7
5	2.2	2.1
6	2.6	2.5
7	3.0	2.9
8	3.5	3.3
9	3.9	3.8
10	4.3	4.2
20	8.7	8.3
30	13.0	12.5
40	17.3	16.7
50	21.7	20.8

″	14	13
1	0.2	0.2
2	0.5	0.4
3	0.7	0.6
4	0.9	0.9
5	1.2	1.1
6	1.4	1.3
7	1.6	1.5
8	1.9	1.7
9	2.1	2.0
10	2.3	2.2
20	4.7	4.3
30	7.0	6.5
40	9.3	8.7
50	11.7	10.8

″	12	11
1	0.2	0.2
2	0.4	0.4
3	0.6	0.6
4	0.8	0.7
5	1.0	0.9
6	1.2	1.1
7	1.4	1.3
8	1.6	1.5
9	1.8	1.6
10	2.0	1.8
20	4.0	3.7
30	6.0	5.5
40	8.0	7.3
50	10.0	9.2

Proportional parts

The −10 portion of the characteristic of the logarithm is not printed but must be written down whenever such a logarithm is used.

44° (224°) (315°) **135°**

′	L Sin	d	L Tan	c d	L Ctn	L Cos	d	′
0	9.84 177	13	9.98 484	25	10.01 516	9.85 693	12	60
1	9.84 190	13	9.98 509	25	10.01 491	9.85 681	12	59
2	9.84 203	13	9.98 534	26	10.01 466	9.85 669	12	58
3	9.84 216	13	9.98 560	25	10.01 440	9.85 657	12	57
4	9.84 229	13	9.98 585	25	10.01 415	9.85 645	13	56
5	9.84 242	13	9.98 610	25	10.01 390	9.85 632	12	55
6	9.84 255	14	9.98 635	26	10.01 365	9.85 620	12	54
7	9.84 269	13	9.98 661	25	10.01 339	9.85 608	12	53
8	9.84 282	13	9.98 686	25	10.01 314	9.85 596	13	52
9	9.84 295	13	9.98 711	26	10.01 289	9.85 583	12	51
10	9.84 308	13	9.98 737	25	10.01 263	9.85 571	12	50
11	9.84 321	13	9.98 762	25	10.01 238	9.85 559	12	49
12	9.84 334	13	9.98 787	25	10.01 213	9.85 547	13	48
13	9.84 347	13	9.98 812	26	10.01 188	9.85 534	12	47
14	9.84 360	13	9.98 838	25	10.01 162	9.85 522	12	46
15	9.84 373	12	9.98 863	25	10.01 137	9.85 510	13	45
16	9.84 385	13	9.98 888	25	10.01 112	9.85 497	12	44
17	9.84 398	13	9.98 913	26	10.01 087	9.85 485	12	43
18	9.84 411	13	9.98 939	25	10.01 061	9.85 473	13	42
19	9.84 424	13	9.98 964	25	10.01 036	9.85 460	12	41
20	9.84 437	13	9.98 989	26	10.01 011	9.85 448	12	40
21	9.84 450	13	9.99 015	25	10.00 985	9.85 436	13	39
22	9.84 463	13	9.99 040	25	10.00 960	9.85 423	12	38
23	9.84 476	13	9.99 065	25	10.00 935	9.85 411	12	37
24	9.84 489	13	9.99 090	26	10.00 910	9.85 399	13	36
25	9.84 502	13	9.99 116	25	10.00 884	9.85 386	12	35
26	9.84 515	13	9.99 141	25	10.00 859	9.85 374	13	34
27	9.84 528	12	9.99 166	25	10.00 834	9.85 361	12	33
28	9.84 540	13	9.99 191	26	10.00 809	9.85 349	12	32
29	9.84 553	13	9.99 217	25	10.00 783	9.85 337	13	31
30	9.84 566	13	9.99 242	25	10.00 758	9.85 324	12	30
31	9.84 579	13	9.99 267	26	10.00 733	9.85 312	13	29
32	9.84 592	13	9.99 293	25	10.00 707	9.85 299	12	28
33	9.84 605	13	9.99 318	25	10.00 682	9.85 287	13	27
34	9.84 618	12	9.99 343	25	10.00 657	9.85 274	12	26
35	9.84 630	13	9.99 368	26	10.00 632	9.85 262	12	25
36	9.84 643	13	9.99 394	25	10.00 606	9.85 250	13	24
37	9.84 656	13	9.99 419	25	10.00 581	9.85 237	12	23
38	9.84 669	13	9.99 444	25	10.00 556	9.85 225	13	22
39	9.84 682	12	9.99 469	26	10.00 531	9.85 212	12	21
40	9.84 694	13	9.99 495	25	10.00 505	9.85 200	13	20
41	9.84 707	13	9.99 520	25	10.00 480	9.85 187	12	19
42	9.84 720	13	9.99 545	25	10.00 455	9.85 175	13	18
43	9.84 733	12	9.99 570	26	10.00 430	9.85 162	12	17
44	9.84 745	13	9.99 596	25	10.00 404	9.85 150	13	16
45	9.84 758	13	9.99 621	25	10.00 379	9.85 137	12	15
46	9.84 771	13	9.99 646	26	10.00 354	9.85 125	13	14
47	9.84 784	12	9.99 672	25	10.00 328	9.85 112	12	13
48	9.84 796	13	9.99 697	25	10.00 303	9.85 100	13	12
49	9.84 809	13	9.99 722	25	10.00 278	9.85 087	13	11
50	9.84 822	13	9.99 747	26	10.00 253	9.85 074	12	10
51	9.84 835	12	9.99 773	25	10.00 227	9.85 062	13	9
52	9.84 847	13	9.99 798	25	10.00 202	9.85 049	12	8
53	9.84 860	13	9.99 823	25	10.00 177	9.85 037	13	7
54	9.84 873	12	9.99 848	26	10.00 152	9.85 024	12	6
55	9.84 885	13	9.99 874	25	10.00 126	9.85 012	13	5
56	9.84 898	13	9.99 899	25	10.00 101	9.84 999	13	4
57	9.84 911	12	9.99 924	25	10.00 076	9.84 986	12	3
58	9.84 923	13	9.99 949	26	10.00 051	9.84 974	13	2
59	9.84 936	13	9.99 975	25	10.00 025	9.84 961	12	1
60	9.84 949		10.00 000		10.00 000	9.84 949		0
′	L Cos	d	L Ctn	c d	L Tan	L Sin	d	′

Proportional parts

″	26	25
1	0.4	0.4
2	0.9	0.8
3	1.3	1.2
4	1.7	1.7
5	2.2	2.1
6	2.6	2.5
7	3.0	2.9
8	3.5	3.3
9	3.9	3.8
10	4.3	4.2
20	8.7	8.3
30	13.0	12.5
40	17.3	16.7
50	21.7	20.8

″	14	13	12
1	0.2	0.2	0.2
2	0.5	0.4	0.4
3	0.7	0.6	0.6
4	0.9	0.9	0.8
5	1.2	1.1	1.0
6	1.4	1.3	1.2
7	1.6	1.5	1.4
8	1.9	1.7	1.6
9	2.1	2.0	1.8
10	2.3	2.2	2.0
20	4.7	4.3	4.0
30	7.0	6.5	6.0
40	9.3	8.7	8.0
50	11.7	10.8	10.0

Proportional parts

134° (314°) (225°) **45°**

N	0	1	2	3	4	5	6	7	8	9
1.0	0.0 000	100	198	296	392	488	583	677	770	862
1.1	953	*044	*133	*222	*310	*398	*484	*570	*655	*740
1.2	0.1 823	906	989	*070	*151	*231	*311	*390	*469	*546
1.3	0.2 624	700	776	852	927	*001	*075	*148	*221	*293
1.4	0.3 365	436	507	577	646	716	784	853	920	988
1.5	0.4 055	121	187	253	318	383	447	511	574	637
1.6	700	762	824	886	947	*008	*068	*128	*188	*247
1.7	0.5 306	365	423	481	539	596	653	710	766	822
1.8	878	933	988	*043	*098	*152	*206	*259	*313	*366
1.9	0.6 419	471	523	575	627	678	729	780	831	881
2.0	931	981	*031	*080	*129	*178	*227	*275	*324	*372
2.1	0.7 419	467	514	561	608	655	701	747	793	839
2.2	885	930	975	*020	*065	*109	*154	*198	*242	*286
2.3	0.8 329	372	416	459	502	544	587	629	671	713
2.4	755	796	838	879	920	961	*002	*042	*083	*123
2.5	0.9 163	203	243	282	322	361	400	439	478	517
2.6	555	594	632	670	708	746	783	821	858	895
2.7	933	969	*006	*043	*080	*116	*152	*188	*225	*260
2.8	1.0 296	332	367	403	438	473	508	543	578	613
2.9	647	682	716	750	784	818	852	886	919	953
3.0	986	*019	*053	*086	*119	*151	*184	*217	*249	*282
3.1	1.1 314	346	378	410	442	474	506	537	569	600
3.2	632	663	694	725	756	787	817	848	878	909
3.3	939	969	*000	*030	*060	*090	*119	*149	*179	*208
3.4	1.2 238	267	296	326	355	384	413	442	470	499
3.5	528	556	585	613	641	669	698	726	754	782
3.6	809	837	865	892	920	947	975	*002	*029	*056
3.7	1.3 083	110	137	164	191	218	244	271	297	324
3.8	350	376	402	429	455	481	507	533	558	584
3.9	610	635	661	686	712	737	762	788	813	838
4.0	863	888	913	938	962	987	*012	*036	*061	*085
4.1	1.4 110	134	159	183	207	231	255	279	303	327
4.2	351	375	398	422	446	469	493	516	540	563
4.3	586	609	633	656	679	702	725	748	770	793
4.4	816	839	861	884	907	929	951	974	996	*019
4.5	1.5 041	063	085	107	129	151	173	195	217	239
4.6	261	282	304	326	347	369	390	412	433	454
4.7	476	497	518	539	560	581	602	623	644	665
4.8	686	707	728	748	769	790	810	831	851	872
4.9	892	913	933	953	974	994	*014	*034	*054	*074
5.0	1.6 094	114	134	154	174	194	214	233	253	273

If given number $n = N \times 10^m$, then $\log_e n = \log_e N + m \log_e 10$. Find $m \log_e 10$ from the following table:

Multiples of $\log_e$ 10

$\log_e 10 = 2.3026$	$-\log_e 10 = 7.6974 - 10$
$2 \log_e 10 = 4.6052$	$-2 \log_e 10 = 5.3948 - 10$
$3 \log_e 10 = 6.9078$	$-3 \log_e 10 = 3.0922 - 10$
$4 \log_e 10 = 9.2103$	$-4 \log_e 10 = 0.7897 - 10$
$5 \log_e 10 = 11.5129$	$-5 \log_e 10 = 9.4871 - 20$

*From A. E. Richmond, "Calculus for Electronics," 2nd ed., McGraw-Hill Book Company, New York, 1958, 1972.

N	0	1	2	3	4	5	6	7	8	9
5.0	1.6 094	114	134	154	174	194	214	233	253	273
5.1	292	312	332	351	371	390	409	429	448	467
5.2	487	506	525	544	563	582	601	620	639	658
5.3	677	696	715	734	752	771	790	808	827	845
5.4	864	882	901	919	938	956	974	993	*011	*029
5.5	1.7 047	066	084	102	120	138	156	174	192	210
5.6	228	246	263	281	299	317	334	352	370	387
5.7	405	422	440	457	475	492	509	527	544	561
5.8	579	596	613	630	647	664	681	699	716	733
5.9	750	766	783	800	817	834	851	867	884	901
6.0	918	934	951	967	984	*001	*017	*034	*050	*066
6.1	1.8 083	099	116	132	148	165	181	197	213	229
6.2	245	262	278	294	310	326	342	358	374	390
6.3	405	421	437	453	469	485	500	516	532	547
6.4	563	579	594	610	625	641	656	672	687	703
6.5	718	733	749	764	779	795	810	825	840	856
6.6	871	886	901	916	931	946	961	976	991	*006
6.7	1.9 021	036	051	066	081	095	110	125	140	155
6.8	169	184	199	213	228	242	257	272	286	301
6.9	315	330	344	359	373	387	402	416	430	445
7.0	459	473	488	502	516	530	544	559	573	587
7.1	601	615	629	643	657	671	685	699	713	727
7.2	741	755	769	782	796	810	824	838	851	865
7.3	879	892	906	920	933	947	961	974	988	*001
7.4	2.0 015	028	042	055	069	082	096	109	122	136
7.5	149	162	176	189	202	215	229	242	255	268
7.6	281	295	308	321	334	347	360	373	386	399
7.7	412	425	438	451	464	477	490	503	516	528
7.8	541	554	567	580	592	605	618	631	643	656
7.9	669	681	694	707	719	732	744	757	769	782
8.0	794	807	819	832	844	857	869	882	894	906
8.1	919	931	943	956	968	980	992	*005	*017	*029
8.2	2.1 041	054	066	080	090	102	114	126	138	150
8.3	163	175	187	199	211	223	235	247	258	270
8.4	282	294	306	318	330	342	353	365	377	389
8.5	401	412	424	436	448	460	471	483	494	506
8.6	518	529	541	552	564	576	587	599	610	622
8.7	633	645	656	668	679	691	702	713	725	736
8.8	748	759	770	782	793	804	815	827	838	849
8.9	861	872	883	894	905	917	928	939	950	961
9.0	972	983	994	*006	*017	*028	*039	*050	*061	*072
9.1	2.2 083	094	105	116	127	137	148	159	170	181
9.2	192	203	214	225	235	246	257	268	279	289
9.3	300	311	322	332	343	354	364	375	386	396
9.4	407	418	428	439	450	460	471	481	492	502
9.5	513	523	534	544	555	565	576	586	597	607
9.6	618	628	638	649	659	670	680	690	701	711
9.7	721	732	742	752	762	773	783	793	803	814
9.8	824	834	844	854	865	875	885	895	905	915
9.9	925	935	946	956	966	976	986	996	*006	*016
10.	2.3 026	036	046	056	066	076	086	096	106	115

x	e^x	$\log e^x$	e^{-x}	x	e^x	$\log e^x$	e^{-x}
0.00	1.0000	0.00000	1.00000	0.50	1.6487	0.21715	0.60653
0.01	1.0101	0.00434	0.99005	0.51	1.6653	0.22149	0.60050
0.02	1.0202	0.00869	0.98020	0.52	1.6820	0.22583	0.59452
0.03	1.0305	0.01303	0.97045	0.53	1.6989	0.23018	0.58860
0.04	1.0408	0.01737	0.96079	0.54	1.7160	0.23452	0.58275
0.05	1.0513	0.02171	0.95123	0.55	1.7333	0.23886	0.57695
0.06	1.0618	0.02606	0.94176	0.56	1.7507	0.24320	0.57121
0.07	1.0725	0.03040	0.93239	0.57	1.7683	0.24755	0.56553
0.08	1.0833	0.03474	0.92312	0.58	1.7860	0.25189	0.55990
0.09	1.0942	0.03909	0.91393	0.59	1.8040	0.25623	0.55433
0.10	1.1052	0.04343	0.90484	0.60	1.8221	0.26058	0.54881
0.11	1.1163	0.04777	0.89583	0.61	1.8404	0.26492	0.54335
0.12	1.1275	0.05212	0.88692	0.62	1.8589	0.26926	0.53794
0.13	1.1388	0.05646	0.87809	0.63	1.8776	0.27361	0.53259
0.14	1.1503	0.06080	0.86936	0.64	1.8965	0.27795	0.52729
0.15	1.1618	0.06514	0.86071	0.65	1.9155	0.28229	0.52205
0.16	1.1735	0.06949	0.85214	0.66	1.9348	0.28663	0.51685
0.17	1.1853	0.07383	0.84366	0.67	1.9542	0.29098	0.51171
0.18	1.1972	0.07817	0.83527	0.68	1.9739	0.29532	0.50662
0.19	1.2092	0.08252	0.82696	0.69	1.9937	0.29966	0.50158
0.20	1.2214	0.08686	0.81873	0.70	2.0138	0.30401	0.49659
0.21	1.2337	0.09120	0.81058	0.71	2.0340	0.30835	0.49164
0.22	1.2461	0.09554	0.80252	0.72	2.0544	0.31269	0.48675
0.23	1.2586	0.09989	0.79453	0.73	2.0751	0.31703	0.48191
0.24	1.2712	0.10423	0.78663	0.74	2.0959	0.32138	0.47711
0.25	1.2840	0.10857	0.77880	0.75	2.1170	0.32572	0.47237
0.26	1.2969	0.11292	0.77105	0.76	2.1383	0.33006	0.46767
0.27	1.3100	0.11726	0.76338	0.77	2.1598	0.33441	0.46301
0.28	1.3231	0.12160	0.75578	0.78	2.1815	0.33875	0.45841
0.29	1.3364	0.12595	0.74826	0.79	2.2034	0.34309	0.45384
0.30	1.3499	0.13029	0.74082	0.80	2.2255	0.34744	0.44933
0.31	1.3634	0.13463	0.73345	0.81	2.2479	0.35178	0.44486
0.32	1.3771	0.13897	0.72615	0.82	2.2705	0.35612	0.44043
0.33	1.3910	0.14332	0.71892	0.83	2.2933	0.36046	0.43605
0.34	1.4049	0.14766	0.71177	0.84	2.3164	0.36481	0.43171
0.35	1.4191	0.15200	0.70469	0.85	2.3396	0.36915	0.42741
0.36	1.4333	0.15635	0.69768	0.86	2.3632	0.37349	0.42316
0.37	1.4477	0.16069	0.69073	0.87	2.3869	0.37784	0.41895
0.38	1.4623	0.16503	0.68386	0.88	2.4109	0.38218	0.41478
0.39	1.4770	0.16937	0.67706	0.89	2.4351	0.38652	0.41066
0.40	1.4918	0.17372	0.67032	0.90	2.4596	0.39087	0.40657
0.41	1.5068	0.17806	0.66365	0.91	2.4843	0.39521	0.40252
0.42	1.5220	0.18240	0.65705	0.92	2.5093	0.39955	0.39852
0.43	1.5373	0.18675	0.65051	0.93	2.5345	0.40389	0.39455
0.44	1.5527	0.19109	0.64404	0.94	2.5600	0.40824	0.39063
0.45	1.5683	0.19543	0.63763	0.95	2.5857	0.41258	0.38674
0.46	1.5841	0.19978	0.63128	0.96	2.6117	0.41692	0.38289
0.47	1.6000	0.20412	0.62500	0.97	2.6379	0.42127	0.37908
0.48	1.6161	0.20846	0.61878	0.98	2.6645	0.42561	0.37531
0.49	1.6323	0.21280	0.61263	0.99	2.6912	0.42995	0.37158
0.50	1.6487	0.21715	0.60653	1.00	2.7183	0.43429	0.36788

*From A. E. Richmond, "Calculus for Electronics," 2nd ed., McGraw-Hill Book Company, New York, 1958, 1972.

x	e^x	$\log e^x$	e^{-x}	x	e^x	$\log e^x$	e^{-x}
1.00	2.7183	0.43429	0.36788	1.50	4.4817	0.65144	0.22313
1.01	2.7456	0.43864	0.36422	1.51	4.5267	0.65578	0.22091
1.02	2.7732	0.44298	0.36060	1.52	4.5722	0.66013	0.21871
1.03	2.8011	0.44732	0.35701	1.53	4.6182	0.66447	0.21654
1.04	2.8292	0.45167	0.35345	1.54	4.6646	0.66881	0.21438
1.05	2.8577	0.45601	0.34994	1.55	4.7115	0.67316	0.21225
1.06	2.8864	0.46035	0.34646	1.56	4.7588	0.67750	0.21014
1.07	2.9154	0.46470	0.34301	1.57	4.8066	0.68184	0.20805
1.08	2.9447	0.46904	0.33960	1.58	4.8550	0.68619	0.20598
1.09	2.9743	0.47338	0.33622	1.59	4.9037	0.69053	0.20393
1.10	3.0042	0.47772	0.33287	1.60	4.9530	0.69487	0.20190
1.11	3.0344	0.48207	0.32956	1.61	5.0028	0.69921	0.19989
1.12	3.0649	0.48641	0.32628	1.62	5.0531	0.70356	0.19790
1.13	3.0957	0.49075	0.32303	1.63	5.1039	0.70790	0.19593
1.14	3.1268	0.49510	0.31982	1.64	5.1552	0.71224	0.19398
1.15	3.1582	0.49944	0.31664	1.65	5.2070	0.71659	0.19205
1.16	3.1899	0.50378	0.31349	1.66	5.2593	0.72093	0.19014
1.17	3.2220	0.50812	0.31037	1.67	5.3122	0.72527	0.18825
1.18	3.2544	0.51247	0.30728	1.68	5.3656	0.72961	0.18637
1.19	3.2871	0.51681	0.30422	1.69	5.4195	0.73396	0.18452
1.20	3.3201	0.52115	0.30119	1.70	5.4739	0.73830	0.18268
1.21	3.3535	0.52550	0.29820	1.71	5.5290	0.74264	0.18087
1.22	3.3872	0.52984	0.29523	1.72	5.5845	0.74699	0.17907
1.23	3.4212	0.53418	0.29229	1.73	5.6407	0.75133	0.17728
1.24	3.4556	0.53853	0.28938	1.74	5.6973	0.75567	0.17552
1.25	3.4903	0.54287	0.28650	1.75	5.7546	0.76002	0.17377
1.26	3.5254	0.54721	0.28365	1.76	5.8124	0.76436	0.17204
1.27	3.5609	0.55155	0.28083	1.77	5.8709	0.76870	0.17033
1.28	3.5966	0.55590	0.27804	1.78	5.9299	0.77304	0.16864
1.29	3.6328	0.56024	0.27527	1.79	5.9895	0.77739	0.16696
1.30	3.6693	0.56458	0.27253	1.80	6.0496	0.78173	0.16530
1.31	3.7062	0.56893	0.26982	1.81	6.1104	0.78607	0.16365
1.32	3.7434	0.57327	0.26714	1.82	6.1719	0.79042	0.16203
1.33	3.7810	0.57761	0.26448	1.83	6.2339	0.79476	0.16041
1.34	3.8190	0.58195	0.26185	1.84	6.2965	0.79910	0.15882
1.35	3.8574	0.58630	0.25924	1.85	6.3598	0.80344	0.15724
1.36	3.8962	0.59064	0.25666	1.86	6.4237	0.80779	0.15567
1.37	3.9354	0.59498	0.25411	1.87	6.4883	0.81213	0.15412
1.38	3.9749	0.59933	0.25158	1.88	6.5535	0.81647	0.15259
1.39	4.0149	0.60367	0.24908	1.89	6.6194	0.82082	0.15107
1.40	4.0552	0.60801	0.24660	1.90	6.6859	0.82516	0.14957
1.41	4.0960	0.61236	0.24414	1.91	6.7531	0.82950	0.14808
1.42	4.1371	0.61670	0.24171	1.92	6.8210	0.83385	0.14661
1.43	4.1787	0.62104	0.23931	1.93	6.8895	0.83819	0.14515
1.44	4.2207	0.62538	0.23693	1.94	6.9588	0.84253	0.14370
1.45	4.2631	0.62973	0.23457	1.95	7.0287	0.84687	0.14227
1.46	4.3060	0.63407	0.23224	1.96	7.0993	0.85122	0.14086
1.47	4.3492	0.63841	0.22993	1.97	7.1707	0.85556	0.13946
1.48	4.3929	0.64276	0.22764	1.98	7.2427	0.85990	0.13807
1.49	4.4371	0.64710	0.22537	1.99	7.3155	0.86425	0.13670
1.50	4.4817	0.65144	0.22313	2.00	7.3891	0.86859	0.13534

x	e^x	$\log e^x$	e^{-x}	x	e^x	$\log e^x$	e^{-x}
2.00	7.3891	0.86859	0.13534	2.50	12.182	1.08574	0.08208
2.01	7.4633	0.87293	0.13399	2.51	12.305	1.09008	0.08127
2.02	7.5383	0.87727	0.13266	2.52	12.429	1.09442	0.08046
2.03	7.6141	0.88162	0.13134	2.53	12.554	1.09877	0.07966
2.04	7.6906	0.88596	0.13003	2.54	12.680	1.10311	0.07887
2.05	7.7679	0.89030	0.12873	2.55	12.807	1.10745	0.07808
2.06	7.8460	0.89465	0.12745	2.56	12.936	1.11179	0.07730
2.07	7.9248	0.89899	0.12619	2.57	13.066	1.11614	0.07654
2.08	8.0045	0.90333	0.12493	2.58	13.197	1.12048	0.07577
2.09	8.0849	0.90768	0.12369	2.59	13.330	1.12482	0.07502
2.10	8.1662	0.91202	0.12246	2.60	13.464	1.12917	0.07427
2.11	8.2482	0.91636	0.12124	2.61	13.599	1.13351	0.07353
2.12	8.3311	0.92070	0.12003	2.62	13.736	1.13785	0.07280
2.13	8.4149	0.92505	0.11884	2.63	13.874	1.14219	0.07208
2.14	8.4994	0.92939	0.11765	2.64	14.013	1.14654	0.07136
2.15	8.5849	0.93373	0.11648	2.65	14.154	1.15088	0.07065
2.16	8.6711	0.93808	0.11533	2.66	14.296	1.15522	0.06995
2.17	8.7583	0.94242	0.11418	2.67	14.440	1.15957	0.06925
2.18	8.8463	0.94676	0.11304	2.68	14.585	1.16391	0.06856
2.19	8.9352	0.95110	0.11192	2.69	14.732	1.16825	0.06788
2.20	9.0250	0.95545	0.11080	2.70	14.880	1.17260	0.06721
2.21	9.1157	0.95979	0.10970	2.71	15.029	1.17694	0.06654
2.22	9.2073	0.96413	0.10861	2.72	15.180	1.18128	0.06587
2.23	9.2999	0.96848	0.10753	2.73	15.333	1.18562	0.06522
2.24	9.3933	0.97282	0.10646	2.74	15.487	1.18997	0.06457
2.25	9.4877	0.97716	0.10540	2.75	15.643	1.19431	0.06393
2.26	9.5831	0.98151	0.10435	2.76	15.800	1.19865	0.06329
2.27	9.6794	0.98585	0.10331	2.77	15.959	1.20300	0.06266
2.28	9.7767	0.99019	0.10228	2.78	16.119	1.20734	0.06204
2.29	9.8749	0.99453	0.10127	2.79	16.281	1.21168	0.06142
2.30	9.9742	0.99888	0.10026	2.80	16.445	1.21602	0.06081
2.31	10.074	1.00322	0.09926	2.81	16.610	1.22037	0.06020
2.32	10.176	1.00756	0.09827	2.82	16.777	1.22471	0.05961
2.33	10.278	1.01191	0.09730	2.83	16.945	1.22905	0.05901
2.34	10.381	1.01625	0.09633	2.84	17.116	1.23340	0.05843
2.35	10.486	1.02059	0.09537	2.85	17.288	1.23774	0.05784
2.36	10.591	1.02493	0.09442	2.86	17.462	1.24208	0.05727
2.37	10.697	1.02928	0.09348	2.87	17.637	1.24643	0.05670
2.38	10.805	1.03362	0.09255	2.88	17.814	1.25077	0.05613
2.39	10.913	1.03796	0.09163	2.89	17.993	1.25511	0.05558
2.40	11.023	1.04231	0.09072	2.90	18.174	1.25945	0.05502
2.41	11.134	1.04665	0.08982	2.91	18.357	1.26380	0.05448
2.42	11.246	1.05099	0.08892	2.92	18.541	1.26814	0.05393
2.43	11.359	1.05534	0.08804	2.93	18.728	1.27248	0.05340
2.44	11.473	1.05968	0.08716	2.94	18.916	1.27683	0.05287
2.45	11.588	1.06402	0.08629	2.95	19.106	1.28117	0.05234
2.46	11.705	1.06836	0.08543	2.96	19.298	1.28551	0.05182
2.47	11.822	1.07271	0.08458	2.97	19.492	1.28985	0.05130
2.48	11.941	1.07705	0.08374	2.98	19.688	1.29420	0.05079
2.49	12.061	1.08139	0.08291	2.99	19.886	1.29854	0.05029
2.50	12.182	1.08574	0.08208	3.00	20.086	1.30288	0.04979

x	e^x	$\log e^x$	e^{-x}	x	e^x	$\log e^x$	e^{-x}
3.00	20.086	1.30288	0.04979	4.50	90.017	1.95433	0.01111
3.05	21.115	1.32460	0.04736	4.60	99.484	1.99775	0.01005
3.10	22.198	1.34631	0.04505	4.70	109.95	2.04118	0.00910
3.15	23.336	1.36803	0.04285	4.80	121.51	2.08461	0.00823
3.20	24.533	1.38974	0.04076	4.90	134.29	2.12804	0.00745
3.25	25.790	1.41146	0.03877	5.00	148.41	2.17147	0.00674
3.30	27.113	1.43317	0.03688	5.10	164.02	2.21490	0.00610
3.35	28.503	1.45489	0.03508	5.20	181.27	2.25833	0.00552
3.40	29.964	1.47660	0.03337	5.30	200.34	2.30176	0.00499
3.45	31.500	1.49832	0.03175	5.40	221.41	2.34519	0.00452
3.50	33.115	1.52003	0.03020	5.50	244.69	2.38862	0.00409
3.55	34.813	1.54175	0.02872	5.60	270.43	2.43205	0.00370
3.60	36.598	1.56346	0.02732	5.70	298 87	2.47548	0.00335
3.65	38.475	1.58517	0.02599	5.80	330.30	2.51891	0.00303
3.70	40.447	1.60689	0.02472	5.90	365.04	2.56234	0.00274
3.75	42.521	1.62860	0.02352	6.00	403.43	2.60577	0.00248
3.80	44.701	1.65032	0.02237	6.25	518.01	2.71434	0.00193
3.85	46.993	1.67203	0.02128	6.50	665.14	2.82291	0.00150
3.90	49.402	1.69375	0.02024	6.75	854.05	2.93149	0.00117
3.95	51.935	1.71546	0.01925	7.00	1096.6	3.04006	0.00091
4.00	54.598	1.73718	0.01832	7.50	1808.0	3.25721	0.00055
4.10	60.340	1.78061	0.01657	8.00	2981.0	3.47436	0.00034
4.20	66.686	1.82404	0.01500	8.50	4914.8	3.69150	0.00020
4.30	73.700	1.86747	0.01357	9.00	8103.1	3.90865	0.00012
4.40	81.451	1.91090	0.01227	9.50	13360	4.12580	0.00007
				10.00	22026	4.34294	0.00005

TABLE 7. DERIVATIVES*

In this table, u and v represent functions of x; a, n, e represent constants ($e = 2.7183 \cdots$); and all angles are measured in radians.

$$\frac{d}{dx} x = 1 \qquad \frac{d}{dx} a = 0$$

$$\frac{d}{dx}(u \pm v \pm \cdots) = \frac{du}{dx} \pm \frac{dv}{dx} \pm \cdots$$

$$\frac{d}{dx}(au) = a\frac{du}{dx} \qquad \frac{d}{dx}(uv) = u\frac{dv}{dx} + v\frac{du}{dx}$$

$$\frac{d}{dx}\left(\frac{u}{v}\right) = \frac{v\dfrac{du}{dx} - u\dfrac{dv}{dx}}{v^2} \qquad \frac{d}{dx}\sin u = \cos u\frac{du}{dx}$$

$$\frac{d}{dx} u^n = nu^{n-1}\frac{du}{dx} \qquad \frac{d}{dx}\cos u = -\sin u\frac{du}{dx}$$

$$\frac{d}{dx}\log_a u = \frac{\log_a e}{u}\frac{du}{dx} \qquad \frac{d}{dx}\tan u = \sec^2 u\frac{du}{dx}$$

$$\frac{d}{dx}\log_e u = \frac{1}{u}\frac{du}{dx} \qquad \frac{d}{dx}\cot u = -\csc^2 u\frac{du}{dx}$$

$$\frac{d}{dx} a^u = a^u \log_e a\frac{du}{dx} \qquad \frac{d}{dx}\sec u = \sec u \tan u\frac{du}{dx}$$

$$\frac{d}{dx} e^u = e^u\frac{du}{dx} \qquad \frac{d}{dx}\csc u = -\csc u \cot u\frac{du}{dx}$$

$$\frac{d}{dx} u^v = vu^{v-1}\frac{du}{dx} + u^v \log_e u\frac{dv}{dx} \qquad \frac{d}{dx}\operatorname{vers} u = \sin u\frac{du}{dx}$$

$$\lim_{x\to 0}\frac{\sin x}{x} = 1, \quad \lim_{x\to 0}(1 + x)^{1/x} = e = 2.71828 \cdots = 1 + 1 + \frac{1}{2!} + \frac{1}{3!} + \cdots$$

$$\frac{d}{dx}\sin^{-1} u = \frac{1}{\sqrt{1 - u^2}}\frac{du}{dx} \qquad \frac{-\pi}{2} \leqq \sin^{-1} u \leqq \frac{\pi}{2}$$

$$\frac{d}{dx}\cos^{-1} u = -\frac{1}{\sqrt{1 - u^2}}\frac{du}{dx} \qquad 0 \leqq \cos^{-1} u \leqq \pi$$

$$\frac{d}{dx}\tan^{-1} u = \frac{1}{1 + u^2}\frac{du}{dx} \qquad \frac{d}{dx}\cot^{-1} u = -\frac{1}{1 + u^2}\frac{du}{dx}$$

*From Richard Stevens Burington, "Handbook of Mathematical Tables and Formulas," 4th ed., McGraw-Hill Book Company, New York, 1965.

$$\frac{d}{dx}\sec^{-1} u = \frac{1}{u\sqrt{u^2-1}}\frac{du}{dx}, \quad -\pi \leqq \sec^{-1} u < -\frac{\pi}{2}, \quad 0 \leqq \sec^{-1} u < \frac{\pi}{2}$$

$$\frac{d}{dx}\csc^{-1} u = -\frac{1}{u\sqrt{u^2-1}}\frac{du}{dx}, \quad -\pi < \csc^{-1} u \leqq -\frac{\pi}{2}, \quad 0 < \csc^{-1} u \leqq \frac{\pi}{2}$$

SHORT TABLE OF INTEGRALS*

(u and v denote functions of x; a, b, and C denote constants.) Interpret symbols for inverse relations to be principal values.

1. $\int df(x) = f(x) + C$

2. $d\int f(x)\, dx = f(x)\, dx$

3. $\int 0\, dx = C$

4. $\int a f(x)\, dx = a\int f(x)\, dx$

5. $\int (u \pm v)\, dx = \int u\, dx \pm \int v\, dx$

6. $\int u\, dv = uv - \int v\, du$

7. $\int \frac{u\, dv}{dx}\, dx = uv - \int v \frac{du}{dx}\, dx$

8. $\int f(y)\, dx = \int \frac{f(y)\, dy}{dy/dx}$

9. $\int u^n\, du = \frac{u^{n+1}}{n+1} + C \qquad n \neq -1$

10. $\int \frac{du}{u} = \log_e u + C,\ u > 0 \qquad$ or, $\log_e |u| + C \qquad u \neq 0$

11. $\int e^u\, du = e^u + C$

12. $\int b^u\, du = \frac{b^u}{\log_e b} + C \qquad b > 0,\ b \neq 1$

13. $\int \sin u\, du = -\cos u + C$

14. $\int \cos u\, du = \sin u + C$

15. $\int \tan u\, du = \log_e \sec u + C = -\log_e \cos u + C$

*From Richard Stevens Burington, "Handbook of Mathematical Tables and Formulas," 4th ed., McGraw-Hill Book Company, New York, 1965.

16. $\int \cot u \, du = \log_e \sin u + C = -\log_e \csc u + C$

17. $\int \sec u \, du = \log_e (\sec u + \tan u) + C$

$$= \log_e \tan \left(\frac{u}{2} + \frac{\pi}{4} \right) + C$$

18. $\int \csc u \, du = \log_e (\csc u - \cot u) + C = \log_e \tan \frac{u}{2} + C$

19. $\int \sin^2 u \, du = \frac{1}{2} u - \frac{1}{2} \sin u \cos u + C$

20. $\int \cos^2 u \, du = \frac{1}{2} u + \frac{1}{2} \sin u \cos u + C$

21. $\int \sec^2 u \, du = \tan u + C$

22. $\int \csc^2 u \, du = -\cot u + C$

23. $\int \tan^2 u \, du = \tan u - u + C$

24. $\int \cot^2 u \, du = -\cot u - u + C$

25.* $\int \frac{du}{u^2 + a^2} = \frac{1}{a} \tan^{-1} \frac{u}{a} + C$

26. $$\int \frac{du}{u^2 - a^2} = \begin{cases} \frac{1}{2a} \log_e \frac{u-a}{u+a} + C = -\frac{1}{a} \coth^{-1} \frac{u}{a} + C & u^2 > a^2 \\ \frac{1}{2a} \log_e \frac{a-u}{a+u} + C = -\frac{1}{a} \tanh^{-1} \frac{u}{a} + C & u^2 < a^2 \end{cases}$$

27. $$\int \frac{du}{\sqrt{a^2 - u^2}} = \begin{cases} \sin^{-1} \frac{u}{a} + C & a > 0 \\ \sin^{-1} \frac{u}{|a|} + C & |a| \neq 0 \end{cases}$$

28. $\int \frac{du}{\sqrt{u^2 \pm a^2}} = \log_e (u + \sqrt{u^2 \pm a^2})\dagger + C$

29.* $\int \frac{du}{\sqrt{2au - u^2}} = \cos^{-1} \frac{a - u}{a} + C$

30. $\int \frac{du}{u\sqrt{u^2 - a^2}} = \frac{1}{a} \sec^{-1} \frac{u}{a} + C = \frac{1}{a} \cos^{-1} \frac{a}{u} + C$

31. $\int \frac{du}{u\sqrt{a^2 \pm u^2}} = -\frac{1}{a} \log_e \frac{a + \sqrt{a^2 \pm u^2}}{u}\dagger + C$

32. $\int \sqrt{a^2 - u^2}\, du = \frac{1}{2}\left(u\sqrt{a^2 - u^2} + a^2 \sin^{-1} \frac{u}{a}\right) + C$

index